WINSTON S. CHURCHILL
HIS COMPLETE SPEECHES
1897–1963

Author and Lecturer, 1931

The Editor ROBERT RHODES JAMES is a principal officer in the Executive
Office of the Secretary-General of the United Nations. He was Director of the
Institute for the Study of International Organisation, University of Sussex, from
September 1968 until September 1973, and has been a Fellow of the Royal
Society of Literature since 1964. His publications include *Rosebery; Gallipoli;
Churchill—A Study in Failure, 1900-1939;* and the highly acclaimed *Lord
Randolph Churchill.* Mr. Rhodes James is a Fellow of All Souls College, Oxford.

Published by Chelsea House Publishers in association with
R. R. Bowker Company (a Xerox Education Company)
Copyright © 1974 by Chelsea House Publishers
(A Division of Chelsea House Educational Communications, Inc.)
70 West 40th Street, New York, N.Y. 10018
All Rights Reserved
Printed and Bound in the United States of America

Managing Editor: Karyn G. Browne
Associate Editor: Jeanette Morrison
Assistant Editors: Jan Schwartz, Deborah Weiss, Michele Sacks
Editorial Consultant: Leon Friedman
Research Staff: Robert Freeman, Jeanne Kassler, Edward Matyjesyck,
Christopher Phillips, Steven Issacson, Deborah Larned, John Bartrum,
Steve Richman, Robert Stenza

The publisher gratefully acknowledges the help
of the Butler Library staff of Columbia University, New York,
in aiding the researchers to gather and reproduce the manuscript.
Acknowledgment is also given to Mr. Geoffrey Block and his staff
of the Conservative Research Department, London,
for their guidance and assistance.

Library of Congress Cataloging in Publication Data
Churchill, Sir Winston Leonard Spencer, 1874-1965.
Winston S. Churchill: his complete speeches, 1897-1963.

1. Churchill, Sir Winston Leonard Spencer, 1874-1965.
2. Great Britain—Politics and government—20th century—Sources.
I. James, Robert Rhodes, 1933-   ed. II. Title.
DA566.9.C5A38   942.082'092'4   74-505
ISBN 0-8352-0693-9

WINSTON S. CHURCHILL HIS COMPLETE SPEECHES 1897–1963

Edited by
ROBERT RHODES JAMES

Volume V
1928-1935

CHELSEA HOUSE PUBLISHERS
in association with
R. R. BOWKER COMPANY
New York and London

1974

Contents

VOLUME V: 1928-1935

RECOVERY AND ISOLATION: 1925-1938

xii   Contents

TRADE

May 24, 1928

House of Commons

It was not my intention to join in a discussion on these extremely grave and complicated topics. While no one complains of the right hon. Gentleman having taken the occasion for debating these serious matters, I am sure he has only to cast his eye around the House to realise that this is not the occasion on which they could be pursued to any definite conclusion. Opportunities will not be lacking in the further course of the Session nor will they be long withheld when we may get to grips with these issues. Neither the Parliamentary Secretary nor I would attempt to suggest that all is well with British trade or that His Majesty's Government have not most serious preoccupations in regard to the state, particularly, of our basic industries employing the greatest mass of manhood and labour. We have made it the central part of our work in the closing days of this Parliament to propose a Measure, remedial in its character, wide in its scope, far-reaching in its intentions, which will occupy this Parliament for the rest of its life. We shall begin, when we return, the discussion of that Measure on the Second Reading of the Finance Bill and during the day and a half allotted to the Apportionment and Rating Valuation Bill. The effects of this remedy, partial if you will, but sincere and important, which we have devised and for which we are labouring, will be thrashed out on the Floor of the House. More information will be forthcoming as to its effects. We have then a remedy and a definite practical step to propose.

I accept all that the right hon. Gentleman said about the serious conditions of our basic industries which afford employment to the wage-earners. I trust that, if it be found that the remedy which the Government have proposed is sincerely conceived, has been honestly studied, and is the result of sufficient Departmental and technical labour, that it will be treated with reasonable fair play, that it will be examined from the point of view of people who are really worried about the condition of our industry and would like to see things better. I know that, with an election only a year or 15 months ahead, it is beyond human nature that a party point should not be taken on this side or on that, but, under those party points and above those party points, let us at any rate embark on those discussions with a sincere desire to extract from the proposals of the Government whatever may conduce to the general welfare.

Mr. Lloyd George: Shall we then get full information with regard to those proposals?

Mr. Churchill: Fuller, but not necessarily full—step by step. We are entitled to unfold our plans as we go, but, at the same time, it is obvious that, as the discussions develop, the necessary facts must be in the possession of those who take part in them. I only rose out of respect to one who occupies the position of the right hon. Gentleman as a party Leader, and who has played so great a part in our affairs. I welcome the cry of alarm which he has raised, and I say that, in view of that alarm, we have a right to claim from him earnest consideration of the practical proposals which we make, even if they are not complete or perfect; and we have also the right to expect from him a severe restraint in the use of the cheaper and commoner forms of party politics, and which, on Saturday afternoons, and particularly during the Whit-suntide vacation, he is very frequently tempted to indulge.

FINANCE BILL (RATING REFORM)

June 5, 1928

House of Commons

No one could complain of the tone and temper of the speech of the right hon. Gentleman. It was the result of careful reflection; it was expressed in language almost entirely devoid of prejudice, and, for my part, as the result of that speech, I am only for the moment left with one question to ask—Is that all you have got to say against the scheme of constructive rating reform which we have proposed? After six weeks of careful consideration, during which all the keenest and sharpest brains in the Labour party have been continuously applied to the immense field that we have opened up, with a target covering the whole horizon, this excellent, moderate, suggestive speech—a speech, I must say, largely borrowed—represents all that they have to say at the present time on this subject. I think they have shown a far sounder appreciation of the real importance of this scheme to the country and to its productive industries and its labouring masses, than has been shown by their much more precipitate allies on the Liberal Benches. I ask the House, and I ask the country, to note very carefully the attitude of scrupulous reserve which has been adopted by the Labour party upon these Budget proposals.

What are the two criticisms which the right hon. Gentleman has been able to select for adumbration this afternoon? He says that the Petrol Duty will be a burden. That is the first criticism. I have never denied that the tax on petrol will be a heavy one. I am very sorry, indeed, that I have had to impose a tax at all, and only a much more grievous need in another direction has led me to make this demand upon the motoring public, in order to find the money necessary to take a forward step. After all, it must be remembered that I am proposing constructive policies on the morrow of the disaster of 1926. More than £80,000,000 has been taken from the revenues of four poor years. But for that, I could have proposed all that we are proposing now and carry it into effect without placing a tax upon petrol. But, in all the circumstances, I submitted to the House, when the Budget was introduced, the broad argument as between the struggling basic industries on the one hand and this buoyant motor traffic on the other, as between our railways with the great interests and labour interests involved in their reasonable treatment and the ever-expanding cost of our road system. There is also the contrast between the position of our coalfields and the ever-growing importation of foreign liquid fuel, and surveying these three groups of alternatives, I submitted to the House and the country the proposition that it was well worth while getting this considerable revenue from a tax upon petrol and petrol-driven transport, and devoting it to the relief of the basic industries from the extremely onerous and invidious incidence of the rates. But I will never deny that it is an evil, or that I wish the revenues of the country had been such as to enable me to dispense with such a tax.

The right hon. Gentleman's second point, and the alternative which he suggests for the tax on petrol, I gather, is the taxation of land values—[An Hon. Member: "The rating of site values!"]—the taxation of land values or the rating of land values. The right hon. Gentleman read a speech of mine of some years ago, and one which, I am bound to say, was familiar to me, because I have taken the trouble to re-read some of those statements quite recently, and I am bound to say that, leaving out what you may call the partisan gloss, which, in times of sharp political conflict is prone to be introduced into our deliberations—leaving all that out, I am not at all convinced that, among my arguments in favour of the rating of undeveloped urban land upon its true value, I employed any which were lacking in lucidity or reason. In the years that have passed a good many things have happened, and we must take notice of these events. In the first place, a whole group of these land taxes were imposed. [An Hon. Member: "Never!"] A whole group of these land taxes were imposed by the right hon. Gentleman the Member for Carnarvon Boroughs (Mr. Lloyd George) when he was Chancellor of the Exchequer—Increment Value Duty, Reversion Duty and Undeveloped Land Duty.

Mr. MacLaren: Were these taxes on land values?

Mr. Churchill: They were certainly taxes directed to absorbing what is called the unearned increment of the land. They were all imposed, and after 11 years the whole group of these taxes proved a total failure. They yielded in the 11 years only £1,300,000, and so disgusted was the right hon. Gentleman with the result of the taxes that he abandoned the whole policy when he was Prime Minister, in 1920. The right hon. Gentleman suggested that he was out of the country at the time the taxes were dropped, but I can assure him his memory has played him false. I have verified the records. I make not the slightest suggestion of want of candour.

Mr. Lloyd George: That these taxes were abolished without my knowledge and consent is not what I meant to suggest. That would have been a very unfair insinuation against the Chancellor of the Exchequer. If I conveyed that impression I can only express my regret. It is not what I meant. It was in reference to the statement made by the right hon. Gentleman the Member for Carmarthen (Sir A. Mond) as to something he had said when the matter was being discussed. I was not there when the discussion took place, but I have not the faintest doubt that I was consulted and assented to it.

Mr. Churchill: I am not making the slightest reflection on the candour or the good faith of the right hon. Gentleman. After all, the torrent of events that swept across us in these tremendous years through which we have passed must necessarily have made it difficult for any Minister who has played the part he has done and been concerned with such a multitude of affairs to remember exactly what the particular course was. The fact is that the right hon. Gentleman presided over both meetings of the Finance Committee of the Cabinet in 1920 which decided on the changes of taxation in the Budget of that year. This was before he went to the San Remo Conference and he presided over both those meetings at the beginning of April, 1920, and agreement was reached on all the changes in taxation.

Mr. Lloyd George: I certainly accept that.

Mr. Churchill: And when the present Foreign Secretary, then Chancellor of the Exchequer, was challenged in the House of Commons by Members who said, when the repeal of these taxes was announced, that he repealed them while the Prime Minister was away, he said:

> That is a foolish observation. The hon. Member obviously does not understand Cabinet procedure. Does he think that a decision of this kind was taken in the absence of the Prime Minister or without his full concurrence or approval? We have unanimously come to the conclusion that the proper course to pursue is to repeal these duties.

And again, speaking of the right hon. Gentleman:

> He has one great quality not given to every man, and that is that in middle age and after middle age he can still learn. He is no coward who fears to own a change of mind and admit altered conditions. He is no pedant who refuses to alter any views which he first took up when a case was first presented to him.

Apparently, the right hon. Gentleman is still continuing his course of instruction. I accept his statement that he was an assenting party to the repeal of these taxes. That is a very considerable thing, that the Minister and politician who put the greatest drive into this case that has ever been put into it should, at the summit of his powers, after 11 years of exhaustive experiment, not feel the slightest hesitation in being responsible for the complete repeal of these three taxes.

But about site values and land values—of course there is a lot of politics in them. Further, there are a lot of officials in them. When the valuation process was brought to an end by a later Government it was possible to retrench 4,000 officials, who would have to be replaced before this policy could be taken up again. [An Hon. Member: "Not at all!"] That is what I am advised. In addition to that, the right hon. Gentleman took into consideration the great disappointment of the yield. And so, though there may be a great deal of politics and a great many officials, and no doubt a great deal of litigation, as we have proved from what occurred, there is very little money in this policy. The idea that we could use the rating of site values as a substitute for this powerful, fruitful fiscal engine of the petrol tax is one of the greatest delusions. If we had to enter into a long discussion at present upon site values, that would be the surest way of obstructing all practical creative reform in the direction of the relief of rates on industry, and the rest of this Parliament would be spent in very exciting but utterly sterile arguments on the subject of land values, and on the principles which you should apply to their rating or taxation, and we should not make the slightest progress towards the very solid, serious task we have set ourselves to accomplish. Therefore I do not intend to make more than one general observation upon the question of site values, except to say that it is the best method of stopping the rating relief of industry. But I will make this one further observation, and I will make it in an interrogative form. Why did Mr. Henry George fail? He was a great advocate of the single tax and he has one disciple, at any rate. Why did he fail, and why is it that his disciples are unable to carry on their political faith in modern times?

Colonel Wedgwood: Because people turn their coats too often.

Hon Members: What have you done?

Mr. Churchill: The right hon. Gentleman spoke then with less than his usual courtesy and with more than his usual obliviousness of his own record. I well remember the time when no one was more scathing in his denunciation of Socialism than he. Now, by a perfectly natural transition of mind, by a steady process of regeneration, he has reached a certain conclusion. He has reached finality. He has got to the bottom, as it were. I do not in any way belittle the logic or the argument about the rating of land. What I say is that very great experiments in this field have been made and that they were found to have failed to such an extent that they were abandoned by their author.

Let me return to the question why Henry George failed in his single tax proposal. It was because he had been studying the world as it had been for generations and centuries, and arrived at certain conclusions on that basis, and the conclusion he arrived at was that land was practically the sole source of all wealth. But almost before the ink was dry on the book he had written it was apparent that there were hundreds of different ways of creating and possessing and gaining wealth which had either no relation to the ownership of land or an utterly disproportionate or indirect relation. Where there were 100 cases 20 years ago there are 10,000 cases now, and that is why radical democracy, looking at this proposition of the single tax—there are two enthusiastic single taxers left in this House—has turned unhesitatingly towards the graduated taxation of the profits of wealth rather than to this discrimination in the sources from which it is derived, and that is what we have done. Let me point out what has happened in the last 18 years. When this question of site values was being discussed in the Budget of 1909 the Income Tax and Super-tax together stood at the maximum, at 1s. 8d. in the £; it is now 10s. Death Duties were 15 per cent. on the highest estates, whereas they now reach 40 per cent. There is not the slightest doubt that very vast changes have taken place in the whole of the methods by which taxation is raised, and those who wish to embark on any controversy upon the taxation of land values in the future must address themselves to the facts as they exist in this completely changed situation.

I leave the only two points the right hon. Gentleman the Member for Colne Valley (Mr. Snowden) on behalf of the Labour Opposition has brought forward in connection with our rating scheme. I am very glad to know that is all they have to say upon the subject. Other criticisms have come from other quarters, and especially from the Liberal party, who have been extremely active in finding fault, and who have placed an Amendment on the Paper with which I propose to deal, as it touches a very direct issue, and I propose to deal with it in detail. The criticisms which the Liberal Opposition have made in the country are mutually destructive. The first is that it is a very bad scheme and it ought to be brought into operation much earlier. Of course it all turns on money. I should be delighted to bring it into operation earlier, but we have to consider money and the necessary administrative and legislative steps that must be taken. I have not the money to bring this scheme, or any part of it, into operation earlier. I have said that £80,000,000 has been lost by the events of 1926. It is a great effort to do what we are attempting to do at a time so soon after those events. The excision of the Kerosene Duty from our proposals aggravates my difficulties. I do not, however, propose to suggest to the House any alternative taxation to make good the omission of kerosene. I count upon the expanding revenue of the country and upon further economies which must be pursued from year to year to bridge the gap. In any case, the finance is secure for at least three years, but I have nothing more to give in the present year, and the benefits, such as they are, must be awaited with patience. After all, 18 months is not very long to wait, and six weeks of it have gone already.

The second self-destructive criticism has emanated mainly from the right hon. Gentleman the Member for Carnarvon Boroughs [Mr. Lloyd George]. He has pursued a double line of attack. First of all, the relief ought to have been concentrated on the basic and unprosperous industries, much more concentrated than the Government propose. Secondly, and alternatively and simultaneously, he says that the relief ought to have been dissipated and spread over the whole area of the distributing trades and of ordinary residential ratepayers. You have the maximum concentration advocated in one breath and the maximum dissipation in the next. There is a very great deal to be said for concentrating the whole of the relief upon the basic industries, and we have done so in regard to the railway part of our proposals. We have been guided in the main policy by a fundamental principle. It is this, that the instruments of production ought not to be taxed but only the profits resulting from their use. That is our principle. We hold that it is economically unchallengable. Why should we fear to apply it boldly? I expect, if we had concentrated our relief upon the basic industries, the right hon. Gentleman would have been the first to rise in his place and to remark on the favours we were giving to a handful of trades at the expense of all the other producers. Under these circumstances, it is much better and much safer to follow a general principle which has been carefully selected to produce the results at which one is aiming and trust to the workings of that principle irrespective of the hard cases it may produce.

Does the right hon. Gentleman consider that it is practicable to pick and choose between the prosperous and the unprosperous industries? The Liberal Yellow Book suggested no such discrimination, and I am bound to say that it appears utterly impossible to make such a discrimination. The right hon. Gentleman has in many speeches he has been making about the country pointed to this and that hard case, this wealthy company which gets relief, this poor class of residents who do not get relief, this declining industry which ought to have more, and so forth. But I suggest that it is utterly impossible to pick and choose between these different industries. If, on the other hand, we were to extend the scope of the scheme to cover all the householders and all the distributing trades, we should dissipate the whole fruits of our proposals. We should reduce the relief to industry to one-fifth of what we are now giving. And what we are now giving amounts only to 4s. a ton on steel on the average. In fact my whole doubt and misgiving has been that the levers at our disposal are not big enough and not strong enough. If they were three or four times as strong, I should be much surer and much more confident. The right hon. Gentleman complains that the distributors do not receive the relief and that the residential ratepayers do not receive it. This would imply a dissipation of the resources at our disposal which would render their employment utterly sterile. We should have spent our £26,000,000, but industry would not be able to appreciate that any change had taken place. We should have lost our money and used up the limited resources of the State and have not altered in any appreciable degree the evils with which we are seeking to grapple. If I had only been considering what I might call benevolent giving, the giving of easements or indulgences, a relief to the general mass of the population, to take one-fifth or one-sixth off the rates would not attract me at all. Long before I did such a thing as that, I would take the tax off tea and sugar which would cost just about the same and which, I have not the slightest doubt, would reach a much wider and lower level of society than the petty general saving over the whole area of the rates. Therefore, I submit to the House that it would have been a great error for us not to concentrate our relief upon the productive industries.

The right hon. Gentleman has gone further and said that we should pick and choose among those industries—Labour Members have confirmed this view—and leave out the prosperous and give all the relief to the unprosperous. It is utterly impossible to do any such thing. No doubt the right hon. Gentleman finds it very convenient to go about the country and hold up the right hon. Gentleman the Member for Carmarthen (Sir A. Mond) and Mr. Courtauld to public prejudice, and, no doubt, get loud cheers from those ignorant of economics and envious of wealth. But you could not pick and choose only between industries. You would have to pick and choose between different concerns in the same industry. The changing fortunes of these businesses from year to year would render it utterly impossible to frame any scheme of reimbursement to the local authorities on this basis.

The right hon. Gentleman not only suggested that you should pick and choose between industries according as they were prosperous or unprosperous, but he suggested other discriminations. Apparently, you are to pick and choose between them accordingly as they are industries the Liberal party like or industries which the Liberal party do not like. Beer, Tory beer, that is to be denied, but cocoa: "Come along my dear! All is well." I have been asking myself where the right hon. Gentleman has got this idea of picking and choosing. I think I have it. He got it from the 1918 election. It is the coupon system. It is an attempt to revive it for the benefit of British industries. I should like to ask the right hon. Gentleman this question: He contends that this proposal of the Government will put £400,000 a year into the pockets of the brewers, because of the relief in rates. Who does the right hon. Gentleman suppose pays this £400,000 a year in rates on the brewing industry at the present time? Does he really suppose that it is the brewers who all these years have been making this sacrifice out of their own pockets in respect of what is admittedly a legitimate element in the cost of production? No, he is paying, I think, too great a tribute to their hearts and too little to their heads. We have another suggestion as to where the burden of the rates on beer has been thrown hitherto. Our suggestion is that it has been paid by the people who drink the beer, and our further suggestion is that a relief in the cost of production in a prosperous trade like this will infallibly make its way to the consumer by economic laws and the working of open competition.

Lieut.-Commander Kenworthy: Have you any promise of that? Have you an undertaking?

Mr. Churchill: I am not basing myself on individual promises, but on the work of inexorable laws. Of course, in businesses which are actually paying the rates out of their capital, or in businesses which are paying a portion of the rates out of their capital, or whose rate of profit is below the normal profit of competing firms, in such concerns the first use of the relief will be to stop the denudation of the capital funds and to enable industries to keep their doors open and their people employed. When you come to more prosperous trades which are in contact with competition, external and internal, world-wide and domestic, the only conclusion which any sound econo-mist can draw, and certainly the only conclusion which any Free Trader can draw, is that the diminution in the cost of production will make its way back in quantity, in quality, or in price, through a thousand channels, traceable or untraceable, to the broad mass of the consumers and wage earners throughout the country. If you do not pick and choose, in the distribution of your relief, between one industry and another, then you must face the consequences of applying your general principle. Let us see what are the consequences of applying our general principle. Here we have a direct conflict of opinion. The Liberal party have placed an Amendment upon the Paper, in which an extraordinary statement occurs. It states that the scheme

> will give a greater measure of relief to flourishing industries than to those which are depressed.

Let us examine this statement. Of course, the burden of rates is the result of two factors—assessment and poundage. These are mutually and reciprocally reacting factors but poundage is the dominant factor in the difference of burden between areas. Where the poundage is high you find the industries depressed and where the industries are depressed you find almost invariably that the poundage is high. A general revaluation of rateable property is proceeding at the present time and will be completed next year. This new valuation will, of course, be the basis upon which our plans will proceed. We are not using any earlier year or any incomplete valuation.

Having thus cleared the ground, let me now examine how the distribution will actually take place between the so-called flourishing and the so-called depressed industries. There is no actual definition of a flourishing or of a depressed industry. Any decision on that point must necessarily be arbitrary. Therefore, I select four main tests by which to tell what is a depressed industry or an industry which is not flourishing. Here they are. The first is that unemployment is abnormal; the second, that the ratio of rates to profits is excessive; the third that the profits are subnormal and the fourth that the profits have been decreasing in recent years. These are, I think, four very fair guides of a depressed or a not-flourishing industry, but there are three other factors which ought to be taken into consideration. The first is whether the industry provides wages for very large masses of manual labour, the second, is whether it is unsheltered, and the third is whether it is markedly concerned in the export trade. If all these seven qualifications are present, it will be agreed that the industries helped are the ones which we want to help. Let us see if we can find a group of trades which, broadly speaking, would fulfil all these conditions.

Last Autumn when I was studying this question and when I was anxious to find some criterion, some general principle which would enable me to carry relief to the basic industries, without invidious discrimination, the first set of figures which I examined was a statement of the ratio of rates to profits. Here I was able to rely upon the Inland Revenue. Every year for the purpose of Income Tax assessments a sample is taken by means of confidential returns of the whole trade of the country. Many thousands of concerns are individually examined and the results of this examination enables a forecast of the Income Tax yield to be made with what most people consider to be uncanny precision. For 1923 a specially detailed study was made into the profits, turnover, rates and reserves of industry, and their relationships. It was made by the direction of my right hon. Friend the Member for Colne Valley for the purposes of the Colwyn Committee. Therefore we have two sources of information—first, we have the annual sample of profits, covering the whole range of British industry, on which the Income Tax estimate is based and, secondly, we have the relation of rates to profits which was revealed by this very detailed and special investigation relating to the year 1923.

The Inland Revenue classified the 30,000 samples of productive industry into 15 main trade groups, which cover the whole of productive industry, except transport, public utilities, and agriculture. These 15 groups comprise nearly 8,000,000 workers, and they account for more than 800,000 of the unemployed. The figures which I studied last autumn were calculated for 1925, which was the last normal year, 1926 having no relation to normal times. I noticed immediately that six of these groups stood out from the others in that the ratio of rates to profits was excessive; far beyond what it was in the case of the rest of the groups. I have now, of course, comparable figures for 1927, and the conclusions which I am going to put before the House are based upon the Inland Revenue figures which have been used to forecast the Income Tax revenue for the current year, similar to those which were used last year with an accuracy so great as to be within about 1 per cent. of the actual receipt.

The percentage of rates to profits throughout the whole of the 15 groups is 7.8; but the six trade groups which stand out have an average of 20 per cent., while the other nine trade groups, which we may call the less depressed or the more flourishing, have an average percentage of rates to profits of only 4.6 per cent. Here is a great line of distinction. Let us see which are the trades which fall on the higher side and which on the lower side of the dividing line. Mines; Wool; Cotton; Iron; Steel, Shipbuilding and Engineering; Bleaching and Dyeing; and Metals, excluding Motor Car manufacture, which for the purposes of the Inland Revenue calculations has been included in Metals, but which perhaps it would not be proper to include in the depressed group. In these six trade groups the ratio of rates to profits is four or five times as high as it is in the other nine. In the case of Mines the ratio of rates in profits in 1927 was 27 per cent.; in Wool, 15 per cent.; in Cotton, 23 per cent.; in Iron and Steel, Shipbuilding and Engineering, 20 per cent.; in Bleaching and Dyeing, 14 per cent.; in Metals, 13 per cent. Look at the other nine groups—Building and Timber, 7 per cent.; Leather, 7 per cent.; Chemicals, 4 per cent.; Food, 6 per cent.; Other textiles, 5 per cent.; Paper, 4 per cent.; Drink, 2 per cent.; Tobacco, 2 per cent.; Pottery, 5 per cent.

There is evidently a vast line of cleavage between these different groups of industries which is marked by the burden of rates upon them. Are not the groups which I first mentioned, together with agriculture, those industries which everyone would admit are the depressed industries of the country? I do not say that these are all of the depressed industries, but they are the major depressed industries of the country, and the average rate of unemployment in those industries was, according to the latest figures, 13 per cent., ranging as high as 23 per cent. in shipbuilding. That compares with the average rate of unemployment throughout the whole country of 9.6 per cent., and with the Blanesburgh figure of what might be considered normal unemployment of 6 per cent. These six depressed trade groups are all unsheltered. They all show a lower volume of profit than they had four years ago. They show considerably less profits than they had even so recently as 1925. Lastly, together, these six depressed trade groups constitute the main staple of our export trade, which is the most directly in contact with foreign competition all over the world.

If you look at the other nine groups you see that they include some trades with abnormal unemployment, like the large building trades, and other trades which would repudiate with indignation the suggestion that they were flourishing, like the glass and pottery trades, but, in the main, you may say of these groups as a whole that they are sheltered and holding their own. The ratio of rates to profits in these nine groups is 4.6 per cent. and the unemployment is far below the average of the previous class. Therefore, it seems to me that a perfectly clear line can be drawn between these depressed groups and these not depressed or flourishing groups. The average burden of rates to profits in the first group is 20 per cent. and in the second group 4.6 per cent. That is a terrific difference.

Now let us see how the rating relief is divided between these two classes. Remember, that I am challenging the Liberal suggestion that a greater measure of relief goes to the flourishing industries than to those which are depressed. There are many in the second group which are not flourishing, but in the first group practically you may say that they are all depressed. Let us see how the money is divided between these two classes. The first group of the depressed industries made in 1927 much less than half the profits of the second group. You might almost say that they made little more than one-third of the profits of the second group. They made actually £67,000,000 of profits compared with £162,000,000 of profits made by the second group, although they employed just as many men. Just as many millions of labour employed, and only about one-third of the profits made, and the first group carry on their shoulders double the unemployment of the second group! See how the relief is divided between these two. Including the railway and canal relief, which will be passed on to the basic industries, £14,250,000 of our £26,000,000 goes to these depressed, basic, unsheltered, exporting and large manpower employing group of industries, and £5,500,000 goes to all the others, including the building trade and many industries which may be characterised as depressed. This group of industries which may be classed as depressed gets nearly three times as much as those which are classed as flourishing industries and this does not include the depressed industry of agriculture.

There remains the question as to whether this state of affairs will be sensibly altered by the new valuation which is now proceeding. When firms are doing badly they can claim at any time their rights at law to a reduction; and we have taken into consideration in our estimates the revision downwards which is taking place in the depressed trades. We have reduced our estimate of the cost to the Government of the relief from about £28,000,000 to £26,000,000 as a result of the changes which are taking place in the relative position of the depressed trades.

When you come to the less depressed or more prosperous trades they are waiting for the ordinary process of revaluation, because it is probable that, if they are affected at all, in the main the movement will be upwards and not downwards. I am advised that £1,000,000 would be a generous estimate of the increased net burden which would fall upon the whole of the not-depressed, the flourishing group, as the result of the revaluation, and this assumes that over the whole of this group, including the building trade, prosperous and non-prosperous alike, the increase in assessments will, after any reduction in poundage has been taken into consideration, increase their rate burden by as much as 20 per cent. If that is so, you will have to add £1,000,000 to the £5,500,000 which I mentioned as going to the not depressed group. But what is the effect of such an incident on the figures I have quoted? It does not in the slightest degree affect the validity of the argument I have used, and that argument shows that the Liberal statement that more relief is going to the flourishing than to the depressed industries is not true; that the exact contrary is the truth; and not only the exact contrary, but the exact contrary multipled four or five times over.

I see the right hon. and learned Member for Spen Valley (Sir J. Simon) in his place, and I believe he is going to follow me or speak in the course of this Debate. I invite him to deal with this matter. He has committed himself to the statement that the bulk of the relief goes to the flourishing trades. In face of the figures I have given, which I am certain cannot be challenged, will he withdraw that statement and expunge from the Order Paper of the House of Commons one of the most grotesque falsehoods which any great party has ever placed upon it? I am astonished that such a statement should have received the responsible approval of the Liberal party. They always tell us that they have the intelligence of both the other parties put together. We know that they have great advantages in examining these matters, great resources with which to embark on research, and they have just given us the Yellow Book with all their clever thinkers writing and studying these matters. It is most disconcerting to find such a grotesque error, such a ghastly departure from actual facts, appearing in their responsible official Amendment. I have paid as much attention to the Liberal Yellow Book as anybody else, and, if this is the method by which it has been constructed, if this is the opinion which has animated those who have compiled it, my confidence in its pages is greatly shaken.

I am going to pursue this argument one step further. I have already said that the test by industries as to whether they are depressed or flourishing is not adequate, you must take account of the firms within those industries which may be depressed or flourishing. The resources of the Inland Revenue enable me to carry this probing one stage deeper. I am going to deal with trades in the depressed group. First, Iron, Steel and Engineering. We estimate that one-quarter of our rate relief will go to the firms which are making four-fifths of the profits in that trade and that three-quarters of the rate relief will go to the firms which are only making one-fifth of the profits, or actual losses. In Shipbuilding, 7 per cent. of our rate relief goes to those firms that are making three-quarters of the profits and 93 per cent. of the relief goes to those who are making only one-quarter of the profits, or making actual losses. In Metals, under one-half of the relief goes to those making nine-tenths of the profits and the other half of the relief goes to those who are only making one-tenth of the profits, or actual losses. In Cotton, one-fifth of the rate relief goes to those firms making seven-tenths of the profits, and four-fifths of the relief goes to those firms making three-tenths of the profits. In Wool, one-half of the rate relief goes to those firms making four-fifths of the profits, and the other half to those firms making one-fifth of the profits, or actual losses. In Bleaching and Dyeing, 56 per cent. of the relief goes to those firms making 85 per cent. of the profits, and 44 per cent. of the relief goes to those making 15 per cent. of the profits, or actual losses.

When you pursue the distribution of this relief below industries and into individual firms, it is certain that the overwhelming mass of the relief is going to those who need it most. Not only are the less flourishing or depressed industries helped four or five times as much as the so-called flourishing trades, but the depressed firms in these industries are also helped in a multiplied degree compared to prosperous firms. Such are the facts deduced from a study of the Inland Revenue figures upon which the almost incredibly accurate forecasts are made from year to year by Chancellors of the Exchequer.

I have only one more observation to make; I leave the facts and come to the theory underlying the Liberal Amendment. Their facts are wrong. They have been completely demolished; not a single vestige or scrap of solid basis is left for them. They are the reverse of the truth. Even if their facts were accurate, it would be impossible in practice to apply them on account of the difficulties of machinery, and, if it were possible to apply them, the theory on which they rest is wholly fallacious. I ask, is it right to try and discriminate between prosperous and non-prosperous industries? It is quite true that we are giving £5,000,000 or £6,000,000 to industries which in the main do not fall in the category of depressed industries. Are we right in doing it? If this country is going to move with the times, if it is going to pay for its imports, provide employment for its people and provide revenue for the Exchequer it is absurd to develop a hostile attitude towards flourishing industries. The character of our industry is constantly changing. It is moving forward into the higher ranges of manufacture, and while we are seeking to relieve the main body which is lagging behind, and, particularly, the rearguard, it would be madness to hinder the advance guard of our industries, which is continually gaining valuable positions for the future.

I am sure the position which has been adopted by the Liberal party under the guidance of the right hon. Gentleman the Member for Carnarvon Boroughs is one which is entirely out of harmony with all their main doctrinal principles. The right hon. Gentleman has always been a man of expedients, never a man of theme and system. The great services which he rendered to the country were rendered by instinct and nimbleness in dealing with point after point as they arose, but they did not take the form of laying out a smooth and ordered scheme either in politics or in strategy. In this case, he has induced the Liberal party to take up a position which is absolutely subversive of the main economic creed of orthodox free trade. This attack upon prosperous industries because they are prosperous, this suggestion that they ought to continue to bear this invidious burden because they are doing well, is not merely unorthodox, but squalid in its character. This kind of argument which he uses, the attitude he adopts towards Mr. Courtauld, is exactly the same as that which the present Stalin Government in Russia are adopting towards Kulaks or industrious peasants. This is their general attitude towards the mass of the peasants, and, incidentally, they have killed the soul of Russia and are now in a position where they can be made the target for political propaganda and abuse. I commend this ghastly error to the attention of Liberal doctrinaires. So far as His Majesty's Government are concerned, we repulse these crude and barbaric ideas. If any country harbours them it will cut itself off from all share in that general expansion of material comfort and enjoyment which scientific capitalistic civilisation, properly corrected by democratic institutions, has now to offer all over the world.

[Later] I did not attempt to deal with anything but the first part of the scheme, which is the relief of productive industry. The second part of the scheme is the reimbursement of the local authority. In the process of reimbursement of the local authority, a process of readjustment which will help necessitous areas will come into play. That subject will occupy the Autumn. For the present, we are dealing only with the scheme for relieving productive industry. The only relief, under this part of the scheme, which the local authority will get, is if industry should revive within its area in consequence of the reduction of the rate burden. It is the second part of the scheme which will deal with necessitous areas.

RATING AND VALUATION (APPORTIONMENT) BILL

June 7, 1928

House of Commons

I am sure that we shall most of us agree with the earnest impulse which lies at the back of the impassioned speech to which we have just listened, but it was a pity that the hon. Member [Mr. Lansbury] was so precipitate in condemning the policy on which His Majesty's Government have now embarked as to say that it was the most idiotic scheme which could be suggested, because, after all, he has not seen the whole policy. Nor does he know at all what will be the ultimate effects of this policy, when it is unfolded in the course of a year, on his own constituents, or whether it will make a better or worse provision for them. It would be wise, before condemning the results of the policy and its conception as utterly idiotic, to make quite sure what it is you have before you. At any rate, there is one thing I can say in reply to the hon. Gentleman, and that is that the effort is a sincere one. He has reminded me of 20 years ago, when we first set up the Employment Exchanges in this country, and he says what a fraud and disappointment they have been, or words to that effect.

Mr. Lansbury: I said that they have not solved unemployment.

Mr. Churchill: Of course, they have not solved all the problems. They have not solved them any more in England than in countries as distant and as different in their characteristics as the United States and Russia—[*Interruption*]—and Russia. At any rate, one may say that they have become an absolutely vital and integral part of British social life and that there will never be a Government in this country which will uproot, eliminate, or destroy this organism which was then brought into being. For myself I would say that this effort which we are making now is at least an effort of sincerity. I do not wish for a moment to exaggerate its results, and I do not claim for it at all what the hon. Gentleman and his friends are so often ready to claim for their own proposals—that it will be a cure-all and immediately remedy the immense disparities and causes of discontent in our modern civilisation. All I can say is that this is a sincere effort, and the hon. Gentleman and those who sit with him and behind him will make a great mistake if they imagine that it is in their party interests to set themselves precipitately against a careful study of this project.

I am called upon at the end of this long Debate to deal with the salient points which have emerged. It has been a Debate in which the attendance has not been large, but in which the quality of the speeches has been extremely well maintained. Let us just see what these salient points are, not only in the course of this discussion, but since the Budget was opened and the general policy announced. First of all, I think I may say that to-night a certain number of false assumptions and wrong-headed opinions have been definitely swept out of the path of our future discussions. There is the contention that this policy gives more relief to the flourishing industries than it gives to the depressed industries. That has been placed on the Order Paper of the House on the high authority of the right hon. Gentleman the Member for Carnarvon Boroughs (Mr. Lloyd George) and the right hon. Gentleman the Member for Spen Valley (Sir J. Simon)—the highest combination of fire and judgment that you can possibly imagine. They have committed themselves to that proposition, and, as a result of this discussion, I venture to say that it has been entirely destroyed. The exact reverse is the truth.

I was looking to-night at some figures which have been brought under my notice and I find, for instance, that the great firm of Courtaulds made last year £4,500,000 of profit for their shareholders. They paid only £45,000 in rates. You find in the iron and steel and engineering trades between 400 and 500 concerns making together a similar volume of profits. There 400 or 500 firms taken together, although they make no more in profits than the firm of Courtauld, pay 20 times the rates which are paid by Courtauld's, and under our scheme they will obtain 20 times the relief. Cases like that can be multiplied to any extent you like. [An Hon. Member: "What about assisting Courtauld, then?"] What is the use of suggesting that the whole of this scheme should be held up because under the application of a common principle there is one particular firm that does not need it? [Hon. Members: "Why not?"] I am quite prepared to face all the taunts that you may make about particular firms which are in a good position which will gain some advantage out of this scheme. I am prepared to face that rather than depart from the general principle which we are applying to the whole of industry, because the moment you allow yourself to be guided by spite and envy you get into difficulties.

The second suggestion, I think, that has been demolished is the "pick and choose" plan. It is admitted that it cannot be carried out. You cannot pick and choose between the different industries of the country, between the prosperous and the unprosperous. If you are to apply your principle, you must apply it with uniformity. The third suggestion which has been demolished in these Debates has been the suggestion that you should spread your relief, such as it is—little enough we have to give, and hard enough to get it—over the whole area of shops and houses. Obviously, if you spread £26,000,000 over the whole of the rateable area and over all forms of rateable property the relief you would give to any one firm and to productive industry as a whole would be inappreciable, and would not have any noticeable effect in altering the course of events or give any real stimulus to our productive industry. If, on the other hand, you were to try to offer three-quarters relief all over the whole area of the rates, the cost would be prohibitive to the central Government, amounting to £130,000,000. What would happen to local government if they were all to be pensioners of the central Exchequer and their ratepayers were to decide on the expenditure of money in the provision of which they would have no further concern?

Then the right hon. Gentleman the Member for Colne Valley (Mr. Snowden) challenged the distinction which we have drawn between the productive and the distributive industries. He said that production and distribution are like a pair of scissors, but it is not true. It is quite true that they work together, but very great distinctions can be drawn between production and distribution and I shall try to draw one or two of those distinctions. In the first place, production in this country faces on the whole worldwide competition, whereas distribution has closed markets. Of course, there is great competition between distributors within those closed markets, but foreigners do not come into this country to run railways or fleets of motor cars and so forth. I say that is a distinction. Here is another difference between the two. The basic productive industries are flagging and failing, and flagging and failing in an alarming degree, and on the other hand the distributive industries as a whole are doing quite well. [*Interruption.*] I can hardly call the export trade distribution. The distributive industries have done very well since the War and are holding their own. But supposing you were to apply this present scheme of ours to the distributive industry, how would it work out?

I have explained, and I trust proved, that in regard to the productive industries the vast bulk of the relief will go to the depressed trades. I think that the reverse would happen in the distributive trades. The pressures under which the distributors are working are quite different from those under which the producers are working. The producer seeks places where rates are lowest, but the distributor does not mind how high the rates are, because he can pass it on to the consumer. Whoever heard of a shopkeeper leaving a town because the rates were high? Whoever heard of a suggestion that Mr. Selfridge should leave Oxford Street because of the burden of rates there, and go out and set up an establishment in open fields in Hendon or Edgware? The best place for a great emporium to set up is in the town even though rates may be high there, whereas in the producing trade some of the concerns simply cannot carry on unless they find relief from their present rates burden. I have no doubt whatever that the distinction that has been drawn and which I drew in opening the Budget between the productive and the distributive trades is one which the more searchingly it is examined the more true and unshakable it will be found. So I say that in all these respects we may claim that the result of this discussion up to the present moment has left the Government position absolutely unshaken. [*Interruption.*] Who is now suggesting that you should pick and choose? Who is now disputing that more relief goes to the depressed than to the flourishing industries? Who is now really maintaining that we should spread this £26,000,000 widely—bread and scrape—over the whole country?

There are some points which have not yet been disputed. One is that there ought to be on the whole a fairer balance as between the competition of road and rail. We believe that the railways have not had entirely fair play against road competition, heavily subsidised as the latter has been by reason of the inadequate share which it has paid in respect of the damage to roads. That we have heard nothing about. Then there is the question of coal versus oil. That is an issue which certainly requires a great deal of thought, because if we could by any means produce from our own coalfields a modern fuel either liquid or pulverised, it would give to basic industries in the twentieth century something of the great advantage they had enjoyed during the whole of the nineteenth century. I have not heard a word about that.

Then there is the question of wider areas for local government. There may be local and parochial disputes about that but, in principle, one knows that there are real advantages in the field of local government to be gained by wider areas. And lastly, there is the question that some relief should be given to necessitous areas in a form which would achieve a broader equalisation of rates. I say that there are four points which we have completely demolished and four other points, salient points, in this scheme which have not been in any way disputed. The right hon. Member for Colne Valley yesterday made a most extraordinary assertion and one which his party ever since he uttered it have been occupied in trying to whittle away. The right hon. Member for Carnarvon Boroughs made a sort of friendly covering apology for it in the course of his speech this afternoon. The right hon. Member for Colne Valley said: "Rates, as such, are no burden on industry." I might say disease as such is no burden on anybody. It is all a question of the incidence. It is one of the most extraordinarily unwary statements that has ever fallen from the lips of an experienced politician. He also indicated that they were infinitesimal in their burden on industry—as such, no doubt. If you take a pair of opera glasses and look at an object in the ordinary way and then turn them round so that the object is diminished, you will get exactly the mental process through which the right hon. Gentleman has gone. [An Hon. Member: "As such!"] Yes, as such.

Before this scheme was broached we were told that rate relief was the most vital thing for the country. I will not read all the statements which were made—Liberal and Labour statements—but as soon as the Government introduces a proposal the right hon. Gentleman comes forward and says, "What is this for? What is the good of all this?" [An Hon. Member: "As such!"] As such. Of course, it is rather discouraging in a way. In the discussions since the Budget was introduced no one has hitherto attempted to prove that the boon to industry will not be substantial. But now the right hon. Gentleman has committed himself to denying that proposition. I am going to give a few instances in order to show how grave is the need of industry and how important will be the relief it will get. A few days ago I gave a list to the House of the industries which could beyond challenge be called depressed, and I mentioned seven conditions which should be fulfilled.

These industries constitute two-thirds of our export trade; some £500,000,000 of exports are accounted for by these industries, and they obtain three-quarters of the whole of the relief which we give to industry. That is, industries covering two-thirds of the export trade of this country receive three-quarters of the whole relief to industry. No one can doubt that that is going to be a great help to our export trade, and no one can doubt the way in which it will help the export trade. [An Hon. Member: "How?"] It will help it by increasing its competitive power in every market into which our goods enter. We cannot pass the rates on to the foreign consumer. The export market is outside our control. Our trade has to go into the markets of the world and enter into competition with other countries, and everyone knows that contracts very often turn on the smallest fraction. I believe, indeed it is impossible to doubt, that the concentrated effect of £14,500,000 per annum in relief to this group of industries, which covers two-thirds of our export trade, will make an appreciable difference in our competitive power. After all, we are a crowded island and have to buy four-fifths of our bread from abroad, and the easing of the burden on our export trades by a strong and concentrated thrust of this character is not a matter which anyone can afford to sweep aside as a negligible thing in our economic life.

The hon. Member who spoke last asked, "What is the good of all this? What about coal?" I do not pretend that it will solve the problem of coal but, at any rate, it will be a help. I am not pretending to solve the whole problem, but I would point this out. The right hon. Member (Mr. Snowden) spoke of this relief to coal as being worth 3d. per ton. That is not so. Our calculation is that, with the railway freight relief— [Hon. Members: "Oh, oh!"] Why should you not count that as well? It is worth 6-1/2d. per ton on the average over the coal trade.

Mr. Shinwell *rose*. [*Interruption*.]

Mr. Churchill: Hon. Members will not be sorry if it is so. Is that no help?

Mr. Shinwell: You cannot ride off like that.

Mr. Churchill: I hope I may be allowed to continue my argument. [*Interruption*.] It really is not a proper way of carrying on a Debate in a representative House like this.

Mr. Shinwell *rose*—

Hon. Members: Order, order!

Mr. Churchill: May I be permitted to resume my argument? I am in possession of the House, and I hope that I shall be allowed to proceed.

Mr. Shinwell: You ought to give way.

Hon. Members: Name, name!

Mr. Batey: Tell us about coal.

Mr. Churchill: I hope I may be permitted to go on with my argument. The hon. Member has no right to call upon me to sit down while I am in possession of the House. Are hon. Members opposite really so uncomfortable about this policy that they are going to silence a speaker by interruptions of this kind? I do not mind in the least, and I will gladly answer any questions when the proper opportunity arrives. I was trying to say that the relief given to coal by this Measure amounted to 6-1/2d. per ton averaged over the whole field. The burden of the mining royalties is estimated on the average to be about 6-1/4d. It is the first time I have ever heard from any representative of the party opposite that the mining royalties are not an incubus and a burden on the coal industry. I have heard speech after speech in Debates for the last 20 years showing what a relief and help it would be if the mining royalties were lifted from the back of the coal industry. But nobody has ever proposed to lift these royalties from the back of the coal industry. All that they have suggested is that the Exchequer should buy out the royalty owners and should collect the royalties itself. That would be no help at all to the mining industry. Here we are giving something which it is admitted affords a benefit to the mining industry as a whole, in which both parties, employers and employed, share under the wage-sharing agreement; we are giving relief to that industry as a whole as great as if we had completely eliminated mining royalties. The state of the coal trade at the present time shows, under the most recent ascertainments, in every single district throughout the country an actual loss, and yet we are extracting £3,500,000 a year from this trade in respect of rates. How long can we go on in regard to the weaker pits?

An Hon. Member: As long as you are in office.

Mr. Churchill: It will go on until the steps which we are now taking become effective. I now turn to the firms and industries included in the list which I gave to the House on Tuesday last, and which I classified—I admit roughly—as depressed, or at any rate as not flourishing. Of the firms that are in this list I have extracted from the table a very large number which are either making no profits at all, or are making actual losses, or are making less profits than the rates which they pay. Simply from these trades—Iron, Steel, Shipbuilding and Engineering; Metals; Cotton; Wool; Bleaching and Dyeing—simply from those five groups of trades there are firms which pay £75,000,000 in wages and salaries, and which are providing a livelihood for at least 500,000 or 600,000 persons—firms every one of which is either running at a loss or is making less profits than it pays in rates. Therefore, you may say that over the whole of this vast area—and, mark you, there is not one of us on either side of the House who has not got some of these firms in his own constituency—over the whole of this vast area you have got businesses which are gradually approaching the moment when, after having paid rates out of capital for a number of bleak years, they will find that they are becoming exhausted and that they will have to close down. Is that not a matter which is of great consequence to industry? Is that not a matter which is of great consequence to this country? Is the fact that there are 600,000 people living on firms which are actually waterlogged not a matter of deep and earnest concern? How are our trade union leaders to get any sort of strong pressure for lifting the level of wages? [Interruption.] I say that there are 1,100,000 unemployed at the present time, and if nothing is done you may have the prospect of another 200,000 or 300,000 being added to them.

You may say that our scheme is wrong, but, believe me, it is not a scheme which you can afford to treat with derision here or on any platform. I say that it is of consequence to all those who care about the workers. It is said that our scheme is of no assistance to the shopkeepers, but is the potential closing down of these firms all over the place of no consequence to the small shopkeepers who serve the people who work in these firms; small shopkeepers whose credit has perhaps been strained to the limit by the disastrous consequences of the industrial civil war of 1926? To say that those shopkeepers are not included in this scheme is beside the point. I say that they have no greater interest than that these firms which are now so hard pressed and in regard to whose position the burden of rates may well be the determining factor, should be enabled to continue to keep their doors open and employ their men. Having said that in answer to the statement and suggestion of the right hon. Gentleman for Colne Valley that rates as such are no burden on industry, I have a suggestion to make to him that, dating from to-morrow, he should begin a pilgrimage about the country. I suggest that he should go to Newcastle and to Sheffield [Hon. Members: "Dundee"]. I suggest that he should go to Dundee—[Interruption]. I suggest that he should go to the rural areas and that he should say to the workmen and to the people who are managing the actual businesses by which they live, that he should say to the farmer— [Hon. Members: "To the brewer"] —"Rates as such are no burden on industry." I cannot think of any better way in which the right hon. Gentleman could employ the next twelve months.

But I leave the right hon. Gentleman, and, if the House will bear with me for a few minutes more, I would rather not sit down without paying my respectful tribute to the speech of the right hon. Gentleman the Member for Carnarvon Boroughs. I administered, I trust with due respect, all things considered, a mild Parliamentary castigation to the right hon. Gentleman on Tuesday last. I did it for his own good, and in the brief process of time which has elapsed I see that it has had a very salutary effect, because the right hon. Gentleman spoke in a most chastened mood to-day and he conducted a series of retirements, under cover of the heavy fire of his oratorical artillery, from a good many indefensible positions. We have no longer the assertion from him which figured on the Order Paper a little while ago about the flourishing industries getting more than the depressed industries. He has abandoned the idea of our having to choose between the flourishing and the depressed firms.

Mr. Lloyd George: No.

Mr. Churchill: I certainly understood he had. Well, it may be that the right hon. Gentleman requires another dose. He even went so far as to say that he would give even-handed treatment to the brewers in the scheme which the Liberal party would bring into play—that he would draw no distinction between brewers and any other class. That is very important, but it certainly is not in harmony with the kind of thing which the right hon. Gentleman has been saying on public platforms and elsewhere. He even referred to Mr. Courtauld who is described as "the rich Mr. Courtauld," and "the man who never asks for anything" and so forth.

Mr. Lloyd George *indicated dissent*.

Mr. Churchill: Well, it was not so much what the right hon. Gentleman said as the nasty way he said it. However I note the improvement and it will encourage me on future occasions to continue the treatment as far as may be necessary. There is one matter on which I should like to offer an explanation to the right hon. Gentleman. He evidently was rather annoyed at my reference to the Election of 1918. I did not know that the right hon. Gentleman had anything to reproach himself with over the coupon Election of 1918. Anyhow I am not going to reproach him nor are the great bulk of those who sit on this bench. We were all in it. The great majority of those who sit on this bench followed him and the late Mr. Bonar Law in that Election, and responded to his appeal to make a common front against the common foe. It was not, in any way, a discreditable transaction. On the contrary I approved of it then and I approve of it now. [Hon. Members: "And would do it again!"] Yes, I would do it again. I must say, however, to be quite frank, that I have not been quite tactful or considerate in not remembering sufficiently how much the personal and political position of the right hon. Gentleman has changed since that date.

Mr. Lloyd George: And your own.

Mr. Churchill: No, on the contrary, mine has not changed at all. The right hon. Gentleman from time to time still speaks of the common front against the common foe, but it is a different common front and the opposite common foe. I had not sufficiently paid attention to this alteration in his views and in his attitude, and, therefore, I must express regret if by any tactlessness I have caused him some embarrassment towards the friends with whom he is once again happily reunited. Passing from that point let me deal with what the right hon. Gentleman said. His speech consisted of two parts, namely, a complaint and a plan. So far as the complaint was concerned, it related entirely to a Bill which His Majesty's Government have undertaken to introduce in November next. All his criticisms referred to that Bill. I think when we are advancing a policy of such great complexity, admittedly open to argument on every point, we are entitled to unfold our plan stage by stage. There is nothing in what is now before the House—[Hon. Members: "Hear, hear!"] Little things please little minds. There is nothing in the policy which is now before the House which is not complete in itself. We are providing in the Budget for the money. We are providing in this Bill for the division between the classes of property to be relieved and those not to be relieved. In the autumn we propose to lay before Parliament in legislative form our Measure for the reimbursement of the local authorities. We are not going to be hurried one inch in the unfolding of our necessary plan and, let me say, that the profound ignorance and lack of comprehension displayed by all the most learned and intelligent of the Liberal party—I say nothing of the other party opposite—in regard to that portion of the scheme already before them, should alone prevent us from overloading their consciousness at the present time.

The right hon. Gentleman referred to the Liberal scheme, which as far as I can make out takes the form of making the relief of the able-bodied poor a national charge on the Exchequer. You could hardly have a more vicious plan. You weaken the responsibility of the local authorities, to whom, nevertheless, you must entrust the business of administration. You afford no effective control to the Exchequer which has to pay the Bill. You overburden the already congested business of the national Parliament with continuous disputes about the difficult question of unemployment benefit. Just on the morrow of the House of Commons having decided to free itself, to a large extent, from a vast burden of uncovenanted benefit, you reimport that system into the very centre of our political affairs, and I am assured that if the policy which is proposed by the right hon. Gentleman and his friends in the Yellow Book, and to which he has affirmed his allegiance to-day, were brought into play inequalities of a serious character would arise. For instance, if you put the relief of the able-bodied poor on to the Exchequer, here are some of the effects which, I am assured, would be felt by industry in different cities. Industry in Sheffield would get a relief of one-seventh of its rates; in Newcastle, of one-sixth of the rates; in Middlesbrough, of one-tenth; in Merthyr, of one-fourteenth; in Bolton, of one-thirty-secondth; in Birmingham, of one-thirty-sixth. Those are the reliefs which would be given to industry as a result of the operation of this part, at any rate, of the right hon. Gentleman's scheme. How does that compare, as far as giving a stimulus to industry is concerned, with our plan of giving three-fourths.

Now, Sir, of course we appealed for and invited co-operation in this policy, but I must quite frankly say that I never expected to get it. I was quite sure that we should have to fight every inch of our road, and I think we must be prepared to do so. There are, of course, anomalies and hard cases which could be brought up to baffle the policy of legislation, to darken counsel, and to create prejudice and unpopularity, but I do not believe that an opposition relying only on hard cases and anomalies and inconsistencies can really hold its own against the advance of a concerted and symmetrical scheme. As to all that will be necessary to carry this scheme through, I assign no limits at the present moment to the efforts which will be necessary, but, at any rate, you may be quite sure that both in the relief of productive industry and in the handling of this large rating question, we shall make a good job of what we have set out to do. There will be hard cases, but there is no need really for us to be afraid of that. After all, we are only striking off shackles. The great triumphs and successes of Liberalism in the nineteenth century came from the fact that they were consistently, over several generations, advocating the striking off of shackles on enterprise, trade, and the social life of the country. What we are doing now is to strike the economic shackle of rates from the industries and agriculture of the country, and you cannot tell exactly how, or exactly when, or exactly in what form the benefit will inure, but that everything will be better, somewhat better and somewhat easier, as the result of this removal of a great adverse factor in the efficiency of our production, no one can doubt. When you embark on a course of restriction or repression, caution and hesitancy should rightly impose themselves upon you; but when you are embarked upon a course of relief and liberation, advance with courage.

RATING REFORM

June 8, 1928

Conservative Clubs Association
Smoking Concert, London

I advise you to be in good fettle, as we are in for a fight. So far as one can pierce the veil which hangs before the future, we will probably be at it ding-dong this time next year. (Cheers.) The year before the General Election is one of the most critical and important periods in political life. We have not only to fight for the principles and causes which Conservatism guards, but we have also to carry through in the year before that election a large scheme of constructive policy fraught, we believe, with high and hopeful consequences for our productive industries and for our agriculture. (Cheers.)

The scheme which, on behalf of the Government, I have laid before the House of Commons when the Budget was presented is one of the most extensive and complicated pieces of constructive social and economic reform which has ever been produced in this country. It is folly to tax for local or national purposes the tools or plants of productive industry and agriculture. Let us tax, if we need, the profits which result from industry, but let us not throw sand in the machinery or put a brake on the wheels which are turning to earn our daily bread, by imposing a heavy and invidious system of rating upon our acutal productive plant. If the Government had had fair play, and had not been compelled to face hideous labour and industrial disputes, we would have been possessed of about £80,000,000 more money, and there would have been no need to have imposed the tax upon motorists. I wish it could have been so. Nevertheless, we will all agree that the motoring community has accepted this burden in a patriotic and public-spirited manner—(cheers)—because they know that the money is not be be used for doles or sops, but is going to be used as a powerful lever of an important reform. In placing a tax upon foreign imported liquid fuel we are giving—I do not say a full or complete measure—but a certain measure of legitimate protection to our great coal industry and a powerful stimulus to all those modern processes of extracting oil from coal or making pulverized fuels which are of the utmost importance to us.

The measure relating to rating reform will be presented by Mr. Chamberlain in the House of Commons this autumn. Although it will be a measure full of difficult points, about which legitimate differences of opinion may arise, I have no doubt that it will be carried through with a great and growing body of agreement. It is my firm belief that Conservative candidates at the next election will be able to fight under a declaration of an effective lowering of their rates, not only upon protective industry and agriculture, but upon all classes of the population. (Cheers.)

Both the Labour and Liberal Opposition had been intending to fill this year with denunciations of the rating system and demands that industry should be relieved. They were also proposing to point to the Conservative Government as the government which had no ideas, policy, or plans on these important topics. When the scene was so swiftly transformed a certain amount of irritation was inevitable on their part. (Laughter.) They were simply eaten up with chagrin that this wide field, which they had hoped to exploit for their own purposes, is now firmly occupied by the Government. Just as they were preparing to set up their various rival jack o' lantern platforms, under their various flags, from red to white (laughter), and arrived with all this tackle at the gates of the field, they found the whole ground laid out with the broad foundations of the great work of constructive reform which the Conservatives had already taken in hand. (Cheers.) So they had to unsay all they had said and to reverse all the arguments they had intended to use. Mr. Snowden had to get up in the House of Commons and say that the rates as such were no burden upon productive industry. Mr. Lloyd George had to get up and say: "While I am all in favour of relieving productive industry, this is not the way to do it." I wonder whether any way which the Government had proposed would have encountered from Mr. Lloyd George anything but partisan opposition. "Whatever I do, and whatever I say, Aunt Tabitha tells me it isn't this way." The Government are going to carry out our policy, and if for reasons which I cannot with courtesy analyze too closely Mr. Lloyd George places himself in direct opposition to the policy, we will have to do our best to bowl him over. (Cheers.)

There will be undoubtedly a hard fight, and the issues are of great importance. The responsibilities of the Conservative Party were never so great as they are now in any period of peace. The Liberal Party, which used to be the guardian of many of our liberties, has ceased to have the power to discharge that function, and the Conservative Party has the duty of guarding the liberties of this country against new and dangerous forms of attack. When the Government go to the country we will have a good record to put before the electors. The Prime Minister has realized in a manner which could hardly be dreamed of the ideals of Tory democracy which Lord Beaconsfield created and which, if I may be allowed to say so, were powerfully vivified after his death by Lord Randolph Churchill. (Cheers.)

The Conservative Party has pursued in the past four years a national policy, without grudges to pay off or favours to bestow; we have maintained peace and have brought about an appeasement of those terrible quarrels between France and Germany—an appeasement which gives us the assurance that the future will not be darkened by war clouds. We will further be able to show that we have achieved a notable advance in the cause of inter-Imperial trade. (Cheers.) There never was a time when there was less friction in the Empire or when the forces which make for closer cooperation and unity were working with greater force and strength.

MOTOR TAXATION
June 14, 1928

Treasury, London

I wish to acknowledge the public-spirited and broad-minded attitude with which the motor industry and motorists received and accepted the disappointment and shock which it was my fate to have to administer two months ago. I know that it was a vexatious piece of information to the motorists throughout the country that the long desired petrol tax should come, only to bring with it no marked relief in the general burden of the licence duties. Personally I was very sorry indeed that had to be so. I would have been glad if I could have carried out this larger scheme of relief to productive industry without trespassing at all upon your [the deputation's] domain, and I could have done it if in the last two years we had not had the greatest and most disastrous industrial struggle that has ever occurred in this country, that cost upwards of £80,000,000 to the Exchequer. In those circumstances it has been a matter of great difficulty for me to formulate and propose a constructive policy of relief to industry.

The taxation of imported liquid fuel, which is to an important extent a rival of our coal industry, is, I believe, in accordance with a far-sighted view of national interests. There is also a feeling that motorists of every class are on the whole not the least buoyant members of the community and, therefore, we felt that in our difficulty, and not for the purposes of giving any dole, but as a lever for carrying out a great national measure of relief to productive industry, we might come to that class.

I notice from reports which have reached me from many parts of the country that some of the country omnibus companies are actually collecting from the passenger for a single journey a halfpenny, and in some cases a penny, additional charge, and giving the passenger a receipt on which is stamped "Payment of petrol duty." If the tax represents as much as a halfpenny a mile on the running costs of one of the large omnibuses, the collection of a halfpenny or a penny for the petrol tax from each passenger travelling in an omnibus is profiteering, and as the subject of fares has been raised here I take the opportunity of drawing public attention to it.

I can see no prospect at the present time of a further reduction in the general horse power duty. We are already giving £1,250,000 in reductions, and I have no resources at the present time, especially after dropping the kerosene duty, out of which a further reduction of the horse-power tax will be met.

There are, however, two questions which may be carefully studied for the future. One is that of the second-hand motor-car, and, while I cannot make any promise, I will be glad to be placed in a position to study the matter in more detail for the purposes of the future. Then there is the question of the horse-power tax prejudicing our power-to-market motors adequately in the Dominions to produce vehicles which effectively hold their own against American mass production. That is a more complicated question and I am not quite sure that there will be quite the same unanimity about it.

Owing to the conditions of the horse-power tax the motoring industry has obtained a very complete control of its own home market, but the importance of securing an effective influence in obtaining a substantial and indeed preponderating share in the Dominions market is so great that the matter ought to be studied. The production of a vehicle which will effectively meet Dominion needs seems to me to be one of the very first problems to which motor manufacturers should address their minds, and I will study any proposal which will have the effect of facilitating this object. But there, again, I can not be held to be making any promise.

I certainly cannot contemplate any further surrender of revenue at the present time. With regard to mitigations which could be given in view to the imposition of the petrol tax, we put our whole hand on the table straight away, and in consequence are not really in a position to find any more money in the present year.

PRAYER BOOK MEASURE

June 14, 1928

House of Commons

The debates on the Revised Prayer Book provoked some of the finest Parliamentary oratory of modern politics. Although accepted by the Lords, it was twice rejected by the Commons. It aroused intense passions–but principally outside the Church.

I shall not attempt to follow the right hon. and gallant Member for Newcastle-under-Lyme (Colonel Wedgwood) in the deeply-moving passages of which his speech consisted. If I venture to trespass on the attention of the House it is only very briefly to explain, in the first place, a personal point of view, and for a few moments to examine the subject which is under discussion from a definitely more secular angle than that which has directed most of the speeches to which we have listened with so much interest this afternoon and yesterday. Personally, I do not like the new Prayer Book. It contains some things which I should feel bound to vote against if they were presented separately, and if I could do so without injury to larger issues. Moreover, on purely sentimental grounds, I regret the departures which it contains from the old-fashioned and archaic wording to which we have all been accustomed from our childhood, and especially in the Marriage Service. I do not like those departures from the old forms. On the other hand, I do not for a moment take the responsibility of rejecting the whole Measure on account of these dislikes and grievances, and therefore on the last occasion I abstained from voting. The development of the controversy seems now to have raised practical issues of a larger and graver character, outweighing my own personal feelings, and requiring a decision which I feel it would not be right for any one of us to shirk.

Like most Members in this House, I think, I have no guidance from those I represent. The religious opinion in my constituency is divided, as it is, I suppose, in the constituencies of nearly everyone here. The subject was in no sense an issue at the last General Election. Men's minds were directed and their votes were cast upon topics which bore no relation to the problem which is now before us. Therefore, like a good many others I expect, who have been sitting through these Debates and the very remarkable one of last December, I have been forced to examine the matter in the light of a new and to some extent unforeseen situation, and also to examine it in the light of what one may, as far as one's judgment goes, imagine to be its potential consequences. I have listened to all these Debates, and the point of view which I venture to submit to the House—as I say, very briefly indeed, for I know there are others far more qualified than I am to take part in the discussion who are waiting to speak—has never been so well expressed by anyone who has spoken as it was in the very impressive speech of the hon. Member for the Brightside Division of Sheffield

(Mr. Ponsonby). I say, with him, that it is our duty to examine this matter, not as members of this or that Church or communion—I examine it not as a member of the Church of England, but as a Member of the House of Commons.

We are compelled to take a decision about the affairs of a great religious community. This community ask, by the recognised means of corporate expression which is open to them, for a wider interpretation of their freedom in spiritual matters. If they were asking for penal powers against their members, or against members who did not agree with them, then, indeed, I could conceive that Parliament would assume its most vigilant air, and cast its most jealous eyes on anything in the nature of repressive or constrictive measures; but when they are asking only for a wider measure of freedom and for an optional alternative form of worship then, I say, undoubtedly the onus of proof rests upon those who invite us to refuse their demands. The primary presumption with which we approach this decision as Members of the House of Commons must obviously be against the denial of liberties which are lawfully demanded. To refuse to a religious community a wider latitude in spiritual matters is a very objectionable step for any modern Legislature to take. It appears to be contrary to the spirit of religious toleration which, I am quite sure, would rule the House of Commons in the case of any other faith or sect among the hundreds which exist side by side within the circuit of the British Empire. So far as I am aware, the large majority of the Church of England, utilising the only means of corporate expression open to them, and wishing to dwell together as a common Protestant body, ask for this widening of their spiritual liberties.

Doubt is thrown upon the validity of this demand. [*Interruption.*] All human processes of expressing corporate opinion are vitiated by imperfections. There never has been any process by which opinion can be measured and expressed over wide areas or great numbers of persons which do not enable the minorities to impugn the character of the decision, or to say that the decision was not representative, or that motives were perverted, or that some incidental circumstance intervened to vitiate the character and validity of the decision. If you are going to take that line, then I do not see how expression by an organisation on a large scale is possible. As a member of Parliament, owing my position in this House to these same expressions of corporate opinion which now are vitiated from many points of view by imperfections of which everyone is a judge, I feel bound to accept the corporate expression of the wish of the Church of England as representing the main opinion of that religious body, and especially of those who are responsible for carrying on its future life and work.

Only overwhelming reasons—that is my submission, though I quite agree everyone has his opinion—could justify our frustrating their constitutionally expressed desire. And so I would ask, "Do these overwhelming reasons exist?" Here again everyone must judge for himself. Personally, I do not think they do. I can quite understand the attitude of those who hold the opposite opinion, but, personally, I cannot think that any of the objections, which would be overwhelming if well-founded, have been proved. I do not believe that we are in the presence of an impending reversion of the Church of England to Roman Catholicism or a break-up of the Reformation settlement. Although it is quite true that this new Book contains features which I, for one, regard as regrettable and undesirable, I cannot see that there is the slightest truth in that suggestion. I agree that no one can really trust more than his own opinion and express more than his own conviction on this subject. I was very much impressed with the account of the Lausanne Conference given by a Member on the Labour benches at the close of last night's Debate in which he quoted the judgment upon this particular Measure of all the Protestant sects and creeds of Europeans gathered together representing all the orthodox Free Churches, and he read out their view as follows:

> The Ecclesiastical Committee, after careful consideration, reported that in their view the Measure of 1927 did not appear to affect the constitutional rights of His Majesty's subjects, and were of opinion that it should proceed.

They go on to say that the Revised Measure which they have also considered in no way leads them to alter their opinion. That is not a matter of individual opinion; it is an opinion expressed by all the Protestant groups in Europe, and clearly they do not consider that anything in these proposals affects the foundation of the Reformation settlement, or constitutes anything in the nature of a reversion by the Church of England to Roman Catholicism. Therefore, the overwhelming reasons for rejecting this Measure are not present, and in their absence the case against the denial of wider spiritual freedom holds the field.

These thoughts are reinforced by separate sets of considerations of an extremely practical character, and I will mention them very briefly to the House. What, in fact, are the powers of Parliament in these days over spiritual matters? Our legal constitutional rights are unchallenged, and about that there is no dispute. I confess that I am very sceptical of the powers of the House of Commons to enforce its will in spiritual matters upon anybody, and still more to pronounce a judgment upon such matters. But while I am sceptical of our competence to arrive at a final decision, no one can say that at the present time the attitude of the Church is aggressive; in fact, it seems to me to be a most submissive attitude in the face of the most unexpected rebuff which it received last winter, the result of which has been these amended proposals. They have pruned from their proposals certain unessential stumbling blocks which were commented on in the Debates of that time, and they have now come back to the House of Commons.

The Church stands at the Bar of the House of Commons and waits. That, to me, is a most surprising spectacle. Here you have the greatest surviving Protestant institution in the world patiently listening to Debates on its spiritual doctrines by twentieth century democratically-elected politicians who, quite apart from their constitutional rights, have really no credentials except goodwill. It is a strange spectacle, and rather repellent. Under the surface, things are not quite the same. Thirty years ago, I used to think that people could be ordered about as if they were a troop of dragoons, but that is not possible to-day in religious matters. In these modern times no one can deny that the vote of any lay assembly like this, which includes a large number of persons belonging to separate rival communities, are unqualified–[Hon. Members: "Why?"]–I am expressing my view, and I have every intention of expressing my view without modifying it in the slightest degree. I assert that in an assembly like this, a large majority are unqualified to deal with the theological issues which are involved. To suppose that such a body in the twentieth century is going to determine the spiritual observances of a religious community is a very difficult matter to accept, and it is repulsive to the modern mind. I am sure such a view would be instantly repudiated by any religious body which claims divine sanction for its work. Therefore, it seems to me that if the Church of England is refused the spiritual relief for which it asks, an undoubted severance will, in fact, take place from that very moment. I am not in the counsels of the Church, and I speak for no one but myself, but I apprehend that the Church would thenceforward declare its own policy, and it would be for Parliament, if the Church diverged too far, to take the initiative and take action against the Church in consequence of its diversion.

There, in fact, lies the sole remedy of Parliament. In the present age the State cannot control the Church in spiritual matters; it can only divorce it. I have seen it suggested that the State could strip the Church of its material belongings, take away its cathedrals and confiscate its stipends. All our history shows that such action has no effect whatever in spiritual affairs, except to influence people in the contrary direction. The refusal of the wider freedom which is now contemplated means the moral separation of the Church and State of this Realm. As to when and how material separation would be effected, that all depends on circumstances and the time, although in such matters time is not necessarily a vital factor. The moral link would be broken by an adverse vote to-night, and I cannot feel that the regrettable features in the New Prayer Book are important enough to justify so precipitate and far-reaching a decision. Parliament should use its constitutional rights with tolerance and moderation, if only for the fact that a violent assertion of its rights may render them obsolete for ever.

I have only one other observation to make, and it is, what will be the immediate consequence of this vote? Either way it must be very unfortunate. I regret that the controversy has reached us in this form, but it has reached us, and we have before us a choice of evils. I have been anxiously asking myself which set of evils is the lesser. In any case, someone will have to carry on the spiritual and daily work in the life of the Church, and if Parliament should dismiss the Church's request, who will carry on that work? Somebody will have to carry it on, and I do not think it will be my right hon. Friend the Home Secretary. The Bishops, the clergy, and the Church Assembly, who alone can give the Church guidance, will have been repudiated by the House of Commons if this Measure is rejected. They will be unable to resign. They will be in the position of a Government which has been defeated on a vital question and is unable to resign.

Mr. Thurtle: Why cannot they resign?

Mr. Churchill: I do not think you could have a more melancholy spectacle than that. No doubt the Bishops will do their best, but no one is going to accept the vote of 14th June, 1928, as giving any spiritual guidance in regard to the religious body that will have to carry on the work of the Church. The Bishops will have no authority except in so far as they separate themselves from Parliamentary domination. I am not speaking for the Bishops. I have no right or claim to speak for them. I am only giving my own view. If this Measure be rejected, there will be a state of no law in the Church—[Hon. Members: "Why?"] —and an increasing divergence of practice. If the Church breaks up into different sects, Low, Broad, and High, and if its dominant practice in future years diverges from the essential Protestant character of this country, it is always open to the State to apply its final remedy.

Some people talk easily and airily about disestablishing the Church, but it seems to me that it is much easier said than done, and I do not envy any Government that has to enter upon the disestablishment and disendowment of the Church of England. The Liberals will not have the power, and a very exceptional situation would be required to make it likely that either a Conservative or a Labour administration would plunge into such a controversy. My contention is that the rejection of this Measure will inaugurate a period of chaos—[Hon. Members: "No!"] —which could only be corrected by disestablishment, but which would not be corrected by any party in any period which we can now foresee. I have yet to learn that there is a worse alternative than that, and that is the alternative which seems to me to follow almost inevitably from the dispossession of the Church authorities from the control and guidance of their own spiritual affairs. In such a situation, one has to decide whether one wishes to see structures and unities dissolved, or whether one is on the side of those who wish to see the continuity of English life carried forward in a spirit of mutual forbearance. I have no doubt where I stand on that issue. I do not wish to see the mitred front of the one great remaining Protestant Church in Europe irretrievably broken into discordant fragments. I would like to see the English people—and this is an English matter mainly—make a further effort to work together for the sake of preserving those English institutions which have largely formed the nation and which are ancient because they have been flexible.

"SIX DIFFERENT OPPOSITIONS"

June 23, 1928

Conservative Meeting,
Hale Park, Widnes

It was one of the definite objects of the Government when the gold standard was reintroduced to cause a steady reduction in the cost of living. According to figures supplied by the Inland Revenue, the greater cheapness of ordinary commodities, not making allowances for any alteration in wages, raised the true value of wages of workpeople in this country by more than £100,000,000 during the present Government's tenure of office. That is £100,000,000 fructifying in the pockets of the people, and every shilling is gathering a fuller and richer return in the vital interests for which it is exchanged.

I do not pretend that my Budget proposal to relieve productive industries and agriculture is a cure-all policy, but I submit that it constitutes a solid, timely, and practical contribution to the most urgent of our immediate economical problems. If you are in search of a cure-all policy that will rid the world of poverty, hard work, and injustice, and enable every one to realize in a moment the most airy dreams of their fancy, it is to the Socialists you must go. (Laughter.) They will be able to promise you all those things, and as long as you are not able to visit Russia you will not have any certain first-hand evidence of the ghastly failure when they tried to perform these promises.

Each of the two main Opposition parties is split into three sections—at least there were only three sections up to last night. (Laughter.) This is the latest, but I must confess I have been busy to-day, and I may be a little bit behindhand. There are, at any rate, only three well-defined, healthy, vigorous, and quarrelsome sections in each of those two parties. Their internal quarrels are their own affairs, and I am bound to say that they seem to pay a great deal of attention to them. These six different oppositions try their utmost to win the prize for being the best at abusing the Government. They all endeavour to enhance their reputation and advance their sectional interest by obstructing and denouncing the policy of the men in charge of affairs, each of them trying to excel the other in vituperation.

The attitude of the Socialist Party is one of hopeful bewilderment and vituperative abuse. So far as the rating proposals of the Budget are concerned, they have not yet found out quite what they are all about, although they have got the unfavourable idea in their minds that on the whole they are rather a good thing for the working classes. I say vituperative abuse because it is almost obligatory of these gentlemen to lavish their censures on the Government.

It is almost life and death to a moderate Socialist or Labour leader to be able to abuse the Conservative Party. It is the only way in which he is able to defend himself against the attacks of those more extreme than he. Many of the trade union leaders are very good-natured, good-hearted fellows by temperament, and may be called moderate Conservatives, patriotic, and perhaps a little too jingo for some tastes. I sympathize deeply with them in their unhappy task in having to work for class hatred and having to mouth those doctrines of spite and envy which did not originate at all in these islands, but which have been borrowed or lent from abroad.

The Liberal Party say: "We are the champion scolds; we are better at it than anyone else. If it is a case of criticizing the Government we are able to cause greater disturbance than anyone. We are the crab-apple. We will back ourselves to beat all records in finding fault." I am willing to adjudge them the palm in this cheery competition. They are more experienced politicians than the Labour Party; they have better-trained minds; they have keener personal rivalries and larger vocabularies.

With regard to our rating proposals—my anxiety is that what we are doing, great though it be, will not be enough, but I say if it is not enough we shall have to go further along that path we have taken or along other paths that will open out from it.

[Editor's Note: Churchill explained the Government's two-fold remedy for "the present vicious great burden" on industry and necessitous areas.] At the end of the month the Government have undertaken to publish a memorandum explaining the general outline of what we are going to do. I will not anticipate more than to say that you will find it will carry a notable measure of relief to those areas which need it most, namely the depressed industrial areas, and it will give a widespread measure of relief to the great mass of the general ratepayers of the country. It will not impose burdens on anyone. (Cheers.)

The measure of rating reform will come into operation at the same time as the relief to productive industry and agriculture so that there will be a connected policy with accumulative effect. Each is good and both together more than twice as good.

MISS AMELIA EARHART

June 25, 1928

*Women's Committee of Air League of
British Empire Luncheon, London*

Eight years ago it was my task at a gathering similar to this to pay some tribute to Messrs. Alcock and Brown when they arrived on this side of the Atlantic after their reckless and lucky flight, the first that had ever spanned the broad Atlantic. It seemed then only a very short while since I remembered my wife coming to my room with the thrilling news that Bleriot had flown the English Channel. Last year I found myself engaged in welcoming Mr. Lindbergh—(cheers)—who was the first to fly the Atlantic alone. And now, this day, I am extremely honoured that I should have been asked to add a few words of sincere appreciation to the many tributes that have been paid to Miss Earhart, the first woman to fly the ocean.

Each of these flights that were successful have been marked by special features. The first of all must always hold that unique quality. (Cheers.) But this latest flight is marked by certain characteristics which are most valuable and hopeful for the future of aviation. With the multiple engine machine we must couple the marvellous feat of navigation performed by Commander Stultz, who, in spite of weather conditions of the most extraordinary embarrassment and danger, managed to steer a true course and arrived within a mile, or a few miles, of the actual point for which he was making. (Cheers.) If we combine these two features we will see that although the courage which was required for this attempt is not diminished we seem to be getting nearer the time when an element of certainty and assurance will be introduced into what has been an extremely hazardous adventure.

FINANCE BILL (AMENDMENTS)

June 25, 1928

House of Commons

It is not because I have nothing to say that I have not so far intervened in this discussion; it is because I have nothing to give. But I should not like to allow the speeches which have been made to pass without a very few words; and, in particular, the observation which was made by the hon. Member for Spennymoor (Mr. Batey) calls for immediate correction. The hon. Member said nothing had been done to bring down the cost of living. When opening the Budget I gave figures, which had been carefully studied before they were made public, showing that, after taking into consideration the changes which have taken place in wages during the last four years, the reduction in the cost of living has added £100,000,000 a year to the purchasing power of the present wage-earners.

The Chairman: The hon. Member for Spennymoor (Mr. Batey) made a statement in parenthesis, and the right hon. Gentleman has replied, but I do not think this point can be pursued.

Mr. Churchill: I want to go no further than to prevent a statement obtaining currency that we are proceeding on the basis of there being no reduction in the cost of living.

Mr. Batey: What have you done towards it?

Mr. Churchill: We have given a very substantial reduction, and it is in relation to that substantial reduction that the Tea Duty must be considered. That duty was very largely reduced by the right hon. Gentleman the Member for Colne Valley (Mr. Snowden). If my memory is right, I think pressure was brought to bear upon him by some of the Liberal Members of that Parliament to make still larger reductions.

Mr. E. Brown: And Conservative Members.

Mr. Churchill: And they were supported by Conservative Members. But the right hon. Gentleman did not feel able to go further, though no doubt he would have liked to make a bigger reduction. I have endorsed his action year by year. I have made the full sacrifice of revenue which was entailed by the remission of duty he made in 1924. I think tea is actually taxed less now than it was before the War. After all the evils which have come upon us from the burden of taxation which is pressing upon so many classes, this old duty, a duty kept on long after the Sugar Duties were removed in bygone days, now stands at a lower level than before the War. Nevertheless, I in no way recede from the view I have expressed on more than one occasion in these discussions, that the Tea Duty is one which anyone in a responsible position would gladly see mitigated or removed from our tariff list. It undoubtedly is a tax which affects the poorest people and on what I may call primary or basic comforts.

It is right and proper that the incidence of this tax should be carefully studied by the House of Commons, and that hon. Members should follow out its ramifications and be acquainted with the actual manner in which particular families are affected by it, and I should be very glad if it were in my power to make some revision of this duty, either total or partial, but I have, as I have had to say on other occasions, heavy expenses to meet. The mere fact that the reduction in the cost of living increases the purchasing power of the pound sterling tends to diminish my revenue as well as to reduce prices in all quarters. In addition to that, I have already in this Budget had to face the loss of the duty upon kerosene, and I have also to face the probability of greater expenditure in regard to the rating relief which we have in view than I originally allowed for. Having all these matters to take into account, I am bound to ask the Committee to excuse me from making any effort to fulfil their wishes this afternoon, although I can say with absolute candour and sincerity that I should be very glad indeed if it fell to my lot to deal with the Tea Duty by giving a substantial mitigation.

[Later] No one would quarrel at all with the contention of the hon. Gentleman that tea which has been condemned should not subsequently be admitted to this country after having been re-exported. No doubt the hon. Gentleman has some particular case in mind, but I feel sure that it must be an exception to the general manner in which our Customs Duties are administered. If it was due to an administrative error, I have no doubt, now that the hon. Gentleman has drawn attention to it, that steps will be taken to see that such an error shall not occur in the future. As to the question whether reasons should be given by the Customs authorities specifying the grounds on which they reject any particular parcel of tea, I am inclined to think that that would throw too great a burden upon the Customs officials.

[Later] The right hon. Gentleman the Member for Colne Valley (Mr. Snowden) has directed the Committee to an Amendment which would certainly, if it were accepted, secure us a combination of the worst of all possible courses, and all the arguments which he used against the tax would be continued in principle, but the advantage to the Revenue would be virtually destroyed. I can understand direct opposition to the Duty on Petrol, but to say that we should impose a duty of a penny upon petrol is in my opinion most unhelpful, and, if I may say so without offence, to set up the whole machinery of this duty merely to place a penny upon it would be obviously futile. The Amendment would involve a loss to the Revenue of £8,750,000 this year and £11,250,000 next year. Of course, if the right hon. Gentleman felt that the proposal which he was making was so unjustifiable in itself that he considered it necessary to state in a perfectly candid manner, a brutal manner, that what he wished to do was to wreck the tax, why go through this farce of reducing it from 4d. to 1d.? I am quite sure that the right hon. Gentleman wishes to wreck this tax, and he knows that if he were successful in wrecking the tax he would wreck the Budget and the policy dependent upon it, and in particular he would succeed in wrecking the scheme of rating reform on which we are working, and would destroy our projects for relieving the necessitous areas, a substantial measure of relief to productive industry and complete relief of rates to agriculture.

I think the right hon. Gentleman has been courageous and candid in taking this attitude of direct and general challenge to the whole proposals which are now being considered. That is what the Amendment amounts to. There is no doubt whatever that without the aid of this tax it would not be possible to make any further progress with the policy which has been unfolded, and we wish to take note of the position which the Opposition have adopted on this question. When the right hon. Gentleman proceeded to detail his arguments there were several points which I think called for reply. In the first place, he represented this tax as one which would fall mainly upon the working classes. I do not think his figures—I will have them examined before the Report stage in detail—will in the slightest justify this contention. The proportion of the tax—I have not got it in my memory at the moment—which is paid by the omnibuses and chars-a-banc is a very small part of the total tax. [An Hon. Member: "It is two-thirds."] No, it is not so at all. The commercial vehicles constitute a very important part of the tax, but our case is, and has always been, that they are at the present time not paying to a proper extent for the damage which they do to the roads, and that they are virtually—

Mr. Riley: May I call your attention—[*Interruption.*]

The Deputy-Chairman (Mr. Dennis Herbert): The hon. Member knows that he cannot speak if the hon. Member who is speaking does not give way.

Mr. Riley: He ought to give way.

Mr. Shinwell: He is always talking about vituperation. Why does he not stand up to it?

Mr. Churchill: The hon. Gentleman had plenty of time, but I shall be perfectly willing to allow the hon. Gentleman to interrupt me if he wishes.

Mr. Riley: May I remind the Chancellor that a question was asked him last week on this very point of the proportion of the burden between privately-owned cars and commercial cars, and the reply of the Chancellor was this. The question was:

> Mr. Robinson asked the Chancellor of the Exchequer—

That is not the question, but, when I produce the answer, he will realise that it is two-thirds commercial vehicles and one-third private vehicles.

Mr. Churchill: I leave it to the Committee to judge whether the hon. Gentleman has made any contribution to the Debate. I stated that only a small proportion of this duty will be collected from the use of hackney vehicles. I have now got the figure, which fully justifies what I stated from my recollection of the facts. Only 16 per cent. of the consumption of petrol may be traced to hackney vehicles, and this covers many other kinds of hackney vehicles, besides the omnibuses and chars-a-banc which are used for the working classes. All the statements put forward by the hon. Gentleman are absolutely unfounded. The great bulk of this duty is paid either by the pleasure or well-to-do traffic or by commercial vehicles. As to the pleasure or well-to-do traffic, it can perfectly well bear this addition to its burdens, and it has been accepted with commendable good will. So far as commercial traffic is concerned, I was about to argue, when I was interrupted and much reproached for not immediately giving way and reproached for being afraid to face the disclosures—never were fears less founded—

Mr. Snowden: This was the question which was put to the right hon. Gentleman on 14th June:

> If he will consider the abolition of the tax on petrol used for commercial purposes?

and he replied:

> I regret that I cannot see my way to adopt the hon. Member's suggestion, which would entail the reduction of the yield of the Duty by about two-thirds.—[Official Report, 14th June, 1928; col. 1158, Vol. 218.]

Mr. Churchill: What has that got to do with the taxation on the working classes? Really, this has not the remotest connection with the facts. When it is sought to justify the original statements, fresh statements are made which have not the remotest connection with the original case. I was proceeding to argue, when I was interrupted on several occasions by hon. and right hon. Gentlemen opposite, who were not in a position to make helpful contributions on the subject, that our case for additional taxation of commercial vehicles is based on the fact that we contend that they are virtually subsidised as against rail traffic, in spite of the tax they bear at present, owing to the great extent to which they cause wear and tear to the roads, not only on account of their weight, but on account of the mileages they run. The ordinary man, who takes his motor bicycle or small car out at the week-end, makes the very slenderest call upon the roads, but the licence duty he pays is computed as though he were using them continuously. On the other hand these commercial vehicles, which play such a valuable part, I readily admit, in our national life, run enormous mileages and of course the mileage of omnibuses are the greatest of all.

I am of opinion that the right hon. Gentleman is perfectly correct in stating that, in some of the country districts, there has been profiteering by some of the omnibus companies. The tickets, which he produced on the Second Reading of the Finance Bill, and others which have been sent to me, leave me no doubt that an altogether excessive charge is being imposed in a certain limited area and over certain limited services on those who use those omnibuses. The calculation is that the duty adds a halfpenny a mile to the cost of running an omnibus. If a halfpenny is collected from 15 or 20 passengers in that vehicle, then it is perfectly clear that profiteering of a very gross character almost amounting to an imposture has made itself apparent in some districts.

Mr. Hardie: You are the father of the crime.

Mr. Churchill: I am the father of a great many things. If they are all to be viewed together, I shall be prepared to recognise my progeny. It always happens, when new taxes are imposed, that here and there considerable difficulties and abuse arise, but competition and, I trust, public opinion in this case will have a salutary effect. The right hon. Gentleman then spoke of the non-road-user of petrol, and indicated that that was a heavy burden on the industry of the country. Out of 805,000,000 gallons of imported petrol, only 50,000,000 are used for the non-road purposes, so that, at any rate, that evil is one the limits of which are comparatively narrow. But I have never attempted to argue that this tax is not a burden. I wish I were in the position to carry forward the large scheme, on which we are engaged, which causes so much perturbation to right hon. Gentlemen opposite, and which the right hon. Member for Colne Valley would gladly hamstring if he could, without this taxation, if that were in my view at all possible. If we had not had the prolonged industrial troubles of 1926—no matter who was responsible—undoubtedly the revenue of the country and our finances to-day would be in such a position that we would be able to carry forward this policy of rating relief without imposing any new duty.

In all the circumstances, it would have been impossible to have gone on without imposing new taxation and I am most gratified and surprised at the manner in which it has been accepted from one end of the country to the other. I thought it a most serious matter to impose this duty, and I thought it would raise a great storm. We went forward ready to face that storm because of the importance of the objects to which we wished to apply the money. But it has been a matter of great relief and satisfaction to me that the general good sense of this country has accepted this tax as one which might well and reasonably be imposed at the present juncture, and has endorsed the view of the Government, that the tax will be far less burdensome in its effect upon our wellbeing than the direct burden of rates on industrial and productive enterprise, and has shown itself ready and willing to accept the burden, because it is the only means by which a far greater evil than the tax can be removed from our industrial and economic life. The right hon. Gentleman with the utmost frankness challenged our general policy. We for our part will be ready now, and at any future time, and in any circumstances, to meet him in direct competition.

[Much later] As far as I am able to comprehend the argument of the hon. Member for Bethnal Green, South-West (Mr. Harris), he wishes to exclude from the Customs Duties such oils as were not actually landed before the 25th of April, which is the operative date. At any rate, that is the effect of his Amendment. The word "imported" has a technical meaning. Section 7, Sub-section (2) of the Finance Act, 1901, enacts:

> As respects the first levying or repealing of any duty of Customs (including any duty imposed by this Act), the time at which the importation of any goods shall be deemed to have had effect shall be the time at which the entry of the goods under the Customs Act is delivered instead of the time mentioned in Section forty of the Customs Consolidated Act, 1876.

The entry is the formal document, and it is to that that we attach the significance of the word "imported." What is entered is imported. If the Customs duty on oils had been imposed in the usual form, the cargo steamer or oil tanker, or other vessel, on which entries had been passed before the 25th April would have escaped, although the vessels had not been discharged. There are three classes. There is the oil which is actually in the country, and which is covered by the Excise Duty; there is the oil which has not yet been entered, and there is the oil which, although it is deemed to be entered is still on board ship. What reason is there for exempting the last except it be that those persons who have oil which was entered but not landed would be able to put the duty in their own pockets? I cannot conceive that there is any advantage in leaving this gap between the Customs Duty and the Excise Duty. Obviously, in all forms of taxation there is a certain amount of leakage. Not everything that is taken from the public reaches the revenue, and we are often reminded that in other forms of taxation there is a certain amount of evasion. But I cannot see why those people who have entered their oil and imported it, though they have not actually landed it from the ship, should be in a privileged position and be able to charge the enhanced price of the duty on the oil, although they have not borne the tax. The Excise Duty is an important part of this year's oil revenue. There will be a certain amount of difficulty in its collection, but it has been well accepted and the oil companies have been most helpful in regard to it. By this Excise Duty we have gained £3,500,000 which otherwise would not have been collected; not on the oil which was entered but not landed, but on the whole of the imported oil in stock we have gained as much as £3,500,000 on account of the tax. If we had not done that, I think the vast bulk of it would have gone to the importer. I cannot accept the Amendment. [Amendment negatived.]

[Later] Of course it must be admitted, at the outset, that where this Duty affects petrol or turpentine or white spirit used in the manufacture of other commodities, a situation of a rather more complicated character arises than is evinced in the general working of the Duty as a whole. Quite a number of different trades are affected in different ways and to different degrees. There are the trades which use turpentine or white spirit as an ingredient for their finished products and where the ingredient remains in the finished product. There are trades which use white spirit or turpentine as an ingredient, but where the ingredient does not appear in the finished product. Lastly, there are trades which use turpentine or petrol or white spirit as a solvent pure and simple, and recover what they have used, or the bulk of it, again and again. Wherever the oil is used as an ingredient which manifests itself in the finished product we give a rebate on the export; but where it is used as a solvent or as a disappearing ingredient there is much more difficulty.

I have come to the conclusion, very regretfully, that I must ask the Committee to support the Government in resisting the whole series of these Amendments for exemptions from the general duty. They do not cover a very wide field. Out of 800,000,000 gallons which we are dealing with, only 50,000,000 gallons are for non-road uses. We are now concerned with only one-sixteenth, therefore. If we were to begin giving exemptions, I do not know where the process would end. I am sure that every single demand met or exemption given, even where a hard case was shown, would open the door to another case so closely akin that at once another exemption would have to take a place by its side. So we should move on from point to point, from trade to trade, and from exemption to exemption, until the whole working of this Duty would cease to be the simple proposition that it is now and would become the most intricate matter of exemption and allowance and so forth.

It must be remembered that one of the reasons which the oil companies put forward to justify their charge of an extra penny on the old Petrol Duty was the amount of labour caused by the exemptions which were given in all kinds of directions. We have tried to secure the collection of this tax with the minimum diversion in any direction to private interests, and in order to do that very strict and austere requirements were necessary in excluding anything in the nature of exemptions. I ask myself whether the hardship amounts to such substantial proportions that we ought to abandon these principles. In the main, and so far as this group of industries is concerned, it is only a very small part of the area of the tax and they will, to a large extent, be safeguarded against any unfair incidence of the tax so far as foreign competition is concerned, both by means of the duty on importation and the drawback on exports. That is our intention. For the rest, they are undoubtedly entitled to pass the tax on to the consumer and in one way or another, I have very little doubt, they will be able to do so. There may be some very minor instances where they will not be able to pass the whole of it on to the consumer because of foreign competition, but these instances are all very small and are not to be compared with the grave issues which will arise once we start breaking in on the sanctity and integrity of the tax.

Moreover, it must be remembered that there is an off-set to this burden in respect of the rating relief. Some of those concerned showed me figures which were calculated on the pessimistic view of their misfortunes and an equally pessimistic view of what they were going to get in the way of relief. Even on this showing, it will be found that a very considerable off-set, if not a complete off-set in these cases will be afforded by the rating relief. Whether that be so or not, there is no tax which you can impose which does not tread on somebody's toes. Wherever you begin with the imposition of taxation, there are some trades which are affected more than others. Last year, to my great regret, I had to put something extra on tobacco. I had to get that taxation as far as possible from the profits of the tobacco industry, and we are getting the increased revenue without any increase in the cost of cigarettes. Wherever you turn in these matters of taxation, you cannot do anything without its being said that there is a little more imposed on this class than on that class, or a little more on this trade than on that trade, or that you have given some little advantage more here than you have given there.

If you are to proceed upon the basis that you must never give any favour, however small, to a flourishing industry, and you must never inflict any injury, however small, upon any industry which is not prosperous, then you had better buy a large consignment of plaster of Paris in which the House of Commons should ensconce itself. Of course, there is no tax which is not bound in some way or other in its ramifications to cause some anomaly or hardship. So far as this duty is concerned, we are like people in a diving bell; we cannot afford to open a single chink, otherwise the water will rush in and we shall be drowned. In giving the rebate which has been asked for by the hon. Members who moved the Amendment on their paints, their varnishes, or their colours, I have no doubt that I should be drawn into giving a rebate on feeding stuffs, petrol used in dyeing and cleaning, the making of gloves, and so forth, and from that I am sure that I should come up against the fishermen who, apparently, although they use kerosene to drive their boats, use petrol sometimes to start their engines, and I should also be up against the Minister of Agriculture, whose farmers are using a small quantity of petrol in order to get their kerosene-driven tractors into initial activity. If we were to concede any one of these points we should erect a whole complicated system of administration which would vitiate the working of the duty and probably cause a depletion in the Revenue which in the present stringency I am not able to afford.

[Later] If I had realised that my hon. and gallant Friend [Sir A. Sinclair] was going to consume so much of his energy and our time in the very powerful oratorical effort which he has made, I would have interceded before and shortened our deliberations. I have been asked to give some information as to the actual burden of this tax upon British industry. Of course originally, when kerosene was included in the Budget proposals, I proposed that the oil tax should not apply either to the fishing industry or to the agricultural tractor; but when the tax on kerosene was dropped and it became desirable to simplify our procedure, I mentioned in my speech that the exemption would no longer apply in the case of the agricultural tractor, which only uses a very small quantity of petrol for starting purposes. I did not then mention the case of the fisherman, but as it subsequently appeared that exactly the same considerations applied, I authorised the withdrawal of the exemption which under the new conditions would be operative only in so far as petrol was concerned. *De minimis non curat lex.* In the first place it is calculated that the total consumption of oil by Scottish boats is 4,800,000 gallons a year. The petrol which is used is estimated at 175,000 gallons. Therefore, the tax on that works out at about £3,000. Of course one does not want to place any burden at all on this industry. I do not think that the amount, spread as it is over perhaps 2,000 boats, can be held to be a crushing or harsh burden. Nevertheless, of course, one must always remember that what may be very small from the point of view of the Government is not small to the consumer.

When we come to the case of England, the situation is slightly different. Where petrol is used practically entirely for the starting up of the engine, it does not cause serious difficulty, but it has emerged that there are numbers of small boats which are found to use petrol not only for starting purposes but for running. They are two-man and three-man boats. Their average consumption would be, of course, considerably higher than that of the boats which use petrol only for starting purposes. It is estimated that the number of these boats would amount to 715. The cost of the duty falling upon the English and Welsh fishing industry is estimated to be £6,000, spread over the whole industry. Of that £6,000, it is probable that two-thirds may be assigned to the small vessels which use petrol not only for starting but for regular propulsion. So far as the boats which only use petrol, either in England or Scotland, for the purpose of starting, are concerned, I doubt if it would ever be worth their while to embark on the elaborate process of reclaiming the money, but it may be worth while in the case of those vessels that are dependent on petrol as the sole means of propulsion. If it were possible to set up a system of repayment, of recovery, for that is the only way in which it could be done, and if everybody in England and Wales—I have not calculated the figures for Scotland—claimed, not only those wholly dependent on its use for propulsion, but also those who use it only for starting, that would involve 9,000 separate repayments in respect of sums which would usually amount to under £1 each. The expense of such a system would be very considerable in proportion to the money involved. It is calculated that the administration cost might well be 25 per cent. on the £6,000 involved for England and Wales, and no doubt a similar proportion in respect of the £3,000 in the case of Scotland.

I should feel about this that it must be looked at in regard to the treatment which Parliament gives to the whole problem. If I were quite sure that this particular matter could be settled as a single, solitary exception to the whole of the Petrol Duty, I should be very disposed to give it careful consideration between now and the Report stage. If, however, it were to be used merely as a means of pressing forward the case of the commercial traveller, the doctor, the agricultural tractors, which are also getting their rating relief, and so forth, and were to be used as a means of involving us in all these complications, I should in the general interests of the tax as a whole, ask the

Committee to support me in resisting the Amendment. We will see how we get on. I will readily undertake between now and the Report stage to study very carefully this elaborate system and see if there is a way by which these small sums can be reclaimed without undue delay, red tape or cost. I will consider it with a desire to avoid these very laborious, costly and inconvenient arrangements. Rather than have it said that on this industry of very poor men—who face the storms and dangers of the sea and gather by their hard toil what is on all hands admitted to be a very frugal and meagre competence—we are placing some extra burden, I would be willing to face both the trouble and expense, provided at the same time that I could feel an assurance that the concession we were making would not lead to our being involved in further more serious and less defensible exceptions which would largely vitiate the efficiency of the duty.

[Later] Mr. Crawfurd: If I understood the right hon. Gentleman aright, he says in effect that if he agrees to this concession it is on the understanding that other concessions should not be pressed.

Mr. Churchill: No.

Mr. Crawfurd: It is a totally unwarranted interference with the liberty of the House of Commons for the right hon. Gentleman to suggest that because he is prepared to grant one concession he is not going to give completely unbiased consideration to other Amendments.

Mr. Churchill: I am the last person to make an unwarranted interference with the liberties of the House of Commons. On the contrary, I have always endeavoured to defer to the wishes of the House and as far as it is possible to invite them to share in the business of shaping our legislation in these matters. The last thing in the world I intended to indicate was that any Member was not within his rights in moving any Amendment, but if a whole series of Amendments is to be moved which would limit the duty, and the Committee pressed me on the whole of these Amendments, then I should be in a very difficult position. My hope is that we shall now be able to pass from this duty without very much difficulty, and then I shall be able to make proposals for relieving the fishermen.

Lieut.-Commander Kenworthy: My hon. Friend asked leave to withdraw. If you still allow the Amendment to be withdrawn I only want to say that I realise that the Chancellor has tried to meet us on this point.

[Later] Mr. Tomlinson: I beg to move, in page 2, line 18, after the word "gallon," to insert the words: "or petrol for tractors used for agricultural purposes and."

Originally, it was the intention of the Chancellor to give this remission. I should like to quote his words:

> The tax on light oils used in agricultural tractors, of which there are 23,000, for the purpose of tillage, but only for the purpose of tillage, in all its stages will be remitted.

When he gave the concession on the Kerosene Duty he rather ungraciously withdrew this concession which was made to agriculture. It is possible to make out quite as strong a case for arable farmers as the case that has been made out for the fishing industry. Hon. Members who represent agricultural constituencies in whatever part of the Committee they sit, will realise the very serious position of arable farmers. The cost to the Treasury is so small and yet is of such importance to those engaged in this industry that the Chancellor might very reasonably be expected to take this matter into consideration together with the other matter. I hope that he will be willing to give this remission.

Mr. Churchill: Certainly, this is a very small question compared with the general incidence of the tax. I am informed that the tractors in almost every case use kerosene, and it is necessary only to use relatively a very small quantity of petrol for starting up. Once the tractor is started up, properly handled, it gives as satisfactory results on kerosene as on petrol. Tractors which can only run on petrol are altogether exceptional, and the makers of one of the leading kinds of tractors recommend the use of kerosene in preference to petrol. This proposal differs, it will be generally admitted, from the proposal in regard to fishing boats. [Hon. Members: "Why?"] I will give two reasons why. First, it is undoubtedly true that when I withdrew the Kerosene Duty I told the House there and then that we did not propose any longer to exempt this petrol which is used for starting up agricultural tractors. On the other hand, I did not say anything at that time with regard to fishermen. That is one reason. The other reason is much more important. No one has obtained more from these proposals than the farmer. He will be entirely free from rates and will be relieved of all future anxiety as to whether the rates go up or down. In view of the fact that the farmers are getting very substantial relief, I certainly think that it is going too far to ask that we should complicate the matter by entering into separate discussions with people who only use a minute quantity of petrol. Nothing could be more calculated to illustrate the difficulty of making the concession which I wish to make with regard to the fishing industry than that it should be made the basis by the hon. Gentleman for his Amendment for giving a concession which would be inconvenient and complicated in practice.

Mr. Lamb: Will my right hon. Friend tell us what he said at the time he introduced the Petrol Duty? May I remind him of another remark which he made? When he was giving relief in respect of the Kerosene Duty, he said, in reply to those who contemplated getting out of the payment of the Petrol Duty by using kerosene, that it would be possible for them to do so.

Mr. Churchill: My hon. Friend will permit me to interrupt him. I was dealing entirely with motor cars. The tractors are different types of engine. They are simpler and, in some ways, cruder types of engine, and the inconveniences which might result from using kerosene—and which I am advised on the highest expert authority would result from using kerosene in motor cars—are such that they do not present themselves at all with regard to agricultural tractors. [Amendment negatived.]

[Later, on an amendment to exempt petrol engines running on rails] Inquiry has been made, and it appears that there are certain cases where there are one or more of these vehicles in use on private lines where there are quarries, etc., and various constructional works, and which might be to some extent affected. I cannot undertake to compensate all those who might be affected by this tax. The Committee has already resisted the requests of others who are affected to a greater extent, or at any rate just as directly as those who are the promoters of such works as I have referred to. Moreover, it will be found that in the vast majority of cases in which these rail-borne, petrol-driven engines are employed, there is also at the same time the rating relief enuring to the constructional enterprises concerned. These sand-pits are included in the general definition of properties which constitute productive industry by means of manual labour. Therefore, this case, again, is quite differentiated from the case of the fishermen.

[Later] There are many difficulties which oppose an aeroplane rising in the air, or a wide adoption of that form of locomotion, but the addition of 4d. on the Petrol Duty will not be an appreciable addition to these. Under the present rules, aeroplanes which set out for foreign flights will be treated in the same way as ships taking in bunker oil, and it is now sought to extend this privilege to internal flying. That would be entirely out of accord with the whole method of the Customs Duties. There is no ground for such a distinction, and it would be inconsistent with our general practice. Moreover, if the light aeroplane case were granted, I should find myself in a very delicate position after having resisted the proposals just made with regard to fishing and agriculture. It must also be remembered that we have done a great deal to foster civil aviation in this country and have given large subsidies which compare favourably with those given by foreign countries. I think it is very much better that aviation should be treated like all the other activities than that it should be given a small special favour.

Miss Wilkinson: Suppose that an aeroplane is proposing to go for an ordinary joy-ride in the United Kingdom and just goes for 20 miles to Calais and then turns back. Would it have its petrol free?

Mr. Churchill: That would be one of those hard cases which proverbially do not make good law.

INDUSTRY AND THE PETROL TAX

June 26, 1928

Treasury, London

I am afraid that I must confront all the requests that have been made [by the deputation from the Federation of British Industries] with a general answer. It is on the general policy that I have to take my stand. The old petrol tax proved a most inefficient tax and had to be abandoned because there had been so many complications and so many leakages that it could not be satisfactorily administered. A fresh start is being made, and every exception will afford ground for a demand for others, and I do not feel that I can run the risk of compromising the simplicity and the integrity of the tax. Although it may be that there are firms and industries which will lose more by this particular tax than they will gain by the rating relief, they are very small exceptions to the general trade of the country.

The trades which have been mentioned fall into three separate classes. The first are those in which hydro-carbon oils are used as an ingredient which remains in the finished product. This category includes paints and varnishes, and boot, floor and metal polishes. So far as foreign competition is concerned, similar products which are imported will be taxed on their equivalent oil content, and so far as the export trade is concerned, a drawback will, of course, be given on the amount of the ingredient contained in the exported article. The second class is where oil is used as a solvent and is not an ingredient at all. That includes rubber manufactures, leather manufactures, etc. In many cases the oil is used as a solvent repeatedly. It is used as an instrument of production, and it will clearly not be possible to tax foreign imports or give a system of drawbacks because there is no oil in the finished product. With regard to both these groups, obviously a tax of this character is one which will be borne by the consumer in the long run, even though for the moment any particular trade or firm may have to bear a part of it.

The third class is where oil is used as an ingredient which does not remain contained in the finished product. This happens in the case of synthetic camphor and terpineol and certain other chemical products. It is of course a fact that we are unable to charge the oil duty on the foreign import or to give a drawback to the home producer, but I cannot vitiate the whole machinery of the tax for the purpose of meeting this particular difficulty. As regards turpentine, I am advised that it is a competitor of white spirit, but as this has been challenged, I am willing for those concerned to discuss the point with the Board of Customs. This does not mean that I am opening the door to a concession.

I cannot hold out any hope of complicating the oil duty by the series of exemptions which the deputation has asked for. When any Budget is produced and any tax proposed, some disturbance is caused, but my hope is that the hardships caused by the oil duty will be greatly outweighed by the general advantage of the Government's scheme to the nation as a whole.

RATING RELIEF

June 26, 1928

Conservative Party Central Council Meeting,
Hotel Cecil, London

There are a great many new industries in this country which have come into existence in the last generation, and these are of the greatest possible value. They are new industries on a modern and scientific basis. They give a great deal of employment. They provide an important and an increasing factor in our export trade, so important to us who have to purchase abroad by the products of our skill and industry the necessities for carrying on our life and industrial processes. These industries that have come into being also afford an ever-growing and very important stream of refreshment to a revenue which, for many causes, in various directions, undergoes shrinkage.

subject," and they try to whittle away the whole value of the policy. That is what they say in the House of Commons, but that does not prevent Labour members and Liberal members coming in numerous deputations—including some of the most representative and influential people on their side—to see me and other Ministers, and begging that some portion, even a small portion, of this scheme, which they say in the House of Commons is worth nothing, may be put into effect to help our basic industries before things get worse. (Laughter and cheers.)

Now, in order to carry out this scheme, we have had to impose a tax on petrol, and that tax upon petrol will undoubtedly have an effect in stimulating to a certain extent the commercial production—the scientific production is already possible—of liquid and pulverized fuel from our own great resources of coal. If that were so—if perhaps in another generation it were found that a very large portion of our liquid fuel production was achieved by scientific processes applied to British coal—and that is an event to which I look forward with great confidence, though we may not, many of us, live to see it—but, if that should be so, then I am sure that those who come after us will point to this Session of Parliament as a most noteworthy Session in which a far-seeing policy was instituted which steadily fostered these scientific policies and processes and enabled our country to use its coalfields in the middle of the twentieth century with the same great effect in the world as it did in the bygone days of Queen Victoria. But, nevertheless, I, of course, admit that this tax on petrol is in itself a disadvantage. I would gladly have used the money for the purpose of relieving the horse-power tax as so many motorists have so long asked.

Unhappily, social and industrial troubles have arisen—the general strike, the elements of spite and malice which so greatly complicated the work of peace upon the coalfields and protracted the long stoppage—elements which, I am sorry to see, are active at the present time in endeavouring to impede every step towards industrial good will and conciliation and cooperation in industry. If it had not been for those disastrous events in 1926 I should probably not have had to ask for this sacrifice of the motoring community. But they have accepted it in a sporting and patriotic spirit. (Cheers.) You know perfectly well that there is practically no ill-feeling or resentment about this petrol tax, and it gives us the means of taking this most important constructive action in the present Parliament. All the work will be done, and when we present ourselves at the election it will be with the work achieved and behind us, with only the fruit of our labours to be gathered in and enjoyed by the country as a whole. (Cheers.)

Now, what is the scheme? In the first place—although this is the second part of the scheme—we are trying to deal with these necessitous areas by a system of adjusting the rates throughout the country, which will lead to a very marked relief in those areas which are at the present time most heavily burdened by the rates arising from unemployment. This scheme will be unfolded in a Memorandum which will be published this week by my right hon. friend Mr. Neville Chamberlain, the distinguished and successful Minister of Health. (Cheers.) It will be found that this scheme gives notable relief where relief is most needed, imposes no unfair burden on any part of the ratepaying community, and gives a very wide measure of general relief from one end of the country to the other.

But this scheme is the foundation. It relieves the necessitous areas in an important manner, but it does not relieve them by giving them doles; it relieves them through the application of sound general principles which cannot vary between one district and another, but which, having been most carefully considered, are capable of universal application to the country as a whole, and will produce the beneficial result of correcting the present injustices which are observed. Far and above a scheme for local government, it will move forward perennially and automatically, every five years, until ultimately a very close and intimate association is established between the needs of localities and the resources which are at their disposal.

So that, in the first instance, you have this great measure of rating relief, the measure for which will be passed in the autumn, which has the effect of reducing the burden in the necessitous areas. Now, what are these necessitous areas? They are the same ones as those I have just been describing to you. They are areas where there are great basic industries engaged in the export trade, which industries are flagging under the present burden and are the cause of great unemployment. These industries will first of all receive relief through the general rating scheme, but then, on the top of that and with the accumulative effect, the relief to productive industry, which I announced in the Budget and of which we have been talking principally up to date, comes into play. First, the rates are reduced where reduction is most needed, and then three-quarters of the reduced rates is taken off the productive industries after they have already been reduced by the second part of the scheme. So, here you have one wave on top of the other. In addition to that there is the relief in freights. Our railway freights are, as I have said, a great burden. The railways are to be relieved of three-quarters of their rates, but they will not keep it themselves. They made no difficulty about passing it on. They gave the most immediate cooperation, because, obviously, they hope that greater traffic will ensue as the result of larger employment, and from that they will gain an advantage in their business and their employees will gain a greater assurance against being retrenched or discharged through the slackening of business. (Cheers.) This freight relief is concentrated upon the heavy basic industries of coal, iron and steel, and one or two others. I emphasize the relief to those who have no other means of transporting their goods than by rail, because their goods are of such a heavy character and quality that it is essential that they should be transported by rail and they have no alternative means of road transport open to them. These are the main proposals and changes of the scheme which we have put forward in regard to industry.

So far as agriculture is concerned, the proposals are simple. We are removing, once and for all, the agriculturist entirely from the area of the rates. He will no longer, in the future, have the slightest anxiety about variations of assessment and about fluctuations in the poundage of his rates. We trust that this will be a measure which will not only give relief, but, what is not least important to agriculture, a feeling of confidence in the future. Such is the policy upon which we are engaged.

Now, I invited cooperation from our opponents in this policy. After all, it is a national policy. It is not a party matter. The days have really gone by when we can afford to play party politics with the great industries of our country. The need of finding the means to keep this immense, overcrowded population alive in this small island is so urgent and dire that it ought to be a patriotic and even sacred duty of all parties in the State to treat any sincere and well-intentioned proposal with the utmost respect. Therefore, I invited cooperation, but I will frankly tell you that I did not expect to get it—(laughter)—and when I did not get it I was not unduly disappointed. I am here to tell you to-day that, if the people of this country mean to have this rate relief, if they mean to have agriculture out of the rates, and they mean to have these three-quarters reductions on the rates on productive industry, with all the advantage that gives to the small shopkeepers where the people are in employment in the neighbourhood—if they mean to have this large reform of the rating system, they have got to fight for it, and they have got to fight for it in the year that lies before us. It may not even be a year before we shall engage in a political struggle, and at that struggle they have also got to fight because, undoubtedly, one of the issues in that struggle will be whether or not these reliefs which we have in prospect are to be carried to the industries and the agriculture which need them so sorely, and the necessitous areas, or whether they are to be intercepted and cast away by political partisanship and obstruction.

So we have a year before us, and we have a programme which has only to be learnt by the speakers of the Conservative Party to command the attention of democratic audiences in every part of the country. There is not a constituency which is not involved. There is not a constituency in which you cannot point to factories which are on the borderline of closing down, and which will be able to continue and to keep their people in employment, and that will react upon the shopkeepers and the whole of the trade of the district. There is not a part of the country and there is not a trade which is not one way or another affected, and affected, mind you, through the application of a perfectly sound economic principle which, having been observed and proclaimed, must be applied without fear, favour, or affection.

FINANCE BILL (SUGAR AND MATCH DUTIES)

June 26, 1928

House of Commons

Everyone knows that the hon. Member [Mr. Alexander] and some of his friends, including the most influential, view with a critical if not an hostile eye the development of Imperial preference which has been undertaken during the last 10 years with the general and overwhelming assent of the great majority of the people of this country. We are also aware of the repeated pledges which have been made on behalf of the next Chancellor of the Exchequer in a Socialist Government, to the effect that all indirect taxation is to be swept away, including particularly the taxes on tea and sugar, and that the sum is to be made good by an increase in direct taxation; through increases in Income Tax, Super-tax and Death Duties. I do not think we need go into these matters this afternoon. If it so be that in a year from now the right hon.

Gentleman the Member for Colne Valley (Mr. Snowden) has so changed his situation and is sitting here—

The Chairman: The right hon. Gentleman is now opening up an argument which I shall not be able to prevent other hon. Members from following.

Mr. Churchill: With great respect, I was not intending to stray from the question as to whether the Sugar Duty should be repealed or not, but when we are confronted with definite proposals for the repeal of that duty, I submit that I was in no way transgressing the limits of Debate in indicating that that might lead to serious inconveniences in other directions.

The Chairman: All Ministers in their ardour for their cause unconsciously widen the bounds of discussion. Other hon. Members cannot be stopped from following them, and it is therefore necessary to utter a word of warning at the first possible moment.

Mr. Churchill: I will follow any guidance which you may think good enough to give me, and will confine myself to saying that should the right hon. Member for Colne Valley be called upon to assume this responsibility in a short space of time, we shall watch with the greatest care whether he will be able to carry out the pledges which have been made on his behalf and repeal the duty now under discussion, and other duties which have been mentioned. We are also aware of the doubts which have been expressed in some quarters about the policy of encouraging the development of the sugar-beet industry in this country, and I am sure that it is easy to make a serious case against it. At the same time, there is a tremendous case to be made for it as an experiment. It was an experiment approved by the party opposite and carried out by us, and it has not yet been completed. Heavy expenditure has been incurred by the firms which started the industry at the outset and, undoubtedly, they are being rewarded and getting back their capital expenditure and outlay. It is part of our policy that they should be prosperous and that others should be encouraged to imitate their example, so that the industry will take root. Whether it will or not is unknown. Whether we have really lit a new fire which will warm British commercial and economic interests, or whether we have just lit a bonfire which will blaze away only so long as the material lasts and then die out, cannot yet be known.

But the bounty has been reduced already as a first step, and in this year I am counting upon that in my calculations. As far as I am aware the industry is holding its own vigorously. Whether it will reveal qualities of permanent survival, it is not yet possible to foretell. It is an experiment, a costly one, but one which, if it succeeds, will add an entirely new feature to agriculture and industry in this country.

But these matters, to which I do not propose to address my attention this afternoon, are matters of general interest, and I would rather deal with the more specific matters referred to by the hon. Member for Hillsborough (Mr. Alexander) with a great deal more moderation than was practised in the House or out of it by his Leader, the right hon. Member for Colne Valley. Let us see what the right hon. Gentleman said to his own constituents on the 1st May:

This plan between Mr. Churchill and the sugar refiners has been con-cocted during the past few months and preparations made for it in order to bamboozle the public. The shares of one of the refining companies rose some weeks ago. This was on the knowledge these people had of what Mr. Churchill was going to do. £2,500,000 has been added to the ordinary shares of that one sugar refining industry during the last six weeks.

That statement contains a number of extremely offensive aspersions and charges which I believe, which I am sure, are quite untrue. In view of the fact that these allegations have been revived to-day by the hon. Member for Hillsborough, the Committee will wish me to enter upon the topic with some explicitness. The right hon. Gentleman said that a plan has been concocted "to bamboozle the public," and that I am a party to that plan. I give the House my assurance that there is absolutely no truth in it. When I make that statement I expect hon. Members to believe it. When other hon. Members make statements I believe them, unless other facts are brought to our notice which make it, unhappily, impossible to accept them. I took no part in the negotiations with the sugar refiners except that I saw them a year ago when they came in a deputation to me, and I must say that they impressed me with the fact that we were doing them an injustice; that the working of Imperial preference and the beet subsidy were, in fact, putting them in a very invidious position.

After that I never saw them in any negotiations. They were conducted by the Board of Customs and Excise, who informed me that proposals were being made to them which would have the effect of procuring reductions in the price of sugar greater than the corresponding loss to the Revenue. It occurred to me that this might be a feature which I could use in connection with the proposed duty on oils in order to relieve some of those who would be prejudicially affected by the taxation of kerosene, and also that there was an opportunity to rectify what undoubtedly was a case of real hardship and injustice to an important British industry, brought about directly by the Government's entry into the field of competitive production. But I confined myself to reading the reports which were submitted to me and took no part whatever in the discussions on this matter until the very latest period before the Budget was finally settled.

A few days before the actual date of the Budget I saw articles appearing in the newspapers criticising the proposals which had been put to me from the Board of Customs and Excise, and it was evident that those who were circulating these articles and paragraphs were fully acquainted with the plan which the Board of Customs and Excise had discussed with the Sugar Refiners' Association. I was offended at this and considered very carefully at first whether I would not delete the project altogether from the Budget. I raised the question *de novo* with the Board of Customs and Excise and said that there appeared to be a leakage of confidential information which was very unusual in regard to the many people we have to consult when preparing a Budget, and that if that were so and there had been an improper use made of this information, I should not allow this proposal to appear in the Budget.

I received what appeared to me to be quite conclusive answers, not only to the attacks made on the merits of the policy, but on the specific point of behaviour into which I was inquiring before I was committed to the proposal that I made to the House when the Budget was opened. When I decided to put this proposal in the

Budget, it was with the full knowledge of all that could be said against it and after having previously examined the question of whether those with whom we had negotiated had been guilty of improper disclosure of confidential information. I am quite sure that the parties with whom the Customs and Excise were dealing were not those responsible for this matter becoming, as it did, very largely public property. The Refiners' Association, of course, are only one of the interests involved in this matter. The proposal had its reaction on other sugar interests, and the Customs advised the refiners to get into touch with representatives of home-grown sugar and Empire producers in order to arrive at a scheme acceptable to all. How could they avoid doing that? Surely it was necessary for them to try to present a scheme for the acceptance of the Chancellor of the Exchequer, and to be able to say that behind it all the varied interests were ranged and that there was general agreement.

They took this step, and the proposal of the Refiners' Association consequently became known to a considerable number of people, including the London representatives of the Mauritius and Queensland producers, who had to communicate with their clients abroad. On 6th March the Customs received a deputation from the Sugar Federation of the British Empire, and very soon after there appeared in the Press a cable from Queensland to the Agent-General objecting to the proposals of the Federation and resigning from it. At this time the general nature of the proposals of the refiners was known throughout the trade. What was only a matter of surmise, which was not unattended with very great risks, was whether in the ultimate result I should accept this scheme which had been negotiated by the Customs, or whether I should reject it.

I do not see how it was possible for the refiners to avoid consulting these other interests. Observe that they were consulting interests other than their own, which in important respects were adverse interests; and it was these adverse interests which began the agitation and sent round carefully prepared articles to the various newspaper offices and generally endeavoured to prejudice the proposals. I do not myself see how blame can be attached to the interests which were in favour of the proposal because in the process of consulting other interests, which were adverse, the matter became public property. I am satisfied myself that it was not through any breach of confidence on the part of the British refiners that the matter had become public property.

Now I come to the more serious allegation, namely, that the reduction in the price of sugar which has taken place since the Budget—which the right hon. Gentleman opposite on 25th April said would not take place but which did in fact take place—is not a real reduction, but is a mere pretence, that the price had been worked up beforehand to an artificial level, and that it was a very cheap concession for the refiners to make a reduction after having carefully prepared an increase for the purpose. I do not think that that is true. I am advised by the Customs that it is not so. I take full responsibility for everything that I say and I do not base myself upon any authority but my own. Nevertheless, in dealing with these intricate matters, in examining the movements of prices and so on, naturally I fortify myself with the advice of my experts. I am advised that it is not true to say that there was any such artificial rise, that the prices were put up in order that the Exchequer might be promised a reduction after the measures that they were taking.

If you look over the course of sugar prices from the beginning of 1927 to the present time, it would appear, broadly speaking—and subject to minor fluctuations, which appear over the whole series of years back to 1924—that there has been a steady diminution in the price. In January, 1927, the price of Tate and Lyle granulated sugar was 33s. 10-1/2d. to 34s. 4-1/2d. a cwt. In April it had fallen to 32s. 4d.; in August it was 30s. 10-1/2d.; in January 29s. 10-1/2d.; in February 29s. 4-1/2d.; in March 29s. 1-1/2d.; and in April it rose to 30s. 7-1/2d. I see nothing in those prices to indicate any attempt to create an artificial foundation for a subsequent reduction. Anyone who likes to look will see that the price movements are not beyond the scope or scale of those which usually take place. But it is not only a question of the actual price of refined sugar. The price in this country is governed by the world price of raw sugar, and the important point in this matter is not actual prices, but the relation of the selling price of refined sugar to the raw sugar world price.

I have seen all the figures for the last two years for Tate and Lyle's sugar. I have been looking down the differences, and they have hardly varied by more than 6d. or 7d. during the whole of this period, from July, 1926, to the present time. In April of 1927 the difference was 17s. 9d.—the margin between the raw sugar c.i.f. and the selling price of refined sugar duty paid. That was on 12th April, 1927. On 2nd April, 1928, it was 17s. 7-1/2d., and on the 16th it was 17s. 6d.

Mr. Alexander: It is a little difficult to see how those figures help. The right hon. Gentleman is just giving the margin between the raw sugar price and the refined selling price, based on world level of prices, but can he give the actual purchase prices and selling prices. I have made a specific charge of their having made a purchase at a low price.

Mr. Churchill: I am coming to that in a minute. My case is that if you look down the whole of the prices of this firm during the last two or three years, you will find that there has been a steady decline. There is an occasional step back of a 1s. or so, but on the whole there has been a steady decline, and there is no evidence of any attempt to make a rise in price for the purpose of making a subsequent reduction. That is my first point.

Mr. Snowden: Can the right hon. Gentleman give some of the later figures?

Mr. Churchill: The figure in February, 1927, was 33s. 1-1/2d. per cwt., and a year later 29s. 4-1/2d. That is for Tate and Lyle granulated sugar. My second point is that not only has the price steadily declined subject to these minor fluctuations, but that these minor fluctuations are themselves comparable to and connected with similar fluctuations in the price of Cuban raw sugar. Lastly, my point is that the margin between the price at which the sugar has been put on the market and the price at which it is purchased in its raw state in the world market has remained almost entirely constant. I have never attached much importance to the undertaking which these refiners gave, to reduce the price by 2s. 4d. for three months irrespective of world conditions. But they volunteered that proposition. I wished to know what they would do, but I did not specify that particular condition. What I attached importance to was their undertaking that the normal margin between the world price and their selling price shall be decreased by the full amount of relief which we are giving in the Budget. There you have a standard which can be followed evenly, irrespective of the various movements of price in the world market. Their prices have always been a certain distance above the prices of raw sugar and they are that distance above them still less the amount of the relief in the Budget.

Then there is the question of the large purchases, which are said to have been made, of Cuban raw sugar. Here, again, I am really astonished to know that it is a crime to make purchases in advance. A trade which is serving the country with an indispensable commodity is naturally bound to buy ahead. It cannot be successful unless it does so. How can we say that any firms buying for the English market and consumer are not to be allowed to purchase in the world market on terms as advantageous as they can get? [*Interruption.*] I am now replying to very offensive charges which have been made, and I do not propose for a moment to allow them to pass without a most complete reply. I cannot conceive why anyone should not be entitled to purchase freely in the markets of the world and advantageously for their customers. If the purchase is disadvantageous they suffer a loss, but if they are able to make a good purchase of a raw material like that, then if they are still continuing to serve the public on a fair and normal basis, they are perfectly entitled to take advantage of the opportunity. With regard to the abnormal purchase of 150,000 tons of sugar which took place in the autumn of last year, I am advised that it was purchased in October, 1927, long before the Budget changes were thought of.

Mr. Alexander: No.

Mr. Churchill: Certainly as far as I am concerned. I am advised that this amount, which represents not more than 10 weeks' supply, had all passed into consumption before the Budget. So much for this abnormal purchase. It was bought before these matters had reached any decisive stage and was used up before the Budget and it is no good for the right hon. Gentleman opposite to smile sarcastically in face of this overwhelming reply. All these matters will be read and studied most carefully in the country. [Hon. Members: "Hear, hear!"] If hon. Gentlemen opposite are so pleased about it perhaps they will let me continue. It is quite true that further purchases were made in February and March which amounted to 190,000 tons but, as I say, why not? How are they going to carry on their trade if they are not allowed to buy raw sugar in order to be able to supply the public? Why should it be wrong for British refiners to purchase 190,000 tons of raw sugar when at the same time and in the same market the United States sugar refiners bought 370,000 tons? I cannot understand why a matter of this kind should be brought in as evidence to suggest that some plot has been concocted.

Mr. Hardie: Free Trade principles!

Mr. Churchill: It is not contrary to Free Trade principles to buy in the cheapest market. In fact I imagine that if there was one principle which we could take as a prime and paramount principle it would be that. I have dealt with that point but there is one other with which I wish to deal and that is the question of the rise in the shares of Tate and Lyle—[*Interruption.*]

The Chairman: I hope hon. Members will allow the right hon. Gentleman to proceed without interruption.

Mr. Churchill: I am really not anxious to arouse feeling but I would remind hon. Members opposite that a number of offensive charges have been made. I am accused of having concocted a plan to bamboozle the public. If I thought the right hon. Gentlemen opposite believed that I am bound to say I should treat it even more seriously than I am doing. Nevertheless it has been said in public and I am determined that it shall be answered as far as I am concerned. As to the rise in shares of Tate and Lyle it has been said by the hon. Gentleman to-day that they rose from 28s. to 44s. at the date of the Budget. They are, I believe, 41s. to-day. I am informed that no purchases of their own shares have been made this year by any member of the firm of Tate and Lyle. I am authorised to make that statement. This great firm we are told amounts to a monopoly. It is one of the principal firms—overwhelmingly the largest firm—in the industry and, as I say, no purchases of their own shares have been made by any member of the firm. The only transaction that has taken place has been the sale by Sir Ernest Tate of some shares belonging to his late mother which he had to realise as a trustee. This transaction took place before the rise in the price of the shares and the price realised was 31s. The shares have now risen to 42s. I think that statement disposes of the right hon. Gentleman's suggestion that the rise which followed on the giving of confidential information had put about £2,500,000 into the pockets of this industry.

Mr. Snowden: I said into the pockets of the shareholders.

Mr. Churchill: I have the statement here and it is that £2,500,000 had been added to the ordinary shares of that one particular refining industry. I am really surprised that the right hon. Gentleman, with his position and experience, should make so misleading a statement. As a matter of fact the market in Tate and Lyle's shares is a very narrow one and the price responds to very small purchases and sales. The idea that the value of their property has been increased by £2,500,000 as a result of the marking up of these quotations is entirely illusory. If they were to attempt to realise this £2,500,000, which figured so well on the public platform before an audience of course the very first step taken would destroy the value which has since been reached.

Mr. Shinwell: What are market values?

The Chairman: I must ask hon. Members to listen attentively. Nothing would be easier than to interrupt in like manner from the other side.

Mr. Shinwell: What about the other side when they do the same thing? Be impartial.

The Chairman: I must ask the hon. Member for Linlithgow (Mr. Shinwell) to resume his seat.

Mr. Shinwell: What about what they did to me a fortnight ago?

The Chairman: I have asked the hon. Member to resume his seat.

Mr. Shinwell: May I say that when those on the other side do this very thing to me there is no protest from the Chair. [*Interruption.*] An hon. Member sitting near me says that is a lie. Is it a lie?

The Chairman: The hon. Member will please resume his seat when I request him to do so. When he is called upon to speak, he will have exactly the same protection as any other hon. Member.

Mr. Shinwell: I rise to a point of Order, Sir. An hon. Member sitting below the Gangway says that the statement I have just made is a lie, and I ask you if that is an expression which should be permitted.

The Chairman: If any hon. Member addressed another in those terms, of course it was exceedingly wrong, and, if he does it within my hearing, I should have to ask him to withdraw the words.

Mr. Churchill: I have no wish to detain the Committee unduly, but I desire to reply to the statements which have been made from the other side. I was saying that if it were true that we, by our action, put £2,500,000 into the pockets of this industry, or of this particular firm, it would equally be true to say that the policy which we have pursued in regard to beet sugar and in regard to Imperial Preference had, since our tenure of office, taken £3,500,000 out of their pockets, because their shares, which now stand at 41s., stood at 54s. four years ago, and they fell from 54s. to 28s. as a result of the very invidious reactions which followed from measures undertaken by the State for quite different purposes. Therefore, I think that when next the right hon. Gentleman visits his constituents and tells them that the Government have handed over £2,500,000 as a special favour to their particular friends, he might, in fairness, state that even on his own unreal hypothesis, they had previously taken away £3,500,000 from the same favoured trade. So much for this aspect of the proposal.

Mr. Varley: It is a mere coincidence that the shares may have gone up.

Mr. Churchill: Not at all. I said that the firm in question with whom we were negotiating were not responsible for that. That is all I am saying, but there was knowledge and I have explained how the knowledge got about, and that speculators used it and I have explained the effect on the narrow market for these shares. I am defending those with whom we were in negotiation from very gross and wounding and damaging charges which have been brought against them, and which I sincerely believe are neither just nor true.

Let me now explain some of the effects of this step. I am informed that the wages bill of the refiners has been increased by approximately 25 per cent. since the Budget. I do not mean the rate of wages, but the amount of wages paid, and for a full year that means an increase of £300,000 or £400,000. I am informed that the imports of raw sugar during April and May of this year were 116,000 tons greater than in the corresponding period of last year, and that the imports of foreign refined sugar were 46,000 tons less and on the balance 70,000 tons more sugar have been imported into the United Kingdom during those two months. That is a 20 per cent. increase which in a full year would amount to 350,000 tons. The refiners melt has increased by more than 25 per cent., and in a full year that means the use of 100,000 tons more coal and 3,000,000 more jute bags together with a correspondingly increased demand in all the allied trades. A large amount of expenditure has been undertaken or is being sanctioned in alterations and additions to the refineries. I believe that the Greenock refineries, which were closed not by foreign competition but by extraneous circumstances, may shortly re-open. As to the reduction in price about which the right hon. Gentleman was sceptical, the prices were reduced by 2s. 4d. per cwt. on the day following the Budget and a further reduction of 9d. per cwt. has since been made. As I say, I give no guarantee as to the effect of movements in the world market, but I am in possession of assurances from refiners that, while their price movements vary with the movements in the world price, full allowance will be made for the remission of taxation which we have made. That we shall be able to test as time goes on. The only cloud that I can see immediately upon the sugar horizon is that certain retailers are, I

believe, consulting among themselves upon the propriety of raising the retail price of
sugar in order to increase the margin of profit to the retailer. I do not admit for a
moment that anything that has taken place in the Budget has created a situation which
would justify an alteration to the detriment of the consumer, and I trust—and I say so
not unadvisedly—that the hon. Member who has just spoken and the great co-operative
institution which he represents will be forward in assisting the public against being
defrauded of the remission in the Sugar Duty which, at the cost of nearly £3,000,000
to the revenue, we have endeavoured to convey to the country.

Mr. Snowden: I think the right hon. Gentleman would have served his own
interests better if he had permitted this matter to rest where it remained after the
Report stage of the Budget Resolution. I am sure no unprejudiced member of the
Committee who has heard the Chancellor of the Exchequer would regard his statement
as a satisfactory explanation and a satisfactory refutation of the charges made from
this side of the Committee. The most audacious of the statements, or excuses, which
the right hon. Gentleman has made, has been his attempt to throw off his own
responsibility for what took place before the Budget and to put it on to the shoulders
of the Board of Customs and Excise. Did the Board of Customs and Excise enter into
these negotiations for the purpose of carrying through a Budget proposal without the
knowledge of the Chancellor of the Exchequer? I am not asking for an answer.

Mr. Churchill: The answer is: Certainly not.

Mr. Snowden: Very well. The Board of Customs and Excise entered upon these
negotiations with the knowledge and on the instructions of the Chancellor of the
Exchequer, and the right hon. Gentleman has come down here this afternoon to try to
rebut a charge that he himself was responsible for what took place in those few weeks
before the proposal was made in his Budget in regard to the Sugar Duty by saddling
the responsibility upon the Board of Customs and Excise. If I had not heard the right
hon. Gentleman make his confession that he was aware of what the Board of Customs
and Excise were doing, that they were doing it with his knowledge and on his
instructions, the impression would have been left on my mind that he was entirely
ignorant of what the Board of Customs and Excise were doing, until they presented to
him their memorandum.

Mr. Churchill: I really must answer that. The right hon. Gentleman will recollect
that I said that I took the very fullest responsibility for what had been done. What I
meant was that while I authorised these negotiations, I did not concern myself at all
with their details; that I authorised the Board of Customs and Excise to ascertain what
form such project would take when it had been thrashed out with the parties
concerned; and that I myself reserved my power of final decision upon it. I am not
attempting to shelter myself behind the Board of Customs and Excise.

Mr. Snowden: The right hon. Gentleman is not now attempting to shelter
himself behind what the Board of Customs and Excise do, but that is certainly the
only impression that could have been obtained by listening to the early part of his
speech. He began by quoting some remarks which I made in a speech which I delivered
to my constituents a few weeks ago, in which I had associated the Chancellor of the
Exchequer himself with what took place in regard to the manipulation of sugar prices,
anterior to the introduction of the Budget, and then the right hon. Gentleman went on

to say that it was not he who was responsible, that he had had nothing to do with these negotiations, that, as a matter of fact, he had not met these people during the weeks preceding the introduction of the Budget, that he had met them about 12 months before, and that that was the only direct communication which he had had with them. The right hon. Gentleman was trying to get out of a difficult situation by creating the impression that it was not he but his subordinates who were responsible for what took place.

Mr. Churchill: That is not what I said.

Mr. Snowden: We will let the report of the right hon. Gentleman's speech settle that to-morrow. I am quite sure that what I am saying is what the right hon. Gentleman said, or that at any rate it is the only possible impression that could have been conveyed to his hearers by what he was saying. What is the charge of the right hon. Gentleman? His charge is that I said that the negotiations which had taken place in the weeks which preceded the introduction of the Budget had bamboozled the public.

Mr. Churchill: That is not what the right hon. Gentleman said.

Mr. Snowden: Will the right hon. Gentleman read the words?

Mr. Churchill: I will read the words:

This plan between Mr. Churchill and the sugar refiners has been concocted during the past few months and preparations made for it in order to bamboozle the public.

That is the report of the statement of the right hon. Gentleman to which I am taking objection.

[Later] I hope the Committee will be ready to dispense with further discussions on this matter and allow us to make a little progress. We have great and important business still before us and it certainly seems to me that we shall be continuing the Debate into the small hours of the morning, which I hope will not be necessary, if we do not make more rapid progress than we are making at the moment. This is an extremely small point and should not detain the Committee for any length of time. I have the duty of raising the revenue in one way or another for the year. In 1916 a duty on matches was imposed by the Government of that day, and at the same time a duty on mechanical lighters was imposed as well. The two were treated as absolutely complementary, and I notice that the right hon. Member for Colne Valley in one of the Debates said that so long as there was a duty on matches there was a *prima facie* case for imposing a duty on mechanical lighters. At any rate, nothing could be more absurd than to impose this burden on the match industry without any sort of equalising protection from this rapidly growing competitor to the match industry.

There is no question at all of favouring the match industry, not in the slightest. They are subjected to what is nothing less than an unwise bounty fed competition. Since 1922 we have given the strongest possible preferential bounties to the mechanical lighter substitute, and to take this duty off altogether and allow a trade to be ruined year after year, and the revenue on which we are depending reduced effectively year after year, would be an unwise procedure. What we have to do is to protect our revenue and give fair play to the match trade. Instead of talking about international combines and world finance, hon. Members opposite should come down to the simple point of the workpeople who are engaged in this match industry. I have not the actual figures of the number of people employed in England in making matches, but we are not bounding ahead so rapidly that we can say we are approaching a stage when we are holding our own in the supply of matches. There is absolutely no question of giving any favour to the match industry. The Joint Industrial Board of the match industry on which employees as well as proprietors are represented made a strong appeal some years ago that they should be free from the unfairly stimulated competition of the mechanical lighter and pointed that the match industry was heavily taxed whilst this new development was not. Why should it be an improper thing for us if we put a tax on matches to make sure that the tax is effective. I am informed that on the last occasion this matter was debated it was asked that there should be a reduction on the countervailing excise duty and on behalf of the Government it was stated this matter would be considered before the Committee stage. I have given careful consideration to the matter and while there are arguments on both sides and very strong arguments too for a duty which favours the home produced article I think in all the circumstances it would be better to adhere to the original form in which the duty was imposed and that is what we propose to do. It is not necessary to go into the question of the international treaties but as the hon. Member has put the question I will tell him that the Treaty referred to is the Anglo-German treaty. The great majority of these mechanical lighters come from Germany and by this treaty it was understood that both countries would do their best not to penalise or injure each other's special forms of exportation. It was a thoroughly friendly agreement. There is no question of our being entitled to do what we are doing so far as the imposition of this duty is concerned. It certainly would create a more invidious aspect if we were to differentiate against the foreign importation.

I am endeavouring to protect the revenue from matches not indeed to free but to reduce the pressure and the burden which a heavy tax on matches would create having regard to this hitherto untaxed importation and I do not think anything less than 6d. would be effective. I am not at all sure that more would not have to be imposed. If the Customs and Excise Duties were higher there might possibly be room for some differentiation, and possibly in future years the question of the Anglo-German Treaty will have undergone some revision, but at present the Duty is so low, and only barely sufficient to protect the match revenue from serious inroads, that I think, after weighing the matter very carefully and consulting the Financial Secretary, it would be better to leave it in the form in which it was introduced.

[Later] I am in charge of everything included in the Budget of the year and I am responsible for everything in the Finance Bill. I accept the fullest responsibility for every proposal it contains. But since when, I should like to know, has an individual Member of the Opposition the right to dictate to the Government how they shall use such forces as are at their disposal or how they shall transact their business? The process of long and intricate discussion, when one topic succeeds another and one Amendment follows swiftly on another, has necessarily to be divided between a number of Ministers if full justice is to be done to each proposition; and the

Committee is to have the guidance and services of Ministers which it no doubt requires. But, in regard to the general merits of the matter, this follows the procedure which we have appointed and prescribed by the White Paper. So far from hon. Gentleman opposite having any ground for complaint that this procedure has led to an undue adoption of Safeguarding, there has been a very strong feeling among the party which, at any rate, is dominant in this House of Commons that the procedure of the White Paper has very rigidly and narrowly restricted the Safeguarding which it was intended by Parliament should be imposed and enforced. For my part, I would say that owing to the collapse of the Liberal party, and owing to the very shaky knowledge of economic subjects possessed by the Labour party, the Free Trade forces in this House are in a state of collapse, and they are exceedingly fortunate in not being asked to consent to much more stimulating propositions than those I have made.

FINANCE BILL

June 27, 1928

House of Commons

The well-informed speech to which we have just listened has placed the Committee in the middle of this complicated and at the same time interesting subject. I have a difficult situation to face, the seeds of which were sown in the days of my predecessor. In the first place, undoubtedly, we have had to pay a higher rate for Treasury bills in late years than was the case four years ago. In the second place, Savings Certificates, as I explained when introducing the Budget, which are a most valuable vehicle of public thrift, are now coming back to the Exchequer for encashment, not so much in increasing numbers, but with a much longer period of interest in their mouths, as it were. They return with eight, nine or 10 years' interest, instead of four, five or six years which they carried in the days of my predecessor. In consequence, I have had to face very largely increasing claims for Savings Certificates interest on the annual revenue. That being so, it was necessary to examine the whole position of the Savings Certificates, and, on investigation, it was found that the payment of, I think it is, £21,500,000 a year would be a fair measure of the real liability which we were incurring and had incurred. Obviously, the extent to which that liability was not being provided for has always constituted a deduction from the nominal figure of the New Sinking Fund. We had not in our Budget accounts presented that fact clearly to the world. I think the hon. Gentleman drew attention to it. It was mentioned in several of our Debates and the whole matter was brought before the Colwyn Committee. I will not say that they approved, but they acquiesced in it in all the circumstances. The difference between this sum and the amount actually paid should have been subtracted every year from the nominal amount of the New Sinking Fund. I have now accepted this burden, which was greater than that which my predecessor the right hon. Gentleman the Member for Colne Valley (Mr. Snowden) was called upon to pay. I was faced with the prospect of encashments carrying interest of between £15,000,000 and £20,000,000, and perhaps larger figures in future years.

That being so, I felt bound to review the whole position of our New Sinking Fund. It was really not worthy of our credit to go on providing a nominal Sinking Fund of £50,000,000 in face of these fresh borrowings each year. I preferred to regularise the proceedings, and to set aside a sum equal to the new liability incurred. At the same time I thought it would be a wise measure, sound in itself, and based upon respectable precedents, while at the same time not imposing too heavy a burden on the taxpayer for the actual debt charge, if we reverted to the old principle of an accumulating fixed debt charge. I find I did more than justice to Mr. Gladstone in the matter in opening the Budget, because Mr. Gladstone, although he had opposed the method of the accumulator, afterwards for many years carried it out. As is so often the case, though he opposed it in Opposition, he for many years subsequently followed the policy when in office.

As far as the principle of the accumulator is concerned, there is no doubt that, after it has run for a certain number of years, the favourable position created is such that, human nature being what it is, there is always a danger of those lapses from financial virtue which have been so properly stigmatised as raids. I cannot myself visualise accurately a situation where the Government in 1978 will be providing £355,000,000 for the service of the debt, while knowing that the Government of 1979 will not have to provide a penny. That is hardly how it will work. But still I believe it will be a very good guide within the lifetime of many of us here if we push ahead with a figure of £355,000,000 a year. That is an impressive figure, nearly £1,000,000 a day, and I see, from comments which have reached me from many parts of the world, that the decision to adopt this course in our generation and to make an absolutely sincere effort to rid ourselves of this burden of debt within a period covered by the lifetime of most of us in this Chamber has created a marked impression of the strength and permanent stability of British financial policy.

The hon. Member pointed out, however, that if, for the first time in my experience, any piece of good fortune came my way in the shape of a substantial fall in the rent of money, and we were able to convert our debt from the present basis to a 3-1/2 per cent. basis—that is a contingency which must be looked for, it will almost certainly come as the years pass by—that then this fixed debt charge would absorb the relief which might otherwise have gone to the taxpayer. That certainly is not my intention. I made a specific declaration to the contrary. The £355,000,000 a year wipes out all our indebtedness, external and internal, in a period of 50 years on a 4-1/2 per cent. basis, and nothing is credited to the growing accumulator except the extinction year by year of blocks of debt through the operation of the Sinking Fund. No account has been taken of the possible diminution in the rent of money, and if it should happen that the happy circumstance to which he has referred should arise in the future, I have always contemplated that that would be a windfall which the Chancellor of the Exchequer would be fully justified in devoting to the relief of taxation. There would be a recalculation. What would happen? Supposing we were to convert our debt to a 3-1/2 per cent. basis and save £30,000,000 or £40,000,000. It may be more—£50,000,000 or £60,000,000—I have not the exact figure in my mind.

Then a recalculation would be made of the amount necessary to obliterate the total debt within the limits of the original 50 years' period, and the figure of £355,000,000 would be reduced accordingly. I should think that would be the right and proper way of dealing with the situation, supposing we had a windfall. What we are aiming at is the extinction of the debt in 50 years. That is the target, and if a smaller sum sufficed to do it, owing to a fall in the rent of money, that smaller sum would be a perfectly legitimate figure for the Government of the day to fix.

Let us now look at the question of how the accumulator works. The principle of the accumulator is that, first of all, we pay out of the £355,000,000 the interest and the management charges on the debt, apart from Savings Certificates. In the second place, we pay the specific Sinking Funds, which now amount to £50,600,000 a year. In the third place, we pay the interest on the Savings Certificates which are actually encashed in the year. In the fourth place, we pay the Depreciation Fund on 5 per cent. and 4 per cent. War Loans, if any. These are Loans to which a Fund is attached contingent upon their falling below a certain level of prices. It only comes into operation when the price of either loan in the market falls below the appropriate figure. Of course, the Finance Branch of the Treasury so manipulates, if I may use the word, or would always be ready so to manipulate the Fund, as far as they could, to keep the loans up to those figures. They are perfectly entitled to purchase stock to keep up credit and prevent the Treasury incurring further liability. But once that liability has been incurred, then that is the fourth charge upon the £355,000,000. If there is any surplus left over, after all these charges have been met, that is devoted to the general purposes of redeeming debt. Although it begins small, it will grow each year until finally it becomes an immense sum, eating up great chunks—I beg pardon; I must be careful what words I use—great sections of this debt each year.

Mr. Snowden: I have not taken part in the discussion, but may I intervene to ask a question? The Chancellor of the Exchequer is making an extremely interesting and lucid statement, but may I ask him what is included in the figure of £50,600,000? That, I assume, includes the American debt and the sums that are allocated to the debts which have specific Sinking Funds attached.

Mr. Churchill: That is a very proper question to ask. There are a number of our loans to which specific Sinking Funds are attached, and these, of course, constitute part of the obligation of the Government towards the service of those loans. Gradually they have increased. In my time, a new 4 per cent. stock has been created to which a £10,000,000 a year Sinking Fund is attached. The £50,000,000 Baldwin Sinking Fund had been largely absorbed by these different Sinking Funds and before I made this recasting of the debt charges, about £47,000,000 was in fact already earmarked to what I may call contractual Sinking Funds. Therefore, we have very little free margin. There was also disclosed in the present Budget what were called invisible Sinking Funds which arise from the interest on the Victory Bonds in the hands of the National Debt Commissioners and repayment of certain Dominion Loans to us. The Victory Bonds, at any rate, when transferred into the public accounts in the new form, also constitute a further lien, as it were, upon the Sinking Fund as the money originally charged to the Budget as interest on these Bonds has in future to be found in the same way as the contractual Sinking Funds. Thus we reach the broken figure of

£50,600,000. Anyhow, that money has to be found and, if it were not found in any year, it might be argued not merely that we were not balancing the Budget, but that we were reducing the security on which the public creditor has relied hitherto.

I was about to say that the accumulator of £355,000,000, reinforced by the £14,000,000 liberated by the amalgamation of the note issues in the present year, is sufficient, over the six-year period up to 1933, to provide an average of £71,750,000 a year for the Sinking Funds and the Savings Certificates together. I take the year 1933 because that year covers a new burden which we shall have to bear. We have to look forward in that year to an additional £5,000,000 payment to the United States of America, and therefore I took a six-year period in order that this adverse factor should come into our calculations. But, in spite of this adverse factor, and overriding this adverse factor, we maintain over the six-year period £71,750,000 for the Sinking Fund and the Savings Certificates. The specific Sinking Funds requires something over £50,000,000, leaving £21,500,000 a year available for interest on the certificates. That figure is slightly in excess of the actuarial requirement. I stated it wrongly a moment ago. It is estimated that the Savings Certificates will require £20,250,000 per annum on the average over the next six years.

Thus we shall be maintaining over that period, a difficult period, and after taking into consideration this impending addition to the American debt charge the strict statutory and specific Sinking Funds and, in addition, providing the whole of the interest on the Savings Certificates. An amount like £355,000,000 is a gigantic sum for the taxpayer to provide year after year, and I am not aware of any country in the world which at any time can show any effort of financial rectitude equal to that. No doubt the right hon. Gentleman the Member for Colne Valley will find fault with me for not making the amount bigger, but it is possible to go too far in these matters at any given time. The average for the period 1928-1933 is £71,750,000. I do not in the slightest degree contrast that in an invidious sense with the procision made by the right hon. Gentleman the Member for Colne Valley, but undoubtedly we are making a greater effort than the right hon. Gentleman was called upon to make in 1924 because the figure this year is £78,500,000 as against £57,000,000. This £57,000,000 is calculated after giving full credit for the invisible sinking funds in his year and it is made up by £45,000,000 New Sinking Fund, £7,000,000 Savings Certificates interest, £3,250,000 for Dominion loan repayments and £1,750,000 for Victory Bonds interest.

I am not in the least attempting to claim any exceptional virtues in this respect, and I shall not do so unless I am attacked. There are people who have endeavoured to confront me with a very awkward argument. They say, on the one hand, that I have not provided enough Sinking Fund, and, on the other hand, when I have increased the Sinking Fund they ask, "Where is all your economy in expenditure?" I have tried to steer a middle course between those two extremes. I think the right hon. Gentleman the Member for Colne Valley in one of his criticisms which he made earlier in our Debates was led into a slip which is quite understandable when one thinks of the complication involved in these propositions and how difficult it is to follow the whole policy which is involved. The right hon. Gentleman suggested that the amount of the Sinking Fund in the six years would be reduced by about £20,000,000. His actual figures were £51,000,000 for Sinking Funds, £14,000,000 for Savings Certificates and £304,000,000 for other interest, making a total of £369,000,000. The fallacy, if I may say so, is that the £304,000,000 includes £13,600,000 for Savings Certificates growing in subsequent years. Consequently £14,000,000 had been counted as an adverse factor twice over, but, making allowance for that, the figures are exactly as I have stated. As a matter of fact, we are paying our full Statutory Sinking Funds, and in addition we are providing the full actuarial charge for Savings Certificates interest.

[Later] I will not go so far as to propound the principle that the end justifies the means, but if the end is desirable and if the means are innocent, one may safely, perhaps, with those reservations, trust oneself to the saying. I am sure the Committee will agree that both those qualifications are present in the existing circumstances. What is the end at which we are aiming? Whatever differences there may be about the rating scheme, at least we are making a great remission of taxation. It is not a new burden or a new expenditure that we are contracting. It is not a new extravagance of any kind. The very large sums of money that are required for the rating scheme are essentially a remission of taxation—I am not saying whether it is wisely applied or not—a remission of peculiarly invidious taxation. And no one can deny that the remission of taxation is desirable in itself. The question of the means then falls to be considered. What means could be more innocent, and indeed commendable, than, after having made adequate provision for the discharge of the liabilities of the State and for the amortisation of its debts, such provision being on a scale far greater than was attempted by any previous administration, to save up the years' surplus for the purpose of giving that remission of taxation in itself so desirable and bring it about at the earliest possible date? In that sense the statement that the end justifies the means is fully to be defended in the present circumstances, with these qualifications. The hon. Member has criticised both the carrying forward into the future of the old Sinking Fund surplus of last year, and the holding of the accumulated surplus of this year in a suspensory fund. But if I were not to take that step, I do not think I could make a proper arrangement for bearing the expense of the scheme.

There is no doubt that the relief of taxation which will come through the rating scheme will substantially exceed, now that the Kerosene Duty has been dropped, and that it has appeared that certain increases in the grants to local authorities shortly to be announced are inevitable, the new revenue from the Petrol Duty, and it is only because I shall have in hand this accumulated fund made up of the prospective surplus for this year and the realised surplus of last year that I am able to see my way to financing the whole of this scheme over the next three years for certain. I hope and trust better days will come during that period and that we may stimulate and accelerate their advent, in which case the normal growth of our revenue and the recovery of our trade, the decrease of our expenditure and the diminution of unemployment, will place us after three years in a position much more favourable than that in which we are at present. I desire, as far as I possibly can, to make the proposal one that does not unduly mortgage the revenue of the future, responsibility for the administration of which may fall to others. I have said I am considering the position in which the Government might conceivably find itself and endeavouring to make sure that they are not left with a future so far mortgaged that they have no reasonable latitude in which to move, and therefore I must ask for this easement both for the past old Sinking Fund and for the surplus of this year. This does not involve any impingement upon Parliamentary control. This Suspensory Fund will be entirely in the control of Parliament at every stage of its existence. If the House should think it right at a later stage next Session or in the year after, to take this Suspensory Fund and devote it to the further repayment of debt and to raise the additional money required for rating relief by other forms of taxation, or if happily it should find itself possessed of resources which I do not enjoy, there is nothing to prevent the full discretion and the effective control by Parliament. Therefore, I feel I cannot accept the Amendment, because although the hon. Member has put his points clearly, nevertheless those points are outweighed by the purpose we have in hand and the necessity which leads us to make these provisions for accumulating in advance sums of money which will subsequently be used beneficially.

[Later] In the early hours of this morning, the Committee was torn by two opposite moods in respect to the Amendment which my hon. Friend has just proposed. On the one hand there was a great demand on this side that his Amendment and his speech should be made under the best conditions at a time when they could be fully reported and studied by the country, and on the other hand the Opposition protested that they were utterly unable to transact any further business unless they were fortified and refreshed by the guidance of my hon. Friend. As I said at the time, my reasons for suggesting that the Clause should be postponed until this afternoon were not of a personal but of a public and general character. There has been a great deal of misconception about the Surtax and the Super-tax, and there have been absurd conjectures on the subject in some quarters. I am glad to think that my hon. Friend did not foster the more absurd and unjustifiable of these delusions.

There is no question whatever of double tax being exacted from anyone in any way. There is, of course, no question of the Exchequer obtaining in any year an additional payment of Super-tax. I think it well that it should be known that my revenue from Super-tax last year was about £60,000,000, and I am expecting to get no more than that in the present year. Consequently these alarming accounts of the Exchequer by some devious method succeeding in obtaining two payments of Super-tax in a single year are utterly unfounded, and I am glad to have an opportunity of making that plain. Although both the Super-tax and the Surtax are imposed in respect of the year 1928, yet they are payable in different years, and are calculated on the income of different years. The Super-tax for 1928 is charged upon the income for 1927, and the Surtax for 1928 is charged on the income of 1928. No one in any circumstances would ever have to pay Super-tax or Surtax for a greater number of years than he has enjoyed a Super-tax or Surtax income, and no one would ever have a liability to pay twice in the same year.

Is not that quite fair? After all, it is only applying to the Super-tax or Surtax payer what has long been the rule with regard to the ordinary Income Tax payer. No one ever questions the fact that the Income Tax payer below the Surtax limit should pay his full Income Tax for the last year of his life. I am sure that there is nothing inequitable or anomalous in the step that we have taken. Neither is there any concealment about it. It is true that our discussion took place at a late hour last year, and for that reason I was anxious that the subject should not be reached at the same time this year. But there was absolutely no concealment of the fact that this would impose an additional charge on the taxpayer. I am not pretending that it does not do so. Of course it does, and is to that extent a new tax. That charge amounts to £1,000,000 a year approximately. That charge, as I explained, was put on the taxpayer as a counterpart to the remission given, I will not say to the taxpayers, but given to other taxpayers in reference to the calculation of income under Schedule E. A million pounds was lost by that, and a million pounds was gained by this. I explained both fully and plainly to the House last year that this was exactly what would occur.

I am not in a position to sacrifice revenue. The simplification scheme, which was studied with great attention by some of the highest experts of Income Tax law and procedure in this House, gained a very great measure of assent, although my hon. Friend has said that the more it was understood the less it was liked. I do not share his view. I do not know how much it will be understood, because even simplification in these matters is a relative term. But that is a very great advance on what was in force before, and that it will gradually be found to open the door to easier processes of collection of the tax, I have no possible doubt. As I have said, I am not in a position to surrender revenue. If the House were to deny me the revenue that I obtain by this addition to the Surtax liability, amounting to £1,000,000 a year and falling to be collected after the death of the Surtax payer, and if I were left to bear the cost of the charge under Schedule E, I should be forced to propose a new addition, which I could only find in the circumstances by a regrading of the Surtax scale to produce an extra £1,000,000.

It would be much better if we adhered to the policy and the proposals which were fully laid before the House last year, and which, as is known well, were not left in any obscurity after the searching criticism by which they were beset in various quarters. I am sure it would be very much better to adhere to that method. I do not conceal for a moment that there is additional taxation. I said so last year. But I cannot surrender any revenue, and if I were denied this I should find it necessary to propose additional direct taxation. Finally, let me say that the Amendment of my hon. Friend does not remedy the evil of which he complains. It does not take away £1,000,000 a year from the Exchequer, but it takes in one holocaust no less than £60,000,000, thus completely disorganising the whole finance of the country, and rendering it utterly impossible to carry out any constructive policy to which we set our hands.

Sir William Davison: The right hon. Gentleman has said that no taxpayer would be taxed on any Super-tax income that he had not received. Is not there a change from the present system? Under the present system no Super-tax payer pays Super-tax until he has had a year of Super-tax income. That is to say, that in the first year during which he has had an income of £2,000 or over he does not pay Super-tax, but that income is the basis of taxation for Super-tax in the following year. It seems to me after what the Chancellor has said that that arrangement is now wiped out and that the Super-tax payer is to pay Super-tax backwards from the very time when he first had a Super-tax income, as contrary to the present system under which he does not pay in the first year. Let me put it in another way. If your income last year was £1,500 and this year £2,000, you do not pay Super-tax this year; you do not pay Super-tax till next year, when it is paid on the £2,000 that you have had this year.

Mr. Churchill: It is no part of our case that there has been no change.

Sir Robert Horne: It was last year.

Mr. Churchill: On the contrary, it was not so. My right hon. Friend is in error in that statement. I said last year:

> In the general scheme of simplification there are various aspects which must be considered together and balanced against each other. It happens in this particular aspect that there is a gain of revenue to the Exchequer, but in another aspect there is a counterbalancing loss. But on the whole, I contemplate, in consequence of the scheme of simplification, that the burden on taxpayers as a whole should be virtually unchanged.—[Official Report, 30th June, 1927; col. 752, Vol. 208.]

Sir R. Horne: I, in common with many other people in the House, understood it in the way I have suggested.

Mr. Churchill: I also said last year, on Clause 41 of the Finance Bill, which relates to the Surtax:

> I fully appreciate the fact that while in certain directions the simplification scheme meant a loss to the Exchequer, in this respect there was a gain to the revenue of an almost exactly similar amount.

Nothing could be clearer than that. It is not my case that there has been no change. There has been a change in respect of Surtax and Super-tax. An increased liability is imposed on the Super-tax payer, but that increased liability does not amount to double Super-tax, as is sometimes suggested; it does amount to the prolongation of a payer's liability for an additional year, collected after his death; it imposes a burden on him which costs in the aggregate £1,000,000 a year; but on the other hand, the revenue by other parts of the scheme is losing £1,000,000 a year, and this extra resource is necessary to us for the balancing of our finances.

[Later] No one can doubt that my hon. Friend has made a serious, temperate and substantial contribution to the discussion of this subject [taxation of co-operative societies]. The question has been raised in this House very often, and my predecessors, for the last 10 years at any rate, have been called upon to deal with it. The hon. Member quoted what was said by the present Foreign Secretary, but whatever may have been the words used by the Foreign Secretary, no action which he took was different from that which has hitherto been maintained under the present administration. My hon. Friend dealt practically with two points—the loss of revenue which results from the spread of the co-operative movement and the undue protection of that movement, compared with the private trader. I have had prepared a Memorandum which has been circulated freely, setting out the Treasury computation of the tax that is paid in accordance with the law by the co-operative societies, compared with that which would have been paid if they had been taxed on the same basis as private traders. This paper shows that the total advantage to the co-operative societies over the ordinary trader or over the ordinary company in matters of taxation amounted in the aggregate only to £100,000 a year. Naturally, that statement was extremely disappointing to those who feel themselves under the pressure of very acute competition from the co-operative societies, and who point out the high contributions which they have to pay to the national revenue.

The Inland Revenue computation has been criticised on the ground that the average of four years puts the figure too low; that the inclusion of the thin year, 1922, vitiates the comparison, because in 1922 the societies did very badly. Since then we have had the figures for 1926, and the Chief Registrar of Friendly Societies has published them. These figures do not in any way upset the computation of £100,000 as being the difference between what the co-operative societies pay now and what they would pay if they were treated in accordance with the method by which the profits of private traders are assessed. On the contrary, the new figures show that the gain to the revenue would be slightly under £100,000 a year. I will give the figures. In 1926, the distributive trading societies, wholesale and retail, had a surplus of £22,800,000, less "divi" amounting to £17,100,000, leaving a balance of £5,700,000. From this should be deducted interest amounting to £4,000,000, leaving a net surplus after payment of dividend and interest of £1,700,000. Add to that depreciation, which we estimate at £1,000,000, and Income Tax at £550,000, making about £1,500,000, and we arrive at a total of £3,200,000. The tax on £3,200,000 in the ordinary way would be £640,000, whereas the tax paid by the co-operative societies is estimated at £550,000. Therefore, the difference on these figures amounts to £90,000.

Mr. A. V. Alexander: Does that figure include the payments of individual shareholders?

Mr. Churchill: I do not think it does, but that is not an appreciable contribution. I am aware that criticism has been directed against the figure of £1,000,000 which is added for depreciation. My hon. Friend the Member for Tamworth (Sir E. Iliffe) is going to submit later that that figure is too low. He has brought forward figures from the Co-operative Year Book which show that as much as £2,000,000 should be added. We have not been able to be convinced by these figures. The £2,000,000 includes the growth of the insurance fund of the co-operative societies, which does not represent profit. However, a departmental investigation on the question of assets and depreciation is now proceeding with the object of ascertaining whether the £100,000 difference between the tax paid by the co-operative societies and that paid under similar circumstances by private traders is too low or not. That investigation is not likely to be finished before the autumn. Anyhow, I do not believe that the result of the investigation, although it may modify to some extent the details, will alter the broad general position.

What is the broad general position? It is, undoubtedly, that under the law as it stands at present, and as it has stood for many years, those enterprises which are owned by people who are below the Income Tax limit—owned by a large number of persons of whom few are liable to Income Tax—have undoubtedly an advantage, an inherent advantage, over those which are owned by people who are not below the

Income Tax limit. This advantage enjoyed with all the formidable power of massed capital on a vast scale, constitutes a formidable menace to the ordinary trader; but I do not see how you can make any greater change in the way in which the Income Tax laws of this country are administered than if you were to invade the primary rights, the primary advantages of those who are themselves in such a small way that they are beneath the Income Tax limits. Those rights appear to be, and they are, of a primary and fundamental character, and I do not see in what way they can be altered by or impaired by any extra burden being thrown upon their possessors in respect of their interest in co-operative societies.

The fact remains that people who have not risen to a certain standard of income are immune from Income Tax and if they choose to band themselves together into societies, Parliament has long considered that their immunity was in no wise to be impaired. That is really at the bottom of the grievance, but for my part I cannot see that any Parliament would be well advised to make an inroad upon these primary immunities and liberties of the small person who has only the most restricted forms of investment open to him, and who is below the Income Tax level. There can be no doubt about the severity of the competition. On the one hand, you have these very small investors immune from the Income Tax burden, and on the other hand you have this immense machine which manifests itself so vastly in every walk of our national and economic life. They are not the only competitors which individual shopkeepers have to face. There are the great multiple shops which are spreading throughout the country and which constitute almost as serious a form of competition as the co-operative movement. My hon. Friend dwelt upon the loss to the revenue which occurs when a private establishment is purchased by a co-operative society.

There must be a certain diminution of tax when property hitherto owned by wealthy persons who are paying Income Tax on a high and progressive scale passes into the hands of a large number of persons who are below the Income Tax level altogether. That is inevitable but the loss is not as great as is supposed. The purchase price will be invested, and the tax will be paid upon the income which is produced by the purchase money. In the second place the co-operative societies pay their tax fully under Schedule A. I frankly say that I am not prepared to advise the Committee to make any change in the working of the law. These matters have grown up slowly. They represent very serious features in our national life, and it seems to me that the inherent right and privilege of the small investor to be immune from Income Tax cannot be restricted or diminished despite the fact that this competition with individual traders has risen to very formidable dimensions. We will pursue investigations into the comparatively small point as to the amount which should be charged for depreciation, and that should be concluded by the autumn. In other respects, I am advised, and, as far as I am able to form an opinion I have come to the conclusion, that there are no grounds at present for making any change in a deeply founded and strongly buttressed system.

Mr. Albery: May I ask one question? Is it not the fact that the small shareholder in a limited liability company is taxed at source, while the member of the co-operative society is not?

Mr. Churchill: There you enter into the field of mutuality, and if you were to attempt to tax mutual trading concerns on the same basis as you tax shareholders in a limited company, you would be undertaking a very profound alteration in the whole of our present Income Tax law.

[Later] I am afraid that I am not in a position to accept the suggestion [to abolish the Betting Duty] of the hon. Member for South Ayrshire (Mr. J. Brown). It is quite true that the Betting Duty, which has been in operation for something like two years, has not yielded the full financial results to the revenue which were expected of it. It is also quite true that a great deal of evasion is undoubtedly in progress, and I think that I must admit that a good deal of discontent and unpopularity towards the Government has been excited among the bookmaking confraternity. These are the evils. On the other hand the Measure was most carefully considered by Parliament; it was supported by an overwhelming amount of public opinion in the country; and even among those who on religious grounds used the moral argument that you should not touch the unclean thing, there was a considerable under-current of opinion in favour of making the person who felt that he could indulge in betting as a practice pay something for the luxury of the excitement that he enjoyed, or hoped to enjoy. Nevertheless the revenue has been substantial. Nearly £3,000,000 a year is being gathered in. Half the yield of the duties on tea, including the chicory group, half the amount that would be required to revert to penny postage or almost the revenue derived from matches—this is the gain from a Duty which, although it causes some political disadvantage to the Government of the day, although undoubtedly it is not working as satisfactorily as we had expected, nevertheless, in no way burdens the productive energies of the nation, and in no way affects its sources of moral or material strength.

I believe that if I were to accept the new Clause, there would be a very considerable outcry, a movement of disappointment, and indeed of resentment, from a very large class of sober and solid persons throughout the country, who feel that betting ought to be made to contribute to the revenue, and now that the duty has yielded such substantial sums, ought Parliament of set purpose to repeal it merely because of the difficulties which beset the duty in the early years?

There is another reason why I am not prepared to withdraw the duty or to modify it in the present year. I do not know yet what is going to be the fate of the Racecourse Betting Bill which is now before Parliament. I have no doubt whatever that, if that Measure becomes law, and when that Measure becomes law—and I am sure that such an institution will in any case be adopted in the course of the next few years—a very considerable reform in British racing will have been effected, and a process will have been set on foot which is bound in the course of years to reduce and eliminate that undesirable personnel which we have incubated in this country to an extent which no other country can show, which is a disgrace in many ways to our islands, and tends to vitiate the noble and national sport of horse racing, to emphasise its undesirable features, and to check the legitimate development which we might naturally expect. I do not know what will be the result of that Measure. It is now about to pass from its chequered career in the Standing Committee, and we shall soon have it upon the Floor of the House, and I must certainly see what is the position of that Measure before I could enter into a discussion of any other proposals for mitigating the Betting Duty or shifting its incidence from the turnover basis to the licence duties which are pressed upon me. Once we know that the Totalisator Bill is going to become law, the question of giving further shape to the present Betting Duty will come into the field of practical politics.

In the meanwhile it is clear to me that the immediate duty of the Customs and Excise is to pursue their efforts at detecting and punishing evasion of the duty. Evasion is going forward on a very great scale. As I have said, bookmakers who are paying their taxes are continually informing me of the evasion which is practised, but when I press for examples and for information which will enable investigations and prosecutions to take place, there is a very singular and rather sinister shrinking from furnishing accurate and detailed facts. Statements are made to Members of the House of Commons of the enormous scale and the open and flagrant manner in which evasion is being practised, but at the same time when one asks for evidence which will enable the law to be set in motion, one is met with what is virtually a complete blank and silent negation. I am told, and I believe there is a good deal of truth in it, that persons whose business is being injured because, while they are paying the tax, others are taking their custom from them through evading the tax, and who have every incentive that business interests can give to induce them to come forward and aid the law—as other traders do when taxes are being evaded by their competitors and rivals—are deterred by physical fear, not merely by fear of trade retaliation or the opprobrium of their colleagues, from giving the information which would enable these practices to be suppressed. That, again, points to the great importance of our setting our racing system on a basis which gradually, over a period of years, will tend to put a stop to this incubation of a crowd of exceedingly undesirable citizens who are growing up at the tail of this great national sport. Therefore, so far from receding from the betting duty or advising the Committee to lend support to the new Clause which is being proposed, I urge that we should give further consideration to making this duty effective by the prevention of evasion, and that we should review the matter when, as I trust, the Totalisator Bill has become the law of the land. If that should occur I hope that I may be able to deal with the position next year, and to make proposals which will place this tax upon a basis more satisfactory to those who are chiefly concerned. But whether it is possible to devise such proposals or not, whether the inconveniences of the present system can be mitigated in any way or not, and whether the evasion which is taking place can be restricted and prevented or not, I am still of opinion that it is an exceedingly sound, practical and useful step for the Government of this country to add £3,000,000 to its revenue by taxing the luxury of betting.

FINANCE BILL

July 3, 1928

House of Commons

I do not take the slightest exception to the manner in which the hon. Member for South-East Essex (Mr. Looker) has put forward his argument, and, though I am not able altogether to meet him, nevertheless I wish to make it quite clear that I am not at variance with him upon the general issue which he has put forward, namely, that the effective value of a licence has been greatly affected by the diminution which has been made in the hours during which licensed premises may remain open. I received a deputation upon this subject a year ago, and after very carefully examining the whole question, I reached the conclusion that undoubtedly a case of some injustice had been made out. I have not found it possible to deal with matter in the present Finance Bill. When last year the subject of the possibility of making some reduction in these duties was raised, the Debate became involved with what was called the small bottle, and I pointed out that it would be impossible to deal with the small bottle issue, an issue which affected off-licence holders, unless and until an attempt were made to adjust the burden which was put on on-licence holders; but I said that, if ever it were found that the general finances of the country would justify a mitigation of the burden on on-licence holders, that would be the time to deal with the question of the small bottle.

I am not in position to do that this year; I think it would be better to await a greater assurance of a surplus before dealing with the question, but I will say now that I hope, and indeed confidently hope, that it will be possible, unless some very unfavourable turn takes place, to make some mitigation of the on-licence duty next year; and, if that should be the position, that will be the time, and then would arise the necessity, for dealing at the same time with the question of the small bottle, which was so strongly pressed upon us by representatives of the Labour party, and, indeed, by hon. Members in all parts of the House. The Amendment would have had the effect of authorising the sale by off-licence holders of small bottles, was supported on the Division I think by the great majority of the Labour party.

Mr. Snowden: They only voted against the Government.

Mr. Churchill: The right hon. Gentleman says that they only voted against the Government. Did they only vote against the Government without any consideration of the merits of the question? Are they not to be held responsible in their constituencies for the topics upon which they vote in this House, and for the Measures which, if they had their way, they would carry into law? I have never heard of such a thing. I surmise that the right hon. Gentleman would be indignant if it were suggested that the Members of the party to which he belongs gave votes in this House caring nothing for the merits of the matter upon which they voted, but merely because they thought that there was some division in the ranks of the Government on the subject and that they might by going into the Lobby embarrass the Administration. I am, at any rate, bound to take note of expressions of opinion given by Members of any party in this House, and, on studying the Division List, I came to the conclusion that there was support from all parts of the House for the treatment of this off-licence question, but most strongly from the Socialist party. I was very much impressed by that, and by the divergence between their views and the view taken by some of the more straightlaced Members of the Liberal party. Feeling bound to give satisfaction whenever I can, I have addressed myself to the study of this question, and I am of opinion that there is a case for the relief of the off-licence holder. I will not burden the Committee with the details of it now, but I am quite clear on this, that it would not be right to make that concession to the off-licence holder unless it was in a Budget which found it possible to make some mitigation of the burdens which now rest on the on-licence holder. I must be guided entirely by what happens to the finances of the country. In this year we have found it necessary to impose additional taxation, no doubt for the purpose of making greater remissions, but the taxation is here and the remissions are still on the road, as has been frequently pointed out, and I have not felt that this was an appropriate time for making other remissions. But it may be that next year—I will not attempt to prophesy—our position will be more satisfactory, and that we shall have some mitigations to bestow without the need of any countervailing burdens. I do not say that it will be so, but it may be so, and if it were so, I should be very glad to deal with the vexed question of the small bottle, in which the Socialist party takes such great interest, and at the same time make a mitigation of the burdens resting on the on-licence holder.

[Much later] I think that some of my hon. Friends in their eagerness are spoiling a case in which there is a great deal of substance by overstating it. This is really not a question of over-riding the powers and rights of the House of Commons by departmental action. The powers of the House of Commons in regard to these matters are excercised through the Inland Revenue. The Board carries out the law as a Department of State and the Courts are above the Inland Revenue to see whether it exercises its functions correctly or not. It is true that there has been a change of practice in this matter, but it is a change of practice which is justified in many directions by precedent. I am not now on the merits of this question. I am only saying that in many parts of our system of direct taxation the practice adopted may vary on this side or on that, and that the practice is at the discretion of the Inland Revenue, subject to the Courts always being the ultimate authority to pronounce upon the propriety or otherwise, or the validity or otherwise, of the actions which the officials take. So we need not go back ot Magna Charta or the Bill of Rights in this subject. As a matter of fact, my hon. Friend the Financial Secretary in the course of his remarks, indicated that we were somewhat impressed by some of the points that had been made in this discussion, and that further consideration will be given to this matter before the Report stage. Of course, if we are forced to a Division, and have to vote on the matter, I shall take that as disposing of it.

[Later] I cannot admit that the action taken by the officials was *ultra vires* or improper. Indeed, I have argued clearly in the opposite sense. At the same time, when a Measure like this, which is full of complicated points, is before Parliament, and I hear arguments used which show that there is anxiety in some particular aspects, then, as I have said, I consider that I may well promise to give further consideration to these points before the Report stage. I do not admit that the action taken by the Government or the officials, who act under the authority of Parliament, has been wrong. It is very probable that the more this matter is ventilated, the more it will be seen that their action has been right in accordance with their authority. I promise to look into the matter, and I hope that I shall be able to give unprejudiced examination to the case, and that I shall not be fortified in the opposite sense by a Parliamentary decision to-night which might well be to reject the contention of my hon. Friend the Member for Cambridge University (Mr. Withers). I hope hon. Members will allow it to go forward to the Report stage without prejudicing it by taking a hasty decision in the matter.

[Later] The subject raised in this new Clause was fully debated during the passage of the Bill through its actual Committee stage, and the opinions of the Government were fully stated by myself and also by the Attorney-General; and, therefore, when my hon. Friend repeats the appeal [with regard to people who may have a considerable income but who die with very small capital] which he made on a previous occasion with his customary lucidity, backed by the knowledge which a lifetime's study of the Income Tax has given to him, and does it with all the ardour with which his championship of the Income Tax payer is invested, I can only deal in my reply with such new material as is needed to complete the answer I have already given. Let us look at the matter from two points of view. First, let us look at it from the point of view of procedure. The hon. Member used the word "surreptitious." He said we had surreptitiously imposed this additional tax upon the public under the camouflage—though that was not the word he used—of a simplification scheme. If there had been any surreptitiousness it has been fully unmasked for more than a year past. As a matter of fact, there was none. At the outset, as soon as we got into Committee upon the Finance Bill last year, it was clearly stated that this involved an extra charge on the tax payer—there was no concealment of that fact—and that it was an offset against the remission which was necessary for the purposes of the simplification scheme in regard to Schedule E. On the last occasion, I read what I said, and I will now read what the Attorney-General said. He said:

The distinction is that in the case of people who come within Schedule E they will pay less Income Tax and Surtax than they would if the alteration were not made. They are put back one year as the scale goes up. The net result will be about to balance the extra amount. Therefore if it were a matter of financial advantage there would be no profit in making the alteration. I say frankly it cannot be the object of this law to gain some advantage to the Revenue because there is no advantage.—[Official Report, 19th July, 1927; col. 351, Vol. 209.]

I also said:

I fully appreciate the fact that while in certain directions the simplification scheme meant a loss to the Exchequer, in this respect there was a gain to the revenue of an almost exactly similar amount.—[Official Report, 19th July, 1927; col. 349, Vol. 209.]

I am not saying this to justify the merits. All I am saying is that the fact that there was an additional charge, which we estimate at over £1,000,000 a year in the aggregate on the Super-tax payer, and that it was balanced by a similar remission, though to a somewhat different class of taxpayers, under Schedule E was clearly before the House last year.

Sir H. Buckingham: Will the right hon. Gentleman justify the statement that there will be a loss of £1,000,000 a year upon the adjustments under Schedule E?

Mr. Churchill: I am for the moment dealing with the word "surreptitious" which my hon. Friend used. I say that all this was brought out most clearly and plainly in the Finance Bill last year. In those discussions we had the advantage of the assistance of the hon. Member who now fills the office of Deputy-Chairman of Committees, and who exposed the matter with the utmost candour, so that there was no manner of doubt exactly how the position stood. Therefore, I say, there has been nothing of a surreptitious nature. The exact, proper, correct procedure was followed throughout, and Parliament and the country have known, in so far as they are able to follow these complicated proposals, that there was to be an extra charge on the taxpayer.

I leave the question of procedure and come to the merits of the change. Is it a fair step we have taken? I am bound to say that the more I have considered it the less I have felt that it is an unjust or inequitable thing to do. After all we are only applying to the Super-tax payer exactly the same measure as is applied to the Income Tax payer. No one pays Super-tax for any more years than he has had a super income. There is no question at all of taxing the same income twice over. For every year that there has been an income there is an Income Tax imposed. That is the law of the ordinary Income Tax payer. All we do in this Bill is to make the law for the Super-tax payer march on exactly the same road, step by step, as the law in regard to the Income Tax payer. My hon. Friend has drawn attention to the hard case of a man who makes a large income for one year, and that the last year of his life, and of the heavy burden which is then imposed upon his widow, the source of income having presumably stopped. An equally hard case, though on a smaller scale—and perhaps all the harder because it is on a smaller scale—arises in the case of a person with an income under £2,000 a year. If that man has succeeded in obtaining a substantial income in the last year of his life, though under the Super-tax limit, after he dies the Income Tax for that year, so far as he has not paid it, is collected from the widow. Therefore, there really is no difference between the two classes, except that the Super-tax affects people who are rather better off than the Income Tax paying class. It should also be remembered that this payment of Super-tax by the executors after death is deducted from the amount of the estate before death duties are charged upon it; although the scales are not similar. It is so.

Sir Robert Horne: I am not disputing it.

Mr. Churchill: Though I do not by any means say the one balances the other, it is *pro tanto* an offset. On the whole I must rest where I was before. First of all, there has been no improper procedure, no ambuscade has been sprung upon the taxpayer. Secondly, I claim that we have merely assimilated the principle of the Super-tax to that of the Income Tax, and that principle has always been accepted, and is accepted now, as right and proper in the case of the Income Tax. If we had not got relief through obtaining this £1,000,000 a year in the process of simplification, we should have carried through the simplification at a loss which the revenue cannot at present stand. My idea was that the simplification should pay for itself. My hon. Friend dealt with that matter and gave us assistance in preparing the whole of that great scheme of simplification, and I am sure he knows that of itself it is a good thing. But I could not carry that out at a loss to the Revenue, and I propose that it should pay for itself, as it will do.

Major-General Sir John Davidson: Did the right hon. Gentleman explain all this last year?

Mr. Churchill: Certainly, and if my hon. and gallant Friend has followed the extracts which I read on this occasion, and also the longer extract which I read on the occasion of the all-night sitting, he would see that it was clearly explained and further that it was amplified and filled in by the very well-informed speeches made by many of those who sit round him at the present time. I am not in a position to forgo this revenue. If I were not to impose this altered form of the Super-tax which was placed before Parliament and provisionally assented to by Parliament last year I should have to seek some additional source of direct taxation to balance the loss. I am sure that the Committee will not press me to do that.

[Much later] My hon. Friend [Sir H. Buckingham] has invited me to say that the right hon. Gentleman the Member for Spen Valley (Sir J. Simon) is wrong. I would not hesitate for a moment to do that if I thought he was wrong, and I never did it more frequently than when we were colleagues of the same Government. Let us see what is the proposal of my hon. Friend. Really, I am a little surprised that with his immense knowledge of the Income Tax he should have allowed himself—in fact, he has allowed himself by his immense knowledge—to be drawn into what most people will regard as a very absurd fallacy. The Committee has just decided by a very large majority that the procedure in regard to Super-tax is to be assimilated to the procedure which has long been adopted in regard to Income Tax. I do not disguise the fact that hard cases might arise. There is the case of a man who all his life has struggled, and at the end of his life produces, say, his first successful book, or invention, or has his first good year of business, and then he dies, and the high income which he made in that year undoubtedly becomes, through the taxation upon it, a charge of a serious character on those he leaves behind. But the House, on the advice of the Government, has rightly decided that the hardship is no more a hardship than what individual taxpayers below the Super-tax level have always endured in similar circumstances. On these grounds, the House has accepted the Government's proposal. My hon. Friend, with very fine argument and logic, arrives at the conclusion that, while it is quite all right that the estate of a man who, only in the last year of his life managed to reach the Super-tax income level, should have to pay the outstanding tax, as the House has decided, that of a man who for 20 years has enjoyed a Super-tax income should be given some special privilege. No proposition could be more removed from reason in the result, however logical the argument may have been to arrive at it. Why should a man who for 20 years has enjoyed a Super-tax income, be treated better than the man who, at the end of his life, has at length arrived at the Elysian fields of Super-tax? Why should you in broad justice treat the man who for 20 years has had a Super-tax income, better than the man who has had to struggle with fortune and only in the last year of his life has reached a Super-tax income? I have paid this objection-able impost since its introduction, and the man who has paid it for 20 years ought to be accustomed to make provision for it as far as he can, and as far as the wickedness of the Treasury allows, every year. But to say that such a man who has had this opportunity and neglected it, after having enjoyed a Super-tax income for 20 years, should be treated better than the man who in the last year of his life has arrived at it, is a proposition which the Committee cannot entertain, and which if it did entertain, would introduce a ridiculous element into the whole theory of Super-tax.

[Much later] I cannot think it possible that this Clause, which was drafted after so much consultation, could have reference to anything but a bona fide statement of procedure and bona fide transactions. Of course, if false statements were presented which were not in accordance with the real facts, obviously the saving grace of this Clause would not apply. That is the impression which I strongly have, and I will make sure that this is the intention of the Clause. I could not possibly pronounce on a matter of law at a moment's notice, but it is the intention of the promoters that nothing which is not bona fide should in any way be safeguarded by the Clause.

Mr. Graham: May I ask whether, in order to be sure on that point, the Chancellor will between now and the Report stage inquire as to whether the effect of these words would, so to speak, be an obsolvitur of the companies or the abandonment of all further steps on the appearance of fresh information which may not represent fraud or be misrepresentation or the withholding of information, in the sense in which the Chancellor speaks—it may be the appearance of fresh details which were not before the Commissioners at the time its decision was reached?

Mr. Churchill: We need not go into details. Of course, I am quite clear that only bona fide disclosures of the trading results of a given year ought to secure the advantages which are afforded by this Clause. If there is a bona fide disclosure of the trading accounts and they say, "This is what we are doing and what we are carrying to reserve; have you any comment to make of an adverse kind on it?" If this is done in a bona fide manner, the company will be effectively protected.

[Much later] No one can deny that there is a plausible case in regard to this matter [of amending the Finance Act of 1926 to refund to credit bookmakers taxes paid on bad debts] more especially when it take the form of asking that the tax should be recovered which has been paid on bets in the case of which the backer has defaulted. Nevertheless, the position, after full consideration, was deliberately taken up, when the tax was originally imposed, that these bad debts in gambling are a necessary and inevitable part of the circumstances with which persons following the profession of a bookmaker are confronted—that they are an essential part of the risks attaching to the profession, and are capable of being taken into consideration by a bookmaker in the general level of the odds which he gives to his clients and the special rules and regulations which form a part of the conduct of this business; and it was considered that it would be far better for us to leave it to the bookmaker to make his charges to his clients for services rendered in facilitating their wagering acts, and to allow therein a proportion for bad debts, than for the State to come along afterwards and investigate all these exceedingly difficult questions as to whether a debt was a bad debt or not. My hon. Friend, if I may call him so, the Member for Dundee (Mr. Scrymgeour) would say that all gambling debts were bad debts in the worst sense of the word, but all these processes would have to be followed out on behalf of the State lap by lap along the course—if I may use what seems in the circumstances to be an appropriate expression—and would involve even greater labour and difficulty than is involved in the enforcement of the tax at the present time.

If we are going to consider at all the Betting Duty and its incidence, I might say—without committing myself in any degree, or making any promise respecting the future—that, as I indicated at an earlier stage in our discussions, I do not close my eyes to a review of the position; but, if we are going to make any such review, I am sure it would be much better to make a general survey rather than deal now with this particular point, which, although a very plausible case can be made on it, is not a point of real substance, does not lead to real embarrassment of the bookmaker, and would only lead the State into further labour without giving relief where relief is most urgently needed.

Mr. Rye: With very great respect to the Chancellor of the Exchequer, I cannot see why this distinction should be made between the bookmaker and the ordinary trader. If an ordinary trader makes a bad debt, he is entitled to deduct it for the purpose of arriving at the income on which he pays Income Tax, and, if a bookmaker has failed to recover a debt, I do not see why he should be placed in any different position from the ordinary trader.

Mr. Churchill: He can deduct bad debts in arriving at his income for the purposes of Income Tax, but he cannot deduct them for the purpose of the operation of this special Betting Duty.

[Much later] My hon. Friend the Member for Loughborough (Mr. Rye) has explained this matter to the Committee very lucidly and correctly. The new Clause which he has moved is the result of discussions between the Treasury and persons representing traders who may be affected by the decision to which he has referred; and it has been examined and agreed by the Parliamentary Counsel who drafted the Measure. It arises undoubtedly out of the recent decision in the Court of Appeal in the case of the Attorney-General *v.* The Metropolitan Water Board. The purpose of the new Clause is, as has been explained by my hon. Friend the Member for Loughborough, to ensure that the provisions of the Income Tax Acts with regard to collection at the source, which require a person paying interest to deduct the tax upon that interest, shall not so operate as to make that person pay a tax on an imaginary profit, but only on an actual profit. I, therefore, have great pleasure in accepting the Clause.

[Much later] I accept this Clause [amending Section 73 of Taxes Management Act, 1880], which has been approved by the Parliamentary Counsel in its present form. Last year by the provisions of the Finance Act continuity of employment was extended to collectors of Income Tax, and this Clause makes it clear that that continuity of employment will hold good whether the collectors are appointed by the Board of Inland Revenue or by the Land Tax Commissioners, an obvious measure of equity and equality. I am obliged to my hon. Friend the Member for Guildford (Sir Henry Buckingham) for having brought the matter forward.

[Later] The Inland Revenue inform me that no additional labour will be caused by allowing this option [of making return of total income to Special Commissioners] to taxpayers who wish to exercise it. It is quite true that it derogates slightly from the principle of one man, one return, but that principle was adopted for the convenience of the taxpayer, and if certain classes of taxpayers wish to go on making their returns, as they do now to Special Commissioners, because, for various reasons, they do not desire to disclose all their income to the local collector, there is no reason why that wish should not be met. The Inland Revenue are always anxious, as far as possible, in this extremely unpleasant duty of tax collection, to meet every wish and to cater for all tastes.

[Much later] The hon. Gentleman asks us to choose between 6th July and 6th September, but it would cause a great deal of difficulty to alter these dates. The question we have to ask ourselves is: Is there any hardship in the present system? Under the present system, the husband and wife can claim to be separately assessed for Income Tax by giving notice by 6th July in the year of assessment, or, when marriage takes place in that year, giving notice before the 6th July in the following year. So they have at least three months to make up their minds. We think that, upon the whole, that is a sufficient period. After all, even if you went to the 6th of September you would still have seven months before the end of the year in which some event making separate assessment desirable might arise. I am advised that the proposal would cause a great deal of difficulty in the ordinary administration of the tax. This question of the date when husband and wife should elect to be assessed separately to Income Tax is bound up with the much larger question of the pooling of the incomes of husband and wife, and that is a very large question. Undoubtedly arguments could be adduced to show that, whereas men and women living together in the bonds of holy matrimony have to pay on the joint income, they could sometimes escape part of the burden if they were not married. No doubt there are cases of hardship, but that change would cost a very large sum of money to the revenue.

The Chairman: I think our labours will be prolonged if hon. Members are tempted to go into those considerations, which I do not think arise under this Clause.

Mr. Churchill: I beg your pardon, Mr. Chairman. The only reason which led me to mention it was to show how very small was the hardship which the Clause sought to remedy as compared with the much larger issue. We cannot accept this proposal.

[Much later] It has been known for some time that the silk trade has been complaining that the drawbacks are inadequate. I would like to point out that these duties have now been working for three years, and I hope that they will continue to go on in the same way for another year or two before they are remodelled. They are duties which have not provoked retaliation. These drawbacks about which so much was predicted, have not been treated as bounties, within the meaning of the legislation in foreign countries, which provide for definite retaliatory measures against bounties on export. The duties have also been attended by a diminution in the cost to the consumer, they have caused some increase in employment, and they have brought in a substantial revenue to the Exchequer.

I think it is much too soon to disturb this extremely complicated system of taxes, to the elaboration of which the House devoted an immense amount of time in the Budget of 1925 and which I trust we shall leave to work in a harmonious manner until at any rate a new Parliament is established to take stock of it.

[Later] I do not suppose for a moment that the hon. Gentleman would suggest that we should alter our whole procedure in regard to awards. Awards, for instance, given to successful commanders in the field are subject to the ordinary rules of taxation, and there is no reason why those special awards which were given after the War should not also bear their proper and due burden. As a matter of fact, a great many of these inventors obtain their information through the fact that they are employed in connection with the military or naval forces, and some of them make large fortunes, while others who have contributed as much put forward no claim at all. I certainly do not see why the ordinary process of the law should be interrupted in order to add to the advantage of those gentlemen who have received awards.

RATING REFORM

July 8, 1928

Conservative Meeting,
Himley Park, Dudley

[Extract] ... Rates are a burden on productive industry in a way that national taxation has never been. Rates vary capriciously with local politics and local fortunes, and are exacted from industries whether they are making any profits or not—in greater proportion—when industries are depressed, because then the whole of the plant is taxed while only a portion is used. Rates constitute at the present time a vicious and invidious feature in the whole of our national economic life, with the result that industries are going to new areas or into the open fields rather than to centres of population, and people who once found a means of livelihood in industry are now finding themselves deprived of it just at the time when the local authority finds itself deprived of the means of relieving their distress.

Eventually, and over a period of time, this new system of rating will bring about complete harmony between the needs and resources of each district, and instead of some districts being unable to provide for the necessary services to maintain their population in health and education, and having to throw themselves on those who happen to be their neighbours, there will be even distributions of burdens and resources from one end of this island to the other.

I believe the petrol tax will stimulate scientific development of British coal in the direction of pulverization, and that the day may come when people will look back to this year and applaud the Conservative Government which looked ahead and sought to stimulate scientific processes by which new life could be given in the future to our wonderful and almost unrivalled coalfields. There are few things more re- markable than the public-spirited manner in which this tax has been accepted by the motoring community, who, so far as I can see from the state of the needs at the present time, are doing their bit.

The Labour attitude [to the Government scheme] has been vacuous, fatuous, and fractious. They have the feeling that the policy is going to be good for the great mass of trade unionists, but they are most anxious that the Government should not get any credit for it. [Editor's Note: Churchill contrasted the Liberal policy of relieving local authorities of the burden of the able-bodied poor with that of the Government, and produced figures to show how much greater the Government relief would be.] One wonders why they go on calling themselves Liberals. (Laughter.)

I do not at all agree with Mr. Lloyd George in the attack which he made on the successful and prosperous employers. It is men like Mr. Courtauld and Lord Melchett who have built up some of these highly complicated new industries which sustain both employment to the people and the revenue of the State. The more I study the campaign of criticism which Mr. Lloyd George has directed against them, the more astonished I am that, having led England at the time of her greatest peril, Mr. Lloyd George should descend to the depth of squalid political partisanship and appear to revel in it.

FOUR YEARS AT THE EXCHEQUER

July 19, 1928

*Dinner to the Chancellor of the Exchequer,
the Directors of the Bank of England, and
the Bankers and Merchants of the City,
Mansion House, London*

Four years have passed since I was called upon to assume the duties of Chancellor of the Exchequer. In the preceding four years there were no fewer than five Chancellors of the Exchequer. That is not including Mr. McKenna, who could have been a fifth if he had wished. (Laughter.) The question arises in my mind how many Chancellors of the Exchequer will there be in the next four years. However, perhaps we will find it easier to moralize on the past than to speculate on the future. I have no doubt that in the City of London very many more successes have been achieved by shrewd moralizations on the past than by daring speculations on the future. Since I am here for the fourth time I will give you my impression of these four years. It has all been uphill. The whole pathway of commerce has been toilsome and hard and very few strokes of good fortune have come to our aid, and when those strokes of good fortune come, they have nearly always been discounted in advance by other unexpected evils. Yet on the whole we have made our way forward—I will not say in the teeth of bad luck—but, at any rate, without any adventitious aid.

The very large remissions of indirect taxation which were made by my predecessor have been paid for by me. The drying up of the receipts from the sale of War stores which made such a remarkable feature of the post-War Budgets, has created a continuous void in our annual revenue. There has been a continuous decline during the last four years in the revenue from the consumption of alcoholic liquors. Vast injury was done to our affairs by the strikes and stoppages in our basic industries in 1926, and in consequence of those I have had to face a condition where there has not been that normal expansion in the income-tax which one has a right to expect from a growing population, and from an advance in civilization; nor has there been that resiliency in the consuming power which one would naturally attribute to the same cause.

I have also had to face the automatic growth of the social services and of the sums which must, under the present arrangements, be contributed to the local authorities for the maintenance of their expenditure. And in all these circumstances I am bound to tell you that I have found it a very difficult matter to avoid reimposing that 6d. which I took off the income-tax and which nobody has ever mentioned to me since. (Laughter.) I have found it very difficult to avoid either the reimposing of that forgotten 6d. or of, in some way or other, failing to maintain the statutory sinking fund. However, I think I am entitled to say, that, aided by my colleagues in the Cabinet, who have sustained the Exchequer at every nasty rut and awkward turning, we have succeeded. The receipts of the War stores as they dried up have been compensated by the settlement of the War debts and the growth of reparations which, at the present time, have reached a figure very nearly equal to what we have to pay to the United States under our debt agreement with that country. We have thus virtually, though not at the moment exactly, achieved the position aimed at in the celebrated Balfour Note. That is one important factor in the situation. We have lost the adventitious revenue derived from the sale of War assets and in its place we have as revenue the result of debt settlement and reparations which is almost equal to our outgoing responsibilities.

The decline in the revenue from alcohol has been compensated by new indirect luxury taxation: the silk tax is going very well—I have never seen any undue hardship inflicted on the population by its imposition—the Betting Tax, now passing into a new form through the happy advent of the totalisator; and, of course, the McKenna duties on foreign motor-cars and musical instruments—I think I ought to say so-called McKenna duties because my right honourable friend has formally at this table on a previous occasion repudiated his paternal responsibility. (Laughter.) I have nourished his cast-off infant, and I am glad to report to him that it is in a sturdy and lusty condition. (Laughter and cheers.) Important economies have been effected in many directions and, to some extent, in the sphere of armaments, although on armaments it must be remembered that we made very great reductions in our Navy immediately after the War and even during the concluding stages of the War in our major construction, and that, in regard to our Army, it has always been conceived on a scale almost incredibly modest compared with the world-wide responsibility of Britain.

New automatic savings have come to hand to meet to some extent the new automatic increases, and I have had from time to time to adopt some expedients described as the shortening of the brewers' credit or the earlier payment of schedule A of the income tax, or some recurrences to the assistance of the Road Fund grossly represented by the ignorant as a mere raid. But by all these means and methods we have in fact maintained not only the remission of indirect taxation granted by the Chancellor of the Exchequer in the Labour Government, but also the remissions of direct taxation which we have been able to achieve. We have not maintained the sinking fund at the statutory figure, but in every year, excepting the year of industrial disaster, we have advanced it by a substantial amount, and hold it to-day at a figure, never surpassed, of £65,000,000, and, in addition, we have provided for the establishment of a universal national system for the whole industrial population of old-age pensions at 65 and of widows' pensions and for improved public services which Parliament desired to institute. We have turned the corner after the disasters of the great strike. Now I am able to say that upon the whole—and it is upon the whole that you must judge these things—we are in a stronger position financially to face the Budgets of the future than we have been at any time during my tenure. (Cheers.)

It is a great source of disappointment and concern to the Government that in the fourth year of our stewardship unemployment should have risen again, and that we should be compelled to resort to some of those remedial measures which we had hoped we had left behind for good in 1925. But it is most important not to draw a false conclusion or to be led into ill-judged or panic moods by the unpleasant fact of the increases in unemployment which are recorded weekly. We must remember first of all that although unemployment is always recorded in the newspapers, the increase in employment does not receive the same prominence. Employment is increasing steadily, and there are in fact, 360,000 more persons within the sphere of industrial insurance and upon the registers as employed now than there were four years ago, and that takes no account, in my opinion, of the ever-increasing invasion of women into hundreds of categories of our national industrial life. The second consideration which I submit is that there is no truth in the idea sometimes mooted that the present increase in unemployment is due to foreign importations. Take the four principal industries which are contributing to unemployment at the present time—coal, cotton, building, and shipbuilding. These together account for half of the existing total of unemployment, and they account for four-fifths of the recent increase in unemployment. If we leave those four industries out, unemployment has actually decreased during the last four years, and has decreased in those four years in spite of the disaster of 1926 and of the wounds inflicted in 1926, which ate deep into the economic energies of the nation.

As to those four industries, the causes of their distress are various. No one can say with regard to any of those four that it is directly due to foreign importation. Take building and shipbuilding, the exact contrary is true. In those trades cheapness of construction is the foundation of their activities and prosperity. Take cotton, which is a great exporting industry. There is in the cotton trade, as in other basic industries, an urgent need of a new impulse of a kind which 100 years ago set such great industries on the path of world ascendancy. Lastly, coal accounts for 300,000 unemployed persons. That is certainly not due to foreign imports of coal, because there are none. It is due to the fact that the coal industry has been putting itself, by most painful processes, upon a more efficient competitive basis so far as man power is concerned. I hope that the processes will not stop at economy in man power, but continue to the other branches—mechanical distributive and selling. (Cheers.) We cannot afford to neglect any aspect of reform in respect to an industry so vital to our prosperity. But the fact remains that now we are producing all the coal that can be marketed at the present time at home or abroad, and we are doing so with 300,000 less men employed than were necessary a few years ago. This imposes upon his Majesty's Government a difficult and only partially soluble problem, so far as the immediate facts are concerned.

In spite of the fact that the problem has been imposed upon us, I say, without hesitation, that the true economic efficiency of the coal industry must be, in any period, the main foundation of our national well-being. We have been ploughing through the aftermath of the War and the aftermath of the industrial strife two years ago. Well do I remember the banquets attended for the first time in 1925, on the eve of the partial breakdown in the coalfields, and the second, in 1926, in the middle of the prolonged stoppage, and how I warned, not those present, who had no need of a warning, but those outside whom my voice might reach, of the grim consequences which would pursue them if a disastrous struggle broke out and was fought to a conclusion. I do not, of course, ignore the possiblity that an extension of the trade of the country will carry out to the coal industry and increase the domestic demand for coal. But when we remember that the existing coalmines produce at least 50,000,000 tons or more than we can market it is clear that a surplus capacity of coal exists which will have to be absorbed before the problem of unemployment can be substantially relieved.

What then are the measures within our power to take which will deal with this strange and difficult phenomena? The special measures required for the emergency will be announced next week by the Prime Minister in the course of the Parliamentary debate. I believe that they will be found to present a broad and well-conceived policy. I am speaking this night, however, not of special measures, but of general measures, and I say of those general measures that we must keep to the high roads even if they are hot and dusty and uphill. (Cheers.) Sound finance, sound currency, honest wages to the workmen, strict discharge of our obligations public and private, is the foundation. Other nations may for a time profit, but this island, with its vital dependency upon world-wide credit and business, cannot afford for a moment to derogate from the strictest standard of financial integrity. (Cheers.) I am inclined to think that when the history of the difficult post-War period is written the decisions which led to the resumption of the gold standard will be found to have played a definite part in the consolidation of the financial strength and even leadership of the country.

I am sure that the start we have received in our policy of sustaining and protecting industry in all parts of the country has been reinforced by the opinion of those best able to judge in the City of London itself. The Government have endeavoured to relieve industry from most invidious burdens—the burden of freights and the burden of rates. Freights we are dealing with only to a small extent, but, nevertheless, we cannot ignore the heavy and even harsh problem which fell upon the basic industries through the rise in freights which followed the Great War. I rejoice to see the efforts which are being made by masters and men on the railways to face the problems which press upon them. I trust it may be in the power of the Government to encourage and aid their efforts. So far as rates are concerned we may, I think, claim to have dealt with them once and for all. (Cheers.) No one will find in the rating problem, so far as industry is concerned, anything worth touching after the Government have finished with it. Rates, so far as agriculture is concerned, were swept away, and, so far as industry is concerned, there is a recasting and readjustment, and after that readjustment has taken place the reduction in the rates, as regards productive industry, will be three-fourths of what you have had to pay.

Without being unduly sanguine I think we may feel that we can face the undoubted difficulties which emerge upon us in the future in a sense and in a spirit of not being unequal to them. They certainly will not be worse than those we have already overcome, but do not let them add to them. Do not let them by any means which it is within our power to control, complicate or aggravate the difficulties which the present economic situation of the world imposes upon Great Britain. This is no time for violent changes. It is no time for exciting political agitation. It is no time for instability or discontinuity in public affairs. We must have a steady stable period, even though to some restless spirits it may seem barren in headlines and in sensation. Unless we can have a steady period of patient effort and a continuous purposeful direction we shall not be able to gather anew our strength or our position relatively or even actually in the modern and rapidly expanding world. (Cheers.)

FINANCE BILL

July 23, 1928

House of Commons

I beg to move, "That the Clause [reducing the Betting Duty] be read a Second time."

The task which I have to perform is one which I know will excite, if not enthusiasm, at any rate approval, because the effect of this proposed new Clause will be a remission of taxation, and a remission of a form of taxation which has drawn upon itself much criticism from the official Opposition. I am proposing to reduce the rate of duty on betting on the course from 2 per cent. to 1 per cent., and the rate on office betting, which is the larger proportion, from 3-1/2 per cent. to 2 per cent. These reductions will take place as from the 1st October, 1928. The first reason which has led us to recommend this course to the House is the desire to mitigate to some extent the temptation to evasion. There is no doubt that evasion to a large extent has been practised in connection with this tax, and those who have not been guilty of evasion have been among those who have suffered most through the diversion of their trade to less reputable quarters. I had in any case to face a certain shortage on the estimated revenue from the tax. The yield was estimated by me at £3,250,000, but I do not think I could have expected much more than £2,500,000, judging by the out-turn of the year so far as it has now gone.

There is no doubt that there are many other attractions competing with racing in this country. Many people who used to go to race meetings as one of their principal pleasures have now found in the motor bicycle, the cinema, and other forms of amusement and diversion, important competing attractions. In addition, there is no doubt in my mind that a certain amount of money which used to be devoted to speculation on racing is now used for speculation on the Stock Exchange. At any rate, the revenues of race meetings have shown a diminution, and there has also been this shortage in the yield of the tax. Although these remissions which I am making will have the effect of reducing the yield of the duty this year from £3,250,000 to £2,000,000, nevertheless the actual net reduction of revenue which I have to face will only be some £600,000 or £700,000. I hope that the reduction in the rate of the duty will add to the efficiency of the tax, and that there will be less evasion and a larger proportion of yield. I should have wished to double the charge for bookmakers' certificates, which is now £10, and to raise it to £20, this year, but for the fact that it would involve a re-committal of the Finance Bill and other somewhat laborious Parliamentary transactions, and I shall have to do that next year. I have mentioned it now in order that no complaint may be made that due notice had not been given. The counterpart of the concession which I have announced is a doubling of the charge for the certificate.

In these circumstances, I commend the new Clause to the House. I am sorry, of course, to forgo the revenue, but am anxious, among other things, to give the totalisator a good start, in order that it may not come as an additional burden upon the course bookmakers. It will be they who will be principally affected by the totalisator, and I am anxious not to add to the burden which they are bearing at the present time. I have been a good deal pressed to change the method of collecting the Betting Duty from the present percentage on turnover to a system of graded licence duties. I am quite ready to look into that, but up to the present no such scheme has been presented to me which would provide any practical means of meeting the many difficulties, and, although a great many important bookmakers are in favour of it, there is a strong minority of opposition among the smaller men. However, I have nothing to say as to that at the present time, except that I am studying the matter, and that, if any practical scheme of grading were to be devised, it would supersede in whole or in part the reduced percentage duty as well as the new doubling of the charge for certificates which would otherwise be imposed next year. I do not myself think that I ought to encourage any expectation that the difficulties will be solved, but, at any rate, I will give fair and careful consideration to any such proposals that may be made. No doubt the right hon. Gentleman the Member for Colne Valley (Mr. Snowden) is looking forward to mocking me on my having to make this reduction, but it ought to be regarded as an entirely satisfactory event. If it can be made during the present year, it is not a matter which anybody, in any part of the house need deplore—

Lieut.-Commander Kenworthy: How much will you get from the totalisator?

Mr. Churchill: The rate of duty on the totalisator has not yet been settled. As the law is at present, it would be the same as on course betting, namely, 1 per cent., but this need not necessarily be the final percentage. As soon as the new authority is constituted, we shall begin the examination of the matter in discussion with them, in order to see what is a fair proportion that the State may properly take. Although the Betting Duty has only yielded something more than one-third of the revenue that was originally hoped for from it, nevertheless I say that even that one-third alone has fully justified its existence, and if at the same time the totalisator marks the beginning of an era of cleaner racing and a diminution in those undesirable elements in regard to which this country has enjoyed a special and almost unique pre-eminence—if this better era should date from the introduction of the totalisator, not only will there be a satisfactory result from the point of view of the Exchequer, but we shall have other reasons to rejoice in the decision which was taken two years ago.

[Much later] I beg to move, in page 3, line 30 at the end, to insert the words:

(8) If, on an application made for the purposes of this Sub-section by the owner of a fishing boat entered in the fishing boat register, it appears to the satisfaction of the Commissioners that the applicant has at any time within the period of six months preceding the date of his application, or within such longer period preceding that date as the Commissioners may in any special case allow, used any quantity of hydrocarbon oil on board the boat, he shall be entitled to obtain from the Commissioners repayment of any duty which has been paid in respect of the oil so used
    Provided that—
    (a) an application for the purposes of this Sub-section must be made in such manner as the Commissioners may prescribe; and
    (b) no person who has previously made an application under this Sub-section for repayment of duty shall be entitled to make a further application until the expiration of at least three months from the date on which the last preceding application was made.
    In this Sub-section the expression "fishing boat" means a boat used for the purposes of fishing by a person gaining a substantial part of his livelihood thereby.

During the Committee stage, I gave a promise that I would do my best to meet the case put forward on behalf of fishing-boat owners in respect of the petrol they use. I promised that I would make a special effort to meet the case of those engaged in the fishing industry, who are among the less well-to-do classes in the country, and I am glad to say that the Revenue authorities, in consultation with other Departments, have been able to devise a Clause which will have the effect desired. It fulfils the promise I gave not only in the sense of an honest effort but also in the sense of the actual result achieved.

UNEMPLOYMENT

July 24, 1928

House of Commons

Among the many illusions of which the right hon. Member for Colne Valley (Mr. Snowden) appears to be the victim, there is one from which I would like to free him. He said that for the future he and those for whom he acts will show us neither mercy nor indulgence. Let him dismiss from his mind the idea that we have ever asked or wished or expected any such aid or assistance. So far as co-operation in the advancement of the common interests of the country is concerned, we have always invited it, but so far as party politics are concerned, so far as the taunts and bickerings of Debate are concerned, we are quite content that the right hon. Gentleman should, on every occasion, here and out of doors, exercise to the full his gift of cold, calculated, well-phrased venom. And, Sir, surely the occasion of a vote of censure was one which was singularly appropriate to the display of this peculiar gift. He has supported a vote of censure ostensibly on the Government, but really, I think, if we look behind this frigid exhibition of malicious invective, we see that what he has really been supporting is a vote of censure on the hard times in which we live and through which we are passing; and I am bound to say that, in collecting materials for his indictment, he showed a singular lack of memory for his own past in the controversies in which we have been engaged and the events through which we have been passing. He said, for instance, that the Government, having given a subsidy to avert the coal industry, did nothing for 12 months. There was not a day in those 12 months when the most earnest efforts were not being made, first by one plan and then by another, to arrive at some solution which would avert disaster.

These efforts are upon record, but what did the right hon. Gentleman do? He was like the deepest diving duck plunging beneath the surface of public affairs, while the vast upheaval of the general strike took place. He was as mum as a mouse, and he sat there peering around the corner nervously while some of his followers came out in the open; and he for his part lay in the background hoping to preserve inviolate his reputation as a respectable Radical, Socialist statesman. Whatever you may say of us or of some of those who sit on these Benches, at any rate we have been engaged in what has been going on, and we have not been absent from the awkward situation at the time when it looked least pleasant, and when there was the least credit or advantage to be got out of it.

This brings me back from the long and discursive tirade of the right hon. Gentleman, ranging from the supply of unlimited machinery to India to many curious and novel suggestions about land drainage, to the real practical issues which are before us in this vote of censure, and on which I should like to say a few words before we go to the Division. The immediate issue before us is coal, as has been the case so often in this Parliament, because unemployment generally, the recent increases in unemployment, and the grievous features of unemployment is so largely due to the unemployment in the coal industry. That is the core and crux of the problem. There is nothing very surprising or unexpected about what has occurred. It was clearly foreseen and stated, I think, by Mr. Cook and others in the course of the negotiations in 1926, that something like 200,000 or 300,000 men might easily be displaced by the extinction of pits which it would not be possible to work on the wage scales for which he was fighting; and, since those troubles have passed, it has been claimed on the full authority of the Labour party that there are at least 250,000 workers in the mining industry who are surplus to requirements, and that even the Labour proposals would offer no prospects of the industry keeping 1,100,000 miners further employed. These facts are concurred in by our advisers. They are set out in impressive fashion in the Report of the Industrial Transference Board. All that was known before. What was not known is how rapidly this condition of affairs would develop, and to what extent the increased unemployment in coal mining might be counterpoised by a general improvement and revival in the trade of the country as a whole. We are actually producing all the coal we can market, and we could easily produce all the coal that we require in a normal year with anything between 250,000 and 300,000 men less than were employed in the industry only a few years ago.

Another serious fact which should be carefully weighed in various quarters is that if the existing mines and existing workers, let alone the unemployed coal miners, were worked to their full capacity, there would probably be a surplus potential output in those mines, even with their present defective organisation, which might well amount to 50,000,000 tons a year. That is a fact which is before us to-night, and anybody must see that a very considerable improvement in home industry would be necessary, apart from the export trade, before this very large surplus capacity of the existing coal mines could be absorbed, or before we should be able to call a larger number of miners back to the pits. This evil of unemployment, which is distressing enough when spread about in the tale of all the different trades of the country, and scattered about in different towns and districts, assumes an extremely distressing and tragical aspect when it is revealed in the concentrated form in which we see it in the depressed coal-producing areas.

The Report of the Industrial Transference Board states this case in a manner which leaves nothing to be improved upon in the forceful and courageous statement of the facts. One might easily say, Why have the Government published this report broadcast and caused it to be produced in public, when it contains undoubtedly the unflinching recital of so many harsh facts? We have done so, among other reasons, because we hope by the presentation of these facts to enlist a measure of national sympathy and co-operation in all parts of the country in liquidating and diminishing as far as possible the grievous and perfectly definite problems with which we are confronted. The problem before us is how to liquidate this 250,000 surplus mining population, and do that, let the House observe, not in a period of prosperity and financial strength, but in the after-math of the great labour stoppage and disputes of 1926, which depleted the capital resources of this country by not less than £400,000,000, and cost the Exchequer at least £80,000,000.

That is the problem, and it is being approached and dealt with at the present moment by various important methods. In the first place, there is the absorption by the coal industry of its own wastage. An agreement has been made that no adults from outside may be recruited for coal mining, and as the wastage in the mines is necessarily very large, through age and one cause and another, that has a most important effect in relieving this problem. In the second place, we are at the present time using the Employment Exchange machinery to facilitate and encourage voluntary movements of miners out of the mining industry into other areas and other trades. I am advised that, apart from the absorption of miners into vacancies within the industry, this voluntary movement of labour has attained the rate of about 3,000 a month.

But the problem we have to face is greatly complicated by the fact that the unemployment in other districts is not diminishing as we had hoped, and, of course, the general state of the basic industries at the present time is depressed. It was for this reason that I submitted on behalf of the Government the rating scheme which constituted the main feature of this year's Budget. That is the scheme which, when it is in full operation, will cost between £30,000,000 and £35,000,000 a year, all going in relief of industry and being directed principally to those very districts and those very industries, especially the mining industry, which are suffering the most at the present time. This scheme of rating reform and relief to productive industry must constitute the main effort of the Government in its dealings with the present difficult situation. It is a large scheme, and I must confess that we have not had much help in regard to it from either of the parties opposite. We have had nothing but jeers and fault-finding. We are told that it is of no value, and that it is vitiated by every anomaly and illogicality. We have not had the least help in, what after all is an effort on an enormous scale to deal with the situation. Nevertheless, appeals have continually been made to the Government to bring in a small portion of what has been described as a quite valueless scheme in order to relieve the coal industry and other industries before the time for the operation of the full scheme arrives.

I have had deputations largely consisting of Members of the party opposite begging that, at any rate, the freight reliefs should be brought into operation at an earlier stage. It has always been my earnest desire to help in this situation, and it is not a case of what the Leader of the Opposition called an eleventh-hour conversion. I have from the beginning kept open the possibility of accelerating the relief of freights. I have always found it very convenient in working out these things to remember that I carefully arrested £4,000,000 of the old Sinking Fund which otherwise would have been swept into the maw of the Commissioners of the National Debt, and I have added it to my balances to face various contingencies which I was sure would arise in the course of this year. We have now decided that the conditions of the present time require us to make this extra effort of bringing a small portion of our scheme into operation before the rest can be achieved.

What is it we are actually willing to do? [*Interruption.*] I think I might have the attention of the representatives of mining constituencies, because this is a matter of real consequence to the people they represent, and I am not dealing with this question in any polemical spirit, and I am sure that they would like to be in a position to form their own instructed judgment. In the first place, we propose what may be called not merely a concentration of relief on freights but a super-concentration, that is to say that the relief upon coal instead of being spread over all kinds of coal is to be concentrated entirely upon export coal, bunker coal, and coal for steel. That is done under the advice which we have received from the people who are interested in the trade, and we believe it will produce the best results. It certainly produces a much more powerful effect upon the cost per ton of steel. Export coal which under the Budget scheme of traffic reliefs would have received 2d. relief, receives under this scheme 7-1/2d. relief, and coal for steel, which would have received 3d. relief, receives 10-1/2d. per ton relief under the present scheme. The effect of the freight reliefs is actually tripled, and this new form of traffic reliefs supersedes, not merely temporarily but permanently, the traffic reliefs proposed in the Budget speech. All the other traffic reliefs proposed in the Budget will remain unaltered. Agriculture, limestone, and so on, will all remain exactly as originally described; coal alone will take this new and more concentrated form.

In addition to the concentration, we propose to accelerate the date at which this relief is to come into operation. We hope to bring it into operation, at the latest, on the 1st December, 1928, instead of on the 1st October, 1929. The only reason why we attach a contingent condition to this is that we do not wish in any way to hamper or prejudice the negotiations that are now taking place with the railway companies for effecting economies in that sheltered trade which are so urgently needed by productive industry, and also because it is necessary for us to make provision to ensure that these reliefs, which we are giving at the cost of the State, will not be taken away by the Railway Rates Tribunal as the result of an application by the railway companies. We shall certainly enact legislation providing that the Railway Rates Tribunal shall not take into consideration these rebates when they are judging what should be the alterations, if any, in the general freights charged by the railway companies.

I have been very glad to learn that so much importance is attached to this section of our policy in various quarters, but I must say that I think the House would be unwise to exaggerate the effect. After all, this is only a fraction of the policy, and the policy as a whole cannot be judged by a partial application. We are relying upon the operation of the rating scheme as a whole, with its very large reliefs to productive industry and necessitous areas, in addition to these freight reliefs, to produce, not indeed a complete cure, but some measure of sensible amelioration. In addition, we propose to extend for two years the system of export credits. We propose also to develop training centres for adults, and also, in a particular measure, the training of juveniles. [*Interruption.*] I am really astonished that hon. Gentlemen opposite do not give me a little more attention. I am afraid that it is a little painful to them to have laid before them the seriousness and strength of the case and of the policy which the Government are pursuing, but in any case these are matters which are of peculiar importance for those whom they represent.

In regard to juvenile training, it is a very remarkable fact that no fewer than 30,000 boys were taken into the coal industry last year. Thirty thousand new boys were brought into that industry last year, when there are 250,000 people for whom there is no employment, and when, even between the ages of 18 and 25, there are

37,000 men unemployed. Yet into this blind alley, into this area so full of chances of unemployment and of failure of employment, 30,000 boys are being taken in, because their labour is cheaper and more profitable to those who employ them. I should have thought a restriction, voluntary, no doubt, but a restriction, and a diversion of this influx of new labour into a congested industry at this time was a most essential part of any plan, and at any rate the opportunity is presented, because this year, as it happens, we reach the fourteenth year after the outbreak of the Great War, when the drop in the birth rate operates upon the juvenile population, reducing it by something like 300,000 a year, and therefore there is going to be a quite exceptional demand for the employment of boys and youths in all parts of the country during the next four years, and we ought to take the fullest advantage of that to encourage these boys to go into the many occupations there are in other parts of the country instead of herding in a hopeless fashion in an industry where, at any rate for the next few years, a very great measure of disappointment and unemployment can only await them. Directions will also be given to the Forestry Commissioners in the setting up of various holdings, which cannot claim very large numbers, that in so far as they can, they shall give a preference, in regard to new applicants, to men displaced from the mining industry.

Lastly, we are making a new effort of very great importance to cope with the question of migration. Already we have succeeded, under the existing machinery, during the last four years in procuring the migration of 264,000 persons at, I am credibly informed, a cost that does not exceed £15 a head. Still, no one can read the Report of the Board without feeling how many obstacles there are that have to be overcome before migration and Empire settlement can attain its proper dimensions. We are approaching this from three separate points of view. In the first place, we are going to endeavour to make the migration of the population more easy by sweeping away some of the obstacles that intervene at present. In the second place, we are going to provide a larger grant for needy migrants to enable them to start when they reach the other side and to obtain the necessary outfit. In the third place, a scheme has been framed for securing the migration of approximately 2,500 boys, 7,000 single men, 2,500 families, and 2,000 single women from the mining districts alone, if the miners are willing to go, at a cost of £600,000 a year. Finally, we have in view schemes of settlement loans to assist the migrants when they reach their new destination in certain circumstances. The whole of this policy of stimulating Empire settlement will certainly involve a new and heavy charge upon the Exchequer which may ultimately rise, though not for some years, to a total of £2,000,000 a year. I have dealt with all the definite and practical steps that we are taking at present to deal with the immediate emergency, and, after a most careful survey of the ground, I am bound to say we have approached the subject from a good many angles and with a very good hope of making a sensible impression upon the grave problem before us.

I turn now from the immediate and practical steps to say a word, if the House will allow me, upon some of the larger issues which have been referred to in this Debate. We ought not to get unduly discouraged, although the times through which we are passing are unpleasant. The history of 100 years ago will well repay a study. We had then, as now, emerged from a great war, and emerged victoriously. We found then, as now, a devastated Europe and an impoverished world. Loaded with debt, then, as now, we treated our debtors with generosity. A 100 years ago, as now, though with much more trepidation and hesitancy, we resumed the gold standard. As soon as the condition of war inflation ceased a hundred years ago, there ensued a prolonged period of hard times, and industrial dislocation, incomparably more severe in proportion to the state of our affairs than anything through which we are passing now. But through all these difficulties we made our way—not, indeed, without much suffering and hardship, but nevertheless with perseverance, and so we shall again make our way if we act with courage and resolution.

Undoubtedly, however, this new 20th century is not in many ways so favourable to us as the 19th century. A new world is growing up around us, far larger than anything previously seen, and filled with giant States and competitors. The desire of so many nations and new States, including our own Dominions, to become completely self-contained, and have within their bounds every form of productive industry, particularly basic industries, has led to a multiplication and heightening of trade barriers, and a check in the expansion of goods transported across the seas, which affects us not only as the greatest exporters of manufactured goods, but also as the world's carriers upon salt waters. I have repeatedly spoken about the unfavourable tendencies which arise from the increasing substitution of foreign imported oil for domestic British coal and of the solution which we may try to find. Taking all these tendencies, there is no one who can view them without anxiety or without vigilance.

I myself do not believe that we shall come through our difficulties by reliance on any particular logical or doctrinaire theory. I do not believe that there is any way in which, by chanting some incantation, we shall be able to produce a solution of the difficulties with which we are confronted. There is the theory of the Manchester School, that all you have to do is to follow the orthodox principles of Free Trade, and hold up your hands and let things drift, and all will be well in the best of all possible worlds. There are still some, though very few, advocates of that policy on the benches in the right-hand corner of the House. Then there is the Protectionist theory that these islands would be far richer, and give employment to all their people, so powerfully voiced by my hon. Friend the Member for Bournemouth (Sir H. Croft), if only Protective duties were placed on all foreign imports. Then there is the belief of the currency specialist that all our evils could be cured by a manipulation of the currency. Lastly, there is the theory of the official Opposition that all you have to do is to nationalise all the means of production, distribution and exchange. I do not believe that the overwhelming majority of this House, irrespective of party and taken as a whole, will put its confidence in any of these doctrinaire solutions.

Now, indeed, I think the modern feeling is more and more against putting reliance upon logical and doctrinaire solutions. While all knowledge continues to expand, as Lord Balfour said to-day, the human faculty remains stationary, and that has induced an experimental mood in all our studies and sciences, a desire to test matters and not to yield oneself completely to clear-cut and logical definitions. At any rate, it seems to me that it is in that spirit that we have to approach our many difficulties, and it is in that spirit that we are approaching them this evening. We have to face all the facts, not only the ugly facts. After all, at the present time this island, with all its difficulties, is still not only the greatest exporting nation of manufactures in the world, but it exports twice the manufactures per head of its population—although there is all this doubt about the fiscal system, and although, undoubtedly, our wages are 50 per cent. above the Continental level, nevertheless we export, against high and hostile tariffs, and against fierce and in many cases unfair competition, double, per pair of human hands, the manufactured goods than can be exported by any other large country on the globe. There are two countries in Europe—Switzerland and Belgium—which are exceptions to this rule. They are small countries, and they are both countries where the duties are exceptionally low, and they stand with us at the head of the list of those nations which have the highest possible exporting capacity.

It seems to me that we ought to consider all these facts, not from the point of view of rigid pedantry, and still less from the point of view of electioneering propaganda. We ought not to hesitate to examine them in a cool and practical spirit, and to make experiments where they claim to be made. First, there is the application of science and higher organisation, not only to coal, but to every form of industrial production. Secondly, there is the removal of the burdens upon industry by the removal of rates, of uneconomic transport charges and also the reduction in the cost of production. And, thirdly, in the fiscal sphere, it seems to me that we ought not to contemplate any fundamental reversal of the fiscal system upon which the whole industrial and economic structure of this country is erected, and with which it is profoundly interwoven. But we are perfectly free, and we ought to be, to study and develop exceptional measures for the special culture of particular trades where advantage can be gained, and where we have shown that advantage can be gained, and we should also carry protective aid, perhaps by temporary measures, in cases where the strain is shown to be greatest, and where it can also be proved that we can give this aid without bringing greater evil in its train. Lastly, it is in the development of our Empire in these many combinations and in the inter-dependence of its industries that we must look to our future destiny.

FINANCE BILL

July 27, 1928

House of Commons

The right hon. Gentleman [Mr. Lloyd George] has, I am sure the House will recognise, contributed another of his helpful speeches to the difficult problems connected with unemployment and the reform of local government which have occupied such a large portion of the Budget scheme and of the time of this Session. He has asked a question, of which I had no previous notice, of which, however, I do not complain. He has asked me to re-balance the Budget of the present year. I did not know that he was going to do so, but I am bound to say that, forecasting as far as I could the position that would arise on this occasion, and thinking that not improbably such a question would be asked, I have no difficulty in setting out what is the total effect of the various changes which have taken place during our discussions. We are dealing with the finances of the present year in the first place, because, as the right hon. Gentleman has not forgotten, our finances are conducted on an annual basis. Every year the Chancellor of the Exchequer makes provision for meeting the expenditure that will fall due in that year.

Let us look at the current year first of all. The Kerosene Duty has been dropped. The right hon. Gentleman said that we lost £3,000,000 on that. That is not so, for the tax was not expected to produce its full yield during the present year, and the loss on the Budget this year from that tax is therefore only some £2,000,000. Then there is the cost of the concessions made in the Betting Duty; that is £1,250,000 this year. But £700,000 or £800,000 of that would have been lost any way. Of course, as regards the revenue generally, there is a wide range of fluctuation in the yield of the different taxes every year, but we nearly always find that what is lost on one tax is counterbalanced on another, and I have no reason to suppose on the experience so far that this will not be the case this year. Then we have accelerated the railway freight relief, part of our general rating relief scheme. That accelerated relief has been concentrated on particular traffics, and includes the relief to agriculture which passed almost unnoticed in the recent Debate; and this also will be brought into operation as from 1st December. But there are only four months of the present year left, and therefore the extra charge which will fall due during the currency of the present financial year is estimated at only £850,000.

I do not know what expenditure will be involved in the present year by the increased programme of Empire migration which was announced by the Prime Minister. Discussions have to take place with our Dominions, and as I must take this opportunity of reiterating, there must be complete and perfect co-operation on both sides. We do not know to what extent those to whom the offer is made of facilities for finding a new home beyond the seas in other lands under the British flag, will take advantage of these facilities; but if I put £500,000 as the figure which will be required, that would appear to me to be making ample provision for what is likely to come into charge before 31st March next. Adding these together, we get an adverse effect upon the Budget of this year of something like £4,600,000, say £4,750,000.

Mr. Lloyd George: What is that £4,750,000?

Mr. Churchill: The loss during the present year on the Budget figures, either by increased expenditure or by revenue concessions made during the passage of the Budget through the House. If we deduct that from the original Budget surplus, which was estimated at £18,750,000 we find ourselves left still with a prospective surplus of roughly £14,000,000. The right hon. Gentleman asked a question without notice, and I am giving the answer.

Mr. Lloyd George: I apologise.

Mr. Churchill: I am giving the answer as I had ascertained it before the right hon. Gentleman put his question, but of course not with that close precision of accountancy which I should have shown had I been aware that he intended to make this point. We are, as I say, looking forward to a prospective surplus of £14,000,000 at the end of this year, after all the concessions which have been made in this year have been paid for, and after taking into account all the additional expenditure which would fall due in this year. Of course, there are the ordinary fluctuations of our revenue and expenditure which no one can do more than guess at. I am certainly not going to undertake to give an *interim* estimate of the yield of the various taxes; that would be most precipitate. So far as I am aware, there is no reason why the Budget estimates as a whole should not be made good. That is the advice which I received at the close of the first quarter of the financial year. Of course it is already clear that we have gained in some directions and that this tends to balance a falling off in other directions. On the basis that the estimates are justified, I estimate a surplus at the end of the present financial year of some £14,000,000 after the £4,600,000 or so has been allowed for. In the balancing of new taxation and the new liabilities connected with the Rating Scheme, I had assumed to carry forward a sum of £14,000,000 and I reinforced myself with the £4,000,000 odd from the old Sinking Fund. Consequently, on the whole, I can say to-day that the provision and the prevision of the old Sinking Fund has broadly speaking balanced the concessions which have occurred during the course of the present Session, so far as the present year is concerned.

I have dealt with the present year. There is not the slightest reason for any feeling in regard to it except one of confidence and congratulation. But I come to the future, going much beyond what precedent enjoins or the House could have required. I have attempted to balance as a separate part of the Budget the cost of the new Rating Scheme and the new revenue, and until the end of the financial year 1930 there should be a surplus. But as you get into periods which are more remote, and if you assume that there is to be no normal increase in the yield of taxation and no improvement in the general trade of the country, and that expenditure continued as at present then, undoubtedly, there will again be a gap which may be considerable between the future revenue and the future new liabilities of the Central Exchequer, but not a gap which could not be bridged quite easily if there were a recovery, as we hope there will be in the next two or three years, in the general trade of the country. Anyhow, it is not as if in this Budget we had been incurring wasteful expenditure, which added to the national burden. What we have been doing is to adumbrate great remissions of taxation, remissions of local taxation, which presses in the most onerous form upon all classes in the community.

This expenditure of between £30,000,000 and £35,000,000 which we are distributing in relief to the rates on productive industry, and generally to facilitate rating reform, is not expenditure like that on Army or Navy or the Civil Services or on pension schemes. It is not comparable to that kind of expenditure; it is, in fact, a remission of taxation. What has been done is that we have undertaken a remission of taxation, a most important remission of taxation, which cannot come into full operation for two years. We have not by this scheme added in any way to the public burdens. The total public burden is to be reduced, and, as I say, reduced not from the point of view of the National Exchequer, but reduced where the burden is most painful, namely, in the local rates. Therefore, I say, that although I have tried as a work of supererogation to peer into the future of the finances of this scheme—The right hon. Gentleman shakes his head. I am trying to give him a full explanation, and whether I secure his assent or not is a matter of total indifference to me.

Mr. Lloyd George: I am sorry that the right hon. Gentleman should feel it necessary to say that. I only shook my head about the statement that it has been a work of supererogation to look into the future. It was a part, and an essential part of his scheme, if he does not mind my pointing it out, to look into the finances of the next four years. Otherwise, there would have been a very great deficit, and he is rolling up the finances of this year and next year in order to meet the deficiencies of two and three and four years hence. It is not a work of supererogation. It was an essential and fundamental part of his scheme.

Mr. Churchill: According to all precedent the actual responsibility of a Chancellor of the Exchequer has been to deal with the finance of the year. But it is agreed—and I have gone on that principle throughout the discussion—that we should look as far as we can into future years, having regard of course to the difficulty of all human prophecies at a considerable distance of time. I say that that is more than has generally been done in the course of an annual statement of the finances. But even with regard to those years ahead, my argument is that all we are committing ourselves to, even supposing that on account of bad trade there should be a hiatus between the revenue and the expenditure of this scheme, is a removal of burdens which at the worst might be judged to be premature. That is a course along which we are entitled to proceed hopefully, endeavouring to lighten the burden of taxation as much as we can and reducing the amount of money at the disposal of the Exchequer as a greater reason for enforcing economy on all Departments of the State.

I have endeavoured to deal in general terms with the questions which the right hon. Gentleman asked. There is no doubt, so far as the finance of this scheme is concerned, that this year we have a substantial surplus, and next year there is likely to be no difficulty in financing it, but in the year after that there may be a certain difference between the revenue and the expenditure, if no good fortune comes to us in any revival of trade. But there are many resources at the disposal of the State for meeting such a difficulty.

The actual total cost of the remission of the Kerosene Duty would be £2,900,000 in a full year. I have no reason to suppose that that estimate will be in any way exceeded. The greatest confidence is expressed by my technical advisers that the new chemical frontier in oils can be effectively defended. We have also undertaken in the future to supply some £2,000,000 a year more for the purposes of the rating scheme which the Minister of Health will introduce in the Autumn. Those two adverse factors, making together about £5,000,000, must be allowed for in the estimates of future revenue and expenditure connected with this scheme which I gave when I introduced the Budget. To that extent, undoubtedly, the position has deteriorated. The State will be, in fact, £5,000,000 worse off for those purposes, but, as I have pointed out, this scheme is not one involving the ordinary onerous expenditure, but constitutes an attempt to alleviate public burdens, and I have every hope that in two or three years time we shall have a relief and revival which will easily enable us to meet the difficulty; if not, we shall have, at the very worst, to consider other resources of taxation. I was hoping to follow this year's Budget with a Budget next year which would possibly contain some mitigation—

Mr. Lloyd George: I am very sorry to interrupt—

Mr. Churchill: Will you let me finish my sentence? What happens in the present case is that concessions which have been given this year reduce *pro tanto* my power of giving further relief next year.

Mr. Lloyd George: I only wanted to point out this. The right hon. Gentleman says the £3,000,000 has been put up to £5,000,000; to the extent of £2,000,000 the Budget position has been worsened. I should like to ask him whether there is not, in addition to that, that separate grant of 1s. which in England and Wales and Scotland runs up to another £3,000,000? One of the difficulties we are experiencing is that the thing has not been explained as a whole, but it appears on the face of it as if there were another £3,000,000 added on.

Mr. Churchill: In the Budget I undertook to place at the disposal of the Ministry of Health £3,000,000 a year in order to ease hard cases which might arise in bringing rating reform into operation. Since then that has been increased to £5,000,000 or so from the Exchequer, and arising out of certain road responsibilities which are transferred to the local authorities, £3,000,000 is also to be found in the future from the Road Fund. So far as the Exchequer is concerned, and the Budget balance is concerned, the addition is £2,000,000, and that does not apply this year.

Mr. Lloyd Geroge: The 1s. special grant is not an issue?

Mr. Churchill: No, that is provided out of the total of £8,000,000—the £3,000,000 which I originally undertook to provide, the £2,000,000 which has been added from the Exchequer, and the £3,000,000 from the Road Fund. I see no reason to suppose that there will be any difficulty in balancing the Budget of future years, and certainly far less than those we have had to face in balancing the Budgets during the strike period in the present Parliament. There is in prospect a certain reasonable and normal expansion of revenue, and this, instead of being used for further concessions, will be first of all devoted to bridging the gap on the rating scheme.

I have answered the right hon. Gentleman the Member for Carnarvon Boroughs (Mr. Lloyd George) as fully as I could upon short notice, and I do not complain of being asked to balance my Budget again. I am bound, however, to draw the attention of the House to the manner in which the right hon. Gentleman the Member for Carnarvon Boroughs has throughout the long Debates in this House and out of doors endeavoured by every resource at his disposal and all the knowledge and wide experience which he has accumulated in his career, to darken counsel and put a spoke in the wheel of reform, and to baffle and confuse the public mind. The right hon. Gentleman has used on every occasion arguments, many of them flatly contradictory one of the other, and arguments so unsound and so degraded in their character that they will hardly bear repeating here. The right hon. Gentleman has even found fault with the Government's scheme because in answer to a request the Minister of Health expressed it in an algebraic formula, as if the application of science and mathematics and the scientific mind to social problems ought to be made a point of ridicule and condemnation of modern schemes.

Where does the right hon. Gentleman stand? Does he wish to go back to the age of pop-guns and rule-of-thumb? These modern times undoubtedly require extremely complicated processes in reforms, and that they should be jeered at and derided because they can be expressed in scientific terms shows the measure of the quality of the opposition which the right hon. Gentleman has applied in the criticisms which he has devoted to this Measure. To-day at the close of the Budget on the Third Reading, I am glad to say that the right hon. Gentleman has added to the various attacks he has made from one quarter and another. He is now urging concessions here and then running over there and saying "What a disaster you have got yourselves into." The whole of the series of these attacks and opposition are the result of the intense feeling of chagrin which has overwhelmed the right hon. Gentleman when he has seen what he thought was a trump card for his party utilised as a means of a great practical reform by his political opponents.

"KALEIDOSCOPIC CONTORTIONS OF LLOYD GEORGE CLIQUES"

July 29, 1928

Conservative Meeting,
Watts House, Taunton

[Extract] . . . I would lead you into too sanguine a mood if I did not point to the darker side of our national affairs at the present time and bring to your notice the urgent need of active measures required to improve conditions.

Under Free Trade a great many new industries have come into existence which have developed in power and wealth and proved valuable in employment while making important returns to the revenue of the country. Side by side there is a great depression in our basic industries, which are the great export trades of this island, which is more dependent on oversea trade than any other community in the world. Those are the industries which are in a state of severe depression at the present time. The figures of unemployment are capable of many explanations, and unemployment does not exist only in this country. No one can fail to regard unemployment as a major preoccupation of the state.

The Liberal scheme [for agriculture] is a matter of committees. The plan is for the landlord to become a State pensioner. All the farmers would apparently belong to the State and would be bought by the County Council Associations, who would turn them out if they bought pigs too cheaply or too dearly. This scheme, laboriously constructed, has for its object not the raising of crops but the raising of votes. The Labour party is as yet unaware of the agricultural problem. They have signified their entry into agricultural politics by describing agriculturists, in the words of Mr. Philip Snowden, as "the pampered darlings of the Tory party."

Under the rating scheme of the Budget, agricultural rates are to cease altogether. It is by this means that the farmer will know that his productive industry is completely freed from its burdens. I did not put this forward as a favour. It is a wise removal of burdens which were hampering production. The rating scheme must be judged as a whole. It is only when the complete scheme is put into operation that its advantages will be felt. Further, it must be aided by the sensible help of the industries themselves and the co-operation of the whole country.

The Liberal party's criticisms of the rating proposals are vacuous, factious, and fatuous. The Liberal party has worked itself into a feverish anger over the proposals.

Mr. Lloyd George claims that we have not picked between the prosperous and the impoverished industries. Nor could we do such a thing as that. Are we to penalise successes and advertise our failures to the world? Mr. Lloyd George says: "Tory beer. Get thee behind me, Satan." Then he turns to cocoa and says: "Liberal cocoa, Liberal cocoa; pass, friend and all's well." Beer seems to be a subject which has got on Mr. Lloyd George's nerves.

The Liberal party with its five hundred candidates can bring nothing but chaos and confusion. The country must stand united to defend the national cause, and vote upon the simple issue against the levelling doctrine and dangerous projects of a half-baked Socialist policy, and against the kaleidoscopic contortions of the Lloyd George cliques. Let us rally under a trusted leader, as wise, sober-minded, and patriotic citizens, for stability and constructive progress and a rational revival.

REPLY TO LLOYD GEORGE

September 24, 1928

Town Hall, Cheltenham

I am breaking the rule that Cabinet Ministers and ex-Cabinet Ministers, and particularly party leaders, should not take part in by-elections. For some years past it has been the practice of the leaders of the parties, like Mr. Ramsay MacDonald and Mr. Lloyd George, to rush about from one by-election to another. As we are within measurable distance of a general election, and as it is very necessary in this wicked world that people who are struck at should not hesitate to strike back, it has been thought right that I should come here. (Laughter.)

When I read Mr. Lloyd George's speech [at Cheltenham on September 22] I wondered whether it was necessary to come to Cheltenham after all. (Laughter.) If that is really all there is to be said against the Government which has administered the difficult and complicated affairs of the country for four years there is no Government in Europe or the United States against which a more serious accusation could not be brought.

I have been responsible for four years for our finances, but they are run now upon a narrow margin. We do not have the fluctuations of revenue and expenditure which occurred in the years immediately after the war. Matters have come down to a peace basis, and we are settling down upon that basis.

Eighty millions were squandered and robbed from the national revenue by the follies of the general strike and the coal stoppage. It is all very well for Mr. Lloyd George and others to come along and criticise the Chancellor of the Exchequer because in the face of a blow like that he has to reach out in this direction or the other to secure revenues to carry on the public services. I take to myself credit for having been able to get through this difficult time, admittedly by using now one shift and now another, without having reimposed any of the remissions of taxation which were made by my predecessor on tea or sugar or having reimposed the sixpence which I took off the income tax in 1925, without having in any way impaired the proper upkeep of the defensive forces of the Empire, without having failed to make an ever-increasing provision for the repayment of the National Debt, and without having imposed any new direct taxation upon the mass of the income tax payers or any burden upon the vital necessaries of popular consumption.

The state of the country is not so black as politicians out of office are accustomed to paint it. My friend Mr. Lloyd George was most gloomy and depressed about our country on Saturday. Everything was wrong. He did not know where to turn to find a bright spot. I have, it happens, spent most of my life in public office, and I must admit frankly in the few years I was out of office I found myself taking rather a gloomy view of the way things were conducted and sometimes getting quite depressed about the fortunes of the country. (Laughter.)

I have no doubt if Mr. Lloyd George had come here on Saturday as Prime Minister instead of as leader, not of the Liberal party, but as leader of the Liberal party in the House of Commons, then you would have had one of the perorations which we admire so much about the Welsh dawn rising over the hills and ripening the rare and refreshing fruits which were to fill the homes for heroes. (Laughter.)

The reduction in the cost of living in the last four years, making allowances for the alterations in the rates of wages, is worth one hundred millions a year in the purchasing power of the mass of the wage-earning public.

I do not profess that an immediate cure for unemployment exists. We are in the presence of very great problems. I must say I despise a public man who, without any conviction in his heart that he can solve these problems, goes about merely crying out against the Government of the day because there is some increase in their severity during their tenure. The Government are not unprovided with a policy, which we do not say will cure unemployment, but which we believe will mitigate it and strengthen our productive industries.

In regard to safeguarding we have the right to say we have made experiments which have been successful. While we contemplate no fiscal revolution we intend to march with strong steps along that path of successful experiment.

The Liberal party, which has ceased to be an alternative Government, suffers also from a weakness of leadership. Mr. Lloyd George has said that Mr. Baldwin is not a driver. I do not know what you feel about it. My belief is that the Conservative party at any rate prefers to be led rather than driven.

Mr. Lloyd George's conduct in the general strike was unworthy of one who had held the position of First Minister of the Crown. There is no doubt whatever that he thought the general strikers had a very fair chance of succeeding, and instead of choosing which side he was on and standing by with firmness he took up an attitude which, if they had succeeded and the constitutional government of this country had been broken down, would have enabled him to come forward as the necessary man to pour oil on the troubled waters and restore the situation.

[Editor's Note: Referring to a speech by Sir John Brunner in 1926, criticising Mr. Lloyd George, Churchill commented]: Mr. Lloyd George is certainly of a most Christian and forgiving disposition. (Laughter.) [A voice: What did you say about

Socialists when you were a Liberal?"] I know the Socialists are in a rather weak position, and I will temper the wind to the shorn lamb.

It is undoubtedly a great public disaster that so many of our fellow-countrymen have ranged themselves under the foreign standard of Socialism. They worship, or imagine they worship, the doctrine of Karl Marx. They wave the red flag and sing out of tune "The Internationale." (Laughter.) They are full of fads and tricks, and although they are no doubt rejoicing in having a real live baronet among them as Sir Oswald Mosley they are quite ready to deprive ordinary people of the simple courtesy of calling them Mr. and Mrs. (Hear, hear.)

Socialism is also starving for want of intellectual support. There was a time when a great many of the grave young men and women were attracted by this doctrine, but now the whole new thought is turning away entirely from this barbaric and re-actionary conception. If Socialists have become more reasonable it is because Conservatives have become more resolute.

The Socialists challenge the basis of existing civilisation, and under them the government would be handed over to the men who organised and managed, or mismanaged, the general strike. The bulk of the five hundred Liberal candidates will lose their deposits, but the Liberals will have the effect of queering the pitch and baffling the electors. Against these dangerous projects of half-baked Socialism and the kaleidoscopic contortions of Lloyd Georgian politics, I urge you to rally the sober minds of patriotic citizens.

CONSTITUENCY ADDRESS

October 22, 1928

Chingford

I am sure that there is an easier and better feeling in important matters between all countries, and especially between great countries. The fundamental guarantees of world peace are stronger than they have ever been. The only cause of dispute during the last two years has not been due to war feeling, but to peace feeling. The only disturbance of peace has been a righteous and general desire to have more of it; in fact, it might be said that if another great war were to break out it would be entirely on the question of how to prevent it. (Laughter.) The nations are now engaged in arguing with each other about how to disarm. I think it would be a pity to push the desire for disarmament to such a point as to raise anxiety or suspicion or ill-will between the great peaceable and friendly communities.

There are moments when a great advance towards disarmament may be made by international agreements. There are also periods when it is probably better to trust to financial pressure and also to the growing sense of world security for progressive reduction in armaments. If we will only allow these forces to operate for a few years I am of opinion that very real and marked results will be obtained. Judged by deeds, I do not think the British record upon disarmament need make us ashamed. We have gone back to a tiny Army, scarcely more than a glorified police force. We are content with an Air Foce which, perhaps, is only half as strong as that of our nearest neighbour, luckily our good friend, and we have given up that supremacy upon the sea which for centuries was the foundation of the might of Britain. I cannot see, therefore, why it should be right to pillory Great Britain as if she was the provoker of armaments, and I think that British politicians who talk in this strain are playing a shabby part to their country, and are doing little service to the cause of world security. Perhaps another opportunity may be coming in the near future to make a notable advance by a different road towards the reunion of Europe.

We are, I believe, to be invited to attend a conference upon the subject of German reparations. The object of that conference is to restore to Germany a power to manage her own financial affairs without foreign control, and also to let her know for certain what is the total which she will have to pay. We have said that we shall be ready to accept such an invitation, and, of course, we will do what we can to help forward any good arrangement which may be come to. I must, however, point out that Great Britian has already made an immense and unequalled contribution to the reduction of the reparations and War debts of Europe. Under the Balfour Note we have declared that we will not take any money from Europe, whether in War debts or in reparations, except what is needed to pay our War debt to the United States. We have renounced all idea of taking money either from our Allies in the late War or from Germany for ourselves. We have forgiven our debtors who owed us two thousand million sterling everything except what was needed to pay our American creditors for the munitions and supplies which we bought from them in the War and expended in the common cause. No other Allied Power has made, or has contemplated anything like an equal sacrifice. Surely no one can expect us to do more. I hope they will not expect us to do more.

We have taken our stand irrevocably upon the principle of the Balfour Note. In the present year we get very nearly as much from Europe as we require to pay the United States. We have to pay £33,000,000 a year, and we are actually getting in the present year about £32,000,000 from Europe. Moreover, from 1932 onwards for several generations we have to pay £38,000,000 a year to the United States, and we have also to provide for that, and provision has been made in the agreements which we have contracted with our Allies to recover that additional liability. We are, in fact, on the point of achieving the position aimed at in the Balfour Note, and we shall do everything in our power to maintain that position in the future. I feel it my duty, addressing my constituents at this juncture, to give you this assurance plainly and publicly before we go any farther into these discussions.

I have no feelings towards Germany except that of good will, but I do not like to see Mr. MacDonald winning the cheer of the German Parliament because he was known to have taken a pro-German and anti-British attitude in the War. I do not like to read extracts from Mr. Lloyd George's articles in the foreign Press full of aspersions and calumnies against this country. If British citizens or British statesmen have anything to say against their own country let them say it here. Here is the place where the attack should be made, where the criticism, direct or implied, should be levelled, and not in foreign newspapers or in foreign Parliaments.

Mr. Lloyd George seems to have a very poor opinion of his fellow-countrymen at the present time. No doubt the English people have their faults, but they are not such a mean and evilly-disposed nation or race as those two ex-Prime Ministers, and eager aspirants to be future Prime Ministers, are busy making out. I am a free-trader, but I urge that the petrol tax will stimulate home production and help to revive the coal industry. There can be only one issue at the General Election: whether there should be a Socialist Government in power or not. I am astounded at the levity with which this dire choice seems to be contemplated in some quarters. Mr. Lloyd George will perhaps be allowed to join the Socialist Government, to give them stability—financial stability—and to teach them Parliamentary tactics. Some of the newspapers are busy arranging a Liberal-Socialist pact. The blushing Liberal bride is to be wedded to the somewhat reluctant Socialist swain. Lord Rothermere will apparently present himself in the guise of the heavy father giving his blessing to the happy pair: "Increase and multiply, my children. Be virtuous and you will be happy. Be economical and you will be rich." The Wedding March, played on organs of a million horse-power, will be "We all go the same way home." (Laughter.)

This is to be, it seems, the latest political stunt. Last time it was the Zinovieff letter. This time it is the Liberal-Socialist alliance. Yet I should like to know what is the difference between this time and last. The only difference is, last time the Socialists had a minority in office, and this time they are claiming a majority in power. What they are asking for is power to rule the country, for which they are utterly incompetent. I do not believe this new coalition is going to come off. I do not think that Mr. Lloyd George wants to join the Socialists. They distrust him, and he despises them from the bottom of his Radical heart. I see no reason, why with good courage and a good conscience and earnest and zealous efforts we should not be victorious in the forthcoming election. I see no reason in the by-elections, the public's temper, the record which we shall present, nor in the policy which we shall pursue.

CONSTITUENCY ADDRESS
October 23, 1928

Epping

[Extract] ... The Liberal Opposition know they never can get a majority in Parliament, at any rate in our lifetime, but they hope by running five hundred candidates of whom perhaps only fifty or sixty will be elected, to baffle the electors and queer the pitch. By so doing they hope to produce a state of uncertainty of balance in the House of Commons which would enable a small group under able leaders to dominate for a time the situation.

That is not good for the country. What is required is firm, steady, and sober-minded government. The last thing we require for our affairs is frantically exciting scenes in the House of Commons, and Governments rising and falling like houses of cards as a result of divisions and debates and Parliamentary convolutions and intrigues. But that is the aim which is openly put forward by the Liberal party at the present time. You remember how little you liked it four years ago, when they put the Socialists in power one day and turned them out the next, and I suppose in the next Parliament they would seek to offer themselves to the Conservatives or the Socialists and put themselves up to auction to the highest bidder. Such a state of affairs cannot be reconciled with good or steady government.

It is not merely putting up five hundred candidates or having able leaders that is going to make a party effective. It must know where it stands on the great matters of the day. The Liberal party in the House of Commons is nearly always divided into three substantial parts, one of which votes with the Government, one against the Government, and the other which walks out. (Laughter.) As for Mr. Lloyd George, who was a man of so much energy and decision in the war, on a number of occasions when he had been called upon to take a decision in the House of Commons he has been unable to express a decided opinion.

RATING REFORM

October 23, 1928

Loughton

[Extract] ... It would be wrong to leave a necessitous area mainly inhabited by poor people without its proper education and sanitary services. It is equally wrong to saddle the whole burden on the four or five districts which happen to be its closest neighbours. By the [rating] system which the Government are adopting the burden will be spread progressively at each stage over the country as a whole. When the detailed proposals of the Government for the future administration of rating services come to be laid before Parliament, it will be found that the fullest provision has been made for making use of local knowledge and experience, and all those who have hitherto cared for the work for its own sake will find ample opportunities of carrying on their public services.

A DISARMAMENT FABLE

October 24, 1928

Aldersbrook

The newspapers have been pressing during the past two months for the publication of all the papers relating to the Anglo-French Agreement, and when at last they had been made public they were very indignant to find there was nothing that anyone could possibly object to in all that had been done. They then complained that it was not all made public before. When there is nothing of any serious consequence to make public it is very difficult to make it public. When an agreement has been reached between Great Britain and France to leave off criticizing various points in each other's technical armaments as a step forward towards the larger measure of agreement, if possible, for world disarmament, there is no reason why it should be made public until the different Powers to whom we communicated it, including the United States, had replied to the communication which we made, and having preferred to await their replies, we did not think it right to move from that position by the criticism or clamour in certain sections of the Press. Now, however, the whole is laid before them, they are disappointed to find that there is nothing or very little in it.

The discussion of the last two years has tended to bring naval, military, and air matters into a position of international consequence and prominence which is not at all warranted by anything in the present peaceable state of the world. Governments have been forced to examine all sorts of imaginary and immature possibilities which will never be translated into reality if any of the great and free democracies of the world are able to make their opinion prevail.

In order not to give offence to anyone, I will use a parable: Once upon a time all the animals in the Zoo decided that they would disarm, and they arranged to have a conference to arrange the matter. So the Rhinoceros said when he opened the proceedings that the use of teeth was barbarous and horrible and ought to be strictly prohibited by general consent. Horns, which were mainly defensive weapons, would, of course, have to be allowed. The Buffalo, the Stag, the Porcupine, and even the little Hedgehog all said they would vote with the Rhino, but the Lion and the Tiger took a different view. They defended teeth and even claws, which they described as honourable weapons of immemorial antiquity. The Panther, the Leopard, the Puma, and the whole tribe of small cats all supported the Lion and the Tiger. Then the Bear spoke. He proposed that both teeth and horns should be banned and never used again for fighting by any aniaml. I would be quite enough if animals were allowed to give each other a good hug when they quarreled. No one could object to that. It was so fraternal, and that would be a great step towards peace. However, all the other animals were very offended with the Bear, and the Turkey fell into a perfect panic.

The discussion got so hot and angry, and all those animals began thinking so much about horns and teeth and hugging when they argued about the peaceful intentions that had brought them together that they began to look at one another in a very nasty way. Luckily the keepers were able to calm them down and persuade them to go back quietly to their cages, and they began to feel quite friendly with one another again.

I hope, however, I will not be asked to bring my parable into any relation with anything that has taken place or is taking place at the present time.

[Editor's Note: Speaking on the rating scheme he dealt with the proposals which he said would be presented to Parliament the following month.] About £50,000,000 a year is being transferred to local authorities as new revenue which will replace old revenue and be in addition to the old revenue. Part of it will be used to indemnify the local authorities for what has been taken away, and the other part will be calculated in relation to the needs of their population. Block grants of the future will be of a dual nature, one side of which will recognize the needs and character of the locality, and at each five-yearly revision it is this side which will grow at the expense of the other. Thus the block grant will increasingly tend to harmonize the resources and the needs of every district.

Before committing ourselves to this policy we had figures worked out parish by parish for a large number of specimen counties, and it is on the basis of those specific figures that the reform will be achieved, not only without a marked increase in rates in any part but with a substantial relief to the highly rated areas and with a large balance of reduction generally throughout the country. The advantages claimed for the scheme are in the first place lower rates and a fairer and more efficient system. In the second place the Exchequer will pay more, but it will know for each five years exactly what it has to pay. In the third place the local authority will know where it stands. There will be a diminution of the interference of Whitehall and an end to the inducement to extravagance which has always attended the administration of percentage grants. A poor district will not be thrown on its immediate neighbour, but the burden will be spread equally over the whole nation. On the other hand, it does not follow that those poor districts will be able to draw a blank cheque upon the State. We have been very careful to make sure that can not occur. Poplar has to be paid for, but not by Epping. It should be paid for by England, but it should not be paid for as Poplar thinks but as England decides.

As the system comes into operation by successive stages industry will be free to go or stay where it will, guided by economic consideration alone, and workmen will be free to live wherever they find it most convenient for their families. A working-class district, if transferred to the area of a new authority, will carry with it automatically a share in the national grant which will make it no longer unwelcome.

CONSTITUENCY ADDRESS

October 27, 1928

Harlow

[Extract] . . . The Liberals are tireless in fault finding. They are perhaps the best fault finders that exist at the present day, and hardly anything escapes their attention.

The Liberal Party are at present engaged in trying to secure a position by which they can hold the balance of power in the next Parliament. They say that they are the only true guides, and that at least 500 candidates are coming forward. Their object is to get into a position by which they will hold the balance of power. That is an arrangement in which there would be no substance, but only a shadow—so in the next Parliament there would be 50 or 60 men, led by able leaders, holding the balance and putting the State up to auction.

The real issue which the electors will have to face within six, or perhaps, I should say, eight months, is whether they are going to instal into office the Socialist Party, which only two years ago was running and managing a general strike. Are you prepared to hand the government over to these men, who declare that even the civilization of the world is wrong?

You will have if the Socialists are returned, an era of Governments rising and falling; of Parliaments honeycombed with political intrigue; and Ministers not standing, as we do, for good or ill to be judged by our actions, but Ministers who will arise knowing that they are only creatures of an era. They will make their little splash, and they will make it by spending money in an attempt to obtain electioneering material.

The position is that there must either be a Tory majority or a Socialist majority, or a Parliament in which it is not possible for any party to have a majority. I am not in the least afraid. All over the country we have great numbers of people taking an active interest in our work, and the women are flocking to our standard. They are marching on towards a great Tory majority at the next election.

SOCIALIST POLICIES

October 29, 1928

Waltham Abbey

[Extract] ... The Government has never pretended to be one of cure-alls and know-alls, but we have tried to give a clean, decent, honest administration to the State and to avoid partisanship. In the region of finance we have tried to pursue a more or less coherent policy. We have endeavoured to reduce taxation which presses on savings, to reduce the income-tax on families in regard to children, and, by reducing the tax on the smaller class of income-tax payers, we claim to have lightened a burden very much felt.

The gold standard was intended deliberately to effect a reduction in the cost of living. It is my claim, made on the highest authority, that the reductions in the cost of living to the wage-earners of the country exceeds by £100,000,000 the reductions which have taken place in wages from time to time. But for the industrial troubles of 1926, we would undoubtedly have done a great deal more than is now possible. But we have ploughed through these troubles without either failing to pay our debts or to pay our way, and have provided money for new social reforms.

The great question of unemployment remains. I do not believe anyone has a complete remedy for unemployment. I am sure that if any party men come forward and say, "We can cure unemployment," they are misleading the people. It would be quite easy to cure unemployment for a few years. That could be done by borrowing on a very large scale, but the result would be exactly that which shipwrecked sailors on a raft experience when they drink salt water to slake their thirst. At the present time we must try to seek for the remedies for the disease and not merely the remedies for the symptom. In the rating scheme the Government claim that we are applying a remedy to the disease. We do not claim that it is a complete remedy, but that it is an effective remedy so far as it goes.

An issue in the next election will be whether a Socialist Government is to be placed in control of the country. That means handing over the Government to the men who only a few years ago were managing and mismanaging the general strike. Mr. Snowden has promised a repeal of duties amounting to £44,000,000 or £45,000,000. Where is the money to come from for the social reforms which the Socialists are so eagerly promising? They promise to gather a surtax, but they will have already given away more than half of its maximum yield, assuming that they are able to collect it.

To make a change of Government at the present time would upset the growth of propserity and consolidation which has been taking place throughout the country. The rating scheme is the greatest chance, the only practicable proposal put forward for helping industries like coalmining and railways. Socialist policies produce misery, squalor, disorder, and misfortune. The Russian people are starving in one of the greatest granaries in the whole of Europe.

CONSTITUENCY ADDRESS

October 31, 1928

Woodford

[Extract] . . . The basic heavy industries are in a state of eclipse. I am not urging that you should give them dopes and artificial stimulants, but that you should relieve them of undue, unfair, and invidious burdens. Rates are the greatest burden of which you can relieve them, and it is the Government's proposal practically to abolish the problem of the rates for them. You ought not to tax the plants and tools of production. Do not cast the sand of taxation into the actual running of the machinery of industry.

We have near here a great district where industries are flagging and in some cases driven away terrified by the high rates. It is bad for the workers, but it is also very bad for the industries, because industries ought not to have to move to brand new spots in the open country from places where there are well-established services for their use.

[Editor's Note: Replying to a suggestion that the Government's proposal had not "caught on," Churchill said]: I never expected that it would catch on before now, because up to the present people have done nothing but pay. All this year I have been taking. (Laughter.) There is the extra tax on the petrol for motor-cars. (A voice, "Shame!") Not at all; it is one of the best things I have done. (The voice: "An absolute scandal. Why not tax the brewers?")

That cry of "shame" illustrates the argument I was making; but next year we shall be engaged in distributing one of the greatest necessary and fertile reliefs of taxation ever devised—upwards of £30,000,000 relief from rates for productive industries and agriculture. That gentleman is crying out "shame" about the brewers. I see no reason why trades should be singled out to be petted or spited. Mr. Lloyd George says that you ought not to give this relief to any of the prosperous trades. There would not be room in Hyde Park to put up all the buildings necessary in which to house the officials for the work connected with deciding which were the trades that were entitled to relief.

Mr. Lloyd George also says, "Fancy relieving the brewer." When he was going on one of his Saturday afternoon oratorical joy rides, his motor-car stopped in some town where there was a brewery on the one hand and a dairy on the other, and his soul was absolutely smitten by the horrible spectacle of a brewery relieved of three-quarters of rates and a dairy not at all. Mr. Lloyd George had not followed the principle. The brewery produces beer, but the dairy does not produce milk. The cow, I am told, has a great deal to do with that part of the story, and the cow and the farm, and all that goes to the production of milk, is not merely relieved of three-quarter of rates, but of the lot, once and for all. I do not agree with this picking and choosing.

You never heard of any complaint about cocoa being let off. Oh, no! But there is a party which says, "Come along, my little dear, sit on the platform": but as for beer, oh, Tory beer—that is shocking.

I consider that the two men—Mr. Courtauld and Lord Melchett—whom Mr. Lloyd George has been holding up to obloquy are great public benefactors. They have started new things in industry in which thousands of people have obtained employment in the silk and chemical trades, and they are holding their own in the competitive markets of the world.

UNEMPLOYMENT

November 8, 1928

House of Commons

If I rise at this early stage it is not only out of courtesy to the right hon. Gentleman who has just spoken, and certainly not because the speech he has delivered was of so formidable a character as to call for an immediate answer, but because I think it will be convenient for the House if at this moment a statement is made on behalf of the Government, addressed broadly to the attack which is made upon them in the Amendment to the Address in reply to the Gracious Speech, and covering the problem and the treatment of unemployment at the present time. I listened to the right hon. Gentleman's speech, which was quite moderate, both in expression and in argument, and, like the Amendment which it supported, conceived throughout in a vein of purely negative criticism and want of appreciation. The only suggestion of a constructive character which the right hon. Gentleman has put forward in this important Debate on behalf of the Labour party for dealing with unemployment, is that we should resume relations with Russia. That was the only suggestion of a constructive character. Anyone who says that the difference which would be produced in our trade with Russia if we once again admit the Soviet Embassy to these islands would have the slightest effect upon the general problem of unemployment, is misleading himself and, if he repeats it, is misleading others.

What was the rest of the speech of the right hon. Gentleman? It was to the effect that all the troubles of unemployment are the fault of the Government; that the present situation is the fault of the Government—of what he called the uninterrupted blundering of the Government. The Amendment says, "You have had four years of office; you have a commanding majority, and yet there is this serious unemployment." It is very easy to say that it is the fault of the Government, but it is almost easier to say that a large part of the misfortunes of the present day are the fault of the Socialist party. Not only is it easier to say that, but it is easier to a very large extent to prove it. Is it not astonishing that the right hon. Gentleman should be so oblivious of the recent past? I think the right hon. Member for Carnarvon Boroughs (Mr. Lloyd George) spoke of the morbid egoism of the Labour party. To that there certainly ought to be added an impenetrable complacency. Has the right hon. Gentleman forgotten the disaster of 1928—the general strike and the prolonged coal stoppage?

Lieut.-Commander Kenworthy: Whose fault was that?

Mr. Churchill: Some £80,000,000 was lost to the revenues of the country and at least £400,000,000 of national wealth was consumed. We have been thrown back for two or three years behind the onward march of other nations in the world. The reserves of industry were exhausted during that period, and the resources of the State to aid misfortune have been grievously impaired. You say: "Whose fault is that? Have you no responsibility for it?" I have never said that all the faults were on one side. Have you no responsibility for it? Have you not admitted your responsibility for it? Has there not been an effort on the part of the responsible leaders of Labour to establish a different and saner policy? Are not the Communists being excluded from the Labour policy as far as possible? Is not Russian interference now being repulsed in domestic affairs? Is not Mr. Cook now discredited? These signs of amendment are welcome, but they are too late. All of us, whatever our shortcomings may be, are suffering from the consequences of 1926, and the price has to be paid. The one supreme, definite, obvious, recent cause of the delay in the general trade revival lies there. We warned you of these consequences beforehand. We warned you that dragging the trade unions into the heart of party politics was bound to add a new complication and a new element of bitterness to the whole industrial life of this country. I am only surprised that the consequences of 1926 in the financial sphere and in the sphere of employment and trade have not been a great deal worse than they have actually shown themselves.

If unemployment is to be used, if this sorrowful problem is to be used as a mere cudgel for belabouring party opponents and the Government of the day, we have a retort which we shall not hesitate to make and which will be readily understood by the electors, but I think it would be—I am sure it would be—a great pity for us to waste an important Debate on this tragic subject in mere party bickering. We ought not to lose patience with each other on a matter of deep concern to us all. We must consider how wide and mysterious the problem of unemployment is, and how many and various and contradictory are its causes in different countries and at different times. Look east and look west. Look west. In the United States, with extremes of capitalism which have not yet developed here, you have nevertheless in the last year seen very heavy unemployment. Look east to Russia where, under the most ruthless expression of Socialism which has ever been tried—with ample power and ample time—in the history of the world, you have also very heavy unemployment. Here you have two great communities each in possession of enormous areas—fertile, rich areas—of the earth's surface, each in possession of almost a continent, pursuing absolutely different policies and systems of government and industry, and each of them is suffering from very heavy industrial unemployment, and neither of them, let me add, is making anything like the provision to aid and succour the unemployed that is being made in this country.

I am not attempting to draw any constructive moral; I am only trying to point out the difficulties and dangers for any responsible person who lays down the law about the unemployment problem. Indeed, I think he is a bold man who claims to have a solution. It is easy to say "Go back to Russia" and I am sure the right hon. Gentleman the Member for Platting (Mr. Clynes) knows that far more effective schemes than that have already been set on foot. But if a man is bold to claim that he has a solution for the problem, he is rash and foolish if he makes such a claim at a time when in his own opinion he has any chance of being called upon to apply it. The right hon. Gentleman told us that he and his colleagues were soon coming into office and into power; he said that our majority would soon completely disappear. I do not share that view. I think hon. Members opposite under-rate the rugged binding strength of the political forces by which they will be opposed. But if their hopes are justified then surely coming responsibilities should cast their prudence before them. They should walk modestly in the sight of all men.

The Amendment speaks of the appalling conditions which exist in parts of our coalfields. Let it not be thought that the feelings of distress which these conditions have caused is confined to any one political party, and certainly I repulse the suggestion in so far as it is made that there is any want of humanity in the British treatment of this problem. There is no country in the world where direct taxation of the rich and wealthy in all its forms is carried so far; there is no country in the world where so great a portion of the national income is spent on the relief of sickness, old age, unemployment, destitution, widowhood, and orphanhood. I have taken some advice on this point and although I admit the figures cannot be taken as precise, yet I think it would be true to say that man for man and woman for woman we in these islands provide two or three times as much, and it may be four or five times as much, as any other country in the world, including the most wealthy and also including the most socialistic countries, for the care of the sick and poor. At the outset of this discussion if there is any disagreement with the measures which are being taken on the ground that they are inadequate to deal with the situation, or if there is any suggestion of inhumanity, let us remember that the British nation and the British Government make a contribution to suffering and privation in their midst with which no other country in the world can compare, and that we to an extent which no other country has attempted take from the wealthy and the rich in order to give to those who are in poverty and distress.

It is in the light of these preliminary observations of a general character that I shall venture, if the House will permit me, to examine the actual facts of unemployment in our midst. It is nearly 20 years ago since it fell to my lot to introduce the first Unemployment Insurance scheme into the House of Commons, and I have followed this subject year by year with continuous attention. No one will underrate the evil, but do not let us exaggerate it. It is grave enough without exaggeration. Let us analyse the general total of unemployment and compare them with the past. Before 1911 unemployment was left entirely to the trade unions, and they rendered indispensable service to the working community. But they only rendered it to the higher ranks of labour, and in the main only to males. My belief is that in the years before the War, there were rarely less than 300,000 or 400,000 unemployed, and that in bad years like the year 1908 the number approached 1,000,000. We now have 1,374,000 unemployed on the register. But the Great War has happened in the interval, and a large part of the capital of Britain and the world has been consumed in consequence. The world all round has grown much bigger. All sorts of countries which were quite ready before the War to buy our basic manufactures now wish to make them for themselves; they wish to become self-contained, and they are increasingly showing themselves capable of doing without many important lines of British goods. Great new coalfields have sprung into activity abroad. White coal has made its appearance and many countries are now using this form of power which used to buy coal from us. There is also the advent of oil as a great motive force. New and more vigorous competitors meet us in every foreign market; old customers are increasingly closing their doors upon our goods. The right hon. Member for Carnarvon Boroughs, in the Coalition days, used to talk about the Great Shop in a district which had become impoverished, and there is a good deal of ground for uncomfortable reflection in the statement which he made. If that is so, if this is to any extent an accurate picture of the events which have occurred in our own lifetime, then surely this is of all others a problem which we should not use for ordinary party purposes; it is one which we should treat as a common problem which British men and women should try and face together.

Coming to an analysis of the existing total of unemployed, if there were nearly 1,000,000 in a year of trade depression before the War, there are now 1,300,000 or 1,400,000 on the register. Let us first remember that the present system of unemployment insurance catalogues and presents each week much which was previously unrecorded. A large proportion of the present total of unemployment represents the normal and not unhealthy working of a nation system of unemployment insurance. At any given moment there are at least 500,000 of the unemployed workmen on the register who only occasionally come upon it, who pay their weekly 7d. for months, sometimes for years, without ever claiming benefit, and when they claim their benefit they are only receiving what they have actually paid for, and often something far less. To apply the word "dole" to workmen in that condition is a most unworthy attitude. They have the same right to draw their insurance benefit in temporary periods of unemployment or when moving from one job to another as any one who draws interest from investments which he has made. The use of the word as applied to such workers is a form of abuse, and I am surprised and shocked to see how very frequently this error is made by superficial observers both domestic and foreign. At the other end of the scale we have the weaker brethren who find it difficult to get their living even in the most prosperous times, who hang heavily and permanently on the Insurance Fund; a fund, let me remind the House, supported partly by State but mainly by industrialist and working class contributions.

Here you have two great classes; one which has paid for every penny it receives and the other which lies like a load on national and working class life. The first class represents nothing but the regular and proper working of an intricate scheme of national self-help against the fluctuations of modern conditions, the second class represents a problem which no government has yet had the strength to treat in a logical and courageous manner. There are 224,000 women at present on the unemployment list who were scarcely ever included in any pre-War total. The fortunes of all these three important classes of unemployed can only be relieved by a general improvement in British trade and by a revival of world and national prosperity. There is a fourth class which is in an entirely different position, and for whom an improvement in British trade and a revival in world trade carries no direct permanent hope of alleviation. I could perhaps speak of cotton, where we have lost a proportion of our cruder markets in which previously we reigned unchallenged. But, after all, the industrial history of the last four years can be summed up in the word "coal." There are 150,000 more coal miners unemployed now that when we came into office, and the general total of unemployment has also swollen by about 150,000. There is equality in those two figures. The aggravation of the problem of unemployment is summed up in the black word "coal."

The position of the coal-mining population, the spread of their misfortunes, the strife that has arisen, have darkened the life of the whole nation, delayed the revival of trade, depleted the finances of the State, and to a large extent have frustrated the hopes of the Government. Let us look therefore into coal. After the War and until three years ago there were 1,200,000 persons engaged in coalmining. There are now 920,000, so that 280,000 persons who two years ago were supported by the coal industry have now been discarded by that industry. Some of them have been absorbed by other industries, but the fact remains that that enormous casting out of labour from the coal industry has taken place; and if it is a grievous misfortune for these men and their families, it is not a misfortune for the coal industry. On the contrary, the coal industry with its reduced staff is now capable, so I am informed, not only of supplying the whole present demand, home and foreign, for our coal, but it can if need be quite easily, without taking on another man, produce 30,000,000 tons of coal more than we are able to sell now anywhere. If and when the time comes, and come it shortly will, when trade expansion takes place, such trade expansion will not bring hope or assistance to this great problem. There are to-day at least 200,000 surplus members of the mining industry who, even with the preference given to miners in the recruitment at the mines, cannot be absorbed for years into the ordinary working of the industry. The existing staff of employés working full time are more than able to supply any demand that even the most favourable conditions that we can hope for would render possible.

There is the problem. It is a limited problem and a grim problem, and it is the last problem that any decent man will approach with any other motive than a desire to help, and it is the last problem which ought to be used as an election cry. Moreover, an aggravation of this problem lies in the fact that this mass of 200,000 men and their families is largely concentrated in particular areas, brooding round the mouths of dead pits and in valleys where the industry has died down, where whole communities suffer together, and where the institutions which should support them fall with the industries by which they live. Lastly, their numbers will not be diminished but may be increased by every improvement in the efficiency of the coal industry, by every well-conceived amalgamation, by every step towards that nationalization which able Labour documents, Liberal Yellow Books and Samuel reports have so strongly advocated.

There is the problem. Shall we not try to face it across all party conflicts and the interests which naturally, before an election, are antagonistic? Cannot we try to face it as much as possible together? Incidentally I may say that this problem of the coal industry is repeated on a smaller scale in the iron and steel industry in almost every particular. The coal industry itself as a living factor has greatly improved. It has cast off its heavy burdens and it has cast them on to society and the State. But it stands to-day in a far superior position to compete in the markets of the world and to supply our own needs, than at any time since the Great War. Although the industry as a whole is indeed still showing a loss on the average on every ton which has been produced in the last few months, the margin is a small one, and the real problem before us is not that of the coal industry—that will solve itself now and move forward as time passes, and rapidly—the real problem is the problem of the displaced coalminers and their dependants, and besides that there is the larger general question of the revival of the trade of the country as a whole.

I have ventured to try to present the issues as I see them. I will now proceed to state the practical steps, and the only practical steps, which the Government recommend to Parliament at the present time to remedy or mitigate these evils. The first and main contribution of the Government is to assist trade and employment generally by a comprehensive rating relief scheme to agriculture and to industry. [*Laughter.*] Well, do not mock, because we are working while you mock. This scheme will relieve productive industry of three-quarters, and agriculture of all, of its rates, at a cost to the national Exchequer of some £22,000,000 a year. In addition there is the further relief on railway freights to agriculture, coal, iron and steel. The rating relief, which the railways will pass on to their customers, will be concentrated in helping those very industries where the need is greatest, and in selecting the particular traffics we have followed the advice received from the industries concerned as to where the relief could best be applied in order to give the greatest benefit.

The railway relief forms a part of the general scheme, but in response to earnest appeals which reached me from the representatives of all parties in the House, we decided that, in order to give immediate assistance, this railway freight relief should be anticipated. At an early date we are going to submit a Vote to the House to enable this relief to begin on December 1. It is estimated that this will throw an additional charge on the Budget this year of nearly £1,000,000, and £2,250,000 on next year's Budget. It will provide for a reduction of 10 per cent. on the selected traffics of agriculture, iron and steel, but it will provide for a reduction on the selected coal traffics—that is to say, coal for export, foreign bunkers, blast furnaces and steel works—of something like 30 per cent. The efficacy of this relief consists in the fact that it is concentrated mainly upon the basic trades, that is to say upon those which employ the largest number of manual workers and in which unemployment is most prevalent.

British industries are classified, for the purpose of unemployment statistics, into 100 groups, and in these 100 groups there are now about 1,000,000 wholly unemployed persons. But of these 1,000,000 half are found in only nine groups, and it is upon those nine groups that more than half of the whole rating relief to industry will be concentrated. In the remaining 91 industrial groups, considered as a whole, unemployment has for the last two or three years remained relatively low; it has actually lessened in the last three or four years. The percentage of persons unemployed in all those 91 groups does not exceed 6 per cent. The real trouble is in the nine groups, and it is to the nine groups that the main aid will go. The improvement in general industry, and especially in basic industries is the first hope of providing new openings for displaced miners. Not only should this concentrated aid to these industries bring direct aid to coal, but, far more, it should enable other industries to absorb the surplus mining population.

I turn aside now to deal with a point to which the right hon. Gentleman referred at some length—the failure of the Government to fulfil pledges in regard to a Factories Bill. We have not included that Bill in the work of this Session. You have invited us to the great assize of the nation. We accept your invitation, and we shall appeal to the country at the first moment after our de-rating Bills have been passed and the necessary financial business settled. How then is there time for a Factories Bill as well as the de-rating Bills? Parliament will have to sit very long and almost continuously. We had to choose between the de-rating Measures which are our main contribution to trade revival and employment, and this desirable factory legislation. Can anyone doubt that it would be wrong to delay a General Election for the sake of the Factories Bill, or to give a Factories Bill at this time priority over de-rating legislation? When de-rating has brought its relief to industry which is now so heavily burdened, the Factories Bill will follow naturally. On the whole the conditions in the factories of this island are better than those which prevail on the Continent of Europe. But you cannot say that British industries are in a more favourable position than the industries on the Continent. I am sure that with trade and unemployment in the position in which they are, it is absolutely necessary that a measure of relief should precede and not follow additional regulations, however desirable.

The second main feature of the Government's policy for dealing generally with the economic conditions of the day is the policy of Empire settlement. The Industrial Transference Board emphasised the importance of stimulating the normal flow of migration to Canada. I would like to take the opportunity of saying what everyone knows, and what cannot be repeated too often, that in the displaced mining community we have not what may be called the ordinary unemployed. We are not dealing with, as it were, any large proportion of the weaker brethren. On the contrary, you have representative groups of British labour, including a large proportion of the very finest specimens that our country can produce. For this class His Majesty's Government have agreed to accelerate and expand the policy of Empire settlement at, it is estimated, an additional cost of £500,000 this year, rising to £1,500,000 in future years.

There is no doubt whatever that a low migrant passage rate would be a great encouragement to steady migration. It is not a question of State-aided passages so much as of individuals availing themselves of an extremely low passage rate. Arrangements will, it is hoped, very shortly be completed with the shipping companies on the North Atlantic service by which they will be able to quote a largely reduced third-class fare to Canada for British migrants. Moreover, we now understand from the Canadian Government, and are most glad to receive the information, that their immigration department will, for the purpose of their regulations, regard persons paying these reduced fares as if they were full fare paying passengers. That is an important fact. Apart from these steps which are being taken to stimulate the general flow of migration, the existing facilities for training and testing migrants who wish to take up work on the land overseas are being expanded by the enlargement and fuller use of the training centres and by the provision of new training centres.

In the third place, I must not omit to speak about a feature of the policy of improving employment by the safeguarding of particular industries after they have made their case before a tribunal. Here I do not think we can overlook the more extreme policy of placing an embargo on certain classes of foreign imports to which the Leader of the Labour party has lately given his adhesion. The position of the Government in this matter is perfectly clear. It has been declared once for all in the Prime Minister's letter of 3rd August. That letter carried with it, needless to say, the unanimous agreement of the Cabinet, both in its negative and in its positive assertions. According to that letter there will be no general system of Protection and no protective taxation of food, but no industry which applies will be prevented from making its case before an authoritative and competent tribunal. That is the platform on which we have taken our stand. Evidently it will be necessary in any particular case for all parties affected, including agriculture, to be able to be heard before the tribunal.

Lieut.-Commander Kenworthy: Including agriculture?

Mr. Churchill: Evidently it will be necessary for all parties who are affected by any application for safeguarding to have a *locus* before the tribunal under that application—all parties, including agriculture. For the rest, it is, of course, futile to prejudge the results of such inquiries. The results, whatever they are, lie in the lap of the new Parliament. Let me make it clear that we shall claim at the Election, full freedom for the safeguarding of any industry which establishes its case on the merits before an authoritative tribunal and which proves that a Safeguarding Duty on its products will do more good than harm to the general trade and employment of the country. Fourthly, in order to stimulate export trade, the original Export Credits Scheme was introduced in 1920. The terms under which this scheme is operated have been altered from time to time in order to make them more suitable and more convenient for manufacturers and exporters. Under the existing legislation, no new guarantees would have been given after September of next year, and the uncertainty of whether the scheme would be continued or not would have deterred firms from undertaking business without that guarantee in the coming year. The King's Speech has already announced the Government's intention of continuing that help to our export trade for a further period of two years and a Bill for this purpose will shortly be brought before the House.

There is a fifth form of help to general industry coming into operation through the new measures for the improvement and extension of our electricity supply, following on the Act which the House passed two years ago. Four schemes have been adopted by the Central Electricity Board, covering an area of 30,000 square miles and a population of 27,000,000. The total capital expenditure involved in these adopted schemes amounts to £17,000,000 and contracts have actually been entered into for £2,750,000. Rapid progress has therefore been made in the last two years, and, from now onwards, this new Act and its consequences will begin beneficially to affect trade and employment.

I leave these general measures and come to the special methods for absorbing surplus mining population. We shall no doubt be pressed in this Debate to embark upon large schemes of public relief works. Most careful study has been made again, during the last few months, by the public departments of possible relief works. On general grounds we are opposed to such a system, especially when directly conducted by the State. It is surprising to see, in the examples which we have lately studied, how meagre are the results in actually relieving the particular problem of unemployment with which we are coping, compared with the outlay in every case. The right hon. Gentleman the Member for Platting said we had the choice between paying for idleness or paying for work. We would find no difficulty in making that choice if he explained to us what were the methods by which we were to be able to choose the one instead of the other. But the general objection to public relief work has never been better stated than by the Leader of the Labour party when in office. On 12th February, 1924, the right hon. Gentleman the Member for Aberavon (Mr. Ramsay MacDonald) said:

> I wish to make it perfectly clear that the Government have no intention of drawing off from the normal channels of trade large sums for extemporised measures which can only be palliatives. That is the old sound Socialist doctrine and the necessity of expenditure for subsidising schemes in direct relief of unemployment will be judged in relation to the greater necessity for maintaining undisturbed the ordinary financial facilities and resources of trade and industry.—[Official Report, 12th February, 1924; col. 760, Vol. 169.]

[Hon. Members: "Hear, hear!"] Then we are all agreed, but, nevertheless, there are two respects in which we propose some relaxation in the rigour of what is undoubtedly the present sound policy. We propose to make certain extensions in the field of land drainage and allied schemes which are at present being assisted out of State funds. The Ministry of Agriculture has a list of suitable schemes, including coast erosion schemes, upon which it will be practicable to employ a certain number of unemployed persons from distressed districts.

Mr. Ernest Brown: Scotland also?

Mr. Churchill: Naturally. I was going to say that, of course, whatever is done in this matter in England will be, in due proportion, applied to the Northern Kingdom.

Mr. Kirkwood: Thre is no scarcity of land in Scotland.

Mr. Churchill: To meet this extension, some widening of the conditions which are at present maintained will have to be made in order that the Ministry of Agriculture may have greater facility and freedom in carrying forward this plan.

Mr. MacLaren: How is this money to be raised?

Mr. Churchill: The money in this case, for these grants for land drainage, will be provided by the Exchequer.

Hon. Members: And coast erosion too?

Mr. Churchill: Yes, but schemes will be framed so as to provide for local contributions in proportion to the national aid. The second extension of grants for public works arises out of the present tasks of the Ministry of Labour. My right hon. Friend the Minister of Labour, who will speak to-morrow, will deal more in detail with this part of the problem and will explain his work in moving men and women from the desolation of the depressed areas into the stream of living industry. [*Laughter.*] Surely it is not a laughing matter.

Mr. Barker: Where are these living streams?

Mr. Churchill: After all, the vast bulk of the trade of this country is flowing with great strength, and the problem we are confronted with is the problem of dealing with the laggard trades and with the individuals in those trades who have fallen behind the general movement of the national trade. A substantial and increasing measure of success is attending the efforts of the Ministry of Labour and, in the actual process of transference from the depressed areas, there is a rate of transfer of something like 600 or 700 a week.

Mr. MacLaren: One per cent.

Mr. Churchill: We were told that nothing ought to be neglected, and do not at all underrate this, or in any way obstruct or belittle this most important function. The process of transference is being facilitated by the training centres where men unused to factory life are being fitted for new trades. These centres are being steadily expanded for the benefit of the depressed areas. If the present rate of transfer can be maintained, it means that in six months something like 16,000 will have been transferred from the depressed areas through the machinery of the Ministry of Labour. If at the same time the expansion of the trade of the country can be stimulated by the general measures to which I have referred, it is obvious that we shall be making, although slowly, progress out of our difficulties. It is said that the work of the Ministry of Labour in transferring labour has already aroused a desire to move among the population from the depressed areas and that it is possible that at least as many men and women are moving on their own account in addition. This policy, if it is to succeed, must have the good will and co-operation of all classes in the community. It is not a question of asking for charity or of asking employers to take men they do not need. All that is asked is that out of the very large number of labour engagements made every week a relatively small proportion should be given to these men who include, as has already been said, some of the best workers in the industrial population.

In order to facilitate and further the transference scheme, and only for that purpose, we propose to re-open, on more favourable terms, the grants for works financed out of loans which are offered to the local authorities through the St. Davids Committee; but we propose to give the more favourable terms only in cases where authorities in the more prosperous areas are prepared to employ a substantial proportion of persons from the distressed areas upon these public works. See how this will help. It is a new principle. We shall, of course, not disturb the present arrangements in regard to the depressed areas, but what we are trying to do is to pull away a proportion of those actually in those areas to more prosperous areas. Therefore, we shall offer more favourable terms to local enterprises set on foot in prosperous areas, provided that in those enterprises there will be employed a substantial percentage of men from the mining districts. This will help the working of the transference of individuals through the Ministry of Labour, because when there is unemployment, in a town which is doing fairly well, and when some employers are asked to take men from the mining areas, they say, "We ought to deal with our own local unemployed first." But if, at the same time, in that town a scheme is set on foot on favourable terms which would not otherwise be set on foot, and which absorbs a proportion of the local unemployed and brings some miners from the depressed areas, that will make it easier for the individual employers in that same town to take their proportion individually of the miners.

The existing conditions requiring a minimum acceleration of five years in the application of the work and excluding road work, will be relaxed in order to secure the maximum response. I have had printed a circular to local authorities of which I have an advance proof here and I have arranged for the circular to the local authorities to be in the Vote Office during the course of to-morrow. The policy of giving preference to miners wherever possible with regard to forest holdings, and particularly to miners with very large families, is also being pursued and will be steadily extended as far as possible having regard to the considerable financial expenditure entailed by each particular case.

I have, I think, presented to the House a series of proposals. I purposely give no total estimate of the numbers hoped to be relieved by these proposals, and no complete estimate of the money required. These proposals as a whole constitute the policy of His Majesty's Government. It is a policy which we shall develop to the utmost of our power. If anyone has helpful and practical suggestions to make which can be dealt with in the present Parliament, now is the time to put them forward. We will certainly consider them fairly, but of course we have already examined and rejected a host of proposals before we chose these and decided upon definite action. You may say you do not agree with the policy, you may say that it is not adequate, but no one can say that there is not a policy, and no one is more interested than His Majesty's Government in bringing that policy to practical and substantial success.

I am very much obliged to the House for having listened to this statement. I thought it very necessary to present our case in a comprehensive form, and I close on a note certainly not of pessimism. There are more people employed in this island to-day than there ever were before. There are 350,000 more people employed in the sphere of industrial insurance alone than there were when we became responsible. This small, overcrowded, overburdened, but still unconquered island has actually found, in the last four years, as many new jobs for British men and women as all the resources of State-aided emigration have been able to provide throughout the whole of the British Empire. Although our pre-eminence in exports is declining, nevertheless we still export, as I reminded the House in the summer, twice as much of manufactures per head of population as any other great country in the world, and apart from population we actually export more manufactures than any country, however populous, in the world.

It is true that the savings of the people are steadily increasing, even in these hard years. The investing power of the nation, both at home and abroad, is still enormous and is still increasing. Many of our leading industries are putting themselves in a far better position to encounter the new stresses of modern competition. Our finances are sound, and our credit is unimpaired. The reliefs of basic industry which we have long planned are now rapidly coming into action. The period of paying and of accumulating funds is nearly over; the period of aid and stimulation to industry is now at hand. And when we hear, as sometimes we do, that in the modern world we are being dwarfed and outclassed, let us in the end remember that we do not stand alone. Although we can see the giants that are growing up in the world all around us, the British Commonwealth of Nations, the British Empire, is actually and potentially the greatest giant of all, and by settling with the British race the vast and mighty lands which owe allegiance to the Crown, and by fostering the ties of Imperial commerce and mutual interdependence between the different parts of the Empire, by every approved method possible, we shall ensure our safe and honourable eminence in the world, however large the world may grow.

"FIELDS OF PEACE"

November 9, 1928

The Lord Mayor's Banquet,
The Guildhall, London

[Editor's Note: Churchill proposed "Foreign Ambassadors and Ministers," and alluded to the absence of the Foreign Secretary, expressing the feelings of the gathering in the delight at his recovery to health.]

This is nearly the twentieth occasion I have attended the banquet, but whenever I have spoken before it was to speak for the Admiralty, the War Office, or the Air Ministry. I was always concerned with acknowledging toasts of military and warlike departments. Now I have been promoted to fields of peace. From the war and its aftermath, we find ourselves coming into the broadening light of a long world peace. It is a source of deep satisfaction that once again the peace of Europe, Christendom, and the civilised world is established.

There is no discouragement of our former Allies in welcoming to-night the representatives of the brave nation from whom we were so terribly sundered in the war. We are shortly to embark upon serious and intricate discussions with German representatives of financial questions. We embark upon that task in which, of course, there will be difficulties, with the very sure confidence that in the midst of all those difficulties and at the end of them all lies a result mutually beneficial to all parties to the discussion and capable of carrying the whole world forward on a surer and truer foundation.

The liberation of German finance and soil from foreign interference or control is an object which we in this country regard as of high value and importance.

Diplomacy is the art of telling plain truths without giving offence. Nothing could be worse than that the public relations of great countries should be covered with a veneer of admirable sentiments and impeccable servility, and that underneath all sorts of feelings and anxiety and aspirations should not find their effective personal expression through the representatives who met together in the different States. I am sure that all the representatives of foreign countries gathered here are capable of putting the real issues and of receiving them. There is one other quality that the important diplomatist should develop. The late Lord Salisbury, when Prime Minister and Foreign Secretary, used to prescribe that our representatives abroad were always, while rendering loyal service to their country, to do the best they could for the country to which they were accredited. I am sure that the Foreign Ambassadors and Ministers present always try to interpret their duties here in this country in that favourable sense. I have no doubt you give full attention not only to all the incidents of daily and political life but also to the easy, tolerant, trustful climate of opinion in which we live together here. I am sure that when they write home they very frequently put in their letters about Britain that she is not so black as she is painted, especially as she is painted by herself. (Laughter.) There has never been, I think, gathered round these tables a body of diplomatists, representatives of great nations in friendly touch with us, to whom Great Britain could with more confidence say, "Report me and my cause aright."

COMMUNISM AND CANCER

November 15, 1928

Royal Society of Medicine Dinner,
Mayfair Hotel, London

The Royal Society of Medicine was founded in the year of Trafalgar, and has pursued a clearly defined object—the classification and increase of knowledge of all parts of medicine and the branches of science allied to it. The Society has behind it a record of service to science and humanity which holds comparison with any scientific or similar body in the world. There is an increasing need to combine and focus all the results of human study in each particular branch.

I hope you will not expect me to lay down the law on the subject of medicine. I have tried my hands at a good many things (laughter), but I am not going to poach on your preserve. I can understand how difficult it is, because its empiricism and its continual contact with the unknown resembles in a good many respects the political profession with which I am directly acquainted. It is a study which in more than one aspect seems to me to revive the daily experience of the politician. Every human being, every living body, has an empire with an innumerable population and many different races, living in vast provinces under different conditions of pressure and climate, subjected to accidents and misfortunes, and usually in a state of internal and external war.

As long as the presiding genius, as long as the central governing control, is seated firmly on its throne, order reigns and harmony prevails throughout the whole combination of that complex organization, but when the central power begins to weaken or is aged or is undermined by any cause, then disorder, discontent, riots, revolts, and revolutions break out. Then we see told in every human body the same story as was told on the pages of history in the decline and fall of the Roman Empire 2,000 years ago, or the decline and fall of the Russian Empire within recent memory.

There is a strong parallel between politics and medicine. Those in politics can see some of the diseases with which medicine is grappling. Communism is a form of cancer. It is a political cancer—the revolt of a single cell which perverted and corrupted those immediately round it and established a foreign principle of life within the body politic, a principle of life governed by laws unknown to the rest of the Empire, entailing endless misery, manifesting itself by the most violent symptoms and requiring remedies about which there is great difference of opinion. (Laughter.) Some say the knife, but all are agreed that the remedies should be prompt and drastic. (Cheers.)

We all know the danger of intervention in the affairs of a foreign country. But this intervention in the affairs of a foreign State is exactly what every doctor has to do every time he prescribes for any patient. The resources of intervention are growing, but the variety of conditions are infinite. I look on the Royal Society of Medicine as a sort of League of Nations applying to the disordered State the remedies which are not merely within the knowledge and suggestion of any one particular Power, but which comprise the collective knowledge and the concerted effort of all that has been achieved by all the organizations of mankind which are directed to the furtherance of human welfare.

The marvel is how much has been achieved in the sphere of medicine. While serving at the Colonial Office I saw something of the immense advance in tropical medicine which has made habitable and healthy vast provinces in which residence was previously attended by death or by a shattered constitution. Marvels have been achieved, but those are only indications of far greater marvels which the future has in store.

I can say with certainty that, however great are the achievements which have been performed in the medical sphere, or however substantial are the results which we are able to show in the political field, nevertheless, we are both asking for more. My audience is, no doubt, looking to me to reduce the taxation of the country—(Hear, hear, and loud laughter)—and to improve its social services, to maintain its defence, and to discharge all its numerous obligations, and politicians look to the medical profession to lay its hands on a great many of those evils in modern life which cause so much concern—in short, we hope that medical men will lay their delicate and inquiring fingers upon those vitamins and other mysterious substances which the people are increasingly assured enable them to be made either fat or lean, well preserved or decrepit, long lived or rapidly disposed of, virtuous or criminal, and happy or despondent. Medicine is reaching forward into those extremely important and delicate fields which so profoundly affect the lives of individuals and the whole outlook of the human race upon the phenomena of life.

IS LABOUR FIT TO GOVERN?

November 16, 1928

West Essex Unionist Association Dinner,
London

[Extract] ... At the last general election we fought to turn out a minority Socialist Government, to terminate a period of political chaos, and to re-establish something that could be looked on as a stable, clean Government. The same issue which was present at the last general election will be present at the coming general election, and in an even sharper form. It is true we have not a Socialist Government to turn out, but we have a Socialist Opposition confidently demanding not office but power. Some people say: "Well, they have been in office before and nothing happened. Why should not they have another chance?"

But the Socialists have never been in power. When they were in office they had the Liberals on one side of them and the Conservatives on the other. They were shepherded along as a man is taken to a station sometimes between two trustworthy police officers. Whatever his condition may be, however he may sway to this side or that of the pavement, you know he is going to get to his destination all right.

I said seven or eight years ago that they were not fit to govern the country. I repeat that they are not yet fit to afford a suitable basis for the conduct of British national and Imperial affairs.

The question at the next election will be whether the men who managed the general strike are going to be his Majesty's Ministers or not. I warn you that if at the next election the Socialists obtain power you are going to see a period of political violence in this country such as happened in the general strike, only more dangerous in some respects and much more prolonged; it is going to inflict immense injury upon the whole process of earning the national income, and an immense weakening of the position of Great Britain throughout the world.

You see other countries by different methods trying to strengthen themselves. If you look across the Atlantic Ocean you will see the Americans by the vote of a vast majority definitely casting their will in favour of the strongest form of national self-assertion. It would be very dangerous at this moment, when you see every other country gathering its strength, if we declined and fell away into mere internal brawling, and handed over our affairs to the weaker elements in the national life.

There are people who say "scrap" the derating bill. The idea that this measure, which represents two years of the best brain power and study that the governing instrument of this country can give to a great social question, could be dropped is too foolish to deserve discussion. In Mr. Neville Chamberlain we have a man who has a genius for local government. There is not a single Minister who would not support through thick and thin his great measure of local and social reform. If I thought everybody was going to say there cannot be this reform because my constituency is going to lose twopence halfpenny, if every effort to reorganise England and carry her forward to a better and stronger life is to be met with scorn and trampled down, then I should feel hopeless for the future of our country.

But I am quite sure the strength of our country will be equal to its needs, and we shall carry the necessary measures whether they be popular or whether they be unpopular, so long as they are sincerely conceived in the main interests of the British people. The idea that a press campaign would prevent a measure of this kind from reaching the Statute-book is also one of those foolish ideas with which I will not further take up your time.

1929

TRADE

January 21, 1929

*Chamber of Commerce Dinner,
Midland Hotel, Manchester*

It is very refreshing to me to be received so kindly by this great company. It is always a pleasure to me to come to Manchester and to find here that, however many intricate adventures—as the chairman has suggested—my course has followed, I am judged with indulgence and kindliness by a very large body of those whose respect and goodwill are very dear to me.

What course is it best for the country to take and what had it better avoid if the present condition of things is to be improved? The state of trade is—as often at this time of year—marked by a distinct feeling of hope. We always begin a new year with new hope; and perhaps this year there is a stronger justification than there has been on other occasions. I, for my part, am certainly on the side of the optimists. I cannot at all join myself with those who think they are serving the cause of our country and its prosperity and livelihood by indulging only in criticism and blank despair. But, nevertheless, if we are to look at the facts—and we must face facts—British productive industry and the general position of Great Britain in the twentieth century are very much less securely established than in the nineteenth century—in the great Victorian era. It is not that our country has gone back or has stood still, or has not progressed or not progressed vastly; it is that the world around has been growing greater at enormous speed and that giants have come into existence in the twentieth century who have altered our relative position in the world. Everyone who looks at the situation now, compared with sixty or seventy years ago, must feel that we have entered upon one of those periods when there is need for an intense effort on the part of the brain, character, and muscle of Britain in order that we may keep fully abreast of the broadening developments of the modern world.

Our position is not such that we can afford to make mistakes. It is not such that we can afford to indulge in the luxury of faction and needless quarrelling among ourselves in economic matters. In party politics it is another matter. But the less there is of it the better. When we come to the vital productive energies of the nation as a whole, its commercial interests and general stability and security, we cannot afford to do the kind of things we used to do in the days when we were so far ahead of every other country, so supreme and safe, that we could indulge in the most violent internal disputations. We cannot afford fierce political agitation; we cannot afford violent disputes between capital and labour. (Hear, hear.) So far as the national bread-winning is concerned, we have got to work together just as we worked together in the war, when national existence was at stake. In the same way now, in these days of peace, national bread-winning is just as vital, or almost as vital, as was the winning of the war, in which all parties took part.

What can the Government do to help British industry? I am strongly of opinion that it is no use to exaggerate what governments can do to help industry and commercial development. They may do a great deal to hinder and hamper; but to help, to foster—that is a most difficult and doubtful sphere. But I will tell what the Government has done, making no party claim, because party is banished from that board. The first thing I will touch on very briefly, because it is a topic to which there is no end, is currency. The Government has laboured to maintain a sound credit for the nation and a stable and honest currency. (Hear, hear.) A community like ours—a wonderful island community—must march along the high road. Nothing would be more dangerous to our world trade and world position than if we were to try and meet temporary difficulties by altering our standards of weights and measures to suit the occasion.

Generally, we have during the present administration carefully avoided either deflation or inflation. We have reached a sound and normal basis, and industry and commerce know now that there are no unpleasant surprises awaiting them in the sphere of currency, that they are upon a well-established and solid level, which as time passes will increasingly be found to be durable and certain. Part of the consequence of the policy we have pursued in currency has been a reduction in the cost of living. It has fallen a full 7 per cent. during the last five years. It is quite true that while a diminution in the cost of living is taking place, manifesting itself, as it does, by a fall in prices, that is, in itself, depressing upon industry. But when it has taken place the return is received in an increased competitive power which aids and stimulates most of all those industries which minister to our export trade. Lancashire industry, which has always had to cut the margin of competition extremely fine, is undoubtedly more securely based at the present time from the point of view of the cost of living, both in respect of the prices which can be quoted for the goods and in respect of the contentment which follows from an easement in the burden of life upon the masses of the people, than it has been in any period in recent years.

In the third place, we have the scheme of rating reform. Rates are obviously a greater burden upon productive industry than the income tax. There are secondary or superfine new industries rapidly developing and becoming very prosperous which are greatly aiding in the race and becoming great factors in maintaining the balance of trade and giving new employment of the highest character; but the basic industries on which the whole fabric and structure of the national life is ultimately founded have, in the last few years, been passing through a period of marked distress and eclipse.

The rating burden falls with peculiar and invidious emphasis on those industries in proportion to the size and bulk of the plant and premises and not of the percentage actually working, or the profits and prosperity. The burden becomes most aggravated in the very proportion as an industry is depressed and suffering from short time. That evil is to be swept away by remitting three-fourths of the rates on productive industry in the currency of the present year. In agriculture the burden will be removed altogether. Freights, too, are to be reduced through the rating concessions to the railways. We have a wonderful system of railways in which a vast mass of our capital is invested and we have a great number of persons who get their livelihood from their profits; and both from the point of view of assisting this heavy industry traffic and of aiding and sustaining the position of our railways, I believe this great provision, translated into rates, coming back to the railways, as we trust it will, in the form of increased custom, constitutes a most valuable and suggestive avenue along which, perhaps at some future time, a fresh advance might be made.

These three methods are by no means all the Government has done in an endeavour to help the producer and to stimulate the trade of the country; but there is no doubt that aiding the producer has now taken a definite place in the forefront of British politics. It claims priority over almost every other aspect in national affairs. In the palmy days of Queen Victoria the producer strode ahead dragging the whole country after him into a richer and larger world. That is not the case now. Anxiety hangs around the councils of those concerned with these vital interests of the nation, and it is the duty of every Government to make it their constant care and study to assist the producer in every possible way without creating further evils and complications.

Let me now say a word about what we ought to avoid as much as we can. First of all, we really cannot indulge in too much politics in this country at the present time. We are going to have a general election. As a politician I ought to be filled with joy, my appetite should be whetted by the prospect of an early attack; but it is not as a politician I am talking to-night, and I must say that nothing will do us less good than violent political conflict from one end of the country to the other—every question judged for the time only by whether it is likely to win or lose votes, no fair criticism or consideration of any proposals either by Government or Opposition because of political interests that are bound to be speedily involved and brought into direct collision.

Such a period is necessary to us. It is a necessary feature in our free constitutional life and no doubt over a long period we gain through our free government and system of associating all classes and parties in the direct conduct of national affairs— we gain in stability and in security a great deal. But so far as the present period is concerned I trust that this next general election will be as short and as sweet as possible. (Laughter and applause.)

We have entered on the age of combination. Our Victorian forerunners, the old economists, had got as far as that it took ten men to make a pin; but they never foresaw the part that combination would play in productive industry. They were much oppressed with the fear of rings and monopolies. The Liberal and Radical view at the end of the nineteenth century, and even at the beginning of the twentieth, was almost entirely based upon prejudice against combinations because of their danger of degenerating into mere price-raising institutions to exploit the public as a whole.

That time is past. A very much broader view is taken now. Every party desires to examine combines and see what part they are to play in industry and the national life in a tolerant and happily non-partisan spirit. Combinations, like individuals, have diseases and vices, but they also have great advantages in stability, buying power, economical and efficient management, concentration of ability, greater security to the workpeople, better service of the public, and in the ability they give us to maintain our position against competition. How can these great organisations be reconciled with the forms of the democratic State and of Parliamentary government so that we may gain the productivity and prosperity which comes with the higher forms of capitalistic competition and combination without losing those liberties which we value more than the acquisition of wealth? (Applause.)

I trust also that we should not imagine that we shall greatly improve our affairs by entering upon a period of political uncertainty and Parliamentary chaos with a Government that does not know where to look for its majority, or a Government that has to keep itself going from day to day by outdoor relief. (Laughter.)

The question really before us is not a reduction of direct taxation; that proposal we will have to consider at the general election is the proposal to increase direct taxation by raising 50, 60, 70, or 80 million sterling from a very limited class. Such a plan would be not only very disappointing financially to those who carried it into law, but would also be deeply injurious in its reaction upon credit, enterprise, saving power, and employment.

My predecessor, possibly my successor—(laughter)—Mr. Snowden, in his salad days, has said that in all matters of direct taxation of income you should not have consideration to what was taken away but only to what was left. This is a test which now might be conveniently applied, and if another £80,000,000 a year were to be raised, as has been proposed, by the surtax, there would be left to a large proportion an income of something between three and four shillings in the pound, without making allowances for the additional charges of the death duties of 40 per cent.

It is quite obvious that the field of taxable endeavour is becoming severely limited when you reach as high a point as 16s. 9d. in the pound apart from death duties. The position we would rapidly reach would be the putting of a premium upon squandering or upon divisions of fortunes, which, while not at all reducing the amount of luxury or the number of people employed in ministering to luxury, would very greatly reduce the rate at which income tax could be levied or the yield to the revenue from these sources, and therefore this idea that these great sums of money could be raised by taxing what are called the idle rich—who are by far the greatest tax gatherers and contributors to the revenue—is pernicious, and if it is inspired as it is, not by a careful study of finance and economic questions, but by a desire to pander to the cheapest motives of the gutter, it is a move which cannot fail to be detrimental to every branch of our productive and commercial life.

There is another thing which I don't think would do us any good at the present time, and that is a stand-up, old-fashioned fight about Protection and Free Trade.

(Laughter.) I cannot see that that would be any help or advantage to the interests of the nation (hear, hear) and the material and commercial interests of the nation. I am glad to think that so far as his Majesty's Government is concerned there is no question of a revolution in our fiscal system or the establishment of a general system of Protection being made an issue at the next election. (Hear, hear.) Undoubtedly there is the most active question of the safeguarding of industries, which establish their case under certain conditions which have been prescribed. But that is a matter which ought to be argued out not as a question for the hustings, but as a question for business men (hear, hear) a matter which ought to be hammered out not by political partisans and candidates greatly desirous of competing against each other for their seats in Parliament, but by people who are aiming only at the objective we all have in view—namely, can we so adjust our national housekeeping as to gain the greater advantage in this direction or that for our own people. (Hear, hear.) And in pleading for this matter being kept out of ordinary Parliamentary politics let me say that I presume here in this audience probably the great majority are Free-traders (hear, hear), as I am myself (laughter), but we should make a very great mistake if we do not readily address ourselves to new facts and new forces in the world. (Hear, hear.)

In illustration of this contention, I refer you to the result of the tax on motor-car tyres which I included in the scope of the McKenna duties. It has led to the establishment in this country of six or seven great new tyre factories. I will not say that the result of such an experiment justifies universal and absolute Protection. It does not. There are many other factors. But I do say it is quite clear that, in the sphere of taxation there are duties which can be imposed which will help industry, which will not increase the cost to the consumer, and which will bring in a substantial revenue to the State; and we should be foolish in our present high state of political and intellectual development in this island to cut ourselves off by rigid or arbitrary limitations from embarking upon such a policy.

We must not be too much concerned with the quarrels and questions of the day before yesterday. We have to face the issues of to-morrow if we are to get through our difficulties. In the general disintegration and collapse of those great military empires of Europe the nationalistic movements of many countries have gained their fullest satisfaction, and Central and Southern Europe are to-day divided into fifteen, sixteen, or more different independent sovereign States on national lines, each with its own military forces, each with its own wall of tariffs, each strongly organised and nationalist.

But such an organisation for the purpose of economic production has a very poor chance if it were ever to be brought into competition with the mass production of the United States of America, which, over the area of a whole continent possessing every natural characteristic, is organised on a universal free trade, competitive basis, and combines the strongest form of federal unit with the greatest development of State rights. It is perfectly clear the issue here does not lie between these movements on the one hand and those strong national expressions on the other. It finds its proper solution in systems of federal government with great local and State jurisdictions and liberties existing beneath them. The British Empire has to move with the times in this respect. There is not the slightest reason why we should not get the greatest develop-

ment of the productive and economic unit and of individual State expression, combined with strong unity at the centre, indispensable for the safety of all.

In economics the same factors are at work, and there, too, we must not fight on
old issues and obsolete, out-of-date questions. People talk as if the question before us
were whether there should be Socialism or individualism, but the world is moving
forward into a period of capitalism and combination, and the problem which we have
to face is the reconciling of this new phase with the democratic and popular system of
government. The problem is not insoluble.

If there were anything I could do to help the cotton trade I would do it to the
uttermost. I have seen with great pain the hard times through which this Palatinate has
been passing. On the whole, I believe the worst is over. There is no doubt whatever
that easier times are coming. In China a more stable system of government is coming
into existence. There is no doubt that great exertions are being made in Lancashire
itself, and surely there can be no higher aim for a young Lancashire man—and I see a
good many as I look around this room—than to set before himself the determination
to revive and restore the Lancashire cotton industry permanently to its great position
in the world—to discover the path by which this community, with its splendid
workpeople, glorious history and tradition, could move on in the new world as
strongly and as efficiently as it moved on in a bygone century. Surely such an aim and
object in life would far surpass anything open to the politician. It would rank with the
philanthropist, with the philosopher, and the great discoverers and inventors; with the
men who have written their names permanently on the history of the nation and the
island, and the benefactors' world of lasting honour.

I know well the efforts you have made. The Manchester Chamber of Commerce
has devoted its energies and attention to the problem of the cotton industry with an
intensity which has not been equalled, and certainly not surpassed, by any similar
body dealing with the problem, and here we are on the eve of the launching of the
very important subject of amalgamation in one section of the cotton trade—a scheme
in which the Bank of England has co-operated in a most unusual manner, almost
unprecedented, and in a spirit of the utmost resolution. I, for my part, set on record
my sincere conviction that by the efforts which you will make, by such aid as may be
given, Lancashire will triumphantly emerge from the undoubtedly difficult and dark
times through which it has been passing, and will, under new conditions and in a
broader and wider world, renew the triumphs which have made it one of the most
memorable episodes in the industrial history of the world. (Loud cheers.)

BATTERSEA BY-ELECTION

February 6, 1929

Town Hall, Battersea

As an old judge of electioneering meetings, I can confidently say that the scene
before me looks extremely healthy. You are engaged in Battersea in what is in itself a

great fight, but what is also a preliminary skirmish of a much greater battle—a general battle which, in a few months' time, will be fought all over the country. I agree that it is a matter of great importance what decision Battersea shall take on the to-morrow. It will not decide the great issues that lie before us, but it will influence them. If you have got a fair fight in Battersea, as Lord Howe has said, you have also got a good candidate. You have got someone whom you know well and who knows London government well.

I have come before you to say a few things about the Conservative record and the Conservative policy, for the Government have a record and a policy. There has been a period of confusion and chaos when no party had a majority and no Government could rely on any organized body of public opinion to support it in the House of Commons. We had three General Elections in the space of 24 months, and all made promises of public improvement at the public expense. The nation is sick of the disturbance. All over the world we had been looked on as being a stable country, yet here we are, more hysterical and changeable in our administration than any of the countries on the Continent of Europe, to say nothing of those across the Atlantic.

The public felt in 1924 that it was high time we had a period of stability, and it was for that that you voted to let the country get strong under a steady Government which did not pretend to cure all the ills from which men suffered nor had a quack remedy for social evils, but would push forward along the straight road and present a sustained policy supported by a solid Parliamentary majority.

The difficulties of carrying on politics after the War are very much greater than those before the War. There were then only two parties, whereas now there are some newcomers who make a lot of noise. The two parties fought each other very fiercely, but now the parties are not so much fighting one another. The Government is trying to solve the grim economic problems of the time, and the Opposition is trying to pull us down. It is an easier business to score off a political opponent than to provide answers for the serious social and economic problems of the day. Anyone can ask what the remedy is. The task of carrying on the business of this great country and the Empire round it requires respectful aid and sympathy from everyone who wishes the country well. We have not been helped by our opponents, as witness the complaints in the addresses of the Labour candidates, and the Liberal candidates too are very fond of fault finding. Has the Government been helped in our troubles in the last four years? If we only had to meet Parliamentary arguments it would have been quite easy, but we have had to meet an organized attempt to upset and impoverish the country and make things worse for the purpose of saying: "There you are! You are to blame." It is in the teeth of difficulties of that character that the Government have had to carry on.

Financial difficulties have been very great. I was robbed of £80,000,000 by the general strike and the prolonged coal stoppage. That money would have enabled me to sweep away taxes. I have had to put on taxes which I would be very glad to take off. This £80,000,000 was stripped from the revenue and £400,000,000 was drawn away from the slowly recovering life energies of the country, so hardly pressed in the struggles of the Great War. It is in the teeth of such difficulties that the Government has established and promoted peace at home. Never has there been a period in modern times when there was greater peace in the industrial world than exists to-day. (Cheers.)

When we could not keep peace at home we have kept order. We carried the greatest measure of social insurance that the Statute Book of any country can show. We have built 900,000 houses at very great expense. I have had to produce £10,000,000 to £12,000,000 for this purpose and the money is increasing. I am glad to see it being spent in rebuilding homes in this country.

People seeing the houses being built with the money have been heard to say, "Ah! The expenditure is going up." What we have had to be on our guard against in these days are the specious and claptrap arguments of the man who tries to have it both ways at the same time. I am sure that London is a place where that kind of fraud is easily detected.

By the policy the Government have pursued we also have definitely procured a diminution in the cost of living which means, I think, at the present time 8 per cent. as compared with 1924. Having dealt with the wage-earning classes and with the old, the weak, and the poor, the Government in its five years' administration now approaches the problem of the producer. We are helping him by safeguarding without any violent change in our fiscal system or any attempt to make it a political issue, but as a business matter carefully selecting industries and safeguarding them against the difficulties with which they have to contend. It cannot be denied that good results have followed from those safeguarding efforts. I think it would be rash to draw an absolute general conclusion from those experiments, but it is not rash having made certain successful experiments to walk further and make new experiments.

Then there is the policy of the relief of industry by taking rates off the producer. If the Derating Bill were the last measure the Conservative Party were to pass it would render an immense service to the country by going through with it at any cost. The Socialist candidate has said that as a result the rates would go up in Battersea. That is absolutely untrue. (Cheers.) A guarantee has been given that there could be no increase of the rates in Battersea for five years, and it is hoped by the Government that when that period has passed a far easier position by the protection of an industry will have been created. The policy of the Government will sweep away from productive industries three-fourths of the burdens from which they suffer, and as far as agriculture is concerned it will sweep the rates away altogether. (Cheers.) Surely the relief from this burden is one of the most needful things that has to be done by anyone who cares about the welfare of the country.

Then we propose to relieve the rates on the railways, but not to give the money to the railways. On the contrary, we said to them: "We give you the relief and you are to pass it on to the consumer." As to the derating policy of the Government, only a few weeks ago a deputation of Labour members came to me imploring the Government to put some part of the scheme into operation a little earlier, and the other day there was a deputation at the Treasury consisting of the Lord Mayor of Newcastle and Liberal and Labour members begging me also to bring the scheme into operation before the time which has been appointed. The Government is making an effort in that direction.

The scheme is one which might conceivably give a fillip to British industry, yet it is of that very scheme that the Labour candidate for South Battersea is going about saying he hopes that the result of this by-election would be to mean its defeat. I do not believe there is any serious politician in the country who would not regard it as most disastrous and destructive if the scheme were defeated.

[Editor's Note: At this stage a disturbance took place at the back of the large hall, and there were shouts of "Turn him out."] Let us be quite friendly and don't have anybody turned out. Let him stay and learn. After all, we are not only carrying on a political campaign; we are carrying on an educative one.

The derating scheme of the Government is a great national effort to improve the position of the country. It is a contemptible thing for a man just in the hope of winning votes at a by-election to try by little grumblings and complaints to invite such a constituency to cast away a scheme to which Parliament has given so many months of time, and to the accomplishment of which all parties are looking forward.

The Liberal Party has newly arrived in Battersea. From beginning to end the Liberal candidate's address was a series of querulous complaints covering almost every aspect of politics. The Liberal Party are very good at making complaints, they are the real prize fault-finders and champion scolds in the political world at the present moment. The weakness of the Liberal leadership in the last five years has been such as to strip the party of any credentials, and no matter how big the fund and how many the candidates without definite leadership it is quite impossible for the Liberals to regain the confidence of the country. What a trick it is to run candidates all over the place and split votes in the hope that no party will have a clear majority. There is no more dangerous, vicious element in public life than that there should be a little group able to go this way and that and move about like pawns on a chess-board.

As regards the Russian question Mr. Lloyd George dares not pronounce one way or another because one section of his party is to vote in one lobby and another section in the other lobby, while the rest are to walk out. All he can do is to follow the bulk of his party and they walk off to Margate to celebrate the Liberal revival. (Laughter.) The Liberals are trying to create a situation of confusion, from which the country had shaken itself so boldly four years ago. They have no chance of being in office themselves or of having the power to conduct the affairs of this country, but they have pledged themselves that whoever is to govern and carry the burden they will try to trip them up.

Mr. Lloyd George, I understand, has been having rough weather, but it is nothing like so rough as Sir Herbert Samuel is going to encounter when he comes back. (Laughter.)

There are, however, larger and graver interests behind all this, and that brings me to the important speech which has been delivered here this afternoon by Mr. Mac-Donald. Judging from the summarized report of the speech which I have received, there was not an argument of any kind in it. It did not contain a single constructive proposal. There was a great deploring of the unfortunate happenings in human life and of the evils of unemployment, and only a vague appeal to the electors to vote for the Socialist Party in the hope that something would turn up.

Mr. MacDonald, it would appear, drew some very curious class distinctions. He is reported to have said that it was not merely the working classes alone who had adopted the doctrines they preach, but quite decent people (laughter and cheers) had also embraced that gospel, and both were marching arm in arm to vote for Labour next time. In addition to the working classes there were millions of decent-minded men and women—people who had been to school and had ideas.

I do not think we should have these class distinctions of decent people here and working classes there. (Laughter.) I have a strong feeling that the great working-class mass of the country has just as high ideas as any other class. Cannot you see in this speech the almost insufferable, indescribable humbug and hypocrisy that animates the Socialist leader, this Socialist intellectual who really showed himself one of the greatest snobs in the land.

It is all humbug and worse than humbug, this building up of class hatred in this country. (Cheers.) All English men and women are equal before the law, with the same rights in the Constitution, the same political liberties, and the same power and authority, whether they are working class or so-called decent people. What is his appeal to vote for these ideas—to ask you to put into power in this country in a few months' time, and to begin on the morrow in this constituency, the very men who two years ago were planning the general strike and trying to carry it out as far as they dared? What are their credentials to run the British Empire? Because they tried to make London walk and could not? The same hands that stopped the tubes, cut off the water, tried to stop electric power, and endeavoured to cast the fortunes of the country into the whirlpool, those same hands are now presented as those which would direct the levers of the British State and regulate the whole traffic of the Empire. Let them give an unqualified answer.

Why should we be plunged into that state of things again just as things are beginning to revive a little? We have a very dangerous and difficult position in the world. Things were different in the 19th century. In the terrible years of the 20th century we have progressed, but the world has grown greater all around us. Ours is a very artificial country, and we are dependent on oversea supplies and world credit. We are in a more artificial position than others are, and we cannot afford, with these great rivals round us, to play the fool here or even to indulge in needless faction. We have to pull together and work together on the essentials of our country. Let us stand together. We got through the struggles of the War, and shouldered burdens because the country was united. The men and women of resolve and patriotism who had something to give out of their hearts to the service of the country stood together. In all the political struggles which are to come, if we combine with energy and conviction, we shall gather for future generations and preserve and hand down to them an inheritance which we have preserved in spite of the perils and tumults of the greatest of all human wars. (Cheers.)

SOCIALISM

February 12, 1929

Anti-Socialist and Anti-Communist Union Meeting,
Queen's Hall, London

On the twenty-first birthday of the [Anti-Socialist and Anti-Communist] Union our thoughts go with warmth and sympathy to one of those associated in its foundation—my old friend Colonel Claude Lowther, who is at the present time suffering from serious illness and to whom we send our warmest sympathy and every hope and wish for his speedy recovery. Twenty-one years have seen a lot of changes in the world. Socialism in that period has become intellectually discredited. It no longer presents itself as a solution of human difficulties or as an effective and practical philosophy to the minds of leading men; it no longer commands the reasoning assent of the pioneers of thought. (Cheers.) During that period we have seen grizzly examples of the ruin which it brought to States, industries, and communities of all kinds, whether it was applied on the largest or on the smallest scale. Show me the parts of the country which at the present time are in the deepest depression, show me the industries which are the most laggard, and at the same time you will be showing me the parts where these withering doctrines have won their greatest measure of acceptance.

If you wish to see the greatest and most terrible example you have only to look at the contrast presented at the present time between the welfare of the Russian and the American people. Socialism to-day is intellectually bankrupt and discredited and has been proved on a gigantic scale and with perfect clearness to be fatal to the welfare of living nations. But we have seen with melancholy feelings how year after year a larger number of our own fellow-countrymen have allowed themselves to drift into an easy acceptance of Socialist doctrines and let themselves be regimented under foreign-made standards of Communist collectivism.

It is, indeed, a melancholy fact and brings me to the main point which I wish to place before you this evening. We are met under the advent of a very serious and critical general election. I deprecate the lighthearted, over-confident, and indifferent mood in which this grave event is treated by thoughtless people. I hope and believe that all will be well but the risks to the country are enormous. On some night in May or June we may go to bed a strong and tranquil nation recovering slowly but surely our prosperity after the Great War. The next morning we may wake up to find that the control of Great Britain and the conduct of its world-wide affairs has been handed over for four or five years to the men who two years ago were managing the general strike and trying to shatter the economic life of the whole land and its ancient Parliamentary constitution.

That to me is a very serious and anxious position. If we wish to save the country from these evils we can only do so by our own exertions. There are no safeguards of any kind in the constitution. We have not even got, as we used to have, the general election spread over a period of six weeks, so that one part of the country could correct and balance an undue swing by the other. No one will know the consequences of their vote, or their neglect to vote, until everything has been decided at one single stroke.

For instance, a man or woman may have some grievance against the Government, which has to carry on all the difficult affairs of the country. They may stay at home, or even vote for some Opposition candidate, never meaning to do more than express their opinion against the Government on some particular point. They may wake up and find that they have helped to launch poor old England upon a voyage the end of which no man can foresee.

Unthinking people frequently say, "What harm did the Socialists do when they were in office four years ago?" At that time they had no power. They were without a majority in the House of Commons. They were kept in office by the charity or folly of the Liberals. They knew that at any moment, if they over-stepped the strict limits of ordinary government and administration, and if they tried any Socialist legislation or finance, or if they threatened to tamper with the Constitution or with the military forces or with the police, they would be turned out at a moment's notice. This gave the Socialist Ministers the power to keep their followers in order. It gave them an excuse for not trying to do any of the foolish and pernicious things that they had promised and said untruthfully that they believed in. When reproached by their extreme men for not doing anything to bring about a Socialist State, they could always say: "The first step we take, we shall be turned out; and we have only just for the first time got into office. Please let us stay a little longer." Therefore on this basis the Socialist Government remained in office for eight months, acting in very much the same way as a Conservative or Liberal Administration would do. It was not until August that the extremists began to lose patience. When they did, their leaders collapsed immediately before them and did whatever they were told. They were told to stop the prosecution of the Communist, Campbell, and to guarantee a loan of 30,000,000 of British money to the Bolshevists. The Government immediately obeyed these orders. And as soon as Parliament could come together, it censured the Socialist Government for its breach of duty and forced them to go to the country, where they received the overwhelming condemnation of the electors.

Quite a different issue will soon be before the country. The Socialists are not asking for office but for power. They are asking for an independent majority over all parties. They are convinced they are going to get it. If they obtain an independent majority in the House of Commons the Socialist Ministers will no longer have any excuse to offer to their followers for not bringing about the Socialist State.

They will be bound to attempt the nationalisation of great industries and services. They have already pledged themselves to lay their uninstructed hands upon the banking system. They will be bound to impose very large additions to the income taxes and to direct taxation generally. They will be bound to bring back the Russian Bolsheviks, who will immediately get busy in the mines and factories, as well as among the armed forces, planning another general strike. I leave you to imagine what the state of the country would be if in the face of a general strike you had a Socialist majority in the House of Commons and if the strike committee sitting in Eccleston Square could play both sides of the game at once and send their orders to the strike pickets and to the Ministers at the same moment.

It was hard enough two years ago, when every one tried their utmost to feed and transport the population, to keep the industries alive, and to keep peace and order in the streets. It is difficult to imagine what the situation would be if the whole machinery of public safety were in the hands of men who only two or three years before had actually been running the general strike themselves. You might easily have a gigantic social and economic breakdown in which Parliamentary institutions would be overturned or brushed on one side and out of which a non-Parliamentary and unconstitutional Socialist regime would come into being as the only force capable of restoring peace and supplying food.

Compared with issues like these, surely grievances about the betting tax or the hours of closing in public-houses or in which small articles could be bought from shops and the ordinary complaints about the day-to-day routine of government seem rather petty. I think men or women would feel very much ashamed of themselves if they found they had let these grave dangers and evils loose upon the country by voting against the Government or simply by sitting at home in unworthy apathy.

There is already an agitation to bring back the Bolsheviks. While they were here we had the worst, the most dangerous and disastrous stikes this country has ever seen. As soon as they were gone we had the best period of peace in industry for a whole generation. I do not want to see the Conservative party weaken in any way its attitude against a subversive and revolutionary propaganda and conspiracy. Whatever may happen, whatever storms may blow. I want to see the strong, stable forces of the country keep together unhampered and uncompromised by any weak surrenders, so that they, at any rate, shall have no responsibility for any evils that may come.

Secondly, in the event of a Socialist Government coming into power, I do not want the new Ministers to be exposed in their earliest days and while they are still inexperienced to the kind of Bolshevist efforts that would certainly be organized by the Russian emissaries and conspirators. I want them to have at any rate a fair chance to do their duty, and above all that it should never be flung in the teeth of the Conservative Party that they brought this peril back into our midst. This aspect seems to me far more important than the comparatively small trade favours that are likely to be given to British merchants and speculators by the Bolshevist Government as the purchase price of getting another footing here. Meanwhile there is nothing to prevent ordinary trade growing up with Russia. The United States, who has never recognized them or allowed them to enter and disturb their country, has done a better trade with them than we have done by all the efforts we have made to conciliate them and the risks we have run. The policy of the Government in this matter is absolutely clear. It was explained only the other day again in the House of Commons by Sir Austen Chamberlain, and I am glad to think that there is no question of its being departed from in any respect.

Let us face facts. In a few months, almost in a few weeks, all the institutions of the country will be put to the test at the same time. No one knows what sort of a House of Commons we will get. No one knows how the new electors will vote. No one knows how many will not think it worth while to use their votes. All we know is that every constituency will be far too large for any one man to see even a quarter of the electors and talk to them and tell them what the issues are. So far as the House of Commons is concerned, they will get a mass impression. It will be given by enormous numbers of people who have never received direct guidance or advice from their Parliamentary representatives, or heard the case stated by responsible persons acquainted with the facts. In the old days they could at any rate talk to the people and argue questions out in every constituency before the people who had to give their votes. But on this occasion the people, so far as they vote at all, will have to vote on their own almost unaided and unguided responsibility. I have profound faith in the good sense of the British people. But certainly no people in the world has ever—so far as I know—had such an immense unfocussed decision flung upon them. No civilized State has ever put all its fortunes so vaguely and incontinently to the hazard.

On the contrary, in the modern world every country, all our rivals, are tightening up their organization. They have rigid, fixed Constitutions or fundamental laws that cannot be altered except by a two-thirds or three-quarters majority. They have strong Second Chambers. They have very strong State Governments or local bodies. They have secondary elections and all kinds of other devices to prevent an unthinking mass vote from sweeping away the whole slowly erected structure of society.

We have nothing of this sort. We put it all on the mass vote by direct election, and no one will know until it is too late what it is they have done. They will only know afterwards, and then they may know only too well. I defy you to show any great community which will so boldly and audaciously run the risks which we are going to run in a few months' time.

Yet of all the communities and civilizations in the world there is none more artificial, more precarious, more menaced at the present time by economic forces than our own. In this small overcrowded island, living at a very high standard of social and economic well-being, compared at any rate to the rest of Europe, we are dependent—as no other country is—on the operations of world-wide trade and world credit and finance. No equally large community has ever in all history depended so much upon the capitalistic system as the 40,000,000 who live in Great Britain. There is no other system by which more than two-thirds of our swarming population can get their daily bread. Injure, rupture, break down the mechanism of their economic life, as the Socialist Party tried to do only two years ago; shatter confidence, destroy credit, throw the industries of the country into disorder, and whole districts will starve. The harm done by the general strike and the coal stoppage set us back for two or three years, while rival nations were going ahead all the time. As the Prime Minister pointed out last week, we had got unemployment down to below a million before the general strike was let loose on us, and now it is up to a million and a third, and will only come down slowly. But think what would happen if a real struggle between Socialism and civilization broke out in this country and really had to be fought out, as fought out it would be. Can you doubt that we are running risks that no other great country at the present time would dare to run? Are we not presuming too much on the good fortune, the Providential protection, which has so far preserved us?

The Liberal party have a grievance, and I admit their grievance. They cannot obtain representation in Parliament which has any relation to their voting strength. Therefore they are taking their revenge upon society. They are pursuing the most wanton and reckless of all policies. They are mad-dogging all the constituencies with 500 candidates, the majority of whom will forfeit their deposits. They are trying their utmost to split the anti-Socialist vote in hundreds of constituencies. Their tactics, or the reasonable consequence of their actions, are to try in every case to put in a Socialist candidate. They hope by this means to bring the Socialist and Conservative parties to something like an equipoise, and then they hope to sit on the balance and make the best bargain possible for themselves. And that is what they call Liberalism. (Laughter.)

Sir Herbert Samuel stated the other day that after the election the Liberal party will not put the Socialists into power, but that does not prevent them from trying to split every vote before the election and make the Socialists as strong as possible. They are certainly gambling in a terrible manner with the vital interests of the State.

It seems to me extraordinary that the Lloyd George Fund, which was built up for the direct purpose of enabling the Conservatives and Liberals to stand up against Socialism, should be used with the consequence of deliberately multiplying Socialist representation in the House of Commons. (Cheers.)

I was taught from my youth up the words of my father, Lord Randolph Churchill. I have never feared the English democracy. I will always put my trust in the real and true opinion of the great majority of my fellow-countrymen. (Cheers.) But how do we know we are going to get the opinion of a great majority? Vast numbers of people may not take the trouble to go to the poll at all. Absorbed in their private affairs they do not realize how serious politics may suddenly become. In a very large number of constituencies Socialists will be returned by minority votes. There will certainly be a great number of people who will say, "Why should not the other side have a chance?" And so there may come into power a Socialist Government, officially declared by itself to be the foe of the whole existing system of society. But that is not the end of the story. It is only the beginning. We may have a Socialist Government based on a minority in the country, pledged to the overturn of every institution we have been able to build up in the course of centuries, regarding the making of profits as a crime and the rent of land and buildings and the interest of money as mere frauds upon the community: but nevertheless a well meaning Government with a lot of respectable old trade union leaders and Radical or ex-Radical politicians filling the offices of State. What guarantee have we that the Ministers, themselves the representatives of a minority, would have the control? On the contrary, we know that the policy of the Socialist Party, and even the composition and character of the Government, are not to be regulated by the Parliamentary representatives elected by the people or by the Prime Minister chosen by the Crown. These great matters will be settled by obscure people sitting in the background, whose names we do not know, whose speeches we never read, whose lives, whose characters, whose personalities are entirely obscure. All we know about them is that their ideas and their basis of power do not arise from the soil of this island. (Cheers.) They are essentially international and regulated in accordance with the international and foreign organizations. The British people have always liked to be governed for good or for ill by men they know. If a Socialist Government came into power they might have a facade of well-meaning and respectable Ministers who were moved here and there like marionettes in accordance with the decisions of a small secret international junta.

I do not fear the taunt which will be flung at me that I am alarmed and downhearted by the situation. Better be sure than sorry. Better be warned in time to take effective action which will ward off these dangers. I am deliberately ringing the alarm bell before it is too late. I wish to disperse this cursed apathy and levity with which the tremendous events of the next few months are being approached in so many quarters.

I have no doubt whatever that sooner or later we will come through all right. We will take good care that we do. We will not have this country smashed up by any sect or faction. We have only to exert ourselves to ward off these dangers. We have not travelled through 1,000 years of history and come through the awful jeopardy of the Great War in order to perish miserably on the morrow of our greatest victory. Mr. Bernard Shaw, the Socialist chatterbox (laughter), has described the effort of Great Britain in the Great War as "the last spring of the old lion." The wish is father to the thought. The old lion is not down yet. He has still the strength and teeth and claws to defend the things he cares about, and I earnestly hope that we shall not be wantonly plunged into a period of convulsion when such extraordinary efforts will be required. (Cheers.) We certainly will not be so disturbed and so distressed if every loyal and faithful anti-Socialist citizen of the country exercises his political rights and discharges his civic duty, and if we stand together in the trials of peace with the comradeship and resolution that carried us through the storms of war. (Cheers.)

PENNY POST

February 14, 1929

Treasury, London

I am bound to weigh with the utmost attention the collective opinion which all these important and varied interests [represented by a trade deputation] have expressed that this reduction in the postal rates is on the whole the most desirable step that can be taken to help the trade of the country at the present time. Of course, upon the merits of a reduction in postal rates we are all agreed. I see as fully as any of those who have spoken the advantages, and I am specially impressed by the Imperial aspect which has been brought to my notice in connexion with the reduction of the Imperial postage rates by the Dominions of Canada and New Zealand. I need scarcely say that the Postmaster-General does not stand in need of conversion upon this point. I have always hoped that the step might be taken by the Postmaster-General and myself jointly during the period in which we are responsible.

But other larger and harsher considerations have struck across our hopes and intentions, and must be weighed together with our desire. The prolonged coal stoppage, following on the general strike, inflicted a grave injury upon the finances of the Exchequer as well as upon the general industry of the country. It involved us in one way or another in a loss of not less than 80 millions during the period through which we are now passing. It greatly hampered my power to give the tax remissions which otherwise might have brightened the closing session of this Parliament; but, nevertheless, I should like to point out that we are making a most substantial and important remission of taxation in the rating relief which will begin to be paid this year. The amount of this relief will be upwards of 35 millions in a full year, and as the yield of the new petrol tax is much less than this, the difference constitutes a relief of taxation which can only be met by economy in the expenditure of the country or by the normal growth of revenue. To undertake so large a remission of taxation at a moment when we are crippled by the disasters of the industrial civil war of two years ago constitutes a very great financial effort, and leaves me in a position necessarily extremely restricted.

I am sure you would not expect me to give you any definite answer to-day: you would not wish me to give you a negative answer: neither would you expect me to anticipate the Budget statement by a positive one, even were it in my power to give one. Of course, one of two things will certainly happen. Either I shall have the money, or I shall not. Now if I do not have the money—and regard must be had to the need of properly financing the rating relief—if I do not have the money, then, of course, this boon to trade of a return to the penny postage—a much cheaper rate than existed before the War, having regard to the new value of money—could only be given if I was prepared to propose new taxation. But I am very disinclined to put on new taxes. It may not be entirely true that "An old tax is no tax," but a new tax is certainly an exceedingly burdensome business for a Chancellor of the Exchequer to carry through in the closing stages of a Parliament.

Therefore if there is no money, those who press for this reform must at the same time be prepared with definite suggestions for raising six millions of revenue, which, even after making reasonable allowance for increased traffic, would be the cost of the concession to the Exchequer. We are told, of course, that economy can produce the desired effect, and I can assure you that every effort will be made to secure economy, which will anyhow be necessary for the financing of the rating scheme. It is quite possible that, should this Government cease to be responsible after the impending General Election, you will find that the period of economy has definitely come to an end.

Immense projects for new expenditure are everywhere being put forward, and are from day to day becoming more prominent on account of the need which politicians at election times feel for obtaining the public support by promising large gifts of public money to the electorate. The air is full of schemes for much greater expenditure, and therefore it seems to me that the best hope of obtaining economies lies in wise suggestions being made during the months that lie immediately before us. We also have, according to our opponents, the prospect of very heavy new taxation—great additions to direct taxation, already higher in this country than in any other country in the world. We are told that many of the duties imposed in the present Parliament must be swept away—the silk duties, the betting tax, the McKenna duties, many of the safeguarding duties are to be swept away with a large sacrifice of revenue. That heavy loss to the revenue would be increased if six millions were struck off the Exchequer receipts through a return to penny postage.

Our future finances seem to me to be facing a most serious and critical situation, and, although we are airily assured that it is quite easy to get 60 or 70 millions a year out of the idle rich, I have yet to be given the names and addresses of a sufficient number of these people to offer the slightest prospect of obtaining the money. At any rate, I should carefully have to consider whether it would be wise in my tenure further to complicate the task of a future Government by depriving them of revenue in addition to that of which apparently they intend to deprive themselves.

But we will consider the alternative that I had the money, and that the Budget prospects were easier than I have a right to expect. In that case, I can assure you that I will most carefully balance this project against competing projects. If we were in the happy position of being able to make new remissions of taxation in addition to the remission which the rating scheme involves, I can assure you that I should give most careful consideration to all that you have said, and in particular to your expressed opinion that this would be one of the best ways of helping trade. I am not yet convinced myself on that point; I am not at all sure that if such a sum of money were available for distribution, there might not be found a more effective way of helping trade. I am not at all sure whether the £6,000,000 which would be required to return to the penny postage would be, even from the point of view of giving satisfaction to the electorate, so attractive as, for example, the repeal of the tax on tea, which would cost an approximately equal sum.

At any rate I think you will see that I am bound to await the end of the financial year and to consider at that time whether my prospects are favourable or unfavourable. If they are favourable, I must weigh most carefully all the competing projects there may be, and be sure that I act in entire consistency with the policy we have hitherto pursued of carrying the public finances forward in a sound manner from year to year, not attempting in any one year unduly to burden the future. We must not, for the sake of gaining a temporary advantage of giving a momentary pleasure, run the risk of its being said that during the lifetime of the present Parliament the finances were allowed to get into an unsound and unbalanced state.

IRISH GRANTS

February 19, 1929

House of Commons

I do not in the slightest degree differ from the account which my hon. Friend has given of the hardships which fell upon the loyalist population of Southern Ireland in consequence of the grave decisions of public policy which were taken by the House of Commons and by Great Britain. I can assure him that it is not with any lack of sympathy with those who have suffered those hardships that I approach what is undoubtedly the thankless and ungrateful task of asserting the reasonable limits of Exchequer control. Some of my hon. Friends who have participated in this Debate have sometimes made severe criticisms of the weak character of our financial control and the manner in which on every occasion when there is pressure the Government yield to the demands of the spending Departments or the the representations of those interested; and I can assure them that having repeatedly to say "No" to cases made, as they often are, as they usually are, with great force, with great plausibility, with a great appeal to the compassionate side, is a very unpleasant part of the work of anyone who has the honour to occupy the high place which I hold. It is a most unpleasant thing, but somewhere in the State, somewhere in this rather fluid organisation of our modern Government, there must reside a principle in the light of which we can say "No" when a certain point has been reached; and it is very dangerous indeed, I think, for the House, carried away by absolutely right feelings, by strong sentiments of generosity—[Hon. Members: "Justice!"]—carried away by a sincere belief that they are expressing what is just, to brush aside or wear down the constituted guardians of the public purse, to overturn the definite long-considered judgment of the Cabinet of the day, and to endeavour to extract from the public Treasury sums of money which the executive Government do not think, in broad right and equity, ought to be handed over.

Let us see how we have proceeded in this matter. In the first instance, I accept altogether the expression which has been used by my hon. Friend who spoke last. The Government have made a succession of forward jumps under pressure. That is absolutely true. It may not be a very complimentary or ceremonious way of describing what has taken place, but in my opinion it is absolutely true and accurate. More than three years ago the plea was put in that there should be a reopening of some of these cases and that there should be *ex gratia* payments in cases which would never have fallen under the ordinary laws of compensation, and naturally I said, as anyone in my position would have said, "Where is this going to stop?" But I was absolutely assured that £400,000 was the outside limit, and the only reason that that figure was not mentioned was that it was believed that if it was mentioned, there would be a tendency to make awards up to the full total of £400,000, whereas probably it would be found that a lesser sum would suffice. However, in agreeing to make *ex gratia* payments we in no way accepted an unlimited liability. Rightly or wrongly, this present Government in no way accepted an unlimited liability, and we in no way set up any tribunal or body of persons to write cheques upon the national account without limit. We said, "All right, £400,000."

Then it was found that £400,000 was not enough, and there was a strong and serious argument about that, and under further pressure we consented to make it £650,000 if my memory serves me right. [An Hon. Member: "£625,000!"] It was £625,000, and that was received with a certain amount of satisfaction and then it was found that the £625,000 was not considered enough. The Committee continued to review cases and to state what they thought was the compensation which might properly be paid, but I must point out that this Committee—I have not a word to say against their credentials or against the manner in which they have done their work— was not a judicial tribunal in any sense of the word. We, for instance, at the Treasury—I have to appear in the odious role of representing the public purse—were never heard in this matter. There was no case where the Treasury counsel could advance arguments against the claims made by the parties, and canvass and criticise their credentials, such as is done when any Income Tax case is fought in any Court with the greatest vigour.

If this were the award of a judicial tribunal, there would be nothing more to be said. We habitually entrust ourselves in financial matters to the Courts of Law, and where a matter is fought out according to law by a properly constituted tribunal, whatever the bill in that particular case may be, the British Exchequer has to honour it. This was not such a tribunal. It was not a tribunal constituted on a legal basis, where both parties to the controversy were represented. It was a tribunal which was dealing with matters admittedly outside any of the ordinary formulations of the law, and, therefore, I have said throughout, not only in the House of Commons, but privately to hon. Members who take such a great interest in this matter, and who rightly take a great interest in it, "You cannot expect the Minister responsible for the time being for the public finances to allow anybody the privilege of writing unlimited cheques upon the public account otherwise than by judicial procedure with both parties represented."

We then came to the final proposal of £1,000,000, and it was accordingly, after prolonged discussion in our conclaves, settled that the Treasury should give £1,000,000 in full and final settlement. My hon. Friend has quoted a good deal from my answer of 20th February, 1928, but there were some parts that he left out which I might perhaps read to supplement his quotations. I said:

> The Government could not bind themselves to act on the advice of the Committee, but would have in their minds a limit of expenditure beyond which they would not be prepared to go, so that, if the Committee's recommendations exceeded that amount, the Government would find it necessary to adjust the payments in each individual case accordingly.— [Official Report, 20th February, 1928; cols. 1197-8, Vol. 213.]

Then I stated that we would give £1,000,000, which was an advance from the £400,000 which we were originally assured, by those who had the cases of these people in their charge, would be sufficient. I then said:

> It remains impossible for any Government to commit itself in a matter of this kind to a liability without limits. I therefore take this opportunity of stating that an increased sum not exceeding £1,000,000 will be held available as required in satisfaction of these claims.
>
> All awards up to £1,000 will at once be paid in full. Of the excess over this figure, 60 per cent. will be advanced on account immediately. The residue of the £1,000,000 will be applied to the recommendations at the close of the Inquiry in so far as they have not been already implemented.

The House will understand the difficulty which naturally arises in reconciling a strict and fair discharge of engagements into which the State has entered with the need of protecting the Exchequer from an indefinite liability.

I should add that this decision must be taken as final so far as His Majesty's present advisers are concerned.—[Official Report, 20th February, 1928; cols. 1198-9, Vol. 213.]

Well, I really do not see what has occurred in the interval which should lead us to alter that decision and I am quite clear that if we were to take, what so far as we are individually concerned, would be most satisfactory and gratifying to us, namely, a further jump in response to pressure, we should be showing that there is no real resisting power in the administration of the Government in regard to matters about which, after prolonged examination, they have come to definite conclusions. After all, what was said by the late Colonial Secretary is quite true. The Government which has had to decide on this matter is not one that is unfriendly to hon. Members nor to the cause they have pleaded. Far from it; those concerned are among the most faithful supporters of the Government, and those for whom they speak are those who have suffered greatly in the cause with which His Majesty's Government have been as-sociated, and it is only after most prolonged consultation that we have reached our conclusion. When, the other day, we reconsidered the matter and reviewed it all again, it was only with a perfectly clear feeling that on the point of honour, on the point of justice, and on the point of a reasonable settlement and decision of these matters, we were doing what was right when we came to the conclusion that we must adhere to the perfectly plain statement we made on 20th February of last year.

Sir W. Davison: At that time, the 20th February, the right hon. Gentleman did not know that there were 1,100 more claims coming in which would have to be dealt with. These claims were only found out since then and, therefore, I submit to my right hon. Friend that it is not climbing down in any way from that decision, but that after that, unexpectedly, 1,100 more claims have come in.

Mr. Churchill: I know the date was extended to admit a further number of claims, and at the time I was assured that it was a matter that was quite negligible, but once the door is open to admit them, there flows in a flood of claims, and that finality which we had reached, on 20th February was once again interrupted. Let us just see what are the facts of the immediate issue before the Committee because I would like the Committee to have it in mind when considering the allegations of hardship and injustice. In round numbers, 4,000 claims were put in, of which 3,175 have been heard. There is still a percentage—about a quarter—unheard. 1,538 were rejected *in toto*, and 1,637 recommendations for compensation were made. Of those 1,637 recommendations for compensation, covering three-quarters of all the claims that had been put in, 1,354 have been paid in full; the whole of those 1,354, including all the smaller people, all the people whose loss was estimated at £1,000 or less, have been paid in full, and only 283 have not been paid in full. We are therefore dealing at this moment with the claims of 283 persons. It is quite possible that there may be additions to that as extra recommendations come in, but that gives the Committee an idea of the figure within which this matter is contained.

There are 283 persons who are involved in this matter and these 283 persons have already received well over £700,000—I do not know whether that is fully appreciated in all quarters of the House—and the question is whether a further sum of £300,000 or £400,000 should be made available for these same people. I am not going to argue that because a person has a large claim he should be treated unjustly, and that only a small claim should be treated justly. Right is right, and I am trying to argue the case fairly, but I have to consider very carefully in this matter the way in which the State has dealt with other classes of claimants in other spheres. These are undoubtedly people who have suffered a great injury, but who nevertheless have suffered much less severely than the people who were dealt with under the Sumner Commission in respect of war damage by air raid or bombardment. These Sumner awards, given by a Commission presided over by a Judge, were scaled down by the British Government in a marked manner in order to reduce the total allocation to a fixed amount. A person who had an award of £100,000 received only 27-3/4 per cent. A loyalist under the present arrangements would receive 60-1/2 per cent. Persons with a claim of £50,000 under the Sumner scale for war damage received 30-1/2 per cent. The loyalists under the present arrangement will receive 61 per cent. The £10,000 claims under the Sumner Commission received 33-1/4 per cent. and under the present scale the Irish loyalists will receive 64 per cent. As we get to the smaller figures they tend more to approximate. The Committee ought very carefully to consider the whole of this position. I believe on the whole that although there is great hardship—I do not deny it for a moment—these sufferers have been dealt with on a better footing than many other large and important classes of persons who suffered from enemy action and violent commotion during the period through which we have passed. I also believe that all the cruder and more primary cases of hardship have been satisfactorily dealt with, and so far as those who still have not received the full satisfaction of their claims are concerned, they have at any rate received substantial payment and are in a far better position than those who had their houses destroyed by the bombs of German aeroplanes or shells from German guns.

I have to carry out a task which is most ungrateful. It would be very much easier for me to take £300,000 or £400,000 out of the Exchequer, and everybody would be all smiles and very agreeable, but I am bound to say that the maintenance of public economy is only achieved by a number of small and disagreeable wrangles and fights, and if that process falls into desuetude and those who endeavour to maintain economy are censured for their exertions, then right down the whole line you will find weakness and collapse. I have noticed steadily in the last few years that throughout the public departments there has been a tendency to save money on the money asked for in the Estimates, which Ministers have pledged their word was essential; there has been a tendency to save money and money has been saved in substantial amounts running into millions. The same tendency is apparently developing this year, and money is being saved, although it has been voted by this House, by subsequent minor frugalities in administration. I am very much in the hands of the Committee in this matter, and I ask the Committee to consider whether they may not be injuring very much larger issues if they put undue pressure upon the Government, against their better judgment and the judgment of those responsible for the public purse, to go, in the case of these

Irish sufferers for whose distress we have the deepest sympathy, altogether beyond what has been held appropriate in the case of others whose pangs are at least as keen.

NORTHERN IRELAND
(UNEMPLOYMENT INSURANCE FUND)
February 26, 1929
House of Commons

Although my hon. Friend the Financial Secretary is in charge of this Debate I thought that I might at this moment briefly put before the Committee some of the larger issues which the Committee should have in mind. The right hon. Gentleman the Member for Colne Valley (Mr. Snowden) has made an uncommonly mild speech so far as its tone and vigour were concerned. He has nevertheless poured out in a feeble and wishy-washy stream the usual succession of violent epithets, charges of bad faith and conduct and of insults to the House of Commons—insinuations at every stage, all with plenty of venom served up cold, but with an obvious lack of any real feeling behind what he says. I venture to ask the Committee to look at this question in its broad and simple outlines. The whole principle of unemployment insurance is that it should be over the widest possible area, because now one trade is prospering and another is failing, now one part of the country is doing well, and another is a distressed area. When you have a sufficiently broad area, the misfortunes of one part of the country and of one particular industry are equated by the better conditions in another. That is the whole principle of unemployment insurance, and of all insurance. But Ulster has only two principal industries, linen and shipbuilding. Cut off by itself, the oscillations would be out of all proportion to the vital strength of this small unit of administration.

Miss Wilkinson: You should have thought of that when you divided Ireland.

Mr. Churchill: But Ulster did not ask for a separate Government to be set up in the northern corner of Ireland. On the contrary, they wished, and their only demand was, to take the rough and the smooth with Great Britain. It was against their wish and in spite of their protests that this form of government was placed upon them. They consented reluctantly, but they consented loyally in order not to block the way to the self-government which was so strongly demanded by the southern part of Ireland. I have always considered that it is the interest as well as the duty of the House of Commons to make a success of the Government in Northern Ireland. The right hon. Gentleman asked what assurance we had that the administration will be thrifty and identical with the administration here. In Ulster the administration of all public services is very frugal and stiff. No lush or lavish expenditure is there. Treasury officals who have examined the matter find that everything is sharply and clearly scrutinised in a way which hon. Gentlemen would perhaps regard as very disagreeable if it were done in detail in any Poor Law matter or unemployment insurance matter in this island.

Ulster also pays a third of the cost of any excess in the unemployment bill in Ulster. By an equalisation arrangement Britain makes good the other two-thirds of the excess; but this one-third of the excess cost of unemployment in Ulster weighs upon that small community, and upon its budget, with far greater force than ten times the amount would weigh upon our affairs.

Then the right hon. Gentleman asked: "Why should they be put in a different position in regard to the debt from what we are in this country?" They are put in exactly the same position. The whole arrangement has aimed at treating Ulster in such a way that she and her people are neither better nor worse off than the corresponding people on the other side of St. George's Channel, and I believe that object has been attained. The right hon. Gentleman asked further: "Why do you suggest that this excessive rate of unemployment will be permanent in Ulster? Are you not suggesting that unemployment is incurable, and that there will be no relief at all as years go on?" That is not the point at all. It is not that we have said that unemployment in Ulster at this high rate will be permanent. What we have said is that so small a unit of unemployment insurance as Ulster will continue to be permanently at a disadvantage compared to the wider unit which operates throughout Great Britain.

What I would like to know is, what other plan could we have adopted? We could have amalgamated the two funds. The right hon. Gentleman gave some countenance to that. The representatives of Ulster were very anxious that that should be done. They certainly asked for no more than what the right hon. Gentleman rather incautiously has admitted he would be ready to concede. That, however, would involve all sorts of difficulties in administration, and might lead to very sharp divergences between the British Government and the Ulster Government on the question of payment of benefits in particular cases, and so forth. But, under the arrangement now proposed, we have the effectual safeguard that Ulster, if her fund costs more than ours because of the extra unemployment, is subjected to one-third of the excess, and, for a country so small, that one-third is the most heavy counter-check you can have.

Now I venture to put one or two very simple points to the party opposite. Rightly or wrongly, the view we take is that these proposals put the working classes of Ulster in no better and in no worse position than their fellows across the Channel. Is Labour going to take the view that they ought to be put in a worse position? If so, in the first instance, it seems to me that it will be very short-sighted. If it were necessary to scrap or reduce the Unemployment Insurance Fund in Northern Ireland, if it were necessary to reduce the benefits or increase the contributions, or break up the fund altogether, we should undoubtedly get an influx of workpeople from Northern Ireland—I leave out of account the humanity of the matter—into those districts which are most distressed, on the Clyde or on the North-East Coast. Would that make things any better at the present time? To show how great is the burden on Northern Ireland, I would like to point out that one of our most distressed areas, the North-Eastern Division of England, with an insured population eight times as large as Northern Ireland, has a smaller percentage of unemployment at the present time. Would it really be worth our while to break up this Northern Ireland Insurance Fund, or by starving it in one way or another, or by burdening that small Government with loans, piling up year after year, to promote a process which undoubtedly would lead to an influx of workers from there into the very industries and the very parts of our country which at the present time are most distressed? I shall be very much surprised if, on reflection, hon. Members opposite would like to identify themselves with such a course.

The other day I read some unfeeling paragraphs in the "Daily Herald":

> Doubtless the Belfast Government, faced with the bankruptcy of the Unemployment Insurance Fund, and unwilling to tap the pockets of its own people, would gladly have got over the difficulty by the simple expedient of increasing the workmen's contributions, or reducing their benefit or scrapping the fund altogether.

But why should we contemplate such matters? These people have just as hard a struggle to get their living as any others, and why should they be worse off than any other of His Majesty's subjects who are represented in this House? I am certain the Labour party will make a very great mistake if they allow the prejudice they feel against the Ulster Government to lead them into taking a wrong line on what is essentially a Labour matter. Just because the right hon. Member for Colne Valley has always had a dislike of the Ulstermen and been very much against them politically, why should the Labour party as a whole take up a position against that working-class population, strike at that working-class population and try to make out that it is in an invidious position compared with others of the same class? What is this we have heard of the solidarity of labour, "Workers of the world unite," and all that sort of thing? The right hon. Gentleman says: "Workers of the world unite—but, as far as these Ulster people are concerned, I have got a down upon them." Then the right hon. Gentleman asks: "Why do you bring this Measure forward when the existing Act does not expire till 1930?" Has not his speech been a very complete answer to that question? [*Interruption.*] We need not go "butting at" each other across the Floor of the House as to who is going to win the next General Election, that rests upon processes which are not yet determined, but this small community in Northern Ireland know that if by any chance—or any mischance—the right hon. Gentleman was responsible for settling this question, they would not get fair treatment. They know that he would be very eager to give them a kick, that he would be extremely glad to see them come a cropper, and that in his malice against the Ulster Government he would not be restrained by any consideration for the working people in that area. I have had a great deal to do with these Irish matters and I feel no relish or enjoyment in that recollection. Each of the parties in this House has got its Irish pet and each has got its Irish bugbear, and people are more inclined to look with severity upon the interests of those they dislike than to ensure fair and impartial administration. As far as I am concerned, I claim to be impartial.

Only last week I was being scarified for taking a particular view upon an Irish matter—to which I still adhere—though I submit to the view of the House. [*Interruption.*] Hon. Members will have to wait no longer than to-morrow to hear me give an answer on the subject of Irish silver coinage affecting the Irish Free State which, I have not the slightest doubt, will bring upon me the reproaches of some of my hon. Friends who represent Ulster. So we are getting it from both sides. But I have been very earnestly desirous that in the settlement of all these Irish matters I should treat both the Governments of Northern Ireland and of Southern Ireland in such a manner as to make for the success of their affairs and to give them the power of continuous life; and further to enable them to deal with the very grievous problems which have been thrust upon them, and cordially to maintain steady contact with the central Government here in relations animated by goodwill. It is not in the least a desire to favour now this one and now that one which has animated me, but a desire that we should make a success of the problems of both these Irish Governments; and in this case, which is one of asking for no more than bare equality, and in which, as I am led to understand by the most critical examination of these proposals, they are getting no more than bare equality in a matter affecting the vital interests of 250,000 working people—in such a matter I do say that if ever there was an occasion on which we should be animated by a generous desire to help one of these Irish Governments, it is this, and the Resolution, proposed by my hon. Friend, constitutes an opportunity for the House of Commons to testify its opinion.

FINANCIAL QUESTIONS

March 5, 1929

Treasury, London

I am very much obliged to you [a deputation from the Association of British Chambers of Commerce] for coming to see me. I dealt with the penny postage when I received a deputation which was headed by some of my friends in the House of Commons and which was very widely representative, and I can epitomize in a few sentences what I said to them. It is, of course, desirable that we should get back to the penny postage, which would, I may say, be a definitely cheaper rate of carrying letters than before the War, having regard to the value of money, but the cost of making that change can only be considered in relation to the state of public finance as a whole, and at the present time the financial position for the future year is not yet fully known to me.

With regard to the obsolescence of plant and machinery, I am interested in the point you make, and if the association likes to discuss this matter with the Board of Inland Revenue, basing themselves on the recommendations made by the Royal Commission on the depreciation of plant and machinery and buildings as a whole, I will arrange for your representatives to be put in touch with the officers of that Department. They will be able to go into it in full detail on either side.

The next point relates to wasting assets. This subject is extremely difficult and complicated and contentious, and I cannot contemplate legislation upon it except after full discussion with all the interests concerned and with an ample field of Parliamentary time. We meet this year under conditions when undoubtedly great uncertainty pervades all our arrangements, and Parliamentary time is certain to be curtailed in view of the General Election. I cannot feel that I should be well advised in including in a Finance Bill this year the extremely complicated clauses necessary to deal with this subject. You will, no doubt, renew your request in a future year. The same really applies to what you have said about removal expenses. I should be glad if you would discuss that with the Inland Revenue, but at the same time I must have regard to the character of the finance legislation this year, and I cannot think this is an occasion for the Finance Bill to be loaded with a variety of very complicated provisions to rectify what are minor defects, if they be defects, in our present law.

With regard to the cooperative societies, an investigation is going forward of what would be the gain to the Exchequer which would result from the cooperative societies being charged to income-tax in the same way as private traders. The investigation has not gone far enough for us to know what conclusion to draw, but it looks, as far as one can see, as if the amount will be probably somewhat larger than the previous estimate of £100,000, but not so much larger as to invalidate the argument which was founded upon that estimate.

With regard to the codification of the Income-tax Law, I think I should be going a little outside the bounds of precedent in the relations between the Treasury and the Chambers of Commerce if I undertook to submit these recommendations, when they are ultimately received, to your body. They affect other bodies and classes just as much as they do you, and I think it would be better that we should simply say that ample time will be afforded for all associations representing the taxpayers to express their views on any such Bill embodying this codification before it is proceeded with in Parliament. I have no doubt you would have an opportunity of making your comments at that time. I should prefer not to suggest anything in the nature of an exclusive discussion upon that matter.

On the general state of affairs I have only this to say, that at the present time I am not informed as to what the out-turn of the current year will be. We started the calendar year in January, as usual, with a very heavy deficit. I think over £130,000,000, due to the fact, of course, that expenditure flows out evenly over the whole year, but the great bulk of the revenue comes in in the last quarter. That deficit has already been reduced by £100,000,000 and is now only just over £30,000,000, with three and a half weeks still to go. Naturally I shall not attempt to make any predictions as to how this three and a half weeks will turn out. Needless to say, I cannot make you partners either of my hopes or of my fears as to the outcome. We are engaged at the present time in surveying the samples of the estimated profits for 1928, on which the forecast of the yield of the income-tax for next year is based. These samples number many thousands, and it is on them that the extremely accurate forecasts are based. The samples have been received and are being examined, but it will not be for another fortnight that I shall have the results, and when I finally get them, I shall, in accordance with the invariable custom, keep them strictly to myself for the time being. But, broadly speaking, I must say I have a feeling—perhaps it is due to a sanguine temperament, but I have a feeling—that things would not go so badly for us in the sphere of trade and industry, and, of course, finance follows upon the state of trade and industry, things would not go so badly for us in the next year or two, as they have done in the past, provided no violent dislocation and disturbance occurs in our affairs.

In recent years we have had these disturbances too frequently. First of all there was the War requiring a whole generation of patient work to repair its damage. Then in the days of the Coalition Government very serious industrial troubles arose. Moreover, there were the painful steps which we had to take for bringing our finances into order and for putting a stop to the great expansion of credit during the War. Then perhaps things were beginning to get a little better by the year 1922, when we drifted into a period of three General Elections in two years. Every General Election leads to all kinds of promises being made by candidates anxious to get into Parliament, who answer all the questions which are put to them in the sense which they think is likely to win them favour and votes, and do not hesitate to commit themselves to projects of all kinds which afterwards have to be paid for. I should not be surprised if those three General Elections together added 40 or 50 millions to the permanent expense of the Government of the country.

Then this period of political confusion was terminated in 1924 by the return of the present Administration with a very large majority and an assured prospect of living its full term, but when we had been only a year and a half in office there occurred the general strike and the prolonged coal stoppage. These have really taken away from me the power to make remissions of taxation to every class which undoubtedly might have been expected during my tenure. We have, of course, reduced the income-tax, and we have also made large concessions to the smaller classes of income-tax payer. We have made a reduction of the sugar duty which has reached the consumer, and I have, of course, maintained all the large reductions which were made by my predecessor in the indirect sphere. And all this in the face of a great disturbance which cost the Exchequer some £80,000,000. It has been a matter of great difficulty to me to do what I shall probably succeed in doing—namely, to liquidate the disasters of the general strike and coal stoppage without any addition to the taxes upon necessaries or to the direct taxation of the country. People do not regard that achievement with very great enthusiasm, but it is, at any rate, a substantial achievement.

However, since those events there has been a period of industrial peace without equal in our records. Every one has pulled together, and, capital and labour being in much closer accord than they have been for a great many years, as might be expected, there are signs of recovery, especially in those heavy industries which have been such a deep cause of anxiety. But now another period of uncertainty seems to be in store for us, and the results of patience and toil and cooperation may well be put back again. These considerations must be present to our minds, but, so far as the Government is concerned, the greatest contribution we can make to the further revival of the country and its trade and industry is to hold steadily on along the well-proved lines of British free enterprise and sound finance, which have been the result of generations of experience in this country, and which, in my opinion, are not likely to be bettered by innumerable kinds of novel and unhappy expedients and bright ideas which might conceivably be the result of the General Election.

As a specific contribution to that revival, we are carrying into effect this year the derating scheme to which you have alluded, Mr. Mitchell, with approval, which undoubtedly constitutes a relief of £35,000,000 of most invidious and onerous taxation—namely, the taxation of productive industry. It is the parting gift which the

Exchequer has been able to confer, in spite of the blows which have been struck at it by the misfortunes to which I have referred. Deducting from the £35,000,000 the yield of the oil duty, you will see that there is a margin of something like £20,000,000. This will have to be made up by growth of revenue, or by further economics in expenditure.

This is the task which lies before us in the future, but the differences between those two, the oil duty and the relief of £35,000,000, constitutes a net remission of taxation and, as I said, of the most burdensome and onerous form of taxation. As to economy, I agree with you that it must be sedulously persisted in. Every one knows that the automatic increases under Acts of Parliament and otherwise, are inevitable, but with those automatic increases to the reductions which we have been able to make on the armaments side of our expenditure and elsewhere. Small as they may appear, they have been achieved by painstaking processes. With those reductions, we have, at any rate, arrested the increase of expenditure which otherwise would have occurred automatically. Whether the events which lie immediately before us are going to be favourable to public economy or not, I can only leave you to judge, but in thanking you very much for coming here to see me to-day I should like to express the confident opinion that, however unsatisfactory our efforts at economy may be thought, we are the most economical Administration that you are likely to see.

Mr. Mitchell: Just two small points, if I may mention them. Of course, we shall be very glad to have the opportunity of discussing with these eminent gentlemen the question of obsolescence and wasting assets, and we will take the opportunity of doing so. As regards the codification of the income-tax, we do not ask for exclusive discussion. We only suggested that it might be published.

Mr. Churchill: It will be; that is the intention.

Mr. Mitchell: Even before the draft Bill; a White Paper in some form.

Mr. Churchill: The question will not arise for quite two years.

Mr. Mitchell: We put it before you for consideration. I am sure we are all very glad to hear you speak in a somewhat optimistic frame, and we hope that the General Election will not have the further unfortunate result of—

Mr. Churchill: Leading to disturbance.

Mr. Mitchell: Leading to disturbance and increased expenses. We hope that the members of Parliament who are standing will not make undue promises which should not be fulfilled.

MOTOR TAXATION AND ROADS

March 7, 1929

Treasury, London

It would not have been easy, I think, for a better statement to have been prepared than that which Sir George Beharrell [spokesman for a motor trade deputation] has just made, and I am very much obliged to you and to him for the pains which have been taken to reduce this difficult topic to broad and simple terms, and for the conciseness with which your case has been expressed. But I cannot feel at all that the picture of gloom and oppression which Sir George has drawn really corresponds to the facts. I am speaking for the moment of the non-commercial vehicles. The users of the non-commercial motor vehicles in this country are, upon the whole, the most fortunate among his Majesty's subjects in every class. They enjoy the immense privilege, convenience and pleasure of this new form of rapid locomotion. I sometimes wonder whether they always realize that the great majority of people in the country do not enjoy these advantages. On the contrary, they find themselves exposed to new disturbances and even to dangers, dangers which last year involved 5,000 deaths and 140,000 non-fatal casualties, that is to say losses equal to those of one of the most famous battles of the 18th century: I sometimes wonder whether the motorist realizes how great are his advantages or that those who do not enjoy them do not always feel entirely contented with their experiences.

I certainly have had many representations made to me of an exactly opposite character to those to which I have listened this morning. I am a motorist myself. Like you I enjoy these conveniences and pleasures, but I certainly feel that it is just to say that so far as the non-commercial vehicles are concerned, you have come here and spoken on behalf of what is, on the whole, the most buoyant section of our vast national community.

Even more remarkable is the position of the motor manufacturers. Their position seems to be one of singular privilege and advantage. They enjoy a very large protective duty, 33-1/3 per cent., against foreign competition; they have also gained very considerable advantages in the home market in regard to certain classes of vehicles in consequence of the incidence of the horsepower tax, which affects prejudicially certain types of foreign cars which otherwise would have been formidable competitors. Moreover, they enjoy these advantages in a Free Trade country where they have the opportunity of purchasing all their requirements for manufacture at Free Trade prices. To those advantages and privileges, which contrast favourably with those of other manufacturers, they have added those of enterprise, great business and inventive skill, and ever improving organization.

It certainly astonishes me to hear that, in spite of these advantages, which so few trades in this country at present share, there should be these serious complaints and that we should be told that the export trade is falling off and, generally speaking, that the motor trade is in a very hard-pressed condition. I certainly cannot entirely, or even substantially, accept the picture which Sir George Beharrel has drawn. On the contrary, great help has been given to the motor manufacturers by the duties which we have imposed, and it certainly would be very discouraging if it could be proved that the British motor trade, even with all these advantages, is not in a vigorous and active condition. But I am sure that it cannot be proved.

How different is the picture which I see when I look at my own position as Chancellor of the Exchequer. During the last five years a series of blows has greatly crippled the power of the Chancellor of the Exchequer to discharge his duties and has enormously reduced his power of alleviating burdens. The general strike followed by the prolonged coal stoppage, cost the Exchequer some £80,000,000, and that alone has placed me in a position of extreme difficulty. I have felt it absolutely necessary to make an effort to revive our basic productive industries, in which unemployment was so rife, by securing to them a relief from the burden of rates. This has involved the imposition of a duty on petrol. It has also led to an ultimate liability to the State considerably greater in amount than the yield of the petrol duty. The gap of about £20,000,000 has to be filled by the normal growth of the revenue and by economies in administration. Thus I am engaged on behalf of his Majesty's Government in making a great new remission of taxation to the producers of this country, and of the most onerous form of taxation, at a time when owing to the general strike and the coal stoppage the finances have been greatly strained.

It is not pleasant to raise taxes; nothing would give me greater pleasure than to be able to make large tax remissions. During this week I have received a succession of deputations, but none of them has impressed me with the feeling of strength and prosperity and buoyancy which the powerful interests you represent have done. You talk to me of the heavy burden of taxation on the motor trade. Is there not a burden of taxation on other trade? Is there not a burden of taxation upon the income-tax payer? Great appeals are made to me to repeal taxes. Deputations have urged the restoration of the penny post. From every quarter these appeals are made, backed with most careful arguments. In some cases they are able to show how their industry is actually declining.

But when I survey the field of motor taxation and the motor trade, I certainly cannot see those signs, and I am thankful indeed that I cannot, of failure which are evident in some other quarters. I have to balance the national accounts, and if remissions are given in one direction the money must be found in some other way. Unless the normal revenues of the country are expanding through great prosperity, there is no means of making remissions except by finding substitutes. It is a question of balancing one set of evils against another. All taxation is evil, and I have to do the best I can to find the least injurious method for the whole country of solving the problems which in an iron ring surround whoever sits in this chair.

There is another balance. The case which the railways would be able to make as to their burdens of rates and as to the effects of the competition of motor transport, would certainly involve pointing out how much more serious is their condition than yours. I have to try as far as possible to hold the balance evenly and fairly between the two.

I do not know yet whether any remissions of taxation will be in my power. But even if remissions were within my power, I should have to weigh your claims against for example, the claims of the indirect taxpayer in respect of taxes on the prime comforts of life, against the claims of the smaller class of income-taxpayer or those of the income-taxpayers as a whole, and if there were a question of making remissions there is a great deal to be said for these various alternative forms of remission. But there is one which we are already making, namely, the relief of rates on productive industry. We must see that the finance of this relief is not endangered.

In these circumstances I cannot at all hold out the expectation of large reductions in motor taxation, and, while I do not at all attempt to forecast what form the Budget will take, I certainly would not wish this morning to arouse false hopes in your breasts. We have all got to face the facts by which we are encircled, and I am sure you would not thank me for encouraging hopes which were not fulfilled.

With regard to the paper which you have handed in showing the cost of the roads over a series of years, I understand you to draw from this the conclusion that motorists pay, and more than pay, in licence duty and petrol duty for the upkeep of the roads they use. This paper I will have examined carefully, but I may say that my advisers traverse the suggestion that this conclusion is a logical outcome of the figures you have given. However, I have no doubt that the Minister of Transport will be quite ready to let his officers discuss the matter with you and also the other figures and comparisons which you have made.

There are probably in your minds certain minor technical questions which you would like to discuss, apart from the general question of the reduction of motor taxation, and opportunity could be taken at the same time to raise these points. Any recommendations which may emerge from these discussions I will promise to consider very carefully, and of course I will examine any additional figures you may furnish in regard to the general weight of taxation, but I should not be doing my duty if I allowed you to expect any substantial remission at the present time.

There is one other matter which you have raised, namely, the further development of the roads. An immense amount has been, and is being, done. I see that in the year when the present Government took office £15,000,000 were paid out of the Road Fund for expenditure upon the roads. The forecast for next year is nearly £23,000,000—a very large increase. We have, I believe, in this country the best roads in Europe. We are spending a great deal more than any of the European countries upon road development, and the complaints of Local Authorities about the burdens thrown on them by motor traffic are at least as loud as any I have heard from motor owners on account of the burden of taxation.

But I am not at all enamoured myself of the idea that unemployment can be sensibly mitigated, still less cured by a great expenditure on roads out of borrowed money, and I believe that widespread delusion exists upon this subject. If the money is to be borrowed without inflation, it can only be taken from the market in competition with all other new enterprises. The same money would be spent, but it would be spent through the hands of the Government, and not utilized by private enterprise. It is difficult, I think, to believe that money spent in a hurried, hasty development of the roads would be better spent than it is now spent by private enterprise in the development of industry. The effects upon unemployment generally of a large policy of road construction would, I am advised, not be appreciable, for the funds for employing labour on the roads would be diverted from other purposes.

Even if there were a large surplus accumulated in a fund like the Road Fund, the problem would not be solved except in a budgetary sense. Such a fund is kept in the form of Treasury Bills, and before those Treasury Bills can be converted into men at work they have to be sold, and they have to be bought by someone who pays for them money which otherwise would be used for some other purpose. If, of course, it were intended to provide by inflation the money for a great programme of public works for unemployment relief, then another set of disasters would come upon us very quickly, and we should go through the grim experiences from which the world is only now escaping. But do not suppose that we are not pursuing a most active policy of road development. Immense sums are being found. The growth of the Road Fund year by year is available for the roads, and the Minister of Transport can show a very great development of the roads for which he has been responsible. That development will continue on an ever-increasing scale.

I end where I began by expressing my obligations to you for the manner in which your case has been presented. I have not thought it right to encourage you to suppose that any large change is possible in the present scales of taxation at the expense of the Exchequer at the present time. In view of what we have gone through and of our efforts to relieve productive industry from the burden of rates, I think you will agree that the problem with which I am confronted is one which leaves me very little latitude. I shall, of course, give the fullest weight to what you have said, and you may be sure that it is certainly not with any desire to disappoint you that I have approached this matter. If I have any power to remit taxes, I must make up my mind as to the forms of taxation which have the strongest claims. And if this turns out to be possible, I do not in any way prejudge the decisions which will ultimately be reached. I thank you very much.

ANGLO-EGYPTIAN FINANCIAL AGREEMENT

March 21, 1929

House of Commons

With your permission, Mr. Speaker, and the indulgence of the House, as this to some extent affects the course of affairs outside, I should like to be able to make a short statement on the subject of the arrangement reached between the British and Egyptian Governments.

I am glad to say that the Egyptian Government have now ratified the financial agreement which was arrived at last month, for the settlement of the financial questions outstanding between the British and Egyptian Governments, and in particular that of Egypt's liability for the Ottoman Guaranteed Loan of 1855.

The terms of the agreement will be presented as soon as possible but it may be useful if I summarise the main provisions in a few words. As regards the 1855 Loan, the Egyptian Government agree to pay the arrears of the Egyptian contribution to the service of this loan which have been withheld since 1924, amounting to £328,600. They also undertake to pay to His Majesty's Government the amount required to cover the service and redemption in future of a share of the loan, which has been agreed at £1,386,000. This liability will be discharged by an immediate cash payment of £302,000 and by 16 annual payments of approximately £90,000 each. In return for these payments His Majesty's Government give Egypt a full and final discharge from all claims in respect of this loan. As regards other matters, the Egyptian Government agree to make a payment of £849,000 in settlement of certain outstanding war claims of the War Office and Shipping Liquidation Departments.

On the other hand, His Majesty's Government for their part undertake to grant Egypt a share (amounting to .464 of 1 per cent.) of British Empire Reparation receipts. The amounts due under this head will be set off against the liability of Egypt for the 1855 Loan, Egypt receiving any surplus and paying over any deficiency: but, provided the German payments continue on the scale of the Dawes annuities, the Egyptian liability for the 1855 Loan should be fully covered by their receipts in respect of reparation.

I have thus summarised the general arrangements. But in view of the reports which have appeared in the Press I feel that I should make clear the position as regards the redemption of the 1855 Loan. His Majesty's Government are not, strictly speaking, under any legal obligation to redeem this loan, nor does the arrangement with Egypt impose on us any such obligation. But we have in the past applied the surplus of the so-called Cyprus Tribute, over and above the amounts required for the service of the loan, to the purchase of bonds and we have by this means acquired altogether £642,400 of the loan, as the nucleus of a sinking fund. During the discussions with the Egyptian Government, it was agreed that these bonds should not be taken into account in calculating the Egyptian share of liability for the loan and we now propose to cancel them.

Further we propose that, in future, the surplus of the payments made both by Egypt and by Cyprus, over and above the amounts required for the service of the outstanding portion of the loan should be applied by the Treasury from time to time either to the purchase of bonds of the loan in the market, if they can be obtained at a reasonable price—in which case those bonds would be cancelled—or to the purchase of British Government securities which would, in that case, be accumulated as a Sinking Fund till the whole of the outstanding loan could be redeemed, after notice, at par. It is estimated that the period required for this purpose will be between 30 and 40 years.

The agreement made represents concessions both on the part of His Majesty's Government and of the Egyptian Government, but I am sure that the House will welcome this settlement of these long outstanding questions between the Egyptian Government and ourselves.

THE BUDGET

April 15, 1929

House of Commons

It is appropriate at this stage to record the comment of The Annual Register *for 1929: "Mr. Churchill had proved himself the most able debater in the party, if not in the House, but as a financier his success had been questionable." Other comments were less charitable, and they have been subsequently endorsed by most historians. But his cooperation with Neville Chamberlain in social reforms—notably for Widows' Pensions—should not be forgotten. Fiascoes such as the Betting Tax—which was virtually abandoned in 1929—and errors such as the Silk Tax were of less importance than the absence of strategy behind Churchill's budgets, which resulted, as his official private secretary, P. J. (later Sir James) Grigg subsequently wrote, in the situation whereby "he was therefore reduced to all sorts of shifts and expedients." Not known at the time was his insistence on the formal establishment of the principle that the Service Estimates should be framed on the supposition that the Empire would not be involved in a major war for ten years. The "ten-year rule" was to have unfortunate—indeed tragic—results, and was to compromise Churchill's own position when he began to call for rearmament in the 1930s.*

The financial year which has just closed resembles its predecessor in various ways. Again, the failure of beer was repaired by the harvest of death. Again, substantial supplementary charges were more than made good by savings from the current Estimates and, once again, the realised surplus exceeded both Estimates and expectations.

Review of Past Five Years

It is usual, in opening the Budget, to compare the current year with the last, but on this occasion, in presenting a fifth Budget, at the close of a Parliament, I feel entitled to look back over the whole period for which we have been responsible. It has been a chequered story. The difficulties have been more prominent than the good fortune. The immense industrial disaster of 1926 has cut a deep gash across the statistical record of our national life. I thought at one time, and I so informed the House of Commons three years ago, that the finances of the Parliament would have been completely ruined by a loss to the Exchequer, which, including the coal subsidy of 1925, was certainly not less than £80,000,000. However, on a review of the past five years, I must admit that matters have worked out a good deal better than I hoped or expected. [An Hon. Member: "Or deserved."] No one has more interest in things going well than the Government of the day and the Minister responsible for the finances of the country. In spite of the injury to every form of national life by the follies of 1926 we have realised a respectable and, as I shall show, a solid surplus in the year that has closed. The material prosperity of this country, whether judged by the condition of its finances, by the volume of its trade or by the saving and consuming power of its people, has maintained a steady advance. For more than two years now we have enjoyed a lucid interval without a general strike or a period of general elections, or a general war. That is the longest lucid interval that I can remember since 1914. Two years' recuperation is quite a long time for this country to allow itself between its ordeals, and, naturally, after two years of peace and quiet there must be a sensible improvement in the general situation.

I will give the Committee a few facts and figures. During the present Parliament the savings of the smallest class of investors, measured by the Post Office Savings Bank, the National Savings Certificates, Building and Provident Societies, and other thrift agencies, have increased by £170,000,000. New purchases of Savings Certificates, which were £31,650,000 in 1926 and £36,000,000 in 1927, have risen under the chairmanship of my right hon. Friend Major-General Seely to £40,850,000 in 1928. The number of persons employed in the insured trades has gone up by 591,000. The cost of living, according to the latest figures, which I only received at the end of last week, has declined by 18 points at least, while money wages over the whole country are almost exactly at the level of 1924. There has been a notable decline in the consumption of alcoholic liquor, accompanied by a progressive diminution in drunkenness. The consumption of working-class indulgences has shown an increase generally, though it is naturally much more marked in the southern parts of the island. Motor bicycles, silk garments, popular amusements, excursions by train and char-a-banc, have all shown a moderate, steady increase, and this in spite of the shocking injuries we have inflicted upon ourselves in the course of the period I am reviewing. But the symptom upon which I dwell with more confidence than any other as indicating the general position of the masses of the people is the increased consumption of tea and sugar. In the palmy days before the great War, the British people consumed each year per head 6.55 lbs. of tea and 81 lbs. of sugar. Last year, after all that had happened at home and abroad, they consumed per head 9.15 lbs. of tea and 90 lbs. of sugar. That is the record consumption of these commodities. The breakfast table duties are the traditional Gladstonian indices of the condition of the wage-earning masses, particularly of the unorganised masses, and especially of the poor. Under all the froth of our turbulent party fights and in spite of all our common faults and shortcomings, it is at any rate satisfactory to note this steady and marked improvement in such an important feature.

Coming now to the commercial sphere. The balance of trade has sensibly improved, and the power of this community to invest capital abroad, thus fostering our export trade, has risen from £86,000,000 in 1924 to £149,000,000 in 1928. New capital issues for home investment in 1928 show a growth of about £100,000,000 over those of 1924. Municipal and industrial issues in the United Kingdom have risen from £70,000,000 in 1924 to £180,000,000 in 1928. Bankers' deposits have risen by £140,000,000, or about 8 per cent. Five hundred million more letters were written and 700,000 more motor vehicles used last year than in 1924. To sum up, whatever may be the fortune of particular industries or particular localities, there is no doubt that we all dwell to-day in a more powerful, more wealthy, more securely founded, and more numerous community than five years ago. There is no doubt that we are steadily improving our own conditions, and that compared with most European countries we are maintaining our old pre-War level. Of course, our progress during these years has been relatively far outstripped by the United States of America, which gained great advantages in the War and has displayed a far higher stability of purpose ever since.

I almost hesitate to mention to the Committee the subject of public economy. We are assured on all sides that the only way to gain the approval of the modern electorate is to spend money as fast as possible and on an enormous scale. The two Opposition parties vie with one another in promises of vast expenditure; the only difference between them is that the Labour party would get the money by taxation and the Liberal party would get it by borrowing. A Surtax of 2s. in the £ levied on investment incomes in excess of £500 a year would, if nothing disappointing happened in the collection, produce £65,000,000 a year provided it was levied on the reserves and investment incomes of companies as well as on the investment incomes of individuals. Such a sum would only be obtained at the cost of a very sharp setback to every index of national prosperity. But the right hon. Gentleman the Leader of the Opposition has already distributed the £65,000,000 at least four times over. The Surtax, originally proposed for the reduction of the National Debt, is now to pay for the free breakfast table, for the replacement of all the McKenna, silk, luxury, safeguarding and key industry duties, as well as for the £200,000,000 or £300,000,000 of the Socialist social programme. I must observe that in this field, at any rate, there will be disillusionment—and disillusionment in our own time.

The Liberal opposition would proceed to capture the great heart of the people by borrowing. The right hon. Member for Carnarvon Boroughs (Mr. Lloyd George) proposes to borrow £200,000,000, and to spend it on roads and telephones in order to cure unemployment. Borrowing, if your credit has been carefully looked after, is often feasible, and it is always an easy way of avoiding disagreeable things like work and self-denial. It saves a lot of trouble. Instead of having to earn the money and save the money, you just go and borrow. What a lucky thing that in this crisis of our fortunes such a brilliant idea should have struck the right hon. Gentleman! Spending money, borrowed or otherwise, while it lasts is always good fun. There must be many hon. Members who from their personal observation or even experience can confirm that view.

Accordingly, the right hon. Member for Carnarvon Boroughs is going to borrow £200,000,000 and to spend it upon paying the unemployed to make racing tracks for well-to-do motorists to make the ordinary pedestrian skip; and we are assured that the mere prospect of this has entirely revivified the Liberal party. At any rate, it has brought one notable recruit. Lord Rothermere, chief author of the anti-waste campaign, has enlisted under the Happy Warrior of Squandermania. The detailed methods of spending the money have not yet been fully thought out, but we are assured on the highest authority that if only enough resource and energy are used there will be no difficulty in getting rid of the stuff. This is the policy which used to be stigmatised by the late Mr. Thomas Gibson Bowles as the policy of buying a biscuit early in the morning and walking about all day looking for a dog to give it to. At any rate, after this, no one will ever accuse the right hon. Gentleman of cheap electioneering.

Economy

I am afraid that after these spacious figures, running into hundreds of millions, the Committee will be ill-inclined to follow with much interest the modest savings we have been able to effect in the course of last year and in the lifetime of this Parliament. Nevertheless, in presenting the public balance-sheet it is my duty to draw attention to them. Our greatest economy in this Parliament has been upon armaments. The Navy, the Army, the Air Force, including the Middle East, which was not included in the military Estimates for 1924, have yielded savings of over £7,500,000 compared with the year of the Labour Government. The Navy had a specially difficult task because the Labour Government, quite rightly in my opinion, laid down five cruisers, which cost Lord Chelmsford's Estimates only £1,500,000, but cost the Estimates of my right hon. Friend the present First Lord nearly £10,000,000. I certainly expected, and I stated so four years ago, a figure for Navy Estimates substantially larger than we have now, and I think that great credit is due to the First Lord of the Admiralty and to the Board of Admiralty for the way in which they have managed to provide for the heavy cost of an increase in the new construction vote, not only without appreciable addition to the Socialist Estimates, but, if you take the increase of the non-effective charges and the transference of the Fleet air arm from Air to Navy Votes into consideration, with an actual diminution of £1,750,000 a year. This represents five years of careful and resolute work which is naturally much against the grain to naval men. But I admire them for the persistency with which they have carried it out.

The Army has been administered by the Secretary of State for War with progressive and increasing frugality. Every single year he has effected further reductions. When he first went to the War Office, in 1921, the Estimates, in the dying momentum of the War, were £80,000,000. When, at the beginning of this Parliament, he went there they were £45,000,000. They are now £40,500,000, and the later diminution has been achieved, not only without loss of efficiency, but in spite of the serious necessary new expenditure on what is called mechanisation.

It was, and I believe it still is, common ground that the Air Force should be expanded into some reasonable defensive relation with those of our Continental neighbours, and programmes were approved six years ago which would have carried the expense of the Air Force in the ordinary course to £21,000,000 this year. The actual expenditure is £16,000,000. It is mainly through the agency of the Air Force and the thrifty genius of Sir Hugh Trenchard that my right hon. Friend the Secretary of State for Air has been able to bring the cost of the Middle East, which before the Cairo Conference of 1921 was £44,500,000 a year, down to just over £500,000 a year at the present time, and to effect a reduction, within the lifetime of the present Parliament, of £4,250,000 a year. In all, the reductions made by the present Government under these four heads—that is, the three fighting services and the Middle East—aggregate over £7,500,000 a year. I hope the Committee will excuse me for mentioning such a trifle, in view of the megalomaniac projects of expenditure which we are told are now so popular.

I turn to the Civil Supply Services. The steady growth of expenditure on the Civil Supply Services existing in 1924, notably housing, health and education, has added £11,500,000 to the public burdens. Old Age Pensions, partly as a result of our legislation and partly by the automatic growth occurring as the result of previous legislation, have increased by £10,500,000. In addition, we are providing in the present year for several services which were not in existence in 1924—Widows' Pensions, beet sugar, schemes for the training of transference of unemployed, additional expenditure on agriculture—amounting in all to £8,500,000, or a total increase of Civil Supply Expenditure from all these causes of £30,500,000. This increase has been partly offset by automatic reductions, chiefly in War pensions through the dying-off of War pensioners and the re-marriage of War widows. This offset amounts to £18,500,000, leaving a net increase of £12,000,000. But I ask the Committee to note—and I ask them to give due credit to this achievement—that by savings elsewhere, year by year and month by month, effected in small sums over wide areas and prolonged periods, His Majesty's Government have been able to show, instead of an increase of £12,000,000 as compared with 1924, an actual decrease on Civil Supply of £5,500,000. It has been able to show that decrease for services which are appreciably larger, more comprehensive, more varied and rendered to a population which is greater by nearly 1,000,000 souls.

In the year just closed I have been able to repeat the salutary process which I started three years ago of a second scrutiny of the spending Departments after the Estimates have been approved by the Cabinet and by Parliament. I took no money in the last Budget for the extra troops in China. I have had to face £3,500,000 worth of Supplementary Estimates—acceleration of the freight relief, £1,000,000; extra Old Age Pensions, £559,000; transference and training of unemployed, £466,000; contribution to the Lord Mayor's Fund, £857,000, and that act of generosity towards the sufferers from Irish injuries on which the House resolved, £385,000, or a total of £3,500,000 odd. But, notwithstanding all this, the actual expenditure on Supply Services is less than the original Budget provision by £2,600,000, entirely through economies of over £6,000,000 effected during the year, by day by day administration, after the Estimates had been passed.

Before leaving this question of economy, may I say that, in my judgment, there is no room for large cuts in the social services. Large cuts in armaments are dependent upon international agreements which, I fear, will not be as easy to reach as we would all hope, and, even so, we are limited by the absolute requirements of the safety of this island and of the community of the British Empire. A process of continued refinement and reduction can and should and must go on, but we cannot break up our social services around which the life of the people has so largely been built. We cannot make any large reductions in the Navy without falling below the one-Power standard, which, in my opinion, would be a fatal decision, or without jeopardising our food and trade routes. We cannot further reduce the police force which we call our Army without failing to retain the Cardwell system of linked battalions upon which depends the whole economy of the garrisons which we have to keep in India and elsewhere overseas. We cannot arrest the development of the Air Force without placing ourselves largely at the mercy of that very neighbour, for subservience towards whom we are repeatedly reproached, and whom the right hon. Gentleman the Member for Carnarvon Boroughs is never too busy to offend.

Gold Standard and Cost of Living

I will now, if the Committee will allow me, come to the question of the gold standard and the cost of living. Everyone knows, or pretends to know, the arguments for and against the gold standard. No one has ever denied that it carried with it privations as well as rewards. My hope and faith is that the privations are minor and temporary and that the rewards will be major and permanent. Everyone knows, for instance, that the gold standard renders inflation impossible and that its introduction deprives the exporting power of a country of the hectic stimulus of a collapsed exchange. Everyone knows that a fall in prices, although it may bring you into truer relation with the outside world and although it is in the long run an advantage of the highest kind, is, while it is taking place, disheartening to the producer at home. Everyone knows that our present policy of paying our debts and maintaining a sound currency implies inevitably high taxation, national sacrifices, and some suffering.

Miss Wilkinson: Class sacrifices, not national sacrifices.

Mr. Churchill: There is among us—I do not know whether the hon. Lady is a member of it or not—a small but highly intellectual school of thought which reaches its fullest expression in Russia, but also flourishes among some of our nearest neighbours, and which proclaims openly that it is much better for a nation to go through the bankruptcy court and start business again—as most of the great Continental belligerents have done in one form or another—and either to repudiate its debts and start again or pay as much in the £ as it finds convenient by writing its currency down to the necessary figure. Happily, we are not called upon to argue about the ethics of such a course because, in any case, it would not be in the interests of Great Britain, which is still the greatest of all creditor countries. The population of this island is maintained by international trade, and anything that makes the purchase of the raw materials and the foodstuffs which we need more costly or more difficult is a direct menace to our livelihood. From this point of view, the producing industries, as well as the entrepot trade, have derived a lasting benefit from the resumption of the gold standard. But this is not all. Nearly one-quarter of our population depends on world-wide operations of credit and commerce for which the stability of sterling is absolutely essential.

The income which we derive each year from commissions and services rendered to foreign countries is over £65,000,000, and, in addition, we have a steady revenue from foreign investments of close on £300,000,000 a year, 90 per cent. of which is expressed in sterling. Upon this great influx there is levied, as a rule, the highest rate of taxation. In this way we are helped to maintain our social services at a level incomparably higher than that of any European country, or indeed of any country. These resources from overseas constitute the keystone, in time of peace, of our economic position, but they depend upon the stability and integrity with which our experienced democracy has hitherto been prepared, under every stress and strain, to maintain the strictest principles of public finance and public faith. Everyone is tempted from time to time by seductive dodges, and everyone from time to time concedes something from the purity of orthodox opinion, but no British Government has yet dared to undermine the hard rock of British financial integrity; and with the mighty economic structure of the United States towering up on our western flank, if ever there was a time when such a step would be disastrous it would be now. Better hard times and a continuing nation than lush, lavish indulgence and irrevocable decline.

We may console ourselves among present discontents by observing that London, in spite of the immense sacrifices made by Great Britain in the War, has regained effectually its solid international pre-eminence in the world, by observing that we are still the greatest international market, that we are able to maintain money rates which are lower than those prevailing in New York, and that the bill of exchange on London, which after the War was seriously menaced, has, in the last few years, regained its time-honoured position as the favourite international instrument and token of commerce.

But I will own that an equally great attraction for me, in the pursuance of this policy, has been that decline in the cost of living which was definitely promised as the result of our allegiance to sound money. I spoke earlier about the increased consumption of tea and sugar. Everyone knows the argument in favour of a free breakfast table, but what is the burden of these remaining taxes on tea and sugar compared to the relief afforded to the consuming public by a decline of 18 points in the cost of living? The identifiable increase in the purchasing power of the wages of insured wage and salary earners alone is equivalent to a remission of indirect taxation of £160,000,000 a year. This takes no account of the proportionate advantages reaped by the enormous number of persons, including the poorest in our midst, unorganised and uncatalogued, from the improvement in the purchasing power of the humble incomes upon which they depend.

National Debt

I now come, having dealt with economy and the cost of living, to the Debt operations of the present Parliament. [An Hon. Member: "What about wages?"] Money wages are equal to those of 1924, taken over the country as a whole. The nominal dead weight Debt has fallen from £7,598,000,000 to £7,501,000,000, or by a total of £97,000,000. But such nominal figures, as I have several times explained, are misleading as a test of the progress made. They fail, for instance, to discriminate between such totally different liabilities as a £100 bond payable next week and a nominal £100 of the old Consols, which need never be repaid, except at the option of the Government, and will in fact never be repaid until some remote date when the interest rates are in the neighbourhood of 2-1/2 per cent. But on a direct actuarial valuation, on the basis of the 4-3/4 per cent. tables—that is to say, taking every separate stock we have issued and calculating its own actuarial value—on this basis, which is the nearest basis we can get to a true scientific valuation, the obligations imposed on the State by the existing debt contracts have fallen in the last four years by £175,000,000. But this figure of £175,000,000 takes full account of all unpaid Savings Certificates interest. If it were open to me to follow the example of every previous Administration in ignoring that unpaid interest, the reduction in the four years would not be £175,000,000, but over £200,000,000. That is not as much as we had hoped, and it is not as much as eminent Liberal economists, or ex-economists, as I am afraid I must say, like the right hon. Member for West Swansea (Mr. Runciman), have often told us it ought to be, but it represents an immense exertion and sacrifice by the taxpayer and the Exchequer. At any rate, the right hon. Member for Carnarvon Boroughs ought not to cavil at it, because it is almost exactly the sum of £200,000,000 which, in trying to win the General Election, he now proposes to borrow and spend in a couple of years. At least we may console ourselves by feeling that the thrift of a Parliament has provided the raw material for another Yellow Book. We have painfully and toilsomely gathered together our meagre savings, and they are now to be butchered to make a showman's holiday.

During this Parliament we have been passing through a period of enormous maturities in respect of the medium term debt consisting principally of National War Bonds, and no less than £1,105,000,000 of debt has fallen due for payment, over and above the ordinary very large transactions upon the Floating Debt. These maturities have come upon us at obligatory moments even in the worst period of 1926, as I said at the time, like Atlantic waves sweeping the deck of a labouring ship, and I have been forced to repay or convert over £1,100,000,000 in four years, that is to say, at an average of £23,000,000 a month during the whole lifetime of the Government, an experience unprecedented. But the greater part of the task is now over. These comparatively short-term bonds have now been largely replaced by long-term debts, and their volume has shrunk from 17 per cent. to 9 per cent. of our total liabilities. An easier period lies ahead. The total Debt falling due in the next four years, which the Government is under compulsion to redeem, amounts to no more than £321,000,000, or much less than one-third of that we have had to deal with in an equal period, and the removal of this recurrent preoccupation and disturbance undoubtedly simplifies the prospects of dealing with the conversion of the 5 per cent. War Loan, which still remains the greatest and most fruitful financial operation likely to be open to the British people. With one single exception every conversion for which I have been fully responsible has effected a saving to the taxpayer, and the total saving from Conversions has been £1,500,000 a year. The one exception was the £62,000,000 of the 3-1/2 per cent. War Loan. This was issued at the beginning of the War at the low rates of interest then prevailing. It was issued under conditions which made it redeemable at par at a fixed date, which fell in my tenure of office, and, of course, the money had to be reborrowed at the post-War rates. That involved us in an annual addition of £700,000 to the charge for the Debt. But for that, the reduction by conversions in the annual public burdens would not have been £1,500,000, but £2,250,000. In the meanwhile—[Interruption]—in spite of all the help which we were given in 1926—in the meantime, by the constant operation of the Sinking Fund, the interest upon the Debt has been reduced by £9,500,000 a year, and with the saving by conversion, the total reduction in the annual cost of our permanent borrowing is £11,000,000 a year.

Why then, it will be asked, has the total annual charge for the service of the Debt increased? There are two reasons. First of all, the accumulated interest on the Savings Certificates encashed, which, in 1924, was only £7,000,000, was in 1928 nearly £18,000,000. If, throughout, the British Government had faced their obligations on these Certificates as we are now doing, there would be no such difference in the two periods. The increase in the charge on account of Savings Certificates has accounted for £11,000,000, and thus the real reduction effected on the other permanent parts of the Debt Charge has been veiled. The second cause is the Treasury Bill rate. In 1928 that rate, contrary to expectations at the beginning of the year, proved high, and the cost of the floating Debt was £5,000,000 higher than in 1924, although the Debt itself was somewhat smaller. The Treasury Bill rates in the last seven or eight years have fluctuated to such an extent as might easily make a difference of £20,000,000 to the

Budget. The Treasury Bill variations are in their nature temporary, and neither the Treasury Bill rate nor the fact that we have faced our obligations on the Savings Certificates should be allowed to obscure the solid and irrefutable fact that the actuarial value of the Debt has been reduced by £175,000,000, and the permanent annual cost by £11,000,000. There is, therefore, no ground for supposing that the exertions of the taxpayer in maintaining the Sinking Fund have not yielded a full proportionate diminution both in lower interest charges and in regard to the aggregate Debt liability.

Surplus, 1928-9

I come to the surplus of 1928. It would seem almost that I ought to apologise to both the Oppositions for the size of that realised surplus. They seem to show almost as little enthusiasm—it is only human nature—when the surplus goes up as they do when the unemployment figures go down. The right hon. Member for Colne Valley (Mr. Snowden) has rebuked me, in his excursions in the Press, for having raided the Sinking Fund. I have not raided the Sinking Fund. I have only carried out the law which Parliament enacted last year. People cannot pretend that they do not understand legislation. If they do not, they ought at this moment to conceal the fact. I have only carried out the law which Parliament passed last year. I have simply fulfilled the statutory requirements of a fixed annual Debt charge of £355,000,000. This was specially augmented last year by £14,000,000 in consequence of the windfall from the currency note account and the total immense sum of £369,000,000 was, as prescribed by Parliament, devoted to the service and extinction of debt. At any rate, the right hon. Member opposite, my predecessor, is in no position to criticise me. I provided last year £57,500,000 for the Sinking Fund out of the fixed Debt charge as against £45,000,000 which he thought necessary when he framed his Budget, and I provided £18,000,000 for the Savings Certificates, as against £7,000,000 which was all he provided—and he had not had a General Strike. The fact is that on these two heads—the extinction of Debt and the prevention of future Debt—I have provided £75,500,000 as against the £52,000,000 which he thought, and which, at the time, I thought proper, or £23,500,000 more money was found last year than he provided. To be quite fair, I ought to make allowance for the concealed Sinking Funds which I mentioned to the House last year, and take off £5,500,000—I am glad the hon. Member for West Leicester (Mr. Pethick-Lawrence) is approving of this—and making allowance for this £5,500,000, I have in fact provided for the extinction of Debt and non-incurring of Debt, £18,000,000 more than the right hon. Gentleman.

I am not using that argument in order to plume or preen myself over the right hon. Gentleman. I am only doing it to protect myself against his future unkindness. I am very glad I persuaded Parliament to assent to this arrangement, and I expect anybody who occupies the position I now hold—[An Hon. Member: "Not for very long"]—we are to have further information about that—will be very glad that the fixed Debt charge has been established. What could be more absurd than to mix up Supply expenditure, which depends upon the decision of the Government of the day and the

House of Commons, with the fluctuations in the world money market? We were all agreed last year that our accounts ought to be simplified so as to separate the healthy growth of revenue on the Post Office and Road Fund from the ordinary Supply expenditure, and to isolate the expenditure which represents the cost of national administration, and the accounts are now presented in that form. But how much more absurd would it be that any Chancellor of the Exchequer should labour for the best part of the year to claw back £5,000,000 or £6,000,000 from the spending departments, and that the Treasury should fight week after week over £100,000, £50,000 or £10,000 of expenditure, and then when this £5,000,000 or £6,000,000 has been saved, as the result of this harassing and unpopular process, the whole fruits of this conflict should be whisked away because the Bank Rate has had to be put up or because more Savings Certificates have been encashed than was foreseen? I do not hesitate to say that if the House of Commons wishes to keep strict control over expenditure and be continually in a position to curb and check the tendencies to profusion of Governments and bureaucracies, the vital step to take is to isolate controllable expenditure from other elements in the Budget, to set it, as it were, on a pedestal or, if you like, in a pillory, where it is nakedly exposed to the public gaze.

That is what we have tried to do, and that is what we have done in fact. On the one hand, the new system of accounting thrusts away from the ordinary expenses of Government the healthy normal growth of reproductive departments, and, on the other hand, we wall off into a separate water-tight compartment all the fluctuations of finance to which we are subjected by the fact that we remain the central money market of the world, and we think it well worth our while to exert ourselves so to remain. Thus there is left for the criticism, censure or approval of the House of Commons, the direct cost of managing and guarding the State. Instead of all these quite different things being jumbled together and a muddled total presented, I have stripped onerous and controllable expenditure of every cover, so that henceforward it can be accurately and stringently examined and measured by the House of Commons. I do not think that this system will be altered in the future. It may be too much to hope that the £355,000,000 fixed charge will be maintained in force for the next 50 years, in which case the Debt would be extinguished, but it certainly ought to be maintained for longer than anyone in this present Assembly lives upon the surface of the globe. But, however that may be, I claim to have placed future Chancellors of the Exchequer in a position where the extravagance or economy of the Governments they represent can be clearly and justly judged.

Forecast for 1929

I come now to the expenditure for 1929. I estimate the Consolidated Fund Services as follows:

	£
Debt interest and Management	304,600,000
Payment to Local Taxation Account	15,000,000

Payment to Northern Ireland Exchequer	5,400,000
Miscellaneous Consolidated Fund Services (including new Agricultural Mortgage Scheme, £500,000; expenses of returning officers at General Election, £420,000)	3,500,000
Total	£328,500,000
The cost of the Supply Services has already been stated at	347,504,000
Total expenditure	676,004,000
(which compares with £682,201,000 actual out turn for 1928)	
Adding rating relief	15,560,000
and Compulsory Sinking Funds	50,400,000
Giving (apart from the self-balancing expenditure of the Post Office and Road Fund) a total of	£741,964,000

I will now forecast, in the light of 1928, the revenue of 1929. Last year Customs and Excise showed a deficit of £8,400,000. That is almost entirely accounted for by beer alone, which showed a shortfall from the estimate of £7,350,000. That is an Exchequer embarrassment, but it is not a national misfortune. The depression of the basic industries and the impoverishment of a large part of the wage-earning classes through the troubles of 1926 are a partial explanation, but in the main there has been a steady decline in the consumption of alcoholic liquor throughout the island. That is due to a change in national habits and to the growth of alternative attractions. After making full allowance for all the improvements in trade conditions which may be expected, I cannot estimate for more than £79,000,000 of beer revenue in 1929. The movement towards greater temperance appears general among all classes, for the wine revenue fell short by £650,000; and, if spirits showed a quite unexpected increase of £300,000 upon the Estimate, that is entirely due to the exceptionally cold weather through which we have passed. In the whole field of this revenue, even prosperity will bring no marked expansion. I think we may all dwell with some complacency upon the results which regulated freedom, corrected by high taxation, have shown compared with those which have followed—or perhaps I ought to say which have flowed— elsewhere from prohibition, tempered by bootlegging.

The sugar remission of last year cost £1,000,000 more than I had expected. That is due to the very rapid shrinkage in imports of foreign refined sugar. Whereas in the three years ending in 1927 the British refining industry had fallen to a 50 per cent. share of the home market, it had already risen to 70 per cent. in 1928 and is still expanding. Contrary to the predictions of the right hon. Gentleman the Member for

Colne Valley, who was very lavish in his predictions and assertions last year, the farthing remission reached the consumer, and so far from being withdrawn after a few months, it was reinforced by another farthing, which was due to the abundance of sugar supplies throughout the world, and to-day the consumer is paying a halfpenny less on an average for granulated sugar than a year ago. There is very little to complain of in that. The Betting Duty yielded £2,250,000 in 1928 owing to the higher rates being in force during the flat racing season. The full yield of this Duty at the new rates established on 1st October, 1928, would be £1,400,000. The new Oil Duty yielded £800,000 above the £12,200,000 which was my final estimate after the exclusion of kerosene. This duty has proved extremely easy to collect, and it has not checked the rapidly increasing use of petrol as much as we thought it prudent to allow for. After considering all that has taken place, I put the Customs for 1929 at £126,000,000, and Excise at £131,950,000, a total of £257,950,000. I have put the Exchequer share of the Motor Vehicle Duties at £4,700,000.

I turn to Inland Revenue. If the Committee will consult the Blue Paper, they will find, in Table 2, details of the Inland Revenue in the year now closed. Income Tax exceeded the Estimate by as much as £4,700,000. This year, we have to face the increased cost of the children's allowances, but even taking that into consideration, I look forward to a receipt, in 1929, of £239,500,000 from Income Tax. The Death Duties yielded the record figure of £80,500,000, showing £8,500,000 above the Estimate, and £3,000,000 above the high yield of 1927. This duty has been substantially underestimated for the last two years, and I feel justified in taking a definitely more favourable view of its prospects than before. Therefore, I put the Death Duties for 1929 at £81,000,000, an increase of £500,000 above the record figure of the present year. Stamps, through the continuing activity of the Stock Exchange and the flotation of new companies, yielded in 1928 £2,000,000 more than the Estimate, and £3,000,000 above 1927.

Mr. Wallhead: What about 1926?

Mr. Churchill: The hon. Member seems to feel very acutely his responsibility for 1926. I estimate for a further growth of £1,000,000 in the current year, making the figure for Stamps £31,000,000. Excess Profits Duty yielded £850,000, notwithstanding repayments of £4,500,000. The Corporation Profits Tax also produced £850,000. I see no reason why these two moribund duties should not repeat in 1929 the yield of £1,700,000 which they made in the current year. The one laggard in the Inland Revenue sphere is the Super-tax, which has fallen short of expectations by £3,800,000. That is partly due to the fact that the acceleration of collection, which was in progress two years ago, has reached the limit. Nevertheless, it is natural to suppose that the Super-tax will reflect the general upward movement of the Income Tax and Death Duties, and my estimate this year is £58,000,000, which is nearly £2,000,000 above the yield of 1928, although substantially below the estimate of that year. It may be for convenience if I just read the forecast for 1929:

	£
Income Tax	239,500,000
Super-tax	58,000,000

Estate Duties	81,000,000
Stamps	31,000,000
Excess Profits Duty and Corporation Profits Tax	1,700,000
Land Tax	800,000
Total Inland Revenue	£412,000,000
This, added to the Customs and Excise	257,950,000
and to the Exchequer share of the Motor Vehicle Duties	4,700,000
makes the total receipts from taxes	£674,650,000

I turn now to the Non-tax revenue. The Committee will see, as the Blue Paper shows, that Non-tax revenue differed but slightly in 1928 from the estimate. It produced £93,966,000, against an estimate of £90,848,000. This surplus was almost entirely due to the Miscellaneous Special Receipts, which benefited by larger Reparation payments than I had allowed for, and by certain surpluses from the disposal of stores and the winding up of war agreements. For 1929, I estimate that the

	£
Post Office net receipts will be	8,990,000
Crown lands will bring in	1,250,000
Receipts from Sundry Loans	30,550,000
Miscellaneous Ordinary Receipts	12,500,000
and Miscellaneous Special Receipts	26,000,000
a total Non-tax revenue of	£79,290,000

being a reduction of nearly £15,000,000 from the figure of last year. This is due to the fact that we have this year no windfall of £13,000,000 from the Currency Note Reserve. Adding together the Tax and Non-tax revenue, and we get, apart from the self-balancing revenue and expenditure of the Post Office and the Road Fund, a total revenue for 1929 of £753,940,000. Thus there emerges, on the basis of existing taxation, a prospective surplus of £11,976,000. We have also in hand in the Suspensory Fund, our nest egg of £22,633,000.

I place these two surpluses, so to speak, upon the mantelpiece, where they can be admired or deplored according to party inclination. Naturally, I am very pleased that the realised surplus should have exceeded, by £8,500,000, the forecast figures which I gave Parliament last year. But the revenue upon which the prospective surplus of 1929 is based has a special charm and virtue of its own. This year there are no adventitious aids and no windfalls of any consequence. We have passed through that period of fortunate but lucky expedients. We stand once more on the basis of permanent and continuing revenue. Moribund taxes have passed out of existence;

revenue has become independent of temporary aids, or raids if you like to call them so; and I can present a balanced Budget with a reasonable prospect of a surplus upon the basis of the revenues which will live and grow.

Review of Revenue

At this point, I shall indulge myself once more in brief retrospect. Let the Committee remember the formidable subtractions from the revenue I have had to face. The remissions of revenue made by the right hon. Gentleman the Member for Colne Valley cost £13,500,000 more in a full year than in the year in which they were made. The special receipts from war stores have dropped by £11,500,000 since his day. The revenue from beer and spirits has fallen during my tenure by £10,500,000 a year. I have remitted £41,000,000 of Income Tax, and £4,000,000 upon sugar. Thus the total adverse tide which I had to face has been over £80,000,000 a year; and beyond this the coal stoppage cost the Exchequer, £80,000,000 spread over four years. In order to avoid the reimposition of severe taxation, I have brought into the revenue of these difficult years £19,000,000 from the Road Fund, £10,000,000 from the brewers' credit, £17,000,000 from the earlier collection of Schedule A, £14,000,000 from the Currency Note Account and unclaimed dividends, £60,000,000 in all. But these non-recurrent receipts are substantially less than the losses of the coal stoppage. [*Interruption.*] I do not want to use a controversial term. We have always agreed to call it the coal stoppage.

There still remained a permanent gap in revenue of over £80,000,000. All this had to be filled. On the other hand, we had the debt settlement and we have the working of the Dawes plan, for which matter the right hon. Gentleman the Leader of the Opposition deserves all due and lasting credit. These have together secured to us increased receipts of over £23,000,000 a year, that is actual receipts of £32,000,000 or £33,000,000. There has been an increase in the Post Office surplus of £4,500,000. The General Exchequer share of the Motor Vehicle Duties is £4,500,000. The general growth of the yield of taxation has been £38,000,000. Lastly, in the place of the £45,000,000 of remitted taxation, we have increased the old taxes upon wines, tobacco and matches by some £6,000,000; and have devised new taxes upon luxuries like silk and artificial silk, the McKenna duties, duties on tyres, and in addition there are various safeguarding duties. Together these yield over £13,000,000 a year. Thus the new receipts of the Parliament aggregate £89,000,000, and more than fill the formidable gap I have described. I thought it would interest the House to realise what changes, in fact, had actually taken place in the character of our taxation.

New Import Duties

Of the group of new import duties, which together yield a revenue of £13,000,000, it is certainly true to say that they are far less burdensome to industry and to trade than the income tax which would be required to replace them. To pretend that they are a burden on the wage-earning classes is pure nonsense. To treat them as if they were on the same footing as sugar, or even on the same footing as beer, tobacco and popular entertainments, is also absurd. Foreign motor cars or motor tyres, foreign pianos, silk garments, or even betting, are not forms of expenditure which compare, at any rate, with tea and sugar as essentials in the cottage budget.

No doubt we shall very soon be arguing on public platforms about the effects of the McKenna, Key Industries and Safeguarding Duties, and certainly that is a contest about which we feel no anxiety. But there are some duties which are not the result of any Committee or any general statutory enactment, but for which I personally am responsible as Chancellor of the Exchequer, and about which I should like to say a word. I take first silk. We have had four years of the Silk Duties. Everyone can remember—if people nowadays remember anything—the long Parliamentary controversy which marked the passage of those duties. According to the right hon.Gentleman the Member for Carnarvon Boroughs I was to be hanged in a silken halter. [An Hon. Member: "Wait and see!"] I am quite ready to wait and see. At any rate, it will be a cheaper halter. Let us see what has happened. The import of foreign artificial silk yarn has shrunk to a quarter; the British export has increased by 50 per cent.; home production has risen from 26,000,000 pounds to 51,000,000 pounds; 21 new factories have been erected in this country, some of them by foreign firms. The insured persons employed in the silk and artificial silk industry have risen from 46,500 when the duties were passed to over 70,000 in 1928. The home price of artificial silk yarn has fallen by 25 per cent., and the quantity available for home consumption has increased by 50 per cent. And as a final result we have an assured revenue of over £6,000,000 a year. It requires a very pedantic purist to frame an indictment against such a duty. When the right hon. Gentleman the Member for Colne Valley has a little leisure, perhaps he will re-read the speeches he delivered against the Silk Duties during their passage, and will compare the assertions and the prophecies of which he is always so free with the facts and results as we know them to-day.

Very much the same story has revealed itself in respect of the protective or quasi-protective and revenue duty imposed upon foreign motor tyres. Six foreign factories have been established in this country, and increased employment has resulted, the export of British tyres has been fully maintained, the import has been diminished by more than a half, and the price of tyres has fallen 15 per cent. since April, 1927.

Mr. W. Thorne: Due to the fall in rubber.

Mr. Churchill: If such results were produced on any scientific question by laboratory experiments no one would say they were decisive, but no sensible or truth-seeking investigator would deny their profound significance and importance.

Betting Duty

However, there is one of the new taxes for which I am responsible which has been a failure, which, indeed, has been a fiasco, and which obviously has caused more trouble than it is worth. I mean, of course, the duty on betting. Here was a project which had behind it a greater backing of public opinion, so far as the newspaper press expresses public opinion, than any other project of taxation of which I have ever heard. Newspapers as widely separated in view as the "Morning Post," the "Star," the "Spectator" and the "Church Times" ardently advocated the duty on betting, and many of those who had studied the subject with great attention thought a revenue of £6,000,000 or £7,000,000 a year, or even more, could be obtained from the taxation of this highly-luxurious dissipation. In practice, however, the duty has failed. The volatile and elusive character of the betting population, the precarious conditions in which they disport themselves, have proved incapable of bearing the weight even of the repeatedly reduced burdens we have tried to place upon them. It has become plain that the collection of this duty in this shape has been vitiated because it has not worked fairly. It is being paid exclusively by the honest bookmaker—who has been unable to avoid it. The very fact that he has paid the tax has placed him at an invidious disadvantage compared with more slippery and unsubstantial rivals. I shall say with the great Burke,

If I cannot have reform without injustice, I will not have reform.

I must admit that in considering this question I have also been influenced by a sense of obligation towards the Labour party, particularly towards the Leader of the Opposition. It is scarcely a year ago since the right hon. Gentleman told the country that His Majesty's Government, in deriving advantage from the duty upon betting, had become a parasite upon damnation. Scarcely a month ago the right hon. Gentleman, seduced by the spectacle of 100 bookmakers' motor cars at the Battersea election, showed himself only too ready to become a parasite upon damnation. [An Hon. Member: "It damned your candidate!"] It is in the common interest that we cannot afford to have the ideals of great parties debased in this manner. We must not lead the weaker brethren into temptation. We must not expose a young, new, callow, half-fledged organisation to the seductions to which, in their immature state, they will infallibly succumb, and it is out of consideration largely for them, and for their reputation, that I have decided that the turnover duty upon betting should be immediately repealed. [An Hon. Member: "How about the motor cars now?"] I shall, however, continue to levy the personal licence duty of £10 upon all bookmakers, and, in addition, a licence duty of £40 a year upon every telephone installed in a bookmaker's office. The yield of these licence duties is estimated at £500,000 a year. We have as a monument of the betting tax, thanks to the zeal of the hon. and gallant Member for Abingdon (Major Glyn), the healthy machinery of the Totalisator, and upon this will be imposed a tax of one-half per cent. of the takings, which I have been led to believe is a fair equivalent to the licence duties upon bookmakers. The cost of these changes will be £850,000 in the current year and £900,000 in a full year.

It will be convenient for me at this point to deal with several minor but not necessarily uncontroversial topics. I have only one new tax to impose this year, and it is a very small one. I have been told that the fact that the rating relief, as given to brewers, distillers and tobacco manufacturers, is capable of being used by people of unscrupulous character and low mentality—such as are certainly not present in this

House—as a means of prejudicing the scheme for giving rating relief to productive industry. Here, again, it is our duty to help our weaker brethren, and not to place a stumbling block in their path. Luckily, there is a convenient method which does not mar in any way the general symmetry of our rating reform scheme or the principle on which it is based. Manufacturers' licence duties have now long been levied, though at very low rates, upon brewers, distillers and tobacco manufacturers. I propose to raise those duties so as to take away from these industries the equivalent of the relief they will obtain under the de-rating scheme. There is not the slightest reflection of stigma upon those industries; on the contrary, some of their leading representatives have publicly stated that they do not wish to benefit by the de-rating proposals, and it is very much to their credit that they have made that statement. The date of the imposition of these increased duties will be arranged, as the Scotch would say, "timeously" with the currency of the relief, and therefore these three industries will neither gain nor lose by our proceedings. The relief they would obtain in the normal working of the de-rating scheme is now estimated at £480,000; and the manufacturers' licence duties will be raised as described in detail in the White Paper, so as to produce a new revenue of like amount.

Liquor Licence Duties

I now pass to a more amiable concession. For many years it has been contended that the Liquor Licence Duties which were imposed in 1910 stand at too high a level in view of the curtailment of the hours of sale. I stated in last year's Finance Bill Debates that this contention was justified so far as on-licences are concerned. I had not then the means at my disposal to remedy the grievance, but I now propose to reduce the licence duties payable by on-retailers by 25 per cent. This concession will take effect on the 1st October next, and will cost £950,000 in 1929-30 and £970,000 in a full year. At the same time, I propose to meet a demand, which has been frequently urged in Parliament for the convenience of the public in general, and to allow such off licence holders in England and Wales as hold a Justices' Licence and only if they hold a Justices' Licence, to sell single half bottles, but not quarter bottles, of spirits.

Harbour Dues

Perhaps I had better dispose at this point of some other modest matters. I have made a provision of about £30,000 a year for reducing Harbour dues in certain cases where they press unduly upon fishermen, especially upon those engaged in the herring fisheries in Scotland and for assisting in the discovery of deep sea fishing grounds or in other ways. In addition certain debts to the Exchequer which weigh upon these fishing harbours and prevent them making full use of the rating relief will be eased either by remission or suspension. Fuller statements on this subject will be made if desired by the Secretary of State for Scotland and the Minister of Agriculture.

There are one or two minor alterations affecting the Stamp Duties on amalgamations and in connection with the motor vehicle duties which will have a small effect on the finances of the year. These will be found set out in the White Paper.

Rural Telephones

Last, but not least, it is proposed to afford to the public, especially in rural districts, certain improved telephone facilities. At present there is an extra charge of £1 a year for each furlong for telephone lines laid more than one-and-a-half miles from the terminal. By increasing the radius to two miles there will be comparatively few points in the more populous regions of this island which will be beyond the reach of the telephone service at ordinary rates. The immediate cost of this concession is £90,000 a year.

Secondly, and in addition, there are about 6,000 post offices—by far the greater part of them in villages—and 1,600 rural railway stations which have at the present time neither telegraph nor telephone facilities. It seems to the Government most desirable that this closer and wider linking up of our country districts with the centres from which they purchase and with one another should be fostered even though in many cases it cannot be justified on a strictly profit-making basis. Accordingly it has been arranged that at least five-sixths of these 6,000 post offices and 1,600 railway stations shall be equipped, for the most part during the next six months, with call boxes at ordinary rates. The remaining one-sixth which constitutes the most unprofitable investment must be left over for the present time. The cost of this will amount to £1,750,000 in the shape of capital expenditure under the borrowing powers of the Post Office. These concessions are no doubt small items—I almost blush to name them—but they fit harmoniously into the general scheme of the Government for fostering basic production.

Precise details of all these matters will be found in the White Paper. The various adjustments which I have mentioned make their inroad upon the surplus. The Betting Duty relief costs £850,000, the Publicans' Licence Duty relief costs £950,000 and the various minor concessions cost the revenue £110,000. On the other hand the increase in the manufacturers licence duties on beer, spirits, and tobacco will be £480,000, leaving a net diminution of the prospective surplus of £1,430,000. Subtracting this from £11,976,000 leaves us still in possession of a surplus of £10,546,000.

Disposal of Surplus

What shall we do with it? Let us, first of all, by way of preliminary digression, address ourselves to the burning question of whether national prosperity can be restored or enhanced by the Government borrowing money and spending it on making more work. The orthodox Treasury view, and after all British finance has long been regarded as a model to many countries, is that when the Government borrow in the money market it becomes a new competitor with industry and engrosses to itself resources which would otherwise have been employed by private enterprise, and in the process it raises the rent of money to all who have need of it. This orthodox view holds, therefore, that a special, even perhaps a double, responsibility rests upon the State when it decides to enter the money market as a rival to the ordinary life and trade of the country. The onus is laid upon the Government to prove either that the need is paramount as in the case of national safety being in danger; or that the work is necessary, and would not be otherwise undertaken; or that the spending of the money by the Government would produce more beneficial results than if it had been left available for trade and industry. No absolute rule can be laid down, but each case must be judged upon its merits and in the prevailing circumstances. We ourselves have certainly not followed any absolute rule. On the contrary, in our desire to induce a speedier return to prosperity and to diminish unemployment we have, during the last five years, ventured upon very heavy capital outlay. We have set on foot and carried into effect of far-reaching and carefully considered programmes of housing, roads, telephones and agricultural development. The expenditure provided for these purposes, either from revenue or from loans raised on Government credit during the past four years, amounts in round figures to £260,000,000. In addition, we have implemented guarantees under the Trade Facilities Act and provided new guarantees for colonial development schemes for a further £40,000,000. We have already carried through a scheme for the re-organisation of electricity supplies at an estimated cost of £40,000,000 or £50,000,000.

The total development expenditure of the present Government during their period of office already exceeds £300,000,000, and there is a further £50,000,000 of commitments in sight. These figures do not include the expenditure, principally on housing and roads, undertaken by the local authorities on the basis of Government grants, which probably fall little short of another £100,000,000. It seems only a very little while ago that we were actually being scolded and criticised from both sides of the House for an extravagant use of cash and credit upon schemes like beet sugar, trade facilities and subsidies in any form. Nevertheless we have pursued the even tenor of our way, and during the course of the present Parliament we have spent, or caused to be spent, or undertaken to spend in cash or credit, over £400,000,000. I believe this great sum has on the whole not been unwisely invested and that much of it will return to us after many days and that we have a better island to live in than we had before. The point I am coming to is that for the purpose of curing unemployment the results have certainly been disappointing. They are, in fact, so meagre as to lend considerable colour to the orthodox Treasury doctrine which has steadfastly held that, whatever might be the political or social advantages, very little additional employment and no permanent additional employment can in fact and as a general rule be created by State borrowing and State expenditure. I am not trying to draw too rigid a line and our own practice does not entitle me to do so, for we have drawn very largely on capital account. I can express my own personal view best of all by a simple illustration which is familiar to all our minds, that of the Boat Race, where the full life-energy and power of the crews must be exerted. There is always an opportunity to the one side or the other to make a spurt, and, if the spurt is judiciously timed and wisely used, it may bring a definite advantage. It may gain a favourable position upon the river, it may possibly even secure a victory. But a spurt is only a draft in an intense form upon the total life-energy of the crew; it exhausts them to a formidable degree; and, if it fails, they are worse off than if they had simply rowed steadily on. Moreover, the race in which we are rowing is not one which has any definite ending. It goes on and on, for reach after reach, and no one can tell at what point any definite advantage can be registered. Certainly, in these conditions, the greatest possible care and deliberation should be used before ordering a spurt from a crew so hard pressed, and nothing would be more foolish, more wrong, more wanton, than for a stroke to make an exhausting spurt, not on any sound calculation of winning the race, but just for the purpose of giving the crowd on Barnes Bridge, under which he was about to pass, something to shout at. I think that all of us will be agreed upon that, or very nearly all of us.

That brings me back, oddly enough, to the proposal of the right hon. Gentleman the Member for Carnarvon Boroughs to spend £200,000,000 mainly on road construction, in addition to the already heavy programme of road and other developments which, of course, is going forward and increasing year by year. The plan of forcing road construction to such an extravagant pitch in a country which already has the best roads in the world, and which is already spending more on its roads than any country in Europe, would, I am sure, not only be of no real or lasting advantage as a remedy for unemployment, but would be positively and gravely injurious to the national welfare. This opinion does not rest only on argument or on belief. Curiously enough, as has lately been pointed out, an almost similar mistake was made 80 or 90 years ago in the frenzied enthusiasm with which the railways were promoted. In the railway construction boom round about 1845, great loans were raised for the rapid building of railways, and armies of men were employed in their construction. The demand for steel rails and rolling stock promised a most vigorous stimulus to other trades; hope and courage were high. But what happened? According to Cunningham's "Growth of English Industry and Commerce," a standard authority, speedy trade depression and financial crisis ensued, from which it took the country several years to recover. Cunningham says, in Volume II, page 828:

> The period of commercial depression was chiefly due to the vigour with which railway enterprise was taken up, and the fact that the ordinary course of commercial transactions was dislocated. In the autumn of 1845, 2,069 miles of railway were opened, with a capital of £64,000,000 odd, while 3,543 miles of railway were in progress, involving capital amounting to £74,500,000. Of course, there was no immediate return on this large amount of capital; it was for the time absolutely sunk; the investment of so much money in forms not immediately productive had the result of injuring many branches of industries and depressing commerce. In so far as the wealth devoted to railway enterprise was withdrawn from circulation in the form of wares, the effects were for the time being disastrous. The proprietors had less means available to purchase goods. Capitalists found their sales diminished; they were unable to replace their stock of materials or to continue to pay wages, until their stores of finished goods were realised; and a general stagnation resulted.

Of course, in the long run, the new railways were the foundation of a new era of prosperity, but that prosperity would have come just as surely, and probably more quickly, if we had maintained a steady methodical progress, and if, let me observe— and this is a point to be noted—the vast canal system, embodying the labours of half a century, had not been incontinently scrapped and sacrificed and ruined for the sake of overdoing a new idea. We ought, I think, to try to learn from the teachings of experience; we ought not, for the sake of a frantic development of roads, to disturb and dislocate the normal productive life of the nation, or strike a precipitate State-subsidised blow at our superb system of railways, in which more than £1,200,000,000 of capital has been sunk, and by which more than 600,000 men get their daily bread.

Road Fund Grants

I have another announcement to make about the expenditure in connection with roads. During the Debates on the Local Government Bill, I declared a further increase in the percentage grants for the maintenance of classified roads and bridges—an increase from 50 per cent. to 60 per cent. in the case of Class I, and from 33-1/3 per cent. to 50 per cent. in the case of Class II roads. That was at a cost of £2,500,000 a year, with consequent relief to rates, and especially to county rates. I am glad to say that the balance of the Fund at the end of the year has turned out to be larger than was expected; it amounts to about £4,500,000. We propose, therefore, now to make a corresponding increase in the percentage grants for road improvements and new construction. For the year 1929, the normal road grants for these purposes will be 60 per cent. of the approved cost in the case of Class I roads, and 50 per cent. in the case of approved schemes for all roads and bridges other than Class I; and, as an induce-ment to local authorities to assist in the transference of labour from depressed areas, we have decided to give an additional grant of 15 per cent. in respect of all schemes on which not less than 50 per cent. of men drawn from such areas are employed, provided that they are engaged through the Employment Exchanges. The additional allocation in the Road Fund Budget for these purposes, as well as for those of accelerating the reconstruction of weak bridges in private ownership on important roads—

Mr. MacLaren: Sending up the land values!

Mr. Churchill: We all know that the hon. Gentleman has a bee in his bonnet on that point—and the replacement of level crossings by bridges, is estimated to bring the total expenditure out of the Road Fund this year up to £23,000,000, as compared with £15,000,000 a year when the Government took office. This substantial contribu-tion towards the aggregate road expenditure of this country, which now approaches £60,000,000 a year, is, in my view, as much as we can prudently afford to take from the national income at the present time.

Returning to the main argument, in our deliberate view unemployment can only be reduced to the normal by the revival of industry as a whole, and especially by the revival of the basic industries. Such a revival will draw men and women now unem-ployed through a thousand channels back into their own trades, or into kindred employment for which their previous training has not unsuited them. That is far preferable to setting the unemployed to work in masses on road construction or other forms of public works, even if such a plan could be carried out upon any large scale for any length of time. In some quarters it has been urged that the Government should seek for opportunities of utilising the national credit for stimulating general trade, and, in particular, for assisting in the process of nationalisation. Such transactions are far better dealt with in the sphere of regular business than by the direct intervention of the Government. What can be done in this sphere is well exemplified by the Lancashire Cotton Corporation, formed under the auspices of the Bank of England. I have reason to believe that the City of London is willing and anxious to assist when similar cases arise in other basic industries.

Railway Passenger Duty

I am glad to be in a position to make one modest, but immediate, contribution to a policy of the modernisation of our industries. There is no doubt that the railways have much more to give to the revival of industry, and especially of basic industries, than the roads. Heavy traffics, bulky agricultural traffics, and, above all, mineral traffics, have no other transport comparable for economy or efficiency with railway transport. Last year we inaugurated a reduction of railway freights upon selected heavy traffics. This is the first instalment of the policy of rate relief to come into force, and it has already amply justified itself. Now we have another contribution to propose, which should make for the greater efficiency of railway transport. For nearly a hundred years there has been a Railway Passenger Duty levied upon the railway companies, yielding to the Exchequer nearly £400,000 a year. The railway companies have repeatedly sought relief from this tax, which they regard as an invidious survival. Subject to the approval of Parliament, I have offered to meet their wishes, but only on one condition, namely, that the capital equivalent of the whole of this relief from taxation, amounting to £6,500,000, should be used as an additional stimulus for the development and modernisation of railway transport. The works contemplated will include such items as port equipment, terminal facilities, marshalling yards, and the adaptation of the railway system for dealing with heavier rolling stock. If Parliament approves of these proposals, the principal railway companies have undertaken to submit a list of schemes which will be put in hand forthwith, and upon which work will be effectively begun within the present financial year. That is all that I have to say at the moment on the problem of railways, but it is by no means all that can be done in that field. The repeal of this Duty will cost £300,000 in the present year.

De-rating

After all, however, the best and surest help we can carry to productive industry, and, through productive industry, to employment, is by a reduction of the burdens which enter directly into the cost of production, or which deplete the capital accumulations upon which, in modern times, industry can alone develop. We have in the Suspensory Fund a realised surplus of £22,500,000. I propose to use this for the purpose of making a very important remission of taxation, a remission of a most onerous and invidious form of taxation, namely, the local rates upon productive industry. After the current payments, three-fourths of the rates upon productive industry, and the whole of the rates upon agriculture, will be abolished. I think I mentioned this last year in my Budget speech, and my right hon. Friend the Minister of Health has had to refer to the subject several times in the interval. This is because it was necessary to obtain Parliamentary authority for the accumulation in the Exchequer of the necessary funds and also to pass legislation to enable them to be applied in the most useful manner.

Of course, it would have been much nicer if we could have kept this quiet all this time and if I could have announced it for the first time now, but unhappily in a world of reality—and Governments and Chancellors of the Exchequer are painfully anchored to reality—it is often necessary to make long preparations in order to secure any large or permanent advantage. However, the necessary laws have been passed by Parliament, the necessary funds have been gathered, and we are in a position to abolish this year three-quarters of the rates upon productive industry of all kinds and the whole of the rates upon agriculture. That is the best, and by far the greatest, gift which it is in our power to bestow. We have saved up for it, we have toiled for it, and we can now bestow it. The £22,500,000 is not needed for the rating scheme in the year 1929. During this year the yield of the Petrol Duty, £15,700,000, will be sufficient to meet the half-year's relief to industry and agriculture, but in 1930 the full scheme of rating relief comes into operation and the Exchequer will provide in relief of local rates nearly £36,000,000 of new money. In that year the Petrol Duty should yield £17,000,000 and £3,000,000 will be provided from the Road Fund, leaving less than £16,000,000 to be taken from the Suspensory Fund, which we hope by that time will be increased by any surplus resulting from 1929. Thus the finance of this vast scheme of tax remission is fully provided for till the year 1931. Thereafter we must look to the normal increase of revenue which, even in these bleak years, has shown a steady annual rise and which during the last year has definitely exceeded expectations.

But, apart from the normal growth of the revenue, there is one special additional factor on which I think I am entitled to dwell. Before the great disaster to the coal industry occurred—[Interruption.] I must describe what happened. Something happened in 1926. To put it in the least controversial way, before what happened in 1926 happened, the principal basic trades of the country yielded profits assessable to Income Tax of £150,000,000 a year. In the present Budget I am counting upon less than £100,000,000 of profits from this same group of trades. It seems probable that a definite and solid revival of prosperity in the basic trades has now begun, but even if these trades do no more than regain in 1932 the levels at which they stood in 1923 and 1924 an addition of at least £10,000,000 would be made to Income and Super-tax on that account alone. Indeed the improved prospects of the revenue and the increase in the Suspensory Fund encourage and justify a further step forward at present in the relief of productive industry.

Agricultural Producers (Rating Relief)

We have been repeatedly pressed to bring the reliefs into operation at the earliest possible date. We have already hastened the freight relief upon selected traffics. Instead of the £18,000,000 in the suspensory fund which I originally budgeted for, or the £14,000,000 which was all I had a right to expect at the end of the Summer Session, we have now £22,500,000. We propose, therefore, to bring the relief of rates upon agricultural producers into immediate operation. The farming community will not have to wait until October. They will be freed from the burden of rates as from the beginning of this month. This earlier relief costs £2,500,000, a sum which in its happily reinforced condition the suspensory fund can properly bear. A short Bill will be necessary before the Dissolution, non-controversial I have no doubt, to allow this further relief and to enable the Exchequer to make good to the local authorities the £2,500,000 which they would otherwise be collecting from the agricultrual producers. The Bill will be introduced immediately after the Budget Resolutions.

I have anxiously considered whether it would be practicable to ante-date in a similar way the relief to manufacturing production. The rates upon agriculture have already for many years been divided under the workings of the Agricultural Rates Acts. They have been divided between productive and residential properties and, therefore, it is a simple matter to remit the rates upon land and buildings used for agricultural production. In the case of industry the frontier line is now only for the first time being drawn between those hereditaments which fall within the scope of our legislation and those which fall outside it. There is no assured basis, therefore, upon which the relief on productive industry can be ante-dated. Industry must still wait until October, but agriculture can receive its relief at once.

Direct Taxation

After allowing for all the minor concessions or remissions, we are still left with a prospective surplus of £10,246,000, out of which I think the taxpayer is entitled to some further relief. The Super-tax payer, with an investment income has received, of course, nothing in the present Parliament, because the relief of £10,000,000 which he gained in 1925 was at the same time, as is so often forgotten, exactly cancelled out by the increase of Death Duties on the same class of fortunes.

Miss Wilkinson: He can only die once, but he gets the relief every year.

Mr. Churchill: The hon. Lady must possess her soul in hope. I can assure her she will not be wholly disappointed. Nevertheless, the Super-tax payer must, I think, be left to contemplate with what equanimity he can the ferocious onslaught which we are assured the Socialist party intend to make upon him. The Income Tax payer, has, however, received substantial relief. He has received a relief of 6d. in the standard rate, and this relief, in the case of the smaller class of Income Tax payer, and especially the man with a family to bring up, has been multiplied several times over by the cumulative rebates and allowances made in the Budgets of 1925 and 1928. I should like the Committee to realise how very important, and indeed decisive, these reliefs have been. Take the case of a married man with three children whose income is all earned. On an income of £400, such a man paid in 1924 £5 1s. 3d. in taxation. He now pays nothing. Such a man with £500 a year paid in 1924 £15 3s. 9d. He now pays £3 3s. 4d. That is equivalent to a reduction in the standard rate of Income Tax of 3s. 7d. in the £. With an income of £600 he paid in 1924 £25 6s. 3d. He now pays £11 10s. That is equivalent to a reduction in the standard rate of 2s. 5-1/2d. in the £. On an income of £700 a year, he paid in 1924 £45 11s. 3d. He now pays £19 16s. 8d., or a reduction of 2s. 6-1/2d. in the £. On an £800 a year income, instead of paying £65 odd, he now pays £33, or a reduction of 2s. 2d. in the £. On an income of £900 a year, instead of paying £86 odd he pays £50.

Mr. Griffiths: Are these miners?

Mr. Churchill: Does the Labour party take no interest in the affairs of the smaller class of Income Tax payers?—a reduction of 1s. 10d. in the £? On an income of £1,000 a year, where £106 odd was paid in 1924, £67 is paid now, a reduction of 1s. 8d. in the £. On an income of £1,500 a year, where £207 was paid in 1924, £150 is paid now, a reduction of 1s. 3d. in the £. Of course, where the income is derived from investments, or where the taxpayer has fewer or no children, or is unmarried, the scales are less favourable, but the reliefs are none the less real and important throughout the whole range of incomes under £1,000 a year. Indeed, an immense process of relief graduated downwards has been carried out in this Parliament, and that large class, comprising more than half the Income Tax payers, all of what are called the black-coated working men, the brain workers, professional men, technical experts, the "intelligentsia," to use the Moscow jargon, upon whose abilities, attainments and exertions the forward movement of scientific civilisation depends—

Mr. MacLaren: Rhetoric!

Mr. Churchill: It is a fact which is brought bitterly home to every country that ignores it—have gained very great and well-deserved benefit, costing in the present year £2,500,000 more than they did in the Budget of last year. I can do no more for this class in this Budget, and my gaze now rests upon the indirect taxpayer.

Tea Duty (Abolition)

I have never had much fiscal sympathy with the consumer of luxuries, and particularly of foreign luxuries. It is to the primary comforts and to some extent virtual necessities of the mass of the population that we should now turn our attention. I have already spoken of the immense boon of at least £160,000,000 a year conferred upon the wage-earners by the reduction in the cost of living. Compared with that universal easement, anything the present surplus can bestow must necessarily be small. We reduced last year the tax on sugar at a cost of £3,000,000 of revenue, and it is to tea that I now turn with feelings of good will. The Committee know, from the annual Debates in this House, that I have long desired to effect some reduction in the Tea Duty. There is no other comfort which enters so largely into the budget of the cottage home, or the still humbler budgets of the old, the weak, and the poor. The reduction or the removal of the tax on tea has been asked for in a long succession of Parliaments.

Its mitigation would always have been regarded by social reformers of every party as an auspicious milestone in the history of the Customs House. There has been a tax on tea ever since the reign of Queen Elizabeth, and I am glad to think that the reign of His Majesty King George the Fifth will witness the total, immediate, and, I believe, final abolition:

> "And while the bubbling and loud-hissing urn
> Throws up a steamy column, and the cups
> That cheer but not inebriate wait on each,
> So let us welcome peaceful evening in."

I said that the remission would be total and I have said so advisedly, and, although over three-quarters of the tea drunk in these islands is produced within the British Empire, Javanese tea enters to a great extent into the cheapest blends used by the poorest people. To maintain for preferential reasons a tax on this foreign tea would therefore exclude from the benefits of remission the very class for whose sake, most of all, this serious sacrifice of revenue is being made.

I am not dealing in the present Budget with the duties on coffee, cocoa and chicory, and although the cocoa group has usually moved up and down the Tea Duty, there is no essential reason why they should be inseparably connected, and there are Gladstonian precedents for the independent treatment of tea. The cost of the abolition of the tax on tea is £6,150,000, in the present year. The repeal will date from the 22nd April next. I have every reason to believe that an effectual reduction of 4d. in the lb. in the price of tea will reach the consumer immediately. With the abolition of the Tea Duty, the proportion of our revenue raised from comforts, that is to say the remaining breakfast table duties, coffee, cocoa, chicory, sugar and also from matches, falls from 4.43 per cent. under the Labour administration to 2.91; by far the lowest percentage ever known.

Balance of Budget

I can now balance the Budget of 1929 with an expenditure under all heads, including the rating relief, the Sinking Fund, and the self-balancing accounts, of £822,584,000 and with a revenue of £826,680,000, leaving a final prospective surplus of £4,096,000. I hope that this surplus may be increased, as the last two surpluses have been, by further savings by the departments during the year, and that in any case this will be sufficient to pay the usual inevitable expenditure on Supplementary Estimates for minor contingencies. My intention is, if I should remain responsible, that whatever surplus is realised at the end of the year, should go, like its predecessors, to strengthen the Suspensory Fund and still further lengthen the period before the full weight of the new rating reliefs measures itself against the expanding revenues of the Exchequer.

Procedure

I will now explain an important departure in procedure upon which we have resolved. It arises naturally and inevitably from the circumstances in which we stand.

Everyone wishes to proceed as soon as possible to the General Election, and all parties are making arrangements on that basis. The limits of Parliamentary time are therefore fixed with much rigidity. We have only a very few days. On the other hand, I must present the Budget scheme for the finances of the year in its integrity. That cannot be done in any Finance Bill which can receive the Royal Assent before the General Election. We therefore propose this year to have two Finance Bills. The first will contain only the necessary provisions to express the Government policy and carry on the public services. All the complicated consequential Clauses will be left to the new Parliament. The Opposition, if successful in the battle, will have the pleasure of passing or repudiating all the machinery Clauses, and will have plenty of time to do so. The first Finance Bill will therefore contain only those—

Lieut.-Commander Kenworthy: You are running away from it.

Mr. Churchill: On the contrary. It will contain only those Clauses necessary to the protection of the revenue, namely, the continuance of the Income Tax and its very small companion, the duty on hops; the repeal of the Tea Duty and of the Betting Duty on turnover, and the repeal of the Railway Passenger Duty. Concurrently with this first Finance Bill, a White Paper will be laid setting forth the draft Clauses left to be dealt with in the new Parliament. They are not of an exciting character at all, but may easily take a long time. It follows from this procedure that we do not intend this Session to move the general Resolution for the Amendment of the Law. It will, therefore, not be open to hon. Members to move a long series of new Clauses setting forth electioneering lures and wiles until after the election has taken place. It will not be possible, for instance, to bring forward new Clauses of a vote-catching character for greatly improving the universe and then forcing the supporters of any responsible Government to vote against them. On the other hand, the Government will facilitate by every means in their power the fullest possible general discussion upon the Budget proposals as a whole, and it may be that the repeal of the Tea Duty, if the permission of the Chair can be obtained, will afford a convenient vehicle for such a Debate. This will conduce to the efficient despatch of public business and the convenience of the House.

General Summary

In this very lengthy statement, during which the House has shown me such exceptional consideration and indulgence, I have thought it right to lay forth fully the financial situation, but I have not attempted to deal with the wider issue of Imperial and social development which will naturally constitute the main portion of the programme upon which His Majesty's Government intend to submit themselves to the country. I have confined myself to that considerable range of business which directly affects the finance of the present year. The main policy which we should pursue in the new Parliament will be set forth by my right hon. Friend the Prime Minister, at what may be called an early and a suitable occasion. I should like, therefore, in presenting my fifth Budget to add a very few words of general summary. Anyone can see that the coal disasters of 1925 and 1926 created a situation very different from that with which I hoped to deal. If I could have foreseen the lamentable course of events, I should certainly not have remitted 6d. from the Income Tax in 1925, but once the standard rate has been reduced to a clear cut figure like 4s. in the £, it would have been very injurious and very vexatious to raise it again. Neither did I wish in any way to detract from the great remissions of indirect taxation which had made the Budget of my predecessor in 1924 memorable. The last three years have been a struggle on my part to avoid reimposing either oppressive direct taxation or trenching upon the relief of the taxation of the comforts of the people which he had given. In this, I claim to have been successful. I have maintained, upon the average of the five Budgets, payments to the Sinking Fund and upon the accumulated interest of Savings Certificates substantially greater than those which were made in former days.

The successful re-establishment of the Gold Standard will still be regarded as a memorable event long after the exertions and sacrifices it has entailed have been forgotten. The preferences upon Empire products, notably upon wine, sugar and tobacco, have been carried to the furthest point that they have yet attained with a remarkable accompanying growth of inter-Imperial trade. I have spoken already of the remissions of taxation which it has been possible to effect. As far as expenditure is concerned, the upward trend has been stopped. It has proved beyond my power to reduce it as much as I had hoped. At any rate, it has been controlled, and it is £6,000,000 less, on a strictly comparable basis, than it was five years ago. Notwithstanding all this, the means have been found to inaugurate and to finance for periods extending far beyond the lifetime of the present Parliament the two most considerable Measures of domestic reform with which I am acquainted, namely, the immense extension of the Pensions and Insurance scheme in 1925, and the relief of productive industry and the rating reform scheme of my right hon. Friend the Minister of Health, in 1928.

I feel that the corner in our economic fortunes may well now have been turned. There are no causes, apart from fresh causes of our own making, which should prevent the next four or five years being easier and more fruitful than those through which we have made our way. The future lies freely in our hands. Reviving trade, lower unemployment, expanding revenues, cheaper money, more favourable conditions for debt conversion, lie before us at this moment as reasonable and tangible probabilities. We can by wisdom and public spirit bring them nearer and realise these long sought for advantages. We can by faction, violence, and folly drive them far away again. The future is inscrutable, and it is equally vain to prophesy or boast, but for my part I have faith in the fair play and august common sense of the British nation, and to their judgment now, and in later years, I submit with confidence the financial record of a Conservative Administration.

Charge of Income Tax

Motion made, and Question proposed,

That—
(a) income tax for the year 1929-30 shall be charged at the standard rate of four shillings in the pound, and in the case of an individual whose

total income from all sources exceeds two thousand pounds, at the same higher rates in respect of the excess over two thousand pounds as were charged for the year 1928-29;

(*b*) all such enactments as had effect with respect to the income tax charged for the year 1928-29 (other than subsection (3) of section twenty-nine and subsection (2) of section thirty-two of the Finance Act, 1926, and section twenty-eight of the Finance Act, 1927), shall have effect with respect to the income tax charged for the year 1929-30;

(*c*) the annual value of any property which has been adopted for the purpose of income tax under Schedules A and B for the year 1928-29 shall be taken as the annual value of that property for the same purpose for the year 1929-30;

Provided that the foregoing provision relating to annual value shall not apply to lands, tenements and hereditaments in the administrative county of London with respect to which the valuation list under the Valuation (Metropolis) Act, 1869, is by that Act made conclusive for the purposes of income tax.

And it is declared that it is expedient in the public interest that this resolution shall have statutory effect under the provisions of the Provisional Collection of Taxes Act, 1913—[*Mr. Churchill.*]

RADIUM RESEARCH

April 16, 1929

House of Commons

In view of the importance of the matter and the public interest attracted by it, the Government arranged for the immediate publication of the Report, and it will be available in the Vote Office this afternoon. It will be seen that the Report deals with the national requirements for radium in medical treatment, in the Fighting Services, and for the purposes of physical research, and with the possibilities of developing new sources of supply. Further, in a full statement as to the use of radium in medical treatment, the Sub-Committee indicate that a great volume of avoidable distress and suffering persists simply because the radium required for the treatment of cancer is not available; and that the acquisition of further supplies should encourage the wider development of the highest skill in its use, and the allocation of more hospital beds to the treatment of suitable cases.

The Sub-Committee expresses the opinion that in order to meet the requirements of England and Wales, and of Scotland, 20 grammes of radium, in addition to the stocks already available, or likely to be available shortly, for general medical use, should be acquired within a specified period, namely, before the end of 1930. The Sub-Committee recommend that the necessary sum, estimated at £200,000, should be raised by a public appeal to which the Government should contribute pound for pound within that maximum sum. The Sub-Committee also propose the setting up of an organisation consisting, first, of a body to hold the funds and purchase and hold the radium, and secondly, of a body to distribute the radium and secure its full use in the manner best adapted to further the advancement of knowledge and the treatment of the sick.

As regards the recommendations of the Sub-Committee on the subject of the organisation, these have been accepted in principle by the Government, but the precise form of the organisation will remain open to further discussion. The Government have accepted the financial recommendation of the Sub-Committee, and they will be prepared to contribute from public funds, up to a maximum of £100,000, to the extent of £1 for every £1 of private subscription for the purchase of additional radium. The Government confidently expect that there will be no difficulty in raising, in a very short space of time, the funds necessary to provide this invaluable addition to the national resources for dealing with one of the most formidable maladies known to us.

THE BUDGET (WAR DEBTS)

April 17, 1929

House of Commons

I think we really must have a little more information about this subject [the Labour policy on the Balfour Note and war debts], and must look into it a little more closely. There was one moment during the statement of the right hon. Gentleman [Mr. Snowden] when I thought he was going to do what everyone in this House, I think, almost in every quarter, would have liked to see him do—

Hon. Members: Nothing of the kind!

Mr. Shinwell: You speak for yourself.

Mr. Churchill: —admit that on the spur of the moment he went beyond what prudence requires and what is demanded of anyone who has the responsibility of having held high office under the Crown and of being among the official leaders of a party aspiring to office and to power. But the right hon. Gentleman only held out this hope in order to dash it to the ground. He said in the most brazen manner that even if he could have considered these matters with the utmost care, and cold and deliberate study beforehand, he could have found no form of words more exactly capable of expressing his meaning than those which he used. Very well. Then let us look into these words with searching attention. I am anxious, above all things, that we should arrive at a perfectly clear understanding of what is the official policy of the Labour party in regard to the Balfour Note and the debt settlements. We have a right to know it. The country has a right to know, the House has a right to know, and the world has a right to know, what is the view which the official Opposition takes of the contractual and responsible and plighted obligations of the State. The right hon. Gentleman said, according to the *Official Report*, which he has quoted:

We have never subscribed, let it be remembered, to the principle of the
Balfour Note. I think that was an infamous Note.

I was astounded at that remark and I naturally asked—it naturally occurred to me to
inquire—who was "We"? I said:

The Labour party.

The right hon. Gentleman then said:

The Labour party! Certainly, we did not. And we should hold ourselves
open, if the circumstances arose, to repudiate the conditions of that Note.

The right hon. Gentleman has now given some account of the Note. He read out from
it some admirable phrases with which he said he agreed, but he has not at all told the
House what was the condition of the Note which he had in his mind that rendered it
infamous and called for repudiation.

Mr. Snowden: I should like—

Mr. Churchill: Pardon me. Let me go on a moment to the three or four lines in
his speech before those I have quoted. I am astonished that the right hon. Gentleman
should like to have those lines quoted, in a sense of relief to him, because they are the
gravamen of the case against him. Three or four lines previously, which I carefully
omitted to put to him till this moment, he used these words:

Perhaps the worse feature of all in the agreements which the right hon.
Gentleman has made is this: That if ever we get more from those annuities
and German reparations than our payments to the United States we have
to reduce the amount of the annuities to be received from our Continental
debtors.—[Official Report, 16th April, 1929; cols. 120-1, Vol. 127.]

It was to that, he said, "We have never subscribed." Let us see where we are. The right
hon. Gentleman said the policy of the Labour party is to welcome a general cancellation of all those debts. How does he reconcile a wish for the general cancellation of all
these debts with this strident assertion that he will insist, if he has the power, on
reclaiming more from ruined Europe, wring harsher terms from ruined Europe, from
Germany, from all the other countries on the Continent, even over and above the sums
of money that we have undertaken to pay in our duty to the United States? That is
the point which I am going to invite, and which the Government invite, the Leader of
the Opposition to deal with.

We have had seven years of these arrangements on the Continent of Europe. Ever
since the Balfour Note was written this country has been able to go into any
international gathering with clean hands and a good conscience. There has not been
any foreign country, even poor little countries from whom we had to demand
payment of their war debts, countries which appealed in piteous terms for mitigation,
to which we have not been able to say, "We have never taken and never will take a

penny more from Europe than what is required, on the other hand, from ourselves."
That has been the foundation of the decent relations of the people of this island and
the Government of this country with all the Governments of Europe, and it has been,
if not the sole foundation, at least the underlying principle, the accepted condition, of
every one of those steps which have been taken in order to place the affairs of Europe
on a more peaceful and solid basis. At this very moment in the international
discussions which are proceeding among the Committee of Experts, of which, as my
right hon. Friend has said, such high hopes are entertained—whether they will be
realised or not I cannot tell—there is a recognition on the part of others and an
assertion on the part of this country that the principles of the Balfour Note must be
maintained; and above all, we place the proud principle that we ourselves will make no
profit or advantage out of this. We will take no more from our Allies or from our
beaten enemies than is required to pay our obligations. And here is the right hon.
Gentleman, who comes forward as an advocate of a peaceful policy, who tries to make
out that he and his party represent the true spirit of the Leauge of Nations,
deliberately saying that if the Labour party have power and office they will hold
themselves free to repudiate the agreements that we have made with Italy and with
France under which no more will be taken from them than is required by the United
States, and will use his power, so far as he can, in order to extract larger sums of
money and make a profit out of those terrible transactions.

There is one other remark which I must make before I sit down. The right hon.
Gentleman used a word, a most offensive word, about a friendly nation and our
nearest neighbour. He accused the nation of being "bilkers," or of "bilking"—an
offensive, slang term from the gutter, used in order to convey hatred and contempt for
a nation with whom we have the closest, most intimate and friendly relations, and
with whom we have been through the most terrible ordeal of history. What is the use
of using such a term? If any Member of a Government had used such an expression
about a nation with whom we have relations, undoubtedly it would have been
considered a fatal step in his career, and I think we have a right to ask of the Leader of
the Opposition some similar attempt to preserve courteous relations between us and
the—[An Hon. Member: "Russians."] We have no relations with the Russians.

Mr. Shinwell: What about the £100,000,000 you spent in Russia. [Hon. Members: "Order!"] Order yourselves!

Mr. Churchill: At any rate, I hope the last word has not been spoken on this
matter. The right hon. Gentleman the Leader of the Opposition has a responsibility.
He has played a distinguished part in the appeasement of Europe, I have testified to it
on other occasions. I have never failed to testify, nor has my right hon. Friend the
Foreign Secretary, to the great contribution of the Agreement of London which
inaugurated the Dawes Scheme. He tells us again and again that he hopes and expects
to be again entrusted with power. Whether that be so or not has yet to be determined,
but at any rate for his own sake and for the sake of his party, for the sake of the cause
of Europe, I invite him to give a more loyal and faithful answer to the question which
has been formally put to him than we have received from the right hon. Gentleman.

[Much later] This is a matter which is really of very great importance, and it
ought to be discussed without any heat. I accept altogether what the right hon.

Gentleman the Leader of the Opposition has said, but what I invite him to do is to reconcile what he has said with these words. [*Interruption.*] It is a perfectly simple point, and a very grave point. The ex-Chancellor of the Exchequer said yesterday:

> Does the right hon. Gentleman then maintain that an agreement which is made by a Government supported by a party which happens to have a temporary majority in the House of Commons commits every other party in the State to the confirmation and the acceptance of that agreement in the future? If that be so, it is a doctrine to which I cannot subscribe.

I have heard with very great pleasure the statement of the right hon. Gentleman the Leader of the Opposition that he has definitely repudiated that remark.

Mr. MacDonald: I emphatically repudiate that method of dealing with statements made in this House. What did my right hon. Friend say? [An Hon. Member: "Twister!"] I am afraid that that interruption reflects more upon the maker of it than upon those against whom it is made. My right hon. Friend's statement was that agreements made are not going to be sacred against revision. Is there any objection to that?

Mr. Churchill: Revision with the consent of the other parties.

Mr. MacDonald: Is there anything in the statement which the Chancellor of the Exchequer has quoted that is opposed to that suggestion?

Mr. Churchill: Certainly. The statement is introduced by the word "repudiate" in the paragraph preceding:

> And we should hold ourselves open, if the circumstances arose, to repudiate the conditions of that note.—[Official Report, 16th April, 1929; col. 121, Vol. 227.]

[Later] I am sure that there is no one, in whatever part of the Committee he sits, who has not extended a full measure of sympathy to the right hon. Gentleman, the Leader of the Opposition. For my part, I think that I may express a very general opinion when I add to that measure of sympathy a mead of admiration, first of all for his loyalty, and secondly for his skill. His loyalty and his skill together have enabled him to treat the matter before the Committee in such a fashion that, in the first place, he covered up the fatal indiscretion of his colleague in vague platitudes and, in the second place, he placed a solid wad and pad of three-quarters of an hour of verbiage between him and the very simple and calm issue upon which Parliament and the House of Commons is determined to have a perfectly clear decision.

I am not going to take up the time of the Committee unduly, and I am not going to try to raise the temper of the Committee by anything I shall say. I am only going to ask for a perfectly clear and definite response because certain issues were raised yesterday. I hoped that they were raised inadvertently, but the right hon. Gentleman the Member for Colne Valley (Mr. Snowden) came down here to-day, and made it perfectly clear that it was no question of words chosen on the spur of the moment. He made it perfectly clear that it was his deliberate, solid political position. I should like to remind the Committee that I gave the right hon. Gentleman a friendly warning yesterday. I am on record in the *Official Report*. The moment that he used this fatal word "repudiation," which in 24 hours had tinkled round the globe, I rose, and he was rather reluctant to give way, but I think that I put it to him in an absolutely calm, and not an irritating manner, whether he had not better just think it over and put it a little differently. [*Interruption*]. Whatever I have to say I am going to say.

The right hon. Gentleman came down here to-day and repeated and reiterated what he had said yesterday, and that raised a very grave issue. After all, the whole modern feeling is that great parties, great countries and great communities are not to be brought into squabbles or controversies or confusions on account of any pique or pride of individuals. The whole tendency of the modern age is that individuals must subordinate themselves to the general movement of large communities. We cannot have our relations with our nearest neighbour destroyed and impaired by the prejudice and ill-feeling, personal ill-feeling, of a single individual, however eminent he may be, nor has anyone a right to twist or distort the foreign policy of a party or of a country merely because in the course of his political activities he has been led into taking up an utterly untenable and indefensible position. Let us just see exactly where we stand in this matter. I am not going to take up the time of the Committee unduly. There are two points at issue, only two points at issue. The first is the point which the right hon. Member for Colne Valley unfolded yesterday when he said to me:

> Does the right hon. Gentleman then maintain that an agreement which is made by a Government supported by a party which happens to have a temporary majority in the House of Commons commits every other party in the State to the confirmation and the acceptance of that agreement in the future? If that be so, it is a doctrine to which I cannot subscribe.— [Official Report, 16th April, 1929; col. 121, Vol. 227.]

Now I understand that is completely withdrawn by the Leader of the Opposition. [Hon. Members: "No!"] Well, is it or is it not? [Hon. Members: "Answer!"] I am not out to press a party point against a Parliamentarian whom I admire as I do the right hon. Gentleman the Member for Colne Valley; it is too important for that. This is the vital basis of the credit of our—[An Hon. Member: "Election!"] —No, you are really wrong if you think that. It is the vital foundation of our national credit. Is it to be understood that, whatever Government is in power, the honourable obligations into which this country has entered will be honoured, however inconvenient they may be, and will faithfully be carried out? That is what I understand to be the declaration of the right hon. Gentleman—[*Interruption.*] —It is so? Now come, he can give an answer to that. [Hon. Members: "Answer!"] I ask that, not to humiliate the right hon. Member for Colne Valley, but to increase the efficiency of the general policy of this country. Anyhow, I will not push it further; but I take it that the statement made in so very few sentences, clear cut, crystal sentences, by the right hon. Gentleman the Member for West Swansea (Mr. Runciman) on behalf of the Liberal party does define definitely the position which is now adopted by the leader of the Labour party.

Mr. MacDonald: In my own words.

Mr. Churchill: In your own words. Now let me come to the second point. The right hon. Member for Colne Valley described the Balfour Note as an "infamous" document, and of all the adjectives that might have been ill-chosen there was hardly one which could have been selected in the dictionary which less described that statesmanlike document, a document which has been accepted of a just cause and which has reconciled nations who have felt that the payment of their debts was a cruel infliction upon them when they were seeking to recover from the War.

The right hon. Gentleman said yesterday

> that if ever we get more from those annuities and German reparations than our payments to the United States, we have to reduce the amount of the annuities to be received from our continental debtors. We have never subscribed, let it be remembered, to the principle of the Balfour Note. I think that was an infamous Note—[Official Report, 16th April, 1929; cols. 120-121, Vol. 227.]

I understand—and must have an answer—[*Interruption*]—that the position of the Labour party is that they agree with the principle of the Balfour Note that we are to take no more from Europe than we have to pay to the United States. Is that so, or is it not so? After all, the country and the world is going to read this discussion, and are you not going to say whether your policy is to take more from Europe than America extracts from us or not? I have never seen a situation where a great leader of a party has been unable to say. [*Interruption.*] I am going to put it to the right hon. Gentleman directly—it is extremely important—whether or not they are going to take more from Europe than the United States take from us? Any man who takes a part in politics must be prepared to face the responsibility, and no man on those benches has the right to make a statement except on the basis that he may be responsible. I am not going to take "No" for an answer. [*Interruption.*] I beg the right hon. Gentleman to give me a definite answer to the question—Is it clearly understood that the policy of the Labour party is not to take more from Europe than we have to pay to America? [Hon. Members: "Answer!"] I do not wish to obstruct the right hon. Gentleman, but has it really come to this, that the Leader of the Opposition dare not rise in his place and give an answer to that simple question? I must admit that the resources of interrogation and argument are exhausted, and I commit and commend to the attention of the country the fact that the Labour party and the late Prime Minister of this country are incapable of answering a perfectly plain and simple question, which has been put to them although it is one which affects the livelihood of the people of this country, and the Leader of the Opposition sits there without daring to open his mouth.

THE BUDGET (BETTING DUTY)

April 22, 1929

House of Commons

Everyone, I am sure, will be pleased and relieved to see [Mr. Snowden] and to hear the right hon. Gentleman disporting himself in a sphere where he is not likely to do any serious harm; in a sphere in which he can use that beloved word, which so readily leaps to his lips, "repudiate," without carrying such far-reaching echoes throughout the world. For my part, I should be the last to begrudge him any momentary satisfaction which he may enjoy by gloating upon the failure, upon what I myself called the fiasco, of the Betting Duty. He is entitled to say: "I told you so." He is entitled to claim from the House of Commons the respect and admiration which it should rightly extend to those who have proved to be true prophets. But, of course, in his general attitude, towards the taxation which it has been my duty to propose during this Parliament, he has placed himself in a position where in the event of any failure by any chance he certainly would be able to say: "I told you so," because there has been no tax of any kind that has been proposed about which he has not made the most confident prediction of failure. It was not upon the Betting Duty that I would particularly advise him to read his previous speeches; it was upon the Silk Duties that I would advise him to consider what he has said in the past.

I frankly admit that the Betting Duty has not succeeded. What are the reasons? I am not going to embark upon a lengthy discussion of the tax. "I come to bury Caesar, not to praise him," or to dispraise him. I have only risen because I did not wish it to be thought that the Government were affording any opportunity for complaint by not sufficiently participating in this tranquil and even lifeless Debate. The main reason why I have felt that we should revise this tax has been the fact that it was honeycombed with evasions. There is no doubt whatever that the bookmaker, the betting fraternity, if I may use such a term in that connection, have been more elusive, less capable of being drawn into the meshes of our fiscal regulations than any other similar body of citizens upon whom it has been sought to lay a burden. Great unfairness arose in regard to the reputable man who had premises, a fixed and definable and recognised position or pitch, which is the expression used in this connection, I think. By the way, the right hon. Gentleman's word "bilked" might really come in here, and might more appropriately have been applied to the book-makers who have succeeded in evading a tax than to the Government of a friendly country. Undoubtedly, great injury was inflicted upon the reputable bookmaker who paid the tax, because he was actually undercut by his less identifiable rival. Therefore, from that point of view I have felt that it was very difficult to defend the continuance of a tax on turnover.

The right hon. Gentleman said that we ought to make a total repeal of the Duty because it attacks a great moral and conscientious principle which, apparently lays it down that on no account must any fiscal discouragement be placed upon an evil like betting. I never felt myself that there was any sound valid good sense behind that argument, although I admit that it has played its part in public thought. When the tax was first introduced, it was extraordinary to me what little part that argument really played in the opposition to the tax. On the contrary, I received deputations from the Free Churches and other religious bodies who were, undoubtedly, protesting against the tax but who, at the same time, did not conceal from me the dilemma of thought in which they found themselves. It was apparent to me that there was a strong religious and moral feeling which felt that if the total volume of betting could be diminished as a result of an impost placed upon it, the matter was one which was well worth considering in a cool and dispassionate spirit.

These Licence Duties, which will, of course, be the subject of full discussion when we meet again after our excursions in the country, will be easy to collect. I am quite ready to discuss their details if I should still be responsible for them. I am not necessarily absolutely adhering to the exact form of the Clause which will appear in the White Paper, but in principle all the inquiries which we have been able to make from a very large section of the betting industry have led us to believe that this revised form of Duty can quite easily be collected, and without undue hardship. Take the case of the bookmaker who deals with very small sums of money and uses a single telephone for that purpose. That question has been raised, but for the present I rest myself upon the Duties, as they are set out in the White Paper, and I have no doubt that the revenue that I have mentioned can be raised in this way.

As to the totalisator, the right hon. Gentleman is going to repudiate that as well as other things. He has endeavoured to throw, as far as possible, that element of uncertainty over the initiation of this new instrument which he is so ready to cast over so many spheres of our daily life and of our fiscal law. We all know how he has declared that there is a whole series of duties which I shall not mention, which he is going to repeal if he has the chance. Industries are kept in a state of uncertainty as to their development because of his indulgence in pure political partisanship; and no doubt in those few words he has done the best he can to do as much harm as is possible in impeding the introduction on our race-courses of an instrument which undoubtedly will have a most cleansing and healthy effect upon the whole life of racing in this country, and also upon the conditions and the character of our race-courses. It is only a small blow that he can strike, and a blow at only a small object, but he strikes it, with that universal malevolence which seems to have taken hold of him at this moment—and quite unaccountably, for he tells us that he believes he will soon be in a place of power and authority, and one would have thought that he would have been mellowed by the prospect and put into a good humour, and also restrained by a sense of approaching responsibility. Notwithstanding that, he chooses to cast this universal web of malevolence, prejudice and uncertainty over a wide field, and in that wide field he has not ignored the smallest as well as the greatest things.

ELECTION ADDRESS

April 27, 1929

Conservative Meeting,
Sevenoaks, Kent

The General Election of May 1929 was a three-party contest, with each party putting up more than five hundred candidates. The Conservatives fought on the theme of "Safety First"; the Labour campaign concentrated essentially on the persistence of unemployment; the Liberals produced the most articulate programme, authored by John Maynard Keynes and Hubert Henderson. The weakness of the Liberal position lay in the continued divisions within the party, and by the fact that their programme was both ahead of its time and beyond the comprehension of most electors. In the event, Labour won 288 seats, the Conservatives 26 and Liberals 59. Baldwin resigned immediately and James Ramsay MacDonald became Prime Minister on June 5.

[Extract] . . . It is probable that but for the general strike and the coal stoppage, unemployment now would have ceased to hang heavily on the minds of thinking men and women, and would have been reduced to normal proportions.

. . . Of the figure of 1,150,000 unemployed, 600,000 was the pre-War normal figure which would probably have come under insurance benefits. Women and juveniles account for 260,000. That leaves a total of about 300,000. For a statesman to go round the country pretending that the whole of the forces of this great centre of a world-wide Empire and all its fortunes should be decided at a General Election by what is remedial treatment to be meted out to 300,000 unemployed is unworthy of the serious attention of an educated electorate.

Nearly one-third of the unemployment in the coalfields of 12 months ago has been eliminated. Juvenile unemployment is decreasing, and will continue to decrease. My hearers should be on their guard against the treacherous tricks which are about to be played upon the country by people who are seeking to exploit the miseries of the unemployed in order that they may find themselves employment of a different character, and who do not hesitate to try to rattle the country into taking wasteful steps of a subversive character calculated to injure our credit and even our national welfare under the pretext that those are the remedies that would cure unemployment.

The Socialist Party have their remedy—taxation. Though this country has the heaviest direct taxation of any country in the world, it is proposed to make a very large increase in the income-tax and other direct taxes.

The whole of the policy they are putting forward is nothing less than a policy of pillage and plunder and is designed to subvert the existing system of society and it is put forward under the pretext of finding some employment for the unemployed.

If the Socialist Party advance under the banner of plunder, I am indeed sorry to see the party led by Mr. Lloyd George with a policy of squander. Plunder and squander—those are the watchwords of our opponents. For all these years we have been exhorted to practise economy and have tried so far as we can to save money here, to reduce expenditure there. We have tried to pay off debts as fast as we can, having regard to the tax made on us by the general strike. When we have been trying to save a little and improve the national credit by the payment of debts, that is the moment that Mr. Lloyd George comes forward and says, "I will cure unemployment by borrowing £200,000,000 and spending it on roads and telephones."

How crude, barbarous, and ignorant is a policy which would gather hundreds of thousands of unemployed together in gangs and set them to make racing tracks for Liberal profiteers to run their cars upon. Far better than this expenditure on roads would be a more energetic development of railroads. That the railroads should be struck at and injured by a wasteful, State-subsidized scheme of road development is, in itself, one of the proofs of the careless and ignorant solution which Mr. Lloyd George proposes for the problem of unemployment.

The borrowing of the £200,000,000 would mean that the State would "barge in" on the money market as a competitor with industry and with every other form of enterprise, forcing the rate of money up, making it more expensive for every man, especially the small man, to obtain the credit he required for the development of his business. If unemployment is to be brought to normal proportions it must be the improvement in the trade of the country.

I greatly regret that the railways have not further advanced in the process of modernization and equipment. Undoubtedly the railways have far more to offer to the heavy industries of the country and to the general trade of the country than the development of the roads. The roads in Britain are already the best in the world, and we are already spending more on them than any other country in Europe. The railways are capable of great modernization and advance, and that is unquestionably one of the practical tasks that could reasonably be undertaken in the scope of the next Parliament.

I am not going into this fight with any fear or doubt of the issue. We have a good record, a great cause, and a trusted leader. Our Socialist opponents are only formidable when they are feared. Only last week in the House of Commons, during the discussion on the Budget, the Socialist Party, once they were tackled by the Conservative forces, were reduced to moral incoherence and physical pulp. Already they are squealing at the criticism to which they are subjected, but that is nothing to what they are going to get when we set about them. (Cheers.)

Let us go into this fight with a good heart, clear convictions, and a firm resolve to do our utmost. Let us be united on a platform broad enough to embrace all those forces which were with us when, over two years ago, we broke the back of the general strike.

It is in the South where conditions are stable and tranquil, and co-operation between the parties was carried to a high point, where the accursed doctrine of class warfare and industrial strife had the least support and acceptance, that there is to be found the greatest measure of prosperity. It is those parts where there is the most hearkening to the pernicious doctrine of Socialism that have suffered most in the last few years. There can be no revival of industry in any district where there is no hearty good feeling and good will and good citizenship between all classes.

THE GENERAL ELECTION

April 30, 1929

Broadcast, London

In making up one's mind about political questions, it is important to go to the root of the matter. Four years ago 5,000,000 tons of coal were cut in a week by 1,200,000 men. This year 5,000,000 tons of coal were cut in a week by less than 950,000 men. That means that the British coal trade, which was the foundation of our industrial strength and one of our most important exports, has become a great deal more efficient and better able to hold its own. That is a good thing for the country. Secondly, it means that the wages available from the proceeds of the coal go to four families whereas they used to be spread over five. That must, in the long run, be a good thing for the miners. But what has happened to the quarter of a million men who hitherto were living on the mining industry and have now lost their jobs? They have been thrown upon the labour market and have (for the time being) joined the numbers of the unemployed. That is hard upon them and very difficult for the Government. However, by stopping outsiders from going into the coalmines, by transferring the displaced miners to other work, and by training young men and boys in the colliery districts in other trades or for settlement in the Empire, we have succeeded already in reducing the number of surplus miners from 250,000 to 130,000, and this process is rapidly going on.

Another root fact is the British system of Unemployment Insurance. No other country has anything like so large and thorough a system. Twelve million workers together with their employers and the State are made to pay so many pence a week while they are in work in order that when the workers are moving from job to job, or particular industries are slack, or men are thrown out by hard weather, they have a means of subsistence provided, which they have earned and paid for in advance. No doubt we have often heard ignorant people describe this as a dole. But provided the man paid his due contributions it is no dole at all, but simply the proper working of a scientifically organized prudence.

There is, in fact (apart from the miners), no standing army of over 1,000,000 unemployed. There are, on the contrary, a much larger number of people who are from time to time unemployed and who then draw the benefits to which they are entitled. If the trade of the country were to improve, hundreds of thousands of people would still lose time moving from one job to another. They would still be thrown out by hard weather and what are called seasonal and cyclical depressions in particular trades. But they would lose less time as trade improved in moving from job to job, and the 11 weeks which is the average benefit drawn by the course of a year now would be steadily shortened. If it were reduced to five weeks then we should be in as good a position, indeed rather a better position, than before the War.

If you understand that system you can easily see how very unsuitable and indeed, vicious is the remedy which Mr. Lloyd George has proposed of gathering larger numbers of unemployed persons to gather into gangs and setting them to make roads for motorcars. In many cases work on the roads would spoil men's hands for their own trades. It would not be suitable work for the older men, who form the largest proportion of those who are longest unemployed. It would interrupt the whole natural recovery of industry, and when the money for the relief work had been spent they might, it is true, have a good many more fine roads for motorists to go forty or fifty miles an hour upon, but the people who had made them would be thrown back upon the labour market, they would return to empty homes and the country would be saddled for several generations with the interest upon the money that had been borrowed and spent.

Mr. Lloyd George said that the election was to be fought on unemployment; but Mr. Ramsay MacDonald said, "I object strongly to the woes and troubles of the unemployed being exploited for election purposes." I hope Mr. MacDonald will live up to that statement during the next few weeks. It is a great temptation to irresponsible people who are looking for votes to say at election times that they have a sure remedy. It is easy to say, "I can cure it; only take my patent medicine and you will be well." The Socialists say, "If only you will nationalize everything and manage everybody's affairs by officials, and fill in plenty of paper forms, you will be cured." The inflationists—the people who think that everything can be put right by manipulating the currency—tell us that they have only to pretend that every 10d. in their pocket is really worth a shilling, and that that will cure unemployment. Lastly, there is Mr. Lloyd George, who said in short, I am not quoting him, "Borrow money freely and splash it about well, and all will come right—as long as I do the splashing." The question to ask yourselves about all these quack remedies is not whether they can make things better—they will certainly not do that—but whether they will not make them positively worse.

The only way in which things can be made better is by a general improvement in British trade. There has in the last four or five years been a considerable improvement. The balance of trade is less unfavourable and 600,000 more people have found employment. The amount of credit available for starting new British enterprises has greatly increased. Many of our industries under the pinch of hard times have adopted the latest machinery and better methods.

Although a third of our capital was spent in the war we are wealthier. There is no reason whatever for being downhearted. On the contrary, our prospects are bright if we do not spoil them.

I find it very difficult to believe that there is any short cut to prosperity. We have to march forward steadfastly along the high road. It may be dusty, it may be stony, it may be dull, it is certainly uphill all the way. But to leave it is only to flounder in the quagmires of delusion and have your coat torn off you by the brambles of waste. It is a good and plainly-marked road; the signposts are all well-known; they were set up by the wisdom and experience of those who have gone before us. Here are some of them:—Peace abroad; steady, stable government at home; clean, honest, impartial

Speeches of Winston Churchill

administration; good will in industry and cooperation between masters and men; public and private thrift. Lighten the burdens of galling rates and so forth upon productive industry and agriculture. Modernize factories and businesses; modernize particularly the railways, which are much behind the times, far more behind the times than your roads. Multiply and strengthen the hold upon markets abroad, especially those priceless new markets which are offered in the Empire. Cheapen the cost of living to the mass of the people as much as possible. That will not only promote contentment, but it will give industries in the long run a greater competitive power in the world market. Avoid chops and changes of policy; avoid thimble-riggers and three-card trick men; avoid all needless borrowings; and, above all, avoid as you would avoid the smallpox class warfare and violent political strife.

The issue at the election is much larger than unemployment. It is the well-being of the whole British people and the position of Britain and her Empire in the modern world. That and nothing less is what is at stake. Powerful, mighty countries are towering up as rivals—peaceful rivals it might be—but rivals none the less; competitors with us in every form of human activity. What are these other countries doing? Is there one that is not trying to make the most of itself? Are they not all engaged in setting up firm and steady systems of government and trying to assert their national rights and interests in the strongest manner? On the Continent of Europe we see many people actually casting down their Parliaments, abandoning the liberties they gained in the 19th century, setting up authoritarian forms of government in order, as they think, the better to take part in the intensified economic and political struggles. Look at the United States. The vast American democracy does not throw many chances away. It had pursued since the War a far more steady and purposeful policy than we have. The American democracy has no doubt many problems which we should not like to have here; but it adds, by every national vote it gives, to the solidity of its institutions, to the security of its capitalist system, and to the advancement of American interests and American power in every quarter of the globe.

These are critical years for the British Empire. Will it with its many communities and widespread races draw more closely together or drift apart and fall to pieces? If we can come through this critical period and draw ever closer together, then, indeed, we should be the equal of any organization yet founded among men, and the British Empire and the United States could walk forward side by side, leading mankind in majesty and peace.

ELECTION ADDRESS

May 7, 1929

Usher Hall, Edinburgh

[Extract] . . . Mr. Lloyd George seems to be unduly hurt because I have advised the electors not to be taken in by quackery, charlatanism, or thimble-rigging. I do not see why he should be when he is perfectly ready to take to his bosom Sir John Simon, who only a few months ago condemned his scheme with full knowledge as a cheapjack project. But I am always anxious not to irritate people unnecessarily, and I hereby announce that I will for the future in this election drop the word charlatan, and will instead use the word cheapjack as applied to Mr. Lloyd George's scheme. (Laughter.)

We are told the only issue in this election is unemployment. Whoever can promise to do the most is to be given the power to decide every other question affecting the whole of this mighty community. That sounds fairly silly. No country makes the provision we do for the victims of unemployment. But there is also the case of the employed, which ought not to be entirely overlooked. Both of the Opposition parties are equally interested in exaggerating and exploiting this evil. They see in it a means of getting votes.

Mr. Lloyd George and those associated with him have quite misunderstood the character of unemployment. They speak as if there were a great standing army, but a constantly changing population of between four and five million persons, some of whom at different times come on the unemployment register. It is absurd to mix up the normal working of our unemployment insurance scheme with the evil of the excessive and abnormal unemployment of the present time, and then to present a muddled total in order to alarm the public and mislead foreign countries. The evil is serious enough without exaggerating it.

We are passing through bleak years. They are our lot after the war. No remedy could be more unsuitable, more vicious, than to withdraw large numbers of people and set them to work in gangs on the roads or on drainage. The bulk of those men would be mostly married and over fifty years of age, and the heavy manual work would be cruel and unremunerative. I ask Mr. Lloyd George does he propose that any unemployed man who refused to join the road gangs should be struck off the unemployment benefit or denied outdoor relief. I think we ought to have an answer to that.

So far from being a remedy, the Liberal scheme would disturb the whole natural flow of industry. It would take away men from the trade in which they would soon get work, and set them to work which might unfit them, perhaps for ever, from resuming their own trade. It would take them from their homes; it would squander on a mere palliative hundreds of millions of money. And at the end of two years we would have to face another demobilization problem.

Firstly, Mr. Lloyd George's diagnosis of the character of the disease is wrong. Secondly, it would be physically impossible to apply the remedy he proposes within the time he mentions; and thirdly, if it were possible to apply the remedy, it would do more harm than good. It would delay trade revival; squander public treasure, and cause more unemployment than it would cure.

Great Britain works on a very small margin at present. If she is wise and careful she will just get through. If she behaves recklessly and in a wanton fashion she will be ruined. If asked what our plan is, I answer in one word, "Persevere." There are no short cuts to prosperity.

I have great hopes of the future relations between the British Empire and the United States. The whole fortunes of the world depends on those relations, and we are determined that the great friendship of the English-speaking world shall move forward year by year. But there is no country in the world which has disarmed as much as Great Britain.

Tonight I have dealt with the Lloyd George policy of squander. To-morrow at Glasgow I will deal with the Socialist policy of plunder.

[Editor's Note: Replying to a vote of confidence in the Government, Churchill said]: Nothing impresses me more than the air of composure, calmness, and even indifference with which in some quarters the serious nature of the present situation is viewed. In a few weeks the whole accumulated fortunes of the country might be flung in the melting-pot as a result of a disgusting and dastardly intrigue, or again the government might be handed over to the very men who not three years ago were endeavouring to paralyse the life of the country. The unemployment problem is being used as a means to baffle and confuse the electors. Five hundred candidates, the best part of them bogus, are being run by the Liberal party in every part of the country for no other purpose than to baffle and confuse the decision and to produce a Parliament which would not have power to give any decision on any great question.

ELECTION ADDRESS
May 8, 1929
Glasgow

[Extract] ... There is something very like conspiracy unwitting in some respects, directed against the well-being of our Parliamentary institutions and against the effective sovereignty of this country. The Liberal party, having done their best to exaggerate the question of unemployment, are now running five hundred candidates, of whom they only expect sixty or seventy to be returned. All the others are simply put forward in order to confuse and baffle the voters in 430 or 440 constituencies, where in the great bulk of cases their men will lose their deposits. They are doing it with the deliberate object of producing a Parliament in which no party can have a majority. They are doing it with the object of being able themselves to put undue pressure first upon the Conservatives, and if that fails upon the Socialists. Is that the kind of Parliamentary government we wish to aim at or which we require for the wellbeing of the nation? I cannot conceive a greater misfortune than that the country should be, as it were, held up to auction in that way.

The Liberals justify themselves when they are criticised in this respect by saying the electoral law is unfair to them. I have not denied their grievance, but I say their grievance, however high you put it, does not justify them in sabotaging scores of seats and delivering them to the Socialists. By doing it they are putting themselves on a level with the ruffian who throws a brick through a plate-glass window in order to draw attention to the fact that he is unemployed. More especially is their conduct unjustifiable when we consider that the great bulk of these five hundred candidates will be supported by the Lloyd George fund which was raised for the express and avowed purpose of enabling both Liberals and Conservatives to make common cause against Socialism, and which is now being used for the purpose of securing the return of as large a number of Socialists as possible. It is an unjustifiable action, a breach of faith, of moral faith, although it may not be amenable to legal process.

Supposing the Liberal party have their way. Great Britain has her enemies. Both Mr. Snowden and Mr. Lloyd George reply by asking, Where are her enemies? I thank God there is no great race of men who are her enemies, but her enemies are widespread and intensely malignant to our continuance as a united Empire. If I am challenged to name them I will do so. There is the Communist Government of Russia, which never stops by night or day its attacks in every quarter of the world upon the peace and prosperity of the Empire. The tried in China to hound down the British, and they are now trying to bring about insurrection in India. What does Stalin wish the result of this election to be? We have enemies in Ireland who are also the enemies of the Free State Government. In Egypt there are enemies.

And are there enemies at home? Mr. Cook has said, "Every man who votes for Baldwin votes for a bloody revolution."

No plan to injure the Empire could be better than that for which the Opposition parties, and especially the Liberals, are steadily working. There is to be a meaningless hiatus of government. Then we are to have another general election.

The Socialists have contributed nothing to the discussions on unemployment except an idea of pillaging the country in order to turn it into a vast West Ham. They attack the Lloyd George unemployment scheme, and then in the next breath say: "We are in favour of it. He has taken it from us." They claim the paternity while they abuse the offspring. (Laughter.)

Although the British direct taxation is the heaviest in the world, and although our social services are the most elaborate and costly, the Socialists now propose to put on a new surtax of £80,000,000 a year. I am advised that the yield of such a tax would be about £65,000,000 a year provided it is not only levied on the incomes of individuals but on the reserves and investment incomes of companies. Such a tax would have the most injurious effect on the saving power of the country and the accumulation of those capital funds without which leadership and command in modern world-wide industry cannot be achieved. Their programme is to be put forward in such a way so as not to frighten even the palest of the pink reds. Their plans for nationalizing the coalmines means nothing less than employing miners at shorter hours and larger wages than the great mass of the wage earners of the country, and this at the expense of the community.

ELECTION ADDRESS

May 10, 1929

Chingford

In 1927, Sir John Simon had been appointed Chairman of a special Commission to examine the future of India and to oversee the progress of the constitutional reform of 1919-1920. The Commission did not consider the question of Dominion Status, and its Report was overtaken by events. In 1929 Simon returned to party politics.

[Extract] . . . I am sorry Sir John Simon has come into the political arena again. I do not say that because of the controversial remarks he has made against myself, because I do not really mind in the slightest.

I am sorry, however, that when he was chosen and undertook to occupy the great position of head of the Indian Commission, and when he is connected with events of profound consequence far outside ordinary party politics, that he should have been so attracted by a desire to plunge into the electioneering scrimmage as to damage, as a result, his influence and prestige which he should have for the purpose of the high task with which he was entrusted, and which he undertook. I suppose that Sir John Simon has been angered by the reference to his speech at Cupar in September, when he described Mr. Lloyd George's scheme of trying to cure unemployment by a patent remedy on borrowed money as a cheapjack scheme. It is a great pity that he should have departed from the position of detachment which it is most necessary that he should keep during this election, and he would have far more fittingly discharged his duty to the public if he had preserved the dignity of retirement and concentration upon his task. He would have far more fittingly discharged his duty that way than by coming into this election, taking advantage of the chivalry which has been extended to him and indulging in the rather cheap pastime of firing under the white flag.

I want to ask the Socialist Party what is the taxation which they propose to meet the cost of the programme on which they are seeking votes. As to the mines, the Labour Party would make them one vast West Ham pauperizing agent in order to keep the miners who voted for them at lesser hours of labour and higher rates of wages than are earned by the vast mass of workers throughout the country. The Socialists are frankly appealing to the basest appetites to which they can cater.

It would be folly to overlook the grave character of the fight with which we are faced. There will be many temptations to do so, because the country is tranquil; there is peace in industry, factories, and mines are working more busily every month. There is less social and class bitterness than there has ever been in this country, less anxiety, more freedom, and more well-being. That is after four and a half years of Conservative administration (cheers) but it is easy to smash up tranquillity. Instead of a Socialist Government about to be swept into the streets Mr. MacDonald is demanding a clear majority to rule the country with a Socialistic Government for five years.

The issue is far more serious than that of 1924. In the interval the only contribution the Socialist Party has made to our affairs was the general strike. Had it not been for the general strike I should have had £80,000,000 more to give away in relief of taxation and £400,000,000 would have been spread about the country in the profits of trade and the wages of the workers. All that vitality has gone, and yet we can still, by pressing steadily ahead, by having a strong united country, show a definite and steady advance, but the advance has been retarded by a least two years while our rivals abroad have moved forward. It would be shameful for any constituent not to go through the process of deciding what to do at this juncture when a majority Government is being sought by men who only three years ago were engaged in a criminal conspiracy against Parliament and the Constitution.

The Liberal Party's policy is one of pure squander to win votes. In a desperate effort to gain the attention of the public Mr. Lloyd George proposed a scheme which I am certain no Government in this country of whatever complexion would try to carry out. The roads proposal is one of the most ludicrous propositions ever put forward by a responsible statesman. Are the unemployed going to be conscripted for the road gang? What will happen at the end of two years?

Further, I want to ask you, is the trade of this country going to recover when all the time we are going to borrow £125,000,000 every year to give it to the unemployed for making roads? Shall not we get to the end of the roads we want? This is roadmaking gone mad. We shall not only run short of money, we shall run short of grass. (Laughter.) This road story is one of the greatest pieces of humbug ever seen, and I believe the reason the Liberal Party has fixed upon it is not because of the unemployed but because it hopes to get support from some of the motorists who objected to the Petrol Tax.

ELECTION ADDRESS

May 13, 1929

Roydon

[Extract] . . . Sir Herbert Samuel has stated that I have described the Liberals as quacks, charlatans, thimble riggers, and card sharpers. This is an absurd untruth. In my broadcast I did not apply such terms to any party or to any person. I only applied them to those, whatever party they belonged to, who undertook to affect a permanent cure for unemployment by, firstly, extensive nationalization of industry, secondly, by inflation of currency, and, thirdly, by borrowing vast sums of money and spending them on making more roads for motorcars.

No one who is not committed to any of these three vicious fallacies is involved in that criticism. Those who are committed to any of them can take their pick of those epithets. The Liberals are being committed against all the traditions of Gladstonian finance to an absurd, erroneous, and vicious policy. If the Liberals succumb to the temptations Mr. Lloyd George is now offering them for party purposes it will not be because they are Liberals, but only because they are electioneering politicians, and therefore I repudiate Sir Herbert Samuel's suggestion that any of these censures apply necessarily to them as Liberals or to the Liberal Party.

I think it is one of the meanest things that has ever been done to exploit unemployment for party purposes. The only object of the people who are running it is to get employment for themselves.

During the past four and a half years this country has been better governed than any other country in the world. The cost of living has diminished by 18 points, which means £160,000,000 a year on the purchasing power of the salary and wage earners. The correspondence of the country has increased by 500,000,000 letters. There has been an increase in the number of motor vehicles, despite the petrol tax, of 700,000. The country is a great, going, prosperous concern, but I warn you that it is easy to throw it by thoughtlessness into dire confusion.

ELECTION ADDRESS

May 14, 1929

Woodford

[Extract] . . . The Liberals have only themselves to thank for the publication of the White Paper. When Mr. Lloyd George's pamphlet first appeared the Government set the public departments to work to examine it and to advise Ministers upon it in all its bearings. Their report to the Cabinet riddled Mr. Lloyd George's scheme. The only reason why the Government did not publish the exact text of the reports they received was that they did not wish to bring the officials into electioneering controversy. The Liberal party then set on foot rumours that the officials had been unable to find any flaw in the Lloyd George scheme, and that the Government were therefore suppressing their report. That misstatement was finally repeated on the authority of Sir John Simon himself. The Government therefore were bound to correct this false impression and to present to Parliament a document embodying the facts and arguments submitted by their officials.

To safeguard these officials from being brought into the electioneering atmosphere, the Ministers in every case assumed responsibility in their own names for the various reports. Both in substance and to a large extent in form the two documents are in harmony.

As soon as Mr. Lloyd George read them he announced that he would deal with them fully in his speech to the Liberal candidates on Monday. I therefore read the newspapers with interest to see how Mr. Lloyd George met these damaging arguments but what happened? Mr. Lloyd George hardly referred to them at all. On the contrary he evidently found they were too difficult to meet. He virtually abandoned the defence of his road scheme and tried to cover up his retreat by bringing out a set of brand new proposals about the railways to which his Yellow Book contained no reference. So far as roads are concerned, in the words of the old rhyme, "He left the baby on the shore, a thing he'd often done before."

The Government has already been working at the railway problem for a long time, and Sir Arthur Duckham's Committee will shortly report upon all the questions connected with the pooling of wagons and modernization of rolling stock. Meanwhile, by the remission of the passenger duty £6,500,000 has been made immediately available for urgent preparatory work upon the railway lines, and when the Government are returned—(cheers)—no time will be lost in dealing with the railway problem.

British railways in their passenger services and in many respects are at a very high level, but the heavy traffic on which basic industries depends is capable of far-reaching improvements and Treasury assistance will, if necessary, be given to bring these about. It is of vital importance that the heavy industries, for which roads can do so little, should have at their disposal a system of rail transport at least the equal in efficiency of any in the world.

ELECTION ADDRESS

May 15, 1929

Waltham Abbey

[Extract] ... I believe that the corner of the nation's economic fortunes is now turned. The future lies freely in our hands. Reviving trade, lower unemployment, expanding revenues, cheaper money, improved conditions of debt conversion—all these lie before us at the moment, not as remote possibilities, but as definite probabilities of the near future. We can, by wisdom and public spirit, acquire these advantages for ourselves. We can, by faction, violence, and folly, drive them away again. That is the real issue upon which this General Election is being fought.

I repeatedly asked what Mr. Lloyd George, in his road scheme, would do for the men who were being set to work on the roads and who could not reasonably be expected to leave their homes. Are these men to be conscripted? Mr. Lloyd George at Llandudno has at last given an answer, and it was a characteristic answer. It was: "It is an insult to the unemployed to say they will not go wherever work is offered."

If you are satisfied with that answer, I am quite sure the unemployed will not be. (Cheers.)

Further, I asked what would happen at the end of the two years to these people who had been gathered together in hutments all over the country. Mr. Lloyd George's answer now was: "I never said it should come to an end in two years. It would be no good starting a scheme like this unless you carried it on for five years."

So, the burden of this debt is to be even heavier. Roads will not make this country prosperous if there is no trade to go along them. We should hamper ourselves in competing with foreign nations if we wasted our substance and strength in making roads beyond those which are required for the economic working of the country.

Mr. MacDonald now says that the Government was responsible for the general strike. Mr. MacDonald and Mr. Arthur Henderson were members of the General Council of the T.U.C., and at the conference of the T.U.C. Executive, held at the Memorial Hall at the most critical moment, Mr. Ramsay MacDonald, speaking for the Parliamentary Party, said "We are in the battle with you." The Government were negotiating and endeavouring to bring about a settlement of the difficulty in the coalfields. Suddenly on a Friday or a Saturday it was announced in all the papers that if we did not give way there would be a general strike as from midnight on the Monday, and all the trades which were to strike were named in the order by what was called the "general staff" of the Socialist movement. Then, because the Government did not give way to such an outrageous threat to wreck the whole country—and that was a Parliament newly elected by the people—we are now told that it was the Government, who were guilty of causing the general strike. That is the same line as the Germans take in saying that if all the nations opposed to them had given way there would have been no war.

ELECTION ADDRESS

May 16, 1929

Fulham

[Extract] ... The Liberal road scheme is much more Lloyd Georgian than Liberal. Who are these experts about whom Mr. Lloyd George is always talking about as being in consultation with him? Some names have been mentioned. There are Professor Keynes and Professor Layton. Professor Keynes is the proprietor or controller of an extreme Radical weekly newspaper and Professor Layton is a candidate. They may be experts, but no one can say they are unbiased. Then there is Mr. McKenna, who has been mentioned but who won't say a word, and if you were to tell me that he and Mr. Lloyd George had been consulting in the preparation of this scheme I should find it beyond the bounds of human credibility.

Sir Josiah Stamp has been mentioned. He is our very trusted and distinguished delegate on the Reparations Conference now sitting in Paris. When I saw him the other day I asked him if his name was not being rather freely used in connexion with this scheme for spending vast sums of borrowed money on building roads. He told me that he had nothing to do with it, and that he did not agree with this policy. There remains only Professor Pigou, the distinguished Cambridge economist. He has remained absolutely silent. Perhaps we shall hear something from him shortly.

The proposals in the Labour Party's programme, if carried out, would cost four times the sum which even their injurious and onerous taxation could raise. To keep a respectable tone the Labour Party proposed, in nationalizing the coalmines, to pay the owners of the collieries and of the mineral royalties a fair price. An estimate had been given to me that to buy the coalmines would cost the nation £250,000,000, and to buy the mining royalties £100,000,000. Therefore £350,000,000 would be raised by taxation and spent by being handed over to the owners of mines and royalties who could then go off with those enormous sums in good Government stock, no longer worrying whether there were difficulties in the coalfields. Those things would be solely the nation's trouble. The reduction from an eight to a seven hours day would alone cost £20,000,000 of loss on the industry. Unless the electors are alert against nationalization they will be saddled with the burden of keeping an immense industry in an entirely inefficient and uneconomic condition.

Mr. Cook, I notice, has been saying that the next trouble in the coalfields will come soon, and that it would be desirable to have a Labour Government in control of the Navy and the Army. I think that it is very necessary to pay attention to that. Why should we put into power men who declare themselves the enemies of our civilization, which, with all its faults, is better than can be shown in any other country in the world?

ELECTION ADDRESS

May 17, 1929

Epping

[Extract] . . . Mr. Lloyd George, by speeches and articles, has made the French feel that he is very hostile to them, and only the other day Mr. Snowden insulted the French in the grossest manner. Oddly enough, both those gentlemen have arrived at a common policy in regard to France. It is to be very abusive and quite defenceless. Their advice will lead us up to the maximum of irritation and the minimum of security. No nation in the world has increased its armed forces so greatly since 1914 as the United States, but we are not alarmed. At the same time, when we had disarmed more than any country in the world, we are entitled to take care that every future step should be considered with care and discretion.

A statesman who puts his country in the wrong when it is going to discuss matters with foreign Powers is not acting fairly. How unfair was it of Mr. Lloyd George to say in Scotland ten days ago that Britain had increased her armaments since pre-War days by £40,000,000. Of course such statements are lapped up eagerly by every foreign country and by every one who wants to put us in the wrong. As a matter of fact, they are quite untrue. If allowances are made for the purchasing power of money, the actual amount spent on British armaments is less to-day than before the War, and it would be very much less were it not for the fact that pensions have grown and the pay of soldiers and sailors has increased. If allowances are made for that, our expenditure on armaments is very much less than before the War, whilst the expenditure of some other countries has nearly doubled.

I think we ought to have fair play in these matters, because we are the country that has set an example to the whole world. We have given up that supremacy at sea which was always held to be necessary for our existence and have shared the trident with other nations. We have worked for the appeasement and consolidation of Europe, and have not hesitated to make financial sacrifices to bring that about. I am one of those who believe we have made sacrifices enough. I am getting a little tired of this malicious propaganda inside our own Empire which always makes out that whatever the foreigners do they are in the right and, whatever our efforts, we are only to be treated with reprobation and disdain. We devised and shaped the machinery of the League of Nations, and British aid has been given it at every stage of its development.

A Voice: Didn't you take 30 millions from the Road Fund?

Mr. Churchill: I did so for a very good reason, and in the same circumstances I would do it again. After the coal strike and the general strike, rather than increase the income-tax or taxes on necessaries, I certainly did take the surplus of the Road Fund. In spite of that the Road Fund is growing year by year, and we are spending more on the roads than any country in Europe.

[Editor's Note: In reply to a question about the incursion of American capital into the country, Churchill said]: On the whole I do not think the introduction of foreign capital in this island is a bad thing so long as it is carefully watched. The country, however, has to be very careful when Americans invest their capital here that they do not get us out of the scientific development of our industries or the foreign markets which those industries serves. This subject is being very carefully watched by various branches of the public administration, who have been specially charged with that task. Broadly speaking, the investment of foreign capital here is not a bad thing and tends to make new opportunities of work.

NOMINATION ADDRESS

May 20, 1929

Epping

[Extract] ... The tranquillity of the country and the absence of fierce political issues make it difficult to excite a full measure of enthusiasm. But, this is only the beginning of the fight, and I expect a very strong rally in the course of this week. Above all, I desire to emphasize that we might have a dull election and a very exciting and momentous result. The well-being and safety of the nation will turn upon the events of a single day—between dawn and dusk, on May 30.

I think that, instead of scattered advocacy or the criticism of a hundred questions, there should be more concentration on the really leading issue of the election. It is quite possible another month from now we shall find ourselves in one of the gravest Constitutional, Parliamentary, and Imperial crises that have ever come about in times of peace.

LORD ROSEBERY

May 21, 1929

Wanstead

He was a great friend, a cherished friend of my father, and I inherited the friendship which was to me a most valued and inspiring treasure. Lord Rosebery was a statesman who always set country before party. In all the great decisions of his life he asked himself the simple question, What will be the best for our country? And he was a statesman who did not adapt himself easily to the movement of ideas in politics. I would say, perhaps, he was not in full harmony with the democratic movements of the present day, and for that he is to some extent criticized to-day. But after all the judgments of our own generation upon the leading figures have to be continually revised by posterity, and for my part I am glad that this opportunity is given me to testify from my own knowledge to the resolute, the earnest, and unfailing patriotism and love of his country, pride in the Empire, knowledge of its history, and profound sagacity with regard to public affairs which always characterized the famous statesman who has now passed away.

ELECTION ADDRESS

May 21, 1929

Wanstead

[Extract] ... I have experienced some difficulty in reaching the electorate. Broadcasting, that wonderful new instrument that would enable vast democracies of the future to live in complete touch with the vital issues of the day, is grudged and doled out minute by minute. After 33 years of experience in Parliament and public life, I was only allowed 30 minutes to speak to 30 millions of people.

The [Liberal] idea that a Government can summon a standing army of unemployed and set them to work on roads without upsetting the whole movement of labour and industry is ludicrous. The Liberal unemployment scheme will cause old-established businesses which went into the money market for funds to re-equip their factories to find that, because of State competition, they would have to pay, not 6 per cent., but 8 or 9 per cent. for their money. That would cause more unemployment than the expenditure of great sums on road gangs can possibly cure.

Nothing is more dangerous at present than change of policy. Nothing could cause greater injury than a period of political instability. If you are to have a House of Commons in which no party has the power to carry on Government effectually, the wildest schemes will be the most successful for the time being and the whole national finance will be seriously endangered.

The Socialist programme is a reckless spate of promises. It contains unbridled promises of expenditure without the slightest plan to make them good. We have too many dangerous competitors to be able to play the fool with our affairs. Great Britain is working on a very small margin. If she is careful she will just get through. If she behaves recklessly she will be ruined and her place in the world will be taken by those who are eager to supplant her. We shall be left out of the forward march in the world, an overcrowded, pauperized island, quarrelling fiercely among ourselves around the embers of a slowly dying fire.

ELECTION ADDRESS

May 22, 1929

North Weald

[Extract] ... Some years ago I said that the Labour Party were not fit to govern. Everything in their conduct as a party in the last four or five years has shown they are not fit to undertake these burdens. They have made an egregious failure of their Parliamentary action. They have greatly lowered the whole character of the debates in the House of Commons, and it is extraordinary that we, all over the country, are considering whether Mr. MacDonald and his friends should be put into power or not, when, less than three years ago, they were the leaders in a general strike which was undoubtedly a constitutional outrage.

ELECTION ADDRESS

May 22, 1929

Epping

[Extract] ... I have been attacked by the Socialists for speaking of a normal unemployment of 500,000 or 600,000. There are necessary movements from job to job and if unemployment of that kind does not exceed an average of three weeks or a month, and is paid for by benefits provided in advance, it must not be called an evil and it is sheer folly to mix that up with the excess and abnormal unemployment which so hangs upon and vitiates the insurance scheme. Nationalization of the mines is having highly important effects. It is good for the miners in the main but hard upon those who lost their jobs and very embarrassing to the Government which found 250,000 men plunged on the other figures of the Unemployment Insurance scheme, when all were hoping that nightmare would pass away.

However, the Government are endeavouring to grapple with it through transference, the aiding of Empire settlement, and the training of juveniles to another outlook in life, and the number of surplus miners has been reduced from 250,000 to 130,000 in two years, and if that policy is continued I have no doubt that in the next two or three years the problem of the surplus miner would cease to be one which would actively play a part in our discussions. The gain to the coal industry will continue, and after all, how are we going to have a firm economic basis unless our coal industry is in a living, thriving commercial condition?

Mr. Runciman, in March, 1926, said of the Trade Facilities Bill that the sum total of credit was fairly well fixed, and that that Bill might provide employment in one direction, but would withhold it in others. Undoubtedly, Mr. Lloyd George's unemployment scheme will hamper productive industry in raising new capital. While it may appear to cure unemployment in parts, it will call up the malady in worse forms elsewhere.

ELECTION ADDRESS

May 23, 1929

Woodford

[Extract] ... The Socialists are so over-confident of victory that they are already showing their teeth. Foreign motor-cars are taxed under the McKenna duties. Coventry is thriving, business is brisk. The public are getting cheaper motor-cars every year, and unemployment in Coventry is practically non-existent. Then the Socialist Party with the Liberals yelping at their tail came on the scene. They declared that they would sweep away the McKenna duties, apparently without the slightest regard for the livelihood of persons engaged in the motor trade. The local manufacturer of motor-cars, Sir Herbert Austin, alarmed at this prospect, said, precipitately, no doubt, that the repeal of the McKenna duties might lead to the closing of his works. The Socialist Party flew into a great rage, and declared they were being intimidated. The local Socialist candidate announced—claiming Socialist Party authority—that a Labour Government would take over the works and run them as a nationalized institution. And Mr. Snowden, who was expecting every minute to be Socialist Chancellor of the Exchequer, menacingly declared, "There is upon the Statute-book a measure known as the Emergency Powers Act, which gives drastic powers to deal with anybody who deliberately conspires to interfere with trade."

So that here we have a perfectly plain threat that the Socialist Party will first of all repeal the McKenna duties on foreign motor-cars, and then, if this should lead to the closing of any motor-car works because it no longer pays to run them—the Socialist Government will treat a refusal by a manufacturer to run his works at a loss as if it were a conspiracy against trade—a great national emergency—and will commandeer the works and will run them at a loss as a nationalized workshop.

Now, who began all this? At the beginning of this story you have a thriving industry giving good employment. At the end of it, after furious industrial and political battles, you have a Socialist Government kicking out the employer and taking over the works and inviting foreign motor-cars to come in, to make quite sure they run the works at a loss. A queer plan for helping British employment! This is only a sample of the general disturbance of trade revival and employment (up again this week, I am glad to say, by 28,000) which will follow upon the return of the Socialists to power with Liberal connivance.

The Emergency Powers Act was intended for real emergencies like the Great War and the general strike. If the Socialist Government could make use of it to take over any works or close down any newspaper on the pretext that a national emergency had arisen, no man's business would be safe. Once the Socialist Government got their blood up and got their pack yelling behind them, they might take over anybody's business and try to run it as a nationalized institution, because he had made some speech they did not like, or because they had some spite or grudge against him. If a newspaper attacked them they might say they were not going to be intimidated. They would take it over and run it as they pleased, alleging a national emergency.

Every business firm, every productive industry, ought to take notice of this threat, first to create trouble and distress for partisan purposes, and second to take over the works of any firm that did not submit to their exactions or persecutions with proper deference. I call upon Conservatives, Constitutionalists and patriotic Liberals to arouse themselves and defend the national welfare against the Socialist threat to commandeer works.

ELECTION ADDRESS

May 25, 1929

Women's Meeting, Wanstead

[Extract] ... It may be found possible to add to the compulsory insurance for wage-earners some supplementary scheme which would enable those who do not belong to what are classified as the wage-earning classes to participate in the benefits of the State scheme, at any rate to some extent. (Cheers.)

I am not making any promise because I scorn to do so without having worked it out and made sure that the money will be to hand. But if we continue to have stable government, if the nation is allowed to go on recovering from its wounds, there will be money for many things in the growing revenues of the country.

The present election is perhaps the dullest I can remember. The main reasons for the tranquillity is that the country has had 4-1/2 years' of stable Conservative Government. What humbug it is to say that this country has been ill-governed in the last 4-1/2 years, or that it has not been progressing and improving. No country in the world has been so well governed during this time. It will be very hard if the tranquillity produced by the Government's stable policy becomes an apathy which permits that Government's defeat.

I have been in political life 30 years and a Minister for 20, and I have never seen a Government freer from class feeling than that of the last 4-1/2 years. The Derating Act gave its greatest benefit to those areas which returned the Government's opponents, to the Socialist areas, the congested districts.

In regard to the silk duties, I recall that Mr. Lloyd George has said that I would be hanged in a silken halter. At any rate, the silk for the halter would be cheaper now than before the duties were imposed.

ELECTION ADDRESS

May 27, 1929

Liverpool

[Extract] ... I do not believe in pessimism, and I am not impressed by the Stock Exchange quotations on majorities. I pay no attention to the gloomy views of concealed satisfaction of the popular Press. There is ample evidence that the nation's prosperity has progressed under the Conservative Government, despite the general strike, for which Mr. MacDonald desires to show that the Government, and largely myself were responsible. Mr. MacDonald's argument is very much like the German contention that, if all the nations opposed to Germany had given way, there would have been no war. Mr. MacDonald has always taken the German point of view in those matters, and his record has chiefly consisted in unexampled desertion of his country in every crisis of her fate.

The Socialist programme is one of promises, plunder, and taxation. Mr. MacDonald and Mr. Snowden have stated that they would repeal the Trade Disputes Act. If they do so they will give a Magna Carta to intimidation. Why should a Catholic trade unionist have to subscribe to running an atheist Socialist candidate? A repeal of the Trade Disputes Act will restore the old vicious political levy.

The Socialists further declare that they would abolish the safeguarding duties. I stand here on a Lancashire platform and tell you that the safeguarding policy, carefully, prudently, and strictly as it has been administered, has not hitherto had any failure of any kind. Mr. Snowden's motive in this promise is to give a sop to the Liberals and gain some support from them in some dirty Parliamentary deal which he has no doubt in his mind.

ELECTION ADDRESS

May 28, 1929

Harlow

[Extract] ... You should dismiss from your minds the illusion that there might be a Liberal Government or a Coalition Government or a composite Government of some kind, and realize that the only immediate practical issue is whether this country should or should not be handed over to the Socialists for, it may be, four or five years.

Mr. Ramsay MacDonald is counting the minutes when, as he anticipates, he will be called upon to have this country in his grip. I think his record ought not to be overlooked. Is he a friend of our country? What was his record in the War and in the general strike? The two greatest State crises in my life were the attempts to overturn this country in 1926 by a great conspiracy to paralyse industry and the struggle of the War, through which we all passed. What did Mr. Ramsay MacDonald do in each of those two crises? Took a line that would have left the country prostrate, first under the heels of the Germans, and secondly under the heels of the general strikers. Is that any reason why he should be returned or should be given the full power to guide all the vast onward march of our country, with its world-wide responsibilities to the one-fifth of the human race comprised in the circle of the British Empire? Ought the disposition of the offices of the Crown, the settlement of all our affairs, to be confided to this man who, on those two occasions, lapsed and slid into a position absolutely unhelpful, if not actually hostile, to the vital interests of the State?

Only a few hours remain before the poll, and I am confident of the result. Victory is in the air. We are on the eve of a decisive manifestation of the steadfastness and perseverance of the nation.

CONSTITUENCY ADDRESS

June 14, 1929

Chingford

Events have fallen out as I warned you they would unless all the Conservative forces gave Mr. Baldwin the same support as they did in 1924. A Socialist Government is now in control of our affairs. They are in office, but fortunately they are not in power. We are to have another spell of Socialist minority rule. The Conservative party, although sadly depleted, is strong enough to be an effective check upon the Socialist Administration.

The Liberal party has dismally failed. Its wrecking tactics have done an immense amount of harm to everyone except the Socialists, and have done no good to Liberals and Liberalism. Their outlook is forlorn. By running five hundred candidates and sabotaging at least forty or fifty seats they have, I believe, gained a dozen more members in the House of Commons. It reminds me of a phrase of John Ruskin's—"A wreckers' handful of coin gathered from the beach to which they had lured an argosy."

However, all this is in the past and we have to look to the future, and I am glad that in the House of Commons there is a fairly substantial anti-Socialist majority. However bitterly this majority may be divided it nevertheless constitutes a safeguard for the fundamental interests and liberties of our country. This is the explanation of the composure with which the nation has accepted Mr. MacDonald and his colleagues. But the situation is nevertheless precarious and might at any time become dangerous.

The Socialist Party has gained office by making promises they could not fulfil, which probably their leaders had no intention to try to fulfil. As long as the Socialists govern the country in a sensible manner and try to do their duty at home and abroad in the general interest of the British people no one will grudge them the valuable educational experience which official responsibility confers. Mr. MacDonald has appealed for two years of peace and quiet in order to allow the revival of trade and industry to continue. No one, least of all those would have just laid down the burden, would be anxious to deprive him of his opportunity. The Socialist Ministers have therefore only to follow the well-tried principles of social and economic progress, to seek peace abroad and maintain order and freedom at home to enjoy a considerable reign. Whether they will do so or will be allowed to do so depends not upon the Conservative party or the Liberal party but entirely upon their own extreme supporters. As long as the Socialist Government drop all this nonsense about Socialism, nationalisation of industry, fantastic expenditure and taxation, wild schemes for "monkeying" with the currency and credit systems on which we depend, and as long as they do not give away the rights and interests of Britain to foreign countries or endanger the safety and unity of the Empire, everyone will be glad that they should have their turn and a fair chance to see if they can make things go a little better.

But, on the other hand, if they are forced by their wild men into extreme courses or even into foolish and disastrous experiments it will be our duty to resist them with the utmost vigour and complete fearlessness.

I wish to make it perfectly clear that I consider that the late Government was a very good Government, and that our late Prime Minister and present leader, Mr. Baldwin, has rendered immense services to the country by his calm, steady, and recuperative period of power, and also by his manly, dignified, and straightforward example on all occasions, whether in good fortune or bad. Whatever our difficulties or dangers may be, we face them united under a leader who claims confidence because he represents the soundest principles of British government and the best traditions of British public life. Do not let us waste time and energy in carping and recriminations, but press forward tirelessly and earnestly with the task for a far greater and more decisive struggle with the Socialist menace, which, believe me, will be the next great political issue.

There are two points upon which we ought to require special assurance at the present time. The first is about the Safeguarding and McKenna duties. We must know

Speeches of Winston Churchill

and we must know without delay what the Government is going to do. This is no time to bring political spite and partisanship into British industry. We cannot afford to disturb, damage, and discourage important industries by making their affairs mere pawns in the party game. As Chancellor of the Exchequer I have borne a direct responsibility for the imposition or reimposition of these duties. To remove them would be a needless, wanton, and entirely superfluous act.

But whatever is going to be done we had better know it at once. In ordinary questions of finance the Chancellor of the Exchequer is always entitled to reserve himself before the Budget, but the removal of the McKenna and Safeguarding duties are not matters of finance. They are pure politics. The new Government knows perfectly well what they are going to do about them, and we ought to be told without delay. I hope you will approve of my supporting Mr. Baldwin in raising this matter at the earliest opportunity.

The second question which seems to require urgent attention affects the safety and power of the country and the whole life and cohesion of the British Empire. I mean, of course, the maintenance of the British navy at the minimum strength necessary to enable us to guarantee the security of our food supplies and our trade and to preserve the necessary contact with the widespread Dominions and possessions of the British Crown. I am very glad to have recovered my full freedom of speech upon this grave subject, with which in one form or another I have been almost ceaselessly concerned during the last twenty years. At the Washington Conference of 1921 we agreed with the United States to abandon altogether that supremacy at sea which we had enjoyed for at least a hundred years, which we had never abused, and which in the late war enabled the United States to participate in the general victory. We abandoned that position willingly and sincerely, and we accepted the new principle that Britain and the United States should be equal Powers upon the sea. I was one of those principally responsible for that decision. It was a tremendous decision, and it is irrevocable.

But that decision implied two conditions. The first was that special regard should be had to the entirely different circumstances of this crowded island, which can be starved in a few weeks, and the great continent in which the people of the United States dwell so safely and so prosperously. It would not, in my opinion, be a fair interpretation of the principle of equal power upon the sea if a mere numerical measure of two fleets, each the replica of the other, were to be made the rule. Then we should not have equality, but under the guise of equality an absolute and final inferiority.

Such a result I intend to resist, and I shall claim your support in so doing.

The second condition which seems to me to be vital to the faithful and successful carrying into effect of the doctrine of equal power upon the sea is that any agreement between Great Britain and the United States must be based upon a tolerant and good-hearted spirit towards naval affairs on both sides of the Atlantic. If naval equality is to lead to a jealous and suspicious scrutiny of every ship and every gun and every armour plate between the two navies it would be much better to have no agreement at all and for each of us to go our own way, acting sensibly and soberly and in a neighbourly fashion, but free and unfettered.

Since Mr. Hoover became President of the United States it has seemed to me, at any rate, that a more comprehending and sympathetic spirit has been imparted to the policy of the United States, not only towards this country but towards Europe in general. It was the intention of the late Government, and particularly of Mr. Baldwin and Sir Austin Chamberlain, to make sure that a similar contribution of goodwill and fair play should be forthcoming from the British Empire. After all, the growth of friendship and mutual trust among the English-speaking people remains the supreme object of world politics and is to-day the surest means of the final and utter expulsion from the thoughts of men of the hideous tragedy and hateful processes of war. We shall await from the new Government a very early declaration of the steps which they propose to take in what I believe is an auspicious hour for the achievement of those high and noble aims.

DEBATE ON THE ADDRESS

July 3, 1929

House of Commons

Everyone will, I think, be willing to extend to the right hon. Gentleman their sympathy and good will in the task which he has undertaken. We admire the courage with which he has addressed himself to a problem so grave, perplexing, and distressing in its character. For my part, having listened to his speech, and recording only the first impressions which are possible when one hears a complicated statement made for the first time, I am bound to say that his statement and treatment of the problem are very moderate and sensible. What does it amount to after all? First of all, there is the £6,500,000 which was to be provided by the railway companies in consequence of my remission of the Railway Passenger Duty. I set out in the Budget the kind of work upon which they had proposed to spend that money. That is going to be carried out; that is not to be reversed. Then use it to be made of the ordinary normal revenue of the Road Fund during the next five years. There has been no intention of diverting those revenues; in fact, I had already said to the House that the whole of those revenues would be made available for road development. [*Interruption.*] I must remind hon. Gentlemen that the only reason that Fund was raided was because of the unfortunate financial consequences which arose from episodes which I am sure hon. Gentlemen opposite, and most of all those on the Front Bench, would gladly see buried in oblivion.

The right hon. Gentleman found these schemes of main road and secondary road development already worked out in the Department when he arrived there, and the money is flowing in under the ordinary growth of the Road Fund at the present time. I think that he is quite right to go on with road development. I have repeatedly said that we should continue to apply the whole of the remaining revenues of the Road Fund, and the increasing revenues, to that development, so, at any rate, there can be no difference between us on that point. That alone accounts for £43,000,000. Then we come to Charing Cross Bridge, Waterloo Bridge, certain developments by railway companies, such as electrification from Liverpool Street, some expenditure on an outer London goods railway, and some other matters of that kind; in the next place, there is to be a relaxation of the conditions under which Lord St. Davids Committee functions. Some of the precautionary conditions are to be swept away in order to enable it to function more freely. In addition, there is to be another Committee set up, side by side with the St. Davids Committee, in order to deal with the public utility side of State-aided enterprises, but the whole of this group—the railways, Lord St. Davids Committee and the new Committee—are all equally to be financed within the limits, so far as the immediate future is concerned, of a power to guarantee sums not exceeding £25,000,000 or to make interest remission for as much as 15 years in the alternative. With regard to the question of removing from industry the children of 14 and old people between 60 and 70 years of age, there is to be a committee on that subject. It is a very good subject for a committee. So far as the expenditure on the Colonies is concerned, there is to be no fresh money at all. The existing loan of £10,000,000, which is in process of being spent, and the expenditure of which has been very frugally and strictly watched, is to be the sole basis of development. The only thing is that some of the precautions regarding it are to be relaxed, perhaps rightly relaxed, and, in addition, a sum of £1,000,000 a year is to be provided from the Budget. It will be seen that all these schemes, many of which are attractive, many of which are useful—the worst that can be said against any of them is that they will not pay—are to be developed upon a sensible and moderate scale, and, although we shall look into these schemes with great attention, examine the financial propositions upon which they rest, and examine their details when they are put before us, I cannot feel that any serious difference will arise between the Conservative party and the Government upon the general method of treating them. Some differences are likely to arise between the Government and the Liberal party on account of the enormous, and I think wise and proper, diminution of the Government schemes from the very expensive and audacious plans which the right hon. Gentleman the Leader of the party proposed.

I say this at first sight upon this statement so ably and agreeably put before us, but, I must say, what a contrast between the speech to which we have just listened and the kind of language and denunciation with which the country has been filled in the painting of the evils of unemployment! What a contrast between the awful perplexity and baffling character of that huge problem on the one hand, and these perfectly useful and practical steps, which, whether they affect unemployment or not, might quite well be considered upon their merits. Since the new Government was formed, I have always been interested in wondering whether the Chancellor of the Exchequer or the Lord Privy Seal would be successful in the obvious collision of their political interests at the present time. I liked to look forward to the day when the Lord Privy Seal, having mounted himself on the furious horse of unemployment, armed with all the projects pulled out of the pigeon holes of the late Administration, would ride full tilt against the Chancellor of the Exchequer, who would be duly supplied with all or most of those cogent arguments by which many of those projects or similar projects had been corrected or turned down in the past. Well, the event has taken place, and I am bound to say, contrary to the opinion I formed of what would take place before I entered this House to-day, I think the Chancellor of the Exchequer has won. So far as the first round is concerned, the first course of the lists, he has safeguarded to a very considerable extent the financial position which was defended by the late Government, in spite of many assaults and many temptations and many unfair attacks to which I hope he will not himself be subjected.

I cannot pass from the right hon. Gentleman's speech to the more general matters with which we should deal at this stage of the Address without saying one word upon the very interesting question of whether large expenditure, or substantial expenditure, of borrowed money upon public works or upon the artificial stimulus of trade will or will not affect the numbers of persons unemployed. I should like to know at the proper time what the Chancellor of the Exchequer thinks about that question. I know what the Treasury view has been in very recent times. Their view has been that unless there is financial inflation, artificial inflation of credit, State borrowings for public works do not and cannot create additional employment. Their view has been that the Government can only take from industry what they wish to spend themselves, and that unless in each case it is proved that the State will spend the money better, that is to say, that the management will be more thrifty, the employment will be more fruitful, that there will be more sagacious profitmaking in the hands of the State, there is no remedy at all, and no diminution of unemployment will take place. Even if the State can spend the money better, then the diminution in unemployment is only the difference between the improved method of the State spending and the ordinary employment which would have been given had the funds been left to be directed by private enterprise. That is the Treasury view, or was the Treasury view, and I think it is a very remarkable contention.

I said when I opened the Budget this year that we had not wholly lent ourselves to that view, because we have ourselves borrowed about £100,000,000 and used it on these or very similar purposes to which the right hon. Gentleman has referred; but it is certainly remarkable that, although we were spending this money on a large scale—a much larger scale than has been mentioned to-day on anything new, though I suppose the old expenditure will have to go on—when we were spending this borrowed money and hoping to stimulate trade here and develop public works there, it did not have any effect upon the numbers of the unemployed, and this seemed to bear out the theoretical contention upon which the Treasury experts have based themselves. It is often said that the Treasury is unreasonable, but the reason the Treasury is so often criticised is not that its arguments are unreasonable but because they are unanswerable. Upon this general question of the State stimulus of industry and the cure of unemployment, I must read to the House some remarks which were made by my right hon. Friend the Member for St. Ives (Mr. Runciman) upon the Trade Facilities Act in 1926. He said:

Whatever good may have been done by—

He did not say much about it at the election—

this artificial means, it is counterbalanced and more than counterbalanced by the delay in the orders which would have been given in the ordinary course had the trade been allowed to recover its own equilibrium in its natural way. The disadvantage of this system is that the Government really cannot perform the ordinary functions which the ebb and flow of trade itself regulates. Any satisfying of the demand ahead of what the world requires is bound to do harm; any selection of individual trades, to the injury of others, while giving employment on the one hand may take it away on the other. . . . The sum total of credit in this country is fairly well fixed, within limits that are, comparatively speaking, ascertainable. . . . If credit is pledged in one direction it is not available in another. It may have provided employment in one direction; it may have withheld it in another. The sum total of employment remains very much the same, whether you do this or not; the disadvantage of it from the point of view of the unemployed is that the unemployed in some parts will be kept longer out of work while the unemployed in other parts are receiving a temporary benefit.—[Official Report, 2nd March, 1926; col. 1289, Vol. 192.]

So far as my experience goes, those observations of the right hon. Member for St. Ives would be hailed by the experts of the Treasury as the purest gospel of wisdom in this matter. [Interruption.] Wisdom is a bad habit! Is that the first result of the hard thinking which is taking place? It seems to be a murky gem. Yesterday, the Prime Minister took occasion to reaffirm the general Free Trade view of his Administration, and everyone knows the strict views of the Chancellor of the Exchequer upon that subject. They are based on fiscal orthodoxy. If they adopt fiscal orthodoxy, let me assure them that the financial orthodoxy which is set forth by the right hon. Member for St. Ives and is endorsed every day by the experts of the Treasury is equally established on a sound and logical foundation, and that it is very unwise to adopt the one and depart from the other. I know that this will not appeal to the right hon. Member for Carnarvon Boroughs (Mr. Lloyd George), because he has never cared two rows of buttons about orthodoxy. When he wants to do a thing, be it fiscally or financially heterodox, he starts out and tries to do it. The Government, however, are going to try this moderate scheme of public works, and, although these do not show much prospect of affecting the problem of unemployment in any appreciable manner, and possible not at all, nevertheless, from the point of view of Empire and domestic development, they contain a great many points to which I think no objection, no opposition, will be taken from this side of the House.

In this task of dealing with unemployment, the new Government have some advantages. They are important advantages which did not fall to us. [Interruption.] Neither myself nor the hon. Member has the privilege of being a Member of the present Administration. They have three advantages; perhaps there are others. In the first place, there are still hopes of a trade revival slowly developing, and that trade revival will, this year, receive the most helpful and hopeful stimulus of the application of the rating relief scheme. Hon. Gentlemen opposite ought not to deride it; they are going to get the benefit of it. When unemployment is reduced, if it is reduced, they will be able to plume themselves upon the fact. At any rate, that is one of the advantages. In the next place, the juvenile population falls this year, and in the following years, by 200,000 or 300,000, or it may be 400,000, in consequence of these years being 14, 15 and 16 years after the opening years of the Great War, in which the birthrate was so lamentably contracted. The last advantage which the Government have over us is that they run no risk of either of the Oppositions attempting to hamper their action or endangering or embarrassing them by letting off a general strike or anything of that kind.

Mr. Maxton: Then I may take it that the statement made at Glasgow by the right hon. Gentleman that the capitalists would take their capital out of the country was merely electioneering, and had no serious intention?

Mr. Churchill: I think the hon. Gentleman has misquoted or misinterpreted what I said at Glasgow. That is all I wish to say about the able and interesting speech of the right hon. Gentleman the Member for Derby (Mr. Thomas). Obviously, these proposals must be carefully examined in detail, and we shall have ample time to discuss them. I now turn to take a more general survey of the political scene. I want to say now what I think is quite proper in the Debate on the Address. I will begin by saying that I think the Government certainly cannot complain of the treatment which they have received from the Press, the public, or the House in regard to the working of our Constitution. We are assured that they are a Government of very able men actuated by the highest motives, and I am sure everyone is very glad to know that. Speaking for myself, politics apart, having lived the greater part of my life in this House, I am glad to see old parliamentarians whom I have known for a quarter of a century, who have played so distinguished a part in our proceedings, having at last their turn and their share in the responsibilities of Government, and tasting what are called by those who have not long experienced them "the sweets of office."

I look forward to hearing the Chancellor of the Exchequer defending the new reparation settlement. I recall the right hon. Gentleman's unmeasured denunciation of the treaties made with France and the United States for the settlement of the Debt. I know the lively expectation which his attitude created in many quarters that there would be a notable improvement in our affairs and the burdens we have to bear should the right hon. Gentleman be able to assume control. Of course, if the Chancellor of the Exchequer can persuade the French to pay more, or the Americans to take less, he will receive from all quarters of the House our most sincere and cordial congratulations, but it would be rather hard if the first important act of his tenure, or almost the first, was to have to defend a European arrangement which left us actually worse off than when the right hon. Gentleman described the position as being "scandalous to the last degree." I shall reserve any further comments upon that subject until the proper time actually arrives.

I also look forward to hearing the Financial Secretary to the Treasury deliver to us a clear exposition of the gold standard and the solid advantages which it will confer upon the country; and generally to defend orthodox views upon financial matters. No doubt the Financial Secretary to the Treasury will be able to do this when his education by the Treasury officials, the Bank of England, and the high financial authorities of the City has been completed. I look forward with interest to events in the future now that the Labour Socialist party has been reinforced by a band of notable converts from the Labour party, or whom the most distinguished are the Secretary of State for India, the Attorney-General, and the Chancellor of the Duchy of

Lancaster. I ask myself, are they converts or are they missionaries? The life of a missionary is one of hazard; he leaves his home and his friends and goes out to dwell among the heathen, living their lives, adopting their customs, sharing their victuals, and hoping that by precept and example he may gradually raise them to a higher outlook of existence and destiny. Certainly, his life must be very exciting, because he is dependent upon the caprice or temper of the natives or their chief. Witness, for example, the sad fate of the right hon. Gentleman the Member for Newcastle-under-Lyme (Colonel Wedgwood), who, after being indulged in a fleeting share of tribal festivities, has now been unceremoniously put into the pot.

Anxiety is also felt for the hon. and gallant Member for Central Hull (Lieut.-Commander Kenworthy), but his friends, and he has many—some of them on his own side of the House—all trust that the Prime Minister will arrange that his parting moments will be cheered by a refreshing draught of that vodka which the Soviet Government is spreading throughout Russia, together with other reforms. I confess that my chief compassion is reserved for victims of a different order. There is also that little band of representatives from the Clyde, including the hon. Member for Dumbarton Burghs (Mr. Kirkwood) and the hon. Member for the Bridgeton Division of Glasgow (Mr. Maxton), who have played such an important part that their lot appears to require our sympathy. Anyone who chooses to read the pathetic Amendment which they have placed upon the Paper will see how pitiful is their cry. They dreamed that they were clearing a pathway along which the toiling millions were to advance towards Utopia, but they wake to find that all they have been doing was to set up a ladder by which the hon. Baronet the Member for Smethwick (Sir O. Mosley) could climb into place and power.

Having taken this preliminary survey of what I may describe as the raw material with which the Opposition has to deal, let me come to grips with some of the points raised in the Speech from the Throne. The first subject I wish to question the Government about is one of procedure. The Debate on the Address is the traditional Parliamentary opportunity for reviewing the whole political situation, and it is the one great opportunity of the year upon which grievances can be discussed. On this occasion the Debate is necessarily somewhat unreal; indeed, it is mainly a ceremonial affair. The new Government have not had time to cause many grievances up to the present, and they have not thought out many of their plans. The Prime Minister has not yet emerged, as he will have to emerge some day, from that region of cloudy generalities and vague ambiguous platitudes in which he likes to indulge and in which he excels.

This Debate has not been a really effective vehicle of discussion, and yet we are told that it is to be the only Debate on the Address which we are to have until October or November, 1930, which is some 15 or 16 months away. My right hon. Friend the Leader of the Opposition made a request yesterday for further facilities, and he used the expression, which I hope the Prime Minister did not overlook, that he would not be willing to lose control of the Address until he had received some assurance that better facilities would be offered for debating the Address. If the Prime Minister had not been speaking with all the responsibility of his office, I should almost have said that he treated the question rather cavalierly. Everyone knows that if the leaders of parties put down Votes of Censure the Government of the day make a practice of according facilities. We all know that Supply days or general discussions are arranged by the Whips on both sides, and in that way we choose the topics for discussion; but really those facilities cannot be compared with Debates on the Address, and they do not restore to the private Member, or to the House, the loss which we should suffer if for nearly 16 months there is no general Debate upon an Address to the Crown. No one wishes to delay or interrupt the business by having Autumn Sessions. We do not want to obstruct the progress of the important Measures which have to be debated, but we do ask, specifically and formally, that in January or February the Government will put down a general Motion of Confidence to which not only leaders of parties but private Members may move Amendments with all the latitude which a Debate on the Address accords them. I hope the House will be accorded at least a week to enable hon. Members to take a further and a fuller review of the political situation which may have developed by that date.

I hope the right hon. Gentleman will accede to this request. He invited us yesterday to join, as it were, in a council of State. I am giving him my counsel now. My counsel, my advice to him is to carry the House of Commons with him in this matter. After all, we who sit on this side represent 14,000,000 electors, and on the opposite side 8,000,000 electors are represented. Fourteen millions to eight is an enormous preponderance. If I may put it in terms which the Lord Privy Seal will understand, it is seven to four. [*Interruption*.] I would ask the right hon. Gentleman to defer to this feeling and accede to this request, which I think is only what is right and fair, and, if he will do so, the necessary details can no doubt be satisfactorily arranged through the usual channels.

Mr. Thomas: Will the right hon. Gentleman tell us what the odds were in the last Parliament?

Mr. Churchill: On a very hasty computation, I think they were very nearly even money.

Mr. Thomas: Oh, no!

Mr. Maxton: May I ask if it is in order to quote the odds across the Floor of the House?

Mr. Churchill: I was speaking, not at all in a sporting sense, but in a purely Parliamentary sense. The second topic on which I should like to address the Government is the treatment which is to be meted out to the Safeguarding and so-called McKenna Duties. There, again, I am sorry to say I think the Prime Minister's answer yesterday was unsatisfactory, both to Free Traders and to those who favour Safeguarding. [Hon. Members: "Which do you do?"] I do both; I am a Free Trader who favours Safeguarding. Of course, I know perfectly well that it will be said that these matters are usually reserved for the Budget; no one has said that more often than I have, and it is perfectly true as regards ordinary financial questions; but this question of the McKenna Duties is not an ordinary financial question—it has nothing to do with finance. No one can conceive that a Chancellor of the Exchequer would repeal these duties and sacrifice £4,000,000 of revenue, if he were in his senses, on grounds of finance. No, the repeal of the McKenna Duties, if it be undertaken, is pure politics. If the duties are removed, they will be removed as part of a political manoeuvre designed to cause friction and antagonism between the forces that are gathered upon the Opposition side of the House.

The right hon. Gentleman, in the days of his irresponsibility, made savage declarations about how he would repeal the McKenna Duties if he had the power. We have heard a great deal about the zeal of the party opposite to reduce unemployment. Here are trades which employ scores of thousands of men. How can anyone deduct those trades, how can anyone make forward contracts—on which steady employment depends—how can they get out the new designs upon which the renewed competitive power of these industries from year to year depends, when there is the threat hanging over them, and the uncertainty enveloping them, as to whether they are suddenly going to have a very high tariff of 33-1/3 per cent., a very high protective tariff, pulled away from them at a single stroke? To remove the duties would be foolish, but it would be wanton and callous in the last degree to prolong the uncertainty and to make the livelihood and the wages of scores of thousands of workmen a mere pawn in a possible party intrigue. I will say no more now, because an Amendment is going to be moved on that subject, and we hope to elicit a further declaration from the Government; but I do say that the Government, in their own interest as well as in the interests of trade, would do well to consider whether, even if they are not going to make any declaration which will relieve the uncertainty at the present time as to what their intentions are, they will not nevertheless give an assurance that, should the duties be removed, prolonged notice will be given before that decision becomes operative. That, at any rate, would give these people some chance of making their plans ahead, and keeping up the supply of work and wages for the very large number of people who are employed in these trades.

While I am within the sphere of the Chancellor of the Exchequer, may I say that I am glad to have elicited from him at Question Time to-day his intentions about the Supplementary Budget. It had three provisions. There was the licence duty on telephones which the bookmakers were to pay. The right hon. Gentleman, by dropping that, makes a needless sacrifice of £500,000 a year of revenue which they were quite ready to pay, which it had been agreed with them that they should pay, and which, at any rate, would provide one-half of the fund of £1,000,000 a year for Empire development about which the Colonial Secretary is so pleased. That is to be thrown away merely, I suppose, because of pique, or not wanting to do anything which might lead to taunts of inconsistency. In the second place, there are the manufacturers' licence duties on liquor and tobacco, which the right hon. Gentleman is going to drop. He said he was perfectly indifferent on the matter, except that, perhaps, he would consider it next year; and now, in spite of the campaign of calumny that there was on the ground that these manufacturers of alcohol and of tobacco— these wealthy and prosperous trades—were to receive large sums of money under the de-rating scheme and so on, when a Measure has been introduced which would neutralise that, the new Government, when they come in, brush it aside as if it were of no account, and thereby show the utter insincerity of all that they have said. Lastly, the licence holders' remission has been swept away. I am sorry for that; it was, I think, absolutely justified. It was a relief which had been announced definitely, and the people concerned, many of whom are not at all wealthy people—for it was arranged

that this money should reach the licence-holder, and not be retained by the brewer—
had no doubt been counting upon it as if it were already theirs by the will and decision
of Parliament. I think that to sweep it away is a harsh act, and I dare say it is an act
which will long remain unforgotten. I dare say the right hon. Gentleman has been
influenced by an unfortunate remark which I made in the course of my Budget speech,
when I said:

> The Opposition, if successful in the battle, will have the pleasure of
> passing or repudiating all the machinery Clauses, and will have plenty of
> time to do so.—[Official Report, 15th April, 1929; col. 65, Vol. 227.]

I suppose the fatal fascination of the word "repudiate," which was used in connection
with his attitude in his unregenerate days, has been too much for him to resist. But the
most noteworthy and almost the only specific declaration with which we have been
favoured is as to the decision of the Government to repeal or revise the Trade Disputes
and Trade Unions Act. That must not pass without definite and early notice in the
course of the Debate on the Address. The Act was passed in a great emergency, with
national approval—[*Interruption*] —and I think the Government are very unwise to stir
this subject again. No doubt they will plead that they do it under duress, and I am sure
they would not have liked to do so if they could have left it alone.

We do not yet know how they propose to amend this Act. Surely, they cannot
possibly intend to widen the restricted scope of intimidation which it involves. Surely,
they are not going to challenge Parliament and the country upon the legality of a
general strike directed for the purpose of bringing pressure to bear either upon the
community as a whole or upon the executive Government. [*Interruption.*] Is it the
contracting-in in respect of the political levy that is to be dealt with? If that be so, I
am bound to say that I think it quite doubtful whether the right hon. Gentleman will
be able to carry that Measure through this House. Why should a Conservative or a
Liberal trade unionist be compelled to go through the invidious process of contracting
out, and facing all the odium inseparable from it, if he does not wish any funds of his
to go to support a party to which he may have a perfectly sincere conscientious
objection? We have all been through a Parliamentary election, and we know what pains
are taken there to ensure the secrecy of the ballot. Every precaution is taken to
protect the voter from undue pressure, and yet it is a far less invidious thing to record
a vote among all the millions that are cast at a General Election than for a man, if he
differs from his mates and his fellows, to stand up and definitely contract out of the
levy, thus bringing odium upon himself. Certainly, it is much better that we should
know at the outset, because, unless these matters are raised, the Government have no
means of seeing what their position will be. As I have said, this is a Measure that ought
to be resisted in the most strenuous manner, and I predict that, whatever changes may
be introduced, the House as a whole will not allow a reversion to the old vicious
conditions which prevailed in this respect.

I have one more topic to deal with, if the House will bear with me. There is a
curious paragraph in the Speech which refers to an examination of the experience of
candidates at the General Election. The Prime Minister has explained that an inquiry

will be set up into the working of the present electoral law, but his language was, in this respect as in others, studiously vague. Like Agag, who, I believe, afterwards came to an unhappy end, he walked delicately, and I think he was quite right, because it is a very critical subject. The Liberal position is clear. They think that they are unfairly treated under the present electoral law, and they demand relief—they demand a second ballot, or some reform which will secure a greater degree of majority representation in the constituencies—[*Interruption*]—a greater degree of majority representation in more constituencies—and they demand it before the next General Election. The position of the Government is also clear. They are the favoured, privileged darlings of our present electoral system; they have had greater advantages than any other party in the country. Naturally, they do not want to give up their favour and their privilege, and do not want a second ballot or anything of that kind; and they do not mean to have it, if I rightly interpret their intentions, before the next General Election takes place.

The Conservative position is different from that of either of these two parties. It is more detached, and it is less determined. We should not have sought for this inquiry or pressed for it, although we are not so favoured under the present system, and have not the same advantages as the Socialists. For instance, although there are, I am told, 280,000 Conservative voters in Wales, Wales only succeeded in returning a single Conservative Member to this House. Although we are not so favoured, the matter, nevertheless, is not a Conservative issue, or one which we should have taken any steps to raise.

It is not a grievance from which we suffer. But now that the Government have declared their intention of holding an inquiry, we are bound to take part in it, and we shall take part in it in all good-will and in all good faith. We certainly could not lend ourselves to any solemn farce of killing the question by delay or by dragging in all sorts of extraneous issues, nor could we join with the Socialist party in trying to extinguish a weaker party. The Prime Minister has opened this question in the gracious Speech and it will have to go forward to a solution. We presume that the precedent of the former Speaker's conference will be followed, apart from the question of the occupant of the Chair, and we presume that the parties will be given representation in accordance with their parliamentary strength and that the reference and other details of procedure will be settled by consultation between the three party leaders. On this basis we shall take our part with a sincere desire to preserve and foster the enduring vitality of those fair and free Parliamentary and representative institutions for which this island is renowned.

I am obliged to the House for giving me such a very patient hearing. I have had to bring a number of topics before them and have not always succeeded in practising that complete restraint which my right hon. Friend said we should all have to observe, but, nevertheless, I feel it is necessary that we should join issue on some of these topics immediately, and I must in conclusion say this. There are gulfs between us in this Parliament. It is no use supposing that we can simply meet together as a council of State. I hope and believe that the floor will prove to be broader than the Gangway, but the gulf between the Socialist party and the rest of the country is in any case impassable. There never has been such a gulf in my experience between a Government and an Opposition. The creation of the Socialist party has been an astonishing thing. I have seen it grow in the course of 30 years from a handful to the largest party in the House of Commons. Many if not most of the men responsible for it are now on the Front Bench, but not all. There is the hon. Member for St. Helens (Mr. Sexton), with whom I remember discussing all these matters 30 years ago. It is certainly an astonishing feat, and they are entitled to rank their life's work as historic. But I cannot say, they would not expect me to say, I think it has been a good or a helpful work.

They have ranged great masses of British people under false and foreign conceived standards. They have built up their power upon doctrines of monstrous error. They have built it up by fomenting class hatred and organising industrial strife. They have dabbled in subversive agitation. They have pandered to rapacious appetites which they know they can never satisfy. It is now their fate, it is indeed their punishment, to have to disappoint those who have believed in them and have believed what they have said, and to discard or explain away the doctrines by which they have risen to great power. It may well be that every British Government, however derived or constituted, has services to render to our common country. It may well be that the impulse from a new angle will be stimulating in our affairs. Those who are the strongest defenders of the existing system of society should also be the first to study the corrections that are necessary of its many abuses and shortcomings. Nevertheless, the central dominating fact of this Parliament remains. As long as His Majesty's Ministers are content to administer and, by administering, to fortify the capitalist system of civilisation on which we have grown great, and on which the United States is growing greater, there is no reason why they should not enjoy, although they are a substantial minority in the country, a lengthy tenure of office. But the moment they attempt to carry into the realm of action any of those fundamental vices and fallacies upon which the whole structure and progress of their party have been built up, and which have been their main inspiration, from that moment they will be swept from power.

DEVELOPMENT (LOAN GUARANTEES AND GRANTS)

July 16, 1929

House of Commons

The Lord Privy Seal opened his speech in a somewhat controversial and even, one might say, truculent mood and tone, but, as he continued, he very soon sank to the querulous, and before he had finished he was frankly in the plaintive state. He was first controversial at my expense, and I rise largely for the purpose of reassuring him, of comforting him, of cheering him up, of making him feel that, after all, it is not quite as bad as he evidently has been led to feel. I intended, and I certainly propose to carry out my purpose, to pay him some compliments and to pay a tribute to him in various respects. Let me begin by assuring him that he is still even after a fortnight at this task, in possession of the sympathy of the whole Committee. I think no one can doubt the difficulty of what he has undertaken. No one can doubt the immense exertions and efforts that it will call for from him; the constant, incessant, strenuous attention to every detail of these schemes, the wearing sense of responsibility, the gnawing worries which arise when one considers all that one has said in the past, the unpleasant contrast which daily develops between promise and performance. From all these points of view, I say that a sympathy, sincere and sufficiently strong to overflow both the Gangway and the Floor, may be extended to the hon. Gentleman.

I will address myself to his scheme as set out in the Resolution. In the first paragraph, he proposes to obtain powers to make loans amounting in the total to £25,000,000 for what I will call—as it is the name which has always been used before—trade facilities. That is all it is. That is the old name. You can invent a new name if you like but that is what it is—trade facilities to help unemployment. On the merits, there is, I think, no objection to be raised against his proposal, at any rate no serious objection. There may be some criticism on details and so forth, and the right hon. Gentleman would be the first to welcome that, but there is no question of any opposition in principle to the idea of using State credit to the extent of £25,000,000 in a trade facilities scheme so moderately conceived, so soberly presented and so carefully hedged about—as the White Paper shows—so strictly limited in scale, and so rigorously disciplined by Treasury experts. On such a scheme, there really can be no immediate or serious controversial difference in any quarter of the Committee.

When I spoke in the Debate on the Address in answer to the right hon. Gentleman I expressed only the first impression I had of his scheme. I had no idea of what it was going to be. I had, in fact, prepared myself to make quite a different speech, pointing out the ruin to our finance which would ensue from a lavish squandering of public money on the kind of scheme with which my right hon. Friend the Member for Carnarvon Boroughs (Mr. Lloyd George) has associated himself and I was agreeably surprised by the general character and tenor of the right hon. Gentleman's speech. Further reflection and a closer study of his speech, of his scheme, and of the White Paper have confirmed all those first impressions which I sustained after listening to his very illuminating, agreeable, and attractive statement. I cannot see any ground principle on which we, as a party, need oppose the Resolution or the Bill which it is sought to found upon it. There is nothing new or novel about it, no startling discovery or departure of any kind.

There is only one point in the right hon. Gentleman's remedies for unemployment which was novel to me, and that was drawn attention to by the right hon. Member for Carnarvon Boroughs, namely, the proposal to get Mr. Courtauld, or some other silk manufacturer, to start up a factory in the Rhondda Valley for the miners who are out of work and for public money to be advanced for that purpose. I do not see in this Resolution any point which covers that, but it is a very interesting point, and I do not express any opinion whether it is a wise provision or not, but, apart from that, I know of nothing that is new in this scheme.

We have had a long and full experience of this kind of schemes of trade facilities which are set out in the first paragraph, not only under the late Government, but under the last three or four Governments. They were originally devised, as all these remedies for, and efforts to cope with, unemployment were originally devised, in the days of the right hon. Member for Carnarvon Boroughs, when the great and terrible crisis of unemployment came upon us in the deflation period after the Great War; and I do not think the Committee would run any risk in lending itself to these schemes. After all, we have had great experience of them. We know perfectly well what happens and the limits within which good results or bad results are to be expected. We have all tried trade facilities, and on a much larger scale than this. Opinions may differ as to what the results were, but all opinions will be agreed that those results are confined within a very limited area of importance. I am glad to see that the money is not to be spent all at once, but that it is only to be spent as it is wanted, that it is not to be borrowed or spent except as it is required. That, I think, is very wise. Fresh powers have to be sought in the event of this £25,000,000 loan for guarantees being exceeded, and so far we shall have an opportunity of re-considering the whole matter, or seeing how it is working out, what progress has been made, and what results have attended the schemes. That is all perfectly correct, and I am sure no one would deny the Government's request.

Now I am going to pay my compliment to the right hon. Gentleman the Lord Privy Seal, which I think he has deserved. I compliment him—and I am sure it will be agreed by all Members of the Committee that it is deserved—on having resisted the temptation—he has told us again to-day how he has resisted it—to be drawn into megalomania. [*Interruption.*] He has resisted the temptation to play up to any of those grandiose and flamboyant schemes with which the right hon. Member for Carnarvon Boroughs hoped he would rehabilitate the Liberal party. I congratulate him upon these schemes, and I congratulate the Treasury on the strictness of their control. No doubt these plans will contain some useful feature. No doubt some desirable enterprises, whether by local authorities, by private authorities, by private capitalists or by statutory bodies will be started a little earlier than they would otherwise have been begun, and others, which perhaps are beneath the threshold of economic utility, will just be lifted into actual existence. No one can doubt that some help will be given in this respect, and it may well be that a number of useful enterprises will be set on foot. But even the right hon. Gentleman, I think, will not claim for his schemes more than that they will be a tonic to industry so far as they go, that they will give it a little fillip. The encouragement in paragraph (1) will give a little fillip, a little titivation of encouragement, a stimulant, a dope, if I might say so, to industry, which perhaps will have good results.

I would praise him also for not hesitating to help private enterprise where it is engaged in public utilities, and, as has been said, though I am not certain whether it was endorsed by the Treasury Bench, not hesitating to help private enterprise in matters so far removed from public utilities as to cover the manufacture of silk stockings, which perhaps would come under the heading of public necessities. At any rate, private enterprise is to be helped and sustained with public money. That is an important development and fortification of the Capitalist system, which is very remarkable, coming from the right hon. Gentleman and his Friends, and I congratulate him on not being hampered by foolish Socialist ideas about profit-seeking being a crime, all that sort of nonsense about rent and interest being exploitation, about private enterprise being the exploitation of the worker. All that nonsense is swept away, and the right hon. Gentleman has not hesitated to cut himself adrift at the outset of his responsibilities from all the nonsense which he and his Friends have talked, so long and so loudly, in Opposition.

I also congratulate him on consulting the business men and the great employers; and, let me say this, that it is their duty to help the Government. Being the Government, they ought to be assisted in non-party matters by anybody, and, if the right hon. Gentleman goes to the great employers of labour and heads of big businesses and asks them, as he has so wisely asked them, for their aid and assistance, they ought not to allow any party or personal considerations to stand in the way of giving the best help they possibly can. The task is heavy enough. So far as I have been confronted by some of these gentlemen, I have said, "It is your duty to help the Government in every way you can to minimise the difficulties of the unemployment position."

But what I liked about the right hon. Gentleman's speech, and especially about the closing portion of it, was the new application of the doctrine which has been called inevitability of gradualness—the inevitability of gradualness in attaining the Socialist ideal. There is certainly gradualness here, and I have no doubt there is inevitability also, but what I am gald to see about it is that the gradualness is in a new direction. It is gradualness, not forward, but backward. What we are witnessing in paragraph (1) of this Resolution is the gradual retreat from the claptrap and folly of Socialism to the firm ground of the modern Capitalist system.

The right hon. Gentleman the Lord Privy Seal has, like Beaconsfield, to educate his party. He has to teach them, and he has been teaching them. He may even have been, as it is sometimes called, "learning" them; and they have a lot to learn. He has to teach them that everything he taught them to say when they were out of office is all wrong, and that what they have to do is to support the opposite when put forward by the very man whom they chose to carry his original doctrines into effect. That is a very stiff course, but I hope they will not mind this salutary discipline. They had some chastisement in public the other day from the right hon. Gentleman, and I understand that at a private conclave this morning further chastening of a more severe disciplinary kind has been administered. That is, perhaps, the explanation of the absence of the hon. Member for Bridgeton (Mr. Maxton). I am glad to see, though, that he has come into the House now, and that he has apparently survived the ordeal. He has returned, I trust, in a sober, contrite, and humble spirit.

I entirely agree with the course which the Lord Privy Seal has taken. Everyone knows that he is a very shrewd and practical man, and, indeed, he would not have lived through all he has done so successfully if he had not got as many lives as a cat, and almost every gift of practical human ingenuity. I think he is absolutely right. It is a very bad thing to deceive people, to gull people. It is very unfortunate that he should have been led into deceiving them and gulling them, but it is far better to throw foolish words aside, and not to translate them into still more foolish action. Therefore, for all these reasons, which I have been endeavouring to express, so far as the Conservative party, for whom I have the duty of speaking, is concerned, we shall make no difficulties about granting the request which the Government made to us in this Resolution.

Paragraphs (2) and (3) of the Resolution, which deal with the grants to public utility undertakings, local authorities, and statutory bodies, are not, of course, comprised within the ambit of the £25,000,000 for guarantees, and we are told in the White Paper that no limit is assigned to the expenditure which may be incurred, but we are also assured that Parliament is to vote in every case upon the details of expenditure and that Parliamentary control will be retained.

Mr. Lloyd George: Is that so?

Mr. Churchill: It is at the end of the White Paper:

> In any case full Parliamentary control will be secured by the necessity
> for a Parliamentary Vote of the grants to be made.

Therefore, you may really say that there is nothing in Paragraphs (2) and (3) except the intention of the Government to produce plans on the subject at a later date, and to submit their proposals to the House of Commons. Nobody could object to that. It is the right of any Government, of every Government, to make any proposal for the spending of money if they think that advantage will result to the community. No one could possibly object to that, but in the absence of any proposals, none having yet been made, we can only await the further development of the right hon. Gentleman's plans. We find ourselves this afternoon in the presence of the Government's complete policy for dealing with unemployment, apart from certain Votes which they will present for the helping by grants of local and statutory bodies. I should like to point out to the Committee that this Motion comprises the whole policy with inconsiderable exceptions. The right hon. Gentleman talked about the £6,500,000 which is to be spent upon the railways, but that was already provided, and arranged for, and announced to Parliament in the Budget. The right hon. Gentleman made the criticism that nothing had been done to establish the principle on which this money was to be spent. The Budget was only in the middle of April, and Parliament was dissolved before the end of May; at the beginning of May, the railway companies were asked to prepare schemes, and the natural time to consider them would have been when they were brought before us. Far be it from me to rob the right hon. gentleman of any credit for any schemes which he puts forward, but I advise him not to base any recommendation to abolish the unemployment disease upon the fact that he received a proposal from the railway companies to dispose of the money which Parliament had already decided that they should have in accordance with the agreement entered into with them before the Election.

There is the question of the road programme. The right hon. Gentleman said that I had turned down a £9,500,000 scheme. There never was any intention of not spending upon road development all the remaining moneys which are derived from the revenues of the Road Fund. That is all that His Majesty's Government are doing; they are merely spending the remaining money—

Mr. Thomas: I made the specific statement that the right hon. Gentleman's Government turned down the £9,500,000 scheme point blank and said that they would have nothing to do with it. I made that statement, and it is true.

Mr. Churchill: It might well be true and yet quite irrelevant to the argument, because the question in all these schemes is not only the question of adopting a scheme at a particular moment before the revenues are there, but of adopting it a year later when the revenues have grown up. Our intentions were, and our public declarations were, that the whole of the money of the Road Fund, or what was left of the Road Fund—[Hon. Members: "Hear, hear!"] . I shall come to that later, and I notice the Chancellor of the Exchequer beginning to get rather uneasy—was to be spent on the development of what we thought to be the best programmes normally year after year, but what has the right hon. Gentleman the Chancellor of the Exchequer done? He used to be the foremost in accusing me of larceny, theft, and I forget what other he used but he used stronger words.

The Chancellor of the Exchequer (Mr. Philip Snowden): "Pilferer" and "plunderer!"

Mr. Churchill: The right hon. Gentleman did much better than that, and I hope that he will be more like his own self, in spite of his cares of office, and that before we get through the Session we shall hear some of his rasping adjectives, for I hope that he is not so crushed down by the weight of official responsibility that he cannot express himself with his natural fluency. What has the right hon. Gentleman done? I took certain lump sums from the surplus of the Road Fund, and I am very glad that I did it, and I would do it again in the same circumstances. In addition to that, I claimed £4,000,000 or £5,000,000 a year under the heading of luxury charges from the Road Fund, and the Exchequer is now enjoying them. That was a raid to deprive the Fund of £4,000,000 or £5,000,000 a year, and the right hon. Gentleman is dabbling of the proceeds of this raid at the present moment. Talk about developing any new expenditure and any new policy! They have simply carried on the policy which was going to be carried out in any case, and have even adhered to the policy of extracting from the revenues of the Road Fund between £4,000,000 and £5,000,000 in aid of the general expenses of the Exchequer. I agree with the right hon. Gentleman the Chancellor of the Exchequer; I think that he is quite rightly holding on to this money, but we cannot have all these heroics from the Lord Privy Seal about how shocking the late Government were, and how magnificent he is in embarking on this road development. Not a farthing is being spent out of the Road Fund that would not have been applied in the ordinary way.

As to Colonial development, which afforded the right hon. Gentleman an opportunity of expressing his devotion to our great and glorious Empire, some parts of which he is visiting at no distant date, he is only spending the revenue of the £10,000,000 which was voted and proposed by the late Government. It is quite true that the money was not spent as fast as we expected, and as fast as it ought to have been. There were, however, very good reasons in each case, and I am bound to say that the highly competent experts of the Treasury in matters of detail were more than a match for the experts of the other Departments in proposing schemes, and they advanced extremely good reasons why particular things ought not to be done and could not be done, and why this and that would not work. For instance, in connection with the Zambesi Bridge, they pointed out that the Portuguese had rights over it if we had proceeded then, and that it would have been found very inconvenient. I agree that there should be a loosening, and I am glad that the right hon. Gentleman proposes to spend this money more freely. It is, however, only the money that was set aside by the late Administration, and the right hon. Gentleman cannot claim to use it as if it were another store of gas with which to inflate his unemployment remedy balloon.

I do not think that I have omitted anything in the scheme of unemployment relief which is before the Committee. I have forgotten one thing, however—Lord St. Davids Committee. I had forgotten that Committee which is stressed so strongly. The right hon. Gentlemen is going to regularise the Committee, to invest them with statutory power, and to widen their scope. The right hon. Gentleman reproached me very much with the fact that we limited the functions of that Committee in 1926, but on what grounds was it done? We read what the Committee themselves said in 1926. They said that:

> Broadly speaking, it would appear that the scheme, which has now been in operation for six consecutive winters has, largely for that very reason, passed the period of its greatest utility, and that if pursued indefinitely to the same extent as in the past, it would be difficult to avoid subsidising work properly undertaken by local authorities in the normal course of their business, and in such case but little could be added to the sum total of work performed in the country.

> In so far as special schemes might continue to be evolved, there is the further objection that they might well have the tendency to divert capital from the normal trade developments which are now to be looked for, and would thus hinder rather than assist the relief of unemployment through the proper channel of trade recovery.

That is one reason why we curtailed the activity of Lord St. Davids Committee. It was by their own advice, and the advice of the very experts and gentleman to whom the right hon. Gentleman paid such a high tribute this afternoon. It may well be that in the three years that have passed since 1926 some leeway which can be made up has accumulated, and that there are local authorities which wish to embark on new work if they can get a little assistance, work which they would not attempt but for assistance. I make no objection to it, and I should apologise to the right hon. Gentleman because, in describing his scheme for remedying unemployment, I omitted to mention the fact that he is endowing Lord St. Davids Committee with statutory authority.

I have so far been in agreement with the right hon. Gentleman, but I fear that I must part company with him upon the suggestion contained in the White Paper that these proposals are going to be a remedy for unemployment. They may be quite good in themselves, and I think that we all pretty well agree about them, but they are put forward as a cure for unemployment and raise issues of a very different order, and I believe that the result which they will bring to the volume of unemployment will be entirely negligible. I will endeavour to support that by three sets of considerations. First of all, take the scale of any of the proposals now before us. They are inconceivably small. The late Government, so abused, so infirm of purpose and feeble in dealing with these matters, spent £100,000,000 a year in loans and expenditure on Colonial, domestic and local developments, and we found no remedy. In 1922, the

Speeches of Winston Churchill

then Financial Secretary for the Treasury, Lord Cushendun, gave figures to the House which showed that £63,000,000 had been provided under trade facilities, and that £63,000,000 worth of schemes had been started. He calculated then that 100,000 men had found employment in virtue of the starting of those schemes. I do not accept that, for I think that it is very questionable whether there was not as much employment killed in other directions as was started by that money. Even if you take that figure and apply it to the £25,000,000 of Paragraph 1, we get about 30,000 or 35,000 men who may be expected to find work, if everything works well and if the whole of this new expenditure operates without detriment to any other industry elsewhere in the country.

Compare this scheme of £25,000,000 in Paragraph 1 with the rating reform scheme of the late Government. When I mentioned this in the Debate on the Address, I noticed scornful laughter on the Benches opposite, but it is our best hope at the present time. I know the sincerity of hon. Gentlemen about the evils of unemployment, and the agony which they see in their constituencies of friends with whom they come in contact on the matter, and I say that it is our best hope. Compare it with this scheme. A relief of £30,000,000 a year for productive industry all over the country operates from next October in perpetuity. The capitalised value of that is £600,000,000, and that is a figure which is comparable to the £25,000,000 about which we are talking now. It amuses me when I read the newspapers to see the different standards by which the actions of the various Administrations are judged. We produce from the labours of two years, and with the gathering together of all the revenues we could secure, past, present and future, this £30,000,000 a year to go as relief to our heavily burdened basic industries, and it is whisked aside as if it were a thing too trifling to be mentioned, whereas the right hon. Gentleman comes forward with £25,000,000 of trade facilities—a little slice cut off the old hambone—and we are told of vast schemes to cure unemployment, and what a gratifying thing it is for the country to see real energy and courage on the Treasury Bench.

I do not believe that these proposals will have the slightest effect upon the number of persons upon the live register of unemployment, or that there will be any appreciable difference at any time with which the present Government are likely to be concerned, or in any time that we shall be able to measure or appraise. They may do good in themselves. Some things may be done which it is a very good thing should be done, and future generations may be quite content, but the limited scale of these proposals excludes them from the category of effectual remedies. With 1,250,000 unemployed at the present time and with over 16,000,000 insured persons, this additional £25,000,000 a year is but a small tonic to stimulate industry.

Mr. Thomas: I am sorry to interrupt the right hon. Gentleman, but I am sure he only desires to be fair. I do not mind his party points, but he must know, as he has read the White Paper, that the £25,000,000 is a fraction compared with Part II.

Mr. Churchill: Quite right.

Mr. Thomas: Yes, quite right, but I want to inform the Committee. Incidentally, he is incorrect in assuming that any of this money must be first sanctioned by the House of Commons. That is not in the Bill, it is not what is intended, and it would be ridiculous if it were suggested.

Mr. Churchill: I am very much obliged to the right hon. Gentleman for giving this information, although he has somewhat interrupted the theme which I was developing, but the last paragraph of his White Paper says:

> in any case full Parliamentary control will be secured by the necessity for a
> Parliamentary Vote of the grants to be made.

That is all I say about that. We never suggested that the right hon. Gentleman had to come to the House of Commons before going on with any scheme, but at frequent intervals he will state his definite schemes and we shall say whether they are good, bad or indifferent. So there is very little disagreement between us. I am dealing only with the proposals actually before us. We have yet to learn his other proposals. The right hon. Gentleman is in the position of a man who comes forward with a remedy for curing a disease, and in this Parliament we are listening with bated breath to his solution of the difficulty. The only solution is £25,000,000 of guarantees, and the fact that he is going to submit to Parliament in due course various schemes for helping the local authorities, as we did to a very large extent year after year, and encouraging them to go forward with local developments. So far as curing unemployment on this scale and dealing with this ghastly problem, which, one may say, ruined the prestige of the Conservative administration in the last Parliament—[Hon. Members: "Hear, hear!"] Yes, I admit that. You used it in a manner to make it most detrimental to those who were in power. But I say that the schemes of the Lord Privy Seal for curing the great problems of unemployment are absolutely visionary and futile. They are good in themselves, but are absolutely futile as a cure. He might just as well go down on to the terrace on some afternoon when the tide is high, take a tea cup from one of the tables, and try to bale out the Thames as imagine that the proposal he is now putting before Parliament is going to be any effective solution of this grim and grey social evil.

I come now to the Treasury argument. The Treasury argument is that the money which the Lord Privy Seal gets to spend in one direction will only be abstracted from a fairly limited supply of credit, and the effects of it will be manifest in unemployment in other quarters. That is their argument, and I hope I am going to hear in this Debate some statement from the right hon. Member for St. Ives (Mr. Runciman). He may have had to make a judicious dive at the General Election to conceal his convictions in order not to impair his newly grown affinity with the Leader of the Liberal party, but now he is safe with us in the new House of Commons—

Mr. Lloyd George: What about Mr. Amery?

Mr. Churchill: We all have our affinities; he might courageously stand up and express his views upon the economic principles of the Treasury case. They definitely say, "Make it just as much as you like, be it on a big scale or be it on a small scale, unless you inflate public credit by the artificial manufacture of credit you will not add to the volume of employment." That is their case, and it is not a mere theoretical case, but is the truth about the existing financial situation. It is contended that there is the fullest use of all the credit available in the banks, with even a tendency to overstrain banking facilities given to industry. That is their case, that is the proposition which they put forward, and I hope we shall hear from the hon. Gentleman in whose name this Resolution stands some exposition of the Treasury views, because it would be most unfortunate, now that all the hopes of the unemployed are concentrated upon the schemes of the right hon. Gentleman, if we found out that after all we were barking up the wrong tree and that no extension of Government credit would in fact create new employment, unless accompanied by an act of financial inflation.

The right hon. Gentleman the Chancellor of the Duchy of Lancaster stated in the course of his interesting speech—his maiden speech from the Treasury Bench was a very able speech if he will allow me to say so, if he had not got into trouble with his noughts—that he knew the Treasury view but that the electors had repudiated it, had pronounced against it at the election. I think that is quite true. Undoubtedly they pronounced against it. Unfortunately, on questions of economic law it does not matter at all what the electors think or vote or say. The economic laws proceed. [*Interruption.*] You may vote by overwhelming majorities that you can cure unemployment by public works on borrowed money, but that will not have the slightest effect upon the results, whatever they may be, which you achieve by your programmes. I am finishing now, and I will not detain the House any longer. I think these large topics ought to be fully explored. It is really only an act of courtesy to the Lord Privy Seal that we should do full justice to the magnitude or otherwise of his proposals.

I am submitting that there is no hope of curing unemployment in any of the proposals we have heard from the Treasury Bench, and I am now going to say that the Government themselves know there is no hope that any of their proposals will, in fact, produce an effective diminution of unemployment. What have we been listening to in the last two or three days? We have been dealing with Unemployment Insurance. The Unemployment Insurance Fund is solvent if the figure of unemployment falls below 1,050,000, on the old basis. The moment the figure of unemployment falls below 1,050,000 the debt of the Fund will begin to be paid off. [*Interruption.*] We had the debt down to £7,500,000 just before the unfortunate labour troubles of 1926. If there is going to be any improvement in unemployment, there was no need for the Chancellor of the Exchequer to take from his slender purse the £3,500,000 which he is proposing to take—I quite agree that on financial grounds it was a respectable and proper proceeding—no need to take that from the slender resources which he will be looking over before the end of the year, and using it to endow the Fund. If he believes that unemployment is going to fall, if he thought the Government remedies were going to have any effect upon the figure of unemployment, it would have been quite easy for him to have let the matter stand over and to have gone in for a little extra borrowing. Then, if matters turned out well, in a very short time the Fund would be solvent again, or on a solvent basis.

But the Government do not believe that. They have taken a more gloomy view than I have felt justified in taking, and I dare say they are right. They are budgeting for a figure of 1,200,000 unemployed running through the winter, and they are making arrangements—I do not say they are wrong—on a scale to enable them to bear the whole of the brunt and weight of this terrible burden of unemployment. They have no serious expectation that the figure of unemployment will fall below 1,000,000 as the result of any measures which the Lord Privy Seal is going to take. In fact, the right hon. Gentleman himself, when dealing with this matter in the Debate on the Address, had already begun to whittle away the figures of the unemployed. He is going through just the process which I went through in the General Election, and some of the very arguments I used he used in regard to what is the normal residue of the unemployed. I remember very well how the right hon. Gentleman the Member for Carnarvon Boroughs (Mr. Lloyd George) and I were found fault with by the "Daily Herald." Though we were much opposed in the particular controversy, we both talked of a certain normal figure of unemployment, and I remember the indignation to which the "Daily Herald" was moved. They seemed to imagine that hundreds of thousands of our working people are condemned to live permanently in this hideous and miserable condition. [Hon. Members: "So they are!"] We have to read the literature of our masters nowadays, and the other day I was reading "Labour and the Nation." It says on page 7:

> For four years more than 1,000,000 workers have been deprived through no fault of their own of the opportunity of adding their quota to the nation's output of wealth.

And on page 20 it says further:

> The Labour party will not be satisfied, as capitalist Governments have hitherto been satisfied, merely with tinkering with unemployment.

And what did the right hon. Gentleman say? I noted it particularly, because he was agreeing with me. He was repeating one of the arguments which I had been using at the General Election. It had sunk into one brain, at any rate. He said:

> When we talk of the live register and deduce from those figures the fact that a million or more of our fellows are unemployed, that gives an entirely wrong picture of the situation to the outsider. The position is not exactly that. Of that total at least 50 per cent. are men and women of many of whom it can be truthfully said that they are unemployed it may be on Monday and find employment before Saturday. That is not a difficult problem to deal with. That is a problem which the Unemployment Insurance Act was intended to deal with.—[Official Report, 3rd July, 1929; col. 91, Vol. 229.]

I am not going to read the whole of it. The House will notice the extraordinary rapidity with which the educative process of Governmental responsibility is having its effect upon the Lord Privy Seal. Only a few weeks have converted him from the phrase about more than a million workers having been deprived through no fault of their own of the opportunity of adding their quota to the nation's output of wealth into the statement:

> That gives an entirely wrong picture of the situation.

Two weeks have translated the right hon. Gentleman from a leader and inspirer of ravening millions into the sleek apologist of power. If those plans had been presented by the late Government, if we had been returned with a diminished majority and had brought those plans forward from the Treasury Bench, they would have been laughed out of court as a remedy for the unemployment problem. They would have been denounced as shams and trivial makeshifts by every Minister who is now prepared to support them. Although I must admit that those plans look innocent, inoffensive, and modest in themselves, they run counter to the orthodox Treasury view, and that is a very serious thing on an economic question. The unemployment problem remains utterly unsolved. Putting it at the best, let us hope that the Treasury are wrong. What is now proposed is only a mild tonic and encouragement to certain particular industries, local enterprises, and private interests which may be beneficial in themselves, but the benefit which can be gained by those private interests and local bodies by the additional employment which may flow from their stimulus will be far more than swept away and counterbalanced by the disturbances which the Chancellor of the Exchequer is making by undermining the whole principle of inter-Imperial trade, by prolonging uncertainty, and by the vicious and heavy taxation which I have no doubt whatever will be the consequence of the pressure and stress which is rife within the party opposite, and which will herald the dawn of the new year.

[Much later] I beg to move, "That the Chairman do report Progress and ask leave to sit again."

The hon. Baronet [Sir Oswald Mosley] entirely misunderstands the position which has developed in the Committee. We are not complaining of the absence of the Minister. We had present a very admirable and engaging representative of His Majesty's Government. We were complaining of the absence of an authoritative exponent of the Treasury. There is not even present the Financial Secretary to the Treasury, although it is his name that is attached to this Resolution. Very grave issues have been raised by the Liberal party on this question of the unlimited powers under paragraph (2), and the inability of the Government to assign any definite figure. We must have an authoritative expression from representatives of the Treasury who have the care of our national finances. There is a general feeling in the Committee that that should be so. In order to express that general feeling I move the Motion. I do so also for the purpose of securing adequate financial advice to the Committee when very large issues relating to public funds are being decided.

It is quite impossible for us to neglect these matters. We are perfectly ready to give the Government the moneys that they require, for any reasonable scheme that will assist in improving employment in the country, but we are not going to provide them with blank cheques. We are not going to allow them, because they are afraid to state the true figures that they have in mind, for fear that they would cause alarm in the City or disgust below the gangway, to remain in a position of vague and convenient nebulosity. We have a right to the presence of the responsible financial advisers of the Government. It is no good the hon. Baronet coming forward. He knows nothing about the Treasury. He is only a sort of ginger assistant to the Lord Privy Seal, and more ginger than assistant, I have no doubt. In order that the Committee might receive proper assistance from the responsible officers charged with the duties of defending the public finances, I move the Motion.

[Later] I would be prepared to withdraw my Motion on the understanding that the Financial Secretary is to come back as quickly as possible to deal with the Resolution which stands in his name. We talk of public engagements, but the House of Commons is a public engagement, and, while an ordinary Member may leave the House, a Minister who is actually in charge of the principal Resolution of the day, especially when that Resolution turns specifically on a topic on which he has primary information, ought to be in his place. I quite understand that the Lord Privy Seal in inadvertence may have told the Financial Secretary that he could go. We know that the Financial Secretary has gone. The Lord Privy Seal says he will not fetch him back, and that he is on his way returning, and I should be ready to withdraw my Motion but for the fact that the Lord Privy Seal went on to say that when he did come back—out of a deference to the House of Commons which I cordially recognise—he could not throw any light on the situation. [Hon. Members: "No!"] Well, that he could not throw any more light on the situation than had already been thrown by the Lord Privy Seal himself. Therefore, I am bound to say that I see no escape from the proposition that we ought to hear the Chancellor of the Exchequer. He may have more important work to do outside than he has here, but it does not follow for a moment that the kind of statement on this financial question, which would be made by the Lord Privy Seal, would be couched in the same terms, poised in the same manner, phrased in the same way as that which the Chancellor of the Exchequer would make. There are different interests and the Chancellor of the Exchequer is responsible more directly in the financial matter than the Lord Privy Seal. Therefore, as he has said that, though he will send for the Financial Secretary, the Financial Secretary can tell us nothing, I am afraid I cannot find any satisfactory ground for withdrawing my Motion. [Hon. Members: "Vote!"] There is no need for hon. Members to get excited. It is a very good thing that people should learn at the very beginning of this Parliament— [*Interruption.*]

Mr. Kirkwood: Stop lecturing.

Mr. Stephen: On a point of Order. I want to ask if the former Chancellor of the Exchequer is in order in handing out this lecture?

The Deputy-Chairman: That is not a point of Order.

Mr. Kirkwood: I think you can stop him all the same.

Mr. Churchill: I am strictly in Order and in possession of the Committee, but, owing to the fact that the Financial Secretary to the Treasury has now returned, I would not stand between him and this Assembly for another moment.

Mr. Lloyd George: The Motion before the Committee is one to report Progress in order to ensure the attendance of a representative of the Treasury. It is quite clear that that representative could not make his statement upon this Motion, and unless this Motion is withdrawn, it is quite impossible for him to speak.

Mr. Churchill: Now that the Financial Secretary to the Treasury has arrived and is ready to give us a statement, I am quite ready to withdraw my Motion to report Progress, and I beg to ask leave to do so.

SPEAKER WHITLEY'S PORTRAIT

July 18, 1929

Speaker's House, Westminster

[Extract] . . . No one knows how many of the amenities and adornments of the House are due to the keen interest which Mr. Whitley took in them. His name will be identified with processes of conciliation and agreement between the Government authorities and their Civil servants and between Capital and Labour in the world of industry.

DEVELOPMENT (GUARANTEES AND GRANTS) BILL

July 22, 1929

House of Commons

I have now had a very few moments to consider the effect of the statement the Lord Privy Seal has made, and I am bound to say it confirms the general impression, and the first impression, I formed when the schemes were presented to the House. It shows that he is proceeding with prudence and caution and with due regard to the susceptibilities and the principles and the authority of the Treasury. I must say I think the debate that took place on Friday and the earlier debate, have really been of very great advantage, because we have clearly ascertained, not the final but the immediate limits of the Government scheme for dealing with unemployment and, as I say, those limits are extremely modest, and rightly so, because undoubtedly it would have been easy for the right hon. Gentleman to put a very sensational figure into his Bill, or into his speeches, and then he would have found he would not have been able to spend the money in the time or would only have been led into wanton and wasteful expenditure.

Therefore, as I say, I think that it is reassuring to the Committee to be in possession of the full statement he has made to us this afternoon. I am very glad that the Government have deferred to the sense of this House now in Committee in placing us in possession of their scheme and of the maximum limit of their scheme as far as the present period is concerned. £25,000,000 is the mass of capital development in respect of which the Government may make grants of interest between now and the next assembling of the House in three months' time. It is quite true that the commitments into which the Government may lead us may extend for as long as 15 years, but even if the commitment is at its maximum of 15 years, as I calculate, the total commitment that can be made in the next three months will not exceed £18,000,000 or £19,000,000 sterling. Taking the 5 per cent. guarantee as covering loans during the whole 15 years within the limit of this £25,000,000 capital development, the total amount will not exceed £1,500,000 a year, or £18,000,000 or £19,000,000 in 15 years.

I do not really feel that I have the slightest reason to alter the view which I have taken throughout this discussion, that this is a very moderate and circumspect proposal. There has never been in these discussions any collusion between the right hon. Gentleman the Member for Carnarvon Boroughs (Mr. Lloyd George) and myself. [*Interruption.*] When I say no collusion I expect to be believed. I expressed the opinion which at first sight was, apparently, the only line to take. I wish only to say that although there has been no collusion, in my view there has been no inconsistency. I took the view throughout, and I take it now, in the possession of this much fuller information, that the scheme is ordinary and sagacious. I said that the Chancellor of the Exchequer won the first round, and in my opinion he has won the second round. That is my view. It is true that the right hon. Gentleman the Member for Carnarvon Boroughs drew attention, and I am very glad he did so, to the serious financial vagueness of this particular provision. The Government have met that, and the Chancellor of the Exchequer has acknowledged the advantage of the measure of the discussions which have taken place in the House.

So that we really congratulate ourselves in both cases. We have a moderate scheme, and we have a correct financial procedure. I am bound to say that I do not see why this limit should not be mentioned in the Bill. The Chancellor of the Exchequer certainly spoke of the subject as if the £25,000,000 could be inserted in the Bill, naturally only of a temporary character, but the Government do not feel that they wish to make an insertion. I should not wish to press them unduly. I am very anxious that they should feel that we have not hampered them in any way in their treatment of this great problem of unemployment. We have never sought to impose a limit upon them. We have asked them to express their view as to what the limit should be. That was their responsibility. They have acted up to their responsibility, and they have told us what the limit is, and for my part I think that it is a very moderate limit. I am bound to say that I do not think they could possibly have adopted a more modest limit as far as this coming period of three months is concerned.

It only remains, as far as this House is concerned, to wish the right hon. Gentleman success in spending wisely and judiciously these limited sums to which he has now the power to commit us. But, before this Clause passes from us, and now that we have before us the limit of the Government scheme, I must reiterate my opinion, which I have expressed several times, that the effect of these schemes upon the volume of unemployment will be utterly negligible. However skilful the right hon. Gentleman does his work, however shrewdly and thrifty he makes his bargains, whatever competent business men he calls to his aid, I must express my conviction that whatever the future course of the unemployment figures may be, they will not be appreciably influenced or affected by anything he has proposed in this Bill, not only in the next two or three years, but during the whole course. The levers which are being applied may be well polished and placed in the right positions, may have heaving upon them the full strength, energy and adroitness of the Lord Privy Seal, but they are levers which are miniature levers. They are not capable of moving this vast mass. We have heard of using a steam-hammer to crack a nut, but it is the other way round. He is throwing a nut into a steam-hammer. I cannot imagine anyone believing that proposals on this scale, however useful they may be in some respects, will be a solution of this hideous problem of 1,200,000 persons unemployed which has played such an immense part in all our political and social controversies, and is undoubtedly the main preoccupation of all who are responsibly concerned, in Office or in Opposition, with the affairs of this country. No, Sir, the evil is gigantic and the scheme is modest in the extreme.

I do not blame the right hon. Gentleman for the course which he has taken. More especially do I think that he has a right to proceed with caution when there is, to put it mildly, very grave doubt as to whether even modest applications will produce modest results, when there is very grave doubt whether the launching of the scheme will have any effect whatever upon unemployment, and will not create as much unemployment by a transference of credit from other quarters. There was a battleship which sank in the Mediterranean many years ago and they endeavoured to raise it, but after six or seven weeks they found they were pumping the Mediterranean in and out of the battleship which was sunk, and it may well be that the Treasury view, which has so consistently been put forward in the many discussions which have taken place since the War, is economically correct. As I have said, I am not in a position to range myself in absolute endorsement of that view in its entirety. I think that the efforts which all of us have made under every Government that has taken place since the War to try to mitigate unemployment by favouring and fostering public works and stimulating enterprises preclude me from taking that view in its entirety. The right hon. Gentleman might perhaps say that there is no such thing as a Treasury view, and that there is only the Chancellor of the Exchequer's view. I do not think that is true. Where it is a matter of politics, of course, only the Minister is concerned, but where you come to highly technical matters, whether connected with the defence forces or with finance or with public health, in some respects, in regard to these technical matters, apart from political matters, the view of these expert officials, who give their whole lives to the study of these questions, is a matter which acquires an independent and separate validity.

Mr. E. Brown: Does it not matter how the questions are put to them?

Mr. Holford Knight: A validity independent of Parliament?

Mr. Churchill: I do not understand that. The point is, what is the truth. The question is, can you by borrowing money and spending it upon public works, diminish the volume of unemployment? If you can, then everyone will be very glad, and we will support the Lord Privy Seal's scheme with greater confidence than we do. If you cannot then, of course, it is no use encouraging hopes amongst unemployed persons that they are going to have relief from their sufferings through the application of a remedy which it is believed will not be effective at all. However that may be, I maintain that the scale upon which the Government proposals have been framed is not of a character to enable any appreciable effect to be made upon this great social evil. I do not intend to press this matter any further, because the right hon. Gentleman has been most conciliatory with the Committee to-day, and the Government has given us further information. I think there is one point, on Report, that I will speak upon when the time comes. Meanwhile I will support the right hon. Gentleman in getting this Clause through.

Mr. Lloyd George: I, also, have had an opportunity since the Lord Privy Seal made his statement of considering this matter and of consulting with my right hon. Friends, and with my hon. Friends who are associated with me, and we are of opinion that the Lord Privy Seal has redeemed very faithfully the undertakings given by the Chancellor of the Exchequer last Friday. I have risen to express satisfaction with the statement that he has made. So far as I am concerned, any opposition or criticism which I was directing against this Clause has been completely mollified. I had some misgivings, on merits, about these grants to these companies, but if the right hon. Gentleman says that he cannot find the necessary opportunities of providing work for the unemployed in the coming winter without embarking upon schemes of this character then, whatever misgivings I may have had, I shall certainly not convert my misgivings into an opposition to his proposals. His responsibilities are very great indeed, and it is the business of the House of Commons to do all in their power, within the means at their disposal, to assist him to carry through his great and very anxious undertakings. For that reason, I wish to express my satisfaction.

May I also express satisfaction at the statement that the right hon. Gentleman made in reply to the hon. Gentleman for Crewe (Mr. Bowen). I have always been a little afraid of the right hon. Gentleman's railway obsession. It is a very natural one and a very honourable one for him, but I have always been a little afraid that he concentrates, in regard to his projects, rather too much upon the railways, to the exclusion of–[An Hon. Member: "Roads!"] Not merely roads, but other things as well. There are a great many other things which I hope the right hon. Gentleman is considering, which could provide employment. I was glad to hear him destroy completely the illusion that if you develop road schemes you necessarily do harm to the railways, or, on the other hand, that if you develop the railways you must necessarily injure the roads. The roads and the railways are both partners in a great undertaking, assisting each other in the transport facilities of this country, and I was very glad to hear the right hon. Gentleman say so. It will completely dispose of a great many arguments which I heard during the General Election, in criticism of certain schemes with which I was associated.

With regard to what was said by my right hon. Friend the late Chancellor of the Exchequer, I fundamentally repudiate everything that he said. I utterly disagree with everything he said, except that he accepted the Lord Privy Seal's proposals. I think that what he said was heresy of the most indefensible character. The idea that if you spend money in this way you will not promote employment and that you may really prevent useful employment in other directions, is a doctrine which I never heard of outside the Treasury, and that doctrine was engendered in the Treasury during the time that it was presided over by the right hon. Gentleman. I certainly never heard of it in the past. When I was Chancellor of the Exchequer, I was responsible, with the full sanction of the Treasury, for setting up the Development Board. It is perfectly true that at that time we did not get as much cash as I should have wished, but I never heard the doctrine put by the Treasury that you might not use national credit for the purpose of developing agriculture and other industries. What is true of agriculture must be equally true of other industries, if there is no credit that you can get without the assistance of the Treasury. The real point is, whether you are spending money for the purpose of making employment, for some purpose of re-equipment and reconstruction and for something that enriches the nation, or whether you are throwing your money away.

Mr. Churchill: I should be misleading the Committee if I ever suggested that the Treasury view is that no development should be done by public money. What I said was that development by borrowed public money would not be beneficial in reducing unemployment.

BARNSLEY CASE

July 23, 1929

House of Commons

This is one of those acutely moving personal questions in regard to which the whole House has opinions irrespective of party. We are all on the same side on the main issues of this case. We all wish to respect in every way the inviolability of the judiciary from partisan comment of any kind in the House. We all wish to safeguard in every way the full freedom of the expression of political opinion at election times, and we all wish to stigmatise, as it should be stigmatised, brutal action and cruelty perpetrated by the strong upon the weak and the young. These matters are common ground between all parties, and I am glad that the representative of the Government on this occasion has said that he cannot let this matter rest where it is now; clearly he cannot do so. This matter has to be fought out. I have the greatest respect for the chairman of the bench of magistrates in question. [Hon. Members: "Name!"] I do not intend to introduce his name, but I will if hon. Members desire it. Otherwise, I do not intend to mention it, because I think it would not be appropriate. I think it is due to him as much as to any of the other parties concerned, that the matter should be probed. We must trust the Government in that matter. We trust to them to act in a loyal spirit and to make sure that the House is satisfied, clearly satisfied, that justice has not been denied, and that all has been conducted in a proper manner. The hon. Member says that the papers will be referred to the Lord Chancellor. I think that may be very right as the first step, and very prudent as the first step, but only as the first step. We shall require to know everything. There is no hurry about the matter. Justice moves slowly and remorselessly upon its path, but it reaches its goal eventually. It is right that the matter should be referred to the Lord Chancellor. The hon. Member for Barnsley (Mr. Potts) has made a speech with which I entirely agree. He said that the matter should be inquired into on the spot. We are not going as far as that. That is not the demand. The demand is that the depositions, the evidence and the notes in the case, shall be brought to the notice of the Lord Chancellor as the highest judicial authority in the country. With that for the moment we are content. We shall not take it further, but when these matters have been so presented and the Lord Chancellor has considered them, we shall require the facts to be fully laid before the House, together with the opinion of the Lord Chancellor upon them.

EGYPT (LORD LLOYD'S RESIGNATION)

July 26, 1929

House of Commons

The Labour Government was anxious to achieve a new arrangement with the Egyptian Government. The ambition proved impossible because of Egyptian insistence upon the restoration of their joint control over the Sudan, ended in 1924 after the assassination of the British Governor-General, and the refusal of the British to concede this point. The British High Commissioner for Egypt and the Sudan, Lord Lloyd, did not approve of the initiative of the Government, and was in effect dismissed by the Foreign Secretary, Arthur Henderson. In the subsequent debate, Henderson revealed that the relationship between Lloyd and Austen Chamberlain had not always been harmonious.

After the speech which the right hon. Gentleman the Member for Darwen (Sir H. Samuel) has delivered, and after the very clear and emphatic manner in which he expressed what I believe is the opinion of the majority of this House as to full Parliamentary discussion before final commitments are made, I can abridge what I was about to have said, and, indeed, I should not have risen at all were it not for the fact that I feel that the position in which matters have been left after the speech of the Secretary of State for Foreign Affairs, [Arthur Henderson], and also after the speech of the right hon. Member for Darwen, is in many respects unfair to Lord Lloyd. There are, of course, two questions at issue, the personal question of Lord Lloyd and his dismissal or resignation, and the general question of the future of Egypt.

I do not dispute the right of the executive Government to choose and change its agents when it requires to do so, but the fullest justification must be offered to Parliament for such changes. In attempting to give that justification to Parliament the Foreign Secretary has gone back over the last four years, and has disclosed the internal discussions which have taken place between the late Foreign Secretary and Lord Lloyd, between the Cabinet and the late Foreign Secretary, and generally has laid these matters, some of them touching extremely delicate points of policy, before the House, the public and the world. I think that the statement that he has made and read out, from the papers so assiduously and eagerly collected and placed at his disposal by those on whom he relies—[*Interruption.*] The right hon. Gentleman must begin by learning that he is not going to intimidate me. I say that the reading of those papers undoubtedly produced a wrong picture, a wrong impression of the actual relationship which no doubt existed between the parties concerned. Lord Lloyd as the man on the spot, facing these difficulties, facing risks in Cairo, naturally had his point of view. The Government here, seeking their general policy of appeasement in these Egyptian and foreign affairs, had their point of view. Why should there not be a free interchange of views? What is there in the whole of this narration to show anything but a healthy, active and closely reasoned discussion proceeding between parties who in the end were unitedly agreed on every grave executive decision?

Does anyone quarrel with the explanation that my right hon. Friend the Member for Bewdley (Mr. S. Baldwin) gave of the duties of representatives of the Crown? They have the fullest freedom for putting forward their views. They put them forward fearlessly. They ought to put them forward fearlessly. Do you want to have puppets, people who sing the tunes that you are habituated to and what you think are popular? You want to know what they really think. You also want to know that when the Executive has reached its decision, the policy on which it has decided will be accepted and loyally carried out. Certainly nothing in the relationship of His Majesty's late Government with Lord Lloyd gave us the slightest ground to complain of the loyalty and fidelity with which he carried out his duties. Again and again he took the view, in the Egyptian atmosphere, which was not the same as the one taken here, but when a decision had been taken, sometimes in one sense or another, he instantly accepted the view which we took. So I say that, while I do not dispute at all that another Government may require a different agent, it is not necessary to reflect upon the official discharge of his duties by Lord Lloyd under the late Administration, nor to represent him in any unfavourable light in that respect.

But I think that the Foreign Secretary, having made this statement to the House, has probably made it extremely difficult for our representatives in every part of the world to express their views with candour and with courage upon these matters, because they will never know that the mere fact that, however well they have done their duty, they have at some stage of discussion expressed a view which is not popular with a new Government which may come in—they will never know that that will not be brought up against them. But, as I say, the late Government had placed their confidence in Lord Lloyd. They knew perfectly well his qualities, and that he had a strong view in certain matters of Egyptian policy, in some cases a stronger view than that which the Government themselves were ready to carry out. But, after all, let us pay some tribute to his work. What were the conditions under which Lord Lloyd went to Egypt? The murder of the British Sirdar of the Egyptian Army had but recently taken place; a very grave state of disorder and anxiety prevailed throughout Egypt, and especially in Cairo; the foreign communities were in the deepest anxiety and looked to us for protection.

Lord Lloyd has been there for four years. It is true that there are many things in the present condition of Egyptian politics which no one would say are desirable in all respects, but those are not matters for which Lord Lloyd had responsibility; they are matters which arise out of that very independence and freedom to manage their own affairs which we have conceded again to the Egyptian people. As far as peace and order are concerned, as far as public confidence and security and tranquillity through- out Egypt are concerned, Lord Lloyd's four years' tenure of office, in conditions so difficult and so varied, is a monument which no aspersions will diminish. I must say another word or two about Lord Lloyd. I have spoken of his relations with the late Government. I must say that I think there has been a certain streak of prejudice in the

Foreign Office against Lord Lloyd—I can speak after four years of intimate knowledge of this matter—partly natural, some of it, very easy to understand. [Hon. Members: "Is that an attack on the Civil Service?"] I will say in this House whatever is in Order. [Hon. Members: "Civil servants cannot reply."] But they have their Ministers to reply for them. I do say that there is a prejudice against one who is not a member of the Civil Service being placed in that position. A man of independent position who has been a Member of Parliament, a man who has access to the Ministers of the day in the Government of the day—such a man, I venture to affirm, is not entirely in accordance with the traditions and feelings of some of the great and powerful departments in this country; and I am bound to say that I noticed more than one instance of it during the last four years.

Now, I come to the question to which the right hon. Gentleman has referred— Was Lord Lloyd treated with the courtesy which he deserved? The right hon. Gentleman read the telegram which was sent in regard to which he has stated that it was difficult for anyone not to have terminated his appointment after receiving such a telegram; or words to that effect. The right hon. Gentleman has told us that it was a very courteous interview. The right hon. Gentleman is always very courteous in his manner, and Lord Lloyd has a very agreeable manner, and I have no doubt that it was a courteous interview, although it dealt with a grave and sad business. I would ask the right hon. Gentleman whether he wishes the House to believe that that is all that has passed between Lord Lloyd and the representatives of the Department over which he presides. Does he really suggest that there was nothing between this telegram, asking Lord Lloyd to come home, and the letter which was presented to the right hon. Gentleman in his room at the Foreign Office? Does he suggest that that is so? Has he any knowledge of any other communications which have been made? I ask the right hon. Gentleman. [Hon. Members: "Answer!"] The House will note the silence of the right hon. Gentleman.

I have asked the right hon. Gentleman whether he has any knowledge that any other communications have taken place. Even to that question he remains silent. Is he aware—[Interruption.]—I am choosing my words—with what sternness the demand was made upon Lord Lloyd to send in his resignation, and how clearly it was intimated to him that, unless he did so, he would be dismissed? Is the right hon. Gentleman aware of that? Is he aware of that? [Hon. Members: "Are you?"] I have Lord Lloyd's statement to me. Lord Lloyd is my friend. He has served under the Government of which I was a Member. I have been, like the right hon. Gentleman, his colleague in the House of Commons for many years before the War, and during the War. So long as Lord Lloyd was a servant of the Government opposite, he made no communications of any sort or kind to me, or to anyone else. He kept himself entirely a servant of the Administration, but when he had resigned his appointment, when he had vacated his appointment, it is perfectly true that he did on that day come to see me. The right hon. Gentleman said that he had knowledge of that. He told Lord Lloyd that he had knowledge of it, and that he took steps to find out who it was that he went to see on that day. Is that really the proper way to treat a high official of the Crown who had just resigned?

Mr. A. Henderson: On a point of Order. I never made any such statement. [Hon. Members: "Withdraw!"]

Mr. Churchill: Perhaps the right hon. Gentleman will say how it was that he knew.

Mr. Henderson: If the right hon. Gentleman has got himself into a difficulty, I am not going to get him out.

Mr. Churchill: I am in no difficulty at all. The right hon. Gentleman himself brought this point out. He chose to bring up, in his great position as Secretary of State for Foreign Affairs, an interview which had taken place between two private persons, and he used that for the purpose of influencing the debate. Therefore, in view of that, may I not ask him on what he based that statement? It was quite true, but on what did he base that statement?

Mr. Henderson: I based it on the statement of Lord Lloyd, who told me that he had "seen Mr. Churchill."

Mr. Churchill: Yes, but after he had heard from the right hon. Gentleman that he was in possession of that information. That is rather a clever shuffle. The point is not of importance, but it illustrates the manner in which this matter has been treated, and the sort of thing that is going on. The right hon. Gentleman says that he based himself on Lord Lloyd's statement to him, but it now appears that he had previously informed Lord Lloyd that he had the information. Let us apply that to the statement of the right hon. Gentleman that no negotiations were going on behind the back of Lord Lloyd. Is it true to say that? Discussions and negotiations were taking place. I am not allowed to mention names, but in another place a Minister of the Crown, yesterday, used the word "negotiations" repeatedly. He said that negotiations were in progress but, "We cannot communicate the progress of these negotiations until they have reached a further point." That was a public, official statement of a Minister of the Crown. Now, the right hon. Gentleman says that no negotiations were taking place; that there had been only two conversations, and the Cabinet committee had only just assembled. It is quite clear that something in the nature of negotiations were going on, and the High Commissioner was not, in fact, informed. It is usual in these matters of importance that when Governments at home begin discussions, they should, in the first place, tell their officer on the spot, while he remains their officer, that they are having discussions and proceeding with the business.

I do not think that the right hon. Gentleman has in any way disposed of the criticism which was made by my right hon. Friend the Leader of the Opposition, when he said that there had been negotiations behind the back of the High Commissioner during the short period since the new Government came in. I say, taking together these negotiations, the telegram which was sent, with the deliberate intention to secure the resignation, the pressure which was put upon Lord Lloyd, apart from what we have been told by the right hon. Gentleman; taking all these three things together, I cannot think that Lord Lloyd has had from His Majesty's Government the treatment which his own perfectly frank and straightforward character and his conduct as High Commissioner in Egypt entitled him to expect. Governments may change their agents, and may choose their agents. Why have the present Government been so very anxious to change Lord Lloyd? It is because, undoubtedly, Lord Lloyd has stood for firmness in defence of British rights in Egypt. That is why he has been singled out and selected for early change.

The fact that a man who, undoubtedly, was identified with the successful assertion of lawful British rights in Egypt, has had to resign, will not be confined in effect only to Egypt. It will raise great difficulties and embarrassments there and elsewhere. This quick and sudden change will cause difficulties all over the British Empire. Administrators, great and small, will have an example before their eyes of the fate which overtakes, under the present Government, public officials and public servants if they stand up with some firmness and stiffness for British rights and interest, and refuse to lend themselves to sloppy surrender and retreat. That is why he was obnoxious, and that is why he has been removed, and I say that it is a very curious action for a minority Government to have taken, at the very time when the Prime Minister has been appealing for national co-operation and goodwill in the treatment of external affairs. It would have been much more prudent and wise to have continued to discuss these matters with Lord Lloyd, and when you had some fault to find with him yourselves, and when you had some grievance with him or some difference had arisen with him in your administration, then you would have had a perfectly good ground for choosing whatever agent you thought would carry out your policy, and it would not have been necessary to go back into the past and to put a completely wrong gloss upon the inevitable discussions, sometimes very keen, which take place behind the closed doors of Cabinets and Administrations.

I have said that much about Lord Lloyd, but I must ask a few questions on the infinitely graver matter of the policy in Egypt. The right hon. Gentleman did not give, I thought, a very precise answer to the questions which were put by the Leader of the Opposition. After all, this is not a matter which can be settled only by general phrases; it can only be settled by precise answers. In the Draft Treaty of 1927 which was discussed with Sarwat Pasha we made certain military proposals, and those proposals were the extreme limit to which we were prepared to go. They were the extreme limit, and only in return for a full acceptance with good will by the Egyptian Government. I want to ask the right hon. Gentleman whether his expression "no change of policy" means that he will not go further in the direction of removing the British troops from Cairo than was prescribed in the Articles of the Treaty discussed with Sarwat Pasha. I think we are entitled to an answer. I trust the Prime Minister will be speaking later in the Debate, and after all he has our interests in his hands in the next few months, and no doubt he will have the largest measure of national support behind him in negotiations in other spheres which he will be undertaking. I appeal to him to give us the maximum reassurance in his power, to let the House separate with the greatest sense of security, in matters about which we are so gravely concerned, and I ask him to answer the specific questions which were asked by my right hon. Friend: Was there any modification of the military provisions; had the Government consulted their military and expert authorities upon them; had they their agreement upon them, and other questions of that kind? May we have the answer to them?

Lastly, will the right hon. Gentleman respond directly to the appeal made to him by my right hon. Friend below the Gangway, and will he give the House an assurance, an absolute assurance, that the future relations of Britain and Egypt will not be compromised in any irrevocable sense by any decision or action which is taken by the Government before Parliament has reassembled? I think it is a fair request to make. I never wish to see the Executive unduly crippled, but considering that the right hon. Gentleman does not possess a Parliamentary majority—it is quite possible that on this Egyptian question he will be in possession of a majority; I do not prejudge it—I do say that, as he is not possessed of a normal Parliamentary majority, he ought to be doubly careful to make sure that he has a majority of the House behind him before, on a matter so controversial and grave as this, he takes irrevocable decisions. Therefore, I ask him to reassure the House that nothing will be settled which will have the effect of altering the present position in Egypt, altering the position adopted in the Sarwat Treaty, without our having had the fullest opportunity of discussing the whole of the proposals before any final decision is taken or signature appended.

WORLD PEACE

August 13, 1929

Canadian Club, Montreal

[Extract] . . . Although I have come to study Canadian conditions, particularly the economic situation and the best means of promoting inter-Imperial trade, I will not touch on this topic until I have ascertained by personal contacts what practical and concrete steps may be taken towards its further development.

No political society has greater interest in world peace than the British Empire, which has all the territory and resources it wants, and requires only the opportunity to develop them under peaceful conditions. I agree with Mr. Hoover that the outlook for general peace has never been better for 50 years.

Great Britain has set a good example to other nations in disarmament, which produced most of the quarrels of the last few years, and has probably been retarded by its greatest advocates.

A more tolerant attitude is needed towards the position of France, whose land armaments others find easy to criticize since they did not take part in France's grim experiences. I doubt whether a defenceless France would give a surer basis for peace. The key to disarmament is good relations and the promotion of common interests between Germany and France, which have been the central object of British policy in recent years.

Great Britain's policy has been to heal the wounds and rancours of war, and there is grave danger in drawing generations of tribute from Germany as a penal consequence of war.

Subject to such reservations as I have already made, I cordially supported Mr. Snowden's stand in respect of the Young Plan of Reparations apportionment, but I hope that the stand will be taken with the minimum of offence to others. I myself made it clear to M. Poincare, who assented, that the Spa percentages should be made the basis of the distribution of Reparations, and I had required that the British Government should feel free to review these various solutions.

The process of self-criticism which is fashionable in Great Britain brings the darkest side of affairs to the foreground and tends to create a false impression abroad. Even after everything has been conceded on the critical side, the British Isles are at present more populous and better off than at any time in their history.

ANGLO-AMERICAN NAVAL RELATIONS
AND IMPERIAL TRADE

August 15, 1929

Canadian Club, Ottawa

[Extract] . . . It has been the prime object of every British Government since the War, to remove all stumbling blocks in the path of friendship between the United States and the British Empire, [such as] the concession of Irish freedom, the merging of the Anglo-Japanese Alliance in a wider pact, and the settlement of War debts according to American wishes. Whatever may be thought of that bargain, it must stand, provided Great Britain secures from her European debtors as much as she is compelled to pay to the United States. The only "live" issue between the two countries is the difficult problem of naval agreement, and the discussion should be conducted on a cool matter-of-fact plane. I was a member of the Ministry which assumed the responsibility for the great decision of policy involved in the Washington Agreement of 1921; but in retrospect I am sometimes disposed to wonder whether its effect upon Anglo-American relations has been wholly beneficial, chiefly because most of the controversies of recent years have arisen from bickerings about the workings of this pact.

The agreement now projected threatens to open up a field of infinite technical discussion, and the attempt to regulate the size of the two navies may in time become fruitful of considerable misunderstanding and friction. [Editor's Note: Churchill pointed to the main elements of difference in the situation of the two countries.] Instead of any parity of conditions there is complete disparity. The application of the principle of rigid numerical equality, whatever the "yardstick" may be, has the danger of missing the real goal that Great Britain and the United States should be equal Powers on the seas.

A fair agreement will be very hard to reach, and if a paper agreement is concluded without the real assent of the two peoples, it may open up a perilous train of mutual suspicion and distrust. It is also questionable whether a rigid agreement will promote the real reduction of naval armaments, because experience of the results of the Washington Agreement has shown that countries built up to the limit allowed them to develop a partiality for large cruisers. Each party will build up to the limit allowed under any new agreement, and Great Britain, with her world-wide commitments, cannot contemplate a reduction of her naval strength below a certain limit, up to which the United States will also build. [Editor's Note: Churchill paid tribute to the sincerity of Mr. Hoover and his comprehension of the difficulties of other nations.] But I cherish fears that a rigid naval agreement may produce a condition worse than naval rivalry, and lead to an unwholesome illumination of international differences. I would prefer that each country resolved to live in amity with another should take its own naval path, and build just the minimum number of ships necessary for its purpose. Rather would I trust in the mutual good will and good faith of the two countries, and their determination to live up to the principles of the Kellogg Pact.

The problem of inter-Imperial trade is of paramount importance. The fundamental question is, how can the different units of the Empire give larger blocks of their business to one another. I assert it would be idle and fatal for any British Party to make food taxes part of its programme, and the Dominions cannot be expected to demolish their protective tariff barriers under which their industries have grown up, but I feel that other avenues await exploration, notably in the field of transportation, and that the modern technique of business may find new solutions for old problems. The questions of inter-Imperial trade should be completely removed from the arena of party politics, and the task of investigating them should first be entrusted to a commission of the foremost leaders of business in the Empire, who would report upon feasible schemes, and provide material for politicians to work out profitable plans. I confess that I myself, although my fiscal orthodoxy is not suspect, take the free-trade view, but I argue that Imperial interests should always transcend doctrinaire creeds if adhesion to the latter proves an obstacle to fruitful action.

IMPERIAL TIES

August 16, 1929

*Canadian Club, Empire Club, and
Board of Trade Luncheon, Toronto*

[Extract] . . . The completion of the Singapore naval base is essential to the security of communications in the Empire. It is nothing more than a resting-place for the British Fleet, and our continued friendly relations with Japan belies the assertion that is is a menace to that nation's security. Australia and New Zealand have already contributed more money for the base than has Great Britain, and its abandonment, as a result of the change of Government at home, would have a disastrous effect. The antipodean Dominions are entitled to expect that, if danger threatens them, the rest of the Empire shall go to their help with full strength, and to do this the Navy must have an Eastern base, where ships can obtain fuel and supplies on their way to Australia.

I am no opponent of self-government and have put through Parliament two of the most daring experiments in self-government ever attempted in connexion with the Transvaal and the Irish Free State, but I have grave misgivings whether Egypt to-day is any more capable of offering the stability of government which international interests in that country and world peace require than she was when Great Britain first stepped in 50 years ago. Conditions in Cairo are grave, with murder and conspiracy rampant, and certain public services, such as irrigation, which were turned over by Great Britain to the Egyptians, have deteriorated under their management.

[Editor's Note: Churchill reiterated the doubts he had expressed in his speech at Ottawa as to whether a naval agreement of a satisfactory character could be arrived at between Great Britain and the United States.] To apply any mere chop-logic numerical parity to conditions so fundamentally different would not lead to what is wanted—equality of power on the sea—but to a condition in which, under the pretence of equality, Great Britain would be relegated to an inferior position. However, no dispute is likely to arise between the two countries which have just signed the Kellogg Pact, and no matter how many ships the United States builds, they will never be used against Great Britain.

[Editor's Note: In closing, Churchill touched upon the question of Imperial trade, and expressed his dissent from the project of free trade within the Empire, and repeated his suggestion that a conference of representative business leaders should be held to explore the possibilities of development of inter-Imperial trade.] Although trade is important, there are other and stronger bonds of Empire, and since the Conference of 1926 nothing but common interests and traditions have held the Empire together. But those are mighty ties, incomprehensible to Europeans, which have drawn millions of men from the far corners of the earth to the battlefields of France, and we must trust to them to continue to draw us together.

EGYPT

August 21, 1929

Educational League Meeting,
Winnipeg, Manitoba

[Extract] ... When I made my last visit nearly 30 years ago, I said that Winnipeg would be a "winner," and my prediction has evidently been fulfilled.

... It is absolutely essential that Great Britain's power in Egypt should be retained for the general welfare of the country, otherwise all the misfortunes which were her previous lot will be thrown back into the mass of Egyptian population. This matter has not been settled yet. We are pledged to consult the Dominions with regard to it. We know Australia and New Zealand are vitally concerned. They hold a strong opinion, and have a right to be heard. I hope that Canada will also form an opinion on the question, and it should be recorded through the proper channels and in the proper manner.

THE MIDDLE EAST SITUATION
AND WAR DEBTS

September 4, 1929

Vancouver, British Columbia

[Extract] ... Under the Balfour arrangement the United States was to get nearly everything from Great Britain that Great Britain got from her creditor-nations in Europe. If Russia comes to her senses and pays up, this money should be kept by Great Britain. My opinion is that the Reparations Conference reached a very satisfactory conclusion. No British Government could have accepted the Young Plan as it stood. Mr. Snowden has been right both in his stubborn resistance and in his final concession. The amount of money in dispute was not large enough to justify the setting back of the whole resettlement of Europe. Nevertheless, the fact remains that the principle of the Balfour Note has been impaired. We could no longer say that we were obtaining as much from Europe, including arrears, as America would receive from us.

It had been my intention, had I continued in office, to take the opportunity afforded by any deviation, however slight, from the principle of the Balfour Note to restate that principle in terms more advantageous to Great Britain. It should have been made clear that the Russian debt to Great Britain of nearly £800,000,000 stood outside the self-denying limitations of the Balfour Note. France and Italy should have been invited to agree to this as an offset to the fresh concession we had made. Perhaps the settlement of the Russian debt may seem remote, but it is by no means impossible. Suppose that in 10 or 15 years Russia resumes the garb of civilization and effects a debt settlement with her creditors, the British taxpayers ought to have some relief from it. The Hague Conference was the moment for obtaining the necessary assent of France and Italy to this restatement of the British position, and I hope this has not been overlooked.

The lamentable occurrences are a bloody foretaste of what would happen in Egypt and India if the protecting and controlling hand of Great Britain were withdrawn. No doubt the harsh dismissal of Lord Lloyd and the proposal to clear the British garrison out of Cairo and Alexandria were interpreted by the Arabs of Palestine as a sign of weakness, and that the time was ripe to strike. The result was massacre and pillage of a horrible character, requiring troops and warships to be hurried to the scene, and probably involving more bloodshed before order is restored. What an object-lesson! What a warning! If the British garrison were withdrawn from Cairo, and if Great Britain repudiated her obligation to protect minorities and foreigners in Egypt, the carnage which has disgraced Palestine would be reproduced in the Nile Valley, with the result that either foreign Powers would intervene to protect their own citizens or we should be compelled to return in far larger strength after great expense and severe fighting. Such must be the inevitable consequence of any want of confidence shown by Great Britain in her mission in the East, or failure in the will necessary to discharge the honourable and merciful responsibilities we have assumed.

For the moment nothing is possible but to support the Government in restoring order and peace in Palestine. No doubt the House of Commons will vote by over-whelming majorities the money or the men needed. The Jews had as good a title to make Palestine their home as the Arabs. There is no reason why Jews and Arabs should not dwell side by side. The Jews have brought great wealth and civilization there. No British political party would repudiate the War-time undertakings to the Zionist movement.

CANADIAN DEVELOPMENT

November 25, 1929

Canada Club Dinner,
Savoy Hotel, London

[Extract] . . . In Canada I had the most friendly reception. It was 30 years since my previous visit, a period that has seen immense growth in Canada in every direction, political, social, and economic. The economic development gives rise to a feeling of the highest hope. (Cheers.) There were pessimists who had asked how Canada could realize an integral and effective unity and achieve a political identity, but to-day the view is changed. In the last 25 years the feature of Canadian development has been the progress to the West, but in the next 25 years the feature will be the new growth to the North. (Cheers.) In the political sphere there have been great and beneficial changes. Old problems have either been solved or swept into the waste-paper basket. The decisions of the Imperial Conference of 1926 have had a great effect and Canada knows that all parts of the Empire have equal status and that the ties that bind us are so flexible and so easy of comprehension that there is no possibility of friction. (Cheers.)

The Empire system is based on freedom and good will, each unit seeking to do its best for the whole combination. We have had to develop the economic relationship between Canada and Great Britain. We want to handle much larger blocks of each other's business. (Cheers.)

I wish to say how much I appreciated the kindly welcome I received in Canada. (Cheers.) The farther West I went I felt that the keen sentiment for England got stronger. The more that Canada realizes the intensity of her own national life and the greatness of her future the more will she find herself drawn into the combination of the British Empire and the more indissolubly will she be united on both sides, the Atlantic and the Pacific, to our Empire and our hopes.

When I was in Canada I spoke of the great questions that affected the future of the Empire, and I found myself confronted with anxious inquiries about how things were progressing in the Mother Country. There was an impression that things were going ill with us and that we were all on the dole. (Laughter.) That was before the latest Bill. (Laughter.) I did my best to reassure them.

INSTALLATION AS CHANCELLOR

December 13, 1929

Bristol University

[Extract] . . . One aspect of university life gives me particular pleasure. Not less than 70 per cent. of the undergraduates have made their way to the University through the technical, primary, and secondary schools of the country and of the West of England. That is a very remarkable achievement.

I remember some five years ago when I held the office which one of our most distinguished graduates to-day now holds, and I remember I was unable to provide a considerable annual sum of public money to facilitate this very purpose and to make sure that there was an unbroken ladder from the primary schools of the country to the highest form of educational achievement. We are a complete democracy. To universal suffrage and direct popular election is now confided all the interests and responsibilities of a world-wide Empire built up through centuries of aristocratic and oligarchic rule. No one can say it is not an audacious experiment. No one can pronounce what the ultimate result will be, but we now hope, we must hope. In this island we have always succeeded hitherto in managing our quarrels and in making the changes which time renders imperative without breaking the golden links which join us to our past. Here in old England we are entitled to a confident hope that all will be well. But we must not only hope—we must act.

ADVICE TO STUDENTS

December 14, 1929

Bristol University

[Extract] . . . I never myself had the advantage of a university education. I was not thought clever enough to profit by it to the full. I was put to be trained in technical matters of a military college, and almost immediately afterwards things opened out very quickly into action and adventure. In those days England had a lot of jolly little wars against barbarous peoples that we were endeavouring to help forward to higher things, and I found myself scurrying about the world from one exciting scene to another. During years appropriate to study and the accumulation of knowledge, I was a pack-horse that had to nibble and browse such grass as grew by the roadside in the brief halts of long and wearying marches. But see how very lucky you all are. You are a most fortunate crowd of quadrupeds, to use a neutral term. (Laughter.) You are admitted to a spacious paddock with the very best herbage growing in profusion. You are pressed to eat your fill. I hope you are going to take advantage of that. . . . The most important thing about education is appetite. Education does not begin with the university, and it certainly ought not to end there. I have seen a lot of people who got cleverer until about 21 or 22 years of age, then seemed to shut down altogether and never made any further progress. . . . Take full advantage of these years when the wisdom of the world is placed at your disposal, but do not spend too much time in buckling on your armour in the tent. The battle is going on in every walk and sphere of life.

DOMESTIC AND IMPERIAL AFFAIRS

December 16, 1929

Essex Conservative Association Luncheon,
Hotel Cecil, London

[Extract] . . . We have to face an anxious and critical situation and it may well be worse before it is better. The Government has not the slightest idea how to cure unemployment. Their only plan is to spend the taxpayers' money on further and better "doles." They are actually budgeting for a live register of unemployment of 1,200,000 during the next three years, and the Bill which we are to pass through the House of Commons this day will certainly add 100,000 persons to that dismal total. So far from curing unemployment every step which the Government has taken will tend in one way or another to increase the number of able-bodied persons who will be reduced to a state of pauperism. In the United States they are reducing direct taxation by £40,000,000, in Germany they are proposing to reduce it by £40,000,000 or £50,000,000. Similar projects are under consideration in France. Those are our great competitors—the greatest civilized nations in the world. All are intending to reduce the burden of taxation with the definite object of improving their world trade.

What are we doing? The Government has already spent £8,000,000 more in the few months they have been in office and have committed us to £20,000,000 of expenditure next year. And all this money goes, not for social betterment, industrial reorganization, or for the revival of trade and industry; it simply goes in "doles." In fact, as the Prime Minister warned his party, they are becoming solely a party of public relief. That very bitter phrase was wrung from the Prime Minister in the stress of his responsibility. If the Labour Party had their way they would reduce the country to one vast soup kitchen. The world regenerators who harshly criticized their predecessors reveal an absolute bankruptcy of ideas, an utter failure of executive action.

But we must not forget that the Government have a jolly plan for dearer coal. The miners have got the Government in their grip. So Mr. MacDonald and his colleagues had the happy idea of getting the coalowners to come into a deal. They are all to join together, Government, miners, and mineowners, and take what they want out of the consumer. I tried my best to give effectual rating relief to help the great productive industries. But all those industries depend on coal. Now the Socialist Government, in order to placate their patrons and masters, the miners, have entered into an unholy bargain with the coalowners to charge, not only the general consumer, but the productive industries of the country, more for their coal. The Liberals were obviously right in pointing out in scathing and penetrating terms the flagitious character of this measure. It is quite likely that virtually the whole of the rating relief of productive industry will be filched back from it in the form of dearer coal. The Government plan means a subsidy, the most offensive that can be produced, given permanently to the coal industry at the expense of the whole nation.

The decision with regard to Egypt is the most urgent and the most fatal of all the decisions likely to be taken in the coming year. The Government are going to take the British troops away from Cairo and make them dig in along the Suez Canal. British troops have been for 50 years in Cairo. They have never been used against the Egyptian people. They have been used only to help the Egyptian people. The Egyptian people have been guided and helped from bankruptcy to great wealth, from anarchy to civilization, by the aid of British administrators, who had behind them the silent strength of the British troops in Cairo. Cairo is not only the Egyptian capital; it is a cosmopolitan city and we have undertaken before all the world the obligation of securing its order and its welfare. So far we have fulfilled that obligation. Now we are to cast it down, and with it all the fruits of 50 years of splendid achievement. Our soldiers are to leave the scene of their patient, peaceful duties and drink distilled water in desert fortifications east of Line 32. I wish to direct the attention of the country to this grave impending event. I am sure it will mean disaster not only for the people of Egypt and of Britain, but for the whole civilized communities of the world. I am sure also that it is a step that will ultimately, and perhaps at no great distance of time, lead to a serious effusion of blood.

But Egypt is only a preliminary. Behind Egypt stands not only the Middle East, with all its problems and perils, but mighty India itself. The very same processes that are thrusting, coaxing, or cajoling us out of Egypt, processes sometimes subtle, sometimes violent, sometimes secret, sometimes open, but never-ceasing, are at work in India. They are at work in India on a far larger scale. Our position in India is wholly different from our position in Egypt. We have rights in India which we do not claim in Egypt. When our interests in Egypt have been surrendered and our duties repudiated there, we must still define our interests and duties in India. But you may be sure that on the day when the British troops evacuate Cairo every enemy of the British Empire in every quarter of the globe will rejoice, and every subversive faction in India will be encouraged by the vision of another day when the last British battalion will be embarking from Indian shores, leaving behind them what Lord Morley, that great Liberal statesman, called "the dull roar and scream of carnage and confusion," coming back to us across the dark distances. The same spirit of pusillanimity, which the Socialists embody, the same lack of conviction in our mission in the East which is liquidating the work of two generations in Egypt, will, if it is not dominated and exorcized, destroy the healing work of 10 generations in India. I urge you to get together, to rally all the forces on whom Britain can rely. I hope and believe we will succeed. We must repel no elements in this country that will fight steadily on our side. At any rate, we will have done our best, and no part of the shame, no unendurable self-reproach will rest on a resolute and united Conservative Party. (Cheers.)

COAL MINES BILL
December 19, 1929
House of Commons

I rise somewhat earlier than I had intended, because I am very anxious not in any way to obstruct or hamper the Prime Minister [J. Ramsay MacDonald] in the momentous speech which he is to deliver at the close of this Debate. I do not wish by any delay on my part to be forced to prolong my remarks beyond the period which, I understand, will be convenient to him. I say frankly that I find great difficulty in winding up this Debate. Usually when important issues are brought before the House of Commons, whoever is charged on either side with the concluding phase of the Debate looks to see first what one side is thinking and then the other, and out of this clash and counter-statement he selects points upon which the House is in doubt or upon which its decision would naturally turn. But on this occasion I have listened to a great part of the Debate, and it seems to me that only one side has been stated.

We have had a series of speeches setting forth all the objections to the Bill. I have never listened to such a series of speeches. There was the speech of my right hon. Friend with all its deep knowledge of practical conditions in the coal industry. There was the speech of the right hon. Gentleman the Member for Darwen (Sir H. Samuel), who impressed us all on this side very much, and lastly, there has been the speech of the Leader of the Liberal Opposition. We have heard speeches like that to which we have listened from the hon. Member who has just sat down, all marshalling the long series of arguments and objections against the Measure, but where is the answer? We have heard no answer. Not a single word has been spoken from the Government Bench since the speech of the introducer of the Bill, and no attempt worthy of the name has been made to reply to any of the dozen serious objections and criticisms which have been brought forward moderately, forcefully but persistently from this side of the House. The Government have sat still as stocks, dumb and silent throughout this Debate and have made no counter-case. Therefore, coming as I do, not so much to take part in the Debate but coming at the end of a commination service to see if I can find some new form in which the curse can be presented, I must apologise to the House in advance if I should be limited rather to the duty of revising, reviving, and reviewing the main arguments that have been adduced against this Measure.

Let us now at the last stage of the Debate, when so short a time separates us from the most important Division which this Parliament has seen, see quite clearly what it is this Bill proposes to do. It is a deliberate and avowed plan of levying a new, indirect tax upon the general public for the benefit of private and sectional interests,

and of levying this tax through the agency of a basic necessity of popular consumption. The right hon. Gentleman the President of the Board of Trade made us a
very lucid, limpid, if lengthy speech the other day. I see that the newspapers in their
tributes to him described his form of oratory as that of a purling brook, limpid and
clear. I must admit that his candour was very apparent. He made no secret whatever of
the fact that the Bill he introduced was intended to have the result of extracting a
new, large sum of money from the pockets of the tax-payers through a dearer price for
coal. I will read to the House the words which I particularly noticed in order that there
may be no dispute about this:

> As regards those public utility organisations, I say not a single word in
> criticism of their work this afternoon.

I thought that that sounded ominous. It always is when anyone begins like that. The
right hon. Gentleman then pointed out that they use between 35,000,000 and
40,000,000 tons of coal a year, and he said:

> Electricity is regulated under two great Acts. . . . Gas is regulated under
> a whole series of Acts of Parliament. Railway companies are regulated
> under the Act of 1921, there are public institutions of one kind and
> another. These are industries which have either some form of guaranteed
> return, or a monopolistic nature, or—

and this is what I want the House to mark—

> or have the power of passing on to consumers increased charges.—[Official
> Report, 17th December, 1929; col. 1267, Vol. 233.]

There is nothing like stating frankly one's position, and if one does it with all the
lucidity and limpidity of a purling brook, all the better. I think it is an advantage in
this discussion that we should all start agreed upon the main point of outset. We are
definitely entitled, and even instructed, on the authority of its author and introducer,
the President of the Board of Trade, to call it the "Dear Coal Bill." Electricity, gas,
railways, and other public utilities, many of them administered by local authorities,
will have to pay more for their coal, and are meant to pay more for their coal, and will
have to recover that from their consumers, from the users of their services, and are
meant so to recover it.

These great services have been singled out for a particular purpose. The struggling railways, with their traffics falling from year to year; gas, which is so vital an aid
to industry, so humble an assistant in the poorest home; electricity, on which high
hopes have been founded and fine perorations are being prepared by the Minister of
Transport—all these are to become the instruments of a new private tax collection for
the benefit of one section of the community, and for the sake of any political
advantage that the Government may think they can get from it. As for the ordinary
domestic consumers of coal, as for the users of industrial coal, as for the agriculturists,

who use coal for many purposes, they will have to pay directly for every sack of coal or consignment of coal that they purchase, and indirectly, in addition, for all the commodities that they purchase which in the future will be manufactured with taxed coal.

This tax is put on to pay the loss which the coal industry is about to suffer because of certain decisions which the Government have taken. They have decided to reduce the hours of miners, or rather, to reduce the length of the shift. Apparently the miners are suffering from short time; that is to say, they are not employed for enough days in each week to enable them to earn the wages that we should like to see them take home to their families. But it appears also that they are suffering from long time; that is to say, they are asked to work too many hours in each of the days when they are employed, and so they cannot have the rest and leisure which they desire. Apparently, also, it costs so much to lower a miner into the pit and haul him up again that the length of time spent below is an important factor, not only in the price of coal, but in the amount of coal which we can sell, and consequently, it is an important factor—within very narrow limits an extraordinarily important factor—in the number of man-day's work available.

One would have thought that this difficulty of the too long shift and of the too little employment in the week could somehow or other have been adjusted within the ambit of the trade, and one would have thought that some arrangement of computing hours, in fortnights or in weeks, would have met all difficulties and have secured to the miner the most satisfactory arrangement of his time and to the mining industry the most profitable employment of the shifts at the coal face. One would have thought that this Government of all others—this Labour Government, intimately associated with the miners, in honourable friendly relation with them—could have done something, with all their special knowledge and their peculiar influence, to work out a system which would have adjusted this difficulty, and that this would have been one of those contributions which it would have lain in the power of a Labour Government to make. Perhaps no other party in the State could have rivalled them in the making of it. However, it was not to be. The Government have promised to reduce the hours of the miners by one hour, and so, as men of honour, as pledges are sacred, they conceive themselves bound to reduce them by at least half an hour. At any rate, we are glad to know that, in the view of the party opposite, debts of honour should always be paid at least at the rate of 10s. in the pound.

No one knows what the cost of this relief will be. I have heard it put at £9,000,000; others say £15,000,000; but at any rate it is a very heavy cost, a substantial new charge upon our resources. Who is to pay? The owners cannot pay, because it is common ground in this Debate that the ascertainments are showing over the last few years a definite loss. Perhaps the figures are exaggerated, but that there is a loss no one disputes. The Chancellor of the Exchequer cannot pay out of his present resources, because he has given them all away for the dole. Perhaps that is putting it too high; we will say that he has given a large proportion of them away in improving the actuarial position of the Unemployment Insurance Fund. The miners certainly cannot be asked to pay out of their wages. And so there remains only one way out—the consumer. It is the consumer who is to pay; it is the consumer who seems to be the line of least resistance. The consumer is in a queer position. He has not got a single friend until, all of a sudden, something happens, and the consumer, hitherto brushed aside as negligible, finds himself a powerful figure, and perhaps the dominant, deciding factor in a political issue. The Government could not fight the consumer, I presume, at the same time as they were fighting the other forces, and, in order to gather their strength, they thought it necessary to come to terms with the owners. They had to square the owners to fight the consumer; and, in order to square the owners, they have had to pay their price. We do not know what the price is, but, whatever it is, the consumer will have to pay.

I am very glad to see the Chancellor of the Exchequer here. I think it would have been more manly and more honest to impose this new indirect tax in the Budget and distribute the money raised in accordance with whatever principle and under whatever conditions the Government thought right to prescribe. It would be far better for the House of Commons and far better for the tax-payer, and we should know exactly the rate that was to be struck, we should know exactly how much money has to be raised, we should have the justification and the purpose to which it was to be put, and the House would have retained power over the taxation of the country. But by this Act of Parliament the taxing powers of the House of Commons are to be handed over to a council of owners, we are to part with our hitherto most jealously guarded right, and £30,000,000, £40,000,000 or £50,000,000 are to be extracted from the pockets of the people by an Act of Parliament passed by this House without any of that protection which the procedure of the House of Commons in financial matters, and in regard to burdens proposed to be cast upon the people, has always provided.

What is the explanation of all this? It is a very simple explanation. Nothing but duress would have led experienced politicians and electioneers, like the Prime Minister and the Chancellor of the Exchequer—I think I will say the Foreign Secretary before I come to the Lord Privy Seal, because the Lord Privy Seal has hardly been showing his usual form in electioneering lately—nothing but duress would have led these experienced politicians into the danger and the uncertainty of being branded as the authors of a policy or, as the right hon. Gentleman below the gangway called it, the calamity of a Dear Coal Bill. Would it have taken the President of the Board of Trade an hour and three quarters to tell us about the grip which the Miners' Federation have upon His Majesty's Government. This limpid stream would have revealed that ugly fact with extreme prominence—40 seats directly controlled by the Miners' Federation and an influence through trade union organisation in many seats which is dominating in the party opposite. There is the scientific conception behind this Measure. There is the social idealism. The Government are not free agents. They have not been in a position to take the right course, nor even to seek it. They have not been able to offer us a helpful solution of the coal problem, or even an improvement in that problem. They have been forced to obey the dictates of sectional and class interests organised and massed in an intimate manner within the structure of their own party, and to adopt the policy of erecting a nation-wide monopoly trust to be set up by Act of Parliament to fix the amount of coal to be got, to fix the prices at which it may be sold at home and abroad and to divide these fixed amounts among the district combines, who are again to divide it among the mines.

That is the proposal. There is no guarantee of reasonable efficiency, such as always has been sought in every measure where compulsory powers are given to private individuals, no guarantee against an overcharge to the consumer, no attempt to reorganise the industry, no attempt to form a big selling pool to deal in the most effective manner with its product, nothing but a powerful combination in restraint of trade, a revival of the obsolete economics and conceptions of bygone generations that there is a static amount of work, a static amount of trade, a static amount of coal to be got and a fixed cost of production, as though all those fallacies had not been swept away by the bold advance of a scientific world. How are the prices that are to be fixed to be distributed? The foreigner is to have the first place. He travels first class. He has the preference. Then we are told perhaps something may be done to let steel and iron, at any rate, get their coal as well as they can now, but about that nothing has been said. In the third class are the public utilities, industrial coal, householders and the general public, who are to pay at a penalised price in order to pay the Bill for the miners' shorter hours, for the compensation or squaring of the mineowners, for the levy to fortify imports into this country with British bounty fed coal and, no doubt, an additional sum thrown in to cover incidental expenses.

When the Government embarks upon such a policy, it is involved in a number of very curious reactions which I shall ask the House to let me mention. First of all, the Government in this policy is bound to favour a particular class of capitalist with whom they have entered into partnership. I am a supporter of the capitalist system but I do not go so far as this Bill of the Socialist Government. There is one advantage, at any rate, of the capitalist system. It continually clears itself of failures. If a capitalist succeeds, he is taxed. If he fails, he is let fail. That is the only method by which the prosperity and productivity of great communities has so far increased. It may be a hard method but it is a healthy method. The more boldly it has been applied in any country, the more rapid has been the advance in wealth, the greater has been the accretion of wealth and the higher has been the standard of living amongst the masses of the population. But the Socialist Government, in their new-found love of the coalowners, are proposing to give the inefficient capitalist a new vested interest and a guarantee of security. In fact, it is a new dole for failure, and it is a new dole for capitalist failure, but only for one kind of capitalist—the coalowners.

I have no wish to reflect upon the coalowners. On the contrary, they have not sought this Bill. They were threatened and they have made a very effective retort to the treatment to which they were subjected. But the coalowners, as capitalists, are not a class to be picked out above all others for favours from the Government at the cost of the public. The landlord, the cotton spinners, steel masters, railway shareholders, a dozen classes have at least as good a claim to consideration, if these good things are to be distributed, as the coalowners. The Government have been committed to a policy of exceptional favours to be bestowed on a particular class of capitalists, which relieve those capitalists from the risks and obligations which are inherent in their position as independent producers under an individualist system.

That is the first reaction. What is the second reaction? The second reaction is what I can only call a novel application of the doctrine of ca'canny. The Socialist mind is always fascinated by the idea of equality, of levelling. Of course, no doubt they would like to level up. That is very difficult. It takes a lot of work to level up. Reorganisation and all that sort of thing, are not so easily done. And so when that cannot be achieved we have to level down. If a mine is equipped with the latest machinery, if it is well-organised, if it is working full time and at the highest economy, it is to be made to slow down by the Bill of the President of the Board of Trade. It is to be made to mark time like the soldiers from Wellington Barracks till the other company catches up. For so many days each week it is to be made to slow down or to stop in order that the inefficient, backward pits shall have their share of the quota. It is very familiar to us. We all know how often the skilful worker or the industrious worker has been made to stop for his less gifted fellow or comrade. Everyone knows the old trade union prejudice. Here we see the ca'canny system applied by Statute, not by prejudice or workshop arrangements, but applied by Statute, not to individuals but to whole collieries, and firms and districts. It is a kind of collective ca'canny. And what does it amount to? That a large number of productive enterprises in this country are to be told in the future, as individuals have been told in the past, that they are not to do their best; they are to be told by law that they are not to do their best.

The third reaction which follows from the policy of His Majesty's Government may be described under the general heading of "Quotas." Having fixed the total cost, having fixed the total coal that may be cut, this total having been divided among the mines, and the price at which it may be sold having been decided by the coalowners' committee, the following situation arises: If any mine wants to cut any more coal—and, obviously, it will be highly profitable to some mines to cut more coal—it must buy an additional quota. We are to have a market in quotas. The quotations of the quotas will be quoted. There will be the "bulls" and the "bears" of quotas, and in the papers: Quotas are cheap to-day. When quotas are bought up, we shall find that a corner in quotas has developed. The efficient mines, which, if they were allowed to work full time, could earn rich profits, and whose economy will be destroyed if they are compelled by this Measure to work short time, have a strong inducement to buy quotas, and the value of the quotas, as the Leader of the Liberal party has announced, will steadily be increased as the number in the market diminishes. Let us see what it is that the purchasers of quotas will be buying. They will be buying the right to cut coal at the highest efficiency. They will be buying the privilege of exercising their initiative and enterprise which hitherto in this country have been as free as air. And they must in the future saddle their successful enterprise with the costs, the high costs, of the purchase price which has been extracted from them to buy up these newly-created monopoly values of quotas from the decaying and dying mines. They will be buying a licence to produce coal efficiently from someone to whom the Government have given a licence with a vested interest to produce coal inefficiently. Where will the money go? The hon. Member for Penryn and Falmouth (Sir T. Walters) has pointed out, that if you are going in for a process of this kind, at any rate, you would suppose that some compensation would to go the miners displaced by this gambling in quotas. Not at all. The money is not to go to compensate the workers displaced. It is simply to go to pay the unsuccessful coalowner for the monopoly value, for the unearned increment value of a newly-created vested interest given to him by the Socialist Government—a Christmas present from Lossiemouth.

We are often asked to remember the human side. There is a human side to this quota story. I am not going to use exaggerated language. I will take the words of the President of the Board of Trade. He said:

> I beg hon. Members also to remember that every colliery that is closed leaves either a village or a derelict community or a social problem behind.–[Official Report, 17th December, 1929; col. 1266, Vol. 233.]

Moderate words, but powerful words. That is also true of the buying and selling of quotas. I look forward a year and imagine what we shall read in the newspapers, say the "Daily Herald," a year hence, after its correspondent has gone down to some village in Durham or South Wales, and finds all the people in that village standing about in the streets. He will say: "What is the matter with you? You were all right a week ago when I came here." "Oh," they say "our quota was sold yesterday. Did not you know?" That is a cold-blooded process. I think that on the whole it is a more cold-blooded way of dealing with the grim facts of life than anything I have ever heard put before this House.

There is the fourth reaction from this strange policy of His Majesty's Government, but again a very characteristic one. All Socialist Governments in every country at all times have signalised their accession to office by inventing new crimes. Anyone acquainted with history knows that that is true without exception, and it has fallen to the lot of His Majesty's Government to invent a new crime–the crime of selling cheap. That is very progressive, very original. Their friends in Russia have only got as far as shooting people for selling dear. This is a refinement and an improvement. Now we are going to punish people for selling cheap. Many laws have been passed in this country to fix maximum prices. In times of emergency many laws are passed to prevent undue profiteering, and the undue taking advantage of the temporary conditions. Maximum prices we can see everywhere. Look at your electrical and public utility legislation, your railways, your tramways–everywhere you see legislation to prevent the public being charged more in relation, it may be, to the earnings, profits, dividends or whatever it may be.

So far as I am aware, and I have made inquiries in several quarters, there is no previous instance in the history of the House of Commons where legislation has been proposed and passed to enforce minimum prices, not maximum prices, and to punish those who fall below them. This is the first time in history that the statutory authority of the House of Commons has been invoked and its penal provisions applied to enforce a minimum price, and to punish capitalists who have not taken enough profits. Properly viewed, this is a Bill for compulsory profiteering. It is no exaggeration to say that there are mines, that could be named on either side of the House, which under a fixed price applicable to the whole of the industry and enabling the whole industry to make a reasonable profit there are mines which, if they sold at that price, will be making profits far greater and far beyond anything that they could have obtained in the free working of the market.

What is the position of the Government in this matter? The President of the Board of Trade made a statement the other day as to how he was going to accelerate and invigorate the work of the Consumers' Council in regard to the cost of food prices to the public. He said:

> The Government intend to submit proposals enabling them to deal with trading interests which refuse to accept the views which the Government may reach after considering the recommendations of the Consumers' Council— [Official Report, 5th November, 1929; col. 815, Vol. 231.]

Here are more penal provisions, but the penal provision is in the opposite direction. I can visualise a poor woman, very likely a widow, who goes to a butcher's shop and buys a piece of meat in respect of which the butcher has been fined for selling it to her too dearly, and she takes it home and fries it on a fire, and the coalowner has been fined for selling the coal to her too cheaply. A strange and wonderful philosophy we are being taught by our intellectual guides!

I would like to deal with an argument which will certainly be addressed or ought to be addressed to me. It may be said: "You make a great fuss about all this, but in the five counties something like these proposals is working at the present time and has been working for a considerable time, and nobody seems to have worried about it." Yes, but there are many things that are done in trade and commerce, in private trade and commerce, which though not illegal certainly ought not to be set forth in the language of a Statute of the House of Commons. Liberal, Radical, Socialist opinion has changed in regard to mergers and combines. When first I came here they were regarded as the arch-bug-bear, but gradually it has been seen that great combinations here and in the United States have produced new services, cheaper and better services for the public, and have given far greater security and better conditions for their employés. Therefore, there is a more reasonable spirit displayed towards great combines.

I welcome that development, but there is all the difference in the world between a combine which is started by private enterprise, with all the salutary influences attendant upon private enterprise, with all the checks that are brought to bear through the competition of others in a wide, free market, and a combine set up by the Government, with the penal provisions of statutory authority which is universal and nation-wide in its scope and sweep. It is right that private enterprise should go and gather wealth were they can by all the means which the law allows. It is right that they should seek to apply their enterprise in the most effective manner, and it is also right that the Government should stand aside as a separate factor to supervise and, in some cases, to assist, and in every way to watch with vigilance and, if necessary, to correct the actions of great mergers and combinations, but in the harmonising of the activities of these combinations with the necessary rights, sovereignties and interests of the democratic State.

We have favoured these combinations in recent years. We talk about them in regard to steel. There has been much discussion about regional mergers. The principle is to concentrate work in the best places and by the best methods and to develop the utmost possible economies and facilities for production. This is not a scheme of that kind. This scheme is merely to distribute a supposedly limited quantity of work over the widest area, and to average out and slow down the whole pace of the industry to that of the average. The policy of steel amalgamation, to which so many people have given attention and concentration, is the exact reverse of the principle of this Bill, which confers enormous powers to limit efficiency, to level down, to average production, to enable proprietors to rest in peace and ease whilst enabling them to charge their expenses in all these uneconomic operations to the general consumer and the industries of the country.

The Prime Minister and the Government have, I think, walked into a trap. They threatened the coalowners. The coalowners have laid a trap for the Government, and they have walked into it, with Mr. Cook, their great friend, prodding them from behind. Now they are in the trap, and well they know it, as anyone can realise who has seen what has taken place in this House. It is a very deadly trap in these times when the lives of Governments and Parliaments are, to say the least of it, precarious. They are in the dear coal trap, and we have seen them running up and down behind bars, whining to the Liberals, whom they have always endeavoured to destroy and devour, to help them to get out, just this once more.

If the Prime Minister was wise, he would be brutally frank. Instead of gaining, as no doubt he will, a pyrrhic victory in the Division Lobby; instead of saddling himself for months ahead with the odium and unpopularity of this Measure, he would, even now, withdraw the Bill. He would, even now, confess what is no doubt the truth that, in all his other preoccupations, he has given neither time nor attention to the Bill, nor has his Cabinet. They have not realised all its implications. They have allowed themselves to slip into it on purely Departmental advice which has not been brought into the common stock of party stress and discussion. That would be the wisest thing to do at this juncture, and to make new proposals next year. Certainly it would be a more dignified course than the course, which I understand the Prime Minister has decided to take, of humbly accepting the ultimatum so brutally flung at him from the Liberal Benches.

As far as we are concerned, we are confronted with the Bill; and, unless a statement of this kind is made we have no other course than to record our votes against it. It is incredible that a single Bill should violate so many principles and affront so many convictions. Conservatives must resist an invasion of property rights, and the restrictions imposed on the owners of mines. We must also resist, and so must all those who represent democratic constituencies, the infliction of dearer coal on the masses of the people. Liberals have shown themselves utterly scandalised, as was natural, by the creation of a new statutory vested interest and a monopoly value. Free Traders are shocked at a reversion to the most obsolete forms of 18th century Protection. Protectionists are amazed that the Government should propose to favour foreign manufacturers with British bounty-fed coal, and yet refuse to consider a duty on imported steel even to the extent of countervailing the bounty-fed element in it. It is not Socialism that we shall vote against to-night. We shall vote against a most repulsive specimen of Syndicalism whereby the Government, under duress, joins forces with a powerful capitalist interest, and with a still more powerful vote interest, in the hope of fortifying their own political strength and with the callous intention of pillaging the wealth of the nation.

EGYPT (PROPOSED TREATY)

December 23, 1929

House of Commons

We have just listened to a speech couched in felicitous and well-balanced terms from the hon. Member for Coventry (Mr. Noel Baker) which shows that the hon. Member has given a very careful study to this question. If I do not follow the line of his arguments, it is because I have a certain amount of ground to cover, and I do not wish to trespass longer than is necessary upon this Debate. First of all, I have a small point, a small discrepancy to which I desire to call the attention of the Foreign Secretary [Arthur Henderson]. I am sorry that I do not see him in his place, because it is a personal point. The House will remember the Debate which took place at the end of last Session on the eve of the Adjournment. My right hon. Friend the Leader of the Opposition asked a specific question of the Foreign Secretary. He said:

> I want to know one more thing, and that is if negotiations have been going on, are going on, or are completed, have those negotiations been carried on without the knowledge of the High Commissioner of Egypt? Those are very plain and very simple questions, and I hope we may have an equally plain and simple answer.—[Official Report, 26th July, 1929; col. 1636, Vol. 230.]

The Foreign Secretary was very emphatic, and he repelled with indignation the insinuation that negotiations had been going on without the knowledge of the High Commissioner. In his reply the Foreign Secretary said:

> There has been a suggestion in the speech to which the House has just listened, and which was made more emphatically in another place, that we had been carrying on negotiations behind the back of the High Commissioner. I challenge that statement most emphatically. . . . May I inform the House that the first meeting of that Cabinet Sub-Committee to consider these proposals with the intention of presenting a report to the Cabinet was held on Monday last, and I think that ought to dispose of the charge that we have been negotiating—at any rate, it appears that a new meaning has been given to the word "negotiating."—[Official Report, 26th July, 1929; cols. 1638-9; Vol. 230.]

The House has now heard that negotiations began in June, and we are now told that these proposals were considered in the early part of June, and we have had a very full account of the course of those negotiations. I do not wish to exaggerate this point, and I make no imputation on the right hon. Gentleman's good faith, but I must say that I think, in the delicate position of the Foreign Secretary, he should look at the two statements which he made, one at the end of last Session, and the other this afternoon in order to see whether there are any important discrepancies which require to be reconciled.

I am going to ask the House this afternoon to consider this extremely difficult question of Egypt in two separate stages. First of all, upon its merits, and, secondly, in respect of the hardly less difficult matter of form and obligation. Whatever may have been the course of events in the last 10 years, whatever view we may take about them, nothing can relieve us of the responsibility of asking ourselves at this stage whether in fact we are actually approaching a good, permanent and peaceful settlement of Egypt. If the result of all that has been said and done is safe and satisfactory, if we shall be able to rest upon this settlement in tranquillity through the years that pass; if we have in fact reached the best solution of this question, then, of course, no other questions would be worth considering. On the other hand, if what we have done should prove that whatever roads we have trodden are leading us now to the edge of a precipice, and are leading us to a far greater chance of strife than of peace, not merely to loss of interest and influence but of life, if it is leading us to continuing friction and bloodshed, then we must examine very much more carefully these questions of form, obligation, and commitments which I admit are also of the first importance.

The first question which I wish to discuss with the Government and place before the country is: Are we or are we not going to have peace as a result of the Treaty which the Government have proposed, and, particularly, as a result of withdrawing the British troops from Cairo. I remember at the time of the entente with France in 1904, when Liberals, Conservatives and Labour men were loud in their rejoicings at this settlement of our disputes with France which they looked upon as a great step towards the achievement of peace, that only one voice was raised against it, and that was the voice of Lord Rosebery who declared that the entente was much more likely to lead to war than to peace. Needless to say, those remarks were judged to be extremely inopportune by everybody. I am sorry to say that I must declare that it is my respectful and earnest submission to the House that the acceptance of this Treaty in its present form and the withdrawal of our troops from Cairo is far more likely to lead to the shedding of blood in Egypt and to a very tense and dangerous situation arising in the Mediterranean than will occur if we go on more or less as we are.

There is no doubt that it is both difficult and unsatisfactory to go on as we are, but we must be very careful, in seeking clarity, in seeking what I would call juridical impeccability, that we do not set in motion a train of events which will lead to shocking and sanguinary disasters. The first question that we ought to ask ourselves— because I recognise that to a large extent the Government are considering these matters from the same point of view as we are—is, what will happen in Egypt when the British troops have evacuated Cairo and taken up new stations in the deserts along the Suez Canal? For 50 years British troops have been in Cairo and just outside it; they have been intermingled with the Egyptian troops. The Egyptian Army has been under British control and guidance. All those troops, British and Egyptian, have dwelt together in amity, in discipline and in comradeship. They have been in close and friendly contact. They have paraded together and have manoeuvred together, and together they have formed the common defence of Egypt against internal disorder or Turkish invasion. Now it is proposed to separate those forces; it is proposed to leave the Egyptian Army, denuded of its British officers, concentrated in Cairo, and it is proposed to withdraw the British Army to the other end of the lists, to fortified camps which are to be constructed in the Canal Zone. I think that the mere act of this separation and of this taking up of opposite stations is pregnant with danger. I fear that it will create new dangers. I fear that it will mean the concrete expression of an antagonism which may very easily ripen, which will almost certainly ripen as the years pass by.

Originally, at the end of the last century, there were only 3,000 or 4,000 Egyptian troops in Cairo. When the liberation of the Sudan from the Mahdist terror was achieved, those numbers considerably increased. When, as the result of the alarming events of 1925 at Khartum, the Egyptian troops quitted the Sudan, the Egyptian Army in Cairo rose from 7,000 or 8,000 to 12,500 men. It has been the constant desire of the Egyptian Nationalists, and of every Egyptian Government depending upon their support, or anxious to gain their support, to increase the size of the Egyptian army as quickly as possible. Two years ago my right hon. Friend was confronted with a proposal of the Egyptian Government to raise the strength of the Egyptian Army in Cairo to 18,000 men, and to equip it with machine guns and many other modern appliances. We were able to dissuade Egyptian Ministers from taking so sinister a step, but we were only able to dissuade them because we were on the spot, and on the spot in force. Although there was no need to use that force, nevertheless its presence had the effect of securing quite quietly, quite politely, and without trouble, the object which we all desired, and which pacifists and disarmament men should be the first to desire, namely, the abandonment of a large scheme of Egyptian military expansion. Once we have retired to the Canal zone, we shall have no means of dissuading the Egyptian Government from any expansion or equipment of their army which they may think fit. Except during the brief period of the Protectorate, we have never had any legal right to do so, but we have had a moral right, and we have had the practical influence which secured the acceptance of that moral right. We may, indeed, have the moral right in the future, but we shall have neither legal right nor practical influence.

Nothing in this Treaty limits the armed forces which Egypt may raise and maintain. They have the wealth—they are very wealthy as the result of 50 years of our assistance; and they will have the sovereign right to raise as large an army as they please, and to equip it and dispose of it as they choose. It is obvious that any substantial increase in the Egyptian Army in Cairo would require the sending of precautionary reinforcements to the British forces on the Canal. For whom else can an increase in the Egyptian Army in Cairo concern except the British forces on the Canal? What other force is there in Egypt, or on the frontiers of Egypt, of any practical consequence that could constitute a preoccupation of the Egyptian Army except the British forces on the Suez Canal? Therefore, if at any time the Egyptian Government increase their army, as they have been long and earnestly anxious to do, and as the Egyptian Nationalists are determined to do, we shall have to make a counter-increase, and a situation of marked tension will arise and speedily develop.

Of course it will be said, and I recognise that it is so, that there is no doubt of our ability, if the worst ever came to the worst, to overcome and even brush aside any force which Egypt might set on foot. We could undoubtedly at any time, as long as we retained the command of the seas, advance upon Cairo and win another battle of Tel-el-Kebir and reenter Cairo. But do we want to do this? Who wants to do it? Is this a situation that we should ever wish to see again? Is this the kind of event that we wish to prepare for? Is this the kind of event that we wish to hatch out in advance? Even if it has been decided to march the British troops out of Cairo, surely, in the interests of peace, in the interests of economy, in the interests of disarmament, the Treaty should at least contain a strict limitation upon the size of the forces which, in times of peace and without consultation with their Ally, the Egyptian Government should raise. To go away from Cairo to the Canal, to lose all decisive influence upon Egyptian policy, and at the same time to leave them free to raise any army they choose, is simply manufacturing explosive in a retort. The British Government may take to themselves the credit of a peace-loving gesture, but the consequences of that gesture, however well meant, may, after a few years, involve serious loss of life.

These matters have already been in the minds of His Majesty's present Government, and they have regarded them in a spirit which in some respects is robust. Lord Thomson, the Secretary of State for Air, is a Socialist Minister, but his political training has not advanced sufficiently to enable him to conceal his misgivings under a perfect veneer of hackneyed phrases. He has remarked significantly, as I observed from the public Press, that armoured cars can reach Cairo from the Canal zone in six hours, provided, I presume, of course, that the roads have not been broken up. What does this significant remark of the Air Minister mean? I ask the Foreign Secretary specifically, because it is no use getting ugly facts covered up and camouflaged over, and leaving the working classes in this country and in Egypt suddenly to wake up and find that armed violence has broken out, and that they are expected to take part in it. [Interruption.] Let us see exactly where we are going. [Interruption.] I ask the right hon. Gentleman specifically—the Under-Secretary can answer me when he speaks, as I presume he is going to do—whether it is part of the plan of His Majesty's Government to keep an adequate mobile force of mechanical vehicles in the Canal zone for the purpose, if necessary, of advancing upon Cairo? I must point out that, if they are not kept in the Canal zone—if, for instance, they are left in England until the emergency arises—then Lord Thomson's assurance has no meaning, and I am sure he would not have given such an assurance on behalf of the Government unless he had honourably intended that reliance could be placed upon it. As a Socialist Minister has introduced this topic of armoured cars into the discussion, I feel bound to bring to the notice of the House the kind of situation which the Government have already been focussing in their minds, and it is no doubt seriously concerning their military advisers. [Interruption.] Laughter may sometimes, not only express feelings, but conceal uneasiness.

I have another point, and I will ask the supporters of the Government to consider it. The Egyptian Army, as hon. Members opposite probably know, is raised by conscription; there is compulsory military service in Egypt. The industrious peasantry of the Delta of the Nile are averse from the profession of arms; they do not wish to serve as soldiers; they prefer to cultivate their fields and lead peaceful, industrious lives, gaining a humble livelihood by their water channels and beneath their date palms; and it is quite impossible to induce them by monetary rewards alone to quit their homes, their villages, and their fields, in order to crunch the gravel on the barrack square or to exchange the implements of agriculture for lethal weapons. They do not wish to be soldiers. Why should they be compelled, against their own inclinations, which are at the moment in harmony with the dearest inclinations of lovers of peace throughout the world, to undergo the rigours of compulsory military training? [*Interruption.*]

If it be decided to evacuate Cairo—I think the House will see that my point is a reasonable one; at any rate, I intend to make my point—if it be decided to evacuate Cairo, surely the least that could be accepted in the Treaty would be that the conscription of the Egyptian peasantry for service in the Army should be simultaneously abolished. The general principle on which the Draft Treaty is framed is one of meticulous similarity and equality. There is equality of status between the two High Contracting Parties, and the Government, as my right hon. Friend has pointed out, have carried this principle so far as to suggest that the whole British Empire shall refer its entire foreign policy to our Egyptian Ally, in the same way as our Egyptian Ally is to refer its foreign policy to us. If we are carrying equality and similarity to such fantastic lengths in the region of diplomacy, surely it would not be too much to ask that an equal provision should be introduced into the Treaty in respect of compulsory military service. I ask, will the Government add to their proposals a provision that neither of the two High Contracting Parties shall adopt or continue compulsory military service unless some great emergency outside Egypt arises? Is that an unreasonable request? Is that a request which any of those who have taken part in denouncing conscription in every part of the world, and who sincerely advocate its abolition, can regard as an unreasonable request? We, too, have advocated again and again the abandonment of compulsory service, and we have not only advocated it, but we have set the example ourselves to all Europe. Are we not, in these circumstances, entitled to make a stipulation of this kind before we sign a Treaty or withdraw our troops? This is at once perfect equity and sound common sense. Those are the two points which I am asking the right hon. Gentleman to consider—first of all a restriction upon the size of the Egyptian Army and, secondly, the abolition of conscription for the recruitment of that army.

I shall no doubt be told that, once the Treaty is signed, all friction and causes of friction and all trouble between the British and Egyptian Governments will have been absorbed in a lasting settlement, a reign of peace and goodwill will ensue, and there will be a new atmosphere. I wish I could believe that this was true. Unhappily, no one who studies the draft agreement, and knows anything about Egyptian affairs, can pretend that all serious causes of friction—"all sources of suspicion," I think, was the phrase the Forign Secretary used—will be disposed of by this Treaty. I take only one very grave cause of continual friction, which has been mentioned to-day on both sides of the House, the British occupation of the Sudan. It is common ground between the Government and the Opposition that the Sudan should remain effectually under British control. No part of the Government's declarations about Egypt have been so outspoken. The answer which the right hon. Gentleman has just given to the point pressed by the late Foreign Secretary appears to me to be all that could possibly have been asked from this side to the House on that subject. The declarations are outspoken and, although I think it is a dangerous thing to introduce a battalion into the Sudan, on account of the disturbance that it will create in public opinion, nevertheless I do not consider that those declarations on this point are unsatisfactory. We have been repeatedly assured that the most the Government will agree to about the Sudan is that it will consider sympathetically the admission of a single Egyptian battalion there as a matter of form and courtesy, simultaneously with the withdrawal of the British troops from Cairo, and we are now told that it will rest with the British Governor-General of the Sudan, irrespective of any provisions in the Treaty, and irrespective of any interpretation that may be placed on those provisions by the League of Nations or otherwise, to order that battalion out again, and nothing can stand in the way of its removal from the Sudan.

From our point of view, that is a perfectly satisfactory answer. But does the right hon. Gentleman really think the Egyptian nationalists will be satisfied with this? Does he really think any Egyptian Government will dare to rest content with it? The connection of Egypt with the Sudan is ancient and traditional. Nothing appeals to the educated classes in Egypt so much as their intimate association with the Sudan. The Egyptian conquest of the Sudan early in the last century was for Egypt national war, and was regarded by her as a great national achievement. The sacrifices and the frightful losses endured in attempts to regain possession of the Sudan and to retain it in the days of the Khedive Ismail were not entirely the exactions of a despotic government. They were supported by strong Egyptian sentiment. Whole armies of fellaheen were dragged from their peaceful occupations by the Government and sent in succession to be destroyed by the fierce Arab tribesmen of the Sudan. To talk about conciliating Egypt, and gratifying Egyptian sentiment, and brushing away all causes of friction and suspicion without conceding them at the least an equal share in the administration of the Sudan is folly. No one can pretend that these causes of dispute will be removed by anything short of that; either you must be prepared to concede the full Egyptian claim about the Sudan, or you must be prepared to face a continued quarrel with all those forces in Egypt at whose behest we are now to evacuate Cairo.

There are other causes of friction which this treaty does nothing to remove— [*Interruption*]. On a matter of this immense consequence—I have not trespassed greatly on the House this Session—I am surely entitled to unfold my case in its integrity. There are other causes of friction which the draft treaty does nothing to relieve. The Egyptian Nationalists, who will be all-powerful in the immediate future, make no secret of their claim that the British troops should not only evacuate Cairo and the neighbourhood, but clear off Egyptian soil altogether. They will never acquiesce willingly or long in the continued presence of an all-powerful British force in the country. Whatever may have been said by Sarwat Pasha, or Mahmud Pasha, or any other of these fleeting figures who arise for the purpose of drawing proposals from various British Governments and disappear as soon as those proposals reach the point of decision, the demand of Egypt is that the British quit the soil of Egypt bag and baggage, and the Nationalist forces which Zaghloul formed and led forward will never be content with less. Zaghloul Pasha again and again made it perfectly clear that nothing short of the complete evacuation of the soil of Egypt would satisfy the national demand which he created, inspired and expressed. [An Hon. Member: "That is not true!"] We may have a difference of opinion on the subject, but I am basing myself on knowledge which has been gathered very carefully for a long period of time. The Government may, with our remaining influence, coax or cajole or coerce the Government of Egypt into accepting the treaty, but they will only accept it as an instalment and as a means of helping them towards their goal, and we shall simply be deceiving ourselves and sowing the seeds of a deadly harvest if we suppose that we can reconcile Egyptian nationalism to exclusion from the Sudan in the terms rightly proposed by the Government, and if we suppose that we can reconcile them to Lord Thomson's force of armoured cars, marshalled within six hours of Cairo. If you are trying to understand and meet another party's point of view, it is surely just as well to face the whole truth and the ugly facts as well as those that are easy and palatable.

Further, when we have gone from Cairo, when our troops have departed, we still have immense responsibilities in Egypt. It is true the Government propose in form to hand over the responsibility for the protection of foreign communities, and the protection of minorities, to the sole control of the Egyptian Government, but the Foreign Secretary has on more than one occasion said, and representatives of the Government in another place have said in terms of almost brutal candour, that, in the event of any failure on the part of Egypt to respect and protect the rights of foreigners or minorities, His Majesty's Government will be entitled to hold that the treaty is broken and that Great Britain will be free to take whatever measures she may think necessary. What can those measures be other than the advance of a military force and, if necessary of a military force and, if necessary, the re-occupation of Cairo? Henceforward we shall be without the power or the influence to prevent things from going wrong in Cairo. We shall nevertheless be watching vigilantly lest they should go wrong. We shall always be forced to nag and press the Egyptian Government where the interests of foreigners and minorities are concerned. We shall always be using the threat of an armed advance and a re-occupation of the Egyptian capital. We shall always be held accountable to Europe and the United States for the safety of their nationals. We shall always continue to take upon our shoulders the burden and the unpopularity of all the antagonisms that may arise between the Egyptian populace and foreign interests and colonies. We shall have no leverage at our disposal except the naked threat of invasion and re-occupation–[*Interruption*]. The League of Nations could not deal with this situation. It could only authorise us to utilise the force that we have and to fulfil the undertakings which we had given, lest the entire country should dissolve into anarchy and confusion.

I have tried to place before the House and the country the dangers now about to be created. I think causes of dispute will grow from year to year. The power of mitigating them in their early stages will be gone. To Egyptian eyes we shall still be the bugbear, we shall still be the interfering Power, the intruding Power, the trespassing Power, the threatening Power, and even, as it will seem to them, the bullying Power. The other European Governments and the American Government will profit from our exertions without suffering our odium. They will have the advantage without the labour. Once again Great Britain will be chained to the labouring oar without ever being allowed to lay a finger on the helm. At the same time, the Egyptians will be placed in a position to retaliate for every interference, however justified, however obligatory, however in accordance with the opinion of the world or the sanction of the League of Nations for every necessary advice that we have to tender by an increase of their military forces, by building up a numerous army under compulsory service and equipping it with deadly instruments of war, and thus forcing us to reinforce our garrison in the canal zone in an atmosphere of ever-increasing tension.

I cannot think that this is a good conclusion to all our work in Egypt. I think that we have deserved better than that. I cannot think that it is a safe course to take if we wish to avoid bloodshed. On the contrary, it seems to me the exact manner in which a catastrophe of violent deeds would be deliberately and almost mechanically prepared. Would it not be far better to leave the British troops in Cairo? Would it not be far better to make it clear that it is our unchanging policy that they shall remain there, and then to concede to Egyptian sentiment and to Egyptian susceptibilities every form of considerate usage and every possible latitude of self-guidance and self-development. That is my counsel. That is the way I shall give my vote at all stages in these discussions. The departure of the British troops from Cairo will be a momentous event. If and when it occurs, it will resound through all Asia. It will be noted by history like the recall of the legions many centuries ago. It will mark the point where great organisms slowly built up, exercising an immense pacifying and unifying influence upon the world, have reached their culmination and have begun the course of decline. I urge the House to resist the departure, but, if it should be within the power of the Government, which I am not sure it is, to carry through this dangerous and fateful step, I ask at least that the departure should be accompanied by a simultaneous restriction in the numbers of the Egyptian Army and the abolition of conscription throughout the valley of the Nile. Surely, that is not an improper demand to make, when it is the aim of the whole world to abolish armed violence from human affairs. Then, at least, if any trouble should arise at any future date, it will be a small and not a large fight to which you will have condemned our soldiers.

I pass from the merits of these proposals to the separate question of the application to which they are put, and here I speak as one who, whatever his personal views may have been—and the right hon. Gentleman has access to our archives and knows what they have been—has borne a share of collective responsibility for all the important decisions about Egypt. During the period of the Protectorate Egypt was, with the formal approval of the allied and associated Powers, including the United States under President Wilson, actually incorporated in the King's Dominions. Our work in Egypt, except for that period, had been conducted on the basis of one of those anomalies which are dear to the oriental mind and by no means unknown to British mentality. For more than 30 years the status of Egypt was declared to be that of a tributary province of the Turkish Empire under temporary British military occupation. Since the abrogation of the Protectorate in 1923, its status has been that of a soverign independent State subject to certain all-important reservations which were in conflict with and largely incompatible with sovereignty, but in respect of which reservations neither party was under any obligation to accommodate itself to the views of the other.

Lord Grey was entirely wrong in assuming that the Declaration of 1922 dealt wholly or mainly with the recognition of Egypt as a sovereign independent Power. I am sorry the right hon. Member for Carnarvon Boroughs (Mr. Lloyd George) is not in his place. As the then Prime Minister, he knows of the situation at that time, and, if he were in his place, he would confirm me in stating, as I now state, that the recognition of independence and the reservations were both integral parts of a single instrument designed to give recognition to Egyptian independence while reserving our necessary rights not only to preserve our own exclusive interests, but to discharge effectively our inalienable responsibilities. The 1922 Declaration cannot be divided; the two parts are integrally united. Then came the proposals of the late Government for the adjustment of the reservations. Those proposals were rejected by the Egyptian Government. They did not go so far as those of His Majesty's present advisers, but they were rejected, and we hold them as having lapsed. The Conservative Opposition, in respect of Egypt, resumes its entire freedom of judgment. It can always be argued that the fact that such proposals were put forward shows that we did not consider that they were necessarily incompatible with British interests. That is a consideration which weighs with us, but it was not a part of an understanding or bargain with any Egyptian party. As far as we are concerned, we are free from the 1928 proposals which were refused.

His Majesty's Government have made proposals which they say are their last word, and they are no doubt committed to them as a Government. If they are accepted, His Majesty's Government must accept the grievous responsibility of presenting them, with or without amendment, to Parliament. We, however, are entitled to go back to the Declaration of 1922, and no reproach can be made against us if we rest upon that Declaration until we are satisfied that a better solution for British, Egyptian, and international interests can be secured. I appeal to the House and to the Conservative party, apart from any other objections that they may entertain, to resist by every means in their power the withdrawal of the British troops from Cairo, and I urge on the Government, if they persist in this fatal step, to insist, by articles mutually agreed upon, that there shall be a limitation of the number of the Egyptian Army and a liberation of the Egyptian peasantry, if only as a parting gift, from the burden of conscription.

The right hon. Gentleman has dwelt to-day on the fact that from three to five years must elapse before the British troops leave Cairo. He rests on that fact with comfort, and he emphasised it to the House. That is only to leave to a future Government a legacy of great danger. As long as the troops are in Cairo none of these dangers will occur, but they will come upon some future Government in conditions of the gravest anxiety. There are other dangers in Egypt which are not remote, and I find it difficult to describe the ineptitude and imprudence of His Majesty's Government in their handling of Egyptian affairs during the short time that they have been responsible. In June, they were in communication with Mahmud Pasha behind the back of the High Commissioner. In August they dismissed Lord Lloyd, thus advertising our impending retreat to every subversive force in Egypt and Palestine. I believe the dismissal of Lord Lloyd and its manner was the direct precursor of the massacres in Palestine—[*Interruption.*] Oh, I do not mean that the Arabs of Palestine rose because they were angry at Lord Lloyd's departure, but because they attributed the sudden striking down of the hand that ruled Egypt and had given it four years of steady Government to an inherent weakness in the British Government, and they thought that the moment was ripe. That is my sincere opinion.

Lord Lloyd went, but Mahmud Pasha remained. What happened? His Majesty's Government, interfering in Egyptian affairs and meddling where they have boasted that no interference is permissible, insisted upon an election taking place in Egypt for a Parliament on a basis of manhood suffrage—manhood suffrage in an electorate, 92 per cent. of whom are illiterate, and, as has been said this afternoon, unable, in consequence of that illiteracy, to enjoy the secrecy of ballot! What does that mean? It could have had no other object and result than the absolute triumph of the Wafd, the Nationalist party, a caucus composed of extreme Anglophobes and the most violent figures in Egyptian politics. This powerful body has so manipulated and intimidated the electors that virtually no other candidates dared to stand. Not a single Liberal dared to stand. The Government have had much more success in exterminating Liberals in Egypt than they have yet had in this country. This interference of the Government in Egyptian affairs destroyed Mahmud Pasha, that "reasonable man" who so gratified and cheered the heart of the Foreign Secretary when he came on what was for him a very unfortunate visit to London. He was flung aside like a discarded and broken tool. No one of his party or political associates dared to present himself for election on the basis dictated by his Majesty's Government. Mahmud has gone, and now you are face to face with Nahas Pasha, the disciple of Zaghloul, the heir of Zaghloul, more extreme than his master. In a few months, therefore His Majesty's Government have annihilated all those Liberal elements in Egypt on which the Milner Report counted in an especial degree. They have confronted themselves only with the bitterest foes of Britain. They have produced a profound degeneration in the Egyptian situation and Egyptian society and encouraged a struggle between the Wafd and the Court, the end of which cannot be predicted.

Long before the five years are up events will occur which will afford evidence of the need of the British troops in Cairo. I do not know how long will be the life of His Majesty's Government, but I believe that they will live long enough to reap some at least of the wrath and evil and folly that they have sown.

There is a sombre philosophy nowadays which I hear in some quarters about Egypt and India. It is said:

> Give them all they ask for! Clear out and let things go to smash, and
> then there will be a case for us to come back again.

The action of His Majesty's Government would bear that construction, and it is, in my opinion, not the worst construction to be put upon it. Such a doctrine is no foundation for the continuance of British fame and power. Once we lose confidence in our mission in the East, once we repudiate our responsibilities to foreigners and to minorities, once we feel ourselves unable calmly and fearlessly to discharge our duties to vast helpless populations, then our presence in those countries will be stripped of every moral sanction, and, resting only upon selfish interests or military requirements, it will be a presence which cannot long endure.

NATIONAL FINANCE
December 24, 1929
House of Commons

An arrangement has been made that this discussion of a naval matter should now come to an end and that for a brief interval another topic, finance, should take its place upon the stage. Let me begin by expressing to the Chancellor of the Exchequer [Mr. Philip Snowden] my regrets at any personal inconvenience which I may have caused to him by the discharge of my Parliamentary duties. I know how heavy is the burden upon him and how short is the interval of leisure he has before he leaves for The Hague Conference on the 6th of January, and I am sorry if the inexorable course of events has led me to curtail that leisure by 48 hours. But I must say that I think the Chancellor of the Exchequer has had during his tenure of office a very great measure of good will, consideration and indulgence from his political opponents and all other sections of the community. I do not think I ever remember a case where so many men and women of opposite parties have been willing to accord the representative of the Government all the consideration in their power. He has been aided and flattered by the Conservative Press and the Liberal newspapers and he has been applauded and encouraged from other quarters of the political scene. He has been given the freedom of the City of London, as we were all very glad to see, and to note that it was conferred so soon. In fact, I said to myself, "It is now or never," and the only argument against it which occurred to me was that the City will have nothing left to give him after the Budget. The great Lord Bacon said in his writings:

> It is an assured sign of a worthy and generous spirit whom honour amends.

No one will deny the right hon. Gentleman's claim to the epithets, but one cannot help being struck by the fact that honour or good will do not seem to exercise upon him that mellowing and softening influence, that widening influence, which so often have attended them. In fact, the more he is treated with consideration and indulgence, the more honour he is shown, the more crapulous and dictatorial he becomes. It seems to me that as he does not respond to this extremely conciliatory treatment it may be well to try whether a change of treatment might not produce a more satisfactory result. If praise and courtesy only result in narrow, bitter partisanship, perhaps a little well-merited chastisement may procure some geniality. Take my own case. The great Lord Bacon, to quote him again, in his essay on "Great Place," says:

> Use the memory of thy predecessor fairly and tenderly; for if thou dost not. . . .

I am glad to see the Leader of the Opposition here, because I know how he likes classical quotations. I will read it again. It is Bacon on "Great Place":

> Use the memory of thy predecessor fairly and tenderly; for if thou dost
> not it is a debt that will sure be paid when thou art gone.

Following that wise example, when I succeeded the right hon. Gentleman as Chancellor of the Exchequer five years ago I was careful to pay a tribute to his work, and I am glad to know that that gave him pleasure and that he has preserved it as a testimonial and repeated it in the House of Commons with gusto. The right hon. Gentleman is welcome to any satisfaction which he has received from that tribute, and he has had no cause to complain of any attack which I have made upon him either in this House or in any part of the country, or in the Debates which occupy undoubtedly a large part of the financial year. I made no comment on his great achievement in regard to the loan, or to his gift of $150,000 to a favoured few, or to his writing down British credit to a figure which I am sure he would have been wise to have avoided formally presenting, labelling, and advertising to the world. The right hon. Gentleman, no doubt, feeling the stress and pressure, is evidently anxious to throw the blame of the difficulties in which he finds himself—allow me to say that he will not find me unwilling to take the responsibility for every difficulty in which I have a share—and of any added difficulties entirely on the shoulders of his predecessor.

In the course of the next few minutes I want to look a little more closely than we have hitherto done at the right hon. Gentleman's achievements and performances during the six months he has held the office of Chancellor of the Exchequer. I come, first of all, to the Hague Conference and Reparations. There the right hon. Gentleman carried on a policy which, as he rightly said, had been declared beforehand as the policy of the British Government. There never could have been any question of our accepting the Young Report as it stood, and that intention was announced to the House of Commons by me before the Dissolution, and I was supported by the Chancellor of the Exchequer and all parties. I certainly considered that the right hon. Gentleman fought a very good fight in the interests of this country, but he fought it in such a rasping manner and in such a needlessly provocative way that I think it is possible that we have lost in other directions a good deal of the apparently small gains which resulted from the right hon. Gentleman's strenuous activities. I must explain, however, that they were not positive gains. The right hon. Gentleman succeeded in not giving away so much as he was asked to give, but he did, in fact, give away—I am not blaming him for it—more than had been given away in the arrangements conducted by the preceding Governments of which he himself was such an unsparing denunciator.

The one serious criticism which I make against the right hon. Gentleman's conduct of these negotiations is that he did not take advantage of the great opportunity offered us to secure liberation from certain declarations which had been made. There is the Balfour Note. The House is familiar with the self-denying clauses, which are omitted in the Treaty agreement with Italy and France, which preclude us from taking any more from Europe than is taken from us to pay our debts to the United States of America, and binds us as regards any moneys that may be paid by

Russia through any revision of her debt policy which may be made, or which is entertained by the United States, to give the benefit of that to those countries with whom we have made settlements. That is the principle of the Balfour Note. When the Balfour Note was proclaimed now nearly seven years ago none of the many high authorities in the Government of that day ever expected that its terms would be realised, and certainly no statesman like the late Mr. Bonar Law, Mr. Asquith, and others I could mention imagined that we should retrieve enough ourselves to pay these obligations. We have, in fact, almost achieved that but not entirely. The right hon. Gentleman was compelled—and I do not blame him—to risk breaking up the Conference for £500,000 a year, and he was compelled to admit an impingement upon the Balfour Note. Although it may be a small impingement, undoubtedly the sanctity of that principle has been broken, and the right hon. Gentleman has consented to its being broken. There was an opportunity to obtain release from the self-denying obligations which we had made, and I should have thought it would have been quite easy at least to say to France and Italy: "Rather than break up the Conference, we will agree to the terms imposed, but it must be clearly understood that, as those terms violate the integrity of the Balfour Note, we claim release from the self-denying clauses, and, if at any time Russia settles her debts and obtains or takes some steps to achieve financial rehabilitation as she may do in years to come, and as it may be her interest to do, then the yield of that relief which may amount conceivably on the terms we gave Italy to £6,000,000, £7,000,000 or £8,000,000 a year and perhaps more, accruing to the British taxpayer should not go simply to reduce the payments of Italy and France.

Similarly, if the United States at any time chose to revise her debt policy and treat all her debtors equally—and there is undoubtedly a growing opinion in the United States in favour of equal treatment for her debtors—if that were so it would seem to be a great pity that we should not be able to gain that advantage because of these self-denying Clauses, for which, I fully admit, the right hon. Gentleman was not responsible, but for which the preceding Government was responsible, and for which I am undoubtedly one of those who have to bear responsibility. But here was a chance, here was an opportunity of getting free, and the right hon. Gentleman, fighting so strenuously as he did, seems to have overlooked this altogether, although I should like to say that I left it clearly on record, in various documents and statements which were made during my tenure of office, that it was my intention, if the slightest infringement of the Balfour Note were to become necessary, to take that opportunity for claiming release. I think that that is a fair and serious criticism. The right hon. Gentleman will have a chance of answering it, but I hope he will not simply confine himself to belabouring me, because I think it is not too late—I hope it is not too late. He is going to the Hague Conference on the 6th of January, and I suggest to him that there is still an opportunity, before matters are finally ratified, to point out that the conditions of the Balfour Note have been ruptured, and that a new situation has arisen. At any rate, I trust that that may be considered by His Majesty's Government, because it is of great and real importance to us.

The right hon. Gentleman attacked my financial record, but I am, under the Rules of the House, not permitted to refer, except in a broad, general and casual manner, to matters which have been raised in the Debates on the same subject in the same Session. All that I will say about the financial record of the late Government is that it is clearly within the recollection of all Members of the House of Commons. We were proceeding on a basis of reviving trade and returning prosperity. We were reducing taxation substantially. We were looking forward to further schemes of social amelioration. We were struck down by the general strike and the coal stoppage. I can recall no instance of any more deadly blow having been levelled at an administration by their political opponents than the launching of that hideous attack, not only upon the fortunes of the Government, but upon the whole prosperity of the nation. The right hon. Gentleman seems to forget all about that. One would imagine that he had never heard of it. Where was he when the general strike was on? I think I have asked that question before. Where was he when that great event took place? He, a leading man, one of the pillars of the Socialist Party, of the Labour Party—where did he go? Why, Sir, he went into hiding. He chose the deepest hole he could find, and, in the darkest recesses of that deep hole, he remained till the fight was over, and then he emerged to throw the blame on others, to exploit the new situation, and to lecture all sides with that impartiality and smug complacency which only finds its rival in the right hon. Gentleman the Member for Darwen (Sir. H. Samuel), in his performance last night. Others had to face the situation which resulted from the general strike and the coal stoppage, and all the rest of my tenure at the Exchequer was occupied in endeavouring to cut through those difficulties without throwing new and heavy burdens on a slowly recovering country.

Whatever may be the unsatisfactory condition of the Exchequer at the present time—and I have no knowledge of what it may be at the present time, nor indeed is it profitable to speculate upon such matters until the out-turn of the year is seen and can be measured—whatever may be the condition of the Exchequer, the right hon. Gentleman has added to his difficulties by agreeing to new and profuse expenditure. He, who used to lecture us upon every penny that was spent, has already, in the short six months he has been in power, added £8,500,000—I am taking the answer he gave to a question—to the expenditure of this year. Whereas in former years I had succeeded in clawing back from the Departments £5,000,000 or £6,000,000 of money actually voted by Parliament, this year, so far from that process operating, there is a new outlet of £8,500,000 of expenditure, and, as the prospective Budget surplus was fixed only, if my memory serves me rightly, at £3,500,000, and as the conditions of the present time certainly do not look too favourable, one must say that a deficit is inevitable from that cause alone, even if it had not arisen in consequence of world causes. But about future years, what has the right hon. Gentleman committed us to? In his answer a few weeks ago he quoted a figure of, I think, nearly £19,000,000, but a great deal has happened since then. He and his colleagues have revised their view as to what should be the conditions under which unemployment benefit should be extended to persons who are in need of it, or who profess that they are in need of it. The right hon. Gentleman has sanctioned a large scheme of lengthening the period of school-time for the youth of this country, and I imagine—I have not the exact figures—that certainly the new commitments which he has made, at a time when he admits that matters are upon a very narrow basis, will amount to £30,000,000. The "Times" newspaper, which is so frequently quoted from the opposite benches—I think very rightly, because it is a most valuable and weighty support and encouraging comfort—in a leading article last week, said that the new expenditure commitments amount to £43,000,000 a year. Perhaps the right hon. Gentleman will tell us, when he rises to speak, how much actual additional expenditures he has let this country in for during his six months tenure of office.

I should like to point out that for this expenditure, although it all falls upon the Treasury, there is very little to show, and it is in no way concerned, or is scarcely appreciably concerned, with any large productive effort which would stimulate the trade and industry of the country. The right hon. Gentleman has said, in one of his moods of self-satisfaction, that it will take him three or four years to get the finances of this country back into the good state in which he left them. He was only in office for a few months on the last occasion. He inherited a surplus of £40,000,000 from his Conservative predecessor. He spent that surplus, as far as he could see, with a desire to gain for himself party election advantages, and he left a somewhat smaller surplus to his successor. Now he hopes to work back to 1924, and he says it will take him three or four years of hard work to bring himself back to that position. If he goes on as he is going now, with £30,000,000 or £40,000,000 of additional unproductive expenditure flung upon the Exchequer during six months of his tenure of office, it will take him three or four years to complete his task, and, when he has completed it in his opinion, the annual expenditure of this country will not be far short of £1,000,000,000.

I have one point with which I must deal for a moment in detail, namely, the right hon. Gentleman's continued harping upon the alleged or so-called bankruptcy of the Unemployment Insurance Fund. He declares that the bankruptcy of the Unemployment Insurance Fund is due to the policy which was pursued by me and by my right hon. Friend the late Minister of Labour, and he attributes the condition of the Fund entirely to that policy. We have a Report from an impartial authority on that subject, and I will venture to ask the House to permit me to read a very short quotation from it. This Report was published in 1927; it is the Report of the Blanesburgh Committee; and this is what it says at paragraph 63:

> We are now confronted by an embarrassing problem which, when we began our deliberations, did not exist. In the first place, the deficit on the Unemployment Fund was then being paid off satisfactorily. With steadily improving trade, the income of the fund was increasing and its expenditure going down. The general strike and the stoppage in the coal-mining industry have changed that situation. The resulting unemployment, as we have seen, increased the indebtedness of the fund from £7,100,000 in April last to over £21,000,000 in December, and there is no prospect that this heavy debt can be liquidated by the time when the new scheme should come into force. In the second place, these industrial disturbances have brought about a marked deterioration in the economic position of the country and have greatly increased for a time the general level of unemployment. At the end of April there were 982,000 persons unemployed; at the beginning of December the figure had risen to 1,506,000.

That is the Blanesburgh Report. The first signature is that of the Chairman and the second is that of the right hon. Lady who is now the Minister of Labour. In view of the clear expression of opinion on these matters by one of his own colleagues, I think the right hon. Gentleman's attempt to throw the blame for the bankruptcy of the Unemployment Insurance Fund on me and my friends on this side of the House really requires some consideration before it is persisted in. At any rate, I leave him to settle with the Minister of Labour, when he next has the good fortune to see her, how he is to reconcile the attack which he made recently with the perfectly clear explanation she has given of the causes of the misfortune to the Unemployment Insurance Fund.

I must say I think the right hon. Gentleman in his treatment of this Unemployment Insurance Fund has perhaps not taken the course which would most conduce to the general welfare of the country. He has advertised and emphasised one cause of its bankruptcy, but even after the General Strike, even in the present lamentable condition of our affairs, it is not true that the Unemployment Insurance Fund was in a state of bankruptcy. Here is a fund which had an annual revenue of between £60,000,000 and £70,000,000, resulting from separate sources of taxation, and which had a debt of £40,000,000. But I do not think £40,000,000 or £50,000,000, would have been too heavy a charge to accumulate at the back of a Fund with such an enormous annual revenue as that. It does not even amount to one year's annual revenue. Look at our own affairs. We have a debt of over £7,000,000,000, that is to say our debt is eight or nine times our annual revenue and, therefore, if the Insurance Fund is in a state of bankruptcy, we are seven or eight times more in bankruptcy. [*Interruption.*] Very little is foreign debt. It may well prove—I will not put it higher, because the right hon. Gentleman has his own difficulties to solve and I know how great they are and how anxious his task is, but it seems to me that he might well have found it prudent not to deal immediately with the increased contribution of the Exchequer to the Unemployment Insurance Fund and to have left the whole situation until he could examine it as a whole with the out turn of the financial year. It may well be that the fund could have risen to £50,000,000 of debts to the State without the disclosure of a deficit in the national accounts and the consequent need of heavy over-taxation.

Here is a point that is borne in upon me by a study of the right hon. Gentleman's methods. It seems to me that he is making a case, by administrative action and by policy, for heaping new vindictive penal taxation of the kind he has spoken of before in such strident and ferocious terms, of a kind which is calculated to raise the spirit and the appetite and the ardour of his followers, and to be of use to him for political purposes and, therefore, no doubt, it would be to his interest to throw whatever burden he can find upon the Exchequer at the same time that he is adding to heavy expenditure, and then claiming that a case has been made out for another large addition to the public burden.

I come now to the last point that I am going to afflict the right hon. Gentleman with, but that is the most important of all. Yesterday he announced to the House and the country his intention to repeal the McKenna, the Silk and the Safeguarding Duties and, somewhat less decisively, the Sugar Duties. I am glad to say he does not contradict me in the interpretation I put upon his answer.

The Chancellor of the Exchequer (Mr. Philip Snowden): I will do.

Mr. Churchill: What other interpretation can be put upon the language he used and the declaration he made? Surely we are not going to be told he only made that statement out of personal vanity, in order to keep these important industries on tenterhooks at his footstool, waiting upon his imperial finger, just in order to say, "You will know what your fate is when my good pleasure is declared." Surely we cannot have that. I should never have accused him of that. It would amount to a callous levity to which there is no parallel in the conduct of public affairs—these great trades all kept hanging about after a statement like that has been made and then, when the Budget comes, to say, "I am glad to announce to you an eleventh hour reprieve. We have decided not to take off the taxes this year, but, of course, I had to keep this as my Budget secret." To let personal considerations of that kind intermingle themselves with the means by which the livelihood of thousands of workmen and the conduct of important businesses are interwoven would be entirely beneath any misconduct I should ever think it right to attribute to the right hon. Gentleman. So, wishing to give him the benefit of the doubt, I take his statement at its clear face value, that he intends to repeal, at any rate, the McKenna, Silk and Safeguarding Duties. If what he said yesterday is the last word he has to speak upon this subject, if he has no further statement to make to-day, I say all these trades, if they are wise, should act from now upon the assumption that the duties are going to be repealed.

There was the right hon. Gentleman's manner, besides his words. It is within the full recollection of the House that he spoke as if he had a personal grievance against these trades, as if, because they had been protected by a tariff, they had done him some wrong and ought to be punished. The whole tenor of his statement was that it served them right, that those who live by a tariff shall fall and suffer by a tariff. I can assure him it is not the fault of the trades. They never asked for this tariff— [*Interruption.*] I know about this. I re-imposed the McKenna Duties without consulting these trades and the silk duties, so far from being asked for by the trade, were vehemently protested against. Messrs. Courtaulds issued a pamphlet against them. He has no grievance against these trades. If he has any spite to display or vengeance to wreak, let him do it on me. I am responsible; let him punish me if he can, but not work off these feelings of antagonism upon organisms of great importance in the provisions of work and wages to our people.

"His manner" I say, but what shall I say of his motive? It is always difficult to plumb motives, and it may be dangerous to impute them. Was it only pedantry that actuated his statement yesterday? I have asked myself if it is free trade conviction. Up to a fortnight ago, I should have rested content with that explanation. Everyone knows that he has always been in the past a bigoted Cobdenite, but, after the publication of the Government Coal Bill, of which the right hon. Gentleman is one of the responsible authors, and which was rightly described from the Liberal benches— and the Liberals are impartial judges—as one of the worst forms of protection, he has certainly no right to plead his unalterable free trade convictions as a reason for his intolerance in this respect.

I accuse the right hon. Gentleman in abolishing these duties of being actuated by motives of political calculation. He is seeking to drive a wedge between the two parties of the Opposition. He is seeking to gain support for the future Budget that he will have to introduce, and, in pursuit of these purely political objects, he does not care a snap of the fingers for the fact that 20,000 more men may be thrown into unemployment. I wonder what the Lord Privy Seal thinks about it all. It seems to me that he is being given what is vulgarly called the dirty end of the stick. First of all, the definition of unemployment is extended in such a way as to swamp the register with scores and perhaps hundreds of thousands of new figures, and then a measure is taken by the Chancellor of the Exchequer in the hope of securing the political defences of his Budget, which undoubtedly is going to throw a large number of men out of employment very speedily, and which, in its depressing influence over the whole range of industry, is bound to have further indirect adverse effects.

I do not intend to detain the House any more. I had no wish to make these reflections. We are going to separate very shortly. It is not a very cheerful or bright Christmas that England is going to celebrate this year, our first Christmas under a Socialist Government. Prices have risen; the tendency of wages is to decline; unemployment has risen; there is great financial disquiet, for which I do not blame the right hon. Gentleman, but which nevertheless has a serious effect. We can see that the recovery of other nations from the Great War has been far more rapid and substantial than our own. The menace, nay, the certainty, of heavy new direct taxation hangs over the country in the New Year. Here, where the burden of direct taxation is already the heaviest in the world, £30,000,000, £40,000,000, or £50,000,000 are to be added to it at a time when Germany, the United States, and, I believe France, are reducing taxation by approximately similar amounts with the direct intention and avowed purpose of increasing their commercial competition with us.

In the Coal Bill, through private agency it is true, new indirect taxation is to be imposed if that Measure passes, and the right hon. Gentleman is just as responsible for that tax, although it may be collected by the coalowners, as he would have been if it had been imposed in the Budget. Between £30 000,000 and £40,000,000 will be added to indirect taxation. Before us in the New Year lies a vista of political turmoil, and, possibly, or rather probably, a momentous General Election. All this political strife and excitement cannot fail to be a drag upon every financial and business force which is making for the growth and strengthening of the Commonwealth. I spoke yesterday of the slow but sure undermining of our position throughout the East, which, let me say, is of vital consequence to the livelihood, to the bread and butter, of millions in this country.

It is a gloomy prospect, a bleak and gloomy prospect, and I think it is hard upon our country that, 11 years after the Great War and the great victory, and after we have done our best, paid our debts, and faced our burdens manfully and charitably, and done all that we can to bring the country together, we should have from one cause or another—the blame no doubt rests not in any one quarter—to face so melancholy a prospect. Britain has deserved better fortune and the only consolation I can offer her on this occasion is that we have at least the remedy for all our evils in our own hands.

1930

COAL MINES BILL

February 4, 1930

House of Commons

Surely we are going to have an answer from the Government to the reasonable request and protest which have been made from this side? The right hon. Member for Carnarvon Boroughs (Mr. Lloyd George) spoke in the sense that it might be an advantage if ultimately this Bill, now so much in dispute, emerged from the House of Commons as an agreed Bill to which all parties had made their contribution. Whether that possibility can ever be realised we do not know, but surely the Government, by taking the course that they are taking to-day, are placing a great and perhaps a fatal obstacle in the path of any general co-operation of the House. We make no complaint, and the Leader of the Opposition made no complaint, of the colloquies and discussions that have taken place between the Government and the Liberal party. People are perfectly free to discuss political action together, and to discuss the details of legislation together when they wish, but there are other questions at issue besides the relations between the Labour party and the Liberal party. There are questions affecting the rights of the House of Commons. After all, those who sit on these benches have some rights. They are far more numerous than those who sit on the Liberal benches, and they have at least a right to have accorded to them the ordinary consideration which is customary in the transaction of public business.

What is the point which is made by the Leader of the Opposition? Until this morning we had no reason to believe that the Government were going to adopt and submit to or acquiesce in the Amendments of the right hon. Member for Carnarvon. The right hon. Gentleman said that those Amendments had been on the Paper for three weeks. We all have a great interest in his exceptional activities in this Parliament, but, after all, even taking the most favourable view of those exertions, an Amendment that stands in his name or that of his followers is not the same as an Amendment put down by the responsible Government of the day, which represents the largest party in the House. I am sure that the right hon. Gentleman himself will see the fallacy of the argument that he advanced against the Leader of the Opposition, that we have no ground of complaint and that no substantial difference had been made when, instead of his name being behind his Amendment, it is put forward on the authority of the Government.

I am assured that the bringing on of Part II of the Bill at this moment unexpectedly, and the withdrawal of Part I, mean that hon. Members on this side of the House have not had an opportunity of preparing and placing on the Paper their Amendments to Part II. For doing that they are entitled to a reasonable time. No long delay is necessary. There is no need to make a serious interruption of Government business. But for the ordinary and practical reasons of Debate there should be at least a single day's interlude, after so decisive a change by the Government, before we are asked to embark on the discussion of Part II. To come down, as a result of what I might call a side deal with one section of the House, and to alter the whole course of Government business, to confront us with the discussion of matters which no one who is not in the secrets of the Government or of the right hon. Member for Carnarvon Boroughs had contemplated would be a subject for Debate to-day—to ask us to do that is grossly unfair. It is more than unfair; it is unwise, because the Government are not themselves in so strong a position numerically in this House or in any other way that they can afford to ride rough-shod over the wishes and feelings of a very large number of Gentlemen sitting in this House.

We have a right to proper treatment. I am surprised that the right hon. Member for Carnarvon Boroughs should be so very inconsiderate to those who, like himself, sit on this side of the House. He may have fixed up some arrangement satisfactorily with the Government. He has, perhaps, compelled them to adopt the proposals which he has put forward. He has made them bend to his will. He has made them go to Canossa. He has made the Government, as the Foreign Secretary said on a previous occasion, "stand on the mat" and await admission. I can quite understand his being gratified. But surely in the moment of triumph, in the moment of satisfaction and glory, he might lend some consideration for others who at any rate voted in the same Lobby as him the other evening. As far as this Bill is concerned, hitherto there has been virtual agreement and co-operation between the non-Socialist parties in the House. The right hon. Gentleman is perfectly entitled, for reasons of his own, to come to some accommodation with the Government, but in embracing a new ally there is no need to spurn those with whom he has previously walked into the Lobby.

After all the right hon. Gentleman frequently talks to us about the interests of small parties in the House. He frequently addresses the Chair and on occasions speaks of how the Speaker and the Chairman of Committees are the guardians of the rights of minorities in this House. In this matter why should he co-operate with the Government to secure unfair treatment of a party almost as large as the Government party? Surely he can deliver the goods to the Government under any arrangement that he has made without at the same time trampling on the fair procedure of the House of Commons and treating in a callous and uncivil manner other Members and parties who have been invited to take part in the discussion of this Bill.

I am sure that if the Government do not treat us fairly in this matter they will not accelerate their business. There are means and methods by which Government business and the progress of complicated Bills can be made much more rapid. But this method, according to all the experience I have had of the House, is most calculated to prolong and exacerbate our Debates. I am going to ask the Government not to sit still like sticks and stones and refuse to make an answer to any kind of appeal which is made to them. I ask them to give us a reasonable opportunity to consider the new situation created by the side-slipping of Part I, so that we can address ourselves to Part II with proper and reasonable Parliamentary notice. In that case I am sure that the loss of a single day will not mean the loss of time in the carrying forward of legislation. But if the Government treat us with scorn and contempt because they have made an arrangement, a very fleeting and precarious arrangement, with their political associates of the moment who at other times are their political foes—if they think that because of that they can afford to disdain us and disdain those who wish to be contributory parties to this legislation, they will render their course of Parliamentary business infinitely troublesome and prolonged.

UNEMPLOYMENT INSURANCE (NO. 2) BILL

February 4, 1930

House of Commons

We are always very glad to see the Prime Minister back again in the House of Commons. We feel much safer when he is here; we know what he is doing; and certainly I think we owe him a debt, in that, with his many grave preoccupations, he should have treated us to such a formidable Parliamentary statement on the subject of the Lords Amendments which are now before the House. Let me say at the very outset, on behalf of His Majesty's Opposition, that in the main we commend the course which the right hon. Gentleman has decided to adopt. The course that he has chosen, and the mood which he has displayed in relation to the Second Chamber, are very much better, wiser and sounder than we have been accustomed to from the Secretary of State for Foreign Affairs, with the assistance of the Attorney-General, who have endeavoured to wipe out the other branch of the Legislature and rule it completely out of all share in our public affairs.

I have mocked at the Government, and shall do so again, when I have seen them run humbly to the footstool of the right hon. Gentleman the Member for Carnarvon Boroughs (Mr. Lloyd George). I have mocked at that because, undoubtedly, it does carry with it a considerable element of humiliation when you see the Government of the country anxious to obtain and enlist the co-operation of a right hon. Gentleman who on frequent occasions has delivered studied insults at honourable and valued Members on the opposite benches. I have never attempted, and should never attempt, to criticise the Government when they show a just and proper deference to the other branch of the Legislature. That is quite a different thing, and on the whole I am bound to say, while in no way prejudging the fate which the proposals that the Government are now making will meet elsewhere, that it is a great improvement upon the mood and the treatment of constitutional affairs by them which we have witnessed during the present Parliament.

The right hon. Gentleman said of the House of Lords that a Labour Government could never receive, or expect to receive, fair play from them. [*Interruption.*] Hon. Gentlemen must use the keen intelligence which is given to them, and endeavour to practise some sense of detachment in judging of our constitutional and political conditions. Has ever a party—a minority party, a minority in this House—been treated with more generosity—[*Interruption.*] If they had not been a Labour party, their numerical position in this House could never have enabled them to rule and sway, quite contrary, in many cases, to the feelings of the majority of the people of this country, so many grave and important events. What have they to complain about? [*Interruption.*] I do not understand this sudden eager, almost furious, attempt to work up a passionate sense of grievance. They are the favoured, pampered darlings—[*Interruption*]—a minority Government every member of whose majority is elected three times as easily as a member of the Liberal party; and then they are ready to cry out. But the right hon. Gentleman, in his crying out, is actuated by careful and calm calculation. He is endeavouring to settle this matter—[*Interruption*]—he has, so to speak, to make a retreat under heavy fire of artillery. I do not criticise him or complain that he has made a retreat and has come forward on this occasion with an entire recognition of the position which the second Chamber still preserves in the constitutional life of the country.

Let us look into this for a moment or two on this general topic. The right hon. Gentleman spoke of privilege and so forth, but he cannot deny that under the Parliament Act, which is the foundation of our modern constitution, the House of Lords have an entire right, if they choose, to reject this Bill. That is the basis of his argument. If that is so, they obviously have a bargaining power, and it was intended by those who passed the Parliament Act—no one had more to do with it than I had; no one took more part in the Debates in the House except Mr. Asquith himself—in the Parliament Act it was intended, and always declared, that a real, effectual bargaining power would be reserved under it to the second Chamber. I cannot expect my Friends on this side of the House to agree with me, but I am dealing with the situation that has now arisen. We always argued that, once the House of Lords had been deprived of an absolute veto upon the proceedings of this popularly elected Chamber, once it had been given limited powers of delay and revision, those powers would become real and effective and that they ought to be used, and should be used on every occasion that was appropriate, and that is what is happening now. You have limited the powers and a new charter has been given to the House of Lords within the limits of the Parliament Act, a charter for which the Foreign Secretary, the Lord Privy Seal, the Secretary of State for India, and I daresay, half-a-dozen on that Bench are as much responsible as I am. Therefore we have entered upon a new era, and I hope a much more satisfactory era, in which the House of Lords is entitled to make a real and an active use of its limited powers in order to revise legislation and to bring a new element into the discussions of this House. After all, whatever vanity we may have about our own Chamber, we must admit that we are subjected to a great number of electoral pressures, and all sorts of things are settled, as we have seen only to-day, across the Floor of the House and behind the Speaker's Chair and so forth. The intrigues that the Prime Minister has been carrying on with the right hon. Gentleman the Member for

Carnarvon Boroughs (Mr. Lloyd George) have shocked me. At any rate, I would suggest that the limited powers of the House of Lords, used effectively and reasonably, will bring into the settlement of these difficult legislative and social questions a new element and an influence without which the House of Commons by itself will not arrive at the best decisions. You will have a richer and a stronger mode of constitutional life if the kind of discussions now proceeding between the two Chambers, and within the limits within which they are proceeding, are permitted to continue to develop.

What is the case? What is the point on which these discussions have arisen? A flagitious Bill. There is no Measure which the right hon. Gentleman's Government have introduced which has more thoroughly deprived them of their prestige, not only in this country, but all over the world, where it is believed, and wrongly believed, that this country is a down-and-out country, that it is simply peopled by unemployed and burdened with ruined industries, and where it is believed that we have, by pursuing undoubtedly passionate policies, sapped the strength and self-reliance of our working-classes. I am not saying that that is what is believed in every country about this island. I know myself when in the United States at the same time as the Prime Minister friends of England on the other side came up and said, "Do you think this new Labour Government will have the courage to sweep away the dole?" One has to explain, of course, our great and elaborate system of Unemployment Insurance which is not understood abroad, but nothing has reinforced the disparagement of this country more than some of the provisions for which the Attorney-General took especial responsibility in regard to "genuinely seeking work." We know very well that there is duress at work—there is duress at work in every Government in power in one part of it or another—and that the decisions embodied in this Bill do not represent those which would have been put forward by legislators who were proceeding in an absolutely calm and uninfluenced atmosphere. Is not this the very kind of question on which the corrective aid of an external opinion, carefully limited by a new constitutional warrant and rendered effective by the very use of that constitutional warrant, should enter into our affairs?

As to the actual provisions of this Amendment, whether it should be one year, or two years, or three years, it is not for us here on this side to interfere in the discussions which are being conducted between the two Chambers. Let them go forward. I have no right or authority whatever to pronounce as to what course should be taken in another place, but I say that this process of collaboration between the two Chambers, this instance of help being sought and accepted and given as between the two Chambers in a matter of this kind, will, I trust, inaugurate a series of useful and fruitful collaborations between the House of Commons and the House of Lords which will conduce to the improvement of our legislation and enrich the public life of the country.

LONDON NAVAL CONFERENCE

February 26, 1930

Navy League Meeting, Cannon Street Hotel,
London

[Extract] The United States, where the Kellogg Pact [of 1927 renouncing war as an instrument of foreign policy] originated, wants to increase its navy relatively more than any other country in the world and Japan wants a 10 per cent. increase, while Britain, on the strength of the Kellogg Pact, has reduced her cruisers from seventy to fifty. Obviously, the Kellogg Pact has made a different impression on the American and Japanese Admiralties from that which it has made on our own. This discordance must strike us—an empire whose fleet is its life—to our very hearts.

We know where Japan stands. We know the position of France and Italy. Every one is familiar with the American desires. But what we do not know is the principle upon which the British Government is proceeding and the relation of that principle to our national safety and imperial unity. We do not know if there is any point—and if so, what point—at which his Majesty's present advisers will make a stand.

We feel we are being pushed, edged and sidled step by step into the acceptance almost at all costs of whatever may turn out to be the general convenience and wishes of the other four powers. We are a passive nation upon which the policies of the other naval nations will imprint themselves. These other powers, without exception, are preparing to increase the relative strength of their navies. From what we can judge by what has been published, all these other nations will increase their naval expenditures as soon as the conference is over.

The rise and expansion of American naval armaments has been the chief event on salt water, except the war episodes, since 1914. On the other hand, Great Britain, which formerly had the supremacy of the sea, has been steadily reducing her fleet from the pre-war period, in ships, gun power and personnel.

It is apparently to be proposed that we, who have led the way in disarmament by sea, on the land and in the air, should make a further diminution, not only of our actual but still more of our relative strength. We ought not to hand over the decisions in this matter to foreign nations, even though they are animated by the most friendly sentiment toward us. British naval requirements ought to be fixed by ourselves alone, because our life depends on the sea, and no group of other nations can be such good judges of these matters as ourselves. The strength of our royal navy cannot be remitted to the responsibility and discretion of our late foreign allies and present good friends.

Arithmetical parity between the British Empire and America means definite naval inferiority for Great Britain. We have never made plans for war against the United States because we are determined no such war shall come between us. It surely follows that the size of the American navy is no concern of ours, or at most is only a matter of friendly and detached interest. We have no reason to add a single vessel to our normal program of fleet requirements, and there are many of us who do not see why our agreement is required to the affirmation of the intention of the United States to build. We ought to build whatever Parliament considers necessary to our safety and our own affairs.

We ask ourselves, are we being played with? Are we really being informed of the true opinion of the naval authorities, or have they changed their opinion, and if so, why? We hope that if there is a difference of opinion between the Admiralty and the Government we should be informed of the true Admiralty opinion; then, as a separate matter, of the Government reasons for over-riding that opinion. . . . But if we accept the figure of 50 cruisers now vouched for by the highest expert authorities as sufficient for our needs how imprudent and unskilful was the diplomacy which announced this enormous British reduction before the Conference had even opened, instead of using it, as it might well have been used, at the critical moment in the negotiations to secure similar concessions from other Powers. What has been the effect of the Kellogg Pact on other naval Powers? All the Powers gathered in London are signatories to the Kellogg Pact. They have all renounced the idea of war as a part of State policy. That, however, led them not to reduce but to seek to increase their Navies. And the United States, whence this famous declaration originated, was led to increase its Navy more than any other Power.

The second simple point is that a treaty between Great Britain and the United States of naval parity calculated arithmetically is not equality. Relations between the two countries are getting more friendly every year. This country has never made any preparations or plans for a war with the United States, because we determined that no such war could ever come. But there are many of us who do not see why an agreement is required to affirm the intention of the United States to build what they conceive to be a navy equal to ours. We ought to build, after hearing unbiased naval advice, whatever Parliament considers to be necessary for our safety. British naval requirements ought to be fixed by ourselves and by ourselves alone, because our life depends on them.

I do not wish, however, to end without associating myself with a practical suggestion made some time ago by Lord Bridgeman. We all wish the Conference to reach an agreement. Instead of pursuing sterile discussions about parities and ratios, which are either misleading or invidious reflections on the naval status of great Powers, let the different delegations table their programmes for the next five or six years in a spirit of neighbourly and sober good will. We seem to be the only great nation which dares not speak up for itself, which has lost confidence in its mission, which is ready to resign its hard won rights. There is a feeling that England under the Socialists is down and out and on the dole. But we are still a considerable people and our hope is that amid the froth and confusion of our present situation the British nation will still have the sanity and resolution to sustain that ancient naval power which across four centuries has so often defended good causes and has never defended good causes in vain.

LABOUR GOVERNMENT'S RECORD

March 6, 1930

Oxford Union Society Debate

[Extract] . . . The Labour Party has been treated with extraordinary fairness and indulgence by the great majority of the members of the House of Commons during their tenure of office. They have received a measure of fair play, leniency, and assistance never extended in my recollection to any Administration and never extended in a lesser degree to the Administration which preceded the present Government.

Under a system of ruthlessly enforced Socialistic and Communistic ideas the whole of the great country [of Russia] is being reduced to slavery, barbarism, and misery. Even religious liberty is being struck at with brutal force, and the whole of a vast people there being kept in chains for nothing except to gratify the doctrinaire theories of men more monstrous than any of which history bears record.

[Editor's Note: Referring to the Coal Bill, Churchill said] : The miners' representatives hold the Government in a grip of steel, and insist on a reduction in the hours of labour from eight to seven and a half day. The special conditions of the coal industry are such that higher economic advantages are gained from a slightly longer day's work. Upon that depends a great deal of this country's power to produce and sell its coal. But owing to the pressure of the Miners' Federation the Government, against its better judgment, is being forced to reduce the hours by half an hour. This will add very heavily to the cost of production and hamper the country's exports. The Government have gone to the coalowners and said to them: "Keep wages at the present figure, and we will give you the power to recover the loss by raising the price of coal to the general consumer." That is very easy money. (Laughter.) Workmen and employers joined together by the Government will take it out of the general community.

No English Socialist has ever contributed anything to the Socialistic creed. All the creed has been borrowed from Germany and from Russia, from which they are trying to get more information. The stock-in-trade of Socialism is to set class against class, to emphasize the difference between wealth and poverty and cast upon the existing social system the blame for all the tragedy which has dogged the steps of mankind from the beginning. They have got their Bolshevist friends back. When their Bolshevist friends were here last time we had the worst labour period we have ever known. Immediately they left our shores we had less loss of work through labour disputes. Now that they are back we shall see whether we shall suffer as we did on the last occasion.

The late Administration had no scores to pay off and no desire to do anything more than to see the whole finances of the country and the country's trade and industry placed on an economic basis. Whatever the present Goverment may say, they must know that the Conservative Party has no conspiracy against them.

The differences between the Liberals and the Conservatives are smaller than the differences between the champions of Liberalism and the disciples of Karl Marx. I remind the Liberals, however, that it is easier to score off your opponents than to grapple with the problems now facing the country. No party at present has the key to the economic riddle. All parties are seeking the best way out. I do not grudge the present Administration its reign of power, it is having an education, an expensive education, in a school which is surprising them. The present Administration in nine months has weakened the position of this country at home and in some, though not all respects, abroad. If you consult the silk industry and the motor industry, both living in uncertainty, you will reach a conclusion whether the Government has or has not been for the general benefit of the community.

UNEMPLOYMENT (INDUSTRIAL AND FISCAL POLICY)

March 13, 1930

House of Commons

The hon. Member [Mr. Baker] who has just addressed the House has contributed a speech which bore the marks of care and study of the subject which is being debated, and which produced a large number of facts which in their proper setting would be extraordinarily significant. I thought that some of the remarks which he made were of importance as showing the change of opinion upon the Socialist benches towards great combines and amalgamations. Certainly, a great many of his arguments were welcomed by hon. Members on this side as showing an appreciation of the new factors which have arisen, principally mass production, and the relation of those factors to the general conditions of employment and to the commodities which are manufactured for the masses of this country. I do not, however, think that at this stage in the Debate I should be well advised to attempt to follow the hon. Member into his catalogue of facts and figures.

I propose to recall the House to the very serious fact that, for the first time in this Parliament, we are moving a Vote of Censure upon the Government of the day, a Vote specially directed to the person of the Chancellor of the Exchequer. A Vote of Censure like this raises, of course, general topics, and certainly they have been very fully discussed, but it also terminates and culminates in a particularly and entirely direct, definite and precise charge against a Minister. Let us see what that charge is. I will state it at the outset and endeavour to sustain it from various angles and points of view. The charge that we make against the Chancellor of the Exchequer is that, without due cause, he has created uncertainty which has been harmful to trade and employment. That is the case and that is the question upon which the House is going to come to a decision.

What is the right hon. Gentleman's defence? I listened to his speech today, and I am bound to say that I am astonished at the simplicity of mind which leads him to suppose that the kind of defence which he offered to the charge preferred against him is going to enable him to make his case good in the country. His defence was this: I am not guilty of all the evils which exist in our State at the present time; therefore I am not guilty of any of them. Does the right hon. Gentleman really think that he is going to get away with that? No one has blamed him even for all the evils which follow inevitably from the arrival of a Socialist Government at the seat of power; still less would anyone attempt to blame him or the Government for all the difficulties, mishaps, misfortunes and uphill toilings which result from world causes and from the movements of economic forces far outside the control of this House, and far beyond the wit of human brains to solve at the present time. We do not blame him for all the evils that have arisen from world conditions or even from the character of the Administration of which he is a member. The question on which the House is going to vote is whether he has aggravated those conditions, whether, having to face a difficult situation, whether being confronted with a hard task and grave problems, whether being surrounded with a great amount of misery and perplexity he has added to those difficulties, he has emphasised and aggravated those misfortunes, and whether he has done so knowingly, wittingly, wantonly, callously.

I readily admit that any Government sitting on those benches during the past few months would have had a bad time. All sorts of things have happened all over the world. Very harsh and forbidding events have happened. Disconcerting things have occurred. Tides and drifts have moved adverse to our prosperity. I readily admit that. I am not posing that as an attack on the Government, although I have no doubt that the right hon. Gentleman, had he been on this side of the House and had we been on the Government side, would have attributed everything, from the scandals in the City and the collapse of the American Stock Exchange, down to the increased figures of unemployment in particular trades or in the cotton trade—I have no doubt that he would have attributed them all to us, and would have made every party score that he could, placing the blame for most of them on to the Chancellor of the Exchequer. Although he would have done that, I freely exclude and exculpate his Government from the blame for these events. [An Hon. Member: "How good of you!"] How good can best be measured in comparision with how bad it might have been.

Of course, the Government were in for a bad time. But the question that we are now going to settle is whether they have made these bad times worse by conscious and deliberate action. Let us have a little look back upon the right hon. Gentleman's public record. He heralded his approach to office by uttering a series of the most ferocious threats against wealth in every form—a very remarkable proceeding for one to adopt who had been Chancellor of the Exchequer in the past and who consciously, and I may say eagerly and even hungrily, wanted to be Chancellor of the Exchequer again. Let us see some of the things that the right hon. Gentleman said. Speaking in the country he said:

> I warn these wealthy city men that a Labour Government will increase their taxation.

Speaking again on 18th May, during the election, he said:

I am not going to say that if a Labour Government comes in there will
be no increase of taxation. Taxation of certain people will be increased.

I want a cheer, please. [Hon. Members: "Try again!"] I hope hon. Members opposite
have not got their muzzles on to-night. Writing for the "Morning Post" the right hon.
Gentleman laid down some principles which would guide him in his future administration and care of the public finances. He said:

> Other political parties regard taxation as a regrettable necessity; they
> believe that incomes should be left to fructify in the pockets of the
> people—a very respectable Liberal doctrine and a Gladstonian doctrine.
> They maintain that taxation is a burden on industry, that it discourages
> enterprise and restricts necessary capital savings. The Labour Party contests
> all these assumptions. It contends that wise national expenditure is the
> most economical form of expenditure.

We have had a specimen of wise national expenditure in the Bill which has been passed
to relieve any unemployed workman of the necessity to prove that he is genuinely
seeking work before he receives an augmented benefit. Then the right hon. Gentleman
went on to say:

> We hold the existence of a rich class as responsible for the poverty of
> the mass and for the social evil of the slums, physical deterioration,
> ill-health, inadequate education and industrial inefficiency. The Labour
> party is determined that the cost of removing these evils shall be paid for
> by the people who are responsible for them.

Do not be frightened; cheer! You cheered loudly enough before you got into office.

> These are the people who have the financial means to do so.

And so on. The right hon. Gentleman proclaimed very clearly the spirit in which he
would assume his responsible duties. He represented taxation, not as an evil, as it is, an
unmitigated evil, as it is, or almost unmitigated, but represented it as a sort of salutary
tonic which would be administered to the country, whereby the idle rich would be
divested of their vast superfluities and the money would be devoted to increasing the
energetic production of the masses of the people. Having used this sort of language and
having done all that he could to create the feeling that some great and fundamental
change would follow his accession to the Chancellorship of the Exchequer, how can
the right hon. Gentleman wonder that there has been a great deal of despondency and
alarm among those against whom his diatribes were directed? It is all very well. The
right hon. Gentleman goes down to the country and makes a speech at some banquet
or other which it is his duty to attend, in which he says that the only thing that is the
matter with the capitalists, or the old country or whatever it is, is that they want a

little more pluck. I say that that kind of statement in the mouth of a man who has been Chancellor of the Exchequer and who is about to become Chancellor of the Exchequer again, and has since occupied that office, is bound to create a sense of great anxiety and great caution among the wealthy classes and the business community throughout the country.

The right hon. Gentleman told us to-day that he was the victim of an organised conspiracy, a deliberate conspiracy. He told us how there was a deliberate policy of certain interests to create unemployment in order to discredit the Government. That is what he said. Does anyone really believe that to be true? I do not believe that the right hon. Gentleman himself believes it to be true. I am sure that the Lord Privy Seal knows that it is not true. I think the right hon. Gentleman is very ungrateful. I have never seen anyone better treated than he has been. I am supposed to attack him. I would point out that I never said a word against him or his finance until he himself tried to shovel his burdens on to me and made a deliberate and unprovoked attack. He is ungrateful. I have never seen a Chancellor of the Exchequer treated better than he has been treated in the 30 years that I have known this House. He was given the Freedom of the City of London, cheered and applauded by the capitalist popular Press. He has never been pressed or harried in any way in this House, up to the present.

The Prime Minister is not here. I do not blame him, because he has other things to do, but I am sure that if the Prime Minister were here he would repudiate, on behalf of the Government, the kind of language that the right hon. Gentleman uses about the leaders of business and finance in this country. "A conspiracy!" To whom do they run, these Socialists? They come into office "to sweep away all this," and it is to be "Goodbye to all that." They come into office, and the first thing that they do in their distress is to run along and find a lot of capitalists to teach them how to cure the unemployment that they themselves profess to be able to cure. Very generously and very readily these leaders of business and finance have come forward and helped the King's Government, as it is the duty of every person in a non-political capacity to do on a non-party and non-political issue. They are conspiring to produce unemployment, no doubt ruining themselves in the process, letting their works stand idle, paying overhead charges and taxes and so forth, conspiring to make an attack upon the Chancellor of the Exchequer by creating a large quantity of unemployment. The Lord Privy Seal is every day seeing business men who loathe the politics of his own party, but who, he knows, are giving the best efforts they can and the fairest and freest advice to help us all out of our difficulties. It is ungrateful.

Let me warn the right hon. Gentleman of one thing. There is no form of delusion more common than the persecution mania. Most of us who have occupied public positions for any length of time get any number of letters from people who imagine that there is a conspiracy against them, "They are hunting me down," "I am being ringed around." These are early days for the right hon. Gentleman to show these signs. We have not even reached the Budget yet. If he is in this condition three weeks before the Budget is introduced, what will he be reduced to by the end of July?

I have spoken so far of the injury and the embarrassment that he has done to the general public fortunes, and to the success of his own party and Administration, by his foolish fulminations against capitalists and wealth and by his assertion of the virtues of severe and punitive taxation. There is one class of His Majesty's subjects and one class of British industries which come in for a double dose of his commination service. Those are the industries which have in one form or another been the subject of protective duties. Everyone knows how numerous those industries are and how various, and, I must say, heterogeneous are the categories into which they are divided. There are the key industry duties, and the McKenna luxury duties, which we owe to the time when the right hon. Gentleman the Member for Darwen (Sir H. Samuel) and the right hon. Gentleman the Member for St. Ives (Mr. Runciman) were assisting Mr. Asquith to conduct the Coalition administration. We have been faithful to the traditions of those duties after their authors have found it convenient to abandon them. The McKenna luxury duties, as the right hon. Gentleman the Member for Darwen directly told us, were imposed during the War for the purpose of reducing freights across the ocean and improving the exchange at a time when foreign luxuries were not required at all in these islands. Whether they are required in these islands now is to my mind an open question, but I cannot for the life of me see why anyone who wants a foreign luxury cannot be made to pay a little more for it. Who on earth is damnified if a person who chooses to pick up an American motor car when a perfectly good English car is available is made subject to some form of taxation?

These duties were re-imposed for revenue purposes. The right hon. Gentleman reminded me that I re-imposed them for revenue purposes, and seemed to think that a bulwark to take shelter behind. My motives were revenue, but nothing can alter the fact that the duties are protective in character. They are protective duties, and very high protective duties. Then there are the Safeguarding Duties, which were imposed consequent upon the Parish resolutions by the foresight, wisdom and penetrating perspicacity of the right hon. Gentleman the Member for St. Ives. We can see the Liberal touch emerging in this class of legislation. Finally, there are, in a category by themselves, the Silk Duties and the duty on tyres, which were not imposed under the Safeguarding procedure, but which were imposed by the Chancellor of the Exchequer in pursuance of what I hold is his indefeasible right to propose to Parliament any duty to which his colleagues in the Cabinet will assent. The total yield of these duties is £12,500,000, and to this you must add the £15,000,000 of Sugar Duties, making, we will say, very nearly £30,000,000 of revenue. The right hon. Gentleman openly and freely declared his intention of sweeping away all those duties at the earliest possible moment, and that is still his position. £30,000,000 of revenue! What becomes of the charge that he makes against me of squandering revenue?

The success of these duties has been very remarkable. Take the whole class of them. Show me any complaint by a trade union organisation. Show me any complaint by an employers' association or an individual employer. Show me any complaint by a Chamber of Commerce. Show me any complaint by any body representing consumers against any of these duties. Show me any public demand for their repeal. Show me any justification in the surplus revenue possessed by the Chancellor of the Exchequer which would justify him in sweeping away all this revenue. On the contrary, the general opinion has moved steadily in the direction, not of sweeping them away, but of making sensible additions to their number and regularising and systematising their character and introducing some more logical principle into this considerable mass of duties which have now been erected and have so far produced nothing but good results. All these duties have been valuable and brilliant experiments, and we are emboldened to go forward, supported by an ever-growing mass of opinion far outside the bounds of party, into this field.

The right hon. Gentleman the Member for Darwen in the course of another of his pedagogic and censorious orations said: "Let us judge of these matters in the light of actual experience." We are quite content with that. That is the whole case. We do not wish these matters treated as questions of party, as a stunt to be managed by the newspapers, but we should like them to be considered at the present time on their merits by persons who have no immediate electioneering interest in the position one way or another. The Balfour Committee, a Committee of very able men, Free Traders in the majority, appointed by the present Prime Minister—the Balfour Committee, after prolonged examination, by a majority, markedly and clearly deprecated the removal of these duties. Now there is a new Economic Committee, an important committee wittily described as a committee from whom no one of note had been omitted. This committee, the new Economic Committee, the members of which the right hon. Gentleman the Chancellor of the Exchequer will probably describe as conspirators, gathered together to come and help the Prime Minister and the Government, a body picked by himself. We should be quite content—we cannot go on working out details and figures on our own, but I place it broadly upon this—to have the question submitted to this Committee whether these duties have been beneficial or not, whether they ought to be removed; and whether they are to be removed or not, the policy should be announced immediately. We should be quite content with that.

After all, we see ourselves in many difficulties. We want to make sure that we are finding the shortest way out of our perils. Why is the right hon. Gentleman so adverse to all this? We have had some old speeches to-night—not so very old either. But there is a speech, a maiden speech, I believe, in the House of Commons, a rather elderly maiden at that time, the maiden speech of the Chancellor of the Exchequer in the House of Commons. He began by saying:

> Might he say to Free Traders on the Ministerial side that it was upon the very existence of these evils, which 60 years of Free Trade had failed to mitigate or palliate, that the right hon. Member for West Birmingham (Mr. Joseph Chamberlain) had founded his appeal to the country?

He went on to say:

> They were prepared to admit that there was a great deal of truth in what was expressed by the right hon. Gentleman the Member for West Birmingham as to the changed conditions of our industries during the past 60 years. Conditions were constantly changing. They agreed with the statement that the time had come when they should take stock of our industrial position.

That is what we are asking now.

> Our industrial circumstances were not what they were 60 years ago, when we practically stood alone among the manufacturing nations of the world.

I almost heard these words repeated by the Leader of the Opposition to-day, though he had not read this speech.

> Since then other nations had become their own producers, and to a great extent they were becoming our competitors in all the markets of the world. Sixty years had falsified the expectations that foreign restrictions upon trade would be removed. There had not been a continuous improvement in the condition of the people during the last 60 years.

That is the Chancellor of the Exchequer, who is the supreme orthodox defender of the most rigidly expressed doctrines of economic Cobdenism.

Mr. Snowden: That was said in support of a Free Trade Resolution.

Mr. Churchill: Yes, and one can gather how much support the Free Trade Resolution received. When the right hon. Member for Darwen derides me, as he has done to-day, for proclaiming myself at once a Free Trader and a Protectionist, he will see that others have trod that path before. The right hon. Gentleman must really take a mental and moral pull of himself, because he is allowing himself to have prejudices against all these protected trades. He says, "They are protected and, therefore, they are malignant and must be punished. I will larn you to be a toad." He cannot receive their representatives. He cannot show himself in the same room; he wants to lay his hands about them, these rank, wicked, cursed protected trades, many of whom have no knowledge of the processes which have led to their receiving these duties. *Odi quem laeseris*; hate those you have injured, or are about to injure. He has proceeded against these trades by a dual process of torture; first, alarm; then, suspense; violent alarm; very prolonged suspense. Anything more elaborate than the machinery he has adopted to create alarm cannot be imagined. He solemnly read out to us a couple of months ago all the arrangements which he was making with regard to the duty-paid stocks in all these trades in case of the duties being removed. He must have known that the revenue then did not justify bringing a single one of these duties to an end. He went through the solemn farce of laying out all the proceeding which would be appropriate with a view of creating the utmost possible concern and uncertainty, and lent to it an extreme air of verisimilitude. He ought to try to be fair to all trades, even though they are protected and to say to himself, "They are all under my wing, and I will do the best I can for all of them, and for all of us." That is the proper spirit for him to address himself to his duties. Instead he comes down here, when we have 1,500,000 unemployed, a number which is probably going to be increased, and talks to us in a mocking way about jews' harps, pop-guns and mechanical donkeys, in a spirit which I can only characterise as worthy of a mechanical donkey. I have little more to say, and I am going to address myself to the question of Budget secrecy.

Hon. Members: What about food taxes?

Mr. Churchill: Hon. Members below the Gangway must make their own speeches and must allow me to make mine. I am directing myself in strict relevance to the Vote of Censure on which we are going to vote.

What is the argument of Budget secrecy? The object of Budget secrecy is the public interest. It is the public interest that the secrets of the Budget should be kept, and that the Budget should be announced in its integrity, because it would be undesirable that there should be forestalments of revenue or other calculations or speculations made upon the plans for the yearly finances. But Budget secrecy means that there shall be no leakage. It does not in the least preclude an announcement by the Chancellor of the Exchequer at any time, if it be thought that it will be better for the common interest, better for the national housekeeping, to have such an announcement. There is no Budget etiquette, no rule to prevent such an announcement being made. Far better to have such an announcement than to have leakages, and are you quite sure there will be no leakages? I wonder very much, when I see the motor trade suddenly lifting its head a little, whether they have not had a hint from some quarter or another to say, "After all it will be quite all right—take it from me."

At any rate, however that may be I cannot tell, but it would be far less objectionable to have a frank and plain announcement by the Chancellor of the Exchequer, and it is ludicrous to suppose that any tradition would be violated by such a statement. The oldest Privy Councillor in the House the right hon. Gentleman the Member for West Birmingham (Sir A. Chamberlain), who was Chancellor of the Exchequer on two occasions, made a precedent. It is quite true that he said, very rightly, that it ought not to be copied—except when special circumstances arise—and I am sure it would have been better for the right hon. Gentleman to have said, "Everyone knows that I would like to do away with these Duties, but there is absolutely no question of my having the finances to do away with them at the present time, and, therefore, I put these trades out of their misery at once." But what does the right hon. Gentleman do? He fixes his eye on the Budget day. That is a great occasion for the Chancellor of the Exchequer. Then he comes down here to the House and unfolds his plan, and we shall all wait with the greatest interest to hear the right hon. Gentleman's plan. But one must not push too far considerations of personal gratification and the theatrical setting of the scene. The right hon. Gentleman wants to come down here on 14th April. He knows perfectly well to-night whether he is going to repeal those Duties or not. I cannot hazard what he will do.

If he does not repeal them what will be his position? Just in order that he might come down here and have all these trades, in which I am told 500,000 people are employed, sitting around in the galleries on every side waiting to hear—[*Interruption.*] There is nothing dishonourable in being in trade. The right hon. Gentleman, as I say, will have them waiting to know what their fate may be, having had their businesses held up, having been unable to make their ordinary forward contracts, having been embarrassed and harassed for months by alarming predictions and threats—all will be waiting and hanging on his words. Then he will tell them, "You are all reprieved, you are all respited and you can go away and live in your present uncertainty for another year. I should have thought that the days had gone by when the personal pomp and circumstance of an individual, the personal vanity of an individual, could outweigh broad matters of interest. We all know the saying: "And wretches hang that Chancellors may shine." We all know how Napoleon before the Battle of Leipzig said, "Do you think I am a man who cares a snap of the fingers for the lives of 100,000 soldiers?" [*Interruption.*] The right hon. Gentleman is using the livelihood of 500,000 people as the raw material of his stage effects. That is the gravamen of the case which we oppose against him to-night. I am not joining with those who proclaim a pessimistic outlook for this country. I agree with the Lord Privy Seal and the right hon. Gentleman the Member for Carnarvon Boroughs (Mr. Lloyd George) that the strength and power of this mighty country is unexhausted, and will be capable in the long run of mounting every difficulty and surmounting every peril. But for the time, the luck is adverse. We have enough to bear and little enough to sustain ourselves, and it is a shame that anyone for motives of pride or prejudice should add a single jot to the burden which is being borne by the self-supporting citizens in every part of the island, when it ought to be the common endeavour of us all to add to the national stock of good fortune.

NAVY ESTIMATES

March 17, 1930

House of Commons

No one, I think, wherever he may sit, will fail to recognise the lucid and at the same time terse manner in which the First Lord of the Admiralty [Mr. Alexander] has laid his first Navy Estimates before the House, and I need scarcely say that with all that he said in tribute to the men of this Service, and in tribute to the high naval authorities, he carried with him the cordial concurrence of those at any rate who belong to the Opposition. Of course, I could not help being struck, during the right hon. Gentleman's speech, by the extreme air of apology which he assumed in speaking of the great Service, the great arm and instrument, upon which the life and the history of this country are both founded. One would have thought that he had something very shocking to explain to Parliament, but that he was anxious to state every extenuating circumstance that could possibly be pleaded for the continued maintenance of the British Navy, even on a scale so considerably reduced as he has described to us. It is true that this Debate takes place at an inopportune moment, and at a very inconvenient moment for the House of Commons. I am not blaming the Government, because they are bound by the ordinary course of the financial year, and, of course, the prolongation of the Naval Conference is a matter not within their control. Still, I think it would have been very much better if this Vote could have been taken even a week or 10 days later, when the Naval Conference would perhaps have been in smoother waters.

This is our regular opportunity for debating the strength and efficiency of the Navy; this is our annual opportunity. We do not get very many in the House; pressure of business stands in their path. It is undoubtedly a period in which there is deep anxiety about our naval position, and in which there is an earnest desire to discuss all sorts of grave matters. The right hon. Gentleman appealed to us, in the course of the Debate, not to make more difficult the task of the Naval Conference. I am sure that his appeal will be responded to on this side of the House, and that at any rate as strict a view of the public interest will always be taken by those who sit on these benches as has in the past been taken by some of those who now sit on the Treasury Bench. At any rate, it seems essential that we should make it clear that any silence which is maintained upon various matters which are the crux of the present Conference must not be taken by the Government as a sign that they have the consent of the whole of the House of Commons in many of the measures which they have proposed, and still less that we, with our present knowledge, are able to say that we consider that the Estimates which the First Lord has just presented are adequate for our security.

I think we ought to have had a full statement, from the Prime Minister or from the First Lord, of the basis of our naval policy. We ought to know what are the standards of naval strength which the Board of Admiralty consider necessary and which the Government have approved, and we ought to know what are the measures that are being taken to maintain them. The Government have brought this Debate on—the first of the three Fighting Services to be discussed—at the earliest moment. They give us virtually no information on any of the vital points, and they seem to exploit to the fullest the argument that any discussion on these vital points will be embarrassing to them in their naval negotiations. We cannot really feel that that leaves us in a very satisfactory position. We have, of course, the assurance that, when the Naval Conference is over, there is to be a full submission of its results to the House and the country, and thereafter the Government will lay the new construction Vote for the year and will take any Supplementary Estimates that may be required. There are, of course, good precedents for such a course. There have been in my own recollection three occasions when it was not found possible to lay the full programme of annual construction before the House on the opening statement of the Navy Estimates, and, therefore, there are good precedents, but we must make it clear that in the interim we in no way assent to the present proposals and Estimates of the Government. We reserve to ourselves most complete and untrammelled liberty to examine the position at a later date.

There are, however, certain points of a purely domestic character which do not affect any other Power, which I think must receive some passing attention. First of all, I allude to the question of cruiser strength. We have been told that the cruiser strength which is thought necessary by Admiralty experts has been reduced from 70 to 50 cruisers. This matter is more complicated than the casual reader of a newspaper would often suppose. The strength of a cruiser fleet depends not only upon its numbers, but upon its newness, and the value of 70, 60, or 50 cruisers can only be judged in relation to the number of old and new vessels respectively that are included in those figures. However, we have been told that the Admiralty now advise the Government that they may remain content with 50 cruisers, not over 20 years old. That is the present declaration. That is an immense reduction on all the previous estimates that were brought before us by expert authority, and most recently brought before us, and when the First Lord boasts as at one moment in his speech he allowed himself the indulgence to boast that, as far as the present Government are concerned, there would be no unilateral disarmament he raised a question which I am bound to take up, and I am bound to ask him, in return, if there is to be no unilateral disarmament—his own phrase—why was this immense reduction in our cruiser strength announced before the Conference began, instead of becoming part of a general process of disarmament? It seems to me this is a very strange and unfortunate diplomacy. It is unfortunate in this sense, that, whereas every other Power states its requirements at the maximum, we begin the discussion with an enormous reduction, and then the argument proceeds on the basis of how much more can be cut off all round. Thus, there is a grave danger and risk, which we feel most concerned about, that the Conference may become a process, not of general naval disarmament, but of disarming Britain, while other Powers become relatively, and, in some cases, actually stronger.

There is another danger in this method of announcing these reductions before entering upon a discussion of this kind, and also of announcing reductions in the actual programme of the year, at this stage. If the right hon. Gentleman had been content to let the programme stand as he found it, in the hope of making a reduction should favourable results emerge from the labours of the Conference, he would have been in the good position, when the Conference had concluded its successful labours, of making a reduction which would be justified by all that had gone before; but now, if for any reason the Conference should not reach a completely successful conclusion—I hope the Prime Minister will follow this—he would have to emphasise the fact that it has not reached a successful conclusion by sending the First Lord to the House to propose a Supplementary Estimate for additional construction. That appears to me to be leading up to exactly the kind of conclusion that you would have endeavoured to avoid, namely, of following on upon a Conference of this character, which I cannot conceive is going to fail altogether, although it may not achieve its full purpose—to follow on upon results which, like so many things in this world, may be mixed and partial, with a Vote which will clearly indicate that those results have not been wholly satisfactory. I am sure it would have been far better not to be so impatient to make a gesture of disarmament, but to proceed frankly on a straight-forward basis to lay all the cards on the table and endeavour to reach a general and joint conclusion.

But, even if the 50 cruisers of 20 years of age were accepted as the basis of the protection of our food and trade routes, what steps are the Government taking to carry out this programme? There is surely no need for secrecy about this. We ought to know what are the programmes that would be necessary to carry out the maintenance of the cruiser fleet on the basis of 50 cruisers not being over 20 years of age. It is not a matter of secret negotiation. It is not a matter of delicate diplomacy. It is a matter of pure arithmetic. The cruisers are all known. They are all in the list. Everyone knows them. Everyone knows the exact date when they were laid down and the date when they will accomplish their 20 years. Therefore, the rate of replacement can be produced with extreme simplicity and accuracy by anyone who chooses to study it. There is no question of running a risk in mentioning such figures to other Powers at the Conference for fear that they would be shocked, because they are capable of making the same calculations that I have had made for myself. I am told that, between now and 1939, approximately 34 or 35 of the present British cruisers will drop out of the line. They will be past the age when they can be considered efficient. If that is so, it would appear that the construction of about four cruisers a year is indispensable to maintain this programme of 50 cruisers of not more than 20 years of age. When the Government have reduced, needlessly, before the Conference, the programme of this year to one cruiser, it is clear that they are not only reducing the standard but they are not even maintaining their own programme.

They are anxious to prove their pacifism and to avoid expense during the current year; they fail to maintain the minimum standard which they have themselves proclaimed, and they are thereby throwing a burden upon the future. They look forward to the day—I can foresee it myself—when they, being an irresponsible Opposition, will use their whole strength to oppose the construction of these very cruisers which, on their own admitted standard, would annually be necessary. The right hon. Gentleman sitting on this side will say, "In our day, we built only one cruiser. We reduced the Navy Estimates by so much. The moment the Conservatives came in up bounded the expenses of the Navy." Yet all this will be part of the execution of a reduced programme to which even the right hon. Gentleman himself has set his seal. The Government ought to have been able to state for this Debate, and I must ask specifically that they will, when the Supplementary Estimate is presented, state exactly what are their series of programmes for the next five or six years ahead to maintain these standards, in order that we may see that they are bearing a just and fair share of the burden of maintaining the naval strength which they themselves think necessary. The right hon. Gentleman said only to-day that the moment the Conservative Government came in in 1924 up went the Naval Estimates. Why did they go up? Because the right hon. Gentleman laid down five cruisers, for which he had had to pay some insignificant token sum, and the full cost came immediately upon us. Really I should have thought it was hardly worth while manoeuvring in that way. The Government will greatly commend any programme of naval policy that they wish to present to the House if it is accompanied by a clearly worked out scheme of maintaining by annual programmes whatever standard is finally selected.

There is another point of a very general character on which I should like to say a word. We hear a great deal about the reduction, or abolition, of battle fleets. Only three Powers in the world have modern battle fleets, and everyone is agreed that it would be sensible to make the existing vessels last another five or six years, and also to reduce considerably the tonnage of these immensely costly capital units. The question whether battleships will be rendered obsolete by submarines or by aircraft is seriously affected by the size of battleships. I sat upon a Committee in 1919 which exhaustively examined the question for many months, and I have always been assured that it is much easier for the capital ship to defend itself against large torpedoes from submarines or heavy bombs from aeroplanes if it is a very large ship than if it is a smaller vessel. I have always doubted whether the submarine would ultimately endanger the battleship or render it obsolete, but the air menace to battleships increases with every year that passes, and, in so far as by general consent all Powers reduce the size of the battleships, to that very extent will you be emphasising the advantage of the new arm over the old and tending to diminish the life of the battleship type.

When we talk airily and hopefully about reducing or abolishing battleships all round, it may be well worth while to consider what reactions will follow from that. What is to take the place of these battle fleets if they are abolished all round? As far as the three great ocean Powers are concerned, their battle fleets are fixed in a certain ratio, but it must be remembered that, as far as Great Britian is concerned in relation to the Continent of Europe, she is able to accept a much lower strength of cruisers and of other small vessels, because she possesses a very powerful battle fleet, whereas the European Powers have not developed their battle fleets since the War. I am quite certain that the abolition of battleships will require a complete re-casting of the whole of our strength in other vessels in relation to the Continent of Europe, and I hope that, when the First Lord speaks on the next occasion, he will endeavour to throw some light upon this extremely difficult and anxious problem.

I ask myself seriously whether it is contemplated at any time that modern navies should consist of ships which are almost entirely unarmoured. The 10,000 ton 8-inch gun cruisers, which, I think, are most erroneously spoken of as if they were real symbols and tokens of naval strength, are mistakenly compared with the pre-War Dreadnoughts. These ships are virtually unarmoured vessels. They are the revivals of the old pre-War "Europa" class, which in my Admiralty days were held up as examples of what should be especially avoided in ship construction. They are ships which cost an immense sum of money, which offer enormous targets and carry a very large number of lives on board, and which are, I say, virtually unprotected from the fire even of guns of their own calibre. The first duty of a warship is to keep afloat. Have we really forgotten the combat of the "Merrimac" and the "Monitor," now nearly 70 years ago, in the American Civil War, when it was conclusively proved in those days that no ship could stand up against modern artillery unless it was protected by strong steel or iron armour? What has happened in the interval to artillery to lead us to suppose that we can now talk of navies in which no battleships exist, but in which every form of naval warfare can be discharged only by unarmoured ships? I hope that the First Lord of the Admiralty will, on the next occasion, also tell us more about the Admiralty view upon these matters, which seem to be of the very greatest consequence.

I have only one more point. I do not wish to keep the House, as there is an Amendment which is to be brought on, but I have a third point which I must mention, as the First Lord referred to it in some detail. There is a reduction of, I think he said, 5,800 men in the strength of the Royal Navy. I always have been of the opinion that 100,000 men was the sort of figure we might well have maintained in times of peace. After all, it has been upon our incomparable, long service, seafaring personnel that our Navy has depended as much even as upon modern appliances. The men take an immense amount of time to train—they begin as boys—and a reduction which can be effected cannot be soon reversed if it is desired later on to increase the Navy. I observe that, whereas before the War we had 146,000 seamen and marines, and after the War under the late Government 99,000, we are now reduced to 94,000—that is a tremendous reduction—and that during the same period the next strongest naval power has increased its personnel from 67,000 in 1914 to 114,000 in the present year—114,000 United States seamen and marines and 94,000 British. I agree that figures are not in every respect entirely comparable, but in the main they are comparable, and I ask, in the face of such figures, what becomes even of the doctrine of parity?

I should like the First Lord to tell us—perhaps he will later on to-day when he has a further opportunity—how they have effected this reduction? Has it been effected on the schools and the shore establishments, by reductions there? Has it been effected upon the number of reliefs in transit? Has it been effected by still further reducing the quarter bills of the ships in active commission, by, for instance, providing crews to man the guns on one side of the ship or only a portion of the armament at one particular time. I am bound to say that I have in the past brought pressure to bear on the Admiralty to reduce to the neighbourhood of 100,000, and I was very conscious of the extremely cogent manner in which the Second Sea Lords of the different periods had always defended their numbers and pointed out how efficiency would suffer and how great a blow would be struck if they were unduly pressed in this respect. It was only last year that I heard a very strong argument put forward for a personnel of 99,000—approximately 100,000—and I therefore feel surprised—as many of us must feel surprised—when the right hon. Gentleman comes forward and without giving any real explanation, except saying that the Third Battle Squadron is to be placed on a training footing, tells us that he has succeeded in striking off no fewer than 5,800 of our naval personnel.

I cannot feel at all contented, or even reassured, by the able statement to which we have listened. Six thousand fewer sailors in the Navy, and still, on the other hand, there are many thousands more upon the dole! So I suppose it will be said that the Government are providing for all the population as thoroughly as before. I should think that it really is an epitome of the message which the present Government have to give to Britain at this time, that all this naval saving, so painfully extracted from the instrument of our protection, pared off from the efficiency and strength of the Fleet, all this £4,000,000 or £5,000,000 which has been saved only forms a small proportion of the additional sums of money which the same Administration is providing for further and better benefits to persons who may not even be genuinely seeking work.

PROHIBITION AND CIVIL LIBERTIES

March 17, 1930

Allied Brewery Traders' Association Dinner,
Savoy Hotel, London

[Extract] . . . The trades represented play an important part in the life of the British nation. It is a matter for congratulation that upon the whole the drink traffic question, as it is called, is more and more passing out of the arena of controversial British party politics. With the decay of the Liberal Party and the rise in their place of the Labour Party there is undoubtedly less inclination to make the question of the liquor trade one of the disputed pawns and counters of the party game. A very different situation exists on the other side of the Atlantic, to which I have recently paid a most interesting visit. There, in the very centre of controversy, is the question of prohibition.

After two months' experience of the full rigours of prohibition I am bound to say that I do not feel one penny the worse. (Laughter.) But there is one feature of the prohibition movement which excites my indignation. There are still people in the United States who obtain indulgence in alcoholic liquor, and among those people I heard the expression "hooch" sometimes used. It caused me great pain. What an expression to describe one of the gifts of the gods to man. It is a coarse, brutish, and squalid expression. On those terms they may reduce all the romance of life to baseness.

It is a most dangerous thing to invade the inward and fundamental rights of individuals. Governments do not exist for the purpose of invading those rights, but to enable individuals to exercise their rights so long as they do not trench upon the interests or the rights of others. The intrusion into the sphere of individual liberty is always followed by evils and by reactions, which produce a whole crop of unfortunate events. The visit to the United States convinced me more than anything else had that the British method of regulated liberty, tempered by high taxation, produces far better results upon the health and temperance of the community, as well as upon the receipts of the Chancellor of the Exchequer. We take the middle road.

THE ECONOMIC SITUATION

March 18, 1930

Wanstead

To add to the Conservatives' difficulties, Lord Beaverbrook—assisted from time to time by Lord Rothermere—had launched a crusade for "Empire Free Trade," and contested Conservatives at by-elections. For a time this movement seemed to pose a real threat to Baldwin's leadership, already under fire from within the Party on other issues.

The political situation is most uncertain. A General Election might come this summer, but, on the other hand, it might not come for quite a long time. No one can tell, but every one must be ready.

The uncertainty is bad from every point of view. It hangs like a cloud over the trade of the country; it prevents Parliament from giving sustained consideration to the many grievous social and economic problems of the day. I have often warned you of the evils which would follow from any period of political instability and Socialist minority rule. I never believed that my words would be so tragically realized and in so short a time. No victorious country has made less progress since the Armistice than Great Britain, and no country is showing less capacity at the moment in coping with its difficulties. Men's minds are now turned almost exclusively upon the economic question. The House of Commons is well suited to deal with ordinary party issues such as had occupied us before the War. It is a feeble instrument to handle the grim economic realities on which the livelihood of millions and the prosperity of the nation depend. Ministers are overweighted and overworked. Their hands are hampered on every side by party exigencies and political theories. The Civil Service, faithful and competent to the last degree, cannot supply constructive inspiration.

I had hoped that the new Economic Advisory Council would make a fresh and authoritative contribution to our national policy and would be invited to express an unbiased opinion upon many of the disputed economic and financial questions of the day. Apparently, however, it has been warned off the really important controversial ground and it appears to be steadily petering out. I am sure that our troubles in trade and unemployment will not be cured by party politicians trying to score off each other and manoeuvring for position and winning an election. They will be cured only when expert, disinterested, free, and non-party proposals are shaped by persons specially competent in industry, business, and finance, and when some political party or other has the strength and courage to adapt a whole scheme so worked out and presented in its entirety to the Parliament of the nation.

Sometimes I feel drawn to the idea that what is wanted, temporarily at any rate, is an additional organ in the Constitution—a kind of sub-Parliament to deal with economic issues and to present conclusions to the Government of the day and to the House of Commons after full, open, brutal, and candid discussion of all the most difficult, delicate, and harassing topics.

It is absolutely necessary for this country, with its overcrowded population, its vast Empire and its threatened trade, to find the right path, and no prejudices or fear of innovation ought to stand between us and that high duty. There are brains in England as good as any in the world. There is knowledge and experience unrivalled in any country. We still have a giant's strength. Joined to our Empire we still have a noble and limitless future. At all costs we must find the right road.

Although I had not at all approved of Lord Beaverbrook's and Lord Rothermere's attempt to form a separate party and split up the Conservative vote in some of the Southern constituencies, I believe that as the result of what had taken place the cause of the economic unity of the British Empire has undoubtedly moved forward by a long march. If the Conservatives are returned to power we will summon an Imperial Conference, from whose discussions no topic will be barred.

If, as a result of these discussions a good plan was made whereby the Dominions would give, not indeed free access to their markets—for that could not be expected—but much freer and more favourable access, and if in return for those great advantages we for our part were required to give them an effectual preference, on their imports of food or raw material, and if the whole scheme when worked out was such as to offer real promise of national and Imperial advantage, of better employment and extended trade, of wider and securer markets, and of more solid Imperial interdependence, then the next Conservative Government would not hesitate to put these issues to the British electorate and would advise them not to cast away what might well be a priceless opportunity, and not to sell, like Esau of old, their birth-right for a mess of pottage.

There would be no protective taxes on food unless the nation upon a direct vote on this definite issue decided that it was in the general interest. Any Conservative candidate is entitled to say to his constituents, "No food taxes unless you vote for them yourselves."

I hope that by this procedure the deadlock which has long obstructed the discussions upon the economic and fiscal unity of the Empire will be satisfactorily removed. If that is so, no small portion of the credit is due to Lord Beaverbrook. He has now taken his position among the leaders of the Conservative Party. He has thereby assumed serious public and personal responsibility and no responsibility will be more exacting than to help to bring the Conservative Party out victorious from the numerous perils and oppositions which surround it.

I have also read Lord Rothermere's programme, on many points of which I find myself in hearty agreement. It is my hope when the time comes Lord Rothermere will also come into line and help the Conservative Party to weave together all these political forces upon which the strength of the Empire depends and bring into power a Government which will seriously defend the rights and interests of Britain in every corner of the world.

Mr. Snowden, who was such a critic of my administration, apparently supposes that all he has to do is to try to put the blame of his misdeed on to me. He thinks he is going to get away with it. I don't think it will come off, but we shall have to see. We have not yet even begun the lengthy discussion of the Budget. We shall see at the end of it who is standing up in the ring.

[Editor's note: Referring to Snowden's refusal to disclose his intentions with regard to the McKenna duties, Churchill said]: It is the greatest instance of personal vanity and the desire for theatrical effect that has ever been produced in this country regardless of the suffering and loss which this may cause to the general mass of the people.

LONDON NAVAL CONFERENCE

March 18, 1930

Woodford

[Extract] ... Why is it necessary for our Government to declare in advance that we will make enormous reductions in the British fleet, while the other powers that have come along put up their claims? It is the most improvident and foolish policy. Here are the other four powers, our Allies in the war, proposing to increase their navies, and proposing that Great Britian should reduce hers, yet no power in the world has greater need for a navy than Britain.

LORD BALFOUR

March 19, 1930

London

[Extract] I have sustained a very keen personal loss, because I have known Lord Balfour since I was a child, and have always been treated by him in 30 years of political life with extreme kindness. Through all the vicissitudes of politics the friendship with which I was honoured continued. . . . He was the greatest member of the House of Commons since Mr. Gladstone. The earlier part of his political work was intermingled with party controversy, but his principal actions were national, and command the gratitude of all.

He it was who, on the outbreak of the Spanish-American War, by a personal decision, turned the policy of Great Britain into a channel definitely friendly to the United States. He it was who, in the black week of the South African War, insisted upon the appointment of Lord Roberts and Lord Kitchener to the chief command, thus restoring the situation. The influence which he acquired in the United States, and the charm which his personality exerted on all, enabled him, in his mission to that country during the War, to procure a measure of good will and cordial co-operation between the two English-speaking peoples which was invaluable. He it was who, at the Washington Naval Conference in 1921, unhesitatingly accepted the principle that Britain and the United States should be equal Powers upon the sea and finally the broader constitution of the British Empire which emerged from the Imperial Conference of 1927 owed its shape and its force to him above all others. These are only some of the chief personal interventions which, according to my knowledge, have marked his memorable influence upon or control of our affairs.

His death cuts us sharply away from the famous past. Politics, society, the world position of Great Britain, all are changed. During the last few months I had the privilege of visiting him several times, and he lay facing with serene philosophy and faith the approaching close of his life. There arose in my mind John Morley's phrase about John Stuart Mill: "A great and benignant lamp of wisdom." It is grievous that it should be extinguished even in the fullness of time.

THE ECONOMIC SITUATION
March 26, 1930
Harlow

[Extract] ... The Conservative Party has adopted as its main constructive policy the development of the economic unity and interdependence of the British Empire. The immediate practical steps have been very clearly explained by Mr. Baldwin and Mr. Neville Chamberlain.

At the General Election, whenever it may come, the Conservative Party will not be committed to the protective taxation of food. The statements which the Socialists and Liberals are, I am sorry to hear, spreading about the division that the General Election will be fought by the Conservative Party on food taxation are quite untrue. We should, however, claim a free hand to negotiate with the Dominions in an Imperial Conference from which no subject would be arbitrarily excluded, and if a good working arrangement emerged from the conference, which gave British manufactures effective and substantial entry into the Canadian and Australian home markets, and if as a part of that arrangement duties on foreign food were required, the Conservative Government of that day would not hesitate to submit the whole scheme in its entirety, on a special referendum, to the direct vote of the electorate. The electors would, therefore, remain complete masters of the situation.

It is no use prejudging a scheme before it has been framed. The first step is to win a General Election, and for that purpose the united energies of the whole Conservative Party will be required. It will not only be necessary to win Conservative seats in the South and Midlands but to carry the war into the industrial and working class areas of the North. I hope that Lord Beaverbrook and Lord Rothermere will put their shoulders to the wheel and use the powers of propaganda and publicity which they possess to educate and convert the hostile areas of the country and to study the problems and encourage the efforts of Conservative candidates in purely working class constituencies. If so they would render great service to the cause they have espoused.

Meanwhile, however, events seem to be taking a new turn. The prominence assigned to the fiscal question, and particularly to food taxes, has had its natural and almost inevitable result of throwing the Liberals and Socialists more closely together. As a first consequence the Liberals are now proposing to help the Socialists to pass the "Dear Coal Bill." Mr. Lloyd George, who had declared it to be an incredibly bad Bill, is now to stultify himself in the most cynical manner by becoming responsible for its passage. The general feeling now is that the election will not take place until next year. Although we must continue vigilant and ready, it may well be that we will enjoy the pleasures of Socialist rule at any rate until 1931.

Naturally the Socialists, who have made such a ghastly failure in handling unemployment, will be anxious to wait in the hopes of an improvement in trade, and Mr. Lloyd George now shows every disposition to give them a further chance. This will mean that the country will be exposed to the ravages of a Socialist Budget, in which Mr. Snowden will have the opportunity of working off his spite upon those sections and classes in the community against whom he is politically prejudiced. The burden of taxation will be heavily increased and the recovery of business and industry proportionately checked. It will also mean that Mr. MacDonald will have the last word upon the surrender of our interests in Egypt and the evacuation of Cairo. Secondly, he will have control of the Indian settlement, with its enormous and historic consequences; and, lastly, he will preside over the Imperial Conference, with its economic sub-conference, which is due to assemble this autumn. The conclusions of this Conference will naturally have a powerful influence upon the immediate future of Empire trade. The prospect is one to cause anxiety and distress among all those who wish to see the prosperity of Britain restored, her strength and fortunes re-established in the world.

The agricultural policy of the Conservative Party has not yet been announced. This is not because it is being neglected, but because it is so important. It is obvious that the farmers cannot grow wheat in competition even with Canada. The difficulty of the English farmer is that he cannot grow wheat at such prices. It is evident that some other means of helping him must be sought. A guaranteed minimum price is the most practical and helpful step which can be taken. That is the policy of the Conservative Party. But further, we also propose to exclude foodstuffs which are either subsidized or dumped in the country at prices which have no relation to the cost of production in the country of origin. In this matter we have the support of the Liberal Party and therefore can command a majority.

THE POLITICAL SITUATION
March 27, 1930
Epping

[Extract] ... It is very important for the electors to understand what is really going on in politics. The key to the present political situation consists in the reform of the electoral law. The Liberals complain that whereas it takes only about 20,000 votes to return a Socialist it takes nearly 100,000 votes to return a Liberal. They demand that something should be done, either by proportional representation or by the second ballot or alternative vote, to enable them to secure representation in Parliament, corresponding to their voting strength in the country. A Conference of all parties is now sitting under Lord Ullswater, but is not apparently making much headway. I had hoped that the attitude of the Conservative Party towards a reform of the electoral law would be such as to enable the two non-Socialist parties to find a certain common measure of agreement. A reform of the electoral law which would secure majority representation would have important advantages.

Events have now taken a very significant turn. The over-shadowing importance which has been given to the fiscal question and to the taxation of food has afforded a common platform to the leaders of the Liberal and Socialist Parties. There has already been, as Mr. Neville Chamberlain pointed out, a somewhat sinister luncheon at Downing Street between Mr. Lloyd George and Mr. Philip Snowden. Following upon that, the Liberals withdrew their opposition to the "Dear Coal Bill," and Mr. Lloyd George, with a singular lack of his customary adroitness, had put forward the perfectly farcical reason that he was afraid of endangering the Naval Conference by voting against the Government. When a man puts forward a reason that is not his real reason it always makes people suspicious. I think that it is more than probable that some understanding was reached between the Liberal and Socialist Parties, behind the backs of Lord Ullswater's conference, for a reform of the electoral law. Such an understanding if reached and carried out may mean that the electoral law will be reformed in a manner most detrimental to the Conservative Party, and that the Socialists will be kept in office until such time as the necessary legislation has received the Royal Assent.

It would be most imprudent and short-sighted for Conservatives, and those who cared about the United Empire, not to realize in good time the formidable nature of the difficulties we may have to meet. We may find ourselves confronted in 1931 with what is called a "Lib.-Lab." combination, which will work the "dear food" cry for all it is worth in our vastly increased electorate of consumers, and who at the same time will have twisted the electoral law into a form most harmful to the Conservative and Imperial interests. I hope it may well be possible, by skilful and prudent conduct, to avoid the dangers to the constitutional cause which can now be clearly foreseen, or that something will happen to prevent those dangers from presenting themselves.

Conservatives must be united among ourselves and have a high spirit of comradeship and loyalty throughout our ranks. The Conservative Party will grow strong and march to victory because it is a broad and free association of the largest possible number of men and women of good will to keep our country powerful and famous. There must be room in every great party for men of many shades of opinion. Parties are organizations aiming at obtaining the control of the Government of the country by gathering to themselves a majority of its citizens and then rating the country in accordance with well-defined general principles. In the General Election of 1924 the Conservatives received at least 1,000,000 Liberal votes. It would be madness to drive those away needlessly when so many enemies are gathering up against the Empire cause. There is nothing in Mr. Baldwin's programme which should alienate from the Conservative Party those extremely important elements. Above all we must not forget that the failure and incompetence of the Socialist Government will be increasingly felt with every month they remain in office, and I look forward with a confidence which outweighs many grave anxieties to a victorious regathering in 1931 of the great forces which triumphed in the election of 1924.

UNEMPLOYMENT INSURANCE

March 28, 1930

House of Commons

The Debate has been characterised by good temper and composure, and certainly the speech that has just been made [by Mr. Sanders] has in no way departed
from the general character of the discussion. I have, in speaking towards the end of the
Debate, to endeavour, as far as I can, to focus the attention of the Committee upon
the essential and well-known aspect of the problem which is before us on this
Financial Resolution.

The problem divides itself into two parts. There is the financial and there is the
social aspect. I come to the financial aspect first, because, though it is important, it is
in my opinion the less important aspect. I hope the Committee will allow me to
review, briefly, the history of the Insurance Fund. This fund, when the late Government took office in 1924, possessed an income from workpeople, employers, and the
Exchequer amounting to nearly £50,000,000 a year. It also possessed, as the Committee know well, borrowing powers up to £30,000,000. These borrowing powers had
been used to the extent of £17,000,000 in 1922, and by the time we came into office
that total had been greatly reduced and the income of the Fund was sufficient to
provide for 1,200,000 persons continuously on unemployment benefit without increasing the indebtedness, and any saving went to the reduction of the charge.

During the first 18 months of our tenure unemployment fell steadily, and in
1925 the debt had fallen to £8,000,000, and for the first time, the only time for a
great many years, the figure of unemployment had definitely fallen below the total of
1,000,000. Under these circumstances, we considered ourselves justified in reducing
the contributions of the employers and of the workpeople, as well as the contributions
from the Exchequer, and we did this under the Unemployment Act of 1925 and the
Economy Act of 1926. The effect of these two Measures was to diminish the income
from the Fund by, I have calculated, £8,000,000 a year, whereas the Chancellor, who
may well be right, very often states it at £10,000,000 a year.

We believed these reliefs to be justified by the improvement of trade and
employment, and even after these reliefs were granted the Insurance Fund was capable
of reducing the indebtedness whenever the figure of unemployment was below
1,000,000. It was then that the party opposite struck its first great blow at employment and at the Unemployment Insurance Fund. It was then these grievous
industrial problems associated with the coal trade and commencing with the General
Strike came upon us. The tax upon the Fund cannot be better described than in the
measured language of the Blanesburgh Report, of which the Minister of Labour is a
signatory, when it was stated:

With steadily improving trade, the income of the fund was increasing
and its expenditure going down. The general strike and the stoppage in the

> coal-mining industry have changed that situation. The resulting unemployment, as we have seen, increased the indebtedness of the fund from £7,100,000 in April last to over £21,000,000 in December, and there is no prospect that this heavy debt can be liquidated by the time when the new scheme should come into force.

That quotation is well known, and are we not entitled to take that as a milestone in this discussion and as a convenient starting point? What ought we to have done on the morrow of these great disasters? We had to survey the whole financial situation, and, in particular, the finance of the Insurance Fund. It was my endeavour, as far as humanly possible, to avoid imposing further disheartening taxation upon the general taxpayer or upon industry at a time when both were painfully recovering from the deep injuries from which they had suffered. I therefore did not increase the contributions of the workpeople or the employers, nor did I restore the Exchequer contribution. I considered, and I still hold the view, that a Fund with an independent income of over £50,000,000 is not compromised or imprudently administered if, during a period of wholly exceptional unemployment, its borrowing powers are used to the full statutory limit, or even to some extent beyond the original statutory limit. Broadly speaking, I have long been of the opinion that the position of this Fund would not be unsatisfactory if its borrowing powers were extended to a figure equal to, say, at least one year of its annual income.

Mr. Wallhead: Was the income of the Fund £50,000,000 after the reduction?

Mr. Churchill: No, it was reduced by £8,000,000 to £42,000,000. Broadly speaking, I have said that a Fund of this kind is not in an unsatisfactory condition if, with an income of £40,000,000 or £50,000,000 a year, it increases its borrowing powers up to the amount of its annual income. That is the view which I have always held. I could not see that any great advantage would be achieved by transferring a large portion of burden from this Fund, with its own independent income, to the National Exchequer, when the National Exchequer had a debt which was eight or nine times its annual income, whereas the Fund had only a debt of less than one year of its annual income. Moreover, I felt that the general strike and the coal stoppage had arisen solely in the industrial sphere and that it would not be desirable or even just, if it could be avoided, to penalise more than they were already penalised the great mass of the nation, including the agriculturists, the shopkeepers and the other unclassified elements in the nation, who, whatever may or may not be said upon the subject of responsibility, clearly had no responsibility for the quarrel which had caused them so much harm.

Fair play and sound finance both seemed on the side of allowing the Insurance Fund to bear its own burden, and there was no evidence to show that, over a long period of time, it would not be capable of bearing its burden. When, in 1928, the partial rationalisation, which had been enforced upon the coalfields, began and threw heavy additional unemployment upon the Fund, while the employment in other branches of industry was not unsatisfactory, but was improving, we considered that we were in the presence of another passing emergency and we, therefore, increased the borrowing powers of the Fund to £40,000,000 for one year only. I repeat that I believed that this was preferable to adding to the burdens of the taxpayers by an increased Exchequer contribution or by restoring the additional pennies to the contributions of the workpeople and the employers.

That was the situation when the Government changed. The new Ministers arrived and took up their duties. In the autumn of last year, 1929, the Chancellor of the Exchequer surveyed the whole of this policy with a very censorious eye. He declared that the Insurance Fund was running into bankruptcy and that that was entirely due to the reliefs that we had granted in the winters of 1925-26 to the employers, the workpeople and the taxpayers. He described these reliefs as being a raid upon the Fund, and used expressions which have been animadverted upon lightly and amusingly by my hon. Friend the Member for Cirencester (Mr. W. S. Morrison). He spoke as if we had robbed the Unemployment Fund of money which was the property of the unemployed. The absurdity of this statement is, of course, obvious. The Fund was not bankrupt. It was in a far better position than the National Exchequer, from every point of view. The cause of the trouble which had arisen in the Fund was not due to the legislation of 1925 and 1926, but to the subsequent great industrial disaster. Remissions of burdens to workpeople, employers and taxpayers ought never to be described by any responsible person in terms of unmeasured opprobrium.

However, the Chancellor of the Exchequer was master of the situation. He immediately invoked the highest canons of finance; he declared his determination. The income of the Fund exceeded its outgoings, not merely over a number of normal years but even at exceptional periods of stringency and depression, but he and his colleague the Minister of Labour brushed aside altogether the idea of increasing the borrowing powers of the Fund. The Chancellor of the Exchequer, with an air of extreme virtue, increased the Government's subventions to the Fund to the extent of £14,000,000 and invented the legend that he was in no way responsible for this addition to the burden of the taxpayer, and that it was solely due to paying off the debts which we, and in particular I, had incurred. When I had occasion to discuss these matters with the Chancellor of the Exchequer across the Table of the House I pointed out that he had made his own task needlessly difficult, that he would run the present Budget into deficiency by this extraordinary expenditure and that he greatly increased the menace to next year's Budget, with all its depressing reactions upon trade and employment.

The Chancellor of the Exchequer wrapped himself in his virtue and treated these arguments with scorn. They might be good enough for a Conservative Government but, for him, no increase in the borrowing powers of the Unemployment Insurance Fund could be tolerated. Why then do we see him this afternoon, less than six months later, proposing to us the very course which he condemned, and proposing to increase the borrowing powers of the Fund to £50,000,000 instead of the £30,000,000 to which they were to drop. On what grounds of logic, of principle or of reason, can the right hon. Gentleman justify the course which he now invites us to take? The income of the Fund is during the present emergency clearly insufficient to meet its outgoings. It is running into debt by nearly £1,250,000 per month or more. Unfortunately, this insolvency and bankruptcy upon which the Chancellor of the Exchequer animadverted so seriously in the autumn are present again in an aggravated form.

The strictures which might be made upon the present position are his own strictures and the strictures of his colleagues. According to his principle so frequently proclaimed, and the other arguments he has hitherto used, it is his duty to increase the Exchequer contribution until the Fund is placed in a currently solvent condition. He has decided not to do that. He has decided to borrow; and to borrow for the very purpose that six months ago he so strenuously denounced. If the Chancellor of the Exchequer was right then he is, on his own showing, wrong now; and if he is wrong now what becomes of the argument that the £14,000,000 additional taxation which has been placed upon the taxpayer was rendered inevitable by the condition of the Unemployment Insurance Fund and that he was merely repairing Conservative neglect? The legend which he has been sedulously promulgating in order to prepare for his budgetary excursions is now shown to be stripped even of the faintest foundation of fact.

But what about the Minister of Labour? The right hon. Lady used even stronger language than the Chancellor of the Exchequer. She described increasing the borrowing powers of the Fund as "dishonest." With much candour and praiseworthy courage she read out the offending quotation from her own speech in order to save other speakers the duty. Therefore I am in no need of having to repeat it for her. "Dishonest" is an unpleasant word, and it is her own word. With extraordinary naiveté she told us to-day that she still adhered to the language which she used in the quotation that she read, and still adhered to the word "dishonest"; and then she added a new expression of her own—that she had embarked upon a rake's progress, a "dishonest" course and a "rake's progress." And she gave the assurance that we were quite ready to accept upon her authority, that she embarked upon this course only with great reluctance.

I must say that I do not judge her harshly, as she judges herself. I do not think at any rate that it is dishonest to borrow up to the limits of a year's income for the maintenance of the Unemployment Insurance Fund. Certainly it seems to me that it is a financial matter about which two opinions may well exist, but into which no dishonesty enters and certainly nothing as worthy of that unpleasant word as to profess high principles in order to disparage opponents and then to desert them ignominiously the first moment that they become inconvenient. I deprecated the addition to the taxpayers' burden imposed by the Chancellor of the Exchequer last year. It is now seen that that addition was not rendered necessary by the state of the Fund; it was rendered necessary only by the desire of the Chancellor of the Exchequer to plume himself on his superior financial virtue and to thank God that he was not as other men are, which decisions and plumings and boastings have now already completely broken down. Why have they broken down? Let us see why.

That brings me to the second part of this argument. 1,600,000 unemployed—a terrible and alarming figure, a figure rightly causing distress and anxiety in all parts of the Committee, a figure which should cause a double measure of self-reproach and heart-searching in those who less than a year ago confidently asserted that they had in their possession knowledge which would enable them to cure, or at any rate to mitigate, the evil of unemployment. Now, at the end of ten months of power, during which they have not been hampered in regard to any suggestion of a constructive character that they have been able to put forward, they find that they have increased by half as much again the total—to us a matter of grave concern—of unemployment.

[*Laughter.*] Surely, it is not a matter to laugh at. I certainly feel great relief from time to time that we have not to bear the burden that is imposed upon Ministers of the Crown, but that burden is redoubled by their own action and their own promises and assertions, and by the harsh and unpitying intolerance with which they judge the loyal efforts of others.

I do not charge the Government with responsibility for the great wave of depression which has swept across the world, for the after-consequences of the bursting of the Wall Street bubble, for the strange mysterious conditions of over-production in so many primary commodities. No doubt the right hon. Gentleman if he had been sitting here, would not have hesitated to try to throw the whole blame upon us. In so doing, he would only have been carrying out his invariable practice during the four or five years in which he conducted the financial business of the Opposition. I shall not imitate that bad example. I know well that the economic forces of the modern world transcend, at the present time, the power of individuals or of individual Governments to foresee or control. I would no more throw the whole blame for the wave of depression which has come across the world, and the increase of unemployment, upon the right hon. Gentleman and his colleagues, than I would give them credit for a fall in the Bank Rate, which arises from concomitant circumstances and causes.

No, Sir, we must proceed with discrimination, and the charge which I am going to make this afternoon is very much more definite and precise. I affirm that, by a wholesale and scandalous relaxation in the conditions of unemployment benefit, the Government have demoralised the whole system of unemployment insurance, and have vitiated to a frightful and almost irreparable extent, the finance and not only the finance, but what is still more important, the character of the insurance system. What have they done? I have said what was their first great blow at employment and at unemployment insurance. Here is their second blow. On the one hand, they have raised benefits at a most inopportune moment and, on the other, they have swept away many of the most important checks and tests which safeguarded the Fund from abuse. The officials of the Employment Exchanges, the humble defenders of the public interest and of the Exchequer interest, have been deprived of their proper measure of support by Ministers and, in consequence of the Debates in this House, and the tone and temper of the dominant party in this House, they have very largely abandoned their painful task of testing applicants and holding firmly the reins of administration. Conditions have been made impossible for them, and anyone who has followed these Debates can see how impossible it is under present conditions for the ordinary official of an Employment Exchange to discharge his duties effectively, not only to the unemployed, but in the interest of the public whose guardian he is.

I would remind the Committee of the law which we have passed. Anyone who has acquired or who may acquire a 30 weeks' qualification, which would cost 17s. 6d., can, under this new Measure, when it comes into operation, draw benefit of from 18s. to 25s. or 30s. a week, according to the family, and can go on drawing that benefit indefinitely. He need never seek work again. He need never prove that he has sought work again. He cannot be asked to prove that he is genuinely seeking employment. In the never-to-be-forgotten words of the Attorney-General, he can sit and smoke his pipe until an offer of employment is actually brought to him, and although the offer may be brought to him, and although directions may be given to him by the officials of the Employment Exchange to repair to this or that place, where he will find a job, he cannot be invited to prove that he has obeyed those directions at any time, and the officials are strictly forbidden either to strike him off or to call upon him to prove that he has endeavoured to carry out the directions which they have given to him. [*Interruption.*] Above all, since the Socialist Government, with the dominating party in this House proclaiming their desire to increase the benefits and further to relax the restrictions; with Ministers who, whatever they may think or feel themselves, know that their own position requires them to shake a warning finger at any official of an Employment Exchange who is found too zealous in the administration of his duties—one of my statements was challenged, but I have now got the quotation, and it is taken from the Unemployment Insurance (No. 2) Bill Financial Memorandum:

> It should be noted that when directions have been given, no dis-qualification can follow unless it is proved that the directions have not been carried out. The claimant cannot be required to prove that he has carried them out.

Hon. Members: Hear, hear!

Mr. Churchill: There is nothing like being agreed upon the facts. Such agreement is a preliminary step to a clarification of the whole problem. The onus is thrown on the officials to prove a negative, and in the face of the mood and temper which sit upon those benches, of course the officials are throwing up the sponge generally. [*Interruption.*]

Miss Bondfield: I cannot allow that statement to pass unchallenged. I must defend the officials from a statement of that kind. It is absolutely untrue.

Hon. Members: Withdraw!

Mr. Churchill: I should never think of withdrawing such a statement. I have said what I believe to be true, and I remain utterly unmoved by the contradiction which I have received. [*Interruption.*] I have a further observation to make, and I am anxious to give the Chancellor of the Exchequer the very brief time which he asked, and which I shall certainly leave to him, but I hope I shall not be interrupted because what I say may not be popular on the benches opposite. If I am interrupted, I shall have to take longer. The Government may say, and probably will say, "This new Act has only just begun to operate, and, therefore, how can it have affected the figures?" It is exactly the Act which would cast its shadow before. The moment the officials of the Employment Exchanges saw the kind of memoranda which the Ministry were issuing and the terms under which they would be governed, naturally they endeavoured to conform to what they believed was the wish and spirit of the authorities under whom they served.

The Minister of Labour showed herself extremely anxious this morning to prove how limited was the effect of the "not genuinely seeking work" condition. She spoke of the two months list, and the dead list, and the queue list, and so forth. The matter is not limited at all to these precise figures. The injury done to the economy and efficiency of the Fund is not to be described in any of these references to particular lists. It is the whole spirit of administration which has been undermined. Hon. Members are angry with me and with my hon. Friend here who said something about reflecting upon the bona fides of the unemployed. While I claim full liberty of debate, I am not anxious to use unnecessarily wounding language. I will use only the language that was used by the Minister of Labour herself in her own official publication. This is what the Minister of Labour became responsible for in the Memorandum to the Unemployment Insurance (No. 2) Bill on the morrow when she was smarting after having her judgment overruled by her own followers, and her hand and that of the Attorney-General forced by the Benches behind her. In their anger, the following remarkable statement was issued with the full official authority of the Minister. The publication of the document is on the responsible authority of the Minister.

Miss Bondfield: Whatever the feelings of the Minister may be, they have not been communicated to the actuary.

Mr. Churchill: But so sweeping and so merciless a condemnation applied to those who had forced this surrender upon the Minister is attributable—I consider reasonably attributable—to a rise of temperature, which had the advantage of securing for us a most valuable insight into the true facts of this matter, which otherwise we might never have obtained. This is what this Memorandum says. After stating that it seemed reasonable that the further number becoming eligible for benefit might be from 80,000 to 90,000, and the annual cost of that would be from £4,000,000 to £4,500,000, it goes on to say:

> Any such estimate must, however, be given with all reserve. These figures relate to insured persons whose unemployment books are lodged at the employment exchanges. The possibility should, however, not be overlooked that the new provision may have the effect of bringing certain other persons into benefit, for example, married women who have done little or no work since marriage, and seasonal workers during the "off-season." These two classes of cases will serve as illustrations of what in the aggregate may amount to a considerable group of new claimants consisting of persons who, so to speak, are not really in the market as competitors for employment, but may hold themselves out as such if they are thereby enabled to qualify for benefit.

An avalanche of new claims is pouring in. The numbers mount continually; the expenses rise by leaps and bounds; heavy further increases, the Minister knows too well, are in prospect, and those increases do not correspond to any proportionate increase in the severity of the depression or the increase of distress. They are coming upon us simply owing to the relaxation of official safeguards which the Government wish to insist upon, but in regard to which they are forcibly overawed. It is only the beginning. The Government have now advertised far and wide for claims for increased uncovenanted doles—for an uncovenanted benefit is a dole of indefinite duration. They have opened the door, no doubt, to much genuine distress, but distress which, I hold, belongs properly to a reformed Poor Law. They have also opened the door to an almost limitless exploitation of the unemployment benefit, and I am justified in saying that by the words I have quoted to the Committee.

The eyes of the country are rivetted morbidly upon these figures week after week, and the whole character and record of the Government is being discredited by them. Against their better judgment they have thrown down safeguards, and consequently they have let loose upon themselves a monstrous embarrassment, which will follow them and harry them at every step, however long their pilgrimage may be. Even worse than the financial damage, is the injury to the unemployment insurance system itself. Other Governments have not been blameless. I admit fully that all the anomalies and iniquities of the present insurance system are not to be charged to the Ministers opposite, but it was hoped that a Labour Government, based as it was upon the founts of the trade union experience which was it its disposal, would have shown itself capable of recasting this problem of unemployment insurance in a statesmanlike manner, removing insurance from the atmsophere of public assistance and placing the Fund upon a sound basis. Instead they have hopelessly confounded the scientific thrift which has been organised among our people against ordinary indigence and misfortune. They have aggravated every anomaly.

Well is it known how some trades pay three or four times as much as they draw, and how others draw three or four times as much as they pay. A man who pays his contributions continuously gets no more benefit in the hour of need than the one who has paid only 17s. 6d. for the 30 weeks. This is not because of accidents between individuals at different times, but it characterises whole classes over long periods. Well do we know how the systematic decasualisation of labour has been practically arrested in many industries owing to the attitude of employers. All these anomalies existed, and they are not to be burdened upon the Government, but they, by their final Act, have aggravated every anomaly, and have justified in the cruellest manner the prejudice and world-wide contempt which has been expressed for the dole.

They have stripped our incomparable insurance system of every vestige of dignity or equity and have converted it into a vast dole-spreading agency. This disaster to the social institutions of the people far outweighs even the financial misfortune which it has entailed. In a few days the Chancellor of the Exchequer will be laying his heavy and not unwilling hands on the taxpayers of the country. He will demand further sacrifices from millions of hard-working men and women, upon whose ceaseless enterprise and effort the progress and wealth of every modern State depends, and without whose loyalty the immense revenues of the State could not be collected. They will know that a substantial and a traceable part of the new exactions to be demanded of them is due to the melancholy demoralisation of unemployment insurance, and the quartering upon them of an ever larger number of persons who need not even show that they are genuinely seeking work.

UNEMPLOYMENT INSURANCE (NO. 3) BILL

April 4, 1930

House of Commons

I beg to move, "That the Debate be now adjourned."

Are we to have no explanation from the Minister in charge of this important Bill, imposing fresh charges upon the Insurance Fund? In order to put myself in order, and to reserve my right to speak later on, I move the adjournment of the Debate as a protest at the fact that no Ministerial speech of any kind has been given in moving the Second Reading of this Bill. We had a Debate on the Financial Resolution on Friday last, and the Minister of Labour then made a statement at the beginning of the debate, but during the whole of that discussion a great many criticisms and questions were raised and serious charges were made against the policy of the Government. We all expected that the Chancellor of the Exchequer would make a full and reasoned reply, dealing not only with the purely financial aspect, with which he was himself concerned, but dealing also with the specific and important questions in regard to unemployment insurance which had been raised, but the Chancellor of the Exchequer, although through the usual channels he was asked how long he required for a reply, said casually that five minutes would be sufficient; and certainly, judged by the adequacy of his answer to the questions raised, five minutes were more than sufficient.

Now we have had no answer as a result of all the experience and criticism of the last few days, and nothing has been said by the Minister on unemployment except the speech which she delivered when the Financial Resolution was moved; and apparently we are to be left all through the course of to-day while the Minister for Labour sits waiting to have a last word. Is that really the way in which to treat the House? I must say that I do not think the present Government will facilitate the course of business by not trying to take an intelligent and respectful part in Debates in this House. To sit silent, hour after hour, waiting for a Division, relying upon a Division to settle the matter, is not the way to deal with these subjects. This question of unemployment is one on which one would expect the greatest amount of leading and guidance from the Labour party, and that they should, as it were, boycott the Debate and offer no explanation or excuse for the situation to the House is a fact meriting, I am certain, severe Parliamentary censure. As a protest against this treatment of this important subject, I ask leave to move "That the Debate be now adjourned."

[Much later] I did not expect to take part again so soon in a Debate on unemployment, but, in view of the fact that practically no attempt has been made by His Majesty's Government and their representatives to answer any of the objections which were propounded by myself and other speakers, I feel it my duty not to allow the Second Reading of this Bill to pass without making another attempt to elicit some further and better justification of their actions and if possible to spur them into extra and increased mental energy. I cannot, I fear, respond to the request of the Lord Privy Seal that we should treat this matter in an entirely detached spirit; that we should treat it as a non-political, or certainly a non-party, question; that we should throw our minds into the common stock and endeavour to make as smooth as possible the path of those who are now responsible for dealing with the problem. It is a very natural appeal for the Lord Privy Seal to make, but we should be either more or less than human if we were unreservedly to assent to it. Our position is that we have been grievously injured, maligned, misjudged, misrepresented, maltreated, driven from the control of events, deprived of the confidence of the Crown, and forced to dwell in the cold shades of Opposition, and that all this has arisen because of the almost unprece-dented—even for electioneering times—outbursts and outpourings of misrepresentation and vilification by which the party opposite deluded the electors and attained, not indeed a majority, but a sufficient representation to enable them to assume the reins of office. How can we forget what they said? The Prime Minister spoke of this question of unemployment as being the acid test by which the Labour party would be judged. In the celebrated Labour appeal to the nation we read:

> The Labour party gives an unqualified pledge to deal immediately and practically with this question. Our schemes have been before the country for years.

After 10 months of office, 1,630,000 are out of employment. The Prime Minister, at Middlesbrough, said:

> Nobody will reduce unemployment to the normal quicker than the Labour party.

So far the progress of "reducing it to the normal" has been to increase it by 500,000 over and above what it was at the time when the Government so easily and hungrily assumed the reins of office. The Chancellor of the Exchequer in the "Daily Herald" said:

> In our first Session we shall deal with unemployment, and we shall bring relief and hope to the workers of the land. We shall not disappoint those who have shown a belief in us.

The Foreign Secretary said:

> Labour's carefully considered plans of social reconstruction and in-dustrial reorganisation and development have undoubtedly caught the imagination of the people.

They may have caught their imagination, which they were well fitted to do, since they existed only in the imagination of their authors. Then there was the First Com-missioner of Works who said:

> These poor people, who pin their faith to our leaders, our programme and our party, will expect us to deal immediately with unemployment.

The moment the right hon. Gentleman gets into office, he becomes merely one of the ordinary suave occupants of the Front Bench, throws aside all his high social and philanthropic enthusiasms, and subsides into the position of a staid, and I would almost say a dignified, official. The Lord Privy Seal said:

> The Conservative Government has no remedy for unemployment except safeguarding and de-rating. Labour, however, is going to solve it by spending money.

Incidentally, I do not know whether that quotation might not be of some use to the First Commissioner of Works and the Chancellor of the Duchy. I make them a present of it. If it is of any use they are welcome to it. It might offer the First Commissioner an opportunity of doing something to carry out the pledges and declarations which he has so freely made. I have given these quotations only to show the expectations which were raised, the promises which were made and the undertakings which were given by the Labour party at the time when they were seeking the votes of the electors. I say that they have been the profiteers of unfairness. But there is a nemesis awaiting them. [*Interruption.*] We have all heard of Time's revenges. I have rarely seen one so swift or so cruel as that which has fallen upon the electioneers who sit opposite, when after 10 months, during which they have had every facility, during which they have been denied no single proposal which they have made, the state of unemployment is worse than ever before. I can only recapitulate the attacks which we have made from these benches, the justified censures which we apply to the Government as a whole and in particular to the Minister specially charged with dealing with this matter. We say that they have failed completely with all remedial or constructive schemes. They have produced no remedial or constructive scheme which they did not find in the pigeon-holes of the late Government or of the Coalition Government of seven years ago.

Mr. Duncan: Unused.

Mr. Churchill: On the contrary, the Government have only applied again schemes which had already been used by their predecessors, and used to the point where they had ceased to have any further efficacy. They have aggravated the distress, much of which was inevitable, I admit, owing to the world war, and the depression in trade; they have aggravated it by undermining the confidence of business and industry and by the state of uncertainty in which they have left important branches of industry. We say that they have swollen needlessly and wantonly the totals of unemployment by a general relaxation of the conditions enabling persons to obtain benefits, which relaxation they have made openly and patently against their better judgment and in deference to pressure from their back benchers.

Mr. Sorensen: Send them into the Army.

Mr. Churchill: We are not talking about conscientious objectors now. I have waited to hear an answer to some of these statements. I gather that they are objectionable to the party opposite. Why then have we to sit through two whole days' Debate and never receive any marshalling of facts or of arguments in answer to these charges? Why is it necessary that the charges should be repeated on a second occasion? Why, Sir, the Minister of Labour in her speech this morning did not even refer to what the Chancellor of the Exchequer stigmatised as my "disgraceful attack" on the officials of the Employment Exchanges? When I was speaking a week ago, she jumped up and said that she did not agree with what I said, and I have been waiting to receive, not a flat contradiction, but a statement of arguments and facts, and I certainly expected to hear this morning a very full and ample statement showing that there had been no relaxation of the conditions under which persons are allowed to receive benefit.

In any case, I pay little attention to charges of making attacks upon officials when those charges are preferred by the party opposite who, on this very subject, never hesitated to attack the officials of the Employment Exchanges and to charge those officials with the meanest forms of persecution. I heard the Home Secretary himself using that word, and, in so far as what I said constituted the slightest criticism of the officials, it has not been to suggest that they have been guilty of persecution; it is to suggest that under the pressure of the new Administration, and of the currents of Socialist opinion, they have lost heart in discharging the extremely painful task of, in many cases, disallowing benefit. They have, as I said, thrown up the sponge, but to say that, is not an attack upon the officials; it is an attack upon the Government whom it is the duty of the officials to serve, and whom, I think, they do serve most loyally. But when they know that there is a Government in power which has got into office by making all sorts of promises to the unemployed, and which is endeavouring to pay its way in office by gradually increasing the funds available for the unemployed; when they know that there is a Government in office which takes as the cardinal maxim of its policy, "The greatest doles for the greatest number"; when they are given a practically impossible task to discharge such as that of finding all these jobs and notifying them to the individuals; when in the case of the individual who has not followed their directions the onus of proof is cast upon them, and when, in addition to all that, this unwholesome and vehement atmosphere of spending money has been created—can one wonder in these circumstances that they have, as I said last week and as I repeat, lost heart and thrown up the sponge in many cases? Can one wonder that there is a general relaxation of those regulations and that administration whose strict enforcement is of vital interest not only to the general taxpayers, but also to the contributors to the Unemployment Insurance Fund who, in the main, are weekly wage earners?

I say that we must request the Government to address themselves fully to the allegations which it is our duty to make against them and against their treatment of this problem, but I wish for a few moments—and I do not intend to stand very long between the House and the Minister—to leave what is necessarily and rightly a controversial atmosphere, and to look at some of the really grave aspects of the present unemployment situation. I have some experience of this subject because nearly 20 years ago it was my duty to unfold to the House of Commons the first scheme of compulsory unemployment insurance which had ever been proposed in any country in the world and at the same time it was my duty to outline and subsequently to bring into existence the whole network of Employment Exchanges which are now an inseparable part of the social organisation of the masses of the people.

Very different were the character and the uses of those systems of insurance and of employment exchanges, in those days, from what they have now become. Insurance was based upon a strictly actuarial foundation; benefits were related to contributions, and the trades selected for special treatment were those which were specially subject to seasonal or cyclical fluctuations. Ample provision was made for the accumulation of large reserves. Each trade was to a certain extent studied separately and none was allowed to make an unlimited draft upon the others, while, as for the employment exchanges themselves, they were intended to give to labour, to the working men or women who have nothing to sell but their labour—and that is the condition of the vast majority of the human race—a market for their labour which should be as wide as the nation and as punctual and as accurate as the London Stock Exchange.

It seems an extraordinary thing that whereas there is a market price varying to the extent of one-eighth or one-sixteenth, or one-thirty-second in all other commodities, labour, the only commodity which the vast mass of the human race have to sell, should always be subject to the accidents of local markets, and should not have a great central organisation of exchange. But we have strayed very far from that consideration. The employment exchanges were primarily designed to find employment, but they have been so overlain with other business, that that part of their work has fallen, I will not say into increasing desuetude, but has increasingly fallen into the background. All Governments since the war have been responsible for these changes and for the degeneration which has introduced itself into the unemployment insurance system and into the working of the employment exchanges, and certainly I, who have been in so many of these Governments, cannot detach myself from that responsibility. The storms that have blown—the greatest that have ever been—have driven us and our pre-War social schemes very far from the courses which we originally planned, but it has been reserved for a Labour Government, which, as I said before, has at its disposal not only the experience but the good will of the powerful trade union world, to strike a heavier blow at unemployment insurance than has ever been struck under the difficult pressures of the past by any of the preceding administrations.

Let me touch upon some of the evil reactions which are to be noted in the workings of the unemployment insurance scheme. First of all, there is the injustice to the permanently or generally prosperous trades—the usually prosperous trades. An extraordinary disparity between contributions and benefit has grown up, and is increasing every day and with every step that the Government take or ask us to take. I will just read to the House a few sentences written upon this subject by Sir William Beveridge, whose authority is almost unquestioned, and who was associated with me 20 years ago in the framing of the original scheme. He says:

> Some industries have ten times as great a risk of unemployment as others; some are now paying in three or four times as much as they draw out, while others are drawing out three or four times as much as they pay in; dock and wharf service for every £11 it contributes towards the cost of its unemployment gets £31 from the direct contributions of other industries, besides £17 from the taxpayer; eight other industries with eight times as many insured persons as docks and wharfs, and paying ten times the contributions are drawing in benefit only the same total.

Are those figures not very impressive? Do they not show the strain which is being placed upon the entire cohesion of this Fund and upon the foundations of this system? Of course, I admit that a certain amount of give-and-take between the different industries was contemplated. The whole idea was that there should be a joining of hands, a linking up together, and within limits you can tolerate these anomalies, but when you reach a certain point, when you aggravate them to the point where these figures begin to emerge, I say that you begin to shake the entire structure upon which unemployment insurance is founded; and if the facts and figures were realised more clearly in these trades, you might very easily be confronted with the strongest possible complaints against a system which is very little better in some cases than the steady transference of money from the pockets of one set of employers and workpeople to another.

Then let us look at the injustice to the regular workmen under this system of insurance, half of whom have actually paid for every penny they receive—at least, that was the case a short time ago—but who are no better treated than those who have paid virtually nothing to it. [An Hon. Member: "Why should they be?"] That is the question that I am raising. Take another case. It does seem to me that men who have been insured for eight or nine years in this Fund, and who have never been thrown upon it at all, never come once upon it, have a right to ask whether this is in fact the best system of raising the money to provide for all the other persons who are unemployed; and it seems to me a very wrong thing that a man who has paid for every penny, who for years and years has had a large balance owing to him individually, if he is thrown out of work temporarily, after a very long period of steady employment should be placed in the same category as persons who have shown themselves utterly incapable of finding the means of earning a livelihood. [An Hon. Member: "Would the right hon. Gentleman argue then that he should die to get his insurance money?"] That has nothing to do with the question.

I am pointing out that whereas these anomalies necessarily exist in a system of insurance, they have now become most serious and grave in our present system of insurance, and I am arguing that they have been made far more grave and brought forward in a much more wounding and direct manner by the changes which have been made during the present Parliament on the authority of Ministers opposite. Take the effect of unemployment insurance at the present time upon casual labour. When these schemes were originally introduced they were only a part of the treatment of the unemployment problem which was then proposed. One of the essential features following on the recommendations of the Royal Commission of 20 years ago was to enforce through the agency of these schemes a rigorous decasualisation of certain trades. A particular trade keeping large waiting lists of persons habitually under-employed was one of the most unpleasant features of those days, and every effort should have been made to purge it, to remove it.

There, again, I am not making this charge against the party opposite at all. I say that the Unemployment Insurance Scheme, in the condition into which it has now got, partly through our Administration, but in the final stage through the contribution of the present Government to the problem, not only does nothing to clear away this casualisation of labour, but is actually fostering it and maintaining it on a very large scale. Whether it be at the docks or in the textile trades, an immense amount of casual labour is being developed and supported by a use of the Insurance Scheme, which was not only never intended for it, but was intended to be an absolute antidote against it.

Lastly, Employment Exchanges have been almost completely diverted from their prime task of finding jobs, and have been burdened and oppressed with the immense labour of administering and distributing Unemployment Insurance benefits. I am going to quote once more from what Sir William Beveridge said about this subject:

> The insurance scheme of 1911, giving in exchange for contributions a strictly limited allowance to tide men over passing depression under a contract which, though compulsory, was to be something like a fair bargain for each man and each industry, has been replaced by a general system of outdoor relief to the able-bodied, administered by labour exchanges and financed mainly by a tax on employment.

That is a very searching phrase—"a tax on employment." I admit to the Minister of Labour and to the Government that this aspect of the problem is mitigated in proportion as further moneys from the Exchequer are placed at the disposal of the Fund. I admit that, but the fact remains that this phrase, "a tax on employment," is well founded, and it seems to me that now that matters have been pushed to the point that they have, and the evils have been aggravated to their present level, we cannot let the matter rest. It might well be that an increase of indirect taxation borne by the whole of the consumers would be preferable to raising the millions for the maintenance of the Insurance Fund directly by a tax upon the regularly employed workmen in the prosperous industries.

    Mr. R. A. Taylor: Now the right hon. Gentleman is quoting Lord Beaverbrook!

    Mr. Churchill: I am not quoting anybody at all.

    Mr. Thomas: Does the right hon. Gentleman make that as a suggestion? It is a very important point. In substance, he says, "let the State take the responsibility for these people outside insurance." Does the right hon. Gentleman make that as a definite suggestion?

    Mr. Churchill: I say that now that you have so strained and shaken the foundations of the whole system of unemployment insurance, and quartered so many persons upon it who are not actuarial contributors, the question of how the burden should be borne must be one of the matters which should be reviewed. Let me also examine—and here I dare say I shall be more in agreement with the Lord Privy Seal than on many other points—the injury which is done to the reputation and the prestige of our country abroad through the manner in which the unduly swollen totals of unemployment are presented to the public. Into those weekly totals go all the millions who have paid for every penny of what they receive, and never ought to be mixed up in what is regarded, to all intents and purposes, as a budget of distress. Into them go over a quarter of a million women who, for the greater part, are living in man-supported homes, and who are a special problem. Into them go hundreds of thousands of persons, as I believe, by the system, in collusion with the employers, of working short time to qualify for benefit, thus really obtaining a subvention in aid of wages. Into them go all the flood of new claims which, it is admitted by the Government, have been added by their recent legislation. Into them go all those who, as the Lord Privy Seal has told us only to-day, happen to be out of work at 9 o'clock on Monday morning but find work during that same day, it may be an hour or two afterwards. Into them go a certain proportion of persons who take advantage of this scheme, who have carefully managed to get themselves qualified; persons who are not in distress, persons who have other means of livelihood, or whose homes have other means of support, but who have found, nevertheless, that under present circumstances they can obtain a qualification. Lastly there go into the totals that remainder of real distress due to cruel misfortune, or due, in some cases, to incapacity or weakness.

All this is rolled together, jumbled together in one confused total, and then used to bellow "Stinking Fish" round the world, to our detriment week after week. I listened to what the Lord Privy Seal said on the subject, and as to the change in the publication of these figures. In view of the base use which was made of the unemployment figures in the last election, it would be impossible for us to deprive ourselves, or the country, of a comparable basis for judging as between the present administration and the last; but the Government have the remedy in their own hands, and I strongly advise them to take it. Let them publish the true figures—the comparable figures may be published as long as they are required, and in political controversy they will be available, but they will fade out as time passes. Let the Minister and the Lord Privy Seal use their experts to draw up figures which represent the actual amount of uninsured distress per week, the true amount, and let them publish those figures, and that will show the extent of the evil from which we are suffering.

God knows it is heavy enough without being exaggerated and swollen by the addition of a lot of altogether irrelevant matters. What are these figures designed to show? I offer this suggestion. They should show the numbers of heads of families or home-breadwinners of either sex who have not been provided for by self-supporting insurance, and who require public assistance. That would be a return which could be made for the appropriate periods and would undoubtedly give a true index of what is happening. You can leave the working of the normal insurance system to other agencies.

I have not attempted to deal with any of the remedies which have been touched upon in the very able speech made by the hon. Member for Shrewsbury (Mr. Duckworth), and others who have spoken. There are tendencies which you can encourage that are beneficial and there are tendencies which you must discourage because they are disastrous. But our difficulty is that we do not know, and we have not found, the underlying principles which would enable us to group together all these tendencies and pursue them in a co-ordinated way. Sometimes, we find that we are pursuing at the same time tendencies which we think will be beneficial, some of which are beneficial, while others are actually harmful. We have not found the underlying explanation, and the world is still at a loss to know how to bridge the mysterious gap between the producing and consuming power. It is a grave question upon which experiment has to be made, and it is one on which the finest intellect of the human race could well be concentrated.

It is strange indeed that production, which involves so much effort and skill, should virtually be unlimited, and consumption, which rests upon the boundless desires and appetites of human beings, should lag behind it. Many experiments have been made, and many of them have proved disastrous. All the latest experiments have

4750 Speeches of Winston Churchill

resulted in disaster. I do not attempt to solve the riddle, but I am bound to say that I do not believe that the key to increasing the consuming power will ever be found apart from a proportionate increase in the economic earning powers of the individual. Certainly, I give full credit to the Lord Privy Seal, under all the pressure to which he has been subjected, with all the harassing troubles through which he has passed, with all the criticism which may be justly levelled against him, and I give him full credit for the way in which he has fearlessly held to the principle that the increase in the earning capacity, and the productivity of labour through rationalisation, must be the life-line of which this country should never let go.

I do not intend to discuss these larger matters, because what we have to discuss this afternoon is quite enough to occupy us. It is a large subject, but it is far more limited. We have the problem of unemployment insurance, and the working of that system before us, and here there is a host of grim and urgent questions which are not insoluble, not unmanageable, but which are crying out for new and lucid treatment, and it is to these problems that this Bill, this costly and woolly palliative, fails to make even the feeblest contribution.

THE BUDGET

April 15, 1930

House of Commons

It would obviously be impossible for any speaker to deal, even cursorily, with the far-reaching proposals and with all the aspects of the Budget which was opened to us yesterday by the Chancellor of the Exchequer, and I only propose this afternoon, in the brief demand that I shall make on the time of the Committee, to endeavour to place before the Committee the broad outlines of the main differences which, as I conceive them, exist between the Government and the Opposition. I acknowledge that the Chancellor of the Exchequer, in his speech yesterday, avoided the whole appearance of recrimination, and conveyed any reflection that he had to make upon his predecessor under the guise of impersonal form. I welcome and applaud this step towards a better line of conduct, and I also note in it that prudence which, from the very beginning of the lengthy discussions which will ensue upon finance, has realised that some caution and good temper should be shown in dealing with opponents. Nevertheless, I feel bound to attempt to disentangle our respective responsibilities for the present state of affairs, and also to contrast the different, and even opposite, policies for which the right hon. Gentleman and I stand respectively.

There are two views which can be taken about taxation. There is the view of the right hon. Gentleman, put forward on many occasions, but most forcefully in his publication "Wealth and Commonwealth." According to the Chancellor of the Exchequer, the wealth appropriated by the idle rich is a deduction from the just share which should go to the remuneration of industry in all its forms; national revenue can be used to secure a juster distribution of the national wealth; taxation can divert the national income into more useful channels; the expenditure of national taxation can be used to stimulate trade and industry; and, lastly, taxation, instead of discouraging individual effort, tends to stimulate it.

That view, whether you think it right or whether you think it wrong, is a clear and intelligible view. If you adopt it, you would naturally seek occasions, and even pretexts, for imposing heavy taxation upon the public. If you were to argue for a largely increased Sinking Fund and for lavish expenditure upon social services, you would do this on the grounds, first, of repairing social injustices, and, secondly, of diverting the money from those whom the right hon. Gentleman calls the idle rich into far more useful channels. But there is another view which has equally been stated by the Chancellor of the Exchequer for the purpose of expressing his entire opposition to it. This is the other view, which I quote again, practically in his own words:

> That national taxation is a regrettable necessity, that it is a burden upon industry, that it discourages enterprise, that Governments best study the interests of the whole nation and of all classes by allowing money, to quote the famous Treasury phrase, to fructify in the pockets of the people.

This is the opposite view from that which the Chancellor of the Exchequer holds. Practically every word is taken from his statement in "Wealth and Commonwealth"— not the phrase about fructifying in the pockets of the people. [*Interruption.*] Fancy being ashamed of that phrase! As I say, both points of view have been stated fairly. I take the second view, which has received a great reinforcement in the present situation of this country, actual and relative. We are the heaviest taxed nation in the world. We are incomparably the most heavily, directly-taxed nation. Our three great competitors, the United States, Germany, and France, are reducing by scores of millions a year their demands upon the direct taxpayer, with the avowed object of increasing their world-financial and world-competitive power. These countries take the view that direct and indirect taxation, particularly direct, are a clog upon trade and a damper upon enterprise, and, if the nation wishes to realise for its own people the immense possibilities of modern scientific production, every possible encouragement should be given to the accumulation of wealth in private hands and the fruitful use of that wealth by active individual effort.

I belong to the school that holds that taxation has reached a point where it has become a grievous impediment in the production of new wealth. High as I rank the Sinking Fund and the Social Services, I am convinced that, under the present circumstances, the emphasis and the main intention of any Chancellor of the Exchequer should be in the direction of an alleviation of the public burden. Therefore, it was my continuous endeavour to reduce taxation, and especially onerous taxation, and even to lean in the direction of reducing taxation in preference, if need be, to austere and drastic repayment of the National Debt.

I hold that we require far less of the State and less of the taxgatherer, not more, in our national affairs, and that those affairs will come round much quicker in so far as

we allow a measure of free play to the saving and creative effort of the commonwealth. Therefore, when I was confronted with the disaster and outrage of the General
Strike— [*Interruption*]. All the laughter of the Socialist party will not efface those
facts from their record. None of their weariness to hear them repeated will prevent me
from bringing them forward from time to time. Therefore, when I was confronted with
these events, with their endless, evil repercussions on trade and finance, I sought to
the best of my ability to spare the taxpayer and to nurse industry through the difficult
and harassing period that followed. That is the whole explanation of the policy for
which I was responsible during the last four years, and it is the only explanation which
I think it necessary to offer for the half suppressed sneers and criticisms and
disparagements which the right hon. Gentleman passed on my financial record. [An
Hon. Member: "You deserved it."] That is begging the question. [*Interruption.*] I do
not in the least mind being interrupted. I am glad to know that permission has been
given.

The results of the general election placed the party opposite in power, and
various political developments since that date seem to have entrenched them there.
The right hon. Gentleman has largely increased expenditure. Apart from the de-rating
relief, for which the money is this year provided, he has added, as I make it,
£26,000,000 to our national load, and he now asks us to impose new taxation upon
wealth of £46,500,000, of which about £34,000,000 arises in this current year. In
fact, we are asked to return to the full severities of war-time taxation, and to do this at
the same time that our rivals in other parts of the world are universally reducing their
already reduced taxation.

I will deal later on with the effects of this taxation, but the first point I submit
to the Committee is upon the question of whether it is necessary to have new taxation
this year at all. I declare that it is not necessary and that it would not be necessary
unless the Government had changed. That is my first main submission. I hold that no
new taxes this year would have been needed. Let us look into that. First of all, there is
the deficit on last year's Budget—a deficit of £14,500,000. £9,000,000 of that was
traceable to the decisions of the present Government as to new expenditure passed
through the House during the winter. Therefore, the deficit did not exceed
£5,500,000. Considering Wall Street, considering the Hatry scandals, considering the
inevitable want of confidence attendant upon the arrival of a Socialist Government, as
well as the general depression throughout the world, that £5,500,000 deficit, the bulk
of it accounted for by the failure of stamps, is not a bad result in all the circumstances.
Of course, it must always be remembered that the present Chancellor had no interest
in presenting a deficit on the finance of last year; in fact, his threat to the sugar trade
alone cost the revenue £1,000,000, and I certainly notice that, in the first week of the
new financial year, the balance of revenue and expenditure was £4,000,000 more
favourable than in the corresponding first week of the year that has closed. At any
rate, I say that nothing in the realised deficit of 1929-30 affords any justification for
an increase of taxation.

Apart from the deficit, is there anything in the forecast of 1930 which the right
hon. Gentleman laid before us yesterday that justifies new taxation? The right hon.
Gentleman's estimate of revenue on the existing basis shows an advance of £5,500,000

above the yield of 1929, and I believe that is, as he said, a conservative estimate. I had arrived, without the advantages which he now enjoys, at almost exactly the same conclusion myself, that it would be a fair basis to work upon to take the yield of last year and to add £4,000,000 or £5,000,000 to the normal increase. De-rating is fully provided for this year and £4,000,000 is left over for next year. There is nothing whatever in this forecast which would have justified an increase in taxation if the Government had not changed.

I come to the Debt. I say there is nothing in the position which justifies a fresh burden. I rather anticipated that the right hon. Gentleman would have attacked the whole principle of the Fixed Debt charge, but apparently, on learning the facts about it, and studying it at close quarters, with the fullest possible information, he accepted and adopted virtually intact all my arrangements for dealing with the National Debt. The Fixed Debt charge of £305,000,000 a year will, as he reminded us yesterday, on a 4 per cent. basis extinguish the Debt in 50 years if it is maintained. That is a prodigious effort. It is foolish and vain even to under-rate the magnitude of that effort of Debt repayment. There is no country in the world where the institution of this scheme was not received with wonder and admiration. You cannot judge the working of the Fixed Debt charge upon the fortunes of a single year. It is premature altogether to judge, still less to condemn, such a system, because the second year or the first two years of its operation are poor compared with what was expected. But look at the current year, with which we have now to deal. The yield of the Fixed Debt charge for Sinking Fund and Savings Certificates in 1930 which was forecasted by me two years ago was £69,000,000 on a 4 per cent. basis. The right hon. Gentleman is budgeting for a far lower rate than 4 per cent. for his Floating Debt. He did not tell us what the rate was. Is there any objection to telling the Committee?

The Chancellor of the Exchequer (Mr. Philip Snowden): It is easy to calculate. Calculate it yourself.

Mr. Churchill: I find it difficult. The right hon. Gentleman did not state it in his speech, and I imagine that there is no secret about it, and perhaps he will have the courtesy at some time or other to inform the Committee upon it. At any rate, I have always been told that a rough calculation of one per cent. fall in the money rate is a saving on our present volume of Floating Debt of something like £6,000,000 a year. But the right hon. Gentleman has said that he is budgeting for £11,500,000 reduction in the cost of the Floating Debt. Therefore, it seems to me, not knowing the exact rate on which these estimates are based, that between £75,000,000 and £80,000,000 will be available in the present year for the service of the Savings Certificates and the Sinking Fund, £23,000,000 of which, he told us, would be devoted to the Savings Certificates. I do not suppose that there is any difference between us on the figures. The sum of £75,000,000 or £80,000,000 is an immense one to be devoted to the service of Debt and Savings Certificates.

When the right hon. Gentleman was last Chancellor of the Exchequer five years ago, the comparable figure devoted to these two purposes was £57,000,000. They are strictly comparable figures. They were calculated for me when I was at the Treasury and announced to the House two years ago. So that in far worse times, and when we are far weaker, we are making a contribution at the present time to the service of Debt and Savings Certificates, which are inextricably interwoven with the results of the Sinking Fund, which is nearly £20,000,000 greater than that which was thought necessary by the right hon. Gentleman five years ago before the great industrial troubles had brought such misfortune upon our affairs. I say that next year an even larger repayment will be effected. The forecasted figure rises to £72,000,000 for next year, and, if the cheap money rates continue, there is no reason why the repayment of Debt and Savings Certificates should not exceed £80,000,000. I am not complaining; I am rejoicing in this, but I say why is it necessary to do more? In my judgment, it is not necessary to do more.

The right hon. Gentleman has taken two steps which he announced to us yesterday. The first is the Clause which we now see on the Paper making it statutory to repay deficits occurring in any year in the finance of the next year. That, of course, is very harmless and very well-meaning. No one can object to it. It is purely illusory. Nobody knows better than the right hon. Gentleman that nothing can abrogate the sovereign power of Parliament, and the Finance Bill of every year is its statutory authority for everything that is done, and for the repeal of every other Statute. There is nothing in that. It is, no doubt, a pious sentiment which may just as well find a permanent resting place upon the Statute Book.

The second step which the right hon. Gentleman proposes to take is to make good the deficit of last year, mainly because it is not additional expenditure, by payments of £5,000,000 this year, £5,000,000 next year, and £4,500,000 the year after. It is an excellent proposal if you can afford it. If the circumstances are so favourable, if you can get the money without doing more harm than good in the process, it is an excellent proposal. But it is a question to be carefully weighed, whether in all the circumstances the right hon. Gentleman would really add to the public wealth and economy by this addition to the burdens which he had already to bear and some of which were of his own creation. Anyhow, I repeat my second conclusion, that, just as there was nothing in the finances of last year—the return of last year or the forecast for this year—to justify taxing us, there is absolutely nothing in the Debt position to justify it. I will come to the reason which leads us into this present unhappy situation in a moment.

Is there any justification for an increase of taxation on account of the outlook for 1931? Still I ask, need we now take measures for 1931? Our finance is annual finance. That is the principle on which everything is based. I think that whether you should take measures for 1931 now or not should entirely depend upon the public convenience and upon your general view of what is most required of the national resources for national interests. I will answer the tacit complaint that £15,000,000 of de-rating relief will come to the Exchequer for payment in 1931 against which there will only be £4,000,000 left in the Suspensory Fund. I feel bound to repeat what solution the late Government would have applied to that problem if they had remained responsible. We had looked to an expansion of trade and revenue. It was not then so ludicrous as it may seem now.

The Income Tax is suffering from a kind of cramp. The Exchequer is not getting its natural, normal and true expansion—the true expansion proportionate to the wealth and accumulated capital of the country and of the growth of population and of the development of industry. Many hundred thousands more people are employed, and many more people are alive here in this Island. There are the annual aggregations of the capital savings of the State. But the Income Tax is not expanding. We are not getting that result. The right hon. Gentleman should ask to see, if he has not already seen them, the returns which were shown to me two years ago of the details of the Income Tax of the great productive trades. I was astounded to find these vast trades, largely the basic trades, coal, iron and steel—all these great trades, which were the foundation of revenue not so long ago contain an enormous number of firms which, though they are carrying on their business, are making no profits or very little profit, and where there are no profits, of course, there is no tax.

Look at it for a moment from the Treasury point of view. We would like them to make profits and to pay tax on the profits. A very little, it seems to me, may lift these trades on to a healthy level. The President of the Board of Trade has borne witness himself to the fact that our measures of de-rating relief had already made a considerable improvement in the profitability of the coal trade. Let the tide of depression ebb ever so little, let the burdens be lightened ever so little, and whole areas of taxable assets which are now submerged will come again into review and will come again into use. That I am certain is the truth of the present situation in the Income Tax sphere. Very, very little, and you will be getting a much retarded expansion of revenue because of a great number of firms and businesses resuming profit-making as well as merely carrying on their work. It was to this that I was looking. It might well have been achieved in 1931. It is not only a question of increasing the volume of trade. It is a question of increasing the volume of profitable trade, for it is on the volume of profitable trade that this important part of the Inland Revenue depends for its expansion. If the recovery had been delayed beyond the year 1931, I quite agree that £15,000,000 more would have had to be found for the de-rating scheme by new taxation.

As everyone knows, I do not accept the Protectionist hypothesis, but I am bound to say, that, confronted with such a need of raising £12,000,000 or £15,000,000 more, I believe it could have been done with far less injury or discouragement to the productive energies of the people at this time if it had been raised by an import duty on foreign manufactured articles, either of a finished or semi-finished character. I observe that Holland, which professes and practices a Free Trade policy, has a general revenue tariff of 8 per cent. *ad valorem* on all manufactured imported goods, but even if in this country you applied it only to finished or nearly finished goods, a very substantial yield could be gained by the Exchequer without any discouragement, but rather, on the contrary, with encouragement to the general trade of the country.

Therefore, I conclude this portion of my argument that there is no justification for new taxes in the past year's deficit, nor in the Debt position, nor in the outlook for 1930, and that it is premature and improvident to decide at this moment upon the task of 1931, and that by so doing you may only cripple the prospects of trade revival in this year, which is already so heavily laden. No, the only cause of all this new taxation is now plainly and mercilessly exposed. It is the additional expenditure of the Socialist Government. There alone lies the reason for the Budget presented yesterday.

I will speak about the character of these additions to our burdens and of the causes which have led to this expenditure later on, but first let me examine for a few moments the new taxation. Nearly £47,000,000 of new taxes are to be imposed. They are all direct taxes, or virtually direct taxes; none are to be passed on to the consumer. They are to be levied upon a very restricted class, already the most heavily taxed but still the most loyally responsive in the whole world. [*Interruption.*] It is not denied. The Chancellor of the Exchequer will not deny it. It is levied 11 years after the War is over. It may be necessary because of the new expenditure to which the Government have committed themselves, but do not let them or their followers behind underrate or be blind to the gravity of their proposals or to the consequences which will follow from them. The right hon. Gentleman the Member for Carnarvon Boroughs (Mr. Lloyd George) spoke of these proposals and likened them to a six-inch shell. They indeed may be a six-inch shell bursting with a shattering detonation in every board room and business house throughout the country.

First let me take the Income Tax. The long battle that I have waged over this 6d. off the Income Tax is over. For four years I successfully defended that remission. I defended it against the assaults of the General Strike—I beg pardon, the assaults of the difficult events of 1926. But at last I am beaten. The Chancellor of the Exchequer and his party have had their way. They have won their victory, and the standard rate goes back, in a time of full and assured peace, to the 4s. 6d. level which had been reduced nearly five years ago. The popularity of the measure is assured by reducing the number of taxpayers involved to limits where the voting power of those who are left may be considered negligible. It is a thumping blow at every form of enterprise and saving, and it will be deeply felt and resented. The Chancellor of the Exchequer himself, in a passage remarkable for him, inconsistent with almost everything he had previously said, made a most valuable and important admission at the close of his speech yesterday, when he said:

> Though I am imposing no new direct burdens on industry, I am fully aware of the psychological effect on trade and commerce of increased taxation even when no material burden is imposed.—[Official Report, 14th April, 1930; col. 2681, Vol. 237.]

But what is the difference between a psychological and a direct effect? What matters to practical men is what happens. Psychological reasons are just as real as any other reasons. The right hon. Gentleman feels deeply the danger of the discouragement of trade. He told us some months ago in a speech in the country that all the business community needed was more pluck, or something like that. Here is his remedy. But at the same time that he is encouraging himself to apply this drastic remedy as a stimulus to greater efforts, he has his own misgivings, which he imparted to us yesterday, and he knows that the step he is taking is one which will discourage trade and will dishearten productive enterprise. A substantial portion of this addition to the standard rate of Income Tax, which causes so much hilarity among the party opposite now, will fall upon company reserves; that is to say, it will fall upon what the Colwyn Committee called money at the very point of becoming fruitful to industry. [*Interrup-*

tion.] It is only a proportion, but still a substantial proportion—one-fifth of the total of £5,000,000. Is that so? I am so glad that the Chancellor and I are in agreement. I cannot guarantee to answer every question on the spur of the moment.

There is another way in which, I am told, the increased taxation as proposed tends to deplete companies' resources. Shareholders will want dividends to give them the same income as before the tax was raised. It is a tendency the most evil and undesirable. The right hon. Gentleman told the Labour Congress a few years ago that no one need fear a Labour Budget except the idle rich. Does he pretend that 6d. on the standard rate of Income Tax, apart from these other imposts, affects no one but the idle rich? Is he really making his task easier by stigmatising the class who will pay him as if they were the worthless wastrels of society?

I come now to Super-tax and Death Duties. I am not going to waste much time or any tears upon the personal sufferings of the millionaires. Where direct taxation uproots families from the homes in which they have lived for centuries it does inflict a great sentimental injury upon them. [*Interruption.*] There is no real gain to British democracy when some family leaves the home of its ancestors and hands it over to a trans-Atlantic millionaire or war-time profiteer. [*Interruption.*] If the hon. Gentleman who interrupts has a keen and poignant feeling about it he will perhaps realise that it is not confined to his party alone. But as far as new wealth is concerned I think that the Chancellor of the Exchequer is probably right in saying that his new taxation will not, in his own words, mean any deprivation of the necessaries of life, or of reasonable luxuries. That may be true, but it has nothing whatever to do with the issues that we have to settle here.

The main part of this new levy will not, I believe, be drawn from personal expenditure; it will be drawn from funds which otherwise would have been devoted to investments. The modern productive millionaire is a highly economic animal. He saves far more than he can consume. He is, although he does not always realise it, the potent ally of the Chancellor of the Exchequer. It is upon the continuous multiplication of these great fortunes that virtually all modern systems of progressive taxation depend for their revenue. It is easy and popular to lead the multitude against such a class, but the question now is whether a point has not been reached when the increased taxation may not begin to defeat its own object, namely, an easily obtained revenue.

Everyone knows the right hon. Gentleman's motto, that in these matters of taxation—I reminded him of it some years ago and he repeated it with gusto only two years ago—you must not look at what is taken away but at what is left. Let us look at what is left. The Treasury calculated for me a year ago that the largest taxpayer who provided annual insurance for his Death Duties would pay in Super-tax, Income Tax and Death Duties, something between 14s. and 15s. in the £ annually to the Exchequer. The present Budget adds 6d. to the Income Tax, 1s. 6d. to the Sur-tax, and 1s. 3d. I suppose, for the insurance of the increased Death Duties. I have not the facilities of calculation that the Chancellor of the Exchequer has, but it is something in the nature of 3s. 9d. in the £. I hope that the Committee will follow these figures. On that basis, the 14s. or 15s. becomes 17s. or 18s., and what is left becomes 2s. or 3s. in the £. I think that that is a very striking result of the taxation which has now been imposed. One wonders whether, when the Chancellor of the Exchequer or his agents arrive to collect the 17s. or 18s. in the £, they will always find the fortune there. It may have been divided, and if it has been divided it falls into a far lower scale of taxation not comparable in its remunerative character to the Exchequer. It may not even be reposing on our hospitable soil; it may have become so fenced about with legal barbed wire that a siege of years may be necessary to obtain it.

Certainly the incentive to run the grave risks of modern business, the incentive for creating new wealth or for accumulating money for reinvestment, seems to be very seriously impaired when, as the right hon. Gentleman says, it is no longer a question of looking at what is taken away, but of looking at what is left, and when what is left does not in these cases appear to exceed 2s. or 3s. or 4s. in the £. If the great incentive to saving and reinvestment on the part of the very rich is impaired, injury will follow to the whole community. It is by this guidance of business and industry by capital that is massed in the hands of individuals who have the power of land planning and of creating the large-scale enterprises which are needed now—the creation of these enterprises on a solid basis by substantial people who are not in a hurry to make their fortunes—it is this process which has been found in every country, and particularly in the United States of America, to be the most swift and powerful means of rationalising industry, of discovering and gaining and commanding markets, and thus creating new wealth and employment.

It may even be true—I have not made the calculation—that the standards of life of the wage earners in all the principal modern communities of the present day vary in proportion to the number of very wealthy citizens in their midst. It is very remarkable. Certainly, it would seem to give food for thought, indeed to all of those who are anxious to obtain the maximum contribution from capital to the well-being of the general community. Certainly, every effort will be made in many businesses to pass on the burden of extra taxation wherever possible. It does not follow that it is always possible, but I firmly believe that there are many cases, when whole classes of competitors are equally taxed, where something will be recovered from the consumer in the form of an increased cost of production and an increased price; and where such articles, showing an increased price, reach the area of foreign competition, our competitive power will be *pro tanto* reduced.

There is a burden which falls, through this taxation, very heavily upon the highly-paid brain worker and the skilled technician, who are absolutely essential in our modern life. To ask the surgeon or the engineer or the scientist or the professional man to pay these very heavy charges at this time is indeed to ask much of him when he knows that this additional burden is cast upon him partly for the purpose of providing out-of-work benefit to persons who need not even be asked to prove that they are genuinely seeking work. Therefore, the Chancellor of the Exchequer seems to me to be running a great risk in what he is doing, and he may be going too far by prejudicing the basis of his existing direct revenue, while hampering the production of new wealth. All these tendencies that I have traced upon the super-rich will operate in a lesser degree upon every grade of taxpayer over whom the Chancellor of the Exchequer is wielding what he has, I believe, called the weapon of taxation. If once the loyal co-operation of the mass of direct taxpayers, for which this country is renowned, were to be shaken, irreparable injury might be done to the whole structure of our taxation system. The right hon. Gentleman is making proposals for preventing legal avoidance. In that, he will get full assistance from all parties in this House, but no legal avoidance provisions, however elaborate, however complicated—as they become complicated they may be found to impinge upon many other legitimate aspects of our national life—can possibly be any compensation for the alienation of the general good will of the main body of Income Tax payers.

We are asked to pay an immense price. The Government are demanding from the nation an immense price. What have they to show for it? What have they to show for all this new expenditure, which I claim that I have proved—I would like to see the argument upset, if it can be—is the sole cause of the heavy additional taxation this year. What have they to show? Here, I have no doubt that the right hon. Member for Carnarvon Boroughs will agree with me in what I am about to say. I cannot see the right hon. Gentleman as well as I did; the Gangway has grown so much broader. It is becoming too blurred and mixed up with the Chancellor of the Exchequer, until one can almost hear the echo of the psalms they chant in common. The right hon. Member for Carnarvon Boroughs will agree with me in asking the question, "What have the Government to show for the £40,000,000 of new taxation which they are imposing upon the country?"

There was the question of the solvency of the Unemployment Insurance Fund. We have heard a lot about that. Its bankruptcy had to be prevented. Large sums of money were voted from the Exchequer for that purpose, but before three months were out the Government came down here and did the very thing which they had sought to avoid. They reopened borrowing and they compromised again that Fund which, at great expense, they said it was so indispensable to rescue. That is all about the solvency of the Unemployment Insurance Fund. It was achieved for three months and afterwards lost again owing to the great expansion of unemployment and unemployment benefit. There have been better benefits paid to more persons out of work, but there has been, as I have said, a demoralisation of the administration of the Fund.

Then we have a handful of oddments and scraps, a few oddments of hard cases in connection with the great scheme of widows' pensions. [Hon. Members: "Oddments!"] Well, it was a scheme which dealt with 12,000,000 widows, whereas the hard cases dealt with, I believe, only half-a-million. All this is mixed up with some complicated tale which the Chancellor of the Exchequer has told about wishing to avoid the step up in 1935, when the existing scale of Exchequer contributions, as originally planned, comes to an end. Well, we have that. The Lord Privy Seal has been given about £2 per head for every extra unemployed man added to the live register during his tenure of office—£1,100,000 or £1,200,000 altogether in order to cure the problems of unemployment.

In effect, the taxpayer has been exposed to the worst of both worlds; at one end, we have had the right hon. Gentleman in the capacity of financial purist and pedant, professing to practise principles of financial orthodoxy, and, on the other hand, we have had the Socialist agitator handing out lush doles with both hands to great crowds, and both are sending in their accounts to the taxpayer. That is all there is. I beg pardon, I forgot one recipient of the Chancellor of the Exchequer's bounty— the bookmaker. The right hon. Gentleman may leave a name execrated by every industrialist, but sometimes it may be remembered with expressions of good will among that confraternity who raise their voices so loudly on the race courses, because of his benevolent action in freeing them from the grinding licence duty of £10 a head. I address myself particularly to the representatives from the Clyde. This is the whole programme. Here is the whole shop window. This is all that we are being given for the £45,000,000 of additional burden which are going to strike a blow at the reviving trade of the country. More than that, it is all that there is going to be, because the right hon. Gentleman, losing confidence in his policy of stimulating industry by taxes, and with grave misgivings, gave us an undertaking that:

> In the absence of unforeseeable calamities or of heavy increases of expenditure, no further increases of taxation will need to be imposed next year.—[Official Report, 14th April, 1930; col. 2681, Vol. 237.]

There is the end, if those words stand, of the programme of the embattled proletariat of "Labour and the Nation." It is worked out. They have come to an end. I wonder whether the hon. Member for Bridgeton (Mr. Maxton) is going to countersign that assurance of the Chancellor of the Exechequer. Nobody disputes the courage of the Chancellor of the Exchequer or his power of standing against opponents in every quarter, but, nevertheless, he may not be able to stand against the pressure that will be put upon him. We know perfectly well that pledges have been given by the party opposite to delude and bribe their voters, that shoals of schemes of expenditure are moving towards this House and that long queues of Bills, all involving further charges, are standing at the turnstile. I can only say that we were told on the Widows' Pensions Debates and on the Unemployment Insurance Debates that these were only instalments. I must say to hon. and right hon. Members opposite, if all your contributions towards the social life of this country is summed up in these foolish, these expensive items that I have read out, if that is all that you have to say to it, then the pain and irritation felt by the Income Taxpayers at the larger burdens that you are going to impose upon them will only be equalled by the pain and irritation felt by the gentlemen from the Clyde at what they are never going to get.

What help will this Budget be to trade? Unemployment is the central feature of our life at the present time. It can only be removed by a trade revival. Is not this taxing Budget the very worst and the most inopportune policy which could possibly be applied to our affairs at this moment? Will it not aggravate the very causes which made the new taxes necessary? Will it not chill enterprise, discourage saving, promote the expatriation of capital, delay the recovery of trade and, indeed, the operation of some great conversion scheme from which we all had hoped so much? All this will be done at the very moment when the opposite processes are at work in all our chief competing countries. Would it not—I ask this not only as an indictment of the right hon. Gentleman but in my own defence—be worth while, I will not say by strict economy but by keeping the expenditure rigidly at a fixed level, even by some mitigation in the process of repaying Debt to the extent of not adding this additional £5,000,000, to try to bring our country round the corner of depression in which it is languishing and open again the high roads to better trade, to buoyant enterprise, to expanding revenues, and to the profits on which those revenues are based? These are all questions which the nation must weigh in the months that lie before us and upon their answer depends in a very large measure the immediate strength and prosperity of Britain.

ARMY AND AIR FORCE (ANNUAL) BILL
April 16, 1930
House of Commons

The Secretary of State for War said that he would not trouble the House with any arguments, that he would not repeat any of the arguments used in the previous Debate. The arguments against the course which he is asking the House to adopt were arguments which on a previous occasion appealed to him so strongly that he testified to his opinion in the Lobby in opposition to the views of a great many of those with whom he is accustomed to act. The proposals having gone to another place, a similar latitude was exercised, and the question which will be before us in a few minutes is not whether we should support the Government in carrying out the proposals which they have put forward as a responsible executive body, but whether the same latitude of opinion, apart from the guidance of the executive, shall not be allowed to the Second Chamber as has been utilised here. My hon. and gallant Friend the Member for Oxford (Captain Bourne) has an Amendment which reduces the difference between the two Houses to a very small point and offers to the Government the opportunity of obtaining this vitally important, and, indeed, indispensable legislation in exactly the form in which they, as a responsible Administration, framed it and brought it forward. I suggest that the right hon. Gentleman should weigh the matter very carefully, because, undoubtedly, it is strictly within the competence of the Second Chamber to carry a modification of this kind, and if they should—of course, I do not forecast what their action may be—adhere to their view, and if they should take the same view as is embodied in the Amendment of my hon. and gallant Friend, they would, after all, only be standing on the same foundation of judgment and authority as was adopted by the Secretary of State for War, by the Secretary of State for India, by, indeed, the responsible Government as a whole when they originally introduced the Motion. The ground on which the Second Chamber would be standing would be a very strong one, and obviously their power to adhere to that ground, if they choose, would be inexpungable. The responsibility rests with the Government of the day for procuring assent for this vital and indispensable legislation, and part of their responsibility will be discharged by paying proper attention to the lawfully expressed views of other parties in the Constitution.

THE BUDGET (SUMPTUARY TAXATION)

April 30, 1930

House of Commons

I should like to take a rather more general aspect on this Amendment, and to ask the Chancellor of the Exchequer whether the £3,000,000 which, I understand, is to be raised by this duty, will be counted in the national statistics upon the direct or the indirect side of our ratio of taxation? It seems to me very important that that ratio between direct and indirect taxation, which has for so many years been followed as an index of the political character of Governments, should be based on sound and true foundations. During the last few years many taxes have been added which are of a different character altogether from those which formerly constituted the basis of indirect taxation. In the old days it was said that indirect taxation is the fund mainly contributed by the mass of the people, and direct taxation is the fund mainly contributed by the well-to-do, and, as far as you are dealing with great articles of popular consumption, tea, sugar, beer, no doubt there is a great deal of truth in that. The index is sound, and that is why it was always the subject of such careful scrutiny from year to year in all the great Budgets at the end of the last century and the beginning of this.

But when you introduce taxes of a sumptuary kind on luxuries—silk, motor cars, musical instruments, and all sorts of matters which are not amongst the staple articles of popular consumption—obviously, you are introducing into the ratio new factors, and in this case the right hon. Gentleman is not really levying an indirect tax at all. It is his boast—one made not for the first time by a Chancellor of the Exchequer—that by private discussions with the leaders of a great trade, by putting pressure upon them, by coming to an arrangement with them—I am not at all criticising this—he has secured from them a yielding up of some of their profits in the form of a direct tax, that being included in the total of indirect taxation. Indirect taxation is paid by the consumer. Here is a tax, the very essence of which is that it is not to be paid by the consumer. Why vitiate the figures by introducing a factor which is obviously entirely contrary to the very purpose for which the ratio of indirect taxation is always quoted? No doubt if the right hon. Gentleman has taken this £3,000,000 by direct taxation from one particular class of producers, he will still emphasise how in his Budget he has carried the ratio of direct taxation much higher than it has ever been carried before, and has lowered that of indirect taxation. But these will be figures produced on an altogether unsound basis, and it seems to me that we require a new classification. I am all for the ratio being strictly followed from year to year as it should be followed, on a strictly comparable basis, and for that purpose sumptuary taxation on articles ought not to be included among indirect taxation. They ought to be in a separate category, and certainly taxes like these, the whole yield of which is to be paid, not by the consumers but by a limited class, ought to be withdrawn from any fair computation of statistics of the ratio between direct and indirect taxation.

THE BUDGET (INCOME TAX)

May 1, 1930

House of Commons

When it falls to the lot of a Member of this House to have to make proposals to Parliament which are necessarily of a serious and disagreeable character, one must always admire those qualities of mind which enable him to lighten the character of his proposals by the charming and agreeable manner in which he commends them to the House and the country. The right hon. Gentleman has addressed us for nearly an hour. [An Hon. Member: "Only half an hour!"] Well, it seemed like an hour. His speech has been devoted to expressing and revealing the deep satisfaction which he has in the functions which he is obliged to discharge, and if anything could equal the satisfaction that he feels in his duties it is his satisfaction with himself. He made a long statement to show how marvellously his financial policy has come to the rescue of our trade, our industry, our finance. By his adroit and far-seeing manipulation of the Floating Debt he has sedulously beaten down the Bank Rate to the level of 3 per cent. He did that all himself. He takes the credit for this episode; it was his own personal achievement. If we were to say at the same time that the unemployment in the country has risen to unprecedented levels, to levels scarcely even achieved after the troubles of 1926, the right hon. Gentleman would say how ludicrously unfair it was to cast upon the Government of the day or upon a single Member of the Government responsibility for results and causes world-wide in their operation, which would have come under almost any administration that happened to be in power. That is the way in which the right hon. Gentleman fortifies himself for his duties. If things go right, he did it himself; it is all his own affair. If things go wrong: "Well, what can you do when world causes are at work against you?"

The right hon. Gentleman seemed to have a great deal of satisfaction about the reduction of the Bank Rate, but there is a school of opinion, which is represented not merely on this side of the House, who consider that it is possible that in his very handling of the Floating Debt he may have aggravated the financial stringency and may have been a discouragement to the starting of enterprise. It is perfectly clear that one of the causes which have led to the remedial event of the reduction of the Bank Rate is the want of enterprise and confidence which prevail throughout the country. I note that the Lord Privy Seal is not laughing. Look at the contrast between the Lord Privy Seal and the Chancellor of the Exchequer; observe it well! The Lord Privy Seal is laughing now. Cabinet loyalty has forced a smile. We consider that the lack of enterprise and the failure in desire to undertake large and important new projects is one of the principal causes, although I do not by any means say the whole cause, of the present state of the money market and of the consequent low Bank Rate.

In the course of his speech the right hon. Gentleman made an unnecessary and an unchivalrous attack upon my hon. Friend the Member for East Aberdeen (Mr. Boothby). My hon. Friend made a remark, which I should have assumed was one on which there would be very little disagreement, namely, that large schemes for dealing with unemployment on broad lines, of which so much was heard from the opposite benches before and during the General Election, had been brought to nothing, or to virtually nothing, by the influence and authority—I do not say whether rightly or wrongly; that is not my argument at the moment—of the right hon. Gentleman and the very powerful Department over which he presides with so much complacency. That was the substance of what my hon. Friend said [Hon. Members: "No!"] What was there for the right hon. Gentleman to devote a long part of his important statement on the increase of the Income Tax to an attack and challenge to my hon. Friend, taking the most unusual course of the Minister in charge of the House sitting down and waiting for a private Member to substantiate a statement so general that it could not have irritated the right hon. Gentleman had it not had a strong substratum of truth. The right hon. Gentleman then proceeded to say that my hon. Friend's statement was wholly untrue, and he had not the manliness to withdraw it. I remember only a few days ago, when an hon. Friend of mine here was speaking, an insulting taunt was flung at him across the Floor by the Chancellor of the Exchequer himself, then acting as Leader of the House of Commons, responsible for the decorum of its Debates. He, who should set an example, flung this taunt across the House and then so adroitly concealed himself by some obscurity of phrasing and a Ruling of the Chair that he himself had not the manliness nor, I will add, the decency to withdraw.

Our attention in this important Amendment is fully engaged upon the challenging question of the right hon. Gentleman. What items, he said, in the bill of the nation would you reduce? I have argued, and will continue to submit to the House, arguments to show that there was no imperative necessity to impose additional taxation in this present year. That is the foundation of the argument upon which I propose to conduct the criticism of his Budget. If the right hon. Gentleman had not added new expenditure, if he had not added £14,000,000 to the amounts supplied from the Exchequer to the Unemployment Insurance Fund, if he had not consented to a profound relaxation and demoralisation of the conditions under which that fund is administered, if he had not provided additional expenditure of £5,000,000 a year not entirely for improved pensions to widows, but for additional benefits to widows and also for an alteration in the finance of that scheme, and if he had not—though it is the least of his faults—added another £5,000,000 to make up for the deficit of last year in respect of the Sinking Fund provisions of this year, on those heads alone enough money could have been provided to equal the amount for the current year provided by the sixpence he is now imposing on the Income Tax. That is our case—that it might well have been possible to have avoided additional taxation this year.

Surely, it is a very sorrowful plight in which the British nation and the British taxpayers find themselves now. 11 or 12 years after the War the standard rate of Income Tax has to be raised by 6d. It is a very grave event. Even if the right hon. Gentleman made good his case that it was necessary, it would be none the less deplorable to have to raise the standard rate of tax which affects the business community of this country at innumerable points, and which involves the taxation of reserves which will be the subject of a further Amendment. To put that further burden upon us at the present time, we the most heavily taxed country in the world, is not a matter to be discussed in so lighthearted a manner or with such an appearance of zest and gusto as in the speech of the right hon. Gentleman. The right hon. Gentleman in the course of his speech recalled to us the kind of thing, which he used to say not long ago in his pamphlets and speeches, about the bracing effects of taxation on trade and industry. It was very difficult listening to his arguments to see why, if those arguments were sound, if as a matter of fact the more you tax the more the wealth of the country increases, why you should stop here.

He made a slighting reference to the question which the right hon. and gallant Member for Tonbridge (Lieut.-Colonel Spender-Clay) put. It was a question which I should have thought cut to the very root of his position. We are interested to know what are the differences which prevail between the right hon. Gentleman and the party below the Gangway, of whose principles the hon. Member for East Leicester (Mr. Wise) has been the exponent this afternoon. What are the differences? We gather they are important differences, but at what point the line is drawn it is certainly not easy for anyone to say. Why does he draw the line at this point and say he will tax no more? Why does he give this pledge which he has given? Let us ask a few questions about this pledge. It is rather an important point on which, no doubt, the right hon. Gentleman would like to give us some information in the presence of his friends below the Gangway. This is what he said in opening the Budget:

> So far as I can see. . . . in the absence of unforeseeable calamities or of heavy increases of expenditure. . . . no further increases of taxation will need to be imposed next year.–[Official Report, 14th April, 1930; col. 2681, Vol. 237.]

What is the meaning of that pledge? After all, the right hon. Gentleman must not, with a cackle of hilarity, pretend that he is going to deceive one side of the House or another. Either he means he is going to keep that pledge, and it is a real assurance to the business men of the country that there will be no further taxation next year, or else he means to insert these very suspicious words "in the absence of heavy increases of expenditure" in order that he shall, as it were, soothe the commercial interests of the country for the time being and yet next year, when the next Budget is to be presented, having consented to some further increases of expenditure, he will be able to make his peace with the hon. Gentlemen below the Gangway. I say that it was a very astonishing pledge for the right hon. Gentleman to give. The question is, are we to put any reliance upon it or not? Will the right hon. Gentleman tell me, for instance, what he means by "in the absence of heavy increases of expenditure"? Will he consider himself absolved from his pledge if, in his capacity of Cabinet Minister, he agrees to some scheme of social reform adding £15,000,000 or £20,000,000 to the expenditure of this country? Will he then feel absolved from his pledge and entitled to impose additional taxation? What is his meaning on that point? Or does he mean that he will not himself consent to increases in expenditure which will lead him to further taxation? Following the right hon. Gentleman's example with my hon. Friend, I will give him a full opportunity to reply.

Mr. Snowden: If the right hon. Gentleman is incapable of understanding plain English words, I am afraid I could not enlighten him.

Mr. Churchill: I think the Chancellor of the Exchequer would have consulted better his interests and his reputation in the country if he had given a more serious answer. He made a most solemn and important statement and pledge, which has been the subject of immense attention both from his own supporters and throughout the country, and he is not prepared to tell us whether he intends to keep that pledge in strictness, or whether he proposes to avail himself of this saving clause about the absence of any increased expenditure in order to make the pledge absolutely worthless. We have a right to know whether he is seeking to trick the traders of this country or the representatives of his party. One or the other is certainly being ill-used and deceived. All the right hon. Gentleman said was that anyone who can understand plain English will know what he means. It is not true. No one in this House knows what it means. The hon. Gentlemen above the Gangway do not know whether he means that he is willing to impose further taxation next year or not, nor do the traders. While he is unwilling to answer that question—not because he could not have answered it, but because he dare not answer it—I say his pledge cannot have any validity or value so far as the trade of this country is concerned.

I am asked how else could the revenues of this country be increased? I believe that if, by taking thought, we were able to avoid further new taxation at the present time, a revival of trade would have the effect of bringing large new areas of taxable capacity into the scope of the Income Tax. I do not know if the right hon. Gentleman has taken the advice I gave him to look at the figures of the great trades in which an immense amount of unprofitable business is being done. If by any means you can get those trades to work and they rise to a profitable level, you would get the £20,000,000 or £30,000,000 without adding a penny to the standard rate of Income Tax. That was the way in which you should have endeavoured to have attacked this problem, instead of, on unnecessary grounds, adding to the burdens already checking and hampering industry. It is not only the burden which is causing, at the present time, resentment and a sense of unfairness. It is the method and the circumstances which have attended its imposition. I, myself, on three occasions, reduced the weight of the Income Tax upon the smaller class of Income Tax payers, but I did not do it at a time when it was necessary to ask from all the other Income Tax payers an enormously increased burden. To ask from the other Income Tax payers very great burdens, and then to narrow the scope of the tax so as to isolate those who are left to pay those burdens, at a time when you are adding to the total burden of the State is, I think, almost unprecedented. There the right hon. Gentleman reveals the spirit of class warfare by which he has been accustomed to gain votes and power in the country.

The question has been raised will his Budget be popular or not? I can quite believe that there are many audiences in this country which would respond with the greatest possible enthusiasm not only to the suggestions which he makes but to those which his friends below the Gangway make. To deprive the Income Tax and Super-tax payers of the whole of their property and hand it over to the unemployed and the poor—that is the proposal which was put forward by the hon. Member for Bridgeton (Mr. Maxton) the other day, and I have not the slightest doubt there are many audiences which would applaud such sentiments. I say that the right hon. Gentleman has left himself absolutely no ground of principle to withstand such arguments; and the case which has been deployed by him to us to-day would cover, if not the immediate transference of wealth, at any rate that gradual steady transfer, until the capitalist classes are entirely eliminated, which was so plainly advocated by the hon. Member for East Leicester in his most soft, purring, sinister, suggestive speech. There is no doubt whatever that the right hon. Gentleman has between him and having to carry out what he is asked to carry out by his supporters, no ground of logic or of reason, but simply the existing remaining force of the governing machine and the resisting power of the great public departments. Can we wonder that trade and industry are anxious and depressed? Can we wonder that the recovery which we are making is so much slower and more painful than that of any other country which emerged victorious or even emerged at all from the Great War?

The effect of the increase in the standard rate, is a melancholy and dismal blow struck at the strength and prosperity of this country. The fact that the tax has been localised upon a small class should be a warning to them all throughout the country of the malice with which they are viewed by those who now wield great power in the State. If it is asked why these new sacrifices, these invidious sacrifices are being demanded, then, let me say that the answer is also one which will justly excite the resentment of the Income Tax payer. We have seen printed on the backs of the Income Tax forms which are sent out, a statement of the expenditure of the country and the means for which this revenue is required. Let the right hon. Gentleman print on the back of his forms, if he is truthful, that more than half of the expenditure of the sixpenny increase on the Income Tax—a large proportion of it at any rate—is required in order that further and better doles may be paid to people who may not even be asked whether they are genuinely seeking work or not [*Interruption*]. If by any chance, as a result of these new exactions and this heavy burden, a surplus should emerge, then the Income Tax payer is informed beforehand that that will be used to sweep away the existing McKenna, key industry and Safeguarding Duties. As I say, I believe that the right hon. Gentleman has done not only a real injury but a psychological injury also. I believe he will find that in alienating the goodwill of the classes who have been by far the greatest supporters of the revenue of this country and on whose high standard of public and civic duty our revenue so much depends, the right hon. Gentleman has struck a serious blow at the foundations of our finance which it may easily be a very grievous matter to repair in the future.

THE BUDGET

May 6, 1930

House of Commons

Surely we are going to have an answer from the Government on this matter, and on the very precise issue which has been raised by the discussion. The Chancellor of the Exchequer made a reasoned statement for having brought forward this Resolution. He gave a very clear reason, but it was not the reason, evidently, by which this matter is actually governed. That is not very pleasant. The reason which the Chancellor of the Exchequer gave us was that, owing to the further restrictions of the zone of Income Tax payers, a certain class of persons would, if the law had been allowed to remain unaltered, have actually been receiving more than they would be called upon to pay. But now it is shown that by far the greater part of this tax will not fall on such persons, but on other persons who will be paying back at least what they receive. The pre-1916 part of this proposal touches the principle of retrospective action in regard to evasion, upon which definite decisions have been taken and the business of the country has proceeded. The right hon. Gentleman says that he expects to get £500,000 from this—half a million a year. Now, by whom is this £500,000 going to be paid and on what process of our national life is it going to impinge? It is going to impinge as a deterrent upon the whole process of insurance. That is the intention and the object. The object has nothing whatever to do with these people between £250 and £225—

Mr. Snowden: The right hon. Gentleman is getting somewhat wide of the point at issue. It is a question of 2s. 3d. instead of 2s.

Mr. Churchill: The right hon. Gentleman was asked what this was worth to the revenue of the year. Can he answer that?

Mr. Snowden: We are not dealing now with the whole subject. This Amendment is dealing with the difference between 2s. and 2s. 3d.

Mr. Churchill: But the Resolution is dealing with the whole subject. I think it will be inconvenient to discuss it in parts. I place myself entirely under the protection of the Chair, but very often it is customary to allow a more or less general discussion on the first Amendment which raises a point in connection with the Resolution, and, basing myself upon that custom, as the matter has been raised, I say: Who is he getting the £500,000 from and upon what process of our national and economic life is this new tax to impinge? It is no use for the right hon. Gentleman to try and pretend that he can get away in a manner of this kind by trying to make the discussion piecemeal, by trying to burke discussion, by having one fragment discussed on one Amendment and another fragment on another. Luckily, our procedure prevents that method from being entirely successful and I hope the House and the country will appreciate what is really intended. I ask the right hon. Gentleman whether he has imposed this duty with a view to obtaining £500,000 a year from the persons who have hitherto enjoyed the privileges granted to them in connection with insurance. If he is, surely, he is taking a very injurious course, and I do not wonder that my right hon. Friend the Member for Northern Cornwall (Sir D. Maclean) was moved to make a qualified protest upon this subject. As my right hon. Friend the Member for St. George's (Sir L. Worthington-Evans) pointed out, these very insurance policies all come into the purview of the death duties. They are an aggregative tax on the estimate which falls in at death.

The process of insurance is surely one which from every point of view, except that of "the road to ruin," should be encouraged by the Government. People make sacrifices to insure their lives in case, owing to the chances, and ups and downs of their walk of life and their employment, they should be cut off at a moment when their families would be left in circumstances of great embarrassment, involving a complete alteration in their mode of life. They make great sacrifices year after year and thereby immense funds are steadily gathered, which funds constitute one of the few processes of collective saving now at work in this country. Hon. Gentlemen opposite may try to sweep away private savings. They may declare that wealth is not to be allowed above a certain scale or standard. But I imagine that they will allow the process of collective saving to proceed. Here is a process of securing vast sums which the State has thought it right and necessary to protect and now the right hon. Gentleman is coming to break in upon this process. Even on their own dismal theories is that a proposal with which hon. Members opposite agree? It is, from his own point of view, the most short-sighted policy that he could adopt. I should have thought that the encouragement of insurance policies was one of the most necessary elements in a wise treatment of British finances at the present time. We see the enormous advantage of this method. We are a nation which has carried insurance in the industrial and social spheres to incomparably higher levels than any other country in the world. Then why should the right hon. Gentleman strike this blow? Is it really worth it?

Of course, the taxpayer is the victim. He is to be left on the rack. If the right hon. Gentleman is to be judged by the efficiency with which he can screw the last bit out of the taxpayer then, on that principle, he would, indeed, be blameworthy if he rejected such a very ingenious little extra turn of the screw as is here proposed. But, on another principle, to a Chancellor of the Exchequer who desires to see the whole forces of this country gaining in strength apart from the individual, such a proposal is most short-sighted and most ill-motivated. I hope we are going to hear from the President of the Board of Trade who has, I see, been brought into this discussion, and who has considerable departmental responsibility in regard to the progress of insurance in this country, some statement to the effect that the Government will reconsider this matter. It really is not worth while. What you gain in the £500,000 a year will probably inflict discouragement upon the actual practice of insurance and will make a loss in the ultimate yield years hence which will far exceed the gain to the revenue. Why break in upon the principle which has been established in regard to these premiums? What is the point of breaking in upon that principle for such a paltry advantage as that which has been described?

I ask the President of the Board of Trade to say that the matter will be reviewed and reconsidered. We are quite aware of the fact that, ploughing with borrowed oxen, the Government have the power to carry it in any form they like. One of the oxen looks like giving at the moment, but, no doubt, the goad, accurately applied, will stir him into his wonted activity. We know all that, but the fact remains that the right hon. Gentleman is doing this quite needlessly. I admit that he has enormous difficulties to face and that in facing them he must necessarily run counter to a great many elements in the nation but in this case he is quite needlessly broadening the irritation and the burden which his Budget inflicts, by casting into it—for what is an inconceivably small sum of money compared with the problem which he has to meet—the whole wide area of these policies of insurance.

LONDON NAVAL CONFERENCE
May 15, 1930
House of Commons

The House is under an obligation to the Prime Minister for the care and pain he has taken to make us a statement on the subject which is now before us. To-day, I must remind the House that we are only discussing a question which you, Sir, have just put from the Chair, namely, whether we should or should not adjourn. This procedure has been adopted at the wish of the Conservative Opposition, because we wish, at this stage, to allow the Government to lay their whole case before us, not only in its diplomatic but also in its naval aspects, so that we may decide what further action it is our duty to take, and, in particular, whether our objections to this Agreement can be adequately expressed by a discussion of Vote 3 of the Navy Estimates or whether they will require to be embodied in some definite Motion put forward by the Conservative party. I say this at the outset to make it clear that we view what is proposed in the Draft Treaty with the most serious anxiety; and I must say that this anxiety has not been removed at all by the agreeable and lucid speech to which we have just listened.

I am going to make some demand on the patience of the House this afternoon. We must recognise, first of all, that the policy of a naval agreement with the United States or other Powers, supplementary to the Washington Agreement of 1921, has been accepted in principle by all parties in Great Britain. The Prime Minister and his colleagues were therefore, it seems, justified in their efforts to arrive at such an agreement. We ourselves had made a series of important proposals designed to avert or slacken naval competition in armaments and make more secure the growing strength of the foundations of peace. Finally, we do not and must not forget that the Clauses in the Treaty of Versailles have bound the victorious Powers to pursue faithfully and earnestly a policy of disarmament, not only naval disarmament, for, as the Prime Minister has reminded us, naval, military and air disarmament all stand together. It is our belief that we have done by action and example more than any other signatory Power of the Treaty of Versailles or indeed of any other Power in the world. That is a course—I am speaking on behalf of this side of the House—which we are determined steadfastly to pursue, so far as the national safety and interest of the British Empire or of the Commonwealth of Nations, if that term be preferred, will allow. I must also recognise that the Prime Minister in his protracted and difficult negotiations, of which he has given us some account this afternoon, has made a personal contribution of forbearance, sincerity and patience which, quite apart from the merits of this Treaty, command general respect in this country. There is no doubt that the visit of the Prime Minister to the United States was the occasion for a marked and impressive manifestation of American good will towards Great Britain, the calling forth of which was in itself a service to the State. In this navy matter, as in this question of India, the Prime Minister and his colleagues are on the stage of history; what they say will be recorded in other volumes than those of the *Official Report* and certainly, in his conduct of these negotiations, the Prime Minister has done or said nothing that is in contrast with the dignity and consequence of the events with which he was dealing.

But I am afraid I did not rise to-day for the purpose of paying compliments to the right hon. Gentleman. Indeed, I apprehend that, if I were to pay tributes, or if tributes to his policy and conduct were paid from this side of the House, that would not commend his policy or his conduct either to the bulk of his own party or to the foreign countries with whom we have been in conference. I, therefore, proceed forthwith to the practical question which lies before us, namely, the wisdom or unwisdom, the merits or demerits of the proposed agreement itself. I think I must make three main submissions to the House. The first is that the Agreement of London is not the natural successor or child of the Washington Agreement of 1921, but, on the contrary, differs fundamentally from it. That is my first submission. My second is that it is not a Treaty of parity at all in the sense that Great Britain and the United States should be equal Powers upon the sea, but that, on the contrary, it is a formal acceptance by Great Britain of definitely inferior seapower. Thirdly, I submit that the London Agreement contains within itself subsidiary provisions which will have the effect of ensuring that that inferiority is attained before the Treaty comes to be revised in 1936. Those are my three main submissions, and I will endeavour to make them good.

The Washington Treaty, might I remind the House, rested upon the basis that Great Britain and the United States should be equal in all the battle elements of their respective Fleets. It was confined exclusively to those elements. It did not raise any question of that disparity which we can imagine to exist between this small, densely populated island, the centre of a commonwealth of nations and dependencies spread all over the world, and lying itself in the closest proximity to European centres, between the entity on the one hand and on the other the vast State, almost a Continent, virtually self-supporting in every essential of life and power, separated by thousands of miles on all flanks from all possible attack. None of the disparity was raised by the Washington Treaty of 1921. It confined itself to the battle sphere. It left unfettered our rights to take the necessary measures, whatever we might conceive them to be, for the protection of our commerce and our food against submarines by means of cruisers, convoy vessels—an expression which should be taken into consideration by naval representatives—and also our rights to make provision for flotillas and small craft as they might be required as long as submarines remain a great factor in the narrow waters and inland seas through which so much of our economic life has to flow. To show how strongly these points were insisted upon at Washington, I need only cite a passage in the instructions which were sent to Lord Balfour, our chief representative, by the Government of that day:

> We welcome your decision to press for the total abolition of submarines. Even if you can obtain this, we wish to be consulted before a final decision is taken upon the limited scales of construction in small craft permitted to the various signatories. The position of Britain, with her world-wide possessions and food supplies, on the other hand clearly requires

an entirely different standard from that acceptable by self-contained nations. We apprehend, however, that there is very little chance of the abolition of submarines being agreed upon, and in this event we must insist at all costs upon absolute freedom in regard to the character and number of all vessels under, say, 10,000 tons. We cannot, in the face of French freedom to construct a great submarine fleet, to say nothing of the submarine and cruiser construction of other Powers, enter into any agreement fettering our liberty to build whatever numbers and classes of cruisers and anti-submarine craft we may consider necessary to the maintenance of national and Imperial life. We feel sure, from our knowledge of your outlook on the whole problem, that you will share this view to the full. Even at the cost of a complete rupture, we feel certain you will not agree to any restriction in this sphere without previous consultation with the Cabinet.

The Prime Minister: Has that paper been published?

Mr. Churchill: No. That is an extract from a telegram of instructions which was sent 10 years ago by the Government of which the right hon. Gentleman the Member for Carnarvon Boroughs (Mr. Lloyd George) was the head.

The Prime Minister: May I ask whether it is not one of a whole series of instructions?

Mr. Churchill: Certainly. It was one of an immense series of telegrams, but it is of immense importance, in studying these grave matters—

Mr. Lambert: Have those telegrams ever been published?

Mr. Churchill: No, but I take the fullest responsibility for the exercise of my own judgment in this matter.

Mr. Lambert: Surely, under the Rules of the House, this is a Cabinet document, and should be published, if it is quoted from.

The Prime Minister: I happen to know the document. Is this a Cabinet paper, and, if it is a Cabinet paper, has the right hon. Gentleman got the usual leave for the disclosure of Cabinet secrets?

Mr. Churchill: This is not a Cabinet paper. This is one of a great series of telegrams which have passed. Many telegrams have been published, and this is most relevant to the immediate matter. Ten years have passed since these messages have passed. Immense publications are being made of telegrams which have been sent and have passed on all sorts of confidential matters, and I should not be doing my duty to the House if, in discussing a matter of this vital importance, I failed to place this grave issue before Parliament with all its lineaments fully portrayed.

Mr. Brockway: On a point of Order. Is it within the Orders of this House that a Member who has been a member of a previous Cabinet should quote from Cabinet documents which he has had in that capacity and which have not been published?

Mr. Speaker: I understood, in the first instance, that that question could not arise, because it was not a Cabinet document.

Mr. Churchill: It is an administrative paper, but anyhow—[an Hon. Member: "Who sent it?"]. That telegram was sent upon the authority of my right hon. Friend the Member for Carnarvon Boroughs.

Mr. Lloyd George: I should certainly have thought, with due respect, that this was a Cabinet document, and I very much regret that my right hon. Friend, seeing that probably this is a telegram which was sent by me, had not the courtesy at least to inform me, because it must have been one of a series of telegrams, some of which it might have been very inadvisable, not from the point of view of the members of the Cabinet, but from the point of view of the relations of the various countries, to publish. I very deeply regret that, at any rate, some opportunity was not afforded me, who happened to be head of that Government, and who probably sent that telegram, of seeing what the nature of the telegram was, and whether there were not other communications. I should have thought, on the point of Order, that this was essentially a Cabinet document.

Mr. Speaker: The right hon. Gentleman, and indeed the House, will realise that it is not within my authority to say whether it is or is not a Cabinet document. I was only quoting what the right hon. Gentleman said who has produced it, that it was not a Cabinet document. I cannot be the judge of that matter.

Mr. Churchill: At any rate, it is not a point of Order. [An Hon. Member: "It is a point of honour!"] It is a matter on which I very readily submit myself to the measured judgment of the House and of this country.

Mr. Toole: Are we not entitled to know who first published this telegram?

Mr. Churchill: That is not a point of Order. On the point which was raised by my right hon. Friend—[Interruption].

Mr. Speaker: The hon. Member asked me, on a point of Order, whether the House is entitled to know who first published the telegram. I can only say that, under the Rules of this House, when a Member is quoting from a document he makes himself responsible for it. Beyond that I cannot go.

Mr. Brockway: Further to the point of Order which I first raised. I appreciate that the Chair cannot decide whether this is a Cabinet document or not, but I suggest that it is possible to put to the right hon. Member the definite question whether this is a Cabinet document or whether it is not.

Mr. Churchill: In my judgment, it is not a Cabinet document, but only one of a series—

Mr. Brockway: In the judgment of your Prime Minister it was.

Mr. Churchill: The hon. Member asked me a question, and I presume he would like me to reply, but I do not wish to reply if he does not want to hear the answer. In my judgment, it is not a Cabinet document. It is one of an unending series of administrative telegrams which have been sent—

Mr. J. Jones: On a point of Order. If the document is not a Cabinet document, who sent it?

Mr. Churchill: Replying to the point of my right hon. Friend the Member for Carnarvon Boroughs. [An Hon. Member: "Run away!"] Who is running away? I am going to be here for another hour. Replying to the point raised by my right hon. Friend—[Interruption].

Mr. Speaker: We are discussing a very important question, and we cannot do so in an orderly manner with so many interruptions.

Mr. Churchill: Replying to the point raised by my right hon. Friend, I would gladly have given him notice of my intention to cite, in one form or another, the

Speeches of Winston Churchill

important instructions which were given by his Government in 1921, but I am bound to say that I thought those instructions would so redound to his credit and reputation that I could not conceive that there would be any occasion where he would wish me to inform him. If I have erred in this matter, I express to him my regret. These were the instructions and the spirit of the instructions which were sent by my right hon. Friend, and on his authority, and on the authority of his colleagues, at a time when he was defending, with resolution and success, the vital interests of this country.

Mr. Toole: On a point of Order. Perhaps the right hon. Gentleman might at least tell us—

Mr. Speaker: That is not a point of Order.

Mr. Churchill: I have been so much interrupted that perhaps I may recall the House to the theme of the argument which I am addressing to it. My argument is that this London Agreement bears no relation to the Washington Treaty, to which it is apparently a supplement, and that the Washington Treaty carefully and specifically excluded all attempts at achieving parity in regard to minor vessels. I have quoted the instructions that were sent by the Government of that day, and I need scarcely say that those instructions were given the fullest effect by Lord Balfour and in the Washington Agreement. The London Agreement, on the other hand, seeks to apply or purports to apply strict parity to the naval forces of all kinds, whether required for battle or for trade and food protection, and, by so doing, brings directly into the foreground of our minds those immense differences in the situation of the two countries to which I have already referred. There, then, is the fundamental difference which the Pact of London has superimposed upon the Washington Agreement of 1921. This is a change of principle of the most profound and far-reaching character, which has certainly not escaped the attention of any country in the world except perhaps our own. That is my first point, and it leads me directly to my second.

My second point is this: What we are asked to agree to now is not a treaty of parity at all. Under superficial and paper appearance of parity, this treaty embodies a solemn acceptance, not only by Great Britain, but by the British Empire, of a permanent secondary position in seapower. We have abandoned, in fact—and when I look at some of the clauses I think we have also abandoned in form—the principle of the one-Power standard to which our naval strength was reduced after the War. Let me remind the House how that standard has been successively reduced. First of all, for some generations we were as strong at sea as all other countries put together. We did not abuse our strength. Next for a long period we adopted the principle of being substantially stronger than the next two strongest Powers combined, the United States not being at that time a factor. Then, when the German danger grew upon us in the early years of this century, we declared our standard of 16 battleships to Germany's 10 and a two-to-one superiority in cruisers and small craft, all Dominion vessels, let me point out, being excluded, and consequently additions to the calculation. I think that is a sound basis, for, after all, the Dominion navies have separate communities of their own to protect, separate difficulties and dangers to face. After the War, at Washington we accepted the one-power standard in all that contributed to battle strength, excluding all other elements necessary for the protection of food supplies.

The Prime Minister asks us to abandon, in effect, the one-Power standard. We are no longer to have a Navy equal even for purposes of battle—I say nothing of trade protection—to the other leading Navy in the world. That is my assertion. Perhaps the First Lord will address himself to it when he comes to speak later in the Debate. I will try to explain on what I base that statement. I am afraid I am going to speak for some time. We are not going to have interests, rights and securities that have been built up over centures dismissed without patient and searching examination. First, let me say in discussing this matter, that war between the two great English speaking peoples is completely excluded from our minds. It has never played any part in our precautions or preparations at any time, and it has been expressly banished in the most solemn and irrevocable manner by the Kellogg Pact. I will therefore use to illustrate my arguments, letters of the alphabet instead of the names of countries. If you have two Navies, "A" and "B," each of which has 20 battleships and 50 cruisers, you have paper equality. But if "A," by sending its cruisers to raid the trade routes of "B," can draw 30 cruisers of "B" to protect those trade routes, the resultant forces available for battle will not be equal. "A" would have 40 cruisers to protect her battle fleet and find her opponent's battle fleet, and "B" would have only 20. The result in the battle sphere—[An Hon. Member: "What about C and D?"] That is a complication going to be still more embarrassing to that nation with the longest trade routes.

I have taken only one illustration, but one has only to read the evidence which Mr. Stimson has been giving before the Senate committee, for the report of which we are indebted to the "Times," in the last few days. Mr. Stimson is a man most high-minded, most fair-minded, most sober-minded, and although, no doubt, in putting his case to the Senate committee, he would naturally make the best of the mission with which he was charged over here, we make allowances for that. Nevertheless, so far as I can see from independent study, everything he has said is absolutely correct. Let us see some of the things he said which have appeared only this morning. I am sure that the right hon. Gentleman is going to give great attention to this. Mr. Stimson spoke of the Anglo-American equality now established by the Treaty in the battleship class which could even "be turned to superiority if the United States should modernise its vessels." He explained how they had put forward a demand for a new great battleship, not because they thought it would necessarily be accepted, but because it would be something to give away, so that they would be sure to acquire the right to modernise their battleships, which in his words would have the effect of giving them the superiority in the battle fleet. He proceeded to say:

> They secured under the Treaty some superiority in the 8-inch class and they had been successful in reducing British superiority in the 6-inch vessels from 26 to 10 down to 13 to 10.

Mr. Stimson went on to say that:

> The United States was to-day free to build 10,000-ton cruisers carrying 6-inch guns if she chose to do so. And, when the relative gun-power of the British and United States cruiser fleets was considered, he thought it would be found that the position of the United States was even better than in respect of tonnage.

Lieut.-Commander Kenworthy *rose—*

Mr. Churchill: I have already got a long way behind time. No doubt the hon. and gallant Member, as one of the protagonists in this discussion, will have the opportunity of addressing the House in good time. My objection is to steer as clear of technical points as possible in order that the House may follow my argument. I have given illustrations and quoted Mr. Stimson, and there is one final test to establish my thesis that we are asked to agree not to parity but to inferiority. Let us compare, therefore, the British and American cruiser fleets, as they will be built, or virtually built, at the end of 1936. I say "virtually," because there are two American cruisers which may only approach the verge of completion. I assume that both countries build according to the Treaty. I have divided the ships into two classes, the modern or new ships and the older ships. Of modern or new ships, Great Britain will have of 8-inch gun vessels 15, and the United States of 8-inch gun vessels, 18. Great Britain of 6-inch gun vessels will have 14 and the United States of 6-inch gun vessels, 9. The total for Great Britain of modern or new ships is 29, aggregating 237,000 tons, and the 27 United States ships aggregate 253,000 tons.

I come to the older ships. We shall have two Emeralds of 7,000 tons and one Adelaide which may come in that class, and 18 small obsolescent 4,500-ton cruisers. As against this, the United States have 10 Omahas of 7,000 tons or upwards. Such are the fleets. But observe nearly all our 15 8-inch gun ships already built or in process of completion. Nearly all the American 8-inch gun ships are still to build, with all improvements in design and power which the naval science of every year makes it possible to bestow on new vessels. Therefore, I have no doubt that they will be superior at every point to the British 8-inch gun ships—at every point science can give them. All the American 6-inch gun ships are new or under 16 years, and they are all of large tonnage. Mr. Stimson makes a great point of that, which, of course, is of enormous importance, where you have to have a considerable radius, stability, strength to resist artillery attacks, and safety in a rough sea. All these are of the utmost consequence.

There are the two fleets, and there is no doubt whatever of these two fleets, as they will be in 1926 cruiser fleets, that of the United States will be definitely superior in strength. That is taking no consideration at all of the different tasks. One has to protect the immense trade routes on which the life of this island depends, and the other is for war unconnected with the bringing in of supplies. But there is a method of testing which of these two fleets will be stronger, because it has been arranged as an alternative that the United States shall be free to construct an exact parity cruiser fleet to our own, a virtual replica as far as possible of our own. By so doing, they will gain 13,000 tons of additional construction. But are they going to do it? They know perfectly well that a far better arrangement for their naval forces and a far better disposition of money for their cruiser fleet will be made by the building which I have set out and not by adhering to an exact replica of our own fleet.

I cannot conclude my argument about parity without dealing with one more point. It is freely stated in the United States, and it is one of the arguments which no doubt the right hon. Gentleman and his colleague the First Lord had to meet, that Great Britain has her large mercantile marine and naval bases all over the world, and that the United States must have a stronger navy to equate this. That is an altogether ill-founded idea. These bases and the merchant ships which we have are not sources of aggressive strength; they are only the vital apparatus by which we compensate ourselves for our dispersed situation and our dependence on overseas food. If the naval power which uses these bases and guards these merchant fleets becomes inadequate, they all sink together in helpless futility. I have used the similitude of the diver. The diver has a helmet, a special dress and heavy boots; he has an air-pipe and pumping apparatus of the most complicated character, but the diver, with all these possessions will not be in a stronger position than the man who is standing on *terra firma* without any of them. If the air-pipe is severed, the diver and his apparatus perish together and to say that we should bring our mercantile marine and bases into this calculation, is to use an argument to which we would never lend ourselves.

In proposing a Treaty binding us to a definite naval inferiority to any other Power, the Government have gone beyond what is wise and right and in harmony with the long and hitherto carefully guarded interests of this country. The signature and ratification of this Treaty will be a memorable and melancholy event in our history. I look upon it with amazement. If anyone had told me that 15 years after the Royal Navy had saved this country from the horrors of invasion, that 13 years after it had saved us from actual starvation, that 12 years after it had brought all the allied nations safely and victoriously through the Great War, we should be sitting here to approve a Treaty which denies us, not supremacy, for that has been given up, but even the right to have a navy equal to that of any other great Power, I would have thought him mad. We on this side of the House may be powerless to save such a position, but we cannot accept the slightest responsibility for it. We cannot invest the act of the Government with national sanction. We hold ourselves free to review the whole situation. I was very glad when I saw in this Treaty the provision which had been inserted for a review in 1935, and I shall have a word to say about that later.

I come to my third point. We are allowed a total of 50 cruisers aggregating 339,000 tons. Leaving the United States out of account, is this sufficient for our needs? The Prime Minister did not think so when he was last in power. On the contrary, he began a programme for the construction of these 10,000 ton 8-inch gun cruisers with an instalment never equalled by the Conservative Government in the succeeding years. The Admiralty did not consider it adequate in 1925; on the contrary, they presented arguments and calculations worked out in elaborate detail for every area showing the cruisers required for every area from which it was necessary for this country to draw its food and raw material. They threatened to resign on their cruiser programme so strongly did they feel. At Geneva, the Admiralty adhered to the same figures backed with an immense amount of technical detail. Let us quote Mr. Stimson again:

> The new British Government came in determined "to do better," and he did not think there was sufficient realisation in this country of "how much they have done." He drew a comparison between the statement of the British minimum cruiser requirements made at Geneva—70 vessels aggregating 420,000 tons—and the present agreement on 50 vessels of 339,000 tons, and described it as remarkable.

We will all agree that it is remarkable. What is the reason which had led the Naval Lords to make such an immense change in the professional advice which it is their duty to tender to the Ministers of the day? It cannot be any improvement in our relations with the United States, or any pact we have signed with them, because we had always excluded the United States as possible enemies from our calculations. We are assured by the Government that it is the effect of the Kellogg Pact and the general improving sentiment for peace which has justified this surprising alteration in professional views. I did not agree with the Lords of the Admiralty in their estimate of 70 cruisers unless many of them were very old vessels. I am none the less surprised, knowing the very solid and detailed arguments on which they based themselves, at their change of attitude and conviction. I cannot understand how expert naval opinion upon the number of cruisers required in particular areas to assure our food supplies can be influenced by the agreement of other Powers to the Kellogg Pact, especially when it has unhappily been followed in almost every case by a marked increase in naval armaments and an increased interest in naval strategy.

I can understand that the argument about improved conditions of peace might well influence the Government and the House of Commons, but I do not see how it is relevant to the purely technical calculations on which all the previous advice of the expert advisers has been based. There is, however, one explanation which suggests itself. Fifty large cruisers of modern type might give us as great a measure of security as 70 cruisers, a large proportion of which were small, old and obsolete. But this explanation is largely swept from us by the extraordinary provision about the 91,000 tons, the significance of which was only realised by the country after the Treaty was made public. Under this provision we are forbidden for the next five years to build up even to our replacement quota of cruisers within the tonnage which is still allowed to us, and we are allowed to build only 91,000 tons. Therefore, during that period we shall be making replacements approximately at 20 years life instead of at 16 years life. I see no objection to extending the life of cruisers by treaty to 20 years, provided that that condition is simultaneously obligatory on every other party signatory to the treaty. But what are we to say to a provision which compels us, whose cruiser fleet is already largely obsolete, and is also our life and protection, to rebuild cruisers after only 20 years, while other parties to the agreement are authorised immediately to replace upon a 16 years basis?

Thus we are neither to have numbers nor quality. We are deliberately to be made to allow the main character of our cruiser fleet to degenerate into obsolescence, while other Powers will be increasing theirs in numbers and modernity, and when the United States will be making enormous and feverish additions to her naval strength. After more than 20 years close connection with these matters, I am astonished that any Admiralty board of naval officers could have been found to accept responsibility—and it is a very grave responsibility—for such a ham-stringing stipulation. The effect is obvious, and I hope that the House marks very carefully the effect; it is to make it certain that our cruiser forces will be reduced to inferiority before the Treaty comes up for revision in 1935 or 1936. That undoubtedly must be considered by us in estimating the importance of the review which we will give to these matters in 1935 or 1936. By then we shall have definitely become the second naval Power.

British affairs, naval and other, have, I think, suffered from lack of will power, through lack of confidence in ourselves or in our duty, and lack of national conviction as to our course. Other countries have their plans and resolves. We drift, seeking the easiest way out, the smoothest course, and taking the line of least resistance. Other countries, much weaker countries, do not hesitate to state their views and intentions and to stand by them. Do they suffer for it? No; they are respected, and deference is shown to their views. We are the passive matrix on which others imprint their claims. Nevertheless, we have not yet reached the position where we need fear to state our views and intentions plainly and resolutely. I have dealt with some of the disadvantages of this Treaty, but what are we going to gain by it? It is called a Treaty of Disarmament. Whom does it disarm? Japan? Japan has secured an increase of her ratio, and she approaches now to within 30 per cent. of the cruiser strength of the British Empire, which is scattered all over the globe. France and Italy? They have gone off to embark, perhaps, on a serious naval rivalry between themselves, which will be the cause of much anxiety to other Powers.

The United States are, of course, making the greatest naval expansion that has been seen. The only Power to be disarmed is the Power which has already disarmed the most; the only navy to be cut down is the Navy of the country that cannot live without sea-borne food. We are told that a great deal of money has been saved. The Prime Minister mentioned £50,000,000, but I have seen £70,000,000 claimed as the saving to the taxpayer in the next five years to be effected by this Treaty. What truth is there in that? The Government's position is that we must build what, in accordance with their views, is the absolute minimum compatible with safety, excluding the United States. We should have had to do that, anyhow, neither more nor less.

What, then, have we saved on it? "Ah," we are told, "we have not got to replace great battleships." I approve of the extension of the life of battleships, it has always been our aim, and we would also have been very glad to see that important additional measures were taken to secure a substantial reduction in their size; but supposing that no agreement had been made and that we had built no more battleships after 1931? Is it certain that the United States would have built any? I think it would be very difficult for the United States to build a series of new and monster battleships if they were the only ones that were being constructed in the world. It would not be difficult through any lack of material or any lack of resources, but it would be difficult because of the moral outlook of very large masses of the population of the United States, and immense opposition would gather against such a policy. This moral resistance would in this case have been re-enforced by practical arguments of the highest significance, namely, that air power, as it increases, will seal the doom of these £8,000,000 or £9,000,000 monsters. Whether that be right or not I am not saying, but at any rate it is an argument which is much supported in the United States, and it seems to me that we need have taken no steps to renew our battle fleet until other Powers embarked on new building.

Therefore, I conclude, but I am only in the region of conjecture, that the agreement reached on battleships is not the result of a bargain or the fruits of this Conference, but the results of the conviction in many quarters, and especially in the United States, that giant battleships are following the mammoth into extinction. Then what money has been saved by signing the Treaty? There is no question of our reducing our normal Estimates by £50,000,000 or £70,000,000, spread over five years. There never was a question of doing more than averting an expenditure which had not yet arrived, and I submit to the House that it is very probable that this new battleship construction would never have come to pass. There is, however, one great prize which might have been gained by this Treaty, which, if gained, would make amends for much. We ask ourselves whether this immense surrender on our part, this sacrifice to which Mr. Stimson has borne unstinted witness, will end the naval controversy between Great Britain and the United States? Shall we reach the position where British and Americans will not worry any more about each other's fleets and leave off ceaselessly comparing them, gun for gun and ton for ton? [*Interruption.*] But we cannot blame the British Nation for being anxious on this matter. After all, we see the Senate of the United States holding the most strict inquiry, examining its officers and representatives, summoning before it admirals and experts, and spending we do not know how many weeks in the most searching examination of every detail of a matter which, after all, is infinitely less important to them than it is in our case. Therefore, you cannot blame us for worrying while we are forced to consider propositions of this kind.

I confess that I would, to end this naval controversy between the two English-speaking peoples, pay a great price—[*Interruption*]—but not any price. But will this Agreement achieve it? [*Interruption.*] I am submitting a reasoned argument to the House and I have not been hurrying, because I really think one ought not to hurry over this. I ask again, Will this agreement achieve it? That is the crux of our discussion. I fear, on the contrary, that this Agreement is only the beginning of a protracted and delicate and difficult controversy between the two countries on technical naval details. Look at the disputes which arose about the simple Washington Agreement. Look at the bitterness which was exhibited about the elevation of the guns, and questions of that kind, and how often we were told that the clever British diplomatists and experts had "pulled the wool" over the eyes of their cousins across the ocean. Look at the bitterness about that simple matter, and conceive what a field for controversy is opened by this enormously complicated Agreement, extending as it does to so many classes of vessel. I fear deeply that this Treaty will create misunderstandings and heart burnings. It has already created misunderstandings and heart burnings on each side of the Atlantic which will hinder and not help the march of the great verities and unities of the English-speaking world. If that be so, all our sacrifices will have been made in vain.

It would have been better to have said that we could not accept numerical parity, because it takes no account of the conditions of our life; it would have been far better to have said, "Let us each build as little as possible and act in a neighbourly manner. Let us each build what we think we require. We are sure that our fleets, however constituted, however contrasted, will, if they act at all, in all human probability act together." That would have been a far wiser answer to have given. The right hon. Gentleman has asked, what would be the effect of giving such an answer on the building of other Powers? He said they would start building, and a repercussion would have been drawn from the United States and another from ourselves. But all that is taking place now. The United States are engaged in building, the Japanese have been given an increase in their ratio; naval construction is going on everywhere, and all that is happening is that we, and we alone, are barred.

Since the War the relations of Great Britain and the United States have become to a very large extent the politics of the world. We in Great Britain can clearly see the course which we should take. We ought to strive to unite the British Empire or British Commonwealth of Nations as closely as possible into one effective whole, so that we can co-operate with the other great branch of the English-speaking peoples on equal terms and as equal partners in high endeavour and equal guardians of peace and progress among all nations. But equality is the foundation of that co-operation. There is the path of safety and honour for all. It is now to be impeded most gravely by action which, though well intentioned, is wrongly conceived and improvidently executed, and I urge upon the House that a far more stringent examination of this issue should be made by Parliament before we commit ourselves to what is certainly a lamentable and may well be an irrevocable decision.

[Much later] I should like to say a word, if the House will allow me. I was certainly not trying, in answer to the unexpected attack of the right hon. Gentleman the Member for Carnarvon Boroughs (Mr. Lloyd George), to lay down any doctrine on these matters which, even when they are compressed into a state of definition, are not such as can be dealt with on the spur of the moment. But I must say this in fair play to the House. I was a Member of the Government which sent these instructions [to Lord Balfour at the 1921 Washington Conference, cited at the beginning of the speech]. I was one of those most closely connected with that part of the policy. The fact is, though I did not disclose it myself, that I actually made the draft which I submitted to the Prime Minister of the time. If I, during the tenure of office of that Government, in the course of my duties as a Minister in the very centre of this policy, had been called upon to defend or explain the policy of the Government, I should have explained it in those very words or almost those very words. I should have said this: "These are the instructions we have sent; this is the sense in which we have acted"; and I must say that I cannot feel, so far as I am concerned, that the lapse of time prevents me from saying what was the policy of the Government in those days, what were the stipulations we made, and what were the limitations. Still less do I feel that I should be inhibited in this matter when I know that the facts have been stated a hundred times, and stated twenty times by me.

On every platform here and in America I have said, "You made a great mistake in saying that we have played you false because we have not the universal parity which you expected at Washington." Twenty times I said we always excluded the cruisers and small craft. There is nothing new in that; it has been stated again and again. When we come to the question of how far these matters are affected by the lapse of time I would point out that it is nearly 10 years ago. That is a very long time, and I certainly do not consider that a Minister deeply concerned with a particular policy is not entitled, after 10 years, to explain in general terms what his view was, and what the course of the Government was.

Now I come to the question of whether I ought to have paraphrased this statement or not. It is true, as the right hon. Gentleman has said, that I could not have had access to the document without his permission. I remember perfectly well the course I took and my action with the Prime Minister in those days in the matter. Instead of rummaging among my archives, I asked that he should supply it to me. It never occurred to me for a moment that there would be all this story about the difference between my reading a perfectly innocent paragraph, the whole substance of which has been published for four or five years, and my paraphrasing it, as I could so easily have done, and perhaps as I ought to have done. I am ready, in the absence of any close definition, to admit that perhaps I ought to have paraphrased it. Instead of saying, "This is what we said," I should have said, "Our instructions to Lord Balfour at Washington were to the effect that he should do so-and-so, but that he was not to do this or that." It would have been quite easy. I think it is possible, on the point of form, that I am in fault, and to that extent, if I am in fault, I am glad to be corrected— and no one can doubt that I have been corrected. It has been the subject of expressions of opinion from almost every quarter in the House, but I ask in fairness, appealing to my fellow Members of the House of Commons, that they should look at the text of the words which I read out and see how completely innocent they are of anything that could have the slightest injurious effect upon our affairs. In order to make them innocuous I did, in fact, leave out deliberately references to certain countries. If hon. Members will do that they will see that in this matter there is no grave and serious breach of the foundations of our public proceedings, but that, on the contrary, a statement has been made which was necessary and relevant to the actual Debate.

I must admit, so far as the right hon. Gentleman the Member for Carnarvon Boroughs (Mr. Lloyd George) was concerned, that he had a ground of complaint against me, in that I did not say to him beforehand, "I shall have to mention the line we took at Washington in 1921." That is the sort of thing that I should have said—that I ought to have said—but I did not happen to see the right hon. Gentleman, and it never occurred to me for one moment that he could have objected. However, if it is his desire to define these matters more precisely, I certainly think that would be very advantageous; but, however you define it, there must be some statute of limitations imposed. After 10 years have passed, or after 20 years, or after 50 years, some freedom must be permitted in the statement of what actually happened, and why it happened, and in this case I rest myself upon a perfectly innocent use of a document which had ceased to have validity for 10 years, and which represented my statement of a course of policy which I had taken a grave and general responsibility in propounding.

FINANCE BILL

May 20, 1930

House of Commons

There will be general agreement that the hon. Member who has just addressed the House ought to take a free and frequent part in our financial discussions, and I can assure him that when it comes to the prolonged stages of the Committee on the Finance Bill we shall welcome his expanding and discursive but useful contributions to a searching examination of the proposals which will be placed before us. The hon. Member ended upon a note of economy. There he is greatly to be congratulated for his courage because he follows a leader, or I believe he follows a leader, whose place is empty at the moment—though I believe his seat is reserved for him when he returns—and whose programme at the last election was the expenditure of borrowed money, up to £200,000,000, to be spent on curing unemployment by building roads and bridges—[an Hon. Member: "And other things!"]—and other things. Whatever may be said for or against such a programme, it cannot be called economy, and the proof that it can hardly be called economy is that the right hon. Gentleman the Chancellor of the Exchequer, even with the strongest incentive and compulsion to act upon it, has not done so now that he is in possession of proper and official information and knowledge. The hon. Member also furnished the Chancellor of the Exchequer with a complete scheme for the revision of the Income Tax. I hope that will have the right hon. Gentleman's attention at an early stage, and that we shall hear to-night some of his first thoughts upon that interesting addition to his labours. Lastly, the hon. Member embarked on some comparisons as to the progress made in reducing the nominal deadweight total of debt. I shall not follow him there, further than to say that if he seeks to have a real, or even a partial comprehension, of our present financial system, he must at the outset realise that comparison of the nominal deadweight total of debt have absolutely no connotable relationship with its actual burden.

This Debate has been marked by carefully considered speeches on both sides, but I cannot feel that there is left to me at the present time any large new field of argument further than what has already been presented on the Budget. What is the first great fact before us? Deep anxiety reigns throughout this island about our financial, economic and industrial position. Every class and every party shares in those anxieties. Unemployment has risen to figures unprecedented even on the morrow of the General Strike. Everyone knows that the short favourable season of the year is rapidly passing away, and that we have before us an autumn and a winter, in which these alarming figures will steadily rise. Trade has fallen off in an extraordinary manner during the worst months, I believe, that have been recorded in normal times for many years. There is a feeling of great despondency in the business and commercial and industrial circles throughout the country. As to remedies, it must be admitted that there is also great doubt and difference of opinion. I never remember a time when one felt the country so much under the influence and oppression of what I would call the down-and-out and under complex, when there was so little resilience, so little real accord or strong conviction over a wide area of public opinion as to the proper method of immediately dealing with our difficulties.

Though there may be great doubts as to the remedies, and although there may be universal accord at the evil, there is a pretty general agreement that the right hon. Gentleman's Budget is not the right way to help at this particular moment, and is not the right treatment that should be administered to our problems at this juncture. We have heard again and again of the evils of direct taxation. When the Conservative speakers put that forward, they are usually met with derision from the other side of the House, but to-day the right hon. Member for Darwen (Sir H. Samuel) used a great many exceedingly searching sentences upon this subject. He said that high direct taxation was a hindrance to industrial enterprise, that it discouraged industry adventuring, that it was a great deterrent to trade, and that industrial organisation must suffer. He used all these terms about the effect of the pressure of high direct taxation upon trade and industry. Therein, of course, he differs from the Chancellor of the Exchequer with his life-long doctrine that high taxation of the idle rich is an actual stimulus to trade and industry, and exercises a bracing effect upon our affairs.

Whatever may be the actual and direct effect of heavier taxation upon trade and industry, I believe it true to say that the psychological reactions are more harmful still. I spoke the other day in an employment Debate of the mysterious gap that existed between producer and consumer in every country in the world. We do not know how to bridge that gap, but all experience has shown that one of the most helpful methods and one of the most certain methods of narrowing the gap is by promoting confidence, enterprise, hope and audacity in the industrial and economic life of any community. In so far as the right hon. Gentleman's Budget has played a part in our immediate misfortunes, although I would by no means attribute all these misfortunes to his Budget, it has played a part undoubtedly in its effect on confidence and on enterprise, of being a real aggravation of the conditions of unemployment and of trade which exists at the present time. Among the psychological effects of this Budget there is undoubtedly the fact that it is conceived in an unfair spirit. I am well aware of the argument that is put by the Socialist representatives below the Gangway, that the rich have the money and that it ought to be taken away from them and given to the poor.

But that is not the position of this Parliament or this Government, nor is it the position which in any way has been accepted by the great mass of the electors of this country. No, Sir, they have not taken that view, but the Chancellor of the Exchequer, who sits there to deal with the actual financial problems of the time, deals with them on that basis. It is a most unwise thing, a foolish step, to produce a Budget of pains and penalties which is deliberately and obviously aimed at taxing only those from whom he is quite sure he can never receive a vote. [*Laughter.*] Hon. Members opposite laugh at that. They make a great mistake in not realising the interdependence of the whole of this community, a vast complex community, which is so interdependent that if any one healthy part suffers that suffering will be spread over every part of the body. In contracting the range of the Income Tax, and at the same moment increasing its burden, the right hon. Gentleman showed a class bias, a partisanship, which ought never to have obtruded itself into his calculations. I say nothing at the moment, except to mention it, of the breach of faith involved in his treatment of the pre-War insurance policies, or of the astonishing argument put forward by himself and the President of the Board of Trade, the latter of whom said, "What does this matter to us? We have got the money." Therefore, apparently, it was of no value to keep faith with those who had contributed it.

Generally speaking, an atmosphere of insecurity and of depression has been engendered and fostered by the Budget of the Chancellor of the Exchequer. If the direct taxpayers, who are the sole object of his attentions at the present time, respond willingly, according to all the traditions which have sustained the revenue of this country, undoubtedly their response and the success of these schemes of taxation, will be used as an argument for a further aggression upon them, for further inroads upon them in future Budgets. The effects of this Budget upon trade and industry will have their repercussions on the revenue, and they will be reinforced by other direct effects upon the revenue itself. Already the balance of the Budget has been destroyed by the increase of unemployment which has resulted since it was introduced. Already the right hon. Gentleman is borrowing, and will be forced to borrow, very large sums upon the Unemployment Insurance Fund, which has been running into the heaviest expenditure since he declared his Budget provisions for the year, and no one can doubt that new expenditure is looming up in the future. The raising of the school age alone is casting a heavy financial shadow over the Exchequer, and, generally speaking, there can be no security, or sense of security, for the classes upon whom the right hon. Gentleman has thrown, and intends to throw, whatever burdens it is his duty to dispose of.

I believe that the limit of direct taxation, if not actually reached, is in sight at the present time. I know that that view is treated with great derision on the opposite side of the House. Figures were quoted by the right hon. Gentleman the Member for Darwen who took an income of £50,000 a year, and showed that, if provision were made for the payment of the Death Duties on such an estate, the actual annual charge upon that income of £50,000 a year would be £50,958. When we talk of the old saying of the right hon. Gentleman that we must not look at what he has taken away but at what he has left, in this minus quantity of £958 a year there is very little left even for him to get fat upon. After all, a revival of trade and industry is the only solution of our difficulties. No other event can enable us to escape from our present position. We have never had in late years the normal expansion of the Income Tax which is the due of any Chancellor of the Exchequer. There has been an almost complete arrest of that expansion.

I am going to recur for a few minutes to the figures to which I have referred more than once, and which I suggest the Chancellor of the Exchequer might examine for himself, with regard to the profits which have been made in past years and in recent years by what are called the depressed industries. I have discovered the figures since I last referred to the matter. Let the House listen to this. In 1913 the profits of the following industries—mining, iron and steel, engineering, metals excluding motors, cotton, wool, bleaching and dyeing and railways—that great group of industries, amounted to £133,000,000. Translating that into present money values, it represents something in the neighbourhood of £210,000,000 or £220,000,000 a year. What were the figures in 1928? The figures for the same industries in 1928, which is the latest year for which I have them—perhaps the right hon. Gentleman can supplement them—showed that, whereas the profits were £219,000,000 in 1913 the comparable yield in 1928 of that same vast group of basic trades was only £96,000,000. What are the conclusions which may be drawn from that? [*Interruption.*] I have tried my best to help the state of trade and the depressed industries, and that was one of the main incentives of the course adopted in the granting of rate relief for those very industries. At the moment, however, I am discussing them from the point of view of the Chancellor of the Exchequer who wants a high yield of Income Tax. Is it not perfectly clear that here you have these enormous industries employing great numbers of people carrying on a very great business, but a very large proportion of them not reaching a profit-making condition, or only reaching a very small profit-making condition, and consequently cutting down the revenues of the Exchequer, and depriving the country of the normal yield of the Income Tax expansion. It is that fact which, more than anything else in my opinion, should attract the attention of those who wish to give good guidance to the country at the present time.

The remedy is to raise these industries to a more generally profit-paying level. If you are able to do so, £10,000,000 or £20,000,000 of additional Income Tax will come into your revenue and enable you possibly to reduce the rate and even further increase the yield. If the right hon. Gentleman were able to reduce the rate of the charge and lighten the burden and restore the confidence which is required, it does not follow by any means that his revenue would fall off in proportion to the reduction of the rate of the charge. He might, if the circumstances turned in a favourable manner, find there would come back to him overflowing revenue as the result of the actual reduction in the charge levied. If it be true that the limits of direct taxation are being approached at the present time—and the pledge, if it be a pledge, which the Chancellor has given that he will not add to the direct taxation next year indicates that he himself is far from disassociating himself from that view—it seems to me—and I repeat what I said upon the Resolution—that we shall be driven to a tariff for revenue purposes. I have mentioned as one possibility which, in my opinion, ought to be considered, and which we should certainly have considered as a purely revenue matter if we had been in power, a duty, and a high duty, upon imported finished manufactured goods.

Taken in conjunction with these figures which I have just mentioned, it must be seen that if the imposition of such a tariff had the effect of stimulating and reviving industry and bringing it up to a profitable level, you would not only get one yield of tax from the duty, but you would get a second yield from the fact that businesses which are now being conducted and are paying nothing to the revenue because they are making no profit would have reached a profitable area and that benefit would pass to the Income Tax. [Hon. Members: "How can you get both?"] Hon. Gentlemen have not followed my argument at all. I am sorry, but I cannot trespass too long on the House and go back upon it. I was pointing out that the duty which would be collected upon these goods would be reinforced by the Income Tax. The Customs Duties which would be collected at the port on this trade by a tariff would be reinforced if the trade were stimulated—[Hon. Members: "Oh!"] Hon. Members may deride it, but let them follow the argument. It would be reinforced by a further addition to the Income Tax.

The right hon. Gentleman asked me on the Resolution to say what my view was as to who would pay the Import Duties. That is a perfectly innocent question. I can answer it at once. Our experience of the Safeguarding Duties has shown quite clearly that there is no absolute rule. Even in these few small duties which have been placed on selected industries, there have been examples shown where it has been proved that the foreigner has reduced his prices by more than the amount of the duty in order to get into the market. That is the fact and one which must be taken into consideration. But even supposing that the consumer pays, it might be well worth his while to pay if at the same time there were a revival of energy and vigour in all our industrial plants and centres, and if a sense of domination and expansion were restored to British industry. I am quite content in this matter to quote the Leader of the Liberal party. He is not here to-night, but he was our Leader in the days when the scheme of Safeguarding was first conceived and brought into reality. What did he say in his formal letter to Mr. Bonar Law on the eve of the 1918 Election? He said:

> I should say that we must face all these questions with new eyes, without regard to pre-War views or to pre-War speeches. I shall look at every problem and consider it from the point of view of what is the best method of securing the object at which we are aiming, without any regard to theoretical opinions about Free Trade or Tariffs.

No one could ask for more than that, and I would ask the Prime Minister, if he were here—I do not think it is much use asking the Chancellor of the Exchequer—why, in the plight in which we stand, and which causes every one trouble and anxiety, has he not thought it worth while to consult, on some of these questions, his new Economic Council which was set up with so much consequence and importance? Why, for instance, could he not have asked his new Economic Council, "Do you think it would be a good thing at the moment"—for, after all, we are practical people—"to sweep away all the Safeguarding Duties, or would it be a good thing to let them alone for a little time at any rate?" Why could he not put that question to this Council? He is not bound by the answer, I quite agree; his Government is responsible: but why could he not put to this new body, which the Government set up and behind which largely they sheltered themselves at the time, such a question as this: "If we have to raise £50,000,000 more, what is the best way in which we can get it without making the conditions of trade and employment worse?" There are also questions connected with currency, connected with the use of public credit—very important questions, very grave and anxious questions, which in my opinion could not in any way be injured if they were remitted for impartial consideration to a body of practical business men and financiers of high repute, such as has been gathered together in the Economic Advisory Council. But the Chancellor of the Exchequer will have none of this. In the right hon. Gentleman we are face to face with a dual personality. Everyone knows the famous example of Dr. Jekyll and Mr. Hyde. [*Interruption.*] On the one hand, we have the severe Treasury pedant, accepting with double joy the narrowest doctrines and dogmas of departmental officials, and on the other hand we have the Socialist agitator endeavouring to excite the masses to the pillage of the wealth of this country. There is, however, this difference between the case of Dr. Jekyll and Mr. Hyde when these two personalities are combined in the Chancellor of the Exchequer, that whereas society gained a great deal by the generous and virtuous actions of Dr. Jekyll and suffered from the brutality and violence of Mr. Hyde, in the Chancellor of the Exchequer we are in the unfortunate position of suffering both from the pedantry of Dr. Jekyll and from the venomous greed and partisanship of Mr. Hyde. It is the pedantry of Dr. Jekyll which has led him to present himself so decorously before the Bankers' Institute, making them ceremonious speeches, full of orthodox platitudes, as to the importance of sustaining the capitalist system, and we have this further aspect of Dr. Jekyll that in order to gratify his narrow and doctrinaire views he not only exposes the whole of the trades protected by the McKenna Duties to prolonged uncertainty, and is leaving them with renewed uncertainty, but is signalising his contribution to our unemployment problems this year by allowing the Safeguarding Duties to lapse. His colleague, the Lord Privy Seal, who sits next to him, with a pensive air, admitted only yesterday the prejudicial effects caused to employment in this country and that his own task was rendered more difficult by the uncertainty in regard to these duties. There may well have been occasion when the right hon. Gentleman could have afforded to indulge his views and his hostility to these forms of taxation, but surely, with unemployment bounding up and with everybody worried and anxious as to what can be done, he might have thought of some more urgent task to undertake at the present time than to face the hostility and the labour of removing this protection from these small industries, which have now grown largely dependent upon them.

This brings me to the speech of my right hon. Friend the Member for Darwen—a most important contribution to our Debate. I am bound to say that whenever I am listening to an able speech by the right hon. Gentleman I am always reminded of a book that I used to read called "Mrs. Caudle's Curtain Lectures." Here there is a difference, because Mrs. Caudle had only one husband, but the right hon. Gentleman and the Liberal party have, on each side of the House, I will not say suitors, but at any rate personalities to whom they are able to impart their wisdom. The right hon. Gentleman said of the Chancellor of the Exchequer that his Budget was trim and grim. So also was the right hon. Gentleman's speech. Professedly impartial, the wise statesman, who takes the middle, temperate position between Conservative reaction and Socialist impatience, contributes a sound, cool, detached, impartial review of the situation. That is the picture which the right hon. Gentleman would like to claim for his attitude. Alas, I cannot countersign his claim. The right hon. Gentleman, acting under the orders, no doubt, of his absent chief, represents, not an impartial tribunal, but a nobbled umpire. He is the unjust judge, the arbitrator who has a fine string of specious, sonorous arguments and reasons to give in support of his judgment, but who gives his judgment according to the party from which he hopes to derive the greatest advantage. I am afraid that the right hon. Gentleman and his friends, still less his leader, are not in a position to take decisions upon the merits of any question. Their decisions have to vary with the ebb and flow of the political combinations which they are considering or rejecting.

Mr. MacLaren: Is this autobiography?

Mr. Churchill: I congratulate the hon. Gentleman on having achieved at least a *tu quoque*; it is something indeed in the art of repartee to get to that primitive stage. Let me not allow my comments upon the right hon. Gentleman's speech to rest solely upon the foundation of assertion. Let me offer some proof. The proof is found above all things in the references which he has made to-day to his attitude upon the Coal Bill. To-day the right hon. Gentleman said, in effect—I am not actually remembering his words—"We had, of course, to suggest some Amendments to particular Clauses of that Bill." But was that the language which he used to the House when it was first being presented? He made us the most impressive speech, in which he described this Bill as inverted Protection. Everyone knows that he hates Protection as much as anything in the world, but I suppose inverted Protection is an even more vicious form of it. Here is one of the worst things that could possibly happen, the worst form of Protection, and in a leaflet—

Sir H. Samuel: We struck out the "inverted Protection."

Mr. Churchill: Naturally, he struck it out after the arrangement had been made. But here, in a leaflet written by some gay and jaunty soul, under the rare and remarkable heading, "Why I have joined the Liberal Party," published by the Liberal Publication Department, I find:

> I cannot understand how the Labour party could have brought itself to give to the coalowners, by law, the power of restricting output,

and so on.

> Every home in England would have to pay more for every bag of coal if the Government got its way. Who showed up this rotten proposal? Not the Tories. Everybody knows it was the Liberals, especially Lloyd George and Herbert Samuel.

Sir H. Samuel: Shall I read the following sentence, or will the right hon. Gentleman?

Mr. Churchill: I will. It goes on:

> If the bad features of the Bill are altered, and we are saved from dear coal, it will be the Liberals we shall have to thank.

The main provision has not been affected. I do not wish to get into a detailed argument, that would not be in order, on this point. But I am not afraid of it, and there will be another opportunity. When this Bill comes back to us from the House of Lords, this "rotten Bill," we shall hear the right hon. Gentleman exerting himself to prove that all the evil features have been driven out and that it only remains for the Liberals and Socialists to unite together to ask the House of Commons to assert its rights. There is the impartial umpire, who, after the manner of his kind, swings from one side to the other according to some occult or secret arrangement made behind the back of Parliament. [An Hon. Member: "What about the Budget?"] I am coming to the Budget, and I dare say the hon. Gentleman will be glad. I say this Budget is a Budget of negation and dismay. It places heavy burdens on the country, and it places them in a manner calculated to cause the utmost despondency and alarm. But, although it places these heavy burdens, there is nothing to show for them. The right hon. Gentleman has piled on new expenditure and has nothing worth while to show for it. I do not know if the House remembers that the hon. Member for West Wolverhampton (Mr. W. J. Brown) made a long and interesting speech. I think there was great justice in his complaint. I disagree with the hon. Member on most topics, but his complaint was that the Chancellor of the Exchequer and the Government had defrauded the electors; they had promised all sorts of indulgences and amenities and improvements and reforms in the social sphere; that they were not able to discharge

Speeches of Winston Churchill

any of these undertakings, and had no intention of attempting to do so. That was his bitter complaint. He said, "Look at your speeches and look at your promises. The statements which are now made mean that we have to drop any hope of any comprehensive scheme for dealing with unemployment." But much more has to be dropped. We are at the end. We have heard about the widows' pensions, the improvements made in the Unemployment Insurance Fund, and some small benefit to civil servants in regard to their pay, but that is all there is left of "Labour and the Nation." The right hon. Gentleman made a speech which has been quoted by the hon. Member for West Wolverhampton. I think it was during the election, in which he indicated that £200,000,000 was not beyond what might well be within the scope of practical finance. He had better be careful how he speaks of his allies. It is no matter what he says to me, but he had better be careful there. He may find that he has involved the Government, not for the first time, in considerable difficulties. The right hon. Gentleman raised this point and he was interrupted by the Chancellor of the Exchequer, who brought out the fact in a part of his speech which was not apparently quoted in the "Times" or any newspaper in which we have a report. He said it was time, but he added that there might be young men in the hall who would live to see this scheme of improving the social services realised. The right hon. Gentleman made a cogent retort when he said he did not think they would have given their votes to the Socialist party if they had known that all the benefits of "Labour and the Nation" were to be reserved for their grandchildren.

There is no surplus in view. The right hon. Gentleman suggested that £14,000,000 might be available, but there is an additional charge in respect of rating relief. If there were a surplus in view, the Chancellor of the Exchequer, by his own folly, needlessly adding to his difficulties, has pledged himself to remove £40,000,000 of indirect taxation. The McKenna Duties, the rest of the Safeguarding Duties, the Sugar Duties and so forth, all are to be swept away. There are £40,000,000 to be swept away before we get to any constructive social programme even if a surplus were in view. Napoleon said to his soldiers, "From the top of these Pyramids 40 centuries are looking down on you." The Chancellor of the Exchequer says to the Clyde, "From the trough of the Treasury £40,000,000 are gaping up at you." This story is drawing towards its close. The Government is utterly bankrupt in ideas. It is content to live on the capitalist system and bask in its pleasures and amenities while at the same time it snarls at it and from time to time inflicts limited but still serious injury upon it. The Government is prolific in surrenders but it is devoid of a single helpful, constructive plan. Shiftless, profuse, futile, spiteful, it is drifting to speedy dissolution amid general indifference to fast gathering contempt.

EMPIRE DAY ADDRESS

May 24, 1930

Badminton Park, London

I am thankful, looking back, that the Conservative Party at the last election did not go to the country telling the lie that they could cure unemployment and parading a lot of crazy schemes to delude the people. Mr. Lloyd George made the wildest promises in the hopes of winning votes. He promised to reduce unemployment to normal, that was to say, to 600,000 or 700,000, within a year without adding anything to the rates and taxes. The shamelessness of that promise was the measure of his hunger for power. Anyone can see where we should have been to-day with this world-wide slump in prices and trade depression.

The Socialist Party promised anything they could to the electors, not only a cure for unemployment, but some splendid new world where all the work did itself, and every one was fully employed doing nothing at trade union rates, and all the taxes would be paid by the idle rich; and no one would need to do anything except go about and kiss all the foreigners he met, and in a spirit of true comradeship hand over to them any possessions England might still have left. Wonderful hopes were centred in the new Labour Government and all the newspapers cheered them as loudly as they possibly could. But what has happened?

A very grim thing has happened; the Socialist Government has run straight into the worst economic blizzard on record in time of peace. Under the storm they have crumpled completely. Although they have been loyally supported by our strong and competent Civil Service, they have failed in such a manner as to show complete incapacity, not only to cure unemployment, but even to face the problem in a manly and mentally vigorous manner. Their collapse is pitiful. But when we remember all the harsh and untruthful things they said about their predecessors, one cannot find much sympathy to waste on them. They asked for it and they have got it. They made their bed and they should lie on it.

They have now been struck a mortal blow by the resignation of Sir Oswald Mosley. Although they may linger on for a considerable time, their reputation and prestige are fatally injured. They know little; they promised everything, they do nothing. Never was a Government so bankrupt in ideas, so feeble in directive energy, hopeless in the presence of emergency.

There is an astonishing passage in the official account of the recent meeting of the Labour Party to discuss Sir Oswald Mosley's vote of censure upon the Government from which he resigned. The meeting, it seems, was rallied by the promise that the Prime Minister, Mr. Ramsay MacDonald, would himself give his attention to the problem of unemployment. Hitherto he was too busy giving away our Navy, or trying to clear out of Egypt, or letting India get into a ferment, to pay attention to such a petty, sordid, local matter as unemployment! Meanwhile, it had unhappily grown up

600,000 since the Socialist Government came into power. So now he is going to look into it himself to see if he could not put it right. It is difficult to find a parallel for such an abject confession of failure and neglect.

There can be no real recovery in trade and industry while the Socialist Government remains in office. Their mere presence casts a blight upon the economic vitalities of the Nation. Mr. Snowden by his Budget attacking capital has aggravated to an extent not fully measured the hard times through which we have to pass. There can be no trade revival without the restoration of confidence in trade and industry. No business man has any confidence in Socialist administration. How could he, considering that the Socialists continually declare it is their intention to destroy the capitalist classes and to take over into their own highly competent hands—as we have seen—all the machinery of production, distribution, and exchange? While that threat overhangs the whole commercial, industrial, and agricultural life of Britain, things will not get any better. On the contrary, they will probably get worse. It is all our own fault. No other victorious country in the world has put a Socialist Government in power.

All the weak and subversive forces, all the defeatist, unpatriotic forces now rule the roost. The spirit of the British race which had come undaunted through measureless perils is now more broken-hearted than it has ever been seen before.

We have only to look at other great civilized nations to see how different their spirit is from ours. They stand up for their rights, they are not afraid when what they think are unjust demands are made upon them to say "No." Far weaker countries than Britain defend their national rights with obstinacy and vigour. Do they suffer for it? No; on the contrary they are respected and even get their way. We alone among nations appear feebly and miserably afraid to call our souls our own. If any ragged gang of subversives in any quarter of the Empire shake their fists at us, instantly the cry arises that we have got to clear out, we have got to apologize for ever having been there, even if we have rescued them from barbarism and anarchy.

Just let us look at what Mr. Lansbury said on Monday night in the House of Commons! He said that no one wanted to do manual work and that he had run away from it at the first chance he had, and he would never go back to it if he could help it! What a doctrine for a Minister of the Crown to preach. Do you wonder there is unemployment and bad trade and lack of confidence and enterprise when a Cabinet Minister boasts himself a miserable workshy? On the principles which Mr. Lansbury inculcated, we should cease not only to be a great power, we should cease even to have a civilized society. What an insult to the working men in this country, who, taking them all round, are the best and most faithful, and the most skilful workers in the world, who are proud of their work or of their craft! You will never cure unemployment or even reduce it while such a spirit prevails. On the contrary, it will get worse and worse; it will feed on the many evils it creates until every resource and energy of the nation is dried up or squandered.

What is Mr. Ramsay MacDonald doing with our Navy? That is what we want to know. What are those compacts into which he is leading us, what are those handcuffs he wishes to slip upon our wrists? Apparently we are not even to have equality with the United States. We are to bind ourselves to have a Navy definitely inferior to theirs, we are to be Number Two. We, who live by the sea, who, if we lose our position on the sea, sink immediately to a fifth-rate Power, are to bind ourselves by treaty permanently to an inferior position. Why should we do this? Why could not we say to our friends in the United States: "Build whatever fleet you like and let us build what we think we need." Why should there not be a declaration of independence for both countries? Why should we have this artificially fomented rivalry between two countries who are never going to war with one another—each trying to tie each other down and interfere in each other's affairs? Why could not we both act in an economic, sober, and neighbourly spirit and each enjoy our own freedom? I will tell you why we cannot do it—because it is the policy of the Socialist Party to beat the life and spirit out of this country and make Old England bow her head in the dust as a preliminary to their pillage of our resources.

I expect you thought I was coming down here to offer all sorts of bribes and promises. We offer no bribes and we make no promises. The nation has its destiny in its own hands. It may, if it pleases, cast away in a single generation all that has been gathered in 100 years. But let us each and all make sure that no part of that shame falls on any one of us. Let English men and women in a high or a humble position, in their public duty or their private life, act and strive for the strength of British and the cohesion of her Empire!

FINANCE BILL

May 27, 1930

House of Commons

In spite of the arguments of the Chancellor of the Exchequer and the appeal made by the Noble Lady the Member for the Sutton Division (Viscountess Astor), I think we are fully justified in proceeding with our Amendment [on the Beer Duty]. After all, as the hon. Member for Silvertown (Mr. J. Jones) pointed out, this is a matter in which enormous numbers of people throughout the country are concerned, and it is right that the Opposition, when considering the finances of the year, should place definitely before the country and before the House the main incidents in our financial system and should year after year state the case for the reduction of certain taxes which are heavy burdens upon the public. Year by year we have heard the party opposite, in bygone years, discuss the taxation of tea, sugar and other burdens upon public commodities, and I think we should make a mistake if we allowed ourselves to be deterred from discussing freely the question of reduction in the cost of beer to the consumer or moving Amendments which would have the effect of giving expression to that view. I know the Noble Lady's views—we have been made very familiar with them—but what astonishes me is that she should proceed with unabated, and I might almost say unabashed, vigour in the reiteration of those views, in face of the ghastly muddle which has been made in her own country in the treatment of the liquor problem.

Viscountess Astor: This is not a question of Prohibition—I am not a prohibitionist—but a question of the reduction of the Beer Duty, which has nothing to do with Prohibition.

Mr. Leif Jones: On a point of Order. Is it in order on this Amendment to discuss the way in which America is dealing with the drink problem? If so, the debate becomes very wide, and there are many sides to this question, and if the whole question of temperance is to be opened up, we shall be debating it all day. [Hon. Members: "Hear, hear!"] I do not shrink from the issue, but I submit that this is not a suitable occasion on which to raise the whole question.

Mr. Churchill: On that point of Order. I submit that I am following the course of the debate. Once the topic has been definitely raised and admitted to the Floor as part of the discussion, it is intolerable that some Members, on one side or the other, should have a right to air their views and that others should be prohibited from making the necessary reply.

The Chairman: At the beginning of the debate I did my best to intimate to Members that Amendments must be dealt with on their merits, and that the debate must not be unduly widened. This is not the occasion for debating temperance or cognate questions in relation to temperance. However, the remark of the right hon. Gentleman came up, and I do not say, if he goes no further than that, that he is out of order.

Mr. Churchill: I shall go no further than that, but, in reply to the speech of the Noble Lady, I must draw your attention to the fact that upon this question she has told us that whenever there is a decrease in the taxation upon beer, the profits are placed in the pockets of the brewers. I think it fair to say two things about that. First of all, it is not true. It certainly was not the case when the present Leader of the Opposition, the right hon. Member for Bewdley (Mr. S. Baldwin), who was then Chancellor of the Exchequer, in 1923 made a substantial reduction in the Beer Duty. There the whole cost, and more than the cost, of the remission was passed on to the consumer. The reduction in the cost of beer to the consumer was substantially larger than would have been warranted by the loss to the Exchequer. In fact, the right hon. Member for Bewdley, as is well known, made an arrangement with the brewers—the same kind of friendly arrangement as the Chancellor of the Exchequer boasted to us he had made in connection with this Budget—whereby, in consideration of a reduction of the national burden, they made a contribution from their own profits in order to give the maximum relief in the cost of beer to the general consumer. Therefore, the Noble Lady is entirely wrong, absolutely wrong—I mean, as wrong as is the difference between night and day—in her statement of facts; but even if it were true that the brewers gained the profits by reductions in the charges put upon beer, it is far preferable that they should get the profit than that the profit should be reaped, as it is in another country, to which I have already referred, by the bootleggers.

At any rate, I must say, from whomsoever we take our guidance on this question, I do not think we ought to take it from the Noble Lady. I do not think she represents at all the point of view which is so definitely expressed and held by the people of this island. The Noble Lady tells us that although the men wish to drink beer and would be glad of some relief in the taxation on beer, the women would be against it. I am not at all sure about that, because my experience has been, in what I have seen and noticed—and here I am entirely in the hands of the Committee, who can judge for themselves as well as I can—that the women do not separate themselves by sex into an entirely different camp from the men, that they are glad sometimes to see that their menfolk are gratified in minor ways, and that it is quite possible that a friendly word from a husband to a wife about gratification for some reduction in the Beer Duty would weigh just as much with a woman as the most enthusiastic temperance speech from the Noble Lady herself.

Nothing constitutes a more false view of British society at the present time than the idea that all the women voters are now banded together in order to take up a fundamentally different position on this question from all the men voters. Such an idea is manifestly absurd, and the sooner the Noble Lady clears her mind when she is fundamentally wrong in her conceptions, the sooner will she be able to take not only an engaging but a useful and well-informed part in our debates. On the general question, it has always been considered the right and duty of the Opposition to voice the grievances of the public against—[*Interruption*]—I am ready to give way, if the Noble Lady wishes to say something.

Viscountess Astor: I want to point out that I was right over the Betting Duty, and the right hon. Gentleman was wrong!

Mr. Churchill: I must, on a point of Order, ask your ruling, Mr. Young, as to whether I should be permitted to reply to that intervention.

The Chairman: I am afraid I cannot be responsible for all these interjections. The right hon. Gentleman must not be drawn from the Amendment.

Mr. Churchill: I will forbear. But let me say that it is not only the right, but the duty of the Opposition parties in the House to present to the Government of the day their objections and the grievances which are felt in the country about the burden of taxes of various kinds. This is one which is felt by very large numbers of persons, and we should fail altogether in our duty if we did not join issue upon it. It is not the responsibility of the Opposition to suggest alternative forms of taxation. That is the responsibility of the Government of the day and the majority. The responsibility of the Opposition is to voice public grievances, and there is not the slightest doubt that this is a very great public grievance among great masses of those hard-working, manual labourers upon whose strong sinews and constant, faithful efforts the structure and foundation of this State depend. Those who take the view of the First Commissioner of Works that the first thing anybody ought to do is run away from manual labour—those who take that sort of view—

The First Commissioner of Works (Mr. Lansbury): The right hon. Gentleman never did a day's hard manual work for his daily bread in his life, and I have done many a thousand. [*Interruption.*] I may say to the right hon. Gentleman that, as distinct from himself, I have worked, and worked very hard, at manual labour, and what I said the other night was that I did not object to rationalisation, because I wanted hard manual labour to be abolished, and that every man who had the chance always left manual labour in order to follow an occupation that did not involve manual labour.

Mr. Churchill: The right hon. Gentleman has repeated the statement, with some modifications.

Mr. Lansbury: No.

Mr. Churchill: He introduced the word "hard."

Mr. Lansbury: No.

Mr. Churchill: I have the passage in my mind, but be that as it may, we can quite see why he has no sympathy with the Amendment, which does appeal to the people who are engaged in manual labour.

Mr. Lansbury: No. I represent—

Hon. Members: Order!

The Chairman: We cannot have this conversation across the Table of the House.

Mr. Lansbury: I represent a Division that is made up of manual labourers more than of any other sort of person, and I have never been asked by a manual worker to vote for a reduction in the Beer Duty. [Hon. Members: "Oh!"] I have never been asked by a workman to vote for a reduction of this Beer Duty. My constituents want less beer drinking, not more, and would be very glad indeed to see this industry taxed off the face of the earth.

Mr. Churchill: The right hon. Gentleman has made a very interesting intervention in our discussion, and naturally I shall observe a very reasonable limitation in following him there, but he has endeavoured to justify the doctrine which he put forward the other night, that it was a right and proper thing for a Cabinet Minister to say he ran away from manual labour at the earliest possible moment. [*Interruption.*] On the contrary, I have earned my living all my life.

Mr. Lansbury: So have I.

Mr. Churchill: And I have never shirked manual work or physical labour.

Mr. Lansbury: Have you ever worked for your daily bread?

Mr. Churchill: Certainly, I have.

The Chairman: I am sure the whole Committee will think that this is very unbecoming.

Mr. Churchill: Naturally, I am in the fullest accord with all that you say about the unbecoming manner in which the First Commissioner of Works is conducting himself.

The Chairman: The right hon. Gentleman should not misquote me.

Mr. Churchill: It is not likely to abbreviate our discussion if the First Commissioner of Works imparts so much heat into them.

Mr. Lansbury: You are responsible. You are insolent.

Mr. Churchill: If the right hon. Gentleman is so angry, as he clearly is, it is because the remark that he made is one that he knows he ought not to have made.

Mr. Lansbury: Not at all.

Mr. Churchill: In the hope of cooling the right hon. Gentleman, let us get back to the impost upon beer. I was endeavouring to conclude when the right hon. Gentleman fell upon me so fiercely. If he likes to come down to the House to delay the progress of the Chancellor of the Exchequer's Finance Bill, we cannot be blamed. One of the real and definite grievances of large masses of the people is the way in which the cost of beer has steadily gone up and the quality has steadily declined. It is not true to regard this entirely as a man's question. There are a great many cases where if there were a reduction in the cost of beer no more beer would be drunk by the individual but more money would be taken home and would be available for household expenses. In many cases, that would be so; therefore, the women have an interest as well as the men in this matter.

Moreover, there is an immense improvement towards practical temperance which makes it all the more necessary to reduce the Beer Duty. Anyone who reads the criminal statistics of this country in regard to convictions for drunkenness, fines for drunkenness, crimes resulting from drunkenness and diseases arising from drunkenness, and compares them with the statistics of another country, to which I do not intend further to refer, they will see how thoroughly justified we have been and why there is a steady movement towards the practice of temperance throughout these islands. The cases of drunkenness have been halved since before the War. [*Interruption.*] I do not agree that it is only lack of money that prevents the working class from getting drunk twice as often as they would do otherwise. I think that is a very wrong reflection upon the character of our working-class population. I agree that the cost of beer and the regulations have something to do with the reduction of consumption, but in the main it is the new interest, the better outlook upon life, the improving education, and the general change in the habits of the community that has had this effect. We have achieved this very important result by departing entirely from the kind of policy of which the Noble Lady the Member for the Sutton Division is so keen an advocate. Now that there is this great improvement in the general habits of the people we have an additional reason why the burden upon beer should be reduced as far as possible. I do not believe that any eloquent arguments which the right hon. Member for Camborne (Mr. Leif Jones) is likely to use about the cold water cure will alter the facts of the situation. The Chancellor of the Exchequer is quite wrong in his suggestion. If I cannot plume myself upon having reduced the burden upon beer by the reduction of the brewers' credit, on the contrary I recovered £10,000,000, which has been a complete withdrawal from the profits of the brewers.

Viscountess Astor: Hear, hear.

Mr. Churchill: The Noble Lady agrees.

Viscountess Astor: Yes, with that.

Mr. Churchill: She is pleased at that. I think she also ought to pay some tribute of gratitude to the brewers who co-operated with the late Government—

The Chairman: The right hon. Gentleman might let me have the benefit of hearing his remarks.

Mr. Churchill: I beg your pardon. I was saying that the Noble Lady might pay some tribute of gratitude to the brewers who co-operated with the late Administration in paying this heavy additional sum into the Exchequer. It was very convenient when it came in. [*Interruption.*] I raised £10,000,000 in two years. It did not come from the consumer; it was not passed on, because there was no increase in the price. It did not come from heaven; that is quite clear. Where did it come from? It clearly came from the brewing trade, just in the same way that the right hon. Gentleman is now obtaining a large concession from them in the increased tax that he is putting on. Where does he suggest that the money comes from? If you are a brewer and you are going to get something in a particular year to which you have long looked forward, and it is taken away from you by a change in the law, you have to make good the deficit to yourself, surely that is just as much taxation as an addition to the Income

Tax. There is a fundamental vice among many Socialists regarding finance. The right hon. Gentleman, apparently, believes that he is going to get this money from nowhere; something for nothing.

As a matter of fact, the right hon. Gentleman has entered into an arrangement with the brewers, very rightly and very properly, following the example of preceding Conservative and capitalist Governments. He has entered into an arrangement with the trade, and is securing from them a contribution in duty towards his Budget, unaccompanied by any passing on of the charge to the public to effect either quantity, quality or price. Thereby, he has established another point of resemblance in method and in outlook which one Chancellor of the Exchequer's policy bears to another. I shall give my vote in favour of the reduction in the price of beer. This is one of the objectives which should be held out in front of the people of this country—a reduction in the price of beer. I would not be afraid to say that on any platform, anywhere, except before some highly selected body of extreme temperance advocates. Reduction in the price of beer is a perfectly legitimate aim and object, and when that reduction is compared with some of the other reductions which the right hon. Gentleman has in view our Amendment is all the more justified, because not only are we proposing something which is greatly desired by very large numbers of people, but we are proposing to give relief to a commodity already far too highly taxed, and we are proposing a relief which, apart from its merits, should be given priority over the £20,000,000 or £30,000,000 of reduction in taxation which the right hon. Gentleman has already promised to remit.

[Later] The Chancellor of the Exchequer, I must admit, has dealt with this Amendment in a calm and courteous manner, which gave pleasure to those who heard him and is an encouragement to us from the point of view of our relations during the discussion of this lengthy and complicated Bill. I hope that he will persist in this great improvement on previous examples which he has given. But if the right hon. Gentleman's speech was an improvement in manner, he fell into errors of logic which were really quite painful. First of all, he fell a victim to the desire to use all the arguments on all sides of a subject at once. What were the two main arguments he put forward against this proposal? The first argument was that the flavour of the beer would be so prejudicially affected, although in this matter he was careful to tell us that he could only speak from hearsay evidence, that it would not be consumed to any extent and that the brewers, consequently, would not avail themselves of the facilities given by the Amendment.

That was his first argument, a perfectly solid argument. But the next moment he told us that the total cost of this concession to the revenue would be no less than £5,000,000 a year, so that apparently a change of which very few people would take advantage would inflict this enormous injury to the revenue. We, therefore, asked the Chancellor of the Exchequer for the basis of his estimate of £5,000,000, and he proceeded to say that he was taking the entire consumption of beer at its present rate of consumption, which was being manufactured from purely British materials, and that then the loss would be £5,000,000. A few sentences before he told us that owing to the deterioration in the flavour the concession would hardly be utilised at all. Really, the right hon. Gentleman must not lose hold of the firm foothold of logical argument at this early stage in our discussions and attempt to use two contradictory arguments at once. However benevolently represented in his speech it does not lead to clarity in our debates.

The other argument he used against this Amendment left me comparatively calm. He spoke of the administrative difficulties. We have heard of these administrative difficulties until we are sick and tired of them. I remember the days, and I have no doubt the right hon. Gentleman does also, when first I came into this House that it was the custom of the Chancellor of the Exchequer to say that it was administratively impossible to graduate the Income Tax. I remember well how I was shown sure and definite reasons, statements and arguments of the highest authority to prove that it had been found impossible to impose a duty on silk. Events have shown by actual experience and practice that when these difficulties are boldly faced and vigorously tackled, the administrative obstacles are often surmounted. The flexibility and experience of the Customs Department is extraordinary. I do not know any branch in which the officials are more capable of addressing themselves to new situations and assisting their political chiefs in finding a solution. I cannot for a moment accept the theory that the administrative difficulties are in themselves sufficient to turn down this proposal, even if it were desirable upon other grounds. At any rate, I am quite sure that the administrative difficulties which stand in the path of this Amendment are incomparably less than the administrative difficulties which the Chancellor of the Exchequer will have to face in the land legislation he proposes to introduce.

What is the remaining argument of the right hon. Gentleman? It is the old argument of the Treaties. That argument may perfectly well be adduced by the Government for not accepting the Amendment, but it cannot be adduced as any reason why we should not move the Amendment, and our moving this Amendment implies that we desire the Government to take all the necessary steps to give effect to it, including, as a sequence, an alteration or modification of such Treaties as exist. The right hon. Gentleman read a Clause from the Anglo-German Treaty. I presume it was the Treaty for which we were responsible. It was framed by the last Labour Government, which we took up and carried through the moment we accepted office five years ago. On the face of it, that Clause would seem very sweeping, but it may well be found that it does not cover all the points. At any rate, we discriminated against the foreigner in respect of home-grown sugar, and we discriminated against the foreigner in regard to home-grown tobacco, to Empire-grown tobacco and to Irish tobacco; and very great benefits have followed from it. The consumption of this cheaper Colonial tobacco has enabled poorer people who never smoked them before to smoke cigarettes, and it may turn out that British beer produced from British materials, if given the advantage of this rebate, would be cheaper than any other beer brewed in this country, and that, in consequence, some of the poorest people who now buy a glass of beer would be able to obtain it for a lesser sum and have a larger proportion of their weekly wage to take home. It has worked out in regard to Empire tobacco, and I do not see why the same principle should not be applied to beer produced from home-grown materials.

The President of the Board of Trade is in his place at the moment, and I trust that he will explain why it is that if we are able to make this discrimination in respect of tobacco and sugar we are not able to make a similar discrimination in the case of the materials for home grown beer? This is just the occasion for the President of the Board of Trade to make one of those excellent speeches, very long, very careful and very lucid speeches, delivered without a note and often without a point. His talents could not be better employed than in illuminating this matter. This is a modest proposal but, nevertheless, a serious one, and I cannot see why it should be brushed aside. Unquestionably, the barley growers would gain a benefit. It would not be large, and would not cost the revenue very much, but they would gain a benefit. It would also be an encouragement to a large number of agriculturists, for the Government would thus take their first step, a small one, towards showing that they recognise that an agricultural problem exists in this country and that they are well disposed towards the rural community. The only conceivable sufferers would be the revenue in the event of it succeeding, but, as has been pointed out already, in proportion as the policy of the Amendment succeeded in that very proportion there would be a revival of barley growing which would more than compensate for any loss to the Exchequer. I will not stand any longer between the Committee and the President of the Board of Trade, whom, I am sure, we are all desirous of hearing.

[Later] I beg to move, "That the Chairman do report Progress, and ask leave to sit again."

I wish to ask the Chancellor of the Exchequer, amicably but pointedly, does he really suppose that he will facilitate and abbreviate the passage of this Bill by moving the Closure, as he has moved it, at a time when we were expecting to hear from the President of the Board of Trade a statement on the matter under discussion, when we had every reason to believe that the President of the Board of Trade was willing to take part in the discussion, and when my right hon. Friend the late Minister of Labour, who had not taken part in the discussion, had risen for the purpose of addressing the Committee? It would not be in order to say anything which would reflect upon the decision to which the Committee came, or to which you, Mr. Dunnico, came, but it is distinctly in order for me to ask the Chancellor of the Exchequer, does he really imagine that he can succeed by these methods with this enormous Bill, with its 50 or 60 complicated Clauses, presenting hundreds of opportunities on which the opinion of the Committee may be obtained by Division and may be compelled to be obtained only by Division? Does he really imagine that he can get this Measure through by proceeding, from the very beginning, with fixed bayonets against its opponents? I paid the right hon. Gentleman a compliment but, I fear, I was precipitate, because he very rapidly, after some smooth words, relapsed to the roughest manner of treatment and he has carried his programme, so far, by means of the Closure.

I suggest to the right hon. Gentleman that even at this stage it would be well to realise that patience and tact are indispensable qualities in a Minister when debating great legislative proposals. I have always held that no man can be responsible for the conduct of a great legislative Measure through the House of Commons, without revealing to Parliament his strength and his weakness, his character and his limitations. The right hon. Gentleman is now at the beginning of one of the most controversial Budgets ever introduced in this Parliament. [Hon. Members: "Oh!"] Certainly, because class legislation and vote-catching opportunism of the most flagrant character represent the spirit of this legislation. Is the right hon. Gentleman really going to help himself by this display of petulance and impatience which leads him to intervene with the brute force of a majority? Anyone who possesses a majority can use it against their political opponents. That is quite true, but never do I remember an occasion when I, as Chancellor of the Exchequer, in charge of a debate of this kind, practically snubbed and brushed aside my own colleague the President of the Board of Trade and prevented him from addressing the Committee on a point on which the Committee were most anxious to hear his views. It is as a protest against the action of the right hon. Gentleman in preventing us from hearing the explanation of the President of the Board of Trade, and in closuring my right hon. Friend the Member for Tamworth (Sir A. Steel-Maitland), that I move this Motion.

[Later] I am bound to say that I listened with very great interest to the speech of the right hon. Member for Camborne (Mr. Leif Jones) which shows him to be possessed of a wealth of information on this subject [of different types of beer] which, if it came from any other Member of the House but himself, would be, to say the least of it, highly suspicious. The facility, the command, the variety of his knowledge, its compendiousness, its completeness, its almost exhaustive character, astonished and delighted us. For the first time, we know accurately the distinction between all these various kinds of beer. It is remarkable how some people get their pleasures. I will warrant that the right hon. Gentleman has in his life derived more pleasure from studying these very wicked drinks for the purpose of preventing their consumption than almost any individual has got through the ordinary indulgences of daily life.

Mr. Leif Jones: Not wicked drinks; foolish drinks.

Mr. Churchill: At any rate, he has derived from them an inverted pleasure. No one can deny the thoroughness of his information. We have had a perfunctory statement from the Financial Secretary to the Treasury, a very polite, very careful very guarded statement, but compare it with the full fresh enthusiasm of my right hon. Friend! There is the object—and there the shadow, the mere reflection! Upon this Clause [placing a duty on imported beer], which deals with the Customs Duty, we have had a debate which has certainly added a great deal to the knowledge which hon. Members have of the subject on which we are voting and deciding. It is not our intention to divide against this Clause. Undoubtedly, some of these beers when imported have a definitely medicinal quality. I have never been brought into contact personally with that aspect of the trade, though I can quite readily believe, as the right hon. Gentleman has told us, that in cases of scorbutic disease these beers may exercise a most valuable and beneficial influence and effect. However, having thoroughly explored this subject we do not propose to put the Government to the trouble and labour of a Division, and we hope that this forbearance on our part will bring from our colleagues on the opposite benches similar consideration when other matters which raise more sharply controversial issues come forward.

[Later] The right hon. Gentleman has been on the horns of a dilemma. He has been weighing and balancing things, and has been advancing with great caution: like an elephant trying a doubtful bridge. Until the last moment I was in ignorance as to the course he intended to adopt. [An Hon. Member: "Surely, you know him."] Yes, one ought to have given him the benefit of the doubt and to have realised that of two positions he would take the more disagreeable one. My right hon. Friend the Member for West Birmingham (Sir A. Chamberlain) was well advised to choose the most opportune moment for raising the question that we should report Progress and ask leave to sit again. This matter touches the convenience of many hon. Members. Undoubtedly, if our proceedings become protracted, they will become very protracted. The appetite will grow with eating. Whether the progress of the Bill will become more marked I cannot say. The right hon. Gentleman spoke of the next Clause as being a small and subsidiary Clause. It raises a large question and must be discussed at length. It deals with the Betting Duty. The right hon. Gentleman is throwing away revenue with both hands: just because he cannot touch the unclean thing. But he gets revenue from liquor, and then laps it up.

I had hopes that the right hon. Gentleman would have considered our suggestion favourably. We are willing to conform to any arrangement to meet the general convenience. As my right hon. Friend pointed out, the Committee which has been considering the hours of the House has reported against all-night sittings. Undoubtedly, the class and character of our business tends to deteriorate as the night advances, although important questions arise. A point for consideration is the work which Ministers have to perform in the early morning of the next day. To-morrow is a very important day. There is to be a Division to-morrow night, I believe. It is very important that we should have a full explanation from the Government to-morrow—we are all waiting for it—and also an explanation of the policy of the hon. Member for Smethwick (Sir Oswald Mosley). I believe the Chancellor of the Exchequer is to reply.

Mr. Snowden *indicated dissent*.

Mr. Churchill: Well, no doubt the right hon. Gentleman will have to be in constant attendance, and he will have important work to do in the morning. From every point of view, especially his own, it is not worth our while continuing the debate at this late hour. However, the matter rests with the right hon. Gentleman. I cannot pretend to have any influence with him. I have no more influence with him than had his late colleague, the ex-Chancellor of the Duchy of Lancaster. The right hon. Gentleman brushes people aside, or tries to crush them as would a juggernaut car. He told us earlier in the evening that he did not care either for my praise or my criticism. He adheres to that. A man of greater importance than the Chancellor of the Exchequer, the great lexicographer, Dr. Johnson, told us that the applause of a single individual is of great consequence. The right hon. Gentleman so easily waves people on one side. One day it is one of his colleagues who is waved out of the administration, another day it is a member of the Opposition who is endeavouring to examine the legislation he brings before the House. When one gets into an important situation like that of the Chancellor of the Exchequer, one has continuously to say to oneself "Modesty." The right hon. Gentleman runs a great risk of creating a spirit of opposition where little exists to-day.

It may well be that the result of a very protracted sitting will have the consequence of developing these all-night sittings into a regular habit, sittings which a Committee has reported so much against, and he cannot blame us if we meet that in a similar spirit. I put it to the right hon. Gentleman whether, having regard to all the circumstances, he would not do well to be content with the three important Clauses he has already got and let us now conclude our proceedings and resume our discussion on the betting law when the Committee will be fresh and invigorated to address itself to a new topic, and when our newspaper Press will be able to record our proceedings.

[Later] I beg to move, "That the Chairman do leave the Chair."

I rise to a point of Order. I wish to ask from you at this stage some further guidance as to the conditions under which we are to be permitted to conduct our debate and under what conditions Members of this House are to be permitted to deliver their speeches and criticisms, if at all. In order to put myself in Order, I propose to conclude by moving, under Rule 68 of the Manual of Procedure, "That the Chairman do now leave the Chair," and, in support of that motion I should like to ask for your guidance, bearing in mind that my hon. Friend behind me was addressing the House and that we found great difficulty in hearing him owing to the organised opposition from the Government benches. [Hon. Members: "And Lord Winterton."] The noble lord did not interrupt my hon. Friend. There was organised opposition from the Government benches. Then the right hon. Member for West Birmingham (Sir A. Chamberlain) appealed to you to secure to the hon. Member the protection of the Chair, and you replied, if my memory serves me correctly, that that was certainly your first care and that you intended to discharge that task, but that it was quite usual from time to time when disorder broke out for the chairman to wait for an opportunity to enforce respect for the speakers on the Opposition side. On that, my right hon. Friend ceased to press his point of Order. We endeavoured to continue the debate, and my hon. Friend below the gangway rose in his place and proceeded with his speech. Thereafter, for two or three minutes, as you will perhaps remember, he was quite inaudible owing to a chorus of interruptions raised from the Government benches every time he attempted to address the Committee.

I must point out to you, in asking for your ruling, that this debate is being continued at the wish of the Government. After we have suggested that all advantages would be served by its curtailment, the Chancellor of the Exchequer has decided that we shall go on with the debate, and therefore it seems very wounding and grievous to my right hon. Friends and hon. Friends on this side of the House that, when directed by the Government to sustain and take part in the discussion, we should not even be allowed to be heard. That is very hard indeed. After this had continued for some time, you rose in your place and made a strong personal and formal appeal to the hon. Gentlemen on the Government side that they should give a fair hearing. That appeal, I need scarcely say, was treated with complete contempt. Not the slightest attention was paid to it by them, and there followed immediately from it your acceptance, in virtue of your plenary authority—which I in no way reflect upon—of the motion for the termination of the debate. That is a frank statement of what has occurred.

I want to ask where, in these conditions, is the protection for the minority, which you were so good as to promise us, when these events occur? What guarantee have we, if we continue the debate, that the moment hon. Gentlemen opposite are anxious to terminate the discussion they will not merely raise this organised clamour, and that the Chair will not then find it necessary to accept the Closure in order to terminate the disorder, in which case the opportunities of debate are denied? This is a very grave matter on which we are most anxious to receive your guidance, because it is perfectly clear that it will be impossible even for a far greater majority than the Prime Minister has now in the House, even for a far greater majority than he commands, to bear down and silence an opposition and prevent them from discharging their Parliamentary duties. Therefore, in order that we may receive your guidance on the subject, and, with the very greatest respect, I move, under Rule 68, "That the Chairman do now leave the Chair."

[Later] It was not without deep feeling, which is shared by a great many of those who sit on this side of the House, that I made the Motion which you have allowed me to put, and I cannot feel that it was needlessly moved, in consequence of the statement you have just made from the Chair to the Committee of the House. In view of the statement which you have made, that in the full extent of your indisputable authority you considered that the Committee had by an overwhelming majority arrived at the moment when it was ripe for decision, it appears to me that I ought not to proceed with my Motion. We all have a common interest in maintaining the dignity of the Chair. We wish our debates to have the greatest freedom, but it is vital for those debates that we should show the utmost respect, and enforce by every power, the authority of the Chair, if only because it is the sole protection that minorities have for their rights and duties. In these circumstances, I ask your leave to withdraw the Motion.

[Later] The Chancellor of the Exchequer is taking a most curious and unreasonable course in depriving himself of this revenue. I believe that the revenue in question is about £70,000 on this [Betting Duty] Amendment, and £200,000 a year on the whole Clause. Let us consider what this money could be used for. Take the national theatre, or national opera, matters in which I know that hon. members opposite are very keen; or take scientific endowment; there might be extra money for light cures or radium. You have this money for nothing—no trouble whatever. The bookmakers have never objected to the tax. Just as in the case of British-made wine, the trade was quite pleased. It gave them definite recognition, a *cachet* a hall mark, an imprimatur on their business.

Mr. Moses: Because it recognised the bookmakers—that is why they were pleased.

Mr. Churchill: They were pleased, and there was the £200,000 a year. If it had been spent on the light cure or radium, then everyone might have been pleased. It seems to have been a matter where everyone could have been pleased, but the Chancellor of the Exchequer has prejudice in his mind. He has the idea that he is putting down betting by singling out bookmakers alone to be favoured, when they do not ask for it and really were not worrying about it at all. This doctrine of the unclean thing really is one of the most remarkable forms of mental infirmity with which this House has been confronted. The "Daily Herald," in its early form, I know, used to give exceptional prominence to betting. This was not a case of ordinary gambling; it is gambling among comrades, really quite shocking, and look at the space given in the official organ of the Labour party, which is managed with some capitalist assistance by a Labour committee, to betting, gambling, and all those forms of the unclean thing that cannot be touched. They can touch it quickly enough when it brings in money to the "Daily Herald," but not for some worthy object. This is a form of mental infirmity, a sort of lesion of the mind from which they are suffering. The President of the Board of Trade, who is so clear headed, must surely feel a serious irritation at this amount of revenue that is being thrown away. It is simply ridiculous, this notion of the unclean thing, while at the same time they do not mind gulping down scores of millions of revenue from the sale of intoxicating liquor.

I am sorry that the Noble Lady the Member for Plymouth (Viscountess Astor) has gone to bed. It would have been interesting to see her relative reaction to the unclean thing in drink and the unclean thing in betting and their competitive priority. There is no logic in the position taken up by the Chancellor of the Exchequer, who, I am glad to see, has returned to the House properly refreshed and able, I hope, to give further guidance and advice to the Committee. I would be grateful if he would address his mind to this question: Why should he refuse £200,000 a year which he can get without the slightest trouble? What is the object? I believe his party keeps a tipster on the "Daily Herald" and are well informed on these matters. This is not the only side to his policy. There is the totalisator. There was a substantial revenue which could have been got without difficulty from this machinery year after year which would have inured to the public well-being. But the right hon. Gentleman is above that. This £200,000 would have paid the salaries of His Majesty's present advisors. It would have been almost poetic in its similitude that Members of His Majesty's Government should have defrayed their salaries by a continuance of these duties on bookmakers.

Mr. Groves: What about dogs?

Mr. Churchill: I am afraid the hon. Gentleman has studied too attentively the sporting columns of the "Daily Herald" instead of devoting himself to the more serious political matters which are, I believe, treated of in some other parts of the paper. The right hon. Gentleman has needlessly aggravated his difficulties in refusing this revenue—small though it be it is still considerable—and still more in failing to utilise the 2 per cent. on the totalisator. He has done it because of some irrational quirk of his intellect, some twist or knot or gnarl in his mental structure. It seems to me that the Debate we have had on this subject is a very fitting commentary on his inconceivable folly and his gross financial improvidence.

[Later] Before the debate ends, is the right hon. Gentleman not going to make some reply to the arguments addressed to him? After all, it is the right hon. Gentleman's wish that this discussion should proceed in the small hours of the morning. When he took that position and attained the ratification of his will and authority over the House, it was to be assumed that he intended to take an intelligent part in our discussions; that he intended to make the necessary contributions to our debates and answer the points raised. Some of the points have been very clear, and I should have thought that it would have been very unpleasant for the right hon. Gentleman to sit there apparently incapable, for some reason or other, of giving an answer. He is raising money from the Income Tax on the profits of bookmakers, and yet saying that he cannot be responsible for the unclean thing by raising money by the taxation of their licences. Surely he has got some answer. Everybody has some sort of answer.

Then take the question of sweeping away this loathsome blemish—but apparently only after 1st November. Up to then he is prepared to obtain the proceeds of gambling and put into his pure and orthodox coffers money which is gained by his direct and intimate association, in his public capacity, with the trade which he has told us is built up from day to day on the ruin of countless homes. He is going more deeply into this business with every step he takes. On the one hand, there is his connection with the "Daily Herald," the official organ of his party. If it were not for the exertions of the "Daily Herald," he would not hold his position on the Treasury Bench. He would not have been there, probably, but for the valuable "Daily Herald." It is all very well to take their aid and assistance and be supported by their active journalism, and then brush it aside as an unclean thing.

Really, for the right hon. Gentleman's own sake, I would advise him to try to make some answer to the arguments. It is not the slightest use sitting there and maintaining a stoney silence. For three or four hours he has contented himself with barking out one single sentence. [*Interruption*.] If it is objected to that I should say "barking," I will say snapping out one single sentence with a peculiar canine inflection. I do not wish to say anything to hurt the Chancellor of the Exchequer. I am anxious that he should have some chance of making some reply. He should be inspired with some desire to distinguish himself in the Debate instead of sitting there with a look of unutterable weariness and boredom on his expressive countenance. It is really quite painful to see. It is his wish that we should debate this now. He sits there unable to answer and unwilling to allow anybody to go to bed. He is forcing us to remain here and he is adding nothing to our discussions. It is unworthy of the great responsibility committed to his care. I ask him to answer the various points raised in the Debate.

[Later] I beg to move, "That the Chairman do report Progress, and ask leave to sit again."

We have had four hours of discussion since the Chancellor of the Exchequer decided we were to continue. During that time we had a very strenuous sitting which has clearly produced a marked effect upon the strength of the Minister in charge of the Bill. For reasons with which I sympathise and respect he has practically ceased to take an active part in the debate. He has simply sat there, hour after hour, with a look of sour disapproval on his face. But we are now coming to the most important Clause and we have disposed of four Clauses and have made a remarkable inroad into the Bill. We are now approaching Clause 5 at five o'clock in the morning when the debates are not followed at all by the country, because the reporting staffs are reduced. We are not at all afraid of our work being reported, but I quite understand that others may not have the same wish and this question of Safeguarding is the most controversial question of the present day. It is the key question at by-elections, and probably it will be the most important point in the forthcoming general election. In every part of the country, the question of Safeguarding is exciting the greatest interest. The Liberal party and other free traders are marshalling their forces and sharpening their weapons. The Labour party are in considerable doubt as to what their course should be. Are we really to assume that the Chancellor of the Exchequer wants this important matter discussed at a moment when the country will not be able to receive any reports? Is he really so alarmed about this topic that he does not wish it to be entered on by Parliament at a proper hour?

In any case, it seems to me that we have now reached a point where we ought to break off our discussion. This Clause, I warn the Chancellor of the Exchequer, is one of an extremely controversial character, and I cannot possibly suppose that it can be easily or simply disposed of. This is like talking to a stone wall. I am not going to appeal to the Chancellor of the Exchequer, because we know the futility of that. Nor am I going to suggest any sort of Parliamentary bargain with him, because, as we well know, the last arrangement made with him was made the ground of an accusation of bad faith against those with whom he entered into the arrangement. Consequently, we are unable to come to an arrangement with him. He has placed himself in a special position different from any other Minister. He is a sort of political pariah for the purpose of our Debates, only, of course, from that point of view, and we are unable to enter into any arrangement with him. But the mere fact that we are precluded from making such an arrangement makes it all the more necessary, and, indeed, indispensable, that he should himself regulate these Debates so as to conduce to proper discussion. He is a little smirched perhaps by the Coal Bill; somewhat smutty from the coal hole, but still orthodox, and I should have thought that it was the very topic that he would have been specially anxious to bring forward at a time when the country would be waiting to hear him.

The Deputy-Chairman: As far as I can ascertain this Clause does not deal with Safeguarding at all; it deals with dumping.

Mr. Churchill: There is Safeguarding against dumping. This was the part introduced by the right hon. Gentleman the Member for Carnarvon Boroughs (Mr. Lloyd George) when Prime Minister, and it is only three or four weeks ago that the right hon. Gentleman said he would introduce legislation to prevent dumping even in the case of food stuffs, arriving too cheaply.

The Deputy-Chairman: We cannot discuss that matter now.

Mr. Churchill: I was only meeting the point that perhaps in referring to this as Safeguarding I was not sufficiently accurate in my description of the subject and I should have said Safeguarding against dumping. There is a lot to be said about dumping. I hardly know another subject on which more general interest prevails, even among all parties. I should like very much to enter into battle with the Chancellor of the Exchequer on the subject, but why cannot we have it at a reasonable hour? Why does the Chancellor of the Exchequer want to smuggle it through at this dim hour of the morning when the pale dawn is just illuminating the monstrosities on the Thames Embankment. I do suggest that he would better consult the dignity of his office, the efficiency of his administration, the smooth and orderly progress of his Bill if, instead of endeavouring to burke this question by relegating it to a period when no record of our proceedings can reach the public, he discussed it at a moment when he is more fit to do himself full justice on his own subject. He would be well advised to accept the Motion which I make, which is not without consideration for the right hon. Gentleman and the progress of his Measure.

UNEMPLOYMENT
May 28, 1930
House of Commons

Motion made, and Question proposed,

That a sum not exceeding £14,784, be granted to His Majesty, to complete the sum necessary to defray the Charge which will come in course of payment during the year ending on the 31st day of March, 1931, for the Salaries and Expenses of the Office of the Lord Privy Seal.

Mr. Churchill: On a point of Order. Is not this debate to be the occasion of a statement by a retiring Minister, who, according to usage and practice, has always on the occasion that it has been made been given full and untramelled freedom in regard to the matters which have led to the severance from his colleagues? Will not the fact that such a statement is to be made—a statement which is awaited with much interest by the House generally and by people outside—have the necessary consequence of broadening the scope of the debate relating to the most important problem of unemployment, with all its aspects, so far as it is possible for us to deal with it within the scope of one day, and will not the general convenience and the general wish of the House make it desirable for the Chair to give that latitude which is usually given when the House so desires it in regard to this discussion, instead of the somewhat alarming series of strict limitations which we have just had the pleasure of hearing?

The Deputy-Chairman: I have taken such advice as is available, and I understand that it has been the long-standing custom of this House that, when a Minister retires, he is entitled to make a personal statement, but, when that personal statement has been made, the retired Minister is entitled only to the privileges exercised by any other Member of this House, and, consequently, in this debate the retired Minister has no privileges other than those shared by any other Member. So far as the discussion is concerned, long-standing custom and long-standing Rules—I think all old Parliamentarians will admit this fact—provide that matters which involve or imply legislation are not allowed to be discussed. This is purely an administrative Vote on the salary of the Lord Privy Seal.

Mr. Churchill: On the point of Order. In the first case, with great respect, will not a limitation of the kind you have suggested render all discussion upon the treatment of the evil of unemployment, upon the emergency of unemployment, wholly impossible? How, for instance, are we at every stage to know that any proposal which is advocated or discussed trenches over the line between administration and legislation? Would it not result in a completely meaningless debate? The second point is this; has it not long been the custom of the Chair to defer to the general wish of the Committee when it is desired to use a Vote in Supply as a vehicle for a free and general discussion?

[Later] I hope that whatever we may think about the many arguments which have been addressed to us to-day, neither the Government nor the Conservative party will allow themselves to be stampeded by the extremely interested arguments addressed to them from below the Gangway on both sides of the House. In this most grave question of unemployment it is of the utmost importance that we should take wise action, and it is perfectly easy to make a plausible case on any of a dozen proposals—or I might even say, if I were to run the risk of falling into Celtic figures, that a hundred possible cases might be presented, all of which sound extremely well, but which, unless they are related to the major verities and unities of the political and economic life of this country, will only produce more harm than good. There are four main processes by which industry might be stimulated, by which a revival in industry might be forced, or actively promoted. I am not speaking of palliatives, I am not speaking, for instance, of unemployment benefit given to persons who are out of work, nor to pensions schemes for old persons, nor indeed to the stimulation of the activities of municipalities. I only refer to the last mentioned so far as to say that, after a certain point, you will find that you are only paying the municipality 100 per cent. or 50 per cent. for doing what it was going to do anyhow.

Leaving out palliatives altogether, there are four main processes by which a revival of industry can be stimulated. The first is the policy of a great loan. You borrow several hundred million pounds and spend it on public works which it would not pay to construct in ordinary circumstances, which will certainly not be paying or economic propositions according to the ordinary tests of life, but which, nevertheless, when constructed may some day have some considerable or important capital value to the island. This scheme is very largely associated with the right hon. Gentleman the Member for Carnarvon Boroughs (Mr. Lloyd George), who made such an interesting speech to-day and to whom I shall refer in a few moments.

The second of these processes is the manipulation of currency. If you can change the pound sterling to something different from what it is, incidentally you make all your calculations on a new basis, and you can work out a rather better set of figures when you call the pound sterling 17s. 6d. or 15s. or 12s. 6d. or even 10s. Very substantial and important changes can be made in the relationship of the various interests in the country and of the various individuals in the country to one another, by the manipulation of currency.

Those who take that view and who study these matters with great attention are so full of affection for their theories that they think there is no problem which cannot be solved by merely gearing up or gearing down the ratio of gold to commodities. Indeed I must confess that I have been tempted in my time by the idea that if you had an archangel to manage these things—a perfectly trustworthy archangel pursuing these operations over a very long period of time—there might be moments when perhaps by such methods he could just lift a difficult economic situation through a peculiarly embarrassing defile. But that is not the point at the present time.

The third process is Protection or Safeguarding, or a combination of Protection and Safeguarding, whereby a great stimulus is given to productive industries through the security of their home market. That is a process to which the hon. Gentleman opposite referred with an insistence which rather shocked almost his only friend on these benches, and it is one which, in these modern times, by affording the possibility of mass scientific production, seems to give very great advantages in the dominance of industry.

Lastly, there is the rather prosaic and simple process of reducing the burdens upon trade and industry. We should all be in favour of that if we knew where we could get the money from. To reduce the burdens upon industry means not only reducing the tax burden on industry, which is now being heavily increased; it means also reducing other burdens, like the transport burden and the distribution burden, which press extremely heavily on industry in this country at the present time. I must avow my partiality for this policy of reduction of burdens. Whatever we may think of the controversial methods, this at any rate is one that, if we could find the money, we would all of us be glad to adopt.

The late Government, in their derating scheme and in the efforts which we made not to add to the taxation of the country, were marching forward on this safe, prudent road of the reduction and mitigation of burdens upon productive industry. Not only were we doing it by the process of reducing rates, but also by the process of reducing freights, on the railways. It is a much better method to reduce freights on the railways than to have a tremendous quarrel with the railwaymen about beating down the standard of life which they have succeeded in establishing. It is far better, if you have to face this question—and undoubtedly our transport charges are much too high—to take the kind of course which we took, by giving what is a virtual subsidy to reduce the cost of transportation. This proved extremely beneficial, although it was applied on a very small scale, and the President of the Board of Trade and other Ministers know perfectly well that highly beneficial results were achieved, especially in South Wales and on the Clyde, by the de-freighting relief given by the late Administration.

The whole problem is where to get the money from, and I have no hesitation in saying, at the point at which our affairs have arrived, that it is my belief that a wisely extended policy of Safeguarding or of tariffs for revenue on manufactures, particularly on the more highly finished forms of manufacture, would produce in the easiest possible manner and with the minimum of psychological injury to the nation as a whole, a very substantial revenue; and here I speak entirely for myself. If those revenues were, in a proportion, devoted to a reduction in the transportation charges throughout this country, and if this policy of reducing transportation charges was followed up by a very strict and searching attempt to reduce the distributive charges and the immense margin which exists between the wholesale and the retail seller in this country—if that were done, it seems to me quite possible that a very large, extended, and combined policy could be presented, which would mean a very marked expansion and stimulus to productive industry in all its forms, and need not necessarily involve the slightest injury to the consumer as such.

I have indicated some of the remedies which have to be discussed, and I have indicated my own preference very clearly. Let me come to the right hon. Gentleman the Minister who is charged with the responsibility of this debate. The right hon. Gentleman started badly, because he started handicapped by all the foolish things he had said before he took office and all the vainglorious undertakings that he or his party had made, but I must admit that he was not the worst; in fact, he was one of the least bad. Most of the things of which he delivered himself were far less flagrant than those of others, and I have never myself seen the justice of his having to be the only person to suffer the blame. If the right hon. Gentleman started badly, I am bound to say that I think we all owe him a debt for having, once he saw he could not in any way fulfil the promises that he had made and make good the anticipations that he had created, scrapped the whole lot, with the greatest decision and resolution, and set himself to work, not to throw good money after the bad, not to follow foolish words by foolish acts, but to propound some fairly sound principles.

First of all, he exposed quite clearly the exaggerations and fraud of the present British unemployment weekly statistics; then he made it quite clear that he would not be a party to foolish stunt plans or great sensational schemes of loans; he made it quite clear that he would not allow the process of rationalisation to be impeded, even though it added to his own difficulties; and, finally, he proclaimed—and this is the lifebelt upon which in the future he is going to get to shore off the seas of history—that the remedy for unemployment could only come through a general revival of the trade and industry of this country.

I come to the speech of the hon. Member for Smethwick (Sir O. Mosley), a very remarkable speech and admirable in every way. It would be impossible to have given a more compendious account of the intricate matters with which he attempted to deal, but, as the speech proceeded, I ask myself one or two questions. I remembered hearing the late Lord Balfour, when he was leading the House—this is only partially attributable to the hon. Member's speech—criticising some speech and saying that there were in that speech some things that were trite and some things that were true, but that what was true was true. I would hardly put it as high as that, but, as the hon. Gentleman proceeded, a sort of feeling came over me, Where have I heard all this before? It seems to me that I have heard a great deal of it before; and, of course, it all comes back to the scheme of the right hon. Member for Carnarvon Boroughs, whom I am sorry I do not see in his place. It is only a variant of his scheme—perhaps a less efficient variant of his scheme. [Hon. Members: "No!"] There is a certain difference, I agree. The right hon. Member for Carnarvon Boroughs said, "We can conquer unemployment," and the hon. Gentleman the Member for Smethwick said, in effect, "I can conquer unemployment," but in principle they are in the same boat, or on the same platform.

This scheme of a great loan to be spent in all sorts of public works, stimulating the construction of roads of all kinds in this already well-roaded country, this scheme and the finance attaching to it, has been examined in every aspect with extraordinary thoroughness over the last 18 months. The late Government examined it. We turned on all our machinery, and we published the result of our examination. We had the incentive to find some very captivating, large policy on unemployment with which to go to the country, but we did not yield to the temptation. When we found that the scheme did not hold water, and would not stand the intensive examination to which it was subjected within the great Departments of State, and within the organism of the Cabinet, we rejected it. We deliberately took our punishment at the General Election. We were jeered at because we were told that we had no great large scheme for curing unemployment; but by our action we saved ourselves, and the phlegm of my right hon. Friend largely assisted to save us from being in the melancholy position in which some other parties find themselves at the present time.

The scheme of the right hon. Member for Carnarvon Boroughs and other schemes of this kind were subjected to examination by another Government. You can hardly exaggerate the differences which exist between me and the right hon. Gentleman the Chancellor of the Exchequer; it is well known that we represent entirely different points of view, but I should like to point out that his Government, when they came into power, had a still greater incentive to find an easy and captivating solution of this grim problem. They, too, had an examination of these complicated matters; they went into the whole matter with an intense desire to do the best they could, and with an intense desire to get out of their straits without doing more harm than they could, and, having examined them, they came to the conclusion that it would not be in the interests of the party to embark on the course recommended by the hon. Member for Smethwick or which was recommended by the right hon. Member for Carnarvon Boroughs. I cannot in the few minutes at my disposal go into any of the arguments on the merits, but I ask the Committee to consider that they must be pretty strong arguments when two Governments, so contrasted and so opposite in their point of view, with every desire to find the quickest way forward and the largest form of practical action, have both, one after the other, turned down these projects.

I am sorry that the right hon. Gentleman the Member for Carnarvon Boroughs is not in his place. I always like to have a Member in his place when I wish to speak about him, but I cannot, for the completeness of the debate, omit a reference to the right hon. Gentleman. I was astonished at the offer which I heard him make to the Prime Minister. We have had to-day a memorable debate, and have assisted at the making, or the attempted making, of history. If I understood the right hon. Member for Carnarvon Boroughs clearly and correctly—and many Members can bear me out—it amounted to this, that he should join a committee as august, as secret, as authoritative as the Committee of Imperial Defence, that he should be given access to every secret of the Government necessary for the discharge of his work, that upon that Committee he should be in consultation with the Prime Minister and other Members of the Government to formulate a policy, or the means of carrying out his own policy, for dealing with the grave problem of unemployment. The precedents which the right hon. Gentleman adduced were perfectly valueless. I am familiar with them. It is true that the late Lord Balfour, after he had retired from all connection with party politics, was invited to join the Committee of Imperial Defence for the study of the great questions connected with Europe and India. It is also true that on the subject of the Channel Tunnel it is customary to consult the leaders of the parties.

How can you compare these two instances with the right hon. Member for Carnarvon Boroughs going over and sitting in council with the Prime Minister and his colleagues upon the central matter of party fighting and struggle in this country at the present time? He would not only be a colleague; he would be more than a colleague; he would be a colleague with none of the advantages of responsibility. When anything went right, he would say, "We put that through; it was our suggestion—Codlin's plan."

If anything went wrong, he would say, "You know how difficult it is to put this old Labour party along." I am friendly with the Prime Minister, although opposed to him in many ways, and I hope that he will not mind my giving him a piece of advice. I should be very careful, if I were he, before I invited the right hon. Member for Carnarvon Boroughs to come over and take charge of the Labour Government. I am sure that, once he were there, with his great knowledge, his immense drive and his grip of every aspect of the administrative machinery of Government, the best course thereafter for the Prime Minister to adopt would be to make a bargain that he should be permitted to go and sit among the Liberal party, and no doubt he would find himself quite happy.

I come, in conclusion, to the speech of the Prime Minister. It is quite true, as the right hon. Member for Carnarvon Boroughs has said, that the right hon. Gentleman has not gripped the crude elements of the statistics of this problem. It is no blame to him, for we know that he exhausts himself in the public service, but this unemployment business is such that it must have the first claim on his attention. We know how he has been engaged on other matters, little though I like them, which have had his wholehearted service, and it was obvious from his speech to-day that he has accepted the figures which have been given to him by the Departments, but it is important to understand how to read them. I remember in the last Budget which I introduced we were spending £100,000,000 a year—and had done so for four years—on stimulating work in defiance of our principles and of Treasury principles, but that is the way things are done. You proclaim a principle, and then see whether you cannot get something on the other side too.

The hon. Member for Smethwick has been rather hard on his late colleagues. I think he proclaimed a good many rather painful stable secrets when he brutally told us that there was no doubt they were actually spending no more on all this Road Fund business than their predecessors had done, doing what we were so much abused for doing. I am quite sure that if my right hon. Friend the late Prime Minister or I myself had, two years or 18 months ago, recited the figures which the Prime Minister went into action on this afternoon we should have been received with a howl of derision by the benches opposite.

I think the Prime Minister would be very well advised to take the advice of the right hon. Member for Carnarvon Boroughs and devote himself to this problem of unemployment in order that he may find every method by which it can be coped with, and also in order that he may hold off foolish and unwise methods which would hamper the natural revival of trade in this country and aggravate the very evils they are meant to cure. I have tried to indicate a few of the means by which this evil can be approached with a view to its mitigation, and it may well be that there is no one method, that it is to be done through a partial application of many and various remedies harmoniously combined in one systematised policy. That may well be the case. I would not exclude anything that would help, so long as it was related harmoniously to the rest of the policy and there were no contradictions, as there often are, between one remedy and the other.

The Committee know that all these remedies will be ineffective unless the whole scheme is clamped together by a growth and revival of public confidence. Confidence is what is needed now. There is great want of confidence. Great anxiety is felt throughout the country, real apprehension. I have never known a time when there was so much apprehension. There is a feeling that anything that is gained will be taken away, a feeling engendered by the Chancellor of the Exchequer when, in apologising to his extreme left, he had to say, "This Budget is only one dose. A succession of doses like this will enable us to extract the greater part of the capital of the country"—or words to that effect. [*Interruption*.] Well, a series of doses like this £50,000,000 is what he contemplated. Can you wonder there is deep anxiety? There is also a feeling, and, I must say it quite frankly, perhaps not altogether justified, that with the Socialist regime in Great Britain this island and this Empire are passing through a period of eclipse which may well be converted into a period of decline.

There is anxiety abroad, and can we wonder at it! Why should the Government complain? Look at all they have said. Look at all they protest they stand for. We know they do not really stand for all that, but look at the way they have proclaimed the nationalisation of the means of production, distribution and exchange, the liquidation of the capitalist system of this country, and so forth; and there is anti-Imperialism in every form. As a matter of fact, they are carrying on in a great many ways with a good deal of sturdy vigour, but can they wonder that anxiety and lack of confidence are caused? They have no theme. The Clyde have a theme. Other parties have a theme, or are developing a theme, but the Government have no theme. They have deluded the masses of their supporters in the country into believing they are about to bring into being some vast, splendid, new world. They have climbed and ensconced themselves upon the structures of Capitalism, and they are shouting to the mob below that they are going to pull them down, while whispering to the bankers and big business that they are going to make them all the stronger. Can they wonder there is confusion and anxiety abroad in the nation; and can they wonder that the electors are showing an increasing reluctance to entrust the task of restoring confidence either to a bankrupt Government or to the eager bidder below the Gangway?

NAVAL DISARMAMENT TREATY

June 2, 1930

House of Commons

The hon. Member who has just spoken is at any rate in agreement with the main point which is adduced from these benches, namely, that we should make careful and searching examination into the details and the consequential reactions of this Treaty before we commit ourselves to it. It is, indeed, a grave matter, and may well occupy the attention of the House. It is not a treaty of parity; it is a treaty of inferiority. As I hold, it is a treaty of inferiority in form and on paper, and it is still more a treaty of inferiority in reality. When one applies what is written on paper to the actual problems of keeping the life and soul of the Empire together, it is undoubtedly a treaty of inferiority. I do not believe that this statement is seriously disputed. If it is all I can say is that we shall have very full opportunities of threshing it out in closest detail upon the Navy Estimates.

I was surprised at the First Lord's suggestion that any naval authority, official or unofficial, would have guaranteed that the British Fleet at the end of this five-year period, having regard to its practical obligations, would be the equal of the United States Fleet. I should have thought that it was not possible to find any authority to support that view. Therefore, I start from the basis that the Treaty is a declaration that the British Empire accepts the position of a second Power at sea. That is a very grave and formidable position from whatever point of view it is examined. Moreover, it is made certain that this position of inferiority shall be established before the Treaty can be reviewed in 1935. That is the point from which I start. We shall have inferiority in fact and in form, and it is beyond dispute that the measures now taken will place use in that position before we have an opportunity of reviewing our position.

My right hon. and gallant Friend the Member for Ripon (Major Hills) and my right hon. Friend below the Gangway both say that there are extremists in every country who are against the Treaty settlement. Of course, if those are the kind of facts upon which hon. Members found their action in a matter affecting the life and welfare of the Empire, then I am sorry for them. Hon. Members should avoid extremist views and should endeavour to find out the facts for themselves, and the true interest of the country would be better served by having a full investigation of the facts. The right hon. Gentleman the Member for South Molton (Mr. Lambert) asked us to put away the war mind. Have we not set an example in this country in that respect and have other countries followed our example? I read the other day in a newspaper a statement made by a naval witness in America. A distinguished Admiral was asked a question about the new cruisers which are to be built for the American Navy, and he was told that the new cruisers would not only be newer but far stronger and more modern than any we possess. I think we in these islands should show equal patience and thoroughness in the examination of questions which are matters of life and death to ourselves. I cannot help but admire the American Senate for the care they give to the foundation of American prosperity and power. In these matters, surely it is not to the Conservative party that the right hon. Gentleman the Member for South Molton should address his rebukes about putting away the war mind.

It seems to me that now we are abandoning our naval supremacy and all claim to it, and that it is merely the question of parity we are debating with another great Power. Never since the reign of Charles II has this country been so defenceless as this Treaty will make it, and never in the reign of Charles II was it so vulnerable. It is said that this does not matter because we have signed the Kellogg Pact, which pledges all nations to the abolition of war, and because war is unthinkable between us and the United States. This Treaty rests upon a self-destructive argument. We are told that war with the United States is unthinkable; we have ruled it out; the Kellogg Pact has abolished it; we do not mind if they have a stronger Navy than we have, or if they have the power, as they certainly would under this arrangement, to interrupt all our supplies of food and raw material. We have such confidence in them that we place ourselves unreservedly in the hands of our English-speaking kith and kin across the ocean.

That is the premise. What is the conclusion which the Government draw? The conclusion from this premise is that we must bring the United States to our council table, and measure swords round the table with the utmost nicety for weeks and months—how long they are to be, how heavy they are to be, how sharp they are to be, what kind of hilts they should have, and so forth. That is a strange conclusion to draw from the premise I have recited. The premise is no war—[*Interruption.*] Surely, we may be allowed to put our case without mockery. You have your majority; you will carry your policy over our heads; but, surely, we may be allowed without mockery to put our case. The premise, as I say; is that we omit the United States from all our calculations. The conclusion is a so-called parity, calculated to an inch, to an ounce, haggled over point by point in every category of ships, we, I think, getting somewhat the worse of it on each of the points. The premise is no competition; the conclusion, the worst form of competition; namely, parity, a neck-and-neck rivalry. The premise is entire detachment from each other's affairs; the conclusion, intense detailed concentration on most unhealthy and, as I consider, altogether unnecessary attention by each country to the other's naval establishment.

Whatever else may be said about this, it cannot be deemed to correspond to any process of truth or of reason. The United States pressed for an extra battleship. The Prime Minister resisted them stoutly, and he succeeded in repulsing their demand. But, if they are no danger to us, if war is unthinkable, if we are to bring them in no way into our calculations, why should not they build extra battleships if they want to do so? For weeks and months the Prime Minister has been arguing and fighting as to whether they should have 18 or 21 eight-inch-gun cruisers. What concern is that of ours? We are now to scrap five of our capital ships, and they are to scrap four—[Hon. Members: "Three!"]. Four; I have the paper here. But what have their ships to do with us, on the assumption that we exclude the United States from all our calculations? We are to delay for five years to allow them to overtake us, but why, if we are not in any competitive relation? It is perfectly clear that the House and the country are in the presence of what I may call a diplomatic grimace.

I propound to the right hon. Gentleman the following exhaustive dilemma: If the idea of a hostile United States is not ruled out, this Treaty is impossible; if it is ruled out, it is quite unnecessary. If war between Great Britain and the United States is unthinkable—and that is certainly our heartfelt wish—what is the true conclusion to draw? Surely, it is to forget and to ignore the United States Navy altogether, and to reserve full freedom to study our own unique problems in our own way. That is the natural conclusion; that is the sensible conclusion; that is the safe conclusion. We have ruled the United States out of our calculations. Why, then, should we calculate about them to a decimal point? Let us address ourselves to our actual dangers. Let us have full freedom to build the Navy we require to shield us from European and Asiatic dangers, and no more than those dangers. Then, having done that, having settled what that standard is, let us by all means invite the United States to build to parity, and to set their own interpretation upon what they require to bring them to that point.

Let me examine the question of the battle fleets. All these conferences have had a tendency adverse to our interests. The Washington Treaty regulated the battle fleets, but it is not the battle fleets that really matter now. That is why agreement has been easy about battleships. It was easy at Washington, and it is easy now. All parties have agreed not to build the battleships that they were not going to build in any case. The right hon. Gentleman, with great success, has forced an open door; a lot of ships that would not have been built will now never be built at all. There are only three Powers in the world that have battle fleets, and they have them at opposite corners of the globe, separated from each other by thousands of miles of ocean. Whichever of those powers crosses the ocean to get at another will suffer the greatest naval disadvantages. Our danger is not that a battle fleet will be defeated in action; our danger is that our food will be cut off in far distant seas and oceans.

The hon. and learned Member for South Nottingham (Mr. Knight), who spoke just now, asked me to define the purpose of the British Navy, and how it differs from those of other Powers. Our purpose is not aggression; it is not blockade. It is clear that, with the naval forces now in the world, we could never enforce a blockade which was not in accordance with the wishes of the United States. That was so in the Great War, but it has been overwhelmingly more so since the War ended. The purpose of our Navy is to secure the arrival of our daily bread. We cannot and we ought not to let ourselves get into a position in which any Power, even the most friendly, has undoubted means of putting irresistible pressure upon us by threatening to starve us out. Such a power, once it existed, would not need even to be exercised to be effective; we should be forced to compliance once it was clear that the supplies of this country could be interrupted.

If trouble comes—I do not believe that trouble will come; I believe that wars are over for our day—it is indispensable that we should be able to survive for two years, and to feed ourselves for two years, so that we could rebuild, as we could in these Islands, with our unequalled resources, the naval power necessary to secure victorious escape from that trouble. By restricting the general battleship programme—which restriction I am not opposing—it must be recognised that we have turned the whole naval effort of other Powers into the building of commerce destroyers. What are these eight-inch gun, 10,000-ton cruisers which the right hon. Gentleman built—the five "Kents"? They are commerce destroyers; and the ones that are going to be built in such great numbers in the United States are commerce destroyers, and the destroyers of the protecting vessels. While the whole naval argument to-day turns upon the attack and defence of trade, we alone being committed to the prodigious task of defending vital supplies—while the whole naval argument turns upon that, the drift of all these conferences and treaties has been increasingly to make it impossible for us to have any security for our food supplies.

I do not wish to plunge into the technical aspect to-night; when we come to the Votes, if the opportunity occurs, I will to into more detail; but I must say this, that our food and other supplies, in a war with a great naval Power, cannot be ensured only by cruisers. We can never have enough cruisers to clear the seas. Even if we had 70, we could not clear the seas in order to bring in our vital supplies. We must rely upon convoy.

Where are the ships to guard the convoys? In the late War we had great numbers of old battleships and armoured cruisers laid up in reserve, with nucleus crews, costing little or nothing. Now there are none. They have all been scrapped by international agreement. There is no material reserve for the British Fleet. That is a loss which falls only on us, because we alone have to bring in our food, and we alone have a reserve of seafaring manhood which would enable us to produce crews for a much larger Fleet than we keep in commission. That is a terrible weakening of our vital defence. Look at the five capital ships which are to be scrapped under this Agreement—the four Iron Dukes and the Tiger. Fine ships! We have spent, I suppose £15,000,000 upon them. The cost of keeping them in reserve would be negligible. They are the very ships to protect our convoys. These heavy ships, with enormous cannon, would each form the centre of a convoy in which 40 or 50 merchant ships laden with provisions might come with safety through areas infested with hostile cruisers to these islands.

The Prime Minister: For how long would you keep them?

Mr. Churchill: I am assured that these ships would retain, if they were properly looked after, value of this kind and for this particular service for at least 10 years.

The Prime Minister: Is that not contrary to the Washington Treaty?

Mr. Churchill: I do not follow that point. My argument is to show that by these agreements we are steadily depriving ourselves of many necessary facilities and advantages which we require and which no other country requires in the same way. Now these ships have to be taken out and sunk, and I ask myself, "Is this economy? Is it making our limited money go as far as possible? Is it getting the best kind of naval defence for the least burden upon the taxpayer?" In a week or two the First Lord will be proposing a new programme. He will come down to the House and ask for two or three more cruisers, and others in future years—£6,000,000, £8,000,000, £10,000,000 more money on new construction—small cruisers, with 6-inch guns. No doubt we need them. We need them at once, but I have no hesitation in saying that we should be far safer with these five big ships for which we have paid £15,000,000 than with three or four of these new, little, weak vessels, much weaker than those constructed by any other Power, that are now to be built at a new additional expense; and here we are throwing away costly, valuable ships on the one hand and being called upon to build new ships at great expense upon the other. Is that economy? Is that the saving of money?

If we are free—and here I address myself again to my right hon. Friend the Member for South Molton—to make our own arrangements for naval defence, it does not at all follow that we should have to spend more. There might be periods in which we should spend less, but we could spend it to better advantage. The two essentials to a thrifty housekeeping of the British Navy—vital and essential points—are, first of all, the power to maintain a material reserve, which we alone can man, when expansion is required and trouble comes; and a second and even more important point is our initiative and freedom of design. This country has always hitherto led the world in naval design. Although it is quite true that the Germans before the War improved on our naval designs, and were better in some respects than we were, nevertheless, in all the essentials of naval design, we have led and still lead the world, for good or for ill. Surely it is a great shame to take away from this country, by international instrument, all that flexibility, that power of varying types, modifying types, which in itself was a restraint on this absurd process of building long series of ships, all of one kind, and matched exactly with their counterparts in another Navy.

All this we lose, but it does not figure in any calculations that have been made at the Conference table. This loss of material reserve falls on us peculiarly. This loss of initiative and design that is almost our birthright and one of our greatest assets is merely swept away and thrown in with the general loss that we have sustained. The First Lord smiles, but I will argue this with him at length, not only to-night, and I hope he will give his mind to these matters. I have given a great portion of my life to them.

The right hon. Gentleman said that if the United States builds, Japan and others will build more, and we should be forced to build more. Let us look into that and see what this Treaty does for us about Japan. I have the highest admiration for Japan. Very good friends they have been to us, and I mention them, not in any invidious or doubting spirit, but see what the Treaty does for us about Japan. We are to scrap five battleships, and the Japanese are to scrap one.

The Prime Minister: The right hon. Gentleman is mistaken; it is a provision of the Washington Treaty anticipated by two or three years.

Mr. Churchill: I am aware of that. My argument is directed to showing the House how extremely detrimental this whole series of arrangements have been both to naval economy and to our own special interests. Besides this, Japan has secured the authorisation to build to within 30 per cent. of the cruiser strength of Great Britain or the United States. Surely that is not a good bargain. Undoubtedly, this Treaty worsens our position relatively to Japan. So also will the competition which this unfortunate discussion has started between France and Italy worsen our relative position in Europe.

I know the right hon. Gentleman will say that it would have been far worse if this Treaty had not been negotiated. He said to-day that, but for the Treaty, shipbuilding would be all the greater. We are told that the United States would build and certainly could build a Navy twice as large. I do not believe she would. I can only record my own opinion, but it is my sincere conviction that the United Sates will build more ships under this Treaty than she would have built without. Do not underrate the American deterrents upon American naval expansion. There are immense pacific forces, active and operative throughout the United States. Thank God for it. They have always held in strict check and often in control what is called the "big Navy" movement there, and we must never underrate those powerful forces. But you have disarmed those forces by this Treaty. A nval officer, an admiral, brought up before the Senate Committee, used a most instructive phrase. He was asked if he approved of the Treaty as a whole, and he said, "Yes, I approve of it because it gives the United States Navy something to hang its hat up on."

Just look at that. All the difficulties of overcoming this volume of pacific opinion, which was so threatening two years ago when the big Navy proposals were put forward, and which forced Mr. Coolidge to modify his proposals and to withdraw them—all this opinion can be overmastered by the answer, "We are only building to the standard fixed by the Treaty. We are only building a Navy up to the limits agreed upon as fair. We are exposed to no possible reproach for forcing the pace in armaments. All this is part of a policy. All this vast expansion of cruisers and armaments is part of an international treaty for the limitation and reduction of

Speeches of Winston Churchill

armaments. It is all settled. There is nothing to do now. The argument is over. The pacifists are routed. There is nothing for the United States to do but open the arsenals, lay down the new slips, and assume, with universal assent, including the assent of Great Britain, the sovereignty of the seas."

I want to know what we gain. We have this Paper here—"An International Treaty for the Limitation and Reduction of Naval Armaments." Is not this the most glaring misnomer that has ever stared at us from an official document? Let me suggest to the right hon. Gentleman the true title of this Treaty. "An international treaty for the limitation and reduction of British naval armaments and for the expansion, actual or relative, of the naval armaments of the United States, Japan, Italy and France." Let me give the right hon. Gentleman another title for this Treaty. "An international treaty for the limitation of the power and the right of Great Britain to safeguard its food supply and for the multiplication and improvement of all means possessed by other nations for interrupting the said food supply." Let me give a third alternative. "An international treaty for stereotyping naval armaments at a very high level to the special detriment of Great Britain." Let the right hon. Gentleman put these three definitions to his Naval Lords and ask whether they are not a more truthful account of this document than the misnomer that appears on its face.

You call it a Treaty of Disarmament. Do not delude yourselves with that. Nothing is going to happen under this Treaty which will give any satisfaction to the Germans in respect of the Clauses of the Treaty of Versailles. On the contrary, they are going to watch a vast process of re-armament going on over the greater part of the world. For the next five years after this Treaty, for which we are making such sacrifices and under which we are losing so much, all the arsenals of the world will be clanging with hammers and riveting machines building new formidable instruments of war. Even our own dockyards will not be idle. We shall soon have the First Lord making the most of all our own dockyards and large increases will be required in naval expenditure. In this Treaty of Disarmament our own dockyards will not be idle. What will they be doing? At great expense they will be fashioning a key which will not unlock the door of our own particular problem. At enormous expense they will be making a ten-foot plank to cross a 12-foot stream and, for that we shall have to pay in Navy Estimates greatly in excess of £50,000,000 and yet we shall not get the security that we require. [*Interruption.*] You may as well consider the facts patiently. It seems to me that from the point of view of the party opposite this is the most unfortunate and sterile ending of their hopes in regard to disarmament.

If it was a treaty of peace and good will among great nations, we might make great sacrifices for that, but there is the crowning disappointment. Since the War the only quarrels and causes of ill feeling among the nations had arisen through these Conferences over disarmament. Every conference except perhaps Washington, which dealt only with battle fleets, which were passing out of the area of seriously controversial discussion, has inflamed the fears and passions of the nations that have taken part in them. A set back has been caused by these Conferences through the well meant attempts of nations not themselves in danger to regulate and cut down the defences of those that are. These conferences have given an enormous advertisement to naval and military men and topics. They have focussed the attention of millions of people upon war topics. They have spread the war mind. They have forced Governments and statesmen to come back from policies of social reconstruction to concentrate upon ships and cannon and strategic problems. The right hon. Gentleman has been so busy that he has not been able even to look at the outlines of unemployment. They have raised the whole basis of debate on national power, prestige and existence. It would have been far better to have trusted the growing confidence that is in the world, and far better to have trusted to the enormous economic pressure of the wasteful expenditure upon armaments, and to have allowed the navies and armies to fall back gradually into the background, as they would have done in the progress of a long peace, shrunk and shrivelled, as they did after the Napoleonic wars, perhaps leaving our country, because of its unique naval needs, with mild primacy, or perhaps not.

This conference is the supreme failure of all conferences. We have seen what it does for our naval defence. But what of other countries? France and Italy—their relations have been definitely worsened. There was no particular assertion of naval competition, but, by bringing this on to the table, you have compelled both these nations to assert a demand for absolute parity which will undoubtedly lead to large naval expenditure. There is tension created between America and Japan which did not exist three months ago. And what of Anglo-American friendship? It is dear to my heart, as I believe it is the foundation of future safety and success. [*Interruption.*] Why not? The United States, as a result of this Treaty, is said to have to spend anything between £100,000,000 and £200,000,000 in construction in the next five years. No nation—not even as wealthy a nation as that—would produce these enormous sums without all sorts of stresses and contentions arising inside the body politic. Every year as the naval estimates of the United States, already two-thirds again as large as ours, bound up £10,000,000 at a time, the whole great issue will be debated. All the big Navy people will point out how vital it is for them to secure themselves against British machinations, and how generous they have been already in making so many concessions to British requests.

In every case the argument will be put forward that it is our large establishment which forces these immense sacrifices from the pacific people of the United States who would gladly have a Navy a quarter, or a fifth, or a tenth of the size which they are now forced to build. Is that going to make for good will? And after five years of this it will all have to be done over again. Once again the great Powers will meet around the table, having focussed their attention upon these details, and measure their swords once more, and this time, in 1935, our sword will be definitely and finally shorter. I cannot think that it is a wise course of policy for us to pursue. I am aware of the fact that newspaper opinion tends to chloroform the nation at this time and to parlayse its mind. In the history of falling or declining Empires, there comes a period when some mistake is discovered. Too late! That is not our case. It is not yet too late. It is still not too late to pause and make a searching examination of this matter before we take a final step. "Oh!" says the right hon. Gentleman. "Every time that a proposal is made, you will ask for this sort of inquiry?" No. This is a unique occasion. We are asked by treaty to accept naval inferiority—that is our allegation, that is our charge—after all these centuries.

Surely, if you hold special inquiries, and invite Members of other parties, to consider a question like the Channel tunnel, surely this vital matter, so vital for the welfare of this country and the Empire, is sufficiently important to be made the subject of a special inquiry. At this stage we seek an inquiry. If the right hon. Gentleman, the Prime Minister of a minority Government, consents to an inquiry, we suspend our judgment upon the Treaty. We are not voting upon the Treaty. We are voting for an inquiry into the Treaty. If the right hon. Gentleman refuses that inquiry, then I say that he and his Government will alone bear the grievous responsibility for an event perhaps disastrous to the safety of this country and certainly of no real service to the cause of the peace of the world.

FINANCE BILL

June 3, 1930

House of Commons

I think that it might well simplify and possibly abridge our proceedings if the hon. Gentleman [Mr. Herbert Morrison] told us exactly, to the best of his belief, what were the financial issues involved in this Amendment, [on motor licenses], and not only in the Amendment but in the Clause. This Amendment, obviously, is a modification of the Clause. It is true that the Clause itself involves only a very small sum, and what is that sum? What is the sum which the Amendment takes away from the yield of the Clause? If we could have that information, we should know what are the dimensions of the problem with which we are dealing.

[Later] I agree with what the hon. and gallant Member for Dulwich (Sir F. Hall) has said. This is really a case where a minor nemesis has overtaken the Government. The original proposal figured in the Budget of last year. Owing to our desire to take the sense of the country on the general political issues we divided the Budget into two portions; the main necessary and operative part and certain provisions of a non-controversial but desirable character which were left over so that they did not interfere with the convenience of the country when their electoral decision was recorded. It was assumed that as soon as the new Government was formed that these comparatively unimportant and non-controversial but nevertheless desirable provisions would be passed through the House in a second and subsidiary Finance Bill. They made their arrangements and adjusted their outlook to the new conditions. It was the Chancellor of the Exchequer who brushed all this aside. He wanted to slight the work of his predecessor. That was the mood in which he came to his office; to show how well he could do it; and he brushed it aside with an imperious gesture of contempt expressed by a brand new broom.

Now a year has passed and the Government has to come forward and stand in a white sheet for their neglect. The Minister of Transport has to say that this is one of the proposals wanted by the Chancellor of the Exchequer last year and that it is a just, legitimate, necessary and desirable feature in our legislation; that it would have been right to do it last year. If it was right to do it last year it is all the more right to do it now. The Government have extended this anomaly, this unfair treatment, for the whole year and now, when we have this enormously complicated Finance Bill, with its almost limitless succession of Clauses and Amendments, they take up the best part of two hours of the time of the Committee in presenting an Amendment to the existing law which ought to have been done last year and which might have been done by general consent last year. In a moment of great embarrassment of Parliamentary business the Government presses it upon the Committee. The Government are entirely and absolutely to blame. The very mood and temper in which they have approached their duties is the cause of their misfortune at the moment. We could have got this without the least trouble.

What is it that we ask in this Amendment? All we ask is that if the Government a year later, having seen the error of their ways, their education advanced by a year's contact with responsibility—or the best approach they can make to responsibility—when all the clap-trap which they talked about on public platforms has been worn off, come forward and indicate their desire to pass what we proposed, and what we should have passed into law last year, we say, "All right, we accept the Amendment; but if you consider accepting our proposal, you should reinstate the proposition in the exact form in which we originally proposed it." We proposed that it should date from January. We are willing to agree with the Government that it should be done at once, but we say that the Government should accept it in the form in which it was originally proposed. One cannot tell what expectations were raised or what arrangements were made. It is important that the legislation of this country should proceed on a definite and solid basis, and that what has been formally proposed by responsible Ministers should be carried into law. The second Finance Bill should never have been rejected and treated in this unceremonious manner, and if my hon. and gallant Friend chooses to go to a Division, I shall give him my vote in order to reinstate this law in the form in which it was originally proposed.

[Later, on Clause 7—Income Tax for 1930-31] I beg to move, in page 5, line 24, to leave out the words "and sixpence."

Before I embark on the general discussion on Income Tax which is raised by this Amendment, I should like to ask the Chancellor of the Exchequer whether he would impart to the Committee his governing ideas as to the extent to which we should endeavour to progress to-night. We have had a discussion on Clause 6, in which the Minister of Transport has been most patient and has given us very full and lucid explanations of every point that has been raised. We have now reached one of the most important Clauses in the whole Bill, and I think it would be advantageous, if the Government have any statement to make, to make it now.

The Chancellor of the Exchequer (Mr. Philip Snowden): I am at all times very anxious not to harass the Committee, but I cannot say that I am satisfied with the progress that has been made up to the present time. I had hoped that we might at this sitting get as far as Clause 11, but, unless the Committee sits very late, I am afraid that we shall not get so far. I think, however, that we must get to the end of Clause 9. I have no wish that the Committee should sit late. I want to take into consideration the convenience of every Member of the Committee, and especially the inability of my predecessor in this office to sit late. It is true that we have now come to the Clause which relates to the Income Tax, and which raises very important matters, but as these matters have been debated at very considerable length in the previous stages of our discussions on the Budget, important as they are, prolonged discussion upon them would not serve any very useful purpose. I do not want unnecessarily to restrict the debate, but I feel that I must get Clause 9, and I think that I might ask for the co-operation of the Opposition in trying to make that amount of progress.

Mr. Churchill: I do not think that, at first sight, anyone would say that the ambition which the Chancellor of the Exchequer has set before himself, to reach the end of Clause 9, is an unreasonable one in the circumstances, although it undoubtedly will involve very considerable contraction of our discussion upon Clause 7, which is the important Clause. I gather that it is the wish of the Chancellor of the Exchequer that we should not be kept here until an unreasonable hour. We will try our best to accelerate the discussion, while at the same time doing full justice to the many important points which arise. There is one circumstance which may somewhat facilitate our task, and that is that you, Mr. Dunnico, have ruled that the extremely important Amendments which we had put down as Amendments to this Clause would be better considered as new Clauses. Therefore, our task is lightened in that respect by your interpretation and Ruling upon the procedure. That being so I will, without more ado, address myself, as briefly as I can, to the immediate issue before the Committee.

This Clause is an extremely important and far-reaching one. The right hon. Gentleman proposes to raise the standard rate of Income Tax by 6d. That is a most melancholy event and one against which I have struggled year after year with every resource and effort open to me. If I had been told when the War came to an end that 10 years afterwards we should be reimposing 6d. on the Income Tax, and that after having gradually worked the tax down to the 4s. level we should have to retrace our steps, I should have regarded it with the keenest feelings of misfortune. The standard rate of the Income Tax is a matter which affects not only the large numbers of people who have to pay the tax but, in its way, casts its influence upon almost every form of our activities and social life. It has been explained how it affects business and enterprise. We know well how it affects the fortunes of individuals. I think the Chancellor of the Exchequer would have been well advised to make further efforts, for this year at any rate, when times are so hard and depression is so widespread, to avert the hardship of the re-imposition of 6d. upon the Income Tax.

I do not believe that this reimposition was necessary. If the Chancellor of the Exchequer on succeeding to office had set before himself, with all his strong determination, an inflexible resolve not to allow the expenditure of the country to increase by one penny, and to make sure that automatic increases were counterbalanced and more than counterbalanced by fresh savings, imposed by his energy and care; if he had been a little less rigid and rigorous in the repayment of debt over and above what is required for the purpose of the fixed debt charge; and if he had set his face against indulgences in the sphere of unemployment and widows' pensions, there would not have been any case this year for the reimposition of this heavy burden. This is the year in which we are passing through, perhaps, the most difficult stage of our immediate journey.

I have on several occasions spoken of the submerged areas of Income Tax, the large proportion of industries and businesses in which the profits yielded bear no real correspondence to what normally may be expected; businesses carried on on a much larger scale than is the yield to the Income Tax, because those businesses are not carried on upon a reasonable and profitable basis. The party opposite have, at the outset, to make up their minds whether they are going to welcome profits made by private industry and by private capitalists and tax those profits, or whether they are going, by every means in their power, to curtail and hamper those profits and then forego the consequent yield to the Exchequer. That is the choice and decision which really lies before them. But they have not clarified their minds; they have deliberately refrained from arriving at any clear mental or intellectual decision upon that point, with the result that we hear continued attacks upon the wealth of those who are called the idle rich, coupled with great regret when the yield of the Income Tax does not show its proper normal expansion. If you want an expansion of the Income Tax, so far from putting an additional 6d. upon it, the wise and shrewd course would be to effect a substantial reduction in the standard rate. No one knows what would have been the effects of a substantial reduction in the standard rate, if it were conjoined with a real re-establishment of national confidence and of enterprise throughout the country. It is quite possible that the right hon. Gentleman might have received from a lower rate of Income Tax, revenue greater than that which he will get from this additional burden.

I speak particularly of the heavy trades, but the phenomena which are present in those trades are equally to be traced in many other aspects of our public life. This heavy taxation, more than any other invisible factor, is making us share in the world depression to a disproportionate extent, and when the world lifts out of the depression, as it will lift, and when the prices begin to rise and business to expand, it is this deadweight burden of taxation which may make us the last country to emerge from the dark defile, and may make us the country to emerge in the most battered and exhausted condition. Therefore, far from extolling the virtue of taxation, far from glorifying in the imposition of this heavy burden, it should be the task and duty of a Government by every means in their power to nurse the country through its difficult periods and to lighten and reduce the demands which they make upon the taxpayers for the maintenance and upkeep of the State.

The right hon. Gentleman, by so blithely placing this heavy addition upon the standard rate of Income Tax, and at the same time showing himself reluctant and unwilling to place any addition upon the indirect taxpayers, and also by restricting the scope of the Income Tax payers thus affected by the tax, has created an invidious condition and has invested his Budget with an unfair character which certainly has caused in this House and outside a distinct impression that he is not being guided by the true canons of finance and is not seeking with that broad impartiality that should belong to whoever holds his great office, to act evenly in the distribution of benefits or in the needful apportionment of hardships and evils; but, on the other hand, he is mingling politics at every step and at every stage in his financial decisions, and is vitiating the purity of the solutions which he offers us by the admixture of extraneous motives which are themselves part of the stock-in-trade of his political popularity.

When we come to an Income Tax of 4s. being raised at a time of peace to 4s. 6d., the old Gladstonian canons of finance and the old views which were taken as to the relative advantages and disadvantages of direct and indirect taxation, must be reviewed and reconsidered. In those days when we were told of the grave injury done to the consumer by indirect taxation, and of the possibility that more would be taken from the pockets of the taxpayer than would be actually gathered into the public coffers, those evils were contrasted with increases in the Income Tax of 1d., or at the outside 2d., on an Income Tax of 5d. or 6d.

I remember well hearing a predecessor of the right hon. Gentleman, the late Mr. Ritchie, reducing the Income Tax after the South African war, and he made a sort of auctioneer's gesture of it and took it off "One penny," "Twopence," "Threepence," and when he uttered the word "Fourpence," the House was almost in a state of collapse from hysteria, there was such enthusiasm and relief. But in those days, when the taxation was practically non-existent, when it was no real burden, when no man making business plans or laying down his own expenditure in the immediate future could be harassed by the inroad of the tax collector, then indeed you might use all the old arguments which may be properly applied to indirect taxation; but now that the first preoccupation of most of the larger Income Tax payers in this country is to find the money to pay their Income Tax, when that is the first charge, as it were, upon their resources and the main cause in many cases of their anxieties, in these days you inflict, in my opinion, a far greater deterrent upon business and enterprise by a further addition to the tax than could be argued even by the most strict Free Trader or economist would be inflicted by a moderate addition to indirect taxation, even though the yield might not in all cases be fully reaped by the Treasury.

As I say, there are many processes which may be allowed to continue, although they have evil effects, because they are on a small scale and can be tolerated and borne, but as the burden rises, as the degree of intensity of taxation increases, so it becomes all the more important to examine all the anomalies, to dwell upon the special hardships, and to canvass with the most searching scrutiny the whole foundation, basis, and character of the tax. There are many aspects of this tax which we shall have to pass in review. Some few we shall deal with this evening, but others we shall definitely raise in the series of new Clauses which we have placed upon the Paper, and which, under the guidance of the Chair, must now be considerably extended. I trust that the right hon. Gentleman will, in his speech, address himself to the main and broad considerations which arise upon the tax. We think that we could best assist him in making progress with his Bill if we have a very full discussion on the general question of the increase of the tax. A very full discussion, Mr. Young, with your permission, would, I think, be in accordance with the wishes of the Committee and its general convenience; and then, when we come to the Amendments, we will dispose of them as quickly as we can and divide upon them, so that we may register our opinions on each point, and at the same time have had the advantage of one general, comprehensive debate.

I have only attempted to inaugurate an open and general discussion in these few remarks, which I have endeavoured to curtail as much as possible. But the right hon. Gentleman must be in no doubt about our attitude, which is one of emphatic protest against the policy of raising the standard rate of the Income Tax by 6d. at the present juncture; a policy which, we are sure, will add to our difficulties far more than it will relieve the revenue problem of the right hon. Gentleman and will, it is quite conceivable, prolong the period of misfortune through which we are passing and possibly leave us, when that period is over, definitely weakened for every purpose of domestic advance or of external progress.

[Later, on the Surtax rate] May I suggest that the Financial Secretary should give some clear indication of the intention of the Government to re-examine this matter before the Report stage? We are anxious to facilitate the progress of business, but the point that has arisen is one of real substance and difficulty. It seems not at all unlikely that the words inserted do not achieve the object they have in view or, if they do achieve it, they raise other difficulties of a constitutional character which it is desired to avoid. I suggest that, instead of carrying the matter further at this moment, the Chancellor of the Exchequer or the Financial Secretary should make it clear that it is going to have the concentrated attention of the Government and the Law Officers of the Crown, and that we shall have an opportunity on report of going into it in full detail and, we trust, in a more satisfactory form.

[Later] I want to make an appeal to the parties of the Opposition, and I take full responsibility myself in saying that we under-estimated the gravity and complexity of the problems which arise on these two Clauses [on the Income Tax and the Surtax]. I must admit that, taking full responsibility for any part that I had in that miscalculation. The right hon. Gentleman proposed earlier in the day not to proceed beyond Clause 9, and it was my belief that, while we might sit on till the very late hours of to-morrow morning, Clause 9 would probably be within the compass of the Government to achieve by that time, but its difficulty has undoubtedly been borne in increasingly on the Committee this evening, and a number of extremely difficult and complicated questions have arisen which have not been adequately discussed. Nevertheless, I did say, taking full responsibility myself, that we did not consider that the proposal of the right hon. Gentleman was unreasonable. Therefore, I must appeal to hon. Members on this side to facilitate the termination of our discussion at the period which was considered to be in accord with the general convenience of the Committee. But I must say that it is clear, from our survey of Clauses 7 and 8, that these issues must be raised in the fullest possible manner upon Report, and I trust that you, Sir, in the Chair, will also bear in mind the abridgement of the discussion on this occasion, which has arisen from a perfectly sincere and natural error, and that you will, in your capacity in the Chair, also guard us from any abridgement of the discussion when the Report stage is reached.

FINANCE BILL

June 5, 1930

House of Commons

Even apart from a discussion on the Question, "That the Clause stand part," which naturally would be abridged in consequence of the full discussion on the first

Amendment, there are certain specific Amendments which could not be disposed of simply by their being put to the Committee. There will have to be some discussion, however accelerated, on the various important Amendments in detail.

[Later] I congratulate the Chancellor of the Exchequer on having deferred to what was the general wish expressed from all quarters of the Committee. The right hon. Gentleman is wise to adopt at the outset a mood of seeking to invite the Committee to share to some extent in the actual shaping of legislative proposals. It is very difficult to do that if the possiblity of debate affecting legislative proposals is excluded, and we are reduced to what is little more than a trial of physical strength and imaginative volubility. Once the Government show that they are willing to learn by the debates—for, after all, almost every prolonged debate in Committee throws light on the subject—and to make their legislation harmonise with the general opinion of the House, we may make more rapid progress than it would be reasonable to expect in the face of an adamantine and inflexible opposition.

We on this side never sought to leave the right hon. Gentleman in the anomalous position of having to allow a rebate of 2s. 3d. on an Income Tax which is chargeable only at 2s. We wish to meet him on that. We recognise that, with the new graduation, that point has to be met, and my right hon. Friend has suggested one method by which it might be met, but we have not the facilities of the draftsmen and the trained legal advisers which are at the disposal of the right hon. Gentleman and it may well be that that purpose can be expressed in some other way. It might not, but the right hon. Gentleman can see perfectly well what we wish, and I gather that if that were conceded, and his difficulty met by another form of words, he would be willing to leave the rest of the Clause out and make it inoperative, and to have no more in the Clause than will maintain the standard rate and the proportion of the rebate to the standard rate for all other cases.

Mr. P. Snowden: I gather that the Opposition do not want to take out paragraph (c), which was the subject of a long point of Order just now, because that is really removing an anomaly which, I think, the Opposition are quite as anxious to remove as we are.

Mr. Churchill: I am only on the specific point and the part of the Clause which relates to this point. I gather that the right hon. Gentleman will study how he can meet the point put forward by the hon. Member for Farnham (Mr. A. M. Samuel). In that case, our general debate upon this aspect might well be abridged.

[Later] I beg to move, "That the Committee do report Progress and ask leave to sit again."

I do this in order to put myself in order so that no remarks which I may now make may impinge upon any discussion which may take place upon the Clause. We have had a very useful day's discussion in which there has been a great deal of good work and good temper displayed, and a certain amount of give and take. The Government have allowed the House of Commons to participate in moulding the legislation for which we are all jointly responsible, and, therefore, seeing that the Prime Minister is in his place, I should like to ask, what are the views of the Government as to the distance we should get to-night and the hour at which we should endeavour to terminate our proceedings? I ask this question early because, whatever the decision is, it is most important that we should utilise the available time to the best possible advantage. If it is decided that we are to make a very long effort to-night, we can examine everything in a most thorough and searching manner, but if, on the other hand, there is a desire to terminate the proceedings at a time which will not expose Members to extreme inconvenience, it will certainly require a great deal of care on the part of Members on both sides of the Committee in order to compress our discussions and make them as fruitful as possible. Perhaps the Attorney-General, speaking for the Government, or the Prime Minister, will let us know what they have in mind. I wish to make it clear that no agreement of any sort or kind has been entered into, either across the Floor of the House or behind the Chair, but we are entitled to ask what are the wishes of our masters in these matters, so that we may arrive at an arrangement for the common good?

The Prime Minister (Mr. Ramsay MacDonald): I respond very gladly to the invitation which has been given to us by the right hon. Gentleman. I do not like to aid and abet in the neglecting of duty of a very thorough and penetrating critic of the Clauses. At the same time, all we want to-night is to get to the end of Clause 16. When we have got Clause 16, which fact has been mentioned before, we shall be prepared to move to report Progress.

Mr. Churchill: I am bound to say that the declaration of business which the Prime Minister has made does not seem to us on this side of the Committee to be unreasonable in view of the progress which has been made to-night and considering the postponement of Clause 12. It seems to us on this side of the Committee that we ought to be able to make a very well compressed examination of the four Clauses which now lie before us. I beg to ask leave to withdraw the Motion to report Progress.

[Later, on Clause 14—Provision as to computation of profits and gains for purpose of charge to tax in two years next after the year in which trade, etc., set up or commenced] We want to get on, and I hope that we may hear from the Chancellor of the Exchequer that he will consider the point as to the further definition of the word "person," by inserting the words "person who is a partner in a firm," or some such words. That question might, perhaps, be considered between now and Report, with a view to making it clear that the intention is to pursue that share of the collective liability of a firm which properly attaches to a partner in the firm, but not to pursue in respect of Income Tax anything which trenches beyond those limits of actual income which hitherto have been the sole basis upon which the tax was levied. There is a considerable point of principle there. I will not ask the Chancellor of the Exchequer for any final or decided statement, but if he would indicate that the point will receive careful attention between now and Report, with a view to the localisation to which I have referred, I think it would enable us to quit this Clause now without further discussion.

[Later, on Clause 15—Amendment of Rule 11 of Rules applicable to Cases I and II of Schedule D] Mr. Wardlaw-Milne: Will the Chancellor, when he is considering the point my hon. Friend has raised, consider whether he cannot abolish this legislation by reference, which makes it so extremely difficult to follow, and whether, before the Report stage, he will have the Clause re-drafted to make it perfectly clear, instead of having to refer to previous Acts.

Mr. P. Snowden: I am afraid I cannot promise between now and Report to solve a problem which has baffled every legislator, I suppose, from the time legislation was first instituted, and that is to abolish legislation by reference. The point here is a very simple one. It involves nothing more than extending the option from three months to twelve.

Mr. Churchill: I do not think we can ask more than that on a Clause which is definitely a concession to the taxpayer. It would, I think, cost nothing to the Revenue to consider a more detailed application of the concession. That, I understand, will be done.

[Later, on Clause 16—Provision as to relief from double taxation on certain profits from sale of goods] On a point of Order. Before any Amendment is brought forward upon this Clause, it might simplify our proceedings if the Government would give us a simple explanation, in ordinary parlance of the purpose, scope and intention of the Clause, and that our discussion should then proceed upon the basis of knowledge of exactly what the Government have in mind, and the points to which they attach importance. We can see whether the points which cause us difficulty can be adjusted rapidly to their point of view.

[Later] I suggest that at this stage the Chancellor of the Exchequer should tell us that he will make an effort to deal with the words "the sale of goods," around which this discussion has played. The words clearly require further definition, both in the direction of amplification and precision. The hon. Member for Luton (Mr. Burgin), who spoke so ably from the Liberal benches, has shown why "the purchase of goods" should be included. I suggest that the Chancellor of the Exchequer or the learned Attorney-General should tell us that this point will be studied by the experts of the Treasury between now and Report, with a view to making the Clause the vehicle of the purposes of the Government.

FINANCE BILL

June 17, 1930

House of Commons

On that point of Order. May we have everything made quite clear? You [the Chairman] have suggested that there should be a general discussion on this particular Amendment, and it is not for us to say that any inconvenience arises from that, but it must not be supposed that we in any way abrogate or invalidate our right to discuss other Amendments fully.

The Chairman: I am not clear to which Amendments the right hon. Gentleman is referring.

Mr. Churchill: There is an important Amendment in the name of my hon. Friend the Member for Barnstaple (Sir B. Peto)—in page 16, line 8, to leave out the words "for the purposes of profit"—which we shall certainly desire to discuss in a manner very different from arranging that it shall go through *pro forma*.

[Later] I have listened to this debate with an increasing feeling of astonishment that the Chancellor of the Exchequer should have seen fit to overload this already complicated and controversial Budget by the introduction of a Clause like this. Whether his officials have taken advantage of his inexperience and thrust before him a number of stock departmental amendments and grievances which they would be glad to have cleared out of the way, and he has not noticed it, nor realised it, or whether there is some other reason, some desire to show favour to some particular Government with whom the right hon. Gentleman and his Government are willing to have specially agreeable relations; which of these may be I cannot attempt to decide, but of this I am sure, that a more foolish course for the right hon. Gentleman to take than to introduce into the Budget a Clause of this kind, which, as has been shown, has vices inherent in it against which Parliament is bound emphatically to protest, is certainly an astonishing course to take. There is, of course, a third reason which has actuated the right hon. Gentleman, and I am inclinded to think perhaps it may be the true one. The right hon. Gentleman is anxious so to cumber the Budget with unessential details, and this sort of trumpery matter which could quite well be left for another year when we were not imposing an additional £50,000,000 or £60,000,000 taxation, as to exhaust and weary the House in the hope that his more general propositions on taxation may escape without the examination which they deserve.

Whichever of these three reasons may have actuated the right hon. Gentleman, the fact remains that he has not been content to allow the practice to proceed upon the basis of the Treasury Minute. He has brought it to our notice and forced us to examine in detail the propositions which hitherto have rested, as it were, under general acquiescence. But he has added a new and more precise definition of the tolerances which have been allowed in the past. Therefore, we are bound to examine it. He knows that by this departure which he has made and by the principles to which he asks us to subscribe—I am not going to dwell upon the extraordinary facts elicited in cross-examination from the Chancellor of the Exchequer by my right hon. Friend the Member for St. George's (Sir L. Worthington-Evans)—he is actually putting a premium upon the employment of foreigners by the consul of a foreign State and a consequent impediment upon the employment of British subjects. This point has been clearly made. It is entirely in harmony with the general logical scheme and outlook of the party opposite and is one which cannot be too widely censured and held up to public animadversion throughout the country as the policy of the Socialist party.

We have to take into consideration the whole issue of reciprocity. This Amendment raises that point directly. It is quite true that in the palmy days of Queen Victoria, in 1842 and thereafter, when this country was at the summit of its power and had reached the highest point in its long history, when in every sphere of trade and finance and on the seas we held an undisputed and almost indisputable supremacy, many tolerances and indulgences were vouchsafed to foreigners. But now in these harder times, when a far sharper competition rules the world and when we find ourselves in no way met by other countries in the spirit in which we guided our policy, we have at every point to go carefully over and count our balance, to examine the whole bearing of any concessions which we may give to foreigners and to make sure that we get the full value for any concessions that we may make.

I recommend the right hon. Gentleman to withdraw this Clause and not occupy the Committee talking about these matters which, on his own showing, need never have come before us but for his spirit of meticulous pedantry which desired to include them. If he refuses to withdraw this Clause, then I ask him why cannot he accept the Amendment which has been moved by my hon. Friend? Why should we give these favours to nations that do not give these favours to us? Why should we discriminate against our own nationals when employed in the consular offices of a foreign State when the foreign State does not similarly give a favour to our nationals when employed under our own consuls in that foreign State?

Of course, if reciprocity were established, and full reciprocity, you would be able to say that it is much better for the consul of Russia or Germany to employ a German or a Russian than to employ an English person on his staff; and, on the other hand, our consuls in their countries would have an advantage and an incentive to employ British persons on their staffs. Let the right hon. Gentleman insist upon reciprocity. Let him embody this Amendment in the Clause. Let him say that it would apply only to people who treat us in the same way as we treat them. The right hon. Gentleman would be routed. Who is the cause of this debate and its prolongation? It is the right hon. Gentleman. Why did he want to stick this Clause on the face of this Bill unless he is asking us to make a new affirmation of principle? If we have to make new affirmations of principle we must make them in relation to the changed circumstances of the times in which we live. The right hon. Gentleman would be well advised even now to withdraw this Clause. If he refuses, then all I can say is that he will be well advised to accept the Amendment. If he refuses to accept the Amendment, it will only be another instance of the unlimited bad weather that he is capable of making for himself.

[Later] The right hon. Gentleman [Mr. P. Snowden] must not endeavour to escape from the very precise point which is directed against it by vague and general denunciations of the conduct of the Opposition nor must he seek to do so by what I think I may describe as insinuations against the conduct of the Chair. The right hon. Gentleman suggested that the Motion which you, Mr. Young, have accepted is an abuse of the Rules of the House and thereby he directly accused the Ruling which you have given. Further, he went on to say that only the Rules of the House prevented him from describing this Motion as of a dilatory and obstructive character or words to that effect. I leave the Committee to judge if that is a decent way of evading the Rules, and if it is worthy of the Chancellor of the Exchequer, as the Minister in charge of the Committee, to say something which he knows is contrary to the Rules of the House and which is a reflection, and has always been judged to be an unparliamentary reflection on hon. Members, and to cover it up and wrap it up in the specious pretence of saying, "I am prevented by the Rules of the House from saying so." All this is done by the right hon. Gentleman in the awkward shift to which he is reduced by the fact that he has cited a Minute but has not been able to say whether that Minute exists or not. He has cited a Minute, but he is not prepared to produce it. Is there any reason why this Minute should not be produced? The right hon. Gentleman spoke about the staff not being obliged to produce material in anticipation of every question which might be put by the Opposition. Of course they are not obliged to do so; but in the brief which is presented to the Chancellor of the Exchequer, if there is a Clause which is intended to take the place of a Minute, it would be quite in accordance with the natural and ordinary process to have the particulars for which we ask. In saying so, I think I speak with the concurrence of my right hon. Friend the Member for West Birmingham (Sir A. Chamberlain), and he and I can claim something like 10 or 11 years of combined experience in the office of Chancellor of the Exchequer.

Mr. J. Jones: In every party bar one.

Mr. Churchill: I am afraid the hon. Member's thoughts are away in other fields, far different from those with which we are now concerned. But I am not going to allow anything to draw the Committee away from the definite point against the right hon. Gentleman. Where is the Treasury Minute? If it exists, there is no conceivable reason why it should not be produced, because we are told that that is the hypothesis on which the argument of the Government proceeds, and that the Clause simply renders the Treasury Minute statutory. The Clause is published, it is in the Bill, and how can it be suggested that there will be any detriment to the public interest in producing the Minute which is said to be the foundation of the Clause? Where is the Minute? It is more than an hour since this matter was first bruited in the Committee, and there has been ample time in which to obtain the Minute. Unless the right hon. Gentleman is able to produce the Minute this Motion is justified, because he has said that it is on the Minute that this Clause is founded, and, if there is no Minute, then the right hon. Gentleman has made a statement to the Committee—no doubt through error and inadvertency—which is found to be related at no notable point to the actual facts. There is not the slightest use in the right hon. Gentleman trying to escape from his difficulty by such methods as he has adopted. We are not in the least surprised at his methods, or at his harsh manner—and we shall probably have less reason to be afraid of him or of those who supported him, with every week that passes. We move this Motion as a protest against the refusal of the right hon. Gentleman to answer this specific question put to him and the failure to produce the Minute; and in the circumstances this Motion, which will be pressed to a Division, ought to commend itself to the general sense of the Committee.

[Later] On a point of Order. May I, with great respect, refresh your memory as to the course which events in this debate have taken? In the first place, my right hon. Friend was engaged in unfolding the case for the Amendment, and made some reference to Russia. You cautioned him that in the main your Ruling was that Russia could not be a substantial matter of debate. Then the hon. Member for Dartford (Mr. Mills) interjected a question which forced my right hon. Friend to reply and to enter much more closely into the matter than he had otherwise intended. Then you, observing the provocation of the hon. Member for Dartford, allowed the right hon. Gentleman to open up the question. Then the hon. Member for Dartford got up and made a speech full of all sorts of definite statements which I should have thought were wholly unfounded and incorrect, statements which we are very familiar with as part of the stock-in-trade of the party opposite. We cannot allow all these untruthful statements to pass, statements grossly erroneous and misleading if they were accepted, because we should lay ourselves open to the charge of failing in our duty. It is impossible after you have allowed that latitude to the hon. Gentleman, that an adequate reply should not be permitted, at any rate up to the point when you intervened. I was myself intending to deal, and am now relying upon you letting me deal, with some of the propositions which the hon. Gentleman has advanced. Now that you have arrested his flow upon this subject, I will of course hold myself strictly limited to replying to the points that he has advanced. I submit, as a point of Order, that when a Chairman has permitted a discussion to be made upon matters of high public policy, it is the right of Members who are deeply offended by those assertions, to have an opportunity of expressing their views.

[Later] On that point of Order. If a specific statement of facts is allowed to be made by the hon. Member for Dartford (Mr. Mills), is it not open for us on this side of the Committee to reply to them?

The Deputy-Chairman: If the right hon. Member for Epping (Mr. Churchill) accepts my Ruling, and the reply is kept precisely to the statement made, I will allow it. But I say at once, quite firmly, that I am not prepared to allow a general discussion.

Mr. Leif Jones: Is it really the case that on this Amendment we can go into the question as to whether any foreign State has at any time defaulted in its financial obligations? The Amendment says: "any foreign state which has made default in meeting its financial obligations." That does not involve, I submit, any particular case where a country has defaulted. That is not within the scope of the Amendment.

Mr. Mills: The terms of the Amendment are hopelessly out of order because they are incoherent. There ought to be some time limit.

The Deputy-Chairman: The hon. Member is not responsible for accepting Amendments. That is the responsibility of the Chair.

Mr. Churchill: I certainly feel strongly disposed to deal seriatim with the various statements of the hon. Member for Dartford (Mr. Mills), but, in all the circumstances of the case, and having regard to the appeal which has been made to us by the representative of the Liberal party not to allow any remarks to pass about any country which might have the slightest irritating effect, I will deal with the proposition entirely in general terms. On the face of it, is it not the most reasonable proposition that could be presented? Is there not a case for excluding from these special favours a State which has defaulted in the payment of its debts? If there were such a State—I will not mention names—which, having borrowed vast sums of money, hundreds of millions of pounds, from a friendly ally, afterwards repudiated flatly and contumaciously all responsibility for repaying a single penny of that sum, is that a State to which you would grant these special favours? If there were a State which not only repudiated the debts contracted by the Government of the country, but proceeded to steal the private property of individuals who had invested their money on public faith and international understanding, would not that be the State which you would exclude from these special favours? If there were a State which was founded upon a doctrine and creed so vile and inhuman that it takes as its fundamental point the breaking of faith with all persons not associated with its doctrine, if there were such a State, is not that the State which we should exclude from our courteous indulgence and usages in this country? That is all that the Amendment says. It is not necessary to go back over a period of 200 years; that would be a long time to go back in search of the State which I have hypothetically mentioned. You might not have to go back over the whole of that time—I do not know. The right hon. Member for Camborne (Mr. Leif Jones) cried out against any remarks which might possibly wound the susceptibilities of any foreign country; now he complains that we do not extend our condemnation to all foreign countries.

Mr. Leif Jones: You do. The Amendment in set terms reflects upon any foreign State which has made default at any time in meeting its financial obligations. I say that Germany has made default, Austria has made default, and France has made default. I say that most European countries within the last 200 years have made default in meeting their financial obligations.

Mr. Churchill: The right hon. Member, in a most offensive way, has mentioned the names of some countries, and the responsibility for any ill-will which may follow must fall upon his shoulders. We have not been the cause of bringing this matter before Parliament. The Government have gone out of their way to insert in this Finance Bill a provision by which, unless this Amendment is accepted, they will bestow special indulgences upon Powers, if such Powers there be, who have defaulted and repudiated their public obligations. I agree that there are strict limits upon the amount of pressure which one country can put upon another in the matter of repayment of debt. You cannot put a great Power in the county court, you cannot obtain a summons against a State or distrain upon their property. The repayment of debt by countries depends very largely upon the measure of their desire to maintain proper credit, and I agree that it would perhaps be unwise for us to press upon the Government the interpretation of this Amendment which would have the effect of denying these privileges to all those countries who may at one time or another, through the depreciation of their currency or some other cause, have defaulted in their payments. But when a case is presented of deliberate, wilful and contumacious repudiation, then I am of opinion that these indulgences should not apply, and it is for the Government to say whether or not contumacious default has taken place. There are defaulting States in the American Union. There are loans given to friendly and allied nations on the Continent, but the gravamen of the charge we are making against any country which is sought to be affected by this Amendment is that it is a deliberate and flagrant repudiation of contractual obligations.

We cannot for a moment exclude from our minds the fact that these defaults may recur in the future. The weapons which one great Power has against another in the matter of the enforcement of debt are very limited. Here is one of your weapons; a small means of putting pressure on a defaulting State; a small minor, non-violent, non-military, method of indicating that certain practices places a country on a lower plane in the civilisation of the world. It is not a question of violent action. You have no power to take violent action, and it would be folly for any country to go to war to collect its debts. More money would be squandered in the first month of the war than the amount of the debt. But let us use the means we have; they are few enough and small enough. In this Amendment we have one method by which we can express our abhorrence and detestation of those practices which places a country guilty of them on a definitely lower level than others. Again I say that we have not raised this matter. We were content to let it lie in the calm and obscure atmosphere to which the custom of generations had relegated it. But the Government, going out of their way in looking for trouble, trying to extend the wider controversy between the parties, have insisted upon our giving these new facilities in statutory form. If these advantages are to be extended, if these courtesies and harmonious usages are to be extended, on a reciprocal basis, at least let it be said that there are some exceptions which we have the wisdom to proclaim and the resolution to enforce.

    [Much later] Surely the learned Attorney-General is not going to leave matters in the position in which they stood when the hon. and learned Member for East Nottingham (Mr. Birkett) sat down. I have rarely heard a speech more precisely directed to the object under debate, more harmoniously attuned to the character of Committee discussion, than the excellent statement which he has made. It seemed to me that there could hardly be a more damaging speech from the point of view of the Attorney-General himself. Not only were his facts traversed, not only was his legal authority impugned, and even controverted, but these sharp arrows were planted in his person by his distinguished legal successor in his old primacy on the Liberal benches. I congratulate the Liberal party on having so rapidly filled the gap. I do not often quote Latin to the Committee, but I will say on this occasion: "Uno avulso, non deficit alter." On the removal of one, another is not wanting. Someone has taken the hon. and learned Gentleman's place who, although not possessing the advantages of official information, has been able to answer him in fact and law and leave him sprawling, a pitiable object. Is he going to sit there silent? You cannot carry on very long in the House of Commons by failing to answer important, serious and difficult questions. The Chancellor of the Exchequer for two hours to-day refused to answer a question which nothing in the public interest withheld him from answering, the answer to which he knew perfectly well. He refused to answer, but sat there stone-walling the discussion.

    In the same way the Attorney-General, bankrupt in argument, scores off, if I may use a fairly popular expression, in a way which we rarely see one Member deal with another in these debates, and he thinks that he is going to get out of it by sitting there smiling. I am glad to see him smile. I have several times been minded to say to those who take part in these Budget debates, "Cheer up!" and it would be a great thing if he smiled and took a buoyant and happy view of life. In spite of all the awful things he may have done, there is no need to go about as if he had seen Banquo's ghost. But this is not a laughing matter; this is not a moment to smile. Having been selected by the Socialist party to give them the strong legal and intellectual guidance which they so particularly require, the hon. and learned Gentleman makes an exhibition of himself and is put on the broad of his back by the hon. and learned Gentleman below the Gangway, and sits still, without making the slightest attempt at a Parliamentary answer. The only contribution of the Chancellor of the Exchequer is a capacious yawn.

    There is another serious aspect to this Clause. It is typical of half-a-dozen that are put into this Bill. The Chancellor is coming forward to demand £50,000,000 or £60,000,000, it may be, of additional revenue from a small class of the taxpayers, a class which he has deliberately narrowed to the smallest possible capacity. The British direct taxpayers are without their equal in the world. No country produces revenue as we have done. Now, added to this very heavy burden, which the right hon. Gentleman argues the necessities of the case demand, are a whole series of petty, vexatious inquisitorial points designed, in my judgment, not to add to the revenue, but to gratify the feelings of personal irritation and spite which the Chancellor has against this class. In the end this may be a very dangerous policy. An enormous revenue is raised by the direct taxpayer. Any one who knows the workings of the Inland Revenue knows perfectly well that the success of any Budget we have seen in recent times or that we may see in the immediate future depends for its yield of revenue on the good will and the loyal co-operation of the mass of the taxpayers. You may devise this dodge and that inquisition; you may invent this new process and stiffen up that particular guard; but if in the process of doing that you have rendered the heavy new burdens odious to the great mass of those taxpayers, believe me for every pound that you save you will lose ten.

[Later] I beg to move, "That the Chairman do report Progress, and ask leave to sit again."

I rise for the purpose of asking the Chancellor of the Exchequer to give us some inkling at this stage of the intentions which the Government have formed with regard to the further course of our business to-night and of their submissions in the matter. [An Hon. Member: "Speak up!"] I conclude with the Motion to Report Progress and ask leave to sit again, and I repeat that for the benefit of my hon. Friend who has just returned from the cricket match. We have not found it easy to make progress to-day because the Chancellor of the Exchequer has not made many helpful answers to the arguments that have been used. He prefers to sit there stonewalling the Debate and rising in his place at intervals to move the Closure. Sometimes he has risen when the Chairman has been unable to accept the Closure, thus showing that he has been unable to judge the sense of the Committee with the same instinct and propriety as the Chairman. What does he intend to do? How far does he wish to go? We have disposed of one Clause and made good progress with a second. They will not add to the revenue nor help to solve the financial problems of the country. All they will do is to work out certain special ideas that the Chancellor of the Exchequer and his friends have on these subjects. I will give the right hon. Gentleman an opportunity at this stage, before I comment further on the situation, to tell us what his intentions are.

Mr. P. Snowden: We have been in Committee now for nine hours, and we have got one Clause. I can answer the right hon. Gentleman in one sentence. This sitting will continue until we have reached Clause 27.

Mr. Churchill: It always makes the thorny path of public business the easier when we are guided by the right hon. Gentleman. I will counsel him, if he is really going to embark on such a lengthy and laborious procedure, to begin his labours—for he is only at the very beginning of them—in rather a better temper than he has just exhibited. The spectacle of rage and malice which was exhibited to us when he rose just now reminds me of an impression I have sometimes seen when walking through a munitions factory and the great glare of a furnace suddenly comes on one.

Dr. Morgan: Get on!

The Chairman: The hon. Member is outside the House.

Mr. Churchill: All I can say is that the proposals of the Chancellor of the Exchequer are preposterous. He asks us to deal with the immense series of Clauses that lie between us and Clause 27.

Mr. J. Wilson: We have to have them at some time.

Mr. Kirkwood: You are getting supporters on this side. Go ahead!

Mr. Churchill: I cannot conceive any course less calculated to facilitate progress. Some of these Clauses are of great importance and complexity. Others are not of such importance, but they are none the less irritating and have added needlessly to encumber the financial provisions. The whole attitude which the right hon. Gentleman has adopted is one calculated to delay the course of public business. From beginning to end of this Budget he has tried to ride roughshod over the House. How, I should like to know, could any Opposition receive the kind of announcement he has made to us? After all, we have our Parliamentary rights as well as he and his friends. He is a Minister in a minority Government dependent on the precarious political co-operation he receives from that bench. He uses tones of arrogance which I have never heard employed in a Government in a majority. He says we are to deal with all these clauses.

Take Clause 19 (Provisions as to collection of tax where appeal pending against assessment). That Clause is one of these little, petty pinpricks to the taxpayer at the time when the right hon. Gentleman is casting this heavy new burden on him. Take Clause 20 (Amendment of law relating to summary recovery of income tax) and Clause 21 (Limitation on amount of sur-tax payable in respect of total income of individual dying within year of assessment). That Clause is one on which, I dare say, there will not be very much trouble. Clause 22 (Valuation for purposes of Schedules A and B to be made quinquennially in Great Britain.) [Hon. Members: "Agreed."] Why should you begin saying "Agreed"? After all, we have been told we are sitting all night. We cannot have at one moment violent threats by the Chancellor of the Exchequer to ill-use the House and squeals for mercy from his followers. Clause 23 (Provisions for expediting in England valuations and assessments for years of revaluation). This is a most serious and complicated Clause affecting the valuation and its relations to the Treasury valuation. Clause 24 (Parishes for purposes of assessment in England.) That perhaps is not a very lengthy Clause, but look at Clause 25 (Appointment of general commissioners in Scotland.) That raises the Scotch aspect of our affairs. That, I should have thought in the best of circumstances difficult to dispose of by the Scottish Members, who take their Parliamentary duties most seriously and have never been known in this House to lack the capacity to state an important case with due prolixity. That is a Clause which might take some considerable time.

Clause 26 (Annual value of property in London for purposes of income tax.) That is a Clause raising questions of difficulty; and finally there is Clause 27 (Provisions with respect to returns, copies of valuation lists and tax assessments in London.) The right hon. Gentleman intends to keep the Committee all through this hot night in order to secure this immense mass of tangled and complicated business. He is trying to carry his Budget not by argument and reason, not by tactful and careful guidance of the Committee, but by sheer brute force. He has his army marshalled behind him. Their bridges and their boats are burned behind them. They cannot escape for some hours. He is using these unfortunates, with their backs to the wall, as it were, to try to press this immense mass of legislation through. I would ask the Chancellor of the Exchequer seriously to consider whether he should proceed in this course of action. After all, there is this present Clause 18, a very important Clause.

Would it not be better to finish that Clause as quickly as possible and then let the House adjourn? What is the reason we are to have this prolonged sitting? A Committee of the House has just reported against these late sittings. Why does the right hon. Gentleman wish to keep us up? We did not put these Clauses down. They are not necessary in any way. They are merely put in in order to make it funny. The right hon. Gentleman proposes that we should sit for all hours of the night on this subject. I am willing to begin this discussion in a most amicable manner, and I have met the right hon. Gentleman in a very fair and friendly manner. If he will wind up his proceedings at Clause 18, which might easily be disposed of in less than an hour or an hour and a half, then we can all return refreshed on Thursday. There is enough material in this great mass of business which he is trying to force through to keep the Committee until three o'clock to-morrow, and in that case another allotted day of Supply is destroyed, because, if the Committee sits until three o'clock, the House can never meet on that day and the Government will have lost the whole of their allotted Supply day. There is a supreme remedy which is provided for Oppositions who are ill-treated in the matter of legislation. I do not know whether the Liberal party will approve of this method of forcing business through. The Finance Bill is a Measure which, from their point of view, has a singular significance, because it is by means of a Finance Bill that a tariff will be carried. No doubt the Government, by overloading the House with petty matters and pressing the debates into all hours of the night, are trying to make a case for a guillotine on the Budget.

The Chairman: That is hardly relevant to the point before us at the moment.

Mr. Churchill: With great respect, I thought that an analysis of the motives and the reasons which have actuated the Leader of the House in pressing this business on Parliament were as much within the ambit of your previous tolerance as which I have already said. But I pass from that, simply pointing out that every step which the right hon. Gentleman has taken in the course of the Budget discussions is consistent with a plan leading up to a guillotine closure. We see paragraphs announcing so in his party official organ, indicating that the ordinary procedure of this House may be swept away in order that he and his friends may carry out their healing process.

But the Budget stands by itself, and once a precedent is set up of a guillotine closure, and it is being prepared beforehand by these all-night sittings, then be sure that if the Liberal party were to support such a procedure, they would destroy the main opportunity they would have of preventing the passage of a tariff Bill, which certainly could only be carried under the application of a guillotine closure.

I have pressed the right hon. Gentleman to reconsider his decision, but I gather we are to have no further word from him, and that we are to go on until this vast mass of business has been disposed of. I gather that is so. I did not expect the Chancellor of the Exchequer to answer. If he sets us this hard task, if he forces us to proceed to examine all the details of this Bill, we will not shrink from the task. We will meet him in the discussions, and we will only hope that the contributions which will be made to our legislation will be such as to render it at least innocuous, and that the contribution which we make to the education of the right hon. Gentleman will carry his command of patience and of good temper one step further than it has yet done.

[Later] The Labour party must be feeling pretty well ashamed of themselves for keeping the Committee sitting up all through the night in order that they may sweat and grind down the clerks of this country. We thought that they were angling for the support of the black-coated workingman, but it is now clear what ideas they have of the hours that clerks should work and the wages they should receive. I could hardly follow all the figures given from the Liberal benches, but it is clear that the remuneration proposed by the Government is an insulting pittance compared with the labours that will be imposed on these clerical staffs and the companies engaged on this work. We know the ideas the Labour party has of work. The President of the Board of Education said he must keep the children at school to save the drudgery of minding machines, and the First Commissioner of Works spoke against manual labour. Therefore, machines and manual work are to be avoided, but the clerk is to work all day for this miserable sum. Could anything more clearly reveal the cynicism that has actuated the Government in their treatment of these clerks in this particular way? Of course, they regard no labour as respectable except the labour that votes for them. That is the frank, naked position. It is because these clerks are not among their political supporters that this miserable remuneration is to be paid to them.

That is one hypothesis. The other is more flattering to the Labour party and to the Chancellor of the Exchequer, who is supposed to take charge of the commercial interests of this country. If the clerks are to be paid properly, and are not to have this brutish, blood-sucking blow, then the burden has to be borne by these companies. At the darkest moment in our economic history, this dreary period of dark misfortune over which the right hon. Gentleman presides with such seraphic glee, he has struck another blow at the companies because, if the clerks are to be properly paid, it is quite clear that a burden must be placed on our commercial and limited liability institutions which will add to their difficulties. Which of the two courses should be followed? What are we to say when we give an account of your actions to the electors of the country? Are we to say that you are desirous that the burden should be thrown upon the companies or sweated out of the clerks? You can take your choice. Whichever it is, I am sure that to keep the Committee up to such a time on such a point is trying to screw the last ounce of work out of the clerical staff. I will not say it is an act unworthy of a Labour Government, but there could be no more revealing act of the utter humbug and hypocrisy characterising their whole policy.

[Later] I beg to move, "That the Chairman do report Progress, and ask leave to sit again."

I really must ask the Chancellor of the Exchequer whether he is not now satisfied that it is quite beyond the compass and power of the Committee to achieve anything like the task which he has prescribed for us? He has placed before us a programme that is quite impossible. I hope he now sees that these Clauses which he has so unnecessarily introduced into the Finance Bill and works of supererogation in which he so delights, are such that, if they are to be examined as they must be, must necessarily lend themselves to protracted debate. These debates have been conducted not only by the Conservative Opposition, but representatives of the Liberal party also have taken a most distinguished part. Consequently we claim that the Opposition on this side of the House, constituting a majority of this assembly, although they may not be able to achieve an actual majority, yet have a moral superiority over the Socialist party which ought to be taken into consideration.

The right hon. Gentleman is really not going the right way about getting this Budget. When he shows an intention to carry by main force what ought to be a matter of tactful persuasion and shows himself ready to brush aside his political opponents and ram down their throats any amount of work he chooses to set before them, then I think it is still the duty of those who have the guardianship of the traditions of this House in their keeping to allow no scamping of the work, tired though we may be of our labours. Even at this stage, I ask whether he cannot make some concession that would enable us to abridge these discussions. Three hours ago it was suggested that we might have wound up the discussion on Clause 18 within an hour. That would have meant that we should not have done full justice to our clerks whose treatment is such a black spot on the labour of this country. If the right hon. Gentleman feels now that he has seen how bleak is the prospect before him and is willing to make a new proposal, I would suggest to him that we should agree to bring Clause 18 to a close before half past four and terminate our proceedings at that. If met in a similar spirit, we should be bound to be at least as good as our word in the matter. I shall no doubt have an opportunity of dealing further with the matter after we have had the reply of the right hon. Gentleman.

Mr. P. Snowden: The right hon. Gentleman is apparently in a state of physical exhaustion, and I can quite understand his anxiety to get through, as he did after having boasted of what he was going to do, before the rest of the Committee a few weeks ago. If he had shown the same anxiety to facilitate business 12 hours ago, I might have been more inclined to listen favourably to the appeal which he has made. I shall certainly not accept the offer he has made. The Committee will search the records of this House in vain for a parallel to the slow progress which we have made to-day. Not one Clause of importance has been passed. I was justified at the beginning of the sitting in expecting, allowing for reasonable debate, that we should get to the end of Part II. I am not prepared to accept the Motion to report Progress. We shall go on, and if the right hon. Gentleman will make a similar proposal, say, about 12 or one o'clock, then I will consider it.

Mr. Churchill: I think the answer of the Chancellor of the Exchequer well repays my effort. He began by boasting exultingly and triumphantly that I, personally, and some other of my hon. Friends, were in a state of exhaustion. Even if we do feel tired, we shall not fail to exert ourselves. Really, the right hon. Gentleman would be wise to accept the Motion or to make some concession. He has got heavy work to-morrow—a Cabinet meeting to attend at 11 o'clock at which he is to make a general survey of the great progress made by the Labour Government in dealing with our general economic affairs and also the congestion of Parliamentary business. Surely, he ought to be reserving himself for that and have some time for slumber and reflection. As far as we are concerned, we have not the least intention of being led into scamping our public duties merely because of the unsuitable hour at which we are compelled to discuss these matters. The right hon. Gentleman has taunted me with having left the last debate two hours before its conclusion. I did so because I had to wind up the debate on unemployment on that very day, and I say quite frankly that I am not capable of giving my attention to such a matter without having two or three hours' sleep. But the work which the right hon. Gentleman has to do is far more important than that which falls to any private Member in winding up a debate. He has the whole finances of the country in his hand. Even if he himself is ready to be carried away by partisanship and to exhaust himself in the struggle, it is really from our point of view desirable that he should be urged to abate something of his ardour and rancour. As nothing I can say will make any impression, it is really not much use my proceeding any further. If I do so, it is not because I have a real expectation of softening his heart, but because I desire to place clearly on record the reasons why we object to this procedure.

It is our duty as representatives of the Opposition to show that this mood and temper, this procedure, these late hours, will not benefit the Chancellor of the Exchequer, but will lead him at every stage deeper and deeper into the mire. The right hon. Gentleman, if he had acted in a reasonable manner, might have been much farther on in his Budget Bill than he is to-day. In the first place, I do not understand why he does not make some friendly gesture on the merits of this Bill. Why does he insist on carrying all these Clauses through? Why not say, "This Clause will cause a lot of trouble, and so we shall drop it." Why have fifty Clauses in this Bill, many of them trumpery, and insist on all of them? We have a right to be consulted on the merits of the Bill and to help in moulding legislation before Parliament. We are going to insist on our right. The right hon. Gentleman is only the head of a minority. Why does he not treat properly those with almost as many votes behind them as his own party? We recognise that he has to carry on the business of the country and get the money, but subject to that, there is a wide field for give and take and compromise. If he were to adopt that attitude, he would make much more rapid progress. If he imagines that he is going to carry this through by plodding on all the night into the next day and then having another all night sitting on Thursday, he is mistaken. Tomorrow the Chancellor of the Exchequer will be considering the position of business in the House of Commons. A shocking condition of congestion lies before us. There is no greater culprit from the Cabinet point of view—

Mr. P. Snowden: Than you.

Mr. Churchill: I am not in the right hon. Gentleman's Cabinet. I say there is no greater culprit than the Chancellor of the Exchequer. I cannot understand why he has deliberately caused this great political failure and deadlock of business. He may imagine that by refusing our Motion to report Progress and carrying on our debate a little longer he will be successful and will make a case for a guillotine or time table Resolution, but I am convinced that the Liberal party will not take a hand in that respect. They will know perfectly well that once a precedent has been set—[*Interruption.*] If I am dwelling in too much detail on the danger of the guillotine procedure, then I shall leave that point. I have given the right hon. gentleman a very fair chance of reconsidering his attitude before we reach the hour of noon which he mentioned so inconsiderately. I shall give him a further chance in the course of the next two or three hours in order to see whether we cannot reach some more satisfactory conclusion than that which he puts before us.

[Later, on an Amendment to Sub-section 4 of Clause 18 dealing with the amount of penalty to be charged for noncompliance with a request for information from the Commissioners of Income Tax] This matter of penalties is very characteristic of Socialist government in every country. First they provide a great number of new offences. Here is an offence taking a whole Clause to describe it, which, before this Finance Bill, had no existence. Now we have been all this time discussing how the penalty is to be inflicted.

Mr. Frank Smith: Cannot we have a penalty for obstruction?

Mr. Churchill: That is a very unparliamentary interruption.

The Chairman: The hon. Gentleman should not make remarks of that sort.

An Hon. Member: He only asked a question.

The Chairman: There was an inference in the question. [*Interruption.*] Questions can be asked in an unparliamentary way; hon. Members ought not to ask questions in that way. It is out of order to impute motives.

Mr. Beckett: I would like to ask if accusations of the sort were not often thrown when the other people were on this side?

Major Colfox: Is it in Order to say in a loud voice that something that may be said is "Nonsense!"?

The Chairman: If done in a Parliamentary way it is not regarded as out of Order in the House.

Mr. Churchill: What has just occurred illustrates very forcibly the evils of these protracted sittings. All tempers tend to be frayed, unparliamentary expressions are flung across the House, and no one can suggest that all the blame is on one side. It is perfectly clear that we have now reached the point where feelings are liable to excitement, and arouse—

Mr. Beckett: On a point of Order. May I ask whether we are now discussing the feelings of the Committee or an Amendment?

Mr. Churchill: On that point of Order. Might I say that, as you have no doubt inferred, I had intended immediately, in almost the next sentence, to move to report Progress.

The Chairman: I did expect that the right hon. Gentleman was going to move to report Progress.

Mr. Buchanan: Further to that point of Order. Is it not customary for hon. Members to move to report Progress first, and then make their speeches?

The Chairman: I have seen it done both ways.

Mr. Churchill: I beg to move, "That the Chairman do report Progress, and ask leave to sit again."

I have thus put myself in order. Now, I want to say a serious word to the Chancellor of the Exchequer. He invited me to raise this matter again at an earlier period. Let me point out to him where we now stand. We have not yet finished Clause 18, and there are still three important Amendments, one in the name of Members of the Liberal party. Then there is the debate on the Clause itself. The Chancellor of the Exchequer says that we are to pass nine more Clauses. What is the use of talking like that? It is perfectly absurd. Each of these Clauses would give occasion for at least four or five divisions, and five nines are 45. It might well be that there would be further troubles in between, but 45 divisions alone would take nearly eight hours without another word being spoken in debate. Even if we simply divide upon the Amendments and the Clauses now before us, we shall be proceeding at half-past one o'clock. So far as we are concerned, we have no intention of being converted into mere automatons, tramping through the Division Lobbies in resistance to the Government. We have every intention of combating their policy not only by our votes but by discussion. Is not the Chancellor of the Exchequer making a great mistake by forcing us to continue at these labours when there is not the slightest chance of his getting even one-third of the way he proposes to go? The only possible consequence can be that the new day which has now dawned, and whose light will soon replace the artificial light from above, will be killed.

Mr. Logan: Why do you not go home and have a sleep?

Mr. Churchill: I was the subject of reproach for having gone home last time, and, indeed, it was almost the only joke the Chancellor of the Exchequer has made—almost the only time that we saw the slightest relaxations of his countenance. I would love to go home, but I cannot expose myself to such taunts and mockeries, and, therefore, I am bound to stay here. But the Chancellor of the Exchequer can set us all at liberty. He will remember the story of the Sibylline Books, and this is the third time we come back offering our books. We offer him the whole of Clause 18 by half-past seven o'clock if he is willing to report Progress then. It may be the last time that this offer will be made, because in these all-night sittings there are two critical periods. The first is at half-past 12, when the last train leaves for the West End. The second critical period is about seven o'clock, when the first reinforcements begin to arrive with the morning light and relieve those who have borne the vigil of the night. We are at present between those two periods, and if the Chancellor of the Exchequer tarries much longer I shall not be able to repeat my offer.

Mr. F. Smith: We do not want your offers.

Mr. Churchill: The responsibility rests with those who reject the offers. But, anyway, why should the hon. Member for Nuneaton (Mr. F. Smith) take the words out of the mouth of the Chancellor of the Exchequer and say the "No" which the right hon. Gentleman is longing to say himself? It is almost his only pleasure, to say "No." He is, in fact, a walking body of negation and now, when he has been kept up all night and rendered totally unfit for the Cabinet meeting, the hon. Member for Nuneaton wishes to rob him of his only consolation. I will now give the Chancellor of the Exchequer an opportunity to reply.

The Chairman *proceeded to put the Question.*

Mr. Churchill: Are we not to have any answer?—*[Interruption]*.

The Chairman: A question has been put to me, and I must be allowed to answer. I cannot make the Chancellor of the Exchequer reply. I rose to put the Question.

Mr. Churchill: On a point of Order. I am quite sure that you would wish to treat with your usual scrupulous fairness Members of the Opposition in this Debate. Out of courtesy I interrupted my remarks to allow the Chancellor of the Exchequer to say whether he would accept the Motion to report Progress or not. Surely, it is without precedent for the Government to make no reply to such a motion, be it only by a grunt.

I sat down to allow the right hon. Gentleman to reply, and almost before a second passed I realised he was not going to reply. My right hon. Friend rose to continue the discussion and it would be very hard if because of the Chancellor's action in not rising to say whether he would accept this Motion or not, we should be deprived of our right to state our case for ten minutes or so. I submit that we should be allowed to do so all the more as no answer has been made from the Government Benches.

The Chairman: As I was proceeding to put the Question nobody was on his feet. I was putting the Question, and the right hon. Gentleman rose at the same time.

[Later] Mr. Churchill (*seated and covered*): May I, as a point of Order, point out to you, Mr. Young, that when you allowed the Motion to report Progress to be debated, to which the Chancellor of the Exchequer has made no answer, I said that it was not our intention to prolong the debate in any way. May I assure you that in pursuance of that undertaking I would suggest to my hon. Friends that at a quarter to six o'clock we should allow the debate to come to a close and take the Division upon the Motion. Therefore the Chancellor of the Exchequer, by moving the Closure, is only prolonging the discussion.

The Chairman: That is not the point of Order. [*Interruption.*] Will the hon. Member who is whistling kindly stop.

[Later] Mr. Churchill: On a point of Order, surely the question is revived which was previously under discussion before the Motion to report Progress was moved?

The Chairman: The right hon. Gentleman rises to continue the discussion?

Mr. Churchill: Certainly. I am under the impression that I was in possession of the Committee, and while I was speaking an hon. Gentleman made an unparliamentary observation.

The Chairman: The right hon. Gentleman was not speaking to the Amendment. He rose to move to report Progress.

Mr. Churchill: With great respect that is not so. I rose to speak on the Amendment, and then I was interrupted by some remark on which I do not wish to dwell any more. When that happened I felt that the temper of the Committee was getting into such a state that it would be better to report Progress. I availed myself of that technical procedure. I broke off my speech on the Amendment. Such is the plain narrative of the facts as they will undoubtedly appear recorded for ever in the Official Report. The Chancellor of the Exchequer having been pressed at all our proceedings, and the Motion to report Progress having been negatived, I was entitled to continue my interrupted speech upon the Amendment. If the Committee will recollect we were at that moment speaking of these penalties. I said that in every country the Socialist party, almost immediately they obtained power, created a large number of new offences, a long catalogue of offences. This Clause, which we have discussed for so long, invents a new offence not hitherto known to the world—that people are to be subjected to penalties of £50, and then further penalties, and the Chancellor of the Exchequer has been considering in what way he can lay his penalties, or mitigate them, or make them more severe. Respectable people are to be subjected to these penalties. [*Interruption.*] Now I am being interrupted. We are not sitting here for our pleasure.

Mr. Beckett: I would like to put it to the right hon. Gentleman that the interruption was not directed at him, but was our greeting to the change of Chairmen.

Mr. Churchill: A most disrespectful observation about the Chair. The hon. Member said that his interruption was made to greet the change of Chairmen. Unless the hon. Gentleman can offer an explanation to the House, it shows that his remark had an implication that only attaches to it. So that I must draw your attention, Sir, to a reflection that has been made upon your predecessor in the Chair.

Mr. Beckett: The interruption was because we thought it was quite time that the Chairman of Committees had a rest, because he has been in the Chair a very long time.

Mr. Churchill: It is customary to accept a statement which an hon. Member makes about his own intentions and actions, and therefore I should not press my point of Order any further. It remains to me only to continue my remarks upon the Amendment, and upon this policy of imposing penalties and creating new crimes. This has been carried to great excess in the United States, and there, as we know, they have a whole list of misdemeanours and offences placed upon the Statute Book of the various States. I have heard it said that there are 13,000 penalties. Laxity in the enforcement of law follows inevitably in its train. That is what you are creating by legislation of this kind, with all sorts of needless offences each involving penalties upon the subject. It is one of the worst features of modern democracy as handled by a Socialist Administration. We are now reaching the full daylight of another day and very soon we shall be in the full scrutiny of the public; and then I hope that we shall not fail to press home upon the Government the vices of this multiplication of petty offences and the attaching to them of objectionable pecuniary fines.

[Later] Is this to be the only answer that the Government are going to make to the Amendment and to the speech which the Mover has delivered? Is this halting, pathetic statement which has come from the Financial Secretary to the Treasury to be the only apology which the Government can make for refusing this carefully prepared Amendment? For my part I heartily agree with the Amendment, and, on behalf of the Conservative Opposition, I can proffer the Mover our energetic assistance. I think it is an Amendment which does great credit to its authors, and is conceived in the very finest traditions of Liberalism, which for many years played a most important and invaluable part in moulding and shaping the expanding liberties of this country. That the hon. and gallant Member and his learned Friend who is associated with him should have drafted this Amendment and placed it upon the Paper constitutes a service which will be deeply appreciated by all those who wish to see a proper relationship maintained between the dignity of the taxpayer and the tax collector.

In the first place the Government are armed with the proper procedure to detect offenders. Do not let us have any talk in the future about the Government being denied means of dealing with the tax evader. Here is proposed a complete method by which any person who is suspected of not having fully discharged his duty to the Revenue, can be proceeded against, and proceeded against effectively and swiftly, but according to the proper standard and regular traditions of accepted British juris-prudence and British decency and fair-play.

No doubt it will astonish the Financial Secretary even to hear this, because there never was a man so swiftly converted into a bureaucrat than he. He simply flung himself into the surroundings of the Treasury, and emerged after a very brief space of time as one of the most complete, self-satisfied bureaucratic officials that we have ever had representing the Government department of the Treasury in this House. No doubt it will surprise the hon. Gentleman very much if I should mention some of the principles upon which this Amendment is founded. First of all, there is the suggestion that, if a man is to be proceeded against, there shall at any rate be a *prima facie* case established, and that this *prima facie* case shall be established against him by reasonable persons—that two of the Special Commissioners shall make an allegation, and that due notice shall be given to the person affected. What is wrong with that? Has the hon. Gentleman already forgotten those principles which he used to profess in by-gone days about the rights of individuals? Why should a man be placed, without his knowledge, under a slur? If allegations are made against him, he ought to be the first person to be informed, and he ought to have due notice. The Mover of the Amendment proposes that the matter shall be referred to a judge of the High Court; that the person against whom an allegation is preferred, whose affairs are to undergo a new and special subterranean examination not known to the Income Tax law, is to have notice, and, after notice, he is to have the right of rebutting the charge made against him. That is the ordinary, normal procedure of British justice and fair-play.

If he can prove to the satisfaction of the court that there is no *prima facie* case, or rather, unless the special commissioners are able to prove that they have a *prima facie* case—the case of a man is not to be rummaged in this way. You would not search a man's house, if you had cause to suspect him, without a warrant. Why treat the whole class of Income Tax payers as if they were criminals?

It has been the one idea of the Socialist Government since they got into power to use that power to hunt and pillage the direct taxpayers of this country. In the whole world there is not a class like the British taxpayer, but if the Government establishes the relationship with them of pitting their brains against the brains of the authorities, it will be a duel instead of a high duty discharged by the taxpayer to render to the State what Parliament has required. If you put it on the footing of a duel, then your devices, dodges and instruments of torture, with which you are filling this Bill, will not be worth the paper on which they are written. You will alter the whole relationship between the Income-Tax payers and the Exchequer. There was a great speech by Mr. Gladstone in which he said this was purely voluntary. If you lose that confidence and goodwill which still exists between the Government of the day—[*Interruption.*] If you once lose that, it will be impossible to re-establish it. Taxation has risen to a high point, and now at this moment you inflict this unwarranted slur on the whole of the Income Tax payers under this inquiry.

The hon. Member who moved this Amendment comes here with the means of preventing evasion. But what do the Government care? They will not look at it. All they want is a general power undermining the whole confidential relationship which has hitherto been preserved as far as Income Tax is concerned. The hon. Gentleman said that there would be no procedure against individuals and that therefore this Amendment was not valid. The Attorney-General became almost metaphysical in endeavouring to explain the relationship between the individual and the class. The Attorney-General has explained that classes alone are concerned. That is not what is intended by the Government. What the Government are going to ask for is particular information about certain persons whom they have reason to suspect.

Mr. Pethick-Lawrence indicated dissent.

Mr. Churchill: I am glad to see they are waking up. There will be a suggestion that this or that wealthy taxpayer is not making a return adequate to the revenues he enjoys. The Commissioners of Inland Revenue will, under the power in this Clause, have a private inquiry and find out what are the securities he holds. I do not complain a bit of that procedure if you inform the man of the charge made against him, if you give him an opportunity to defend himself, and if the matter be adjudicated by an impartial judge.

Mr. Pethick-Lawrence: The right hon. Gentleman has said that what the Government are going to do is to proceed against one or two individuals. That is not correct. It has been distinctly brought out that the Clause does not enable that to be done. The Chancellor of the Exchequer definitely stated that the procedure which the right hon. Gentleman and the Mover of the Amendment envisaged was not possible under this Clause.

Mr. Churchill: The hon. Gentleman has not added to the strength of his position by the interruption, but, however much we may differ from him, the courtesy and good nature we always meet from him is very agreeable. I put to the hon. Gentleman this very plain question: What is there that you legitimately require for the purpose of preventing evasion and securing the necessary information that cannot be given by this Amendment of the hon. Member for North-East Bethnal Green (Major Nathan)? If that does not give you your powers, what do you want? The House has examined this matter for 10 hours with great attention. Is the hon. Gentleman's desire to have a roving commission given to him to make inquiries here and there under penalties, and so forth? We will give you the powers for which you ask, but in return give to His Majesty's liege, whose affairs you are investigating, the information that his affairs are under special scrutiny, and an opportunity to justify himself if he can. If he fails to take advantage of the 28 days' delay, you are absolutely justified in proceeding and making any inquiries you desire.

This is a procedure which will limit the obligations to those cases to which it relates, instead of making it applicable over the whole area. If this Amendment were adopted, all the objections entertained on the ground of the clerical labour thrust upon the companies and the expenses to which they will be put, or the alternative of the shameful sweating of the poor clerk who is receiving a pitiful remuneration just because his firm is not likely to have voted for the party opposite—all these arguments drop to the ground because the number of cases in which it would be necessary to proceed would not be very numerous. The number of returns which it would be necessary to require would not be very numerous nor the returns very lengthy. They would not be the vague, general, fishing and roaming returns. They would be precise returns prepared and proposed for the purpose of establishing a definite charge, and there would be neither great difficulty nor expense in the matter.

The right hon. Gentleman has shown quite clearly that it is not evasion of taxes that the Government are seeking to prevent in this Clause. The Opposition and the Liberal Party have given them the fullest means for dealing with the matter. What they want to do is to lay their predatory, inquisitive and prying fingers on the whole distribution of wealth and securities throughout the country, under the cloak, in the first instance, of preventing the evasion of income tax, and ultimately, no doubt, for some sinister purpose.

[Later] I beg to move, "That the Chairman do report Progress, and ask leave to sit again."

I do so in order to invite the Chancellor of the Exchequer to state what the intentions of the Chancellor of the Exchequer are. On this occasion I shall not make any further offer. The right hon. Gentleman has subjected us to the fullest rigour a majority can apply to a minority in Opposition. He has treated the arguments and representations made to him with supreme, and even insolent, contempt. [*Interruption.*] His only intervention in debate in the last five hours has been that on three occasions he has moved the Closure. Not for the world would I comment upon that because, it is, as it were, Mr. Chairman, sanctified by your acceptance and hallowed by the endorsement of the Committee. That has been the sole guidance on important financial issues which we have received from the high officer of State entrusted with the conduct of the Treasury. [*Interruption.*] We have been treated with severity. The right hon. Gentleman may continue to ride roughshod over the Committee; we cannot prevent him doing so, but he has little enough to show for all the ill-usage. We offered him this very Clause, which now we are to debate in its final form, 11 hours ago in one hour from that time. [*Interruption.*] He brushed that aside.

Anyone who has listened to the points adduced knows they are points of real substance. In fact, I have rarely heard an all-night sitting in which so many intricate points were put forward in serious debate. It detracts from the debate that practically no answer is given from the Government benches. Hour after hour Ministers sit glum, glowering, and scowling on the bench as if, forsooth, they were masters of the House of Commons and no one else is to wink or breathe. On this occasion I am not going to make any suggestion to the right hon. Gentleman to give him Clause 18, but he takes it from us by his arbitrary methods. I invite him to declare his intentions, not because I expect to get anything but a prolongation of what we have suffered in the past, but because it is only right and proper that from time to time the Government should be given an opportunity and be asked to state what its views are as to the course of public business. Are we not going to have an answer?

The Chairman: The Question is—

Mr. Churchill: Are we not to have an answer? [*Interruption.*] No answer? If this is to be the treatment that the Opposition is to receive, the Opposition that has been going the whole of this night, and which comprises both the non-Socialist political parties, together aggregating about 13,000,000 votes in this country, I shall give the right hon. Gentleman warning that we shall use all our powers to procure respectful treatment from the Chancellor of the Exchequer. After all, he is the servant of the House. What right has he to refuse to give the Committee proper guidance in the matter? [*Interruption.*] We know well how they would trample on minorities if they had control. The tyranny of the Socialists—[*Interruption.*] The right hon. Gentleman is a fitting representative of the intolerant spirit—[Hon. Members: "Divide!"] There will be plenty of time to divide. We shall no doubt divide a great deal before we finish! For the right hon. Gentleman to insult the House of Commons by refusing to tell us what his intentions are is an unprecedented act with absolutely no warrant for it, and I will use the whole of the reserves at our command—[*Interruption.*]

Sir K. Wood: I desire to add my protest—[*Interruption*]—to the Chancellor of the Exchequer—

Mr. Churchill: Sir, I rise to a point of Order, to direct your attention to the repeated disorderly interruptions which have already been censured and stigmatised in the course of this debate.

The Chairman: I do not notice anything out of the way.

Sir K. Wood: You will remember—[*Interruption.*]

Mr. Churchill: The proceedings are grossly unparliamentary!

The Chairman: Order! I really did not notice anything the last time, but I must say that this is out of order. This swishing noise all over the place must cease.

[Later] Mr. Churchill: I beg to move, "That the Chairman do leave the Chair."

In view of the unprecedented event which has just taken place, namely, an entire debate upon the Question put by you from the Chair with an obvious conspiracy of silence maintained on the Ministerial Benches, I feel bound to move under Rule 68 that you do now leave the Chair and I make this Motion for the express purpose of inviting the Prime Minister, who is, we believe, in the House, to come to the aid of the Committee in the difficult situation in which it now finds itself. This long and strenuous debate has been conducted with decorum and without ill temper, but I warn the Government that I am bound to draw the attention of the occupant of the Chair to the fact that very strong feelings are excited by the continuous refusal of the Government to take part in the discussion in any way. Their only part in these discussions is simply to remain there, refusing to debate or even to indicate to the House what its future course of business is to be. Such a proceeding is unprecedented.

Mr. Beckett: On a point of Order. In moving the Motion which the right hon. Gentleman is now moving, is he entitled to discuss what the Government are doing? I submit that in a speech on this Motion he is entitled only to discuss the merits or demerits of your action.

The Chairman: The merits or demerits of my action do not come in at all. In moving this Motion the right hon. Gentleman should only state the reasons why he is moving it.

Mr. Churchill: The reasons, as I have stated, are the conspiracy of silence on the Government Benches, the unprecedented fact of a debate with an absolute refusal to answer, the fact that the Committee have no knowledge of how far the Government intend to go, the fact that they contumaciously withheld—

Mr. R. A. Taylor: On a point of Order. Is not this Motion moved by the right hon. Gentleman a Motion on which you yourself have a discretion as to whether it may be discussed?

The Chairman: That is not a point of Order.

Mr. Churchill: I ask that the Prime Minister as Leader of the House should come to our aid at this time, and I ask specifically that he should know that that is the wish of those who sit on this side of the Committee, that the Prime Minister himself should come as Leader of the House and perhaps prevent matters assuming a very different complexion.

[Later] Mr. P. Snowden: On a point of Order. This Motion has been moved under Standing Order 68. I venture to suggest this point for your consideration: Proceedings in Committee of the Whole House may at any time be discontinued by an Order to report Progress or by an Order that the Chairman do leave the Chair. I submit that it is not within the meaning of this Standing Order that a second Order that you do leave the Chair can be exercised after the first has been used; that they are alternatives, but that one is not supplementary to the other, and that as the Committee have just decided that we do not report Progress the right hon. Gentleman cannot use this second alternative. The only difference between the two is this, and this, I think, supports the contention that they are alternative; if the first alternative were adopted and carried the result would be that the Committee could sit again. It would simply adjourn the debate. But in the second case, if the Motion now before the Committee were carried, it would mean the end of the Bill under consideration. I do submit to you, therefore, that it is not in accordance with the spirit or the letter of the Manual of Procedure that after a Motion to report Progress has been defeated the second alternative should immediately be proposed.

Mr. Churchill: On that point of Order. May I submit the historical reasons which have led to these two procedures being incorporated in Standing Order 68?

The Chairman: It is in the Manual of Procedure; therefore it is not a Standing Order that is referred to.

Mr. Churchill: I made a mistake, but if I may be permitted to proceed with the point of Order. The process is quite clear, and everyone knows quite well why there are these alternatives. These two are presented for the purpose, as the right hon. Gentleman ought to know, for which they are now used. It has always been impossible, when the Committee have decided not to report Progress, to repeat that Motion, and for that very purpose those who have safeguarded the procedure have introduced an alternative, to move that the Chairman do leave the Chair. It is intended that when one of these procedures has been used and the minority of the Committee are still not satisfied that the debate is proceeding under proper conditions, it shall be open to them to put the second Motion. There is really no doubt whatever about that.

Proof of this is inherent in the procedure. It has been inserted in the procedure that the Chairman shall have the discretion to disallow either of these Motions if he considers it an abuse of the Rules of the House. I well remember, from my study of the proceedings of the Irish Nationalist party in the years from 1880 to 1885, before the reformed procedure came in, that it was the custom of the Irish Parliamentary party, when dissatisfied with the treatment they received from the Government, to move to report Progress, and to move in succession that the Chairman do leave the Chair, and to continue that process *ad infinitum* until they brought the proceedings of the Committee to a standstill. It was to guard against that abuse of the Rules that discretion was given to the Chairman to refuse a Motion if he thinks there is an abuse of procedure. So far from the right hon. Gentleman's point being correct, he is totally misconceived as to the whole purpose and character of this particular procedure, and I invite from you, Mr. Chairman, a ruling which will make perfectly clear the liberties of the House of Commons. You may not always be in the place of power, or we in the place of Opposition.

[Later] I beg to move, "That the Chairman do report Progress, and ask leave to sit again."

Once more I invite the Chancellor of the Exchequer to state on behalf of the Government what course they wish to pursue. The right hon. Gentleman has had his way. He has held the Committee strictly to business for one of the longest sittings that I can remember in recent times and I do not think that he can feel altogether satisfied with the result. There are much better ways of dealing with a powerful Opposition, almost equal numerically to the Government in power. The right hon. Gentleman ought to jettison without hesitation a large number of the Clauses which have been thrust into the Bill on Departmental grounds and which add to our burden at a time when the congestion of Parliament is increasing with extraordinary rapidity, and he ought at the same time, not merely on small matters but on large matters, so long as they do not imperil the general structure of the Budget, to respect the wishes, even if he does not share them, of those who are his fellow Members. The Government in its position as a minority Government, the remonstrances which have been addressed to him from the Liberal party—all these matters should induce the right hon. Gentleman to desire to come to an arrangement. It is really dreadful to go on wearing the Committee out by a species of physical torment. Obviously this is not the way in which to treat the grave problems of the State. The right hon. Gentleman has not been fighting for any money at all. The last Clause undoubtedly raised a great many disagreeable points of controversy, but one thing we offered as soon as we realised exactly what the character of the Clause was, and that was to make it perfectly certain that he could find out and hunt down the tax evader. We were ready to give him all that power in the Amendment of the hon. and learned Gentleman the Member for East Nottingham (Mr. Birkett) which in his absense was so admirably presented by the hon. and gallant Gentleman the Member for North-East Bethnal Green (Major Nathan). All this has taken place because the right hon. Gentleman has been fighting, not for revenue, not for the purpose of detecting and putting a stop to improper tax evasion, but simply in order that what he chooses to put into the Finance Bill shall be rammed through *ipso facto*, whatever the cost to the convenience of the Committee or to the convenience of the party and to the Government of which he is a prominent feature, if not indeed on all occasions a bright ornament. [*Interruption.*] I am not quite as bright as I should have been if I had had a proper night's sleep. Far worse than a private matter in Opposition is the spectacle of the Chancellor of the Exechequer, already late for his Cabinet meeting, if that has not been put off, simply because he has kept us up all through the night, trying to show that he is the master. He is not the master. This House is a difficult place for any man to try to rule by the use of a majority and the Closure and stern and harsh measures. No doubt Oppositions are sometimes very provoking, but it often happens that, if they are met in a reasonable spirit, and if parts of the Bill which are not really necessary for the finance of the year are freely discarded, and parts which are not necessary for the prevention of evasion are stated in a form acceptable to the Committee, much more rapid progress is made. I make the Motion in order to enable the right hon. Gentleman to inform us what the Government proposes.

[Later] I had hoped when the right hon. Gentleman opened his remarks, that I should have been able to have made my last contribution to this debate by saying that nothing in the conduct of the debate became him so well as his ending of it. But the right hon. Gentleman continued to use a great many hard and highly controversial expressions about the conduct of the Opposition, for which they are quite ready to take full responsibility. But in view of the remarks which he has made, I am forced, in two or three sentences, to put it perfectly clearly on record that the right hon. Gentleman has been thoroughly beaten. He has been forced to eat his words. He told us last night that he was going to sit until Clause 27 had been passed. We told him quite plainly that it was impossible to accomplish even half that distance, but the right hon. Gentleman went on defying the Committee and to-day, on the 18th June, he has met his Waterloo.

"PARLIAMENT AND THE ECONOMIC PROBLEM"

June 19, 1930

Romanes Lecture, Sheldon Theatre,
Oxford University

[Extract] Until quite recent times it was generally accepted that the best way of governing States was by talking. That system, has, however, lost much of its authority. Democracy is careless of the very institutions by which its political status was achieved, and I see the Houses of Parliament alone among the senates and chambers of the world, a living and ruling entity, the swift vehicle of public opinion, the padded arena of the inevitable class and social conflict, the college from which Ministers of State are chosen and hitherto the solid and unfailing foundation of the executive power. I regard our Parliamentary institution as precious to us beyond compare. Never was a body more capable of dealing with political issues than the House of Commons. Speaking generally, in practical politics it has no rival.

I ask you to consider some of the economic issues about which partisans contend loudly and many intelligent people are in doubt. The classical doctrines of economics found their citadels for nearly a century in the treasury and the Bank of England, and were all part of one general economic conception, amplified and expounded in all the Victorian textbooks and endorsed by most modern histories. But we are now in the presence of new forces not existing when those textbooks were written, and it is certain that the present economic problem is not solved at all by those books, however illustrious their authors. We have, however, a harder task before us than the breaking up of old, established conclusions. We have to build another story upon them equally well proportioned and unified. This is the dangerous puzzle confronting ancient and admirable Parliamentary institutions.

[Editor's Note: After taking a "sharp illustration" in the controversy over free or restricted imports, which he described as a matter requiring high, cold, technical and dispassionate or disinterested decision, he said] : I do not believe that the true principles can be discovered by our Parliamentary and electoral institutions, not even if they are guided by a faithful and energetic Press. Again, there is the strange discordance between consuming and producing power. Are we really to believe that no better adjustment can be made between supply and demand? Surely it is upon this mysterious crack and fissure in all our arrangements and apparatus that the keenest minds in the world should be concentrated. I doubt, however, whether Democracy, or Parliamentary Government, or even a General Election would make a decisively helpful contribution.

Are we, or are we not, capable of a higher and more complex economic, fiscal, and financial policy? Are we not capable of evolving a united body of doctrine adapted to our actual conditions and requirements? Could not such a system of policy be presented and accepted upon a national and not a party basis? Could it not, when devised, be taken out of the political brawling and given a fair trial by overwhelming national consent? Here then is the crux for Parliament. Many dangers threaten representative institutions once they have confided themselves to adult suffrage. There are dangers from the right and dangers from the left. We see examples of both in Europe to-day. But the British Parliamentary system will not be overthrown by political agitation, for that is what it specially comprehends. It will pass only when it has shown itself capable of dealing with some fundamental and imperative economic need; and such a challenge is now open.

It must be observed that economic problems, unlike political issues, cannot be solved by any expression, however vehement, of the national will, but only by taking the right action. You cannot cure cancer by a majority. What is wanted is a remedy. Every one knows what the people wish. They wish for more prosperity. How to get it? That is the grim question, and neither the electors nor their representatives are competent to answer it.

Governments and the various parties moving in the political sphere are not free to proclaim the proper remedies in their completeness, even if they know them. All kinds of popular cries can be presented for an election, and each may contain some measure of the truth. None in itself will provide us with the key. For this reason opinion has been turning towards the treatment of the subject on national and non-party lines. The leaders of parties, we are told, should meet together and arrive at a common policy. But these leaders, having their being in the political sphere, would not be able at such a conference to do much more than restate in civil terms the well-known differences and antagonisms which they represent.

It would seem therefore that, if new light is to be thrown upon this grave and clamant problem, it must in the first instance receive examination from a non-political body, free altogether from party exigencies, and composed of persons possessing special qualifications in economic matters. Parliament would, therefore, be well advised to create such a body subordinate to itself, and to assist its deliberations to the utmost. The spectacle of an economic sub-Parliament debating day after day with fearless detachment from public opinion all the most disputed questions of finance and trade, and reaching conclusions by voting, would be an innovation, but an innovation easily to be embraced by our flexible constitutional system. I see no reason why the political Parliament should not choose in proportion to its party groupings a subordinate economic Parliament of, say, one-fifth of its numbers, and composed of persons of high technical and business qualifications. The idea has received much countenance in Germany. I see no reason why such an assembly should not debate in the open light of day and without caring a halfpenny who won the General Election or who had the best slogan for curing unemployment, all the grave economic issues by which we are now confronted and afflicted. I see no reason why the economic Parliament should not for the time being command a greater interest than the political Parliament; nor why the political Parliament should not assist it with its training and experience in methods of debate and procedure. What is required is a new *personnel* adapted to the task which has to be done, and pursuing that task day after day without the distraction of other affairs and without fear, favour, or affection.

The conclusions of such a body, although themselves devoid of legal force, might well, if they commanded a consensus of opinion, supply us with a comprehensive and unified view of high expert authority, which could then be remitted in its integrity to the political sphere.

Let one recapitulate the argument I have submitted to you upon this aspect of political science. The economic problem for Great Britain and her Empire is urgent, vital, and dominant. There exists at the present time no constitutional machinery for dealing with it on its merits, with competent examination and without political bias and antagonisms. The House of Commons, to which the anxious nation looks to provide a solution, is unsuited both by its character and by the conditions which govern its life to fulfill such a task. Nevertheless the task has to be done. Britain is unconquerable and will not fail to find a way through her difficulties. Parliament is therefore upon its trail, and if it continues to show itself incapable of offering sincere and effective guidance at this juncture our Parliamentary institutions, so admirable in the political sphere, may well fall under a far-reaching condemnation.

If Parliament and the Ministries dependent upon Parliament cannot proclaim a new policy the question arises whether they should not, while time remains, create a new instrument specially adapted for the purpose, and delegate to that instrument all the necessary powers and facilities.

FINANCE BILL

June 19, 1930

House of Commons

May I say, with great respect, that this is rather an awkward situation? Such a situation often arises, with perfect good will and good faith on either side, *per incuriam.* Something takes place, or a Clause is put in a particular way, and a Division is taken. Let me, however, recall to you, Sir, and to the Committee, exactly how our business so far has been running this afternoon—

The Chairman: I do not know if the right hon. Gentleman wants to put a point of Order to me, but the responsibility rests upon me.

Mr. Churchill: It is to you Sir, that I am addressing myself exclusively, if I may say so, not only in the purely Parliamentary sense, as is my duty, but also personally, in regard to this matter. It was understood that, if a general debate on the whole Clause took place on the first Amendment, the other two Amendments would be moved with short speeches and disposed of very rapidly—[Hon. Members:

"Formally!"] There is a difference of opinion as to whether it was to be formally or with short speeches. There is not much difference between the one and the other. "Formally" would not exclude short speeches.

The Chairman: There can be no point of Order in regard to that matter.

Mr. Churchill: I am reciting what has happened, because there must not be any misunderstandings; we do not want to get any bad blood into our discussions. These two Amendments were to have been moved, as the Government contend, formally, and, as we say, with short speeches—

The Chairman: I understood that the right hon. Gentleman was raising a point of Order with me, and not with the Government, with regard to the way in which I put the Question.

Mr. Churchill: The way in which you put the Question founds itself upon the events which preceded the putting of the Question, namely, that these two Amendments were to be moved formally, as the Government contend, or, as we say, with short speeches—there is no difference between the two—[*Interruption.*] If we say we will do it, we will do it; and let that be remembered, by the way. There was no clear—

The Chairman: There must have been some mistake at the very beginning. The Question originally was put in the way that I put it, and evidently nobody on the Opposition side of the Committee drew the attention of the Chairman to it at the time.

Mr. Churchill: However it may be, the fact remains that we are not in a position to move these two Amendments—

The Chairman: Only one of them.

Mr. Churchill: We can only move two out of the three. We have lost one of them. We can neither move it formally and divide upon it for the purpose of expressing our opinion upon it, nor can we move it by short speeches. I agree that it is, therefore, irrevocable. "The moving finger writes; and, having writ, moves on." We cannot recall it, even with all your good will or ours. Therefore, we must regard that Amendment as having gone. But I submit to you, Sir, that the fact that this has happened completely disposes of the slightest understanding on the rest of the Clause. I am putting it to the sense of fair play of the Committee—

The Chairman: That is the view of the right hon. Gentleman, but it does not arise on the point of Order as to the way in which I put the Question.

Mr. Churchill: With very great respect, the point of Order that I am putting is not a point of Order purely affecting a technical matter. It governs the important aspect of the general relations between the parties in the House and the Chair during the progress of these protracted discussions, and I suggest that, as we have lost altogether the opportunity of moving and voting upon this Amendment, it is quite clear that, on the remaining Amendments which are saved, we shall revive our right to have the ordinary free and untramelled discussion, and to have a full discussion on the Question, "That the Clause stand part of the Bill."

Mr. Wardlaw-Milne: On the point of Order. I would like to get clearly from you, Mr. Young, exactly what the position is.

The Chairman: I will state it. All that has happened is that the Amendment standing in the name of the right hon. Gentleman the Member for Wood Green has not been saved, and, therefore, cannot now be put from the Chair. That is all that has happened. The blame for that should not be cast upon the Government Front Bench because a mistake was made by the Chairman for the time being, at the time when the agreement was made.

Mr. Churchill: I do not understand that there was an agreement between the parties and the Deputy-Chairman, but my right hon. Friend will take up that point and enlarge upon it further. I understand that a suggestion was made by the Deputy-Chairman, and my right hon. Friend acquiesced in it, but it must not be considered on the same basis as a Parliamentary bargain reached with the Government. It was an understanding for the good conduct of the debate, reached between my right hon. Friend and the Chair. Since, as you have said, though I would never venture to say it, the Chair made a mistake, I suggest to you that it is for the Chair to release us from the slightest obligation in this matter.

The Chairman: This is really not a point of Order. The discussion is taking place over something the Committee has done, perhaps by an error on the part of the Chair, in not having saved an Amendment, and the Amendment of the right hon. Member for Wood Green (Mr. G. Locker-Lampson) unfortunately cannot be formally moved. The only thing left for the Committee is to proceed with the Amendment in the name of the hon. Member for Kidderminster (Mr. Wardlaw-Milne), which I also understood was to be formally moved.

Mr. G. Locker-Lampson: Would it be possible to save it, in a sense, by putting in a manuscript Amendment, a proviso, containing the words which have been left out?

Mr. Pethick-Lawrence: I was going to make some such suggestion myself. If you could see your way, Mr. Young, to accept a manuscript Amendment, which again would be moved formally, and we divide without discussion, that would be a reasonable way out, which would observe what was an understanding between the Chair and both sides of the Committee, and would preserve the hon. Member's right to have a formal vote taken, and it would not take up time.

Mr. Wardlaw-Milne: I want to get it clear. I have no objection to what has been proposed regarding my hon. Friend's Amendment, but you, Sir, have twice stated that it was understood that my Amendment would be put without discussion.

The Chairman: The hon. Member must raise that point when he comes to his Amendment. If the right hon. Member for Wood Green can find a suitable place, I shall be pleased to put his Amendment. It is one of those things that will happen.

Mr. Churchill: It is really most important that we should not begin what may be a very protracted sitting with any misunderstanding. I understand it is settled that this Amendment which was cut out is now to be restored. That being so, our grievance disappears. We will take these three issues in the briefest possible Parliamentary time, but I must make it clear that we must have a reasonable Parliamentary opportunity of discussion on the Question, "That the Clause stand part of the Bill."

Mr. Remer: Many of us on this side, not only on this but on other occasions, do not hear you, Mr. Young, when you put the Question from the Chair.

The Chairman: That is not a point of Order, but this is the first time I have heard it said that Members do not hear me.

Mr. Remer: My point of Order is that you were not heard in the noise and the curious sounds coming from the opposite side.

The Chairman: Perhaps the hon. Member will use his influence with both sides of the Committee.

Mr. Leif Jones: On the point raised by the right hon. Gentleman the Member for Epping (Mr. Churchill), I certainly understood that we were taking a discussion of the Clause on the first Amendment. The right hon. Gentleman himself made a speech which not only covered the Clause but almost covered the Budget. He went so far beyond the Clause as to be interrupted by the Chair. Those who want to get on with the Bill are entitled to ask that we shall not have that discussion repeated on the Question, "That the Clause stand part of the Bill."

The Chairman: I am in the hands of the Committee in the matter. I can give no ruling in regard to that.

Mr. Churchill: I do not want there to be an accusation of bad faith. I contend that a reasonable and brief discussion on the Question "That the Clause stand part" is not barred out by any arrangement. If the Financial Secretary will say that is so, he will be no sufferer by it.

[Later] I beg to move, "That the Chairman do report Progress, and ask leave to sit again."

It may possibly—I cannot say certainly—expedite the course of our discussion if at this stage I interrogate the Chancellor of the Exchequer upon the views which he may have formed as to the progress of our business to-night. In order to do that and to put myself in order, I have moved that we report Progress. The right hon. Gentleman has, no doubt, got in his mind a fairly clear idea of the course that he would like us to pursue this evening, and for fear that I should do anything that might sway the calm flow of his reason by some obstructive ebullition of irritation, I will sit down and invite him to tell us exactly what it is that he would like us to do, and in what manner we can, in his opinion, serve him best.

[Later] Naturally, the right hon. Gentleman [Mr. Snowden], from his point of view, regards the importance of these Clauses differently from us, but there are a great many points concerning them which we are bound to raise. That applies particularly to Clauses 20 and 21. Clause 22 is a most complicated matter to which some of my hon. Friends have given an immense amount of study, and I am sorry to say that they are not united in the view they take of it. Some of my friends move in one direction and some in another, but both, in spite of their varied views, find no agreement with the Chancellor of the Exchequer. That is a Clause, therefore, of importance and substance. I agree that Clauses 23 and 24 rather follow from it. So far as Clause 25 is concerned, that, of course, is a matter not likely to be disposed of in a brief period. Nevertheless, I am bound to say that we shall go into these matters with the hope that the differences between us will not be so great as they have been, and that by 12 o'clock we may not find there is so much difference between us as there was the other night. While I cannot make any agreement, I must express my satisfaction that the Chancellor of the Exchequer has taken us into his confidence at so early a stage and has indicated the procedure which, if we cannot promise to accept, we cannot consider entirely divorced from what we regard to be reasonable.

FINANCE BILL

June 23, 1930

House of Commons

I beg to move, "That Mr. Chairman do report Progress, and ask leave to sit again."

I am very anxious that the course of our discussion shall be as smooth as possible and that the time available shall be employed in as fruitful a manner as we can conceive and, therefore in view of the progress that has been made this afternoon, or rather the little progress, I would ask the Financial Secretary, in the absence of the Chancellor of the Exchequer, whether he can make any further statement as to the wishes of the Government in regard to our proceedings to-night. I would point out how very clearly our objective is marked out for us by the Order Paper. We are dealing now with this immensely important Clause dealing with London valuation. I am entitled to say that the debate has not been conducted solely on party lines. The representatives of 13,000,000 of electors have all expressed growing anxiety at the character of this Clause, and the Government majority in the last Division has borne the deep dint of an increasing amount of Parliamentary misgiving. Unquestionably, the discussion of this Clause must be protracted. After that, we have a Clause which I frankly admit is of less consequence and less fertile in points of principle, dealing mainly with machinery but still important machinery which it is our duty to see is bright and clean and well oiled and efficiently adapted.

We might well have asked that the discussion should come to an end with Part II. I think we can most certainly arrange to gratify the right hon. Gentleman upon Part II at a very reasonable hour to-night, but he has, like a hard taskmaster—though he has not pressed us so hard so far, and I am most anxious to keep the debate in that good-tempered character which it has hitherto borne—asked us to accord him Clause 28. That raises enormous questions with very large sums of money to be taken from the direct taxpayer, and, of course, we must consider that Clause together with other Clauses affecting Estate Duties. The right hon. Gentleman would be well advised to let us know that he will not press matters beyond Clause 28 to-night, because then the Committee will be able to space out the limited time before twelve o'clock or quarter past in the manner which would assure the most useful and effective debate; otherwise, we might easily find ourselves in for another long nocturnal wrangle.

There is another reason to which I must call the attention of the Chancellor of the Exchequer before he replies. As he has been informed by my hon. Friend the Member for Watford (Sir D. Herbert), a very grave flaw has been detected in the drafting structure of the Bill, and we have to submit a point of Order and procedure to the Chair when the time comes which unquestionably will affect the whole group of Clauses from Clause 29 to Clause 33, inclusive. My hon. Friend was well advised in submitting this matter in good time to the Chancellor of the Exchequer and also to your colleague in the Chair, and we have for a considerable number of weeks been studying this point with the highest authorities to which we can have access and have no doubt whatever of the strength—

The Deputy-Chairman: We cannot go into the point of Order at this stage. While information that it is going to be raised is quite in order, the right hon. Gentleman must not go further.

Mr. Churchill: I will not go further than to say that we have the utmost confidence in the strength—though it is not for me to say in the validity—of our arguments. It would be a very great pity if the matter came to be discussed at nine or ten o'clock to-morrow morning after a prolonged and harassing all-night sitting. It would be far better to get Clause 28 to-night, which I believe you can do if we now begin to space out our time to the best advantage and to curtail ruthlessly our discussions, and then start on Wednesday afternoon with this very grave constitutional issue which is to be raised before we discuss the five Clauses dealing with the private company. I have risen early to make this Motion, because, if one leaves it later, there is so little time to be saved, and it would not be possible, with the best will in the world, to compress discussion within those limits.

[Later] We think we should stop at Clause 28 to-night and raise this big point of Order and the new principles involved in the group of Clauses beginning with Clause 29 when we come back on Wednesday. I am sure that is the reasonable and practical course to take. The right hon. Gentleman is not very far from adopting this course, and I shall not say a word to incline him to turn his thumb down or to cast a harshness over our proceedings. We can, I believe, have useful debates up to a quarter past 12 or midnight and finish up Clause 28, and then address ourselves on Wednesday to those principles and those highly technical matters which arise on Clause 29. I cannot make any bargain affecting another day. There is no doubt that if the right hon. Gentleman pursues his endeavours to meet the wishes and views of the Opposition and continues the course of accepting Amendments which do not ruin the principles he has in view, namely, the prevention of improper evasion, and accepts a large number of Amendments which do not upset his principles and prevent business in general being affected by these provisions, such an attitude would abridge discussion. If we separate at the end of Clause 28 to-night, we shall arrive at the discussion of our business on Wednesday without any feeling of rancour or ill-usage from his conduct of our debate this evening.

[Later] I think there is a great deal of force in the suggestion of the right hon. Gentleman the Member for Darwen (Sir H. Samuel). If our point of Order when raised on Wednesday next were to succeed it would have the effect, probably, of leading to the temporary withdrawal of these Clauses in order that they might be amended by the Government before being discussed. In these circumstances, if we finish with Clause 28 to-night, I certainly think we should be well advised not to move for the postponement of Clause 29, but to proceed at once on Wednesday, after the point of Order has been disposed of, to deal with the Amendments either by a general discussion on one Amendment or, in the ordinary way, and in strict accordance with the terms of each Amendment. I am most anxious to have as easy a passage in the Committee as is possible in conformity with our duty of examining this complicated Measure carefully.

[Much later] Mr. P. Snowden: I beg to move, "That the Chairman do report Progress, and ask leave to sit again." Although it is shamefully early we have got to the end of, I will not say the agreement, but the suggestion which was made, and I shall honourably abide by it. I trust hon. Members will feel some righteousness in going home so early and will be in a physical and mental condition when we resume the Committee stage of the Bill even to make more rapid progress.

Mr. Churchill: I do not think that we ought to separate without my offering to the right hon. Gentleman the Chancellor of the Exchequer my congratulations on the solid achievements of to-day. How clear this casts before us the moral *"Suaviter in modo, fortiter in re."* Here you have a sound example of two methods applied in the passage of the Bill—the vinegar and the oil. Which is the better one? The second is a sort of Aesop's fable. There is the traveller with the north wind blowing upon him and the more it blew the more he wrapped himself up, and then the sun came out and shone brightly on the traveller, and he divested himself of his cloak and yielded himself to the genial influence. The right hon. Gentleman has made progress to-day, but only progress in one element, namely, of time—and it is the time element which governs his affairs. I suggest to him to go one step further. Do not let him be checked by arbitrary feelings but go one step further. Let us have some compromise on merits, and we can wind up this business in due time. The right hon. Gentleman has already said he will consider all the Amendments to Clauses 29 and 30 which do not affect the main principles which he has in view and which we share with him, namely, to stop outrageous evasion of taxation. Let him consider carefully whether he cannot make his Budget a Budget of the House of Commons as a whole. He has got to have his revenue and to balance his Budget, we know. We may not like the way he does it, but he has got to have it. But let him consider whether we cannot expedite proceedings on a much larger scale than we have done to-night by some give and take between the two sides of the House and by the acceptance of Amendments which meet the point of view expressed from these benches and also the point of view expressed with so much ability from the Liberal benches. [*Interruption.*] Do not let hon. Gentlemen jeer at the Liberals when they are keeping them in office. Despise not the horse that is bearing you through the battle. I accept the Motion, but I do suggest to the right hon. Gentleman that it would be very well worth his while to consider whether the kind of arrangement which is possible in the sphere of time might not be very profitably extended to the sphere of merits.

FINANCE BILL

June 25, 1930

House of Commons

The Ruling which you have given, Sir, as the result of so much care and reflection, for which we are indebted to you, raises in my judgment the most serious and grave issues, and I feel bound, in accepting any Ruling that falls from you, to express, on behalf of those who sit on this side of the House, deep anxiety at some constructions which may be placed upon the Ruling which you have, in your duty and in your unchallengeable authority at this stage, thought right to give. I feel bound to place on record now some of those grave points which as I gather you have decided—

The Chairman: I think the right hon. Gentleman is now launching out on a criticism of my Ruling. I think, having given my Ruling and believing that I am right, the Committee should now proceed.

Mr. Churchill: With very great respect to you, Sir, it is, as you will readily admit, the duty of Members of the Committee, with proper submission to the Chair, to discharge what they regard as their proper Parliamentary functions and not in any way to be deterred by impatience or disorderly clamour from any part of the House. I am only submitting to you the grave anxiety and the doubt that arises on account of some of the points upon which decisions have been given, which decisions, no doubt, have complete validity as far as this episode is concerned but which, unless they are accompanied by further and fuller Rulings on your part, might easily lead to misconception and to misinterpretation in the future. May I ask, before these very grave Rulings pass into the definite acceptance of our Parliamentary system and custom, whether we are to take it that you have definitely ruled that the word "companies" in itself embraces all companies wherever situated and, if so, how are we to discriminate between the principle which extends the word "companies" to cover all companies and the principle which limits the word "person" to cover only persons of British jurisdiction. That seems to me to be almost a turning point in our Parliamentary procedure and, in accepting your decision, I would only ask for the judgment to be couched in terms which will deal with the far-reaching reactions which must spring from that.

I would also ask you whether, having been called upon in the execution of your office to give these formal and important Rulings which are now passing into our procedure and taking a definite part in the procedure of the House of Commons—precedents which will be cited perhaps for generations—could you explain definitely what is the virtue in italicisation? I had always understood that the typography was purely a matter of convenience—that there was no inherent virtue in the typography, that whether a Clause could or could not be entered upon by the House, ruled on by the Chair and passed by a Committee, depended not at all on whether it was printed in large or small type, in italics or in Roman or any other form, any more than it does upon the colour or character or thickness of the paper on which it is printed. It is a mere device for Parliamentary convenience. But I gather from your Ruling that an entire alteration in the inherent and essential character of Clauses depends upon whether they should be printed in Roman or in italic type, and from that it would appear that your Ruling to some extent is giving the necessary information which would enable the Committee to guard itself against those Ministerial encroachments which my right hon. Friend has mentioned, and which would easily be possible if it were found that Clauses might be altered in their intrinsic character merely by a change in the typography easily and readily at the disposition of the Ministers of the day.

There is one other point. You have said we have lost our right to raise this point of Order because we did not raise it in the Second Reading. You have pointed out that there have been occasions in the past, if I understand your ruling, where these points have been admitted by the Chair in Committee because they had previously been brought to the notice of Mr. Speaker when the Bill was in its Second Reading. If that argument stands upon anything, it stands upon a wrong submission to Mr. Speaker on the Second Reading. Mr. Speaker has said, when the point has been raised, that it is not the time to raise it. Is it possible to establish a claim for the subsequent validity of an objection because it has been raised at a time when it was inadmissible? Are we to lose our opportunity of raising this question at the right time because we failed to raise it at the wrong time previously? I venture to say that these grave changes and innovations in the whole character of our procedure—

The Chairman: I object to the right hon. Gentleman using the word "innovation."

Mr. Churchill: I withdraw the word "innovation" and I substitute the word "interpretation." The interpretations of these very difficult matters which you have been compelled to make in consequence of your duties and in your difficult position require from you further amplification in order that conclusions may not be drawn from them that may sensibly narrow and stiffen the ordinary and long-established procedure of the House. I would venture to ask that these points might receive from you some further elucidation.

The Chairman: On the word "company"—again, I am no lawyer—I take the Budget Resolution, and the word there, to me, is not limited in any sense. That is the only ruling which I can give from the Chair in relation to the word "company." When Clauses are italicised and a Bill has passed its Second Reading, it is an intimation to the Committee that a Money Resolution is necessary before the Clauses can have any life in them. Consequently, if there is no Money Resolution introduced to give life to them, they are not part of the Bill at all.

Mr. Churchill: With great respect—

Hon. Members: Order!

Mr. Thurtle: On a point of Order. May I submit to you—

The Chairman: I have not called upon the hon. Gentleman.

Mr. Thurtle: Mr. Young!

Hon. Members: Name!

The Chairman: I have not called the hon. Gentleman. The point raised by the right hon. Gentleman has to be settled first.

Mr. Thurtle: That is my point of Order.

Mr. Churchill: I venture, with great respect, to intervene to ask you whether the nature of the Clauses would in any way be altered by the fact that they were in italics, and whether if they were not in italics it would not equally be obligatory upon the Chair to deny them existence and to refuse to put them to the Committee?

The Chairman: If the Clauses are not italicised they are part of the Bill as it passes Second Reading. If they are italicised, they are for all practical purposes not part of the Bill committed to the Committee. I also indicated in regard to a Bill which came up for Second Reading with no italicised Clauses, that if there was any objection, such as that which has been raised to-day, it should have been raised before Mr. Speaker. In my opinion, I have no power to order the withdrawal of these Clauses which have been committed by the House. I hope that that is sufficient, and that it is not necessary for me to go any further into the matter. I want to say now directly to the right hon. Gentleman, that I have given my Ruling, and I shall abide by it.

Mr. Churchill: Of course, now that you have definitely given your Ruling, and, if I may say so, have shown very great patience in hearing fully the various objections which we felt bound to submit to you and to argue, it is our duty to accept the Ruling you have given for the purposes of this debate and we do so, but I am sure you will not take it as in the slightest degree reflecting either upon the validity of your Ruling or upon your conduct of this difficult matter if I say that we shall feel bound to bring this matter before the House in order that the grave reactions following from this Ruling may be fully debated and decided upon.

The Chairman: Whether the right hon. Gentleman desires to bring the matter before the House as a House or not does not concern me at the moment.

Sir D. Herbert: I desire to move, "That the Chairman do report Progress, and ask leave to sit again," for the purpose of explaining the position in which some of us find ourselves as a result of, I think I am right in saying, the somewhat unexpected Ruling. My right hon. Friend has suggested, as indeed I indicated a short time ago, that he might think it necessary to put down a Motion upon the Order Paper to discuss this Ruling in a proper way as permitted by the Rules of the House.

The Chairman: The hon. Member cannot move to report Progress on any grounds of my Ruling. This is the second time he has referred to my Ruling.

Sir D. Herbert: I am very sorry if I have transgressed your Ruling in moving to report Progress. I have no intention whatever—[Interruption.]

Mr. Broad: I think it is time that this foolery was stopped in the interests of Parliamentary proceedings.

The Chairman: The hon. Gentleman has no right to interrupt when the hon. Member for Watford (Sir D. Herbert) is on his feet.

Sir D. Herbert: I apologise if I have said anything which appears to interfere with your Ruling. My intention in moving to report Progress is to submit the position—

Mr. Ernest Evans: On a point of Order. Is there any Motion at the present moment before the Committee? If no Motion has been put by the Chair, is the hon. Member in order in moving to report Progress?

The Chairman: I think that the hon. Member is in order in moving to report Progress.

Sir D. Herbert: I shall take much less time in giving my reasons for moving to report Progress than some hon. Members of the Committee have spent in irresponsible talk on the subject. I wish to move to report Progress for the reason that some of us who desire to raise certain points of Order similar to those raised to-day in the House on subsequent stages of this Bill, and by other means, find ourselves in this difficulty, that if we were to be logical we should take no further part in the proceedings on these Clauses in the Committee. I do not think that it would be for the convenience of the House and the Committee as a whole that anything of that kind should take place. In these circumstances, I desire to take this opportunity of saying that we do not, if we remain in the Committee and discuss these Clauses and Amendments, take any responsibility by reason of the fact that we may have joined in the discussion in Committee, for in our opinion when these Clauses come to the House they cannot be regarded as being authorised.

The Chairman: I cannot accept the Motion at this stage.

Mr. Churchill *rose*—

The Chairman: I am exercising my powers as Chairman. I do not think that this is a proper Motion at this stage. [*Interruption.*] The right hon. Gentleman could hear what I am saying if there was not so much noise. I am exercising my power as Chairman, and I do not think that this is a proper Motion to put at this stage, and therefore I decline to accept it, and that should put an end to the matter.

Mr. Churchill: With great respect, your Ruling, of course, terminates the Motion—

The Chairman: That is not a point of Order.

Mr. Churchill: I beg to move, "That the Chairman do report Progress, and ask leave to sit again."

I renew this Motion in order particularly to give the Chancellor of the Exchequer the opportunity of making a general statement, which he had given notice of his intention to make on the whole character of the Clause. I submit that it would be a most convenient procedure for us to take if, after this protracted discussion in which heat has been generated, on a Motion to report Progress so that the matter may generally and thoroughly be discussed across the Floor of the House. I make this submission to you with very great respect, hoping that, at any rate, you will give it consideration at this stage.

[Later] We are in a very difficult position—almost an impossible position. The Chancellor of the Exchequer has studied the Amendments which my hon. Friends on this side, both above and below the Gangway, have had on the Paper for a long time past. He has considered them with the aid of his accomplished advisers, and he has seen that there is considerable validity, even from his own point of view, in many of them. In consequence, he has adopted a number of them; he has put down other Amendments of his own, and, in regard to a third class of Amendments, he has said that he will accept them with some alteration in the wording. The result is that he has virtually transformed this Clause and it is now, to all intents and purposes, a new Clause entirely different in its general presentation and in its general approach to this subject from the Clause originally in the Bill. The right hon. Gentleman said that this was a complicated matter, and the Attorney-General has also admitted its complexity. In such a complicated matter every part, or almost every part, depends upon every other part, and, consequently, if a number of essential points are subject to alteration, the view which one takes of the Clause as a whole and its method of treating the subject, must naturally be subject to change also. I know that the right hon. Gentleman wants to get on with his Bill, but I cannot believe, in view of the situation which has developed, and without a reprint of the Clause in the form in which the right hon. Gentleman now presents it, that a discussion embarked upon to-night is going to carry us very far. I listened to the right hon. Gentleman's very careful and patient exposition of the changes which he is making, and I am bound to say that I found great difficulty in following their actual effect upon the Clause. The hon. Member for Plaistow (Mr. Thorne), no doubt, understood them at once—

Mr. Thorne: Yes, and I understand your scientific method of obstruction. [Hon. Members: "Order!"]

Mr. Churchill: Of course, it would be very easy to get on with our business if every difficult point or argument which was advanced from one side were to be merely swept away by the other side under the general heading of "obstruction." Even if obstruction were a Parliamentary charge, which it is not, even if the hon. Member were allowed under the Rules of Order to apply much harsher terms than that to me, it would in no way induce me to abridge my remarks or shirk any aspect of my Parliamentary duty. I am asking the Chancellor of the Exchequer if he would not be well advised to accept the Motion and allow us to address ourselves to the consideration of this Clause when we have it before us in the form in which the right hon. Gentleman means to propose it. I certainly do not want to appear uncharitable, but the right hon. Gentleman has admitted that flaws have been shown in his original proposals by the Amendments which my hon. Friends have placed on the Paper, and it is not necessarily a very great concession on his part, when a mistake in the drafting of his Clause or in the statement of his proposals has been pointed out to him by the Opposition, that he should seek to put it right. It is not a concession which one need spend all the rest of one's days in being grateful for. If the right hon. Gentleman has profited by the improved drafts suggested from this side of the Committee, so far from our being grateful to the right hon. Gentleman—except that we are always grateful to him when he is kind to us in manner—it is he who ought to be deeply grateful to my hon. Friends who, without the expert knowledge at their disposal which the right hon. Gentleman enjoys, without the prolonged and profound consideration which he has been giving to these matters for months past, have been able to point out to him a way in which he can achieve his object with greater advantage and in a clearer manner. I do not think there is much gratitude to be brought into this proposal.

Mr. Thorne: On a point of Order. Has the discussion which has been going on for the last 10 minutes anything to do with the question of reporting Progress?

The Deputy-Chairman: I am afraid that, from the outset, this discussion has been rather out of order, but the Chancellor of the Exchequer took advantage of the Motion to make certain statements explanatory of the Amendments which he proposes to move and I cannot properly refuse to hon. Members on the other side of the Committee a reasonable opportunity of expressing their opinions on those explanations. I think, however, that the discussion should now be confined to reasons for or against reporting Progress.

Mr. Churchill: I think, Mr. Dunnico, that you will admit—and fortify yourself in your authority in the reflection—that nothing could have been more precisely directed to the exact Motion before the Committee than the argument which I was advancing. Owing to the concession which the Chancellor has made, not to our entreaties, but to our arguments, not a concession made necessarily out of good will to us, but made in submission to reasoning which has appealed to him and his advisers, this Clause has been so completely transformed that it is virtually a new Clause and it is not possible for the Committee to understand it until they see it in its integrity as now presented, and until they see exactly what they are being asked to do. It is only committing us to a long and laborious discussion, which cannot possibly reach a fruitful conclusion, to persist in going further with this debate and from that it follows, I think with reasonable assurance, that the Chancellor of the Exchequer would be well advised to accept the Motion and to put the Clause in its amended form on the Paper in order that when we meet again next week we shall have been able to study fully the new situation which has developed. It is quite true that the right hon. Gentleman may feel that this course would entail some loss of time, but I do not believe that in the long run such would be the case. I certainly cannot conceive that, in the present state of affairs, we are likely to progress far, however late we sit to-night. I am precluded from suggesting that the right hon. Gentleman should postpone the Clause in order to take another Clause because we agreed to withdraw that proposal, but I suggest that he would be well advised to accept the Motion which we shall certainly press to a Division.

[Later] I beg to move, "That the Chairman do report Progress and ask leave to sit again."

I make this Motion in order that I may suggest an arrangement which I think will be for the convenience of the Committee. My suggestion is that we should postpone this Clause until we have received the Amendments printed in their amended form and proceed now with the rest of the Bill. I have been looking at the Clauses from Clause 34 to 47, and, after consulting some of my hon. Friends, I am prepared to say that, as far as we are concerned, if Clauses 29 to 33 were postponed, there would be very good prospects of passing Clauses 34 to 47 to-night. I know those Clauses contain one or two points of substance, but I wish to make it perfectly clear that we should reserve the Schedules for further discussion on another day, and we reserve the fullest liberty in regard to the new Clauses. There is also Clause 12, but I do not think it is suggested that that Clause should be dealt with to-night.

[Much later] I rise to give my support to the Amendment moved by the right hon. Gentleman the Member for St. George's (Sir L. Worthington-Evans) which has been reinforced by the right hon. and gallant Gentleman below the Gangway. I ask the Chancellor of the Exchequer to give his serious attention to the views expressed from this side on this question. This Debt treatment requires to be brought into proper relation with the financial and economic state of the country. You may do far more harm to your credit and reproductive energies by extra taxation than you will gain in the prestige which comes from additional redemption of Debt at this juncture. I ask myself whether, on the whole, we have not cast the emphasis since the War unduly upon a speedy amortisation of old Debts instead of giving a greater stimulus to the creation of new wealth. Of course, the Socialist party naturally applaud the most stringent methods of fortifying the rentier class. There they have their champions. For my part, I think the productive side has to be considered, especially when you are already making an immense provision which has only to be steadfastly pursued across several generations to secure, even within the lifetime of people to-day, a complete clearance of this hideous legacy of the Great War. I consider that the right hon. Gentleman, at the present juncture in our financial affairs, is making an unnecessarily large provision for the redemption of Debt, and I do not believe that I am unsupported by solid financial and political opinion in making that statement.

If I remember aright, the quota in the fixed Debt charge appropriate to this year is over £70,000,000 on a four per cent. basis. The right hon. Gentleman can borrow money at a little over two per cent., owing, it is said, to his careful guidance of the finances, or owing, some say, to the fact that industry is almost dead, and that people will not throw money into enterprises. Whatever be the cause, the fact remains that he can borrow at £2 3s., or even less, in the City from week to week. When he spoke to the bankers and got on so well with them, he said that he was saving about £12,000,000 a year through much cheaper borrowing on Treasury Bills resulting from his extremely skilful reduction of the Floating Debt. If that be so, the £68,000,000 or £69,000,000, which would have been the contribution under the fixed Debt charge to the amortisation of the Debt appointed for this year, will be increased by that amount; in addition to which he has got £10,500,000, to which the right hon. Member for St. George's has drawn attention which comes to him in course of the Reparation payments. The figures for the reduction of Debt this year will be enormous, and yet this is the worst year we have gone through with our unemployment bounding up 100,000 in a fortnight. This is the year which the Government select for laying upon this country, staggering and gasping under its burden, the heaviest burden of Debt repayment. Is it good sense? Is the only thing to do to keep on repaying Debt, no matter where you have to borrow it, and to borrow with one hand and repay with another?

I am sure that the right hon. Gentleman will be well advised to strike out this additional provision. He has had his opportunity of bringing it forward and scoring off his predecessor. My contention is that the right hon. Gentleman, by assenting to new expenditure and by muddling the final months of the collection of the revenue, caused the trouble and that there would have been no deficit if the right hon. Gentleman had not been in power. He has had his score, and he has had the advantage of showing his superior virtue. Now let him drop this nonsense, and come back to the real position in which we stand, where what we require is not to lay all the heaviest burdens of Socialistic expenditure and of financial prudery upon the nation at the same moment, but where we wish as far as possible to give encouragement to industry, and to show that their fortunes are not entirely obnoxious to the Government of the day.

Five million pounds extra over and above the fixed Debt charge, over and above the Reparation money, over and above the great economies on Treasury Bills, is to be provided statutorily in this Measure. Where is that £5,000,000 to come from? I will tell you where it is coming from. It is coming from the additional 6d. on the reserves of companies, on the reserves of productive enterprises. Sixpence is to be taken additional to the present 4s. in order that the right hon. Gentleman shall be able to preen himself on reducing debt. Here is a definite division of principle between the two sides of the House. I wonder whether in their heart of hearts hon. Members opposite are quite such vehement supporters of this principle of rapid debt amortisation? I should have thought that what was required at present was a little encouragement for industry and employment; that they should be given a feeling that they were not, as it were, under the ban and bar of the Government of the day. I suggest to the right hon. Gentleman that he removes from the scope of the increase in the Income

Tax the reserves of limited companies and industrial enterprises, and, in order that his Budget shall suffer no disadvantage, he should strike out—

The Deputy-Chairman: The Amendment before the Committee is that the £5,000,000 should be excluded from this year's payment, and on that the right hon. Gentleman is not entitled to discuss the whole system of national taxation.

Mr. Churchill: Am I to understand that in arguing that this sum of £5,000,000 need not be added to our burdens I am not entitled to mention in passing the strain and stress which could be relieved—

The Deputy-Chairman: I did not rule that. What I have ruled is that the right hon. Gentleman must not discuss the general system of taxation. He has made a reference to Socialist schemes and other matters which do not come under this particular Amendment. He must confine himself to the question of the money raised in the Amendment.

Mr. Churchill: Indeed, I am doing so. I am saying that this money ought not to be paid because it can be found only by making a further inroad upon the already depleted reserves of our industrial and productive undertakings.

The Deputy-Chairman: The right hon. Gentleman was urging the Chancellor of the Exchequer to refrain from placing the extra 6d. of Income Tax on the reserves of limited companies, and I say that is not in order on this Amendment.

Mr. Churchill: Then I trust you will permit me to say that if the right hon. Gentleman were willing to accept this Amendment he would be in a position to give that great remission. I am content to leave it at that. That would be doing something which would be a great encouragement to our industries. But, seriously, I want to ask the Chancellor of the Exchequer—[Interruption.] If you want to mock, we will mock. Why should there be these taunts when, with astonishing chivalry, we are helping you to-night in a manner which, I am bound to say, has gone beyond the limits of generosity? Why should there be these mocking interruptions? Anybody is allowed to have an opinion in this House. [Interruption.] I say to the right hon. Gentleman that if he wishes to facilitate the course of this Budget he ought to try to meet the opinions which are put forward from this side of the House, even when they do not altogether represent his complete view of our financial policy. After all, he is the head of only a minority Government—[Interruption]—he is the Minister of only a minority Government, and the House has a right to be associated with them to some extent in shaping legislation. Why should every suggestion we make be brushed aside? Why should the right hon. Gentleman imagine that simply by threatening us, as he has done to-day, with the Guillotine Closure on the Budget, he will be able to carry—

Mr. McKinlay: Has this anything to do with the Amendment before the Committee?

The Deputy-Chairman: I hope the right hon. Gentleman will confine himself to the Amendment before the Committee, and also that we shall not have these taunts across the Floor.

Mr. Churchill: I certainly claim the ordinary freedom and liberty of debate which has always been given to an Opposition which is almost as strong as the Government of the day. Will not the right hon. Gentleman try to make his Budget scheme more agreeable to the judgment and general feeling of the House, and not adhere to his original plan as if that was the only method by which our affairs could be well conducted? I hope very much that the Chancellor of the Exchequer will be willing to try to meet the reasonable and moderate views of the Opposition. I know it is no use asking the right hon. Gentleman for any concession which places him at a disadvantage, but in this Amendment we are asking him to relieve himself of a portion of the burden which he has thought it right to undertake. I ask the right hon. Gentleman to weigh the facts and not treat the views which we have put forward as if they are bound to be excluded from any consideration of our financial system. We claim a right to take our share in the shaping of legislation, and if we are denied that right, and if reasonable proposals made from this side count for nothing—[*Interruption*]—and are snarled and yawned at by hon. Members opposite, do not let it be supposed that that will deprive us of our effectual resisting power.

FINANCE BILL

June 26, 1930

House of Commons

This is a matter of very great importance [Clauses 46 and 47], but we cannot carry the discussion much further to-night. There is always criticism as to whether any sort of arrangement should be come to, but we have come to one, and, in order to carry it through, I hope the Chancellor of the Exchequer is not going to go back on what he said previously. We have only a few minutes more, and, as we cannot do justice to the matter now, I trust that on the Report stage we shall be able to deal with it. Let it be recorded now that this point has emerged, a very grave and serious point, and on the Report stage of the Bill we must have it dealt with. I suggest that we really must conclude the debate now.

FINANCE BILL

July 1, 1930

House of Commons

It seems to me that the Attorney-General went a considerable distance in admitting the validity of the objections which have been raised on this side of the Committee when he promised to consult the text of the various Finance Acts to see how far the expression "directly or indirectly" was in common usage. In order to bring this matter to a point at which we can take a Division, I would ask the Attorney-General whether and in what way he would fall short of his aim in this Clause if for the word "indirectly" there were substituted the words "or by agent or nominee," as suggested by my hon. and learned Friend the Member for Moss Side (Sir G. Hurst).

Why are the words "or by agent or nominee" not exhaustive in themselves for the purpose which the Government have in view? To what extent do they fall short of the desire and intention of the Government? The Attorney-General has not told us, but he has indicated that he would examine the other Statutes with regard to the use of the word "indirectly." He has shown that he recognises that there are some difficulties attaching to the word "indirectly" which would be avoided by the adoption of a more precise definition. I suggest to the Attorney-General that he should tell us whether the words we suggest would meet his case, or, if not, in what way they fall short of what he has in mind as the main effective practical purpose of the Clause.

In any case we shall take note of his undertaking to examine the text of other Acts. The phrase, "whether directly or indirectly" certainly has a familiar smack about it, but in this particular Clause we want a very precise definition, because the Government are endeavouring to stop an abuse, and they have to thread their way most carefully through a tangle of phenomena so as to select that abuse and eradicate it without damaging the vast growth of perfectly legitimate organisms and practices on which a very large proportion of our business and commercial activity depends, and on which much of the structure of our City finance has been erected. I invite the Attorney-General to choose a precise and limited definition, instead of opening the door vaguely and widely to all sorts of matters which cannot at this moment be accurately foreseen. If he is able to hold out the hope that such a definition may possibly be ready on Report, and that he will be able to meet us on Report, we shall be thankful, but, in order to jog his memory on the matter, and in order to have a quite definite record of this transaction and discussion so far upon the Journals of the House, we shall feel bound to resist the insertion of the word "indirectly," because we would much prefer a precise and positive limited definition.

[Later] I beg to move, "That the Chairman do report Progress, and ask leave to sit again."

I venture at this stage to ask for some enlightenment from the Chancellor of the Exchequer or whoever is representing the Government in the conduct of this Measure at this moment as to the wishes of the Government and their intentions in regard to progress to-day. I would ask the Government to let us know whether they want to sit up very late to-night or not, because many arrangements have to be made for the convenience of Members and the officials of the House and so on, and generally it would be convenient to know what are the wishes of the Chancellor of the Exchequer. I hope that we shall be able to avoid a lengthy sitting, and that the Government will not ask the Committee to make an undue effort on this occasion. We have now no less than three consecutive days of the Finance Bill, and it is most desirable that we should not enter upon the very intricate Clauses 29 and 30 and right on to Clause 33 under conditions when the Committee will be exhausted and when many of our leading luminaries will not be shining but perhaps exhausting themselves, in view of the great responsibilities of their labours on the following day. From every point of view, it is desirable that these extremely complex and technical Amendments should not be taken during all-night sittings.

There is no doubt that one all-night sitting has a tendency to lead to another. Tempers are aroused, interest is excited, cheers are met by counter-cheers, gibes and retorts are met by counter-gibes and retorts, and discussions of the highest propositions may well be discoloured, distorted and distracted if we get beyond the normal hours of life and labour which long custom has rendered appropriate and convenient. I would ask the Attorney-General, as I gather that he has now received an instruction from the highest authority and is able, therefore, to give a clear and independent opinion upon the matter, what are his wishes? It is very pleasant to have the Committee under the leadership of the Attorney-General, because although many of the propositions with which he has to deal are so unpalatable to us, he always handles them in such a suave and amiable manner that one really feels pricks of conscience and compunction when one has to intervene. I hope, therefore, that he will be able to say that we shall be able to get away before midnight, or very shortly afterwards, and that we may resume this very intricate Clause to-morrow afternoon.

[Later] I do not propose to put the Committee to the trouble of dividing on this Motion. I recognise it is difficult for the Chancellor of the Exchequer at this moment to say where he will stop. The Clause is very technical and there are a great many Amendments introduced by the Government. Our attitude must be determined by the action of the Government in regard to some Amendment which some hon. Friends on this side intend to propose. Perhaps we might ask the Chancellor the same question again about 10 o'clock this evening, or somewhere about that time, and he will be more able to judge what it is fair to ask of the Committee on behalf of the Government. Therefore, I ask leave of the Committee to withdraw the Motion.

[Later] I should like to ask whether the Attorney-General would be able to accept the Amendment if the words "or the identifiable proceeds thereof" were inserted after the word "transferred"? That would make the point quite clear and would assert that definite continuity of identity in the property throughout the period of time. Some of the cases which have been put by hon. Members above and below the Gangway—difficult cases—have not been in any way met by the explanation of the Attorney-General. He answered the first case put by the hon. Member for Watford (Sir D. Herbert), but he did not deal with the second point in connection with building development companies. I trust we shall have some answer to these points. It makes one very uncomfortable to see these important Clauses passing line by line on to the Statute Book, knowing that they are leaving behind them at every stage many unconsidered cases of difficulty and hardship, which will be fought out in many wrangles in the law courts, and then will come back to this House, after an interval, in a further crop of legislation. Cannot the Attorney-General rid us at any rate of some of these difficulties?

[Later] Surely we are going to have some reply from the Attorney-General to the important point made by the hon. and learned Member for Altrincham (Mr. Atkinson) about alteration in the value of a property after it had been transferred to a company, and the consequential incidence of the burden of taxes on the transferee. We are surely in a very unsatisfactory position. He tells us that this is the right place to insert this Amendment. Naturally that is so, otherwise, Mr. Chairman, you would not have allowed it to be inserted. In support of the Amendment we adduced a series of homely illustrations, the armchair, the playing fields, the Lancashire business man, all these simple illustrations which were designed to translate this extremely technical matter into terms which could be appreciated by the general public. The hon. and learned Gentleman when he answers tells us that here is the right place to raise the Amendment, but it is not the right place for him to answer the arguments adduced. The proper place will be in Section (2) after paragraph (c). That is not at all satisfactory. What we want to know is, how are the Government meeting these definite objections? Are our fears unsound? Is there no ground for supposing that these difficulties will occur, and why is that so? That is what we want him to tell us, and we have not been told. I think it is profoundly unsatisfactory. Take the point of my hon. and learned Friend the Member for Altrincham (Mr. Atkinson). I hope he will press the point again before we take a Division in order that we may clearly show that there is a ghastly and gaping flaw in the Clause which the Government are proposing.

Mr. Atkinson: I will repeat the question. Is the company to be liable for property with which it has parted 20 years ago when it was worth very little, and when it has been made a property of great value to the people to whom it was transferred?

Mr. Churchill: May we not have an answer to that question. Is it a bona fide anxiety and a real dilemma proposed to the Government? It will not take long to give an answer if an answer exists. If there is an answer, let the Attorney-General not grudge those few words.

[Much later] I beg to move, "That the Chairman do report Progress, and ask leave to sit again."

I understand that it may be for the general convenience if, before we enter upon the discussion of the extremely important Amendment placed before us in the lucid speech of my hon. Friend the Member for Watford (Sir D. Herbert), I give the Chancellor of the Exchequer an opportunity of telling us what his ideas are about the progress which we ought to make to-night and how long he wishes to keep us here.

[Later] No one complains of the tone in which the Chancellor of the Exchequer has addressed the Committee on this point. Of course, our path would be greatly smoothed by the treatment which he may decide to mete out to the Amendments which we may have to move, and particularly to the present Amendment. At the same time, I hope that we shall, without entering into any bargain of any kind, be able to make progress in the direction he has indicated before inconvenience is caused to Members by a protraction of the sitting. If so, I suppose that the debate on the Clause will be taken in the light of day to-morrow, when we shall be able to survey the whole of the Clause as it has been remodelled by the House in the process of the Committee work. It is not only a question of endeavouring to compress discussion within certain limits, but there are questions of merit, one of which we are now discussing, which it is difficult to say might not enter into the arrangement. But if the right hon. Gentleman is able to accept some of the Amendments on this side of the Committee, I do not think that his suggestion is unreasonable. I, therefore, ask leave to withdraw the Motion.

[Later] The inclusion in the Clause of this strange provision, removing the business of holding, dealing in or developing land from the exemption aspect of the Clause, shows a prejudice which has existed in this country for a great many years. Indeed it dates from a time when the possession of the soil constituted almost the sole form of wealth, but the times have entirely changed, and the wealth which is derived from the ownership of agricultural land has become an almost insignificant part of the general system of wealth from which the revenues of the Exchequer are drawn. But the prejudice persists, though the facts have altered. As a result of that prejudice there is an injustice and the result of the injustice has been, to some extent, the position with which the Clause sets out to deal. It is pointed out that, in regard to the taxation of land, the Exchequer no longer seeks to follow the rule of apportioning the burden in proportion to the ability to pay. That principle is abandoned. There is a lot of talk about amenity values and the pleasant life that can be lived in the country and so forth, but the levying of taxation in proportion to the real beneficial yield, the financial return derived by the owner from the property—that principle which, in every other sphere, is acclaimed as dominant and indisputable—is now here cast aside. There is the injustice that Death Duties are calculated on capitalised value which bears no relation to the actual commercial value of the property.

Mr. Leif Jones: The evils of which the right hon. Gentleman is complaining are due to the fact that it is a capital tax—a tax on the capital value of the land, and the capital value of the land is not based on its agricultural value.

Mr. Churchill: That is our complaint. Here is a particular class of property the capital valuation of which for the purposes of Death Duties bears no relation to the return which that property gives, in the actual money power and money advantage which is derived from that form of capital. That is the injustice, and it is not, certainly, an injustice which dates its origin from the arrival in power of the so-called Socialist Government. It has been enforced by every administration, in one form or another, over a long period of years. But while you have that injustice and illogicality, although you may have some plausible explanation of custom behind you, you will have serious injury growing up in the State. I had as Chancellor of the Exchequer to consider these matters, and the late Cabinet considered it with attention, and we were certainly not prepared to say that the highly artificial arrangements which have been referred to for the purpose of enabling landowners to evade Death Duties should continue without further legislation; but it had never been our intention to make any legislation of this kind a feature in our policy without at the same time endeavouring to redress the root injustice which has been referred to by my Noble Friend the Member for Aldershot (Viscount Wolmer) and which has almost without resistance been pressed upon the Committee from so many parts of the Committee. I will take only one instance, and if the right hon. Gentleman were able to meet us now or on the Report stage, it would notably facilitate the passage of this Clause and other Clauses.

Take the question of the inclusion of the amenity value in the valuation for Death Duties, in the case where the estate is passing not by sale—a sale is a commercial event—but by succession. Why should a man have to ransom the amenity value of his own home, where his family have lived for generations, when his father dies, against the bidding of any profiteer or Transatlantic importation, or any new arrival in this country from any part of the world? One can quite understand that there is a certain class of vulgar persons who will pay a very large and fancy price in order to sit in the ancestral seat of some decaying British family; but why should the amenity value be brought into calculation when it is in regard to a man's own home? We have always considered that that was an injustice which must be removed before you proceed to stiffen up this legislation relating to the Death Duties. I cannot see why the right hon. Gentleman could not do it. It would be quite easy to insert a provision to say that the amenity value should not be taken into consideration in assessing the amount for Death Duties except when it passes by sale and not by succession.

What right has anyone to force a man to pay for the amenity value of his own home in competition with the common market value offered by all and sundry who might come and bid for it? It is contrary to every form of justice and fair play. This is an old subject with the right hon. Gentleman, but I hope that he will consider this, because we wish to stop the evasion of Death Duties by artificial, elaborate and deliberate means, but you ought to couple with that the protection of the successor to his own home from being, as it were blackmailed to bring it back over again in competition with all and sundry from any part of the world.

I hope the right hon. Gentleman will consider this point. I propose to put down a new Clause dealing with it. It would go a long way to remove the strong feelings which are naturally aroused by the flagrant statement in print which we see before us that of all the business methods of producing wealth or of organising industry the one selected for special severity of treatment is the business of holding, managing, developing or dealing in land. I hope the right hon. Gentleman is not going to make a very controversial reply.

Mr. Alpass: You have not been controversial!

Mr. Churchill: I have not been controversial. I have put a point of view, but I have tried not to say anything to hurt the feelings of hon. Gentlemen. The principle is that wealth should be taxed. The principle is that the enjoyment and power which money gives should be taxed in proportion, but not that you should apply your taxation in such a way as to force from the man who loves his own home a price, in order that he may stay there, which is far beyond its proper use or money value. I am only suggesting an extension to the amenity value of the principle which Sir William Harcourt himself, and afterwards the right hon. Gentleman the Member for Carnarvon Boroughs (Mr. Lloyd George), in a Budget which was denounced as severe Radical legislation, applied to pictures and other heirlooms. As long as the estate is passing by succession and is not being brought into the market for sale, the amenity value ought not to be included for the purpose of valuation for Death Duties. I hope the right hon. Gentleman will not brush that contention aside at this moment, not only for our own sakes, but for his own.

[Later] We really must ask for an answer from the Chancellor of the Exchequer. We could not let the debate lapse without a statement, and I hope it will be a statement full of good words and not harsh words. Anyhow, however it goes, we could not possibly let a matter of this kind be disposed of without an attempt on the part of the Leader of the House for the time being and the Minister in charge of the Bill to answer the many important and cogent points which have been addressed to him across the Floor of the House. I hope that the right hon. Gentleman is going to give us an answer, because he really will not accelerate his business by sitting silent. [*Interruption.*] If I am interrupted I shall take much longer. The right hon. Gentleman can, no doubt, say what there is to say in four or five minutes, but by sitting silent he may lose ten times that time by reason of the offence he will cause to hon. Members who have brought forward, in a respectful and reasonable manner, grievances which they have felt bound to present. I ask the right hon. Gentleman to take part in this debate, as it is his duty and proper function in the great office which he holds.

FINANCE BILL

July 2, 1930

House of Commons

I beg to move, "That the Chairman do report Progress, and ask leave to sit again."

It would be convenient at this stage, when we have reached the business which we prescribed for this afternoon, that I should invite the Chancellor of the Exchequer to state on behalf of the Government what he has in mind for our labours this evening and also possibly for to-morrow. It will be for the convenience of everyone to know what the outlook of the Government is at this moment. I reserve any further remarks that I have to make, in pursuance of the Motion that I have made, until I have heard the Chancellor of the Exchequer.

Mr. P. Snowden: I thank the Opposition for having so faithfully kept to the arrangement that was made with respect to our business for this afternoon. With regard to the future, I think the next three or four Clauses will not raise matters of such intensity as the Clause with which we have been dealing. The next Clause deals with Estate Duty where life interest is transferred to a private company, and Clause 31 deals with the charge of duty and powers of recovery. I do not think those Clauses are very controversial. Clause 32 raises the question of the valuation of shares in private companies, of which we have heard a good deal in the discussion of Clause 29. This is the ninth day of the Committee stage of the Bill. I should be surprised to hear that any Finance Bill for the last 20 years has taken nine days in Committee. I suggest that we should try to get to the end of Clause 33 to-night. I have no desire to have an all-night sitting, but I am very much afraid that unless we make rapid progress—I mean reasonably rapid progress—before to-morrow evening it will be necessary, however disagreeable, to sit very late, and possibly very early.

Mr. Churchill: And late again.

Mr. Snowden: That is all that I can say at the moment. I hope that the Opposition will meet me and enable us to get the Clauses which I have mentioned.

Mr. Churchill: The right hon. Gentleman is asking what is physically impossible when he suggests that we should dispose of Clauses down to 32 and 33 in the bare four hours that remain before the House would be sitting at a time that would cause considerable inconvenience to a number of hon. Members. Of course, more progress would be made if we sat until 2 or 3 o'clock, as has often been done in former times, but that leads to great inconvenience in regard to Members getting away from the House after the public conveyances have ceased to run or ply for hire. In consequence, it is often found that once we have passed the witching hour of 12.30, things tend to resolve themselves into trials of physical endurance. It seems to me that the right hon. Gentleman might be asking not more than can be accomplished reasonably to suggest that we should dispose of the Clauses down to Clause 33 before midnight to-morrow night. That, I think, would be a very reasonable proposal and scheme for laying out our work. We should certainly endeavour to compress our criticism into that space of time.

That would enable us next week to address ourselves to the very important Clause 12, which has now been put down in its new form. The new form removes a good many of the objections that were entertained to that Clause, and I believe that it is now founded on a large measure of agreement with some of the great life insurance companies. That would seem to be a Clause which might well form the subject of our discussion on whatever day is chosen for the resumption of the Finance Bill discussions next week. After that, we have the whole range of the new Clauses, to which the utmost importance is attached. Some of them embody provisions on which the main shock on this Budget will be taken. I have frequently endeavoured, sometimes perhaps in a controversial style but more often in a friendly manner, to suggest to the Chancellor of the Exchequer that the time has come when he ought to address himself to this problem on wider lines than hitherto. It is not a question of proceeding night after night with amicable arrangements for the conduct of business and the acceptance of Amendments, such as have been readily accepted by the Government during the debates. That is quite all right as far as it goes, but it is not really a method which is adequate for the handling of the great problems with which the right hon. Gentleman is now confronted.

It seems to me that over the week-end some efforts should be made to see whether the differences which exist on this Budget cannot be more or less resolved without the right hon. Gentleman being deprived of the power of balancing his Budget, for which undoubtedly he is bound to fight to the last, or the proceedings of the Committee being unduly protracted. We all wish to avoid such sittings. Meanwhile, the days are slipping rapidly away, and although there remains for the Opposition an enormous amount of work, which could if necessary discharge in the examination of these proposals and in the moving of new Clauses, as well as in the final revision of the Bill with Mr. Speaker in the Chair on the Report stage, nevertheless, the sooner we come to some general understanding so that the Budget has upon it the imprint of the House of Commons as a whole, although it involves much with which we on this side do not agree, it should be possible to accelerate our discussions. I will not say more at this moment, because it may be irritating and perhaps an impediment to the course I am suggesting. But we can hold out no hope of finishing Clause 33 by to-night; even if we sat until 2 or 3 or 5 o'clock in the morning we should not succeed in doing that. The Chancellor of the Exchequer would be quite fortunate if he achieved that by 12 o'clock to-morrow night. He may do that, and it might be possible to break in on one or two of the earlier new Clauses, but certainly not on the new Clause 12. I am giving no undertaking at all; I am only indicating my position as to the time which is required.

[Later] I do not think we can carry the matter further than where it was left by the right hon. Member for St. George's (Sir L. Worthington-Evans) and the comment which has been made by the hon. Member for Watford (Sir D. Herbert). In principle, the desire of the Chancellor of the Exchequer to obtain Clause 12 before we separate to-morrow is not necessarily unattainable, but whether it is attainable or not depends on a study of the Clause in the brief time which remains before it is debated. If it should be found that, contrary to our belief, it still contains many controversial points and that the difficulties have not been met by the discussions between the Government and the life assurance societies, it will be necessary for us to suggest to the right hon. Gentleman that one or two of the other new Clauses should be given precedence. I am not giving any pledge, but it would be premature to assume at this stage that the Clause is not in a form which would enable us to dispose of it to-morrow night.

FINANCE BILL

July 3, 1930

House of Commons

I beg to move, "That the Chairman do report Progress, and ask leave to sit again."

Following what I may now call the usual practice, I think at this stage in our proceedings I might, for the general convenience of the Committee and to facilitate public business, move this Motion for the purpose of ascertaining from the Chancellor of the Exchequer his views, not only upon the immediate progress of the Bill this evening, but, taking a rather more extensive view, upon its future progress. In fact I might ask him—though I have no knowledge of whether the right hon. Gentleman will be able to make any response or not—what his ideas are as regards the completion of the Committee stage. We are now going to embark on what was originally Clause 12 in its revised form, and if that Clause, on examination, is found to be one which can be disposed of with some rapidity, we might come to the other new Clauses to-day, and then, if we work hard and amicably on Monday, we might dispose of quite a number of new Clauses. One or two of these are important. There is one which we are anxious to discuss, which is not yet on the Paper, but I think that on the lines which I have suggested we might, conceivably, map out our work in a manner which would secure the highest efficiency in debate and the least inroads upon the already heavily strained physical energy of the Members of the Committee.

Mr. P. Snowden: I am afraid I cannot say anything about the programme beyond to-day's proceedings. I expressed the hope last night, and I think I repeated it to-day, that we should be able to make considerable inroads on the new Clauses this evening.

[Later] Perhaps at about 10 o'clock I may put another question to the right hon. Gentleman with a view to accelerating business as much as possible. I am not complaining of what he has said, but he must know that if these matters are kept in suspense for a long time, hon. Members become exceedingly anxious and disturbed as to the future progress of the Bill, and tend to dwell with more insistency and thoroughness on some of its aspects than perhaps they would if they understood that the happy relationships established during the conduct of this very controversial

Measure were going to continue. Therefore, I hope that if, say at 10 o'clock, the right hon. Gentleman should feel that the light is shining a little more clearly on his path and that he can discern more accurately the general scope of the further stages which we have to take, he will not hesitate to tell us, for his own sake no less than for ours. I beg to ask leave to withdraw my Motion.

[Much later] I beg to move, "That the Chairman do report Progress, and ask leave to sit again."

I am most anxious that nothing should occur to raise the temperature of this debate at a season of the year when already the physical temperature runs unusually high in these latitudes, and therefore, as I indicated a little earlier in our proceedings, in the hope that we may accelerate our proceedings as much as possible, I ask leave to move to report Progress in order to give to the Chancellor of the Exchequer an opportunity of telling us now with fuller knowledge what he thinks should be the immediate course of our discussion.

Mr. P. Snowden: I regret to have to say that I am not in possession of any fuller knowledge now than I was some two hours ago, and I am sorry that I cannot satisfy the right hon. Gentleman to any greater extent than when I last spoke. The debate on this Clause has gone on longer than I expected. I do not complain; I simply state the fact. When I last spoke, I said I hoped that we might be able to make some inroad upon the new Clause this evening, and I have not abandoned that hope. I shall certainly not ask the Committee to sit after 12 o'clock, and I hope that between now and then we may make reasonable progress. I am afraid I cannot say anything beyond that.

Mr. Churchill: Of course, I am sorry the right hon. Gentleman is not able to give any further indication of his wishes than that which has just fallen from him. This Clause on which we have been engaged is one of very deep interest, affecting as it does at so many points the life of the community. The right hon. Gentleman would, I am sure, be well advised to come to some conclusion in his mind, because we feel, although we may be allowed to go to bed to-night at a reasonable hour, that he would have a grievance—not a legitimate grievance, but a natural grievance, not a grievance against us, but a grievance against things in general, if he had not made considerable progress with the new Clauses. There is not much chance of that, and he will be well aware of the difficulties that lay before us. This particular Clause, although the right hon. Gentleman has agreed it with the experts and the authorities of the life assurance companies, is a matter which cannot be hurried. We have our views and they are disinterested views, and we cannot leave this on the Statute Book simply in the form in which it is arranged with the eager tax-gatherer and these great vested interests in the life assurance companies. We must examine it, and make sure that legislation is not the result of any particular deal or arrangement between the Government and any particular section of the community, but that it represents the settled conviction, after searching examination, of the House of Commons and of the great mass of the electorate of which we are the servants.

I trust that we may get through this Clause before the hour of midnight strikes to wake Cinderella from her dream, but even so, the next step will be to embark upon a question of extraordinary complexity and one which appeals in a special manner to almost every family among the Income Tax payers—the question whether Income Tax should be reckoned jointly or severally between people who are living together united by the matrimonial tie. I am not going to anticipate that on a Motion to report Progress, but it seems to me that this is a subject which arouses the combative instincts of millions of householders throughout the land, and it is only natural, and indeed inevitable, that these combative instincts, so widely excited, should find their representative repercussions in our attitude upon this side of the Committee. We shall have to address ourselves with very great zest and zeal to these matters if we are to make any progress to-night, and rather than delay the proceedings I will ask leave, in order to facilitate progress, to withdraw my Motion, which I made in the hope that the Chancellor of the Exchequer would be able, by a wave of a fairy wand, to relieve us of many of our anxieties. He is not able to do so, and therefore I think the best thing I can do is to ask leave to withdraw the Motion, so that we may immediately address ourselves to the serious difficulties that lay before us.

[Later] The Chancellor of the Exchequer is to be congratulated upon the arrangement which has been made that this debate on Clause 12 should come to a conclusion at 12 o'clock. I rise at this stage only for the purpose of saying that it is not our intention to divide against the Clause in its resuscitated and novel form. Although we consider that it still contains many objections, we must admit that it has been so completely remodelled that it does not call from us at this stage a manifestation in the Division Lobby. But let the Chancellor of the Exchequer not imagine that he is entitled to receive any bouquets for this legislation. On the contrary, he owes it to the House of Commons, and to no one more than the hon. Member for Watford (Sir D. Herbert), that he has been rescued from the fate which lay before him, from the pitfalls into all his untutored steps were remorselessly leading him. What a discreditable transaction is the history of this Clause! Here is the Chancellor of the Exchequer using all the force and power of his office upon his opponents, with the utmost vigour. Having had all the winter to consider these matters, having all the brilliant experts of the Treasury at his disposal, having also at his disposal, if he had only asked for it, all the advice of the great commercial companies and interests who are involved in this aspect of legislation, with mature deliberation he produced his plan he produces it in the Finance Bill, it is printed and circulated, and the House goes into Committee upon that carefully considered plan.

The briefest examination shows that it is vitiated at every point, that it is contrary to reason and logic and good sense, that it would not work and that it would involve immense injury to our affairs. The right hon. Gentleman has to go off tardily and, after the due hour has passed, do the work which he should have done earlier. He has to go and consult those very vested interests which his party exists to insult and undermine. He has to go and meet them in humble parley and, line by line and word by word, redraft and recast his legislation, until the final form of his Clause is utterly unrecognisable from that in which he cast it with the aid of his officials. After he has done that, after he has gone to Canossa or has sat shivering in the courtyard—or would have sat shivering but for the season of the year—of the great life assurance companies, he comes down to the House and tries to convert his humiliation into a positive paean of victory. He tells us that because he has now, at last, made peace with the great vested interests, therefore the alliance of the Socialist Government with great vested interests is complete and that the House of Commons need not concern itself further in the process. In his drafting and redrafting of this Clause, the right hon. Gentleman has exhibited every vice which can be scarified in our legislation. He has shown carelessness in preparation, arrogance in the advancing of his Measure, swift and weak retirement, readiness to arrive at accommodations with those he had been previously prepared to scout and finally a renewal of the original arrogance.

What do we see? His original Clause, a misbegotten abortion, has been withdrawn, and now we are invited to witness the rising from its ashes of a phoenix, assisted by the life insurance companies. This is presented to Parliament as a specimen of the efficiency of Labour legislation in regard to complicated commercial and financial matters. My hon. Friend was absolutely justified in the careful manner in which he exposed the shortcomings of the Chancellor of the Exchequer to the Committee, and my hon. Friend below the Gangway, whose robust interventions in our debates always excite our pleasure, even when they do not command our agreement, who told us off so sharply and who is always ready to tell us off as sharply as if we were a squad of infantry, was not in some at least of the closing passages of his remarks sufficiently recognisant of the services which my hon. Friend the Member for Watford (Sir D. Herbert) rendered to the Committee.

Although we have made our protest against the careless, slipshod, slovenly, slapdash manner in which the Chancellor of the Exchequer has commended his proposals to the Committee, we do not intend on this occasion to carry our proposal into the Division Lobby. We must admit that the skilful advice of the great interests concerned, elaborated as it has been by a Committee of the House of Commons, which has not shirked its duties, has enabled the country to escape most mischievous proposals, which, if we had not banded ourselves together to effective resistance, would at this moment be passing smoothly and remorselessly to their place in the permanent legislation of the country. It is worth while reflecting on the risks we run and the jeopardy we stand in every hour. If a number of private Members in this Committee had not scorned delights and lived laborious days, if they had not sacrificed their time and strength, and endangered their health and confronted the Socialist Chancellor of the Exchequer with a firm resistance, with a hedge of fixed bayonets, this Clause in its original mischievous and atrocious form would already be sailing along on its way to the Statute Book. We have done our duty, and we have had one of the rewards, one of those rare and refreshing fruits that fall from time to time from the tree of Fortune to those who have laboured long. Encouraged by the success the Committee has had in the remodelling of this Clause, we shall devote our energies with even greater force to the further stages of the class-prejudiced, spiteful, fruitless and injurious Measure, of which this Clause is a typical example. [Question, "That the Clause be added to the Bill" put, and agreed to.]

[Much later] Mr. Churchill: I made no arrangement except that which is recorded in the *Official Report*, which can be examined. As to the arrangements made to vary the agreement so that the discussion on the group of Clauses ending with

Clause 33 should be brought to a conclusion between six and seven this evening, I was not concerned with it, but I understood from the Chancellor of the Exchequer that he gave a release from the undertaking, and he cannot, therefore, go back upon it. Never in any circumstances have we made any agreement that anything more than Clause 12 should be got to-night. On the contrary, we expressed grave doubts as to whether that Clause could be dealt with by midnight, and it was only in the event of the right hon. Gentleman withdrawing the original Clause 12 that we made any suggestion of agreement. As far as I am aware, the right hon. Gentleman has not the slightest ground of complaint when he goes home to-night, not only with the group of Clauses up to 33, but also with his new Clause 12. He has got all that was ever suggested or agreed to by us in any of the discussions which happily have taken place in the full light of day across the floor of the Committee. It is quite true that if the right hon. Gentleman had been willing to give us some indication of his intentions with regard to the future Committee proceedings on the Bill, I held out a hope that we might, by sacrificing many things which we consider are essential, have accelerated the progress of business. He refused. I asked him at 6 o'clock, and at 7 o'clock, and at a quarter past ten to give the Committee some guidance as to the future conduct of business. He declined; and, that being the case, he has not the slightest ground for complaint. He makes these complaints when he is angry, but the point is whether he makes them when they are true. He knows very well that we did not agree that he should have more than Clause 12 by midnight to-night unless by indicating the future course of the Bill he rendered the conduct of business easier. This is the statement from yesterday's *Official Report*:

> If the Opposition are willing to agree to the suggestion that we should get through these Clauses and also the new Clause 12 by midnight to-morrow, I would be satisfied.—[Official Report, 2nd July, 1930; col. 2047; Vol. 240.]

Really, I make great allowances for the Chancellor. He has a great burden upon him, and I think he bears it with a great deal of courage. From many quarters foes advance upon him, and he is abused for much that he can control and for more that he cannot control. Therefore, I am not one of those who would hound him down, but I put it to the Committee, in the broad fair play of the House of Commons, whether he has not shown the results of the pressure that is upon him when he charges us with a dishonourable breach of faith and with failing to keep Parliamentary agreements, when those words which I have just read out, placed in my hands by a colleague, can be already nakedly placed before him across the Floor.

Mr. P. Snowden: The words which the right hon. Gentleman has read have no bearing at all on this question, and the *Official Report* will prove that to-morrow. I remember saying, I think it was at 10 o'clock this evening, that we must make an inroad into the earlier of the new Clauses on the Paper, and that, I am sure, is within the recollection of the Committee. I know quite well what the understanding was.

Mr. Churchill: Might I ask one question? What concession did the right hon. Gentleman make? An understanding cannot be unilateral. It is quite true that I offered that we would endeavour to accelerate business if the Chancellor outlined subsequently the future progress of this Bill, but he refused to do so, and he has no right to expect from us our share when he has utterly refused to make any contribution whatever.

FINANCE BILL

July 7, 1930

House of Commons

I beg to move, "That the Chairman do report Progress, and ask leave to sit again."

I do not rise to move this Motion because I wish to do anything but abridge and expedite the proceedings, but we really must know beyond a peradventure, as President Wilson put it, what are the intentions of the Government, and we must make quite sure that there is no misunderstanding of any sort or kind between the two sides of the Committee. We are trying to get on as quickly as we can, but we have been greatly blocked by the long discussion on the private Bill, and there remain only two hours before 12 o'clock for eight pages of proposed new Clauses. It will be extraordinarily difficult to press that in, but I agree that we must do everything in our power. Where does the Government stand in the matter? Are they prepared to facilitate in any way the clearing of the Order Paper up to the point where the proposed new Clause—(*Relief to company reserves*)—standing in the name of the hon. and gallant Member for North-East Bethnal Green (Major Nathan), appears on the Paper? That new Clause should come on in the early part of Wednesday's debate. That is our wish, and it is the wish of the Government. I do not know whether it is possible to get through the intervening business by 12 o'clock, even by not discussing it. The Government should make it perfectly clear that they will not attempt to discuss that proposed new Clause during the small hours of the morning, if by any chance the present programme falls through; otherwise, we may be quite sure that we shall carry the discussion round to two or three o'clock in the morning. Then there is the question of what is to happen after 7.30 on Wednesday. We had better have it out, because the right hon. Gentleman is always ready to say that we have broken agreements, and so on. There is this important proposed new Clause of the hon. and gallant Member for North-East Bethnal Green, and afterwards, the question of the assessment for Death Duties. I am not in a position to guarantee that the matter will be wound up at 7.30 on Wednesday, but we will do our best. We are with the right hon. Gentleman in the hope that the Committee stage should be put out of the way by Wednesday, but let there be no misunderstanding so that he can say that we have broken our word. There is no need for misunderstanding, and we will do the best we can.

FINANCE BILL

July 9, 1930

House of Commons

I feel sure that the Committee will share my feelings of regret at the reply which has been made to this Amendment by the Chancellor of the Exchequer. It all goes to show what I have long realised throughout these protracted debates that the right hon. Gentleman never tries or desires to meet the suggestions of his opponents. The right hon. Gentleman always resents, from whatever part of the House they come, any attempts to co-operate with the Government in framing the financial proposals of the year. The Chancellor of the Exchequer contends that great complications would arise if the principle embodied in this Amendment were to be introduced into our legislation. I hope the Committee will not be misled by that statement. I know how easy it is for high experts at the disposal of the Chancellor of the Exchequer to meet any sane and practical proposition which the Government of the day wishes to be embodied in our legislation. All the difficulties which the right hon. Gentleman has stated are completely dwarfed by the difficulties presented by large chunks of legislation which are now passing through Parliament. The attitude of the Chancellor of the Exchequer has now become an obstinate resistance to any co-operation by the House of Commons as a whole in the financial legislation of the year.

What is the principle which we seek to establish by this new Clause? The hon. and gallant Member who has put this proposal on the Paper has the support of a considerable number of his own party. It is quite possible that this new Clause could be re-cast with the assistance of expert officials in a better form, and I am quite certain that, if the Chancellor of the Exchequer wished to adopt the principle of the proposal, he could easily produce a form of words which would be satisfactory, and which would give the measure of relief to industry which we desire; but the right hon. Gentleman is only aiming at making difficulties. I think he ought to realise how simple is the principle which we are pressing upon him. We contend that the object of the right hon. Gentleman has been wrong in its general emphasis, and has sought to cast its extra burden too heavily upon industry and employment, and to safeguard too jealously the special interests of the rentier class. It is not for me to condemn a strict Debt repayment system, but the question is how to apportion our action to the circumstances of the hour.

Mr. MacLaren: Deal with the new Clause.

Mr. Churchill: I am not to be drawn from my line of argument by interruptions of that kind, and, if I am out of order, the Chairman will call me to order. I was explaining the root principle of this Measure. I consider that the Chancellor of the Exchequer has laid too heavy a hand on industry, and he would have been well advised to have relieved industry to a greater extent, even if he had been obliged to abate his energy in Debt amortisation. This is not the first time that I have put this point before the right hon. Gentleman. There is only one way of doing it. The right hon. Gentleman could express this matter in a much more satisfactory form if he chose to meet us, but he does not want to meet us. We want to have a little less of Potsdam from the right hon. Gentleman and a little more of Geneva. [An Hon. Member: "You make us sick!"] I should be sorry to hear that the right hon. Gentleman is going to be sick, but, if that is so, I hope he will withdraw from the Chamber. I am not going to allow any interruptions of that kind to interfere with making my point.

If the right hon. Gentleman intended now to try and take the House into partnership in his Budget, he could do so by accepting this new Clause, which would only cost him about £3,000,000; or he could achieve the same end by accepting the Amendment which is to be moved later on, and he could undoubtedly find some other means of altering the balance of his Budget without committing himself to any serious loss of revenue. If the right hon. Gentleman would take that course, he would bring the House much more together upon the financial policy of the year than he has done up to the present. The right hon. Gentleman and his friends are pursuing a policy of pure negation, and, consequently, we shall be obliged to record our votes in favour of the new Clause proposed by the hon. and gallant Member for North-East Bethnal Green (Major Nathan). We shall take that course with the conviction that we are striking the right note at the moment, even if the particular form of this new Clause is not all that could be achieved by anyone who had access to the official machinery of drafting. This is a sound and sensible proposal to lighten the burdens of industry, even if the Government have to slow down their debt amortisation.

I am sure that the Chancellor of the Exchequer could express our purpose in a better way if he was only willing to do so. When this new Clause has been disposed of, another Amendment is to be moved with the same object in view. Our object would be met if the Chancellor of the Exchequer would say, "I do not like either of these two forms of words, but I agree with the object in view, and I will re-shape the Budget so that an extra £5,000,000 or £7,000,000 will be given to this object, and I ask the Committee not to press forward this proposal so vigorously." If the Chancellor of the Exchequer would bring forward some other proposal which would effect that end and transfer the sum of money we ask for from one side of the account to the other, our object would be achieved. Is the right hon. Gentleman going to treat us to a "Stone-Wall" Jackson resistance, and merely palm off upon us the stock objections which the Treasury continue to offer to every proposal until they decide to adopt it. If he takes that course, then I am sure he will convince the Committee that reason and friendly persuasion have no effect upon him, and that the only thing he will respect is Parliamentary force expressed by voting strength after protracted discussion at every stage.

[Later] I do not think it is necessary for any protracted debate to take place upon this new Clause, because the issue has been laid very clearly before the Committee by the right hon. Member for Carnarvon Boroughs (Mr. Lloyd George) in the extremely moderate and weighty speech which he has just delivered. The first of the broad issues was already stated by me to be an alteration of the emphasis of the Budget to give a greater measure of relief to industry, even if the process of debt redemption may have to be temporarily slowed down. The other aspect, which has

been put forward by the right hon. Member for Carnarvon Boroughs, the Leader of the
Liberal party in this House, is that this is upon the whole one of the safest and surest
methods of reviving industry and relieving unemployment. All sorts of schemes are put
forward to relieve unemployment, some wise and some foolish, and, as has been
pointed out, immense sums are being disbursed, not to prevent the evil of unemployment, but merely to mitigate its consequences to individuals. Here, for an expenditure
which I have always been advised would not exceed £7,000,000 a year, undoubtedly a
stimulus and encouragement would be imparted over the whole of our industrial
enterprise. Of course, it is quite true that the actual money value is not the whole of
the stimulus. What industry wants to feel at the present time is that the Government
and the Chancellor of the Exchequer wish to come to its aid, wish it well, are anxious
that enterprises should be launched and that a stimulus should be imparted to our
production. That is the desire which industry expresses at the present time.

   I do not think there is very much in the argument that firms which do not make
profits, and consequently do not pay Income Tax, will not derive benefit. If they do
not have to pay Income Tax they do not suffer the evil from which we now ask that
the firms which do make profits should in this respect be relieved. The Chancellor of
the Exchequer speaks as if a remission of taxation was a burden to the taxpayer; he
speaks of it as if he was throwing a great burden on the taxpayer. But if this
expenditure does not exceed £5,000,000 or £6,000,000 a year, the mere removal of
the extra provision which he has made for the Sinking Fund this year, over and above
the German reparations, and over and above the great advantages in the purchase of
Treasury Bills—if that £7,000,000 does not exceed it, or practically balances it, no
burden whatever is thrown on the taxpayer or on the country. All that happens is that
one form of vital initiative which now is singularly under depression and arrest in this
island will be relieved from the break or drag which is preventing its full expansion.

   The right hon. Gentleman was very scornful of the Amendment. He used a lot of
words, taken from his harsh vocabulary, to describe the new Clause in scathing terms.
"Ill-considered" and "absurd"—those were the terms which rang in our ears. The
Liberal party are responsible for the Amendment, and I believe that they have not put
it down without prolonged and careful consideration of its terms on the merits. They
have given a great deal of study and attention to this aspect, and it is a proposal which,
so far as unemployment is concerned, I am bound to say seems much freer from
objections than some others that have come from that quarter. But, at any rate, I see
no sort of inconsistency in an Opposition party putting forward a proposal, the
purpose and intention of which are quite clearly expressed, and, at the same time,
offering to accept from the Government a reasonable measure of amendment of the
actual terms or drafting of the Clause. That seems to me to be an absolutely natural,
simple and straightforward way of approaching the matter.

   The right hon. Gentleman has met these proposals with a dead weight of
resistance, in an uncompromising spirit. He has received the requests addressed to him
with a dull and stern negation. If he had wished to meet the Committee in any way, to
meet those who have put this new Clause on the Paper, he could quite easily have said,
"I cannot accept it in this form, but I will engage to give a relief which will not be less
than £7,000,000 a year to productive industry, and before the Report stage is reached
I will place on the Paper a Clause which will embody this purpose in terms which are

acceptable to the Administration and in harmony with the requirements of the Statute." The right hon. Gentleman has not chosen to do that. He meets us with a steady "No." In those circumstances, while I agree entirely with the right hon. Member for Carnarvon Boroughs, and while we have not the slightest desire to relieve the Government from a single hour of the agony and humiliation that they are condemned increasingly to suffer, nevertheless, if Parliament is to take part in the shaping of legislation, it is inevitable that when proposals are put forward which commend themselves to large numbers of Members, those Members should not shrink from giving their vote in accordance with their honest opinion.

[Later] The Financial Secretary to the Treasury is an apt imitator of his chief. He learns his lessons with sprightly ease, and he has not been long in presenting us with the proofs of his training. What have we at this moment? Another of those disagreeable legacies, and the Chancellor and the Financial Secretary continue to obstruct with a resistance which is sometimes backed by a wealth of argument, and at other times finds no stronger support than the kind of speech to which we have just listened from the hon. Gentleman. The hon. Gentleman says that in the five Budgets that I presented I did not alter the principles of valuation in regard to landed property. That is quite true, but if he will study the records of the Treasury, he will find that I made something like this proposal at the same time that I proposed to deal with the evasion of Death Duties. I thought that the evasion of Death Duties should be stopped, and we have assisted the Government to stop it in this Bill— [*Interruption.*] Well, the Government have accepted the Amendments which we have proposed. They got themselves into a hopeless muddle, and, in spite of all the assistance which they received from the permanent officials, their own brains were not so well addressed to the subject as to enable intelligible Clauses to be presented, and we therefore came to their aid.

At the time when the late Government proposed, in 1928, to prevent the evasion of Death Duties by Clauses which would have the same intention as those of the right hon. Gentleman, but which would have been more carefully drafted, I proposed to my colleagues in the Cabinet that we should relieve agricultural estates from what is undoubtedly a grossly unfair incidence of taxation. Why has there been this attempt to evade the Death Duties? It is because the taxation upon this class of property is grossly unfair. Here you get an immense capital drain or draft upon an estate, which might come at frequent intervals, and you calculate its value on a basis which in no way corresponds to the commercial value. What is all this talk about placing the burden upon the shoulders which can bear it? What is all this talk about the principle of the ability to pay? You have an estate which produces, we still say, £1,000 a year, and it is valued at twice or three times the capital value which would produce £1,000 a year. Why is this excessive and inflated value imposed on these estates? It is because from all parts of the world, and from all parts of the country, the new rich, the profiteering class, come and force up the price of these old homes of England, and exploit the amenity value because they are anxious to seat themselves in the baronial chairs, or to invite their friends to sit in the halls which have enshrined many generations of those who have played a recognisable part in the history of the country.

Why should you market that? Why should you make a son ransom his own home in these commercial times against the bid of all and sundry coming from all parts of the world? Let him pay on what he receives; let him pay to the full without evasion his share of the national expenses from the actual funds and revenue of which he has the enjoyment. To compel him to ransom the amenity value of his own home in the open market in this modern, confused, disorganised world, where so many true values have been destroyed, and where the power of money asserts itself with more naked force every year—why should we compel him to do that? It is a gross injustice. Of course, the Socialists, who wish to level everything, who regard the glorious history of the past as if it were merely a series of disgraceful chronicles of pillage and exploitation, who wish to cut themselves adrift from the continuity of our history and the traditions of British life, to start a new life, like the Soviet Government, on an entirely different basis of ethics, of politics, of economics and of history—from their point of view one can understand that they view with great satisfaction the installation in an English country home of some prosperous pork butcher from Chicago, or some gentleman who, instead of serving his country in the War, piled up a great fortune by the rapid inflation of capital, or by the successful promotion of enterprises of doubtful soundness. These are the heroes whom they wish to ensconce in houses which undoubtedly are honourably interwoven with the history of our country.

I make this appeal on the broadest lines. Nothing is more remarkable than the rapidity with which the new democracy is squandering the treasure and the Empire created by generations of the aristocracy and oligarchy. It was said in the days of the great Lord Chatham that you had to get up very early in the morning to know when there was a new victory; but now you have to get up very early in the morning to know what promise has been given away, what great interest has been squandered, and what great security of the nation has been destroyed. From your own point of view, surely you should tax the money; you should not tax the non-material values. I am only suggesting that there should be applied to landed property the principles conceded by all parties to heirlooms, pictures, works of art and so forth. It is true that we have framed our new Clause to apply generally to all estates, whether passing by sale or succession. If the Government wish to meet us, and if they wish to limit it to estates passing by succession, we should regard that as a satisfactory settlement of this matter. If a man sells his home, he shows that he is regarding it upon a commercial basis, and he should be taxed upon that basis, amenity value as well. If, however, he only wishes to live where his family has lived for generations, it is monstrous that the actual benefit which he enjoys should be overloaded by an enormous super-added weight of amenity value, which is largely arbitrary in its estimate, and to the fixing of which an element of predatory snobbishness undoubtedly enters.

I have a word or two to say to the Financial Secretary and his friends about this. I have no doubt that they are all looking eagerly for their holidays, and will be very glad when the House of Commons, to the existence of which they owe their political positions, will have released them from its somewhat sharp talons; when they can have some breathing space before we begin our conflicts in the autumn. I, too, am anxious to have some rest, and so are my friends on this side, but we have not devoted all this time and attention to the Budget without the intention of obtaining some definite results. An hour or two ago we tried to obtain some results by the use of the weapon of a Parliamentary majority, but, unhappily, that was not entirely at our disposal. The right hon. Gentleman has no particular reason to sleep soundly in his bed o' nights as a consequence of anything that may have occurred to-day. That issue hangs over the Chancellor of the Exchequer until the Report stage of this Measure has been passed. With regard to this Clause it is quite true that we have not at our disposal the weapon of a majority, nor the possibility of acquiring such a weapon. I quite agree that the Government can vote us down, can treat us as they have treated us on other remonstrances we have addressed to them, with lofty disdain.

Mr. March: We had four years of it.

The Under-Secretary of State for Scotland (Mr. Johnston): Why did you not do this when you were in office?

Mr. Churchill: I have explained that it was linked up with another proposal and as I could not put forward the one I left out the other—entirely because of the pressure of time and the amount of work there was upon us. We had very heavy Budgets in those days. We had great constructive schemes, like the Widows' Pensions scheme and the De-rating Bill. We did not send round for a Treasury Clerk and ask him, "How much do we get with 6d. on the Income Tax and 1s. on the Super-tax?" and then take another £20,000,000 out of Death Duties. We did not make up our Budgets in half-an-hour and on a half-sheet of note-paper, as this botched and mis-shapen production was drawn up. We took trouble in those days, and that is why our Budgets were so heavy—loaded, densely packed with carefully thought-out well-intentioned, beneficial—

The Deputy-Chairman: The right hon. Gentleman is making a Third Reading speech.

Mr. Churchill: I was only responding, perhaps at somewhat too great length, to a rather provocative and to me personally wounding interruption. However, I leave that point, mindful of your remarks, and say to the hon. Gentleman that if he gives us no consideration upon this Clause he will not accelerate the course of business. Of course I, like him, am entirely dependent upon the support of others, and with this hot weather, and holiday time approaching, I do not know whether I shall find the same active and ardent assistance as has hitherto been forthcoming on the Budget; but if we are to be treated with absolute scorn, then I will make it my business, if I can get anyone to stand by me, to examine in meticulous fashion the whole process of the Budget during the Report stage. The hon. Gentleman might just as well address himself to this proposition. I warned his chief a week ago that he would run grave risks, would lead his party into grave risks, if he did not attempt in some way or other to meet the wish of the House on the question of giving relief to industry from its present burdens. It is open to him to alter this Clause if he chooses, and to say that he will give the relief only when estates pass upon succession; and unless he does something of that kind he will pay in tears and beads of perspiration, in laborious days and protracted nights, for an obstinacy not founded on any real necessity of the State but arising largely from the temperamental manifestation of the none-too expansive nature of the Chancellor of the Exchequer.

LABOUR GOVERNMENT POLICIES

July 16, 1930

Buckhurst Hill

[Extract] ... I have snatched myself away from an exciting and important debate in the House of Commons in order to come and tell you a little how things are going, and I will return to cast my vote of censure against the Socialist Government.

Nothing goes right in this Government. There has never been a period of so much depression and anxiety that I can recollect. I recognize that there has been a great wave of world depression, and no matter what Government had been in power there would inevitably be hard times. But what I say is that this Socialist Government being placed in power at this juncture, by their very presence, not less than by their actions, has aggravated the whole economic position of this country, and through the economic position has aggravated the general trade situation throughout the world. If you wish to put things right the first step is to throw out of office an unworthy Government which obtained power by making promises not only which they could not perform, but which they have never even attempted to perform.

... But for the fact that the [Egyptian] nationalists would not accept an agreement which the Socialist Government tried to make with them Cairo would have been left ungarrisoned. What has happened in Egypt now? Alexandria has been the scene of a bloody riot, and 16 or 17 people were killed yesterday and 200 or 300 injured. But for the fact that the British troops have not been removed from Cairo, but for the fact that we still have the power to prevent disorder and discharge our obligations to foreign countries to maintain order, as we have promised to do, you would at this moment have something like civil war or revolution raging in Egypt with blood flowing in streams and foreign colonies in that country demanding that England should do her duty or stand out of the way or let some more resolute power fulfil an indispensable function.

In India, things were much better when the Conservative Party left office. The words Dominion status have done nothing but evil. They have led politicians of India to nourish hopes which, I am sure, bad though things are, will not be realized. They have led them to make demands which a year ago they would never have dared to present. The Indian position has been most gravely aggravated by the events of the past year, and we are by no means at the end of our troubles. On the contrary, you must expect the Indian problem will become increasingly serious and grave not only in this country as a controversial matter, but in India itself.

What are we going to do to take hold of our affairs and advance effectually the banner of Britain and her Empire? Certainly we must be united here at home. We cannot afford to quarrel, we cannot afford the luxury of particularist opinion, we have to pool our opinions. We have to ask that at the forthcoming Imperial Conference no reasonable proposal that can be found to offer promises of mutual advantage to

Britain and her Dominions should be excluded from mutual and sincere consideration at the Imperial Conference. To-day we have been refused even that. Mr. Snowden, by a speech of blistering and rigid refusal, has done his best to sabotage all prospects of a satisfactory and fruitful result of the labours of the Imperial Conference.

[Editor's Note: Replying to a question as to his opinion on food taxes, Churchill said] : My opinions on food taxes are those of the Conservative Party, the official opinion and views of the Conservative Party, that we should convene a conference of the Dominions, and that we should discuss freely with them all questions of mutual advantage, and that we should not exclude from that conference the sincere discussion of any taxes which may be found to be beneficial. That is the position which Mr. Baldwin has taken up, and that is the answer which I give to the question.

FINANCE BILL

July 17, 1930

House of Commons

I beg to move, "That the Clause be read a Second time."

I do not observe the right hon. Gentleman the Member for Carnarvon Boroughs (Mr. Lloyd George) in his place on this occasion. I had hoped that he would have been present again to support by his powerful and picturesque oratory the important proposal contained in this new Clause. It may not have escaped your notice, Mr. Deputy Speaker, that a considerable amount of excitement was caused when this matter came before the House on the last occasion, and the proposal received a remarkable measure of support on this side of the House—in fact one may say that it very nearly commanded a majority of the present House of Commons. The Chancellor of the Exchequer, when speaking upon this proposal on that occasion, held out hopes to the right hon. Gentleman the Member for Carnarvon Boroughs that he would consider some proposal based on the lines of this new Clause although expressed in a different way. The principle of this proposal is that we should endeavour to give the strongest encouragement to industry by relieving it of the heavy burdens which press upon it to-day, and which have such a disastrous effect upon employment.

I was very much impressed with the argument used by the right hon. Gentleman the Member for Carnarvon Boroughs when he pointed out how many experiments were being tried to relieve unemployment, and how large sums of money were being disbursed with that object without much chance of success. The right hon. Gentleman pointed out that the assent of the majority of the Liberal party had been obtained for such a proposal as that contained in this new Clause. I know there were some formidable dissentients, but I think I may claim that this proposal had the assent of 65 per cent. of the Members sitting on the Liberal benches, which, I think, is an unprecedented measure of assent. The right hon. Gentleman the Member for Carnarvon Boroughs also pointed out that if the expenditure of this money did not produce the proportionate amount of new employment claimed for it, no money would be spent at all, and there would be no loss to the Exchequer. Therefore, this proposal is as reasonable as it could possibly be made. On these benches, on the last occasion when this subject was considered, we followed the lead of the Liberal party in view of the careful study which it has given to financial matters of all kinds. We have learned something of their diligence and their high authority from the many Yellow Books and other coloured books which they have prepared, and which from time to time they have used to illuminate public discussions on these matters. [*Interruption.*] There is no reason why any hon. Member should object to that. On the contrary I think he ought to be delighted that any contributions to the solution of this problem by the Liberal party should gain such a wide measure of support.

We took the plan of the Liberal party and supported it. We relied on their authority, and on the earnestness and diligence with which they studied this subject. I want to know whether the Chancellor of the Exchequer is going in any way to defer to the speech made by the right hon. Gentleman the Member for Carnarvon Boroughs and his arguments, and whether he is going to defer to the strong expression of opinion in the House which was, in fact, so strong that it almost effected the translation of the Chancellor of the Exchequer to a position of greater freedom and less responsibility. I do not know whether the right hon. Gentleman is going to defer in any way to that expression of opinion. It may be that the right hon. Gentleman does not feel that he is in any danger this afternoon, and that he is on this occasion under no obligation to the Liberal party. But perhaps the Chancellor of the Exchequer will say

"Ease would retract vows made in pain;
As violent and void."

The Chancellor of the Exchequer may not feel disposed to pay any attention to his words, but he told the party below the Gangway that he had the same object at heart as that which was contained in their Amendment, and he hoped to be able to find words, probably couched in different language, to give effect to it. At any rate, in moving this Clause, I offer the Chancellor of the Exchequer, in the first place, an opportunity of letting us know where he stands with regard to this proposal, and what value we are now to attach to the assurances which, I think with a somewhat wry face, but nevertheless quite unequivocally, he gave to the right hon. Gentleman the Member for Carnarvon Boroughs in the hope of averting his ire.

That is the first reason why I felt it to be my duty to put down this Clause. The second was that I thought that it would be a very great pity if a matter which has excited so much interest, and which was the result of so much careful thought and study by the Liberal party, should, as it were, slip aside from our discussions unnoticed, and not be brought forward with all proper formality upon the Report stage. I watched for some days, and studied the Order Paper each morning with anxious care, to see which Members of the Liberal party would set this Clause down on the Paper, and what support it would receive from them. But when, yesterday, some of my hon. Friends who take an interest in this matter drew my attention to the fact that, although the days, and even the hours, were slipping by, towards the time when the Report stage must inevitably be taken, the Order Paper was blank in respect of this important proposal, upon which, as I have said, the Government were almost hurled from power, and upon which within two of a majority of this House have already expressed a favourable opinion, I felt it to be my duty to step into the breach and to place this Clause upon the Paper, in order to enable the party below the Gangway once again to show that, whatever may have been said or done here or outdoors, there are at any rate some important topics upon which the Gangway is narrower than the Floor.

I make no sort of reproach, I say candidly, to the Liberal party on this subject, I should never think of reproaching those whose votes I am anxious to obtain in the Division Lobby; and, therefore, I am in no way commenting upon their neglect to place this Clause on the Paper. Indeed, I know that they have had quite a lot to think about lately, and have been very busy on one thing and another, and doubt this was an oversight. I have repaired the oversight. I have not only enabled them to renew their support of this proposal, but I have given an opportunity to the Chancellor of the Exchequer to make concessions which will, perhaps, reunite the House of Commons on a matter on which it was so acutely and narrowly divided.

As to the merits of the proposal, there really can be very little doubt that to spend the sum of money which this Clause would involve upon increasing and improving the plant of all our great productive works throughout the country would be an incomparably more fruitful and more prudent employment of our limited resources than any of those other schemes upon which millions are being poured out. Still more would it be an improvement upon that immense outflow of public money which has already ruined the Unemployment Insurance Fund, and for which further immense demands are to be made upon us to-morrow. For these reasons—firstly, the merits of the proposal; secondly, to afford an opportunity to the Chancellor of the Exchequer of making a concession; and, thirdly, to express my gratitude and regard for the Liberal party for the care which they have taken in illuminating our discussions on this subject, and the stout-hearted manner in which they have testified to their conviction in the Lobby—I desire, with great respect, to move this Clause.

NAVY ESTIMATES

July 21, 1930

House of Commons

I do not rise for the purpose of continuing the debate at this stage, but only to ask you, Mr. Young, in what way our voting to-day can be arranged so as to give effect to the true opinion of the Committee in its various aspects? The hon. and gallant Gentleman who has moved a reduction has done so because he thinks that the First Lord of the Admiralty is making too great a provision for naval expenditure. On this side of the Committee, we wish to raise the question of not only the inadequacy, but of the wrong character of the naval defence which is now being provided for. These are two separate and two diametrically opposed questions, and I would ask your guidance as to what would be the best method of taking these two quite different decisions of the Committee. I suggest that there are two methods; one is for the discussion to be general and to run on throughout the day, both points of view finding their expression, and for us then to have two Motions for reduction voted on in quick succession, the one representing the views of the hon. and gallant Member, and the other representing the views which are held on this side of the Committee. Another way would be to bring the discussion on this particular Amendment to a close at a comparatively early stage in the proceedings, and then to call on the other Amendment from this side of the Committee.

[Later] So far as this Amendment is concerned, we shall, on this side of the Committee, not give any support to the proposal which has been made by the hon. and gallent Member for Central Hull (Lieut.-Commander Kenworthy) or those who have spoken in the same sense. Our own opinion upon the Estimates put forward by the First Lord we shall take an opportunity of expressing later on, when a reduction will be moved from this side of the Committee. The hon. and learned Member for South Nottingham (Mr. Knight) asked what was the object of the British Navy, and whether it still aimed at closing the seas to any or every other Power.

Mr. Knight: If necessary.

Mr. Churchill: If necessary. Such objects have long passed beyond the power of the British Navy. From the moment when we abandoned the claim to supremacy of the sea which we did in the Washington Conference of 1921, all such ideas, obviously, have ceased to operate in our affairs. It is not the closing of sea routes to others, but to keep them open for the safe arrival of our own daily bread, that the British Navy exists for, and that is the only object for which it exists at the present time. Our sincere anxiety is that even this limited and vital purpose is not in fact within the compass of the British Navy upon the proposals and forecasts for which this Government have become responsible.

The hon. and gallant Member for Central Hull made a long speech to show how enormous and excessive our naval armaments were, but the great feature of the last 15 years, the great feature since pre-War times, has been the immense diminution of British naval power. There has never been such a voluntary contraction in the relative naval power of any great country. Look where you will. Compare the ratio of the United States and the British Navies in 1914 with the ratio that will exist when this Treaty has come into operation. Compare the position of the British Navy in relation to Japan in 1914 with what exists to-day. Japan, a Power with which we have always had excellent relations, is by treaty authorised to build within three cruisers of all that is permitted, not only to these islands, but to the British Empire as a whole, with our world-wide responsibilities and with the task confided to us of preserving the cohesion and the security of peoples spread across the whole of the globe and comprising more than a fifth of the entire human race.

Take the position of the British Navy in relation to France in the narrow seas. Here I must admit that the problem is a very difficult one. There are only three great naval Powers with battle fleets which are, as you may describe them, oceanic Powers— Great Britain, the United States and Japan. These battle fleets are already in a state of arrest, of stagnation, and, according to many highly competent persons, are passing increasingly into the sphere of obsolescence. A great many authorities hold that the day will come, at no great distance, when naval strength will not be expressed in terms of battle fleets and that air power and other causes will tend to throw these hitherto primary elements of naval power increasingly into the background. It is also to be remembered that the only three Powers that possess battle fleets live at opposite ends of the world, separated by enormous ocean distances from each other—[An Hon. Member: "And cannot get at one another"]—and cannot get at one another without the aggressors running the risk of moving across thousands of miles of sea, and consequently these battle fleets, which constitute so large a proportion of our permitted naval strength and of our valid naval expenditure, are increasingly passing out of the practical sphere. But meanwhile other Powers not concerned with the development of these battle fleets, not concerned to compete in that arena, are rapidly increasing all the other classes of vessels, the cruisers, the submarines and the flotillas which in the most direct manner—far more directly than in the case of battle fleets—menace that very daily bread which is the sole concern for which the British Navy exists.

I said in the course of an earlier debate this Session that we have disarmed so much more vigorously and sincerely and effectively than any other nation that we were reduced to a position more defenceless than any that we had occupied since the reign of King Charles II. The right hon. Gentleman very naturally turned the argument against me by asking who was responsible for that. I should explain that I meant, so far as the Navy is concerned, when the provisions of the proposed new Treaty had been carried out. At present the British Navy is not in that position, but when the provisions of this Treaty have been carried out, when the great increases prescribed in every other country have been made effective and our own position has been restricted by the Treaty, it will be true of the Navy that we shall not have any effectual guarantee either that we can bring in our food supplies across the ocean in the face of the cruisers of other Powers or that we can bring them through the narrow waters in the face of the flotillas of the European Powers. As far as the rest of the assertion is concerned, the Army is almost reduced to a police force and the Air Force is only half the strength of that of our nearest neighbour. Never since the reign of King Charles II has this country been so completely dependent upon the good will—which I trust will not be denied—of other Powers, not only in the distant oceans of the world, but also in the narrow seas that wash our very shores. Yet we have listened to speech after speech from the benches opposite as if this country was the aggressor, as if we were the Power which more than any other was spurring on naval competition, as if we were the Power which, above all others, was responsible for the great expenditure on naval armaments which has so unhappily characterised the beginning of the present century. So much for the accusation that we are an aggressive and expanding naval Power.

I am anxious to examine a little more closely the White Paper that the First Lord has circulated. Questions have been asked in this debate of great importance. I take first of all the question of the flotillas. I read the paragraph at the bottom of page 4 as a perfectly clear, plain admission on behalf of the Admiralty that the proper con- struction of flotillas under the Treaty would require 110,000 tons before 31st December, 1936. If it does not mean that, what does it mean? What is the use of drafting this paragraph in this way—every word most carefully calculated—if in fact the

110,000 tons are not to be constructed but only, as the hon. Gentleman pointed out, about two-thirds of that amount? The Financial Secretary to the Admiralty declared that not two flotillas a year would be constructed but only one each year. I am sure anyone who read this White Paper would have been extremely surprised to hear that statement. Obviously this paragraph has been drafted with the intention of giving the impression of a greater naval construction than the Government intend, and thus of allaying doubts and anxieties in the country on the subject of the flotillas. The only other alternative is that the Board of Admiralty and the First Lord together have drafted this paragraph but, owing to the pressure developed even this afternoon below the Gangway on the Government side, it has been thought better to reduce the programme by a third. Perhaps the First Lord will tell us exactly what was the purpose of this paragraph and what the policy of the flotillas should, in his opinion, be.

Let me remind the Committee of a speech delivered in another place by a naval authority of the highest eminence, Lord Beatty—a most remarkable speech, a speech of great moderation, a speech of sobriety and temper, which deserves all the more attention because Lord Beatty has only once or twice in a great many years offered his opinions to the public. I am quoting from views which he has made public not only in another place but also by letters to the public newspapers. I am not solely referring to discussions which have taken place elsewhere. He said:

> The destroyer is the antidote of the submarine. What is the situation to-day? Not only are we restricted but other countries are free. France will have double the number of submarines that we have got, she can build any number of destroyers and flotilla leaders of any size that she likes, whereas we are restricted not only in numbers and in size but in equipment, with the result that in 1923, in flotilla leaders, France will possess 24 of from 2,200 to 2,500 tons, armed with 5.5 inch guns, whereas we shall have only 16 of 1,500 tons with 4.7 inch guns.

That is a very remarkable fact and, if that is true, does it not make very much more serious the statement that the Government are not only not going to build up to the limits prescribed by the Treaty in flotillas but that they are going to reduce the flotilla construction by practically a third? The right hon. Gentleman and his party have very often shown a disposition to be not unduly favourable to our French neighbours. I do not wish to press it in any direct or invidious manner but, in an earlier debate this Session, the First Lord himself spoke in the sense of the importance of reducing French land armaments and generally speaking it cannot be said that His Majesty's Government at present enjoy any special measure of good will in relationship with France. Are they really wise at this moment so to reduce our construction of flotillas and of anti-submarine craft, as well as accepting a so much lower ratio of submarines, that unquestionably when this Treaty has been completed and its provisions carried out we shall be inferior in the narrow seas in submarines and in anti-submarine vessels to our nearest neighbour?

I turn to the question of cruisers. The right hon. Gentleman is proposing to us to build three cruisers. They are to be six-inch gun cruisers. I regret very much that this country, which has little money for naval defence and has to spend what money it has to the best possible advantage, should be prevented from building vessels equal in fighting strength to the contemporary ships that are being laid down in the dockyards of other Powers. There is no comparison whatever between an eight-inch gun cruiser and a six-inch gun cruiser. I suppose that an eight-inch gun cruiser would defeat two or three six-inch gun cruisers or destroy them one by one with the greatest ease. These cruisers are very costly. These six-inch gun cruisers cost, it is pointed out, £1,500,000, or something like that. The right hon. Gentleman admits that they are costly, but perhaps he tries to reassure his pacifist friends by telling them that although the vessels are very costly, nevertheless they are comparatively harmless.

I regret extremely that we should not be in a position to use our limited funds to the best advantage without at all prescribing what are the exact types that should be built. I am sure that this construction of a large number of six-inch gun cruisers over a period of years at a time when other Powers will be building eight-inch gun cruisers, and when France and Italy are free to make a large construction of eight-inch gun cruisers, is unthrifty, infrugal and most injudicious from the point of view of spending the money available for naval defence in the best possible way.

The fact is that we have so tied our hands by treaty engagements and obligations that we no longer have the power to study the British naval problem in its integrity and on its merits. We have to build, not the fleet we require, but conventional fleets: fleets which are prescribed by treaty conditions, and not fleets which would originate from an unprejudiced and expert study of our actual dangers and our actual resources. A great deal of our naval funds is used for our battle fleets, which, probably, will play a very small part in any future combat. On the other hand, we are crippled by this reduction in our total tonnage and expenditure; we are crippled by this reduction in respect of all these vital routes upon which our food supply depends.

The whole policy of these naval agreements has been deeply detrimental to the interests of Great Britain. It has been more detrimental to our interest than any paper statement would show. We have fettered our freedom of construction, and we have lost our originality and initiative in design. We have condemned ourselves to very heavy continuous expenditure year after year because—let there be no delusion—these Estimates and this White Paper do not indicate the slightest relief in naval expenditure. On the contrary, I should have said, looking at the new construction programme outlined in the White Paper, that we must look forward to an increase in Naval Estimates next year and the year after. Yes, a substantial increase as Vote 8 begins to swell under these cruiser programmes. We are not getting any relief from heavy expenditure; all that we are doing is to spend this money in an artificial and conventional manner in a way in which nobody would dream of adopting if we were free to study our own problem in our own way.

Finally, we have done all this without either gaining any credit as a Power for making great concessions in disarmament. We are still held up, especially in our own country, as a State keeping the world in unrest by its naval expense. We have gained nothing there, nor have we made any gain in goodwill between the naval Powers. On the contrary, it is my belief that these negotiations out of which this Vote 8 has originated and this Vote itself are an element, a prominent feature in a process which has enormously advertised and aggravated naval strength and naval rivalries, and which at every stage, not only now but as the years pass by, will foment and refresh a continued stream of international ill-will. If you look abroad, I am certain that on the continent of Europe, but for all these discussions whose fruits are now represented in this Vote, you would have a far easier situation between France and Italy than exists at the present time. As for the United States, our friends, our most closely associated nation, whose Navy will in future be measured meticulously year after year against the British Fleet, year after year as the enormous increase of American shipbuilding becomes necessary—as prescribed by the Treaty, the greatest expansion that any Power has ever made in recent times—and as the heavy burden of Estimates rises more and more, ill-will and criticism will be directed towards this country which we shall be told is, by its armaments, the cause which provokes the United States to undertake the heavy burden and sacrifice. Look where you will, there is not one single redeeming feature in these Naval agreements.

This Vote 8 with its enormous cost, with its extraordinarily misapplied resources, with its inadequacy as far as our real problem is concerned, is a crowning proof of the errors into which we have been led. It is not yet too late. Let us regain our liberty. Let us regain the freedom, to construct the types of vessels we need, and to delay that construction or accelerate it entirely in relation to our own peculiar difficulties and dangers. Let us tell the United States frankly and freely that we are not thinking of building against them; that we proportion our Navy and design our ships in relation to European and Asiatic dangers, and that when we have fixed our programme, we cordially invite the United States to build to equality in those programmes, and to place whatever interpretation upon equality their experts advise them.

I have ventured to address the First Lord upon these matters, but I hope that he is going to clear up the question of the flotillas and the cruisers. I hope that he will address himself particularly to our relation with France in the narrow seas after this Treaty is completed, and I hope that he will, even at this hour, be able to hold out to us some hope that the Government will desist from their fatal policy of hampering British naval construction and forcing us to build a Navy adapted to the Treaty and Paper conventions, but, for all its cost, incapable of rendering us the vital security we need.

PUBLIC WORKS LOANS BILL

July 23, 1930

House of Commons

I do not intend to continue this discussion, especially as the speech we have just listened to from the right hon. Member for Darwen (Sir H. Samuel) has, to a very large extent expressed what I believe to be the general view on these benches. It is our intention in the Division to support the Government in the attitude that they have adopted. I take this further opportunity of congratulating the Chancellor of the Exchequer upon the firmness and determination with which he has repulsed one of the most spiteful and venomous procedures against an individual which I have ever seen in this House. When we look back upon the disaster of the labour troubles of three years ago and all the wrong things said and done, including words in all sorts of quarters, when we remember that leniency has been shown even to men who placed stones on the railway lines, I am astounded that those who have the gravest need to seek oblivion and to plead that bygones should be bygones should have given us the exhibition to which we have been treated to-night.

[Later] What an extraordinary situation! The Chancellor of the Exchequer has admitted and confessed to the House that the Government had taken no real trouble to search up the antecedents of these gentlemen who are now to be added to the Commissioners. The Chancellor of the Exchequer has presented those names, including the name of a gentleman who has apparently served a long term of imprisonment, without even being aware of the facts. [*Interruption.*]

Mr. Marley: On a point of Order.

The Chairman: The hon. Gentleman must allow the right hon. Gentleman to proceed. I will call him to order if he is out of order.

Mr. Buchanan: On a point of Order, may I ask whether an hon. Member is entitled from his seat in the House, to shout another hon. Member's name across the floor repeatedly and offensively?

The Chairman: I will deal with the hon. Member if he is out of order. It is not confined to one side of the House. I did not hear any name mentioned.

Mr. Churchill: Perhaps I may be allowed to develop my argument. We have listened to a good many views from the other side of the House. It is clear that these names have not been examined from the point of view of the merits of the individuals and the work they have to do, nor from the point of view of commanding public confidence or adding to the weight and authority of the Board, when we find that a member is appointed who has a record for striking at the interests of this country during the crisis of the War. We are not now dealing with mere words, however ill conceived or ill conditioned. We are dealing with actions that have been the subject of proceedings before the proper tribunals and punished at law, and for the Chancellor of the Exchequer to come down to this House ignorant of a matter of this kind, which was common knowledge as soon as the names appeared on the Order paper, shows that he has not given proper attention to the real merits of the case.

We know perfectly well why this proposal has been brought forward; it was a desperate attempt by the Government to stave off the anger of their own supporters below the gangway. When the Measure was first brought before the House there was no idea of adding these names. It was only when anger was expressed at the appointment of Lord Hunsdon that the Government sought to find a line of least resistance, not by excluding Lord Hunsdon, but by throwing in additional names to dilute, as it were, the hostility. None of these names would have been put forward at all if the Financial Secretary to the Treasury had done his duty the other day, and had not, in the most cowardly manner, moved the adjournment of the debate. He has had an example from his chief of Parliamentary duty as discharged by a Minister. But the

Chancellor of the Exchequer should not be content simply with flouting his own supporters; he should discharge his duty by examining the character and antecedents of the men whose names are submitted to the House of Commons for inclusion in public bodies of this important character [*Interruption*]. I shall not take much longer if I am not interrupted, although it would be quite easy to dilate on this subject. This proposal is purely political in its character and is not made to improve the Committee. It is an attempt to placate the wrath of the miners' members and other Socialists. Why does the Chancellor of the Exchequer wish to do it now? He has carried his division and we have supported him. Why should we add these further names to a Committee already as large as has been found necessary for its work? As far as we are concerned, we will have nothing to do with this weak and dishonest expedient, nor take any part in placing on a public board at this time a man who has to his record a criminal conviction for malicious injury to this country in time of war.

[Later] I rise to a point of Order for the purpose of asking you whether, in the event of the hon. and gallant Member for Central Hull (Lieut.-Commander Kenworthy) embarking upon the escapades of a particular vessel in the Great War, it will also be in order for hon. Members on this side of the Committee to deal with incidents— [*Interruption*] —if necessary to rebut the statement of the hon. and gallant Member. I submit to you that if these extremely interesting topics are raised on one side of the Committee, they shall be raised on this side.

[Later] Is that your intention, Mr. Young, to put the four names together so that we have to challenge them together?

The Chairman *indicated assent.*

Mr. Churchill: In that case, we shall vote against these names, not in relation to any particular individual, but because we consider they are brought forward by the Government not to improve the character of this Committee but from political reasons. On those grounds we shall give our vote.

FINANCE BILL

July 25, 1930

House of Commons

I gather that it will be for the convenience of the House if I rise at this moment to express on behalf of the Opposition our final words upon the Budget of the right hon. Gentleman. When I knew that this task would fall to me, I took a last look round over the course of our long debates and over the wide field which this Budget, like every other Budget, opens to us, but I am bound to admit and, indeed, to confess, that some considerable reflection left me unable to find very much new that could be said in condemnation of the policy of the right hon. Gentleman. But when I came here this morning I listened to a speech from the right hon. Member for Camborne (Mr. Leif Jones), which gave an entirely new orientation to my thoughts. The right hon. Member for Camborne urged me and those who sit on this side of the House to congratulate the Chancellor of the Exchequer upon the achievements which the conception and the conduct of this Budget represent. I find that a much more fertile field, and if the House will permit me I will endeavour to couch all my remarks in a laudatory vein. Looking round for matters upon which I might pay my tribute to the Chancellor of the Exchequer, let me, first of all, congratulate him on the skill, the tact and the patience with which he has conducted the Budget debates.

I must admit that at first I was a little puzzled by his methods. I could not see why, at the beginning of so complicated a Bill with so many Clauses, he should, as it were, deliberately seek to offend the House; why he should use the Closure in the first few hours of our Committee discussions; why he should throughout the discussions refuse all concessions on merits to his opponents; and why he should seek to go out of his way to pick quarrels now here and now there. Gradually, however, we saw his deep design. The right hon. Gentleman wished to kill a great mass of foolish social legislation. He wished to sweep from the path of the Government such embarrassing and dangerous items as a Trade Dispute Bill and a Bill for the raising of the school age. This purpose became apparent to us as our debates continued, and the moment we saw what the right hon. Gentleman had in his mind we endeavoured to collaborate with him, and as a result we have, I believe, taken three times as long to discuss the present Budget as was required to discuss the very extensive proposals which formed the subject of Budgets of the last few years: and with this further result, that the whole Socialist programme of the Session has been cast aside, and jettisoned, and all those Bills from which the future regeneration of mankind was to be expected, have to be subject to the massacre of the innocents, the only survival being the dear Coal Bill, now, I suppose, the dear Coal Act, which is to keep the home fires burning in the winter. I congratulate the Chancellor of the Exchequer upon his strategy.

The right hon. Gentleman the Member for Camborne wishes me to praise him for his economy. I have found some difficulty with the best will in the world to find a foundation of fact upon which I may rest such an eulogy. After all, the Chancellor of the Exchequer is responsible as a member of the Cabinet for the demoralisation of our insurance system by abolishing the provision which required people to prove that they are genuinely seeking work before receiving the bounty of the State; and he has on more than one occasion needlessly increased the expenditure of the Government by giving a more extended bonus to civil servants in proportion to the cost of living than the scale in this country, which already far exceeds the scale of any other country in Europe, warranted. Therefore, I found some difficulty in responding to the appeal of the right hon. Member for Camborne to praise the Chancellor of the Exchequer for his economy. But I must admit that almost equally important with the expenditure he has contracted under these two heads, in defiance of economy, is the relief which he has secured to the Exchequer by effectively destroying the School Leaving Age (Extension) Bill through and protracted debates upon the Budget and by concentrating upon himself and his Measure such a large proportion of Parliamentary time. I am able to go this far with the right hon. Member in praising the Chancellor of the Exchequer for economy.

Evidently this was a very profound design on the part of the Chancellor of the Exchequer, and in order to carry it into effect it was necessary for him to repress and hold in strict control all the natural amiability of his nature. I am sorry to say that, from a very good motive, in the cause of economy, and in the cause of preventing foolish legislation, he had very often to show us, as it were, the rougher side of his character and he had sometimes to disguise himself as a spiteful, irritated harridan. He has also had to do a thing which I should have thought any Chancellor of the Exchequer would have found extremely repugnant—he has had to present deliberately ill-drafted Clauses on highly technical matters to the House, thus occupying whole days and even weeks of Parliamentary time which could easily have been saved with a little forethought, application, and perspicacity in the Department over which he presides. I recognise the sacrifice, moral and sentimental, in his failure to adopt these rules and methods, and made for a good end, an end which we have achieved in common.

In the second place, I must congratulate him upon his chivalry. I had occasion to speak nearly a year ago, before the Budget was introduced, at the beginning of our financial disputes, of that tolerance and fairness which is enjoined by the great Lord Bacon in regard to the actions of predecessors upon Ministers attaining office. But the right hon. Gentleman has defended my reputation in a manner for which I shall ever be grateful. For one likes to think one's work is appreciated. When one has held an office so difficult and harassing, so surely surrounded with hostile criticisms and so certain to be attended with disagreeable results in one quarter or another—when one has held an office like that of the Chancellor of the Exchequer for nearly five years, one likes to feel that one's work is not wholly condemned. But I must admit that a year ago there were a lot of ignorant, short-sighted and prejudiced people in this country who took quite an unfavourable view of my financial achievements.

It is the right hon. Gentleman who has defended me from these aspersions, and he has defended me not by mere words, but he has defended me by actions, which are stronger than words. I feel very much better about it all now. I can go about and meet people who a year and a-half ago were rather inclined to shake their heads, because in trying to save industry from heavy indirect taxation I employed expedients and devices, legitimate but still unusual, and by using windfalls and discovering hidden resources tried to smooth our financial passage in order that we might recover from the disasters of the great strike without reimposing heavy taxation. [Hon. Members: "Hear, hear!"] That cheer I perhaps should not have received a year ago. It is a proof of how effective the advocacy of the Chancellor of the Exchequer has been in re-establishing the reputation of his predecessor, and for that also I pay him my tribute.

I must also congratulate the Chancellor of the Exchequer upon his impartiality. He has not sought to ingratiate himself with any one section of this House. He has distributed his blessings with even-handed equity on all sides. No one has been left out. There is no Member of the House, wherever he may sit, in whatever quarter of the House, who can really feel himself forgotten. Even those who do not like the right hon. Gentleman, and there are some I am sorry to say, though I hope to change their opinion before I have finished—even those who do not like the right hon. Gentleman very much, would be bound to admit that he has been just as rude to his supporters as he has been to his opponents. The same genial smile which plays upon Mayfair and Throgmorton Street also cheers the would-be workers of the Clyde. The same honeyed tones which restored harmony to Europe at The Hague will presently greet the Dominion representatives when they arrive. This, Mr. Speaker, shows an even disposition which deserves admiration on the part of the House.

Lastly, I must congratulate the right hon. Gentleman upon his great admirer and supporter the right hon. Gentleman the Member for Camborne. What a mellifluous smile would broaden upon the saintly countenance of Mr. Cobden, if only he could see these twin Victorian dodos caressing each other, encouraging each other across the Floor of the House, pledging each other, as it were, in libations of cold water. "Direct taxation" says the Chancellor of the Exchequer "is a stimulus to industry." "Make it a shilling," says the right hon. Gentleman the Member for Camborne. "I doubt if 6d. on the Income Tax is enough; better make it a shilling while you are about it." And so, from side to side, this happy agreement advances from stage to stage. I could not help thinking to myself that if only they added Lord Hunsdon to their triumvirate we should then have what the Prime Minister has called a Council of State, which would really embody all that was most archaic in the three parties. I will venture now in the very few moments during which I will trespass further upon the time of the House, to carry my tribute into a still wider sphere.

The right hon. Gentleman said, quite modestly, some time ago, that it would take him two years to put the finances of this country into thoroughly good order. Well, Sir, we have had one year and we may, I think, take stock of the position at this stage—the Third Reading of the Finance Bill. If I may use a phrase which the Chairman of Committees has heard on more than one occasion, we may "report progress and ask leave to sit again." It must be a great pleasure to the Chancellor of the Exchequer to see the fruits of his labours already becoming apparent in so many directions. Look where you will. Look at the rate of expenditure, rising in the dead level total, rising steadily and swiftly with almost every decision that is taken. Look at the dividends which are being paid by the railway companies and the great industries of this country. Look at the change which has taken place in the values of securities, particularly the industrial securities, upon which the employment of the great manual labouring masses depends. Look at the rate of unemployment. All these reveal the touch of a master hand. We see this great country swiftly responding to Socialist inspiration. Look with great particularity at some of the specific decisions which have ministered to this general recovery. Look very briefly at the Debt policy, the austere, unflinching, orthodox, courageous Debt policy of the Chancellor of the Exchequer: Danton—"No weakness"! If his predecessors may have erred, he will repair the error and correct the fault. He will pay back to the Sinking Fund the £15,000,000 deficit of the last year, even if he has to go round the corner and borrow it.

Look at the great discovery which he has contributed to our finance. He has discovered that you can raise the main proportion of the revenue of this country by taxing the idle rich. That has given great confidence to our mercantile and industrial classes, who felt that they were not going to be heavily burdened in the matter because the right hon. Gentleman has discovered this great truth and possibility; and I must say, for the mercantile and industrial classes, that they seem to be responding to the stimulus which has been given. Take the McKenna Duties and the other duties of a protective character which are now in force. There the right hon. Gentleman has made a manly stand for Budget secrecy. There has been no weakness there. He has thought it necessary to emphasise Budget secrecy to the highest possible point by first of all threatening all these industries with having the conditions under which they carry on fundamentally deranged, and then, in spite of all the clamour which was raised, firmly adhering to his policy of keeping them perpetually in suspense.

Last of all, we had, in the week that has just closed, the Chancellor of the Exchequer's contribution to the success of the forthcoming Imperial Conference. Everyone is looking forward with expectation and anxiety or with hope to that momentous meeting. After all, the Dominion Prime Ministers, busy men in their own countries, travel across vast distances of ocean and land to reach these shores; they only come here once in four years, and I think the Chancellor of the Exchequer was quite right to give them the assurance that at any rate in one quarter a warm welcome awaited them. Then there is the right hon. Gentlemen's policy of diminishing the reserves available for productive industry. There again I am trying, I must say, all through, in response to the appeal made by the right hon. Member of Camborne to put the most favourable construction upon the Chancellor's actions. Of course, these reserves are a source of great preoccupation to companies and to productive businesses. They go on, they accumulate, they gather, and each year, or may be at intervals in a year, the boards of management have to decide whether they will keep them in hand for a rainy day, whether they will use them to replenish their plant, or whether they will make a new issue of dividends or bonuses to their shareholders. The right hon. Gentleman solved all their problems; he put an end to their anxieties; they have not got to worry about it at all. He has taken all the money!

I leave the past, and I leave the present, which we are now enjoying, but what of the future? Here, at any rate, we start fair. There is great confidence in what an hon. Member who spoke earlier in the debate, in his enthusiasm, called "our glorious Yorkshire Chancellor," will do in his next Budget. We know his policy. It is perfectly plain. His policy is to lay the whole burden of taxation upon a limited class. The right hon. Member for Camborne credited me with having been a fidgety Chancellor. There is nothing fidgety about this. Put it on, put it up and keep it there. The right hon. Gentleman has invested the whole of our Income Tax system with an air of permanence and stability. He has shown people quite plainly what they should reckon on. It is a great thing for them to know where they are. It is a great thing for any business to know that there is one feature, at any rate, amid the many uncertainties of life, that is sure and certain. Enterprise and initiative require firm foundations now. They know, at any rate, that their burdens are not going to be reduced in any way. They have an assurance in that respect for the future upon which they can build, or not build, as the case may be.

Then there are the unemployed. They know very broadly what the outlook is for them. They know that nothing is going to disturb them, to find them work, for instance, to revive general industry, to replenish our plant, to stimulate enterprise. They need not worry themselves about that. They are not going to be disturbed by any new-fangled notions of that kind. No, Sir, the policy of the Chancellor is the dole in its integrity and universality. The dole, the whole dole and nothing but the dole. There is the constructive unemployment policy, and these men now know the system on which they may organise their lives, their homes, their marriages and holidays. There is nothing fidgety or disturbing about this aspect of the Chancellor's policy—restful, and sure and calm, and during the winter which is coming on—grim winter—we shall be considering, like we were last year, the prospects of next year's Budget. Industry and trade will be wondering whether the Chancellor of the Exchequer will have further blessings in store for them, if he should be in a position to bestow them, and they will look forward to the next Budget, knowing well the principles on which it will be framed, and knowing by experience the consequences which will follow from the application of those principles. In that spirit, and in those circumstances, British industry may face the future if not without anxiety, at least without ill-founded hope.

EGYPT

July 29, 1930

House of Commons

After the extremely important and deeply agitating matters which have engaged the House for the last two hours, it may require an effort of special concentration for the Committee to contract their attention to such a topic as the state of affairs in Egypt. Nearly 600 persons were killed and wounded in the streets of Cairo and Alexandria during the last fortnight. The riots which took place led to a great destruction of property. A virtual state of siege has been proclaimed in Cairo by the Government. The British troops have been held in readiness, strictly confined within their barracks. British ships have hastened across the Mediterranean; the *Queen Elizabeth* is at Alexandria, the *Ramilles* at Port Said, and another vessel at Suez. The state of the foreign communities has been such as to cause the greatest anxiety, and has led to complaints by them to their Governments, with severe censure of His Majesty's Government in almost all the newspapers of Europe. That is the state of affairs in Egypt to-day.

Is it not providential that the British troops had not in fact been withdrawn from Cairo before this situation developed? Imagine that the treaty which it was vainly sought to negotiate had come into operation and full fruition, and that you had had the events which took place in Alexandria 10 days ago, with the expectation of far greater commotion in Cairo itself—imagine such a situation occurring and there being no British ships nearer than the Canal. Obviously the Government would have had to give orders for the troops to march from the Canal to Cairo, or for Lord Thomson's armoured cars to be sent to Cairo, at the same time as the Socialist Government were compelled to order the battleships of the Mediterranean Fleet to appear off the different Egyptian ports.

That is the situation which has now been disclosed in Egypt. Let me ask the Committee to contrast it with the position a year ago. A year ago Egypt was tranquil. There had been great trouble four years before, but the country had been reduced to tranquillity and there was a complete calm. A foreigner could walk about the streets of

Cairo by day or night as safely as he could walk about London. Nothing could exceed
the tranquillity of Egypt a year ago. But I quite admit that there was one important
circumstance in the condition of Egypt a year ago which could not possibly be left
where it was. It was impossible to allow Egypt to continue in a condition in which all
the work of a Parliamentary assembly was suspended. It was clearly necessary for the
Egyptian Government and the Egyptian authorities, or their British friends and
advisers, to co-operate by every means in their power to reconstruct and revive suitable
institutions which would enable a legislative assembly to be called into being to act as
a counterpoise and corrective to the powers of the Court and afford adequate
expression for the wishes and will of the people. That was a task which clearly lay
before the Egyptian Government and before His Majesty's Government a year ago.

For that task they were well circumstanced by the tranquillity which prevailed
in the country. They were also well circumstanced by the fact that, both Mahmud
Pasha, the then Prime Minister and the then High Commissioner, Lord Lloyd, were
anxiously and hopefully looking forward to the construction of those constitutional
institutions which would have the effect of providing a proper and adequate foundation for Egyptian Government, and one much broader and more capable of progress
than either the present dispensation or a pure protectorate such as has existed in the
past. That was the position then—tranquillity and the possibility of constructive work.
I have described what the situation has been reduced to to-day. We ask the Government how has this great change from peace and the hope of progress to the present
riot and certainty of increasing strife, been brought about in the course of a single
year? Who is responsible for it? What is the responsibility of the Government for it,
and what are the particular acts which have led to this degeneration in the state of
affairs?

Let me retell the tale to the Committee. A year ago, almost to a day, His
Majesty's Government laid their hands strongly and vehemently upon Egyptian affairs.
They procured—they provoked—the resignation of the then High Commissioner. They
procured that resignation in such a way as to cause the maximum of disturbance in
Egypt and throughout the East; in such a way as to give the greatest possible
encouragement to subversive forces and forces antagonistic to the Anglo-Egyptian
connection. They procured that resignation in such a way as to strip Lord Lloyd's
successor of almost every vestige of that influence so precious to Great Britain in the
conduct of her affairs with Egypt. That was the first step. The next step was to
inaugurate negotiations with the Egyptian Government with the object of reaching a
treaty, the main purpose of which was to be the evacuation of Cairo and Alexandria
by British troops, and the withdrawal of those troops to the Sudan and the Canal. This
step, I must explain, overlapped the dismissal of the High Commissioner. Before the
High Commissioner was provoked into resignation, if I may use that expression,
negotiations were far advanced between the Foreign Secretary and Mahmud Pasha,
who was visiting England on other matters; and although we were assured a year ago
that those negotiations were then only at their first, initiatory stage, as a matter of fact
a few weeks later we were confronted with a draft agreement which obviously had
been arrived at a considerable time before.

Mahmud Pasha took the draft agreement. He had not expected to negotiate such
a treaty, but, being well received, being, as the Government described him, "a most

reasonable man," finding himself agreeably entertained by the Government, the negotiations prospered and he took the draft agreement back to Egypt. Not until he reached Paris did His Majesty's Government open to him the full intention of their policy. When in Paris he was informed that the agreement must be ratified by an Egyptian Parliament elected upon a basis of manhood suffrage. If I am asked to specify this disastrous step of the Government which has produced such evil conditions in Egypt, that is the step which I select. From it all these evils have flown and from it, I predict, a long series of evils and embarrassments will continue to flow.

This was a grave interference in the internal affairs of Egypt and it was a mad interference. The election of a Parliament on manhood suffrage in Egypt! Why, even in this powerful country, with generations of prescription and tradition behind it—this country which even now preserves the strong remains of a well-knit political structure—our affairs have not prospered with the wide extensions of the franchise which have been given. But to pretend that the peasants of the Nile Valley, the fellaheens, the slaves of centuries, the slaves of yesterday—aye and, but for the British influence, the slaves of to-morrow—to pretend that the Egyptian fellaheens, 92 per cent., or it is even said 95 per cent. of whom are illiterate, and therefore unable to have the protection of the ballot, could be made the electoral foundation of representative institutions similar to those which exist in Germany, France, Great Britain and the United States, is the veriest farce and the most contemptible casting aside of the duty of mental effort of which it is possible to conceive. It is so easy to say, "Have a general election on a universal franchise and let things rip." That was the contribution which was presented to Mahmud Pasha when he left these shores and arrived in Paris.

I need scarcely say that this decision in the first place destroyed altogether any prospects of negotiating a reasonable treaty. In the next place it destroyed the tranquillity of Egypt, and it destroyed, there and then, Mahmud Pasha, "the reasonable man," the man whom the Government had used so intimately to bring a treaty forward once again between Great Britain and Egypt. The broken instrument was cast aside. Mahmud Pasha did not even take the trouble to make an attempt at carrying on. As soon as he got back to Egypt he asked that a successor should be appointed and disappeared. A stop-gap Government was brought in under Adley Pasha to provide for the installation, after a general election, as to the result of which there was no doubt, of the Wafd party caucus in power. The Wafd made the elections. Although not actually the Government they were obviously the great authority and power, and backed, as was believed, by the influence and good wishes of the British Government, they made the elections most effectively. No one else was allowed to stand at all. Those who voted were dragooned in accordance with the powerful machinery which this corrupt and fanatical caucus is able to employ.

Brutal violence was used where necessary, but in fact there was uncommonly little violence because it was not necessary. Not a single one of the Liberals of the moderate middle element, without which you will not build up the necessary instruments of self-government in that country, not a single one of those very representatives upon whom Lord Milner's report counted so much to serve as the foundation for a future assembly and government, dared to present himself at the poll. They were simply swept aside, and this complete destruction of all the moderate elements resulted from the decision of the Government and from their interference in

Egyptian affairs in dictating to Mahmud Pasha the character of the electoral law under which he was to hold the elections. I shall, no doubt, be told that I have said all this before. It is quite true that I am almost using the notes of a speech which I delivered nine months ago. On 23rd December, I said:

> Mahmud has gone, and now you are face to face with Nahas Pasha. . . . In a few months therefore, His Majesty's Government have annihilated all those Liberal elements in Egypt on which the Milner Report counted in an especial degree. . . . They have produced a profound degeneration in the Egyptian situation, and Egyptian society and encouraged a struggle between the Wafd and the Court the end of which cannot be predicted. Long before the five years are up events will occur which will afford evidence of the need of the British troops in Cairo. I do not know how long will be the life of His Majesty's Government but I believe that they will live long enough to reap some at least of the wrath and evil and folly that they have sown.—[Official Report, 23rd December, 1929; cols. 2008-2009, Vol. 233.]

I repeat those words without hesitation, hoping that they may receive more consideration now than they did when I first used them in the House of Commons. The Wafd came to power as a result of the elections. When they came into power they put into operation what is called the spoils system of which we heard the other day from the Treasury Bench—a vigorous spoils system. They dismissed great masses of officials and put in their own special trusted agents. The mudirs of eight or nine provinces were replaced by the sworn adherents of this secret political society. Only consider the effect of that. If the present regime, the Sidky Pasha regime, lasts in Egypt, it is inevitable that these newly appointed agents of the Wafd should be in their turn removed and replaced by other governors acting in loyal accord with the new régime. Consequently, you will have the whole provincial government administration of Egypt subjected to one disturbance after another to the cruel injury of the fellaheen population.

Negotiations were now resumed with Nahas Pasha, and, as I think, in conditions which rendered them doomed to certain failure. I tried to explain to the House of Commons in December why it was impossible to have any settlement with the Egyptian Nationalists on the basis which the Government had prescribed, and I think rightly prescribed. Although I thought that they were most foolish in offering to move our troops from Cairo, I thought they were wise in the strict attitude which they adopted on the Sudan. I ventured to point out that no Egyptian party would be able to agree sincerely to a settlement which practically excluded Egypt from the Sudan. I said then:

> To talk about conciliating Egypt and gratifying Egyptian sentiment and brushing away all causes of friction and suspicion, without conceding them at least an equal share in the administration of the Sudan, is folly. No one can pretend that these causes of dispute will be removed by anything short

of that; either you must be prepared to concede the full Egyptian claim about the Sudan, or you must be prepared to face a continued quarrel with all those forces in Egypt at whose behest we are now to evacuate Cairo.– [Official Report, 23rd December, 1929; col. 2002, Vol. 233.]

I remember being mocked by some of those who are sitting now upon those benches, though there were more hon. Members there then; I suppose that they are outside discussing the agitating events of this afternoon. I remember being mocked when I pointed out that you would not get a settlement with Egypt on the basis which the Government–quite properly, in my opinion–adopted in regard to the Sudan. You will not get an Egyptian Government which will take the responsibility for cutting the connection to such a large extent between Egypt and its southern province for which such immense sacrifices have been made by Egypt in the past. What follows? The negotiations failed. I think that it is creditable to the Wafd leaders and Nahas Pasha that they acted in a straightforward manner, and that they did not simply take the agreement for what it was worth, and then proceed to use it to get more. Anyone could have told you beforehand that these negotiations, for the sake of which such disturbances were made, were foredoomed to be wrecked on that point, provided that the representatives of the Egyptian Government acted with sincerity, which they did. The Treaty was rejected, so that the whole elaborate process, the costly process of getting rid of Lord Lloyd, of negotiating with Mahmud and the betrayal–I can use no other word–of Mahmud, of the interference with the electoral law in Egypt by the Egyptian Government on the direction of the British Government–

The Prime Minister: Who interfered?

Mr. Churchill: The right hon. Gentleman interfered by directing that there should be a reference of the Treaty to Parliament elected without a change in the electoral law. The installation of Adly Pasha and his caretaker Government in power, the installation of the Wafd in power, the resumed negotiations, the sittings up day and night and the goings on that were heard of in the Foreign Office–for the whole of this elaborate and wearisome pilgrimage the Government had nothing whatever to show. In the end they had nothing to show for nine months of disquieting intervention and interference in the course of Egyptian affairs. But though the Government had nothing to show, the consequences of their action remained. We see them now–two live autocracies facing one another in Egypt. There is an oriental court entrenched by the practical necessities of law and order, facing a corrupt and fanatical caucus which is armed with a Parliament falsely professing to represent some definite expression of the wishes and interests of the people. That is the situation which His Majesty's Government have managed to create. They have segregated Egyptian politics into two extreme categories. It is marvellous how so much mischief could have been scientifically produced. They have segregated and divided Egypt into its two most extreme aspects, and now, having got them at the opposite corners of the ring as it were, His Majesty's Government declare absolute impartiality– like in the general strike, when we were asked to adopt absolute impartiality between the fire and the fire brigade.

They have declared absolute impartiality, but it is not a passive impartiality. The Government are backing both sides. They sent their warships to Alexandria and other ports, to encourage the Government. They made a declaration that the electoral law with its manhood suffrage basis is not to be altered, in order to encourage the Opposition. Both are given their fair, even-handed support. What is it you are doing in Egypt? Is it a prize fight which you are promoting on the brilliantly illuminated stage of Cairo? Is it a fight in which you want to make sure that both sides have an absolutely even chance and are capable of realising the utmost combativeness which is in them, and that there is no danger of a premature termination of the fight or no risk of the spectators complaining that they have not been adequately entertained? Is that the policy? If not, what is it? Is it a scenario of a film that you are making upon the banks of the Nile of Charles I and Oliver Cromwell in an Egyptian setting? Is that what you are doing? Such a spectacle has never been presented to the Chancelleries of Europe as the spectacle of the Government, having first of all created these opposing forces and cleared the arena for their conflict, making quite sure that each shall be kept in the highest possible condition and furnished with all that is necessary to carry that conflict to the most severe and hard-found-out conclusion.

I warn the Government that we are not by any means at the end; we are only at the beginning of this conflict. They have started the conflict, and one cannot tell what form it will take before it is finished. We are told that there should be no interference with the internal affairs of Egypt. The interference has been incessant. There has been interference at every point, and in a manner calculated to promote strife, to foment strife and to protract strife, and the result is that, needlessly and wantonly, Egypt has been cast into confusion and disorder. The Prime Minister and his colleagues have found that it is impossible to disentangle Great Britain from Egyptian affairs. You cannot withdraw to the Canal and to the Sudan, and shrug your shoulders and allow matters to take what course they will in the intervening areas. You cannot possibly do it. British influence must be used to guide and aid Egypt. His Majesty's Government have been forced to interfere. Why have they been forced to interfere? Just because their influence has fallen so low. They have lowered their influence of their representatives in Egypt, and they have lowered the influence which this Parliament, by a consistent policy, has exercised over Egypt, to a point to which it has never fallen since we were concerned with the affairs of that country.

When influence is gone interference emerges—naked, blind and crude. Interference in the shape of the movements of ships and the influence of troops is what the Government have been forced to rely upon. We have to restore British influence. It is a plant of slow growth. It is very difficult to cultivate. You struck it a fatal blow a year ago when, in a rough and almost insulting manner, you struck the High Commissioner from his position—[*Laughter.*] The hon. Gentleman laughs, but we are paying for it. It may be laughable to the hon. Gentleman, but we and all those who are living in Egypt are paying the price of this action. Six hundred casualties in a fortnight, volleys of musketry firing into the crowd and bullets piercing one human body after another are not things to laugh at. We may be wrong in our view of the remedy, and the Government of course may be right, but, at any rate, these are matters which Parliament ought to discuss. I am no party with those who say that the House of Commons should not discuss these grave matters affecting the oriental interests and policies of the Crown. We have to restore our influence, and to use an influence weighty, because it is not unsupported; an influence discreet, because it deals with matters in the early stages; an influence faithful, because it has no other object but the well-being and tranquillity of the country.

We have to restore that influence so that we can make one side concede and another forbear. We have to try to recreate the conditions which were so laboriously and slowly gathered together in the four years preceding the change of Government, and which were so wantonly squandered on the morrow of the accession to power of the party opposite. It is no use waiting until life has been lost and until foreign residents are in danger and appeal for help to their Governments, and when the British Government come in with force of arms, as they have been forced to do on this occasion. It is no use doing that. In our relations with Egypt we must try and make a good job of it, and make things work out well for the general interest of the country, and we must work behind the scenes with all the influence we can towards the achievement of such ends. We must pursue our policy so as to bend the boughs while they are still twigs. All that has been cast aside. We are now back to 1922. The 1922 Declaration specifically provides for the welfare of Egypt, that is to say, of its people, being one of the first steps we must take into consideration. We cannot divest ourselves of the care for the welfare of the population.

We hold no brief for any party in Egypt, and it would be a pity if British parties were to ally themselves in such a way, but we have enduring obligations to secure that good and peaceful conditions of life and labour should come to the peasantry in whose interests we were originally drawn into the country—[*Laughter.*] Everything that Great Britain has done is a source of scorn and mockery to a certain class of citizens, but they, in turn, are held in well-deserved contempt by the overwhelming majority of the people of this country. We cannot lose confidence in our mission, either in Egypt or elsewhere in the East, to serve faithfully the interests of the mass of the population; and far better should we concentrate our attention on that than be drawn into these intricate politics and intrigues with the politically minded section of the community. The Government's policy, judged by its results, has made Egypt a worse place for every class and every race to live in than it was this time last year. They have inflamed all passions. They have complicated every difficulty. They have armed every hatred, and they leave us with a future of weakness and embarrassment, the end of which no man can foresee.

The Prime Minister: I have listened for half an hour or thereabouts to the most highly coloured and inaccurate chapter in history to which a Front Bench politician has ever given voice. . . .

Our mission in Egypt is confined now—not by us, but I think is rightly confined—to the safeguarding of four specific points, and one of those points is our responsibility for foreign life and property in Egypt. To refuse to accept that responsibility would be criminal folly. The right hon. Gentleman referred to something else which is quite inaccurate. He told us that we had had representations, official representations, that there has been a great feeling of unsettlement among foreign nations over what has happened. He has been absolutely misinformed. No such thing has taken place.

Mr. Churchill: I never said "official representation."

The Prime Minister: Really—

Mr. Churchill: The right hon. Gentleman very ingeniously restates his propositions in a form which leads them further away from their original intentions every time. I never said that the Government had had official representations. What I said was that there had been bitter complaints by the foreign community in Egypt, and that the foreign newspapers in almost every country concerned had been very scathing in their comments—or something like that.

INDIA AND EGYPT

August 20, 1930

Conservative Meeting, Minster, Thanet

Churchill had been viewing the Indian policy of the Government—supported by the official Opposition—with unease since its declaration of October 31, 1929, that the granting of Dominion Status, wholly ignored by the Simon Commission, was implicit in the Montagu-Chelmsford declaration of 1917. Churchill, in an article in the Daily Mail *on November 16, 1929, had described the proposal as "not practicable," "fantastic," and "criminally michievous." By August 1930 the gulf between his views and Baldwin's had widened considerably.*

The Times has observed that I have had an unhappy session in the House of Commons. That might well be true—(laughter)—and I propose to tell you plainly why I am unhappy. First, I am unhappy about India. The wild Pathan tribesmen have actually come out of their mountains on to the plains of India and are molesting and insulting a famous city (Peshawar), with a large garrison of British and Indian troops. Such a lamentable spectacle would have been impossible in former times. To go into the mountains to fight an Afridi is like going into the water to fight a shark; but here is the shark coming out on to the beach! Thirty years ago, when I knew something of the Indian frontier, those marauding invaders would have been destroyed or hunted back to their mountains with the heaviest losses. Yet in those days the British forces were not nearly so well armed as they are now. It would almost seem that the same spirit of defeatism in high places, which is so rapidly throwing India into chaos, has paralysed military action at Peshawar. It marks the lowest ebb yet seen of British authority in India. Those tribesmen came only because they had been led to believe that Lord Irwin's Government was clearing out of India and that rich spoils lay open to their raids. There is the sinister feature of the event.

If there is weakness at Simla there is folly at the India Office. The India Office suffered reports to be published without lucid and intelligent contradiction or explanation. Great battles, we were told by the newspapers, were raging round Peshawar. The situation, said the Government of India, was grave and critical. But later on it appeared that not a single British soldier or white officer and only six native soldiers had been killed or wounded in all these great battles and grave events. If the India Office and the Government of India had wanted to create alarm here and cause unrest throughout the East they could not have adopted a more inept and inarticulate attitude. The Peshawar episode is typical of the weakness and incapacity with which the present Government is handling Indian affairs.

Much larger issues are raised by the manner in which the Indian constitutional problem is being dealt with. The Government of India arrested and imprisoned Gandhi for criminal breaches of the law. They now permit him to hold cabinet councils with fellow-conspirators in gaol, while the great governing organism, upon whose calm strength the lives and livelihood of uncounted millions depend, wait cap in hand outside the cell door hoping to wheedle a few kind words out of their prisoner. Already, in the hopes of placating this malevolent fanatic, the Socialist Government has banished Sir John Simon from the Round Table Conference which is to be held in November. Sir John Simon is of all men the man most capable of advising and helping such a Conference. He was the head of a Commission of men of all parties set up by statute to report to Parliament upon the constitutional development of India. He and his colleagues laboured for three years at their task, and they had presented a unanimous Report, in which Conservatives, Liberals, and Labour were all joined together. To exclude Sir John Simon from the Round Table Conference at the behest of a handful of disloyal Indian politicians is a proceeding at once abject and foolish, reflecting nothing but discredit on those responsible for it, whether here or in India.

The original plan, on which all three British parties had agreed, was to send out the Simon Commission, to consider their Report in Parliament, to refer it to a Joint Committee of both Houses before whom Indian deputations could express their views, and then to pass a Bill carrying into law the Report as modified by Parliament, and to give orders to our officials and officers in India to put it strictly and firmly into effect. That was the adopted plan, and that was the constitutional procedure. But all this has now been swept aside in favour of a Round Table Conference, a sort of large lively circus in which 80 or 90 Indians, representing hundreds of races and religions, and 20 or 30 British politicians divided by an approaching General Election are to scrimmage about together on the chance of their coming to some agreement.

I wish to place on record my conviction that it is almost certain that the result of the Conference will be confusion worse confounded. I hope, indeed, it will not be disastrous. It is very wrong to encourage false hopes in the minds of the Indian political classes. They are only a handful compared to the vast Indian masses for whom we are responsible, but they are entitled to be treated with good faith and sincerity. It would be wrong to lure and coax them over here with vague phrases about Dominion status, when it is quite certain that these Indian politicians will not obtain Dominion status in their lifetime. We may not be able to win their agreement; let us make sure we do not lose their respect. In dealing with Indian problems and with earnest men it is far wiser and far safer to be blunt and plain. The Round Table Conference has no power to confer any Constitution upon India. Parliament alone can deal with that. No proposal for Dominion status would pass through, even the present House of Commons. We do not know what the next House of Commons will be like, but it seems certain that is will be less favourable to Dominion status for India than the present

Parliament. Therefore I take this opportunity of stating these facts and truths simply and straightforwardly so as to prevent, so far as a private individual can prevent, the very grave dangers and reproaches of disappointed hopes.

Let me, however, also reaffirm the inflexible resolve of Great Britain to aid the Indian people to fit themselves increasingly for the duties of self-government. Upon that course we have been embarked for many years, and we assign no limits to its ultimate fruition. But I thought the great merit of the Simon Report was in showing that our steps should be turned in a different direction from that followed in the Montagu-Chelmsford reforms. The experiment of magnifying the power of an All-India Assembly has failed. It has produced weakness and inefficiency in government, confusion in the minds of the masses, and has in no way satisfied even those political classes for whose benefit it was devised. It is in the building up of truly representative institutions in the great provinces of India, institutions which shall have their roots deep in the soil and in the life of the Indian masses, that the path of practical progress now lies. Until these local organisms have been effectively developed and are seen to be working well and giving good government and justice to the Indian people, it would be unwise in any way to increase the responsibilities of the Central Assembly—that artificial abstraction of Indian nationalism which only ignorance and folly could identify with India.

Another thing that has been making me unhappy is Egypt. The Socialist Government is eager to scuttle out of Egypt and to withdraw our troops in Cairo, where they have preserved order and made progress possible for 50 years. As this could not be immediately accomplished the Foreign Office, under Mr. Arthur Henderson, seems to be endeavouring to produce an impossible situation by continual interference in Egyptian internal affairs. One would almost think they were trying to breed a civil war in Egypt as serpents might be bred in the Zoo. There is a quarrel in Egypt between a fanatic Parliament and a despotic King. More than 600 people have been killed or wounded in the streets of Alexandria and Cairo last month. Mr. Henderson and his Foreign Office tried to be neutral and impartial by keeping the ring clear and helping both sides to fight their quarrel out to the bitter end. When the Egyptian Parliament rose against the King they sent British battleships to Alexandria and held the British troops in Cairo in readiness to put down the rebellion. As soon as order had been restored for the moment in the streets they told the Foreign Office official, whom they had made High Commissioner, to invite the leaders of the rebellion to lunch in order that they and their followers might not be downhearted. This was the first time that running with the hare and hunting with the hounds had ever been elevated into the deliberate policy of a great Power towards the people of a small country for whose well-being she had accepted an international responsibility.

I am also unhappy about the Navy. The immediately practical peril of the Naval Treaty to us is in Asia and in Europe. We have bound ourselves by a solemn endorsement to restrict out Navy while all others are increasing theirs, so that we should not be able when the treaty has been carried out to defend our trade and interests in the Far East against any hostile Asiatic Power with a modern fleet, nor bring our food supplies through the Mediterranean and the Channel in the face of the French submarines and flotillas. When the treaty has been carried out we shall be defenseless at sea so far as our food supply is concerned, and dependent upon the good will and self-restraint of foreign nations as we have never been since the days of Charles II.

I would like to see the Conservative Party absolutely united upon a programme which would rally to it a majority of the electors of Great Britain; all pulling together, putting aside personal aims or sectional views, working to gather the support of patriotic men and women in every party, and resolved above all things fearlessly and tirelessly to avert the decline and fall of the British Empire. I hope that the Imperial Conference will produce a situation which will enable a practical policy for improving the trade between the Mother Country and the Dominions to be proclaimed by all of us with one voice. It would be wrong for loyal friends to quarrel among themselves. It would be foolish not to wait till the facts are made plain before taking decisions. Then you will soon see this wretched Socialist Government driven from office. Confidence will be restored in Britain and spread from Britain round the world. Industry will be stimulated by a tariff. Agriculture will be aided by a guarantee. The dole will be purged of abusers and imposture; and we shall bear our part in a general revival of national and Imperial strength. (Cheers.)

CONSERVATIVE POLICY

September 6, 1930

*Unionist Association Meeting,
Dumbartonshire, Scotland*

The difficulties of all modern Governments are very great. People expect them to solve economic and social problems which have never yet been solved in human history. When the electors were disappointed they said: "Turn the Government out and give someone else a chance." That seemed all right 18 months ago, but what happened when the newcomers proved to be far less successful than the old? Some impatient people say: "Let us get rid of all the politicians, especially the ones who have any experience, and let us have new methods and new men." We should make a great mistake if we exchanged Parliamentary Government for newspaper government. (Cheers.) The newspapers play a most important part in our modern life, but when they step outside their proper province—a wide and ample province of purveying news and interesting reading, and providing fair organs of public opinion and a forum for free discussion—when they attempt to dominate the State; when they unfairly bias and weight the news they print; when they suppress as far as possible all opinions but their own; when they traduce or belittle all public men who do not show themselves subservient to their will; when they finance and run candidates and confuse elections and split votes; when they dictate policy to party leaders, and even demand the right to choose ministers of the Crown—then they come an abuse which is dangerous to the Constitution and fatal to good government. (Loud cheers.)

The most unpopular Minister of any Government is usually the Chancellor of the Exchequer. (Laughter.) Very fierce fires are playing now upon Mr. Snowden. But the Conservative attack is not the real danger to which Mr. Snowden is exposed. His danger is the combination, ever growing more intimate, between the wild schemes of Mr. Lloyd George and the extreme and violent forces represented by Mr. Maxton and Sir Oswald Mosley. (Cheers.) This combination is now demanding from him new and immense borrowing in the hopes of curing unemployment, and there is no doubt that a large majority of his own party are in sympathy with that demand. A rumour ran round the City last week that Mr. Snowden had resigned. Immediately all gilt-edged stocks rose in value. What a change from last year, when thousands of people met him at Victoria Station and the City of London magnates lavished upon him their highest compliments and honour! It has not taken long to wear the gilt off this gingerbread statesman.

The expulsion of Mr. Snowden and his replacement by, say, Sir Oswald Mosley to carry out the Lloyd George policy of a vast loan for the unemployed to build roads would not effect any permanent cure for unemployment and would be deeply injurious to all our credit and finance. (Cheers.) It would hamper trade and enterprise and delay the revival of industry. Unless the currency is inflated, State borrowing will not create new employment. It will only transfer existing credit and employment from private industry to the State, and the State would probably not use the credit as fruitfully as private enterprise. I thought the London financiers precipitate and short-sighted a year ago when they showered the highest honour upon an unproved Chancellor. They would be more short-sighted still if they now imagine their interests will be served by getting rid of him for Mr. Lloyd George's wild schemes. (Cheers.)

It is almost certain that Mr. Snowden's Budget, in spite of 50 millions additional direct taxation, will end in a deficit. The limits of direct taxation have been reached. Raising the rate of direct taxation further will not raise the yield. There is a measure of common agreement in all parties that a tariff for revenue upon foreign imported manufactured goods is bound to come. Such a tariff will provide the foundation upon which the prevention of dumping and the powers of trade negotiation with foreign countries can best be arranged. It will give that psychological stimulus to British industry which is essential if the advantages of modern mass production are to be gained. The Conservative Party go into action united upon such a policy. (Loud cheers.)

Some of our friends think that the question of food taxes to unite the Empire ought to be made the main and almost the sole issue upon which the Conservative Party will appeal to the country at the next election. I do not agree. I think the first object should be to turn out this wretched Socialist minority Government which is hampering business and enterprise and breeding unemployment at home, and is rapidly liquidating many of our most important interests abroad. That is the practical and immediate issue which I consider far outweighs all others. That is why I have tried to keep out of all divisions and disputes inside our ranks and have done what I can in the House of Commons and on the platform to fight the common foe. (Cheers.) But there are other great questions which are just as important and have as great a claim upon the loyal endeavour of the Conservative Party. The maintenance of our naval security and of the food supply routes across the oceans is vital to our life and existence. Our interest and responsibilities in Egypt and, above all, our position in India are also of the highest importance. It would be a terrible mistake, and even a failure of duty, for patriotic men and women to lose interest in these tremendous matters and to make the question of food taxation the sole test between friends and foes.

Moreover, the Imperial Conference of all our Dominions is now about to open. Such a gathering of responsible heads of the British Empire, drawn together across immense distances of land and ocean, can only be held every three or four years. I am sorry indeed that the present Socialist Government have the charge of that conference, but even they will not be able to prevent our Conservative point of view from being brought to the notice of the Dominion representatives. It is more than possible that the deliberations of this conference will create a situation upon which the Conservative Party will be able to take united action at the forthcoming election. (Cheers.) That, at any rate, is my belief.

The government of India has imprisoned Gandhi for more than a month, and they have been sitting outside his cell door begging him for favors, begging him to help them out of their difficulties. Now we learn, without surprise, that he rejects their appeals. He will not help them at all. On the contrary, he dictates the terms from his prison, which even the meekest of all governments can't accept. So a whole month has been wasted.

But much more than time has been wasted. The authority and dignity of the government has been deeply prejudiced. The prestige of Gandhi has been enormously enhanced. If the government wishes to make a rebel powerful and rally all his supporters around him, there is one sure way to do it. It is to persecute him and supplicate him alternately.

By imprisoning him without trial the government has won for Gandhi the sympathy of millions. By supplicating him they have informed those millions how much they fear his power. In short, there could not be a more perfect plan for fanning and fomenting Gandhi's mischief and adding to his influence than that which the India Office and the government of India have pursued. If Gandhi has broken any law, he should be tried and punished, and while he is serving any sentence imposed by the courts the government ought not to negotiate with him in any manner. The only safe rule is to follow the well-marked paths of law and justice, and calmly to face the consequences of their impartial administration.

[Editor's Note: After outlining the views put forward by the European Association in Calcutta, Churchill said] : I trust that the carefully weighed opinions will not be ignored by their fellow-countrymen at home. India is the most crucial, and in some ways, the greatest, of all our problems at the present time. It may be that the line of political division in Great Britain will in the next year be drawn between those who are willing to abandon India if the Indian political classes so demand, and those who believe that we have an abiding responsibility to the masses of the Indian people and that we should discharge our mission with inexorable determination. (Cheers.)

LORD BIRKENHEAD

September 30, 1930

London

Lord Birkenhead has been my greatest friend for nearly a quarter of a century, so I cannot say very much about him now. He was the most loyal, faithful, valiant friend any man could have, and a wise, learned, delightful companion. He would not, I think, have wished to live except in his full health and vigour. All who knew him well will mourn him and miss him often. But even more is our country the poorer. These are the times when he is needed most. His deeply founded sagacity, his keen, courageous mind, his experience and understanding, his massive system of conclusions, his intellectual independence, his knowledge of all grave issues now pending, make his death at this moment a national impoverishment. His happy, brilliant, generous, warm-hearted life is closed. It has closed in years when he might have made his greatest contribution to the fortunes of the England he loved so well.

THE POLITICAL SITUATION

October 27, 1930

Epping

[Extract] ... The time has come when all the existing duties—safeguarding, McKenna, and key industries—imposed at different times for different reasons, should be regularized and fitted into the structure of a general tariff on all foreign imported manufactured goods. Such a tariff has now become necessary for revenue purposes. We have reached the limits of direct taxation. The rate of duty would vary according to the character of the goods, finished goods receiving the highest rate of duty, and primary manufactures or semi-raw materials the lowest rate. Mr. Snowden, no doubt, will say: "If revenue is your object you ought to put on a countervailing Excise duty equal to the Customs duty in each case." But I have been told that our social services and superior conditions of labour constituted already a tax on industry which in comparison with the rest of Europe might well be computed at between 10 per cent. and 15 per cent. If that is so a tariff averaging a similar percentage would only equalize conditions between Brutish and foreign producers and could not be accused of sheltering inefficiency. Having come to the conclusion that this measure is necessary, I am all for carrying it out in a resolute and effective manner. The imposition of such a tariff would be the occasion and the signal for a resettlement of our fiscal relations with foreign countries. When a country like Great Britain, one of the world's greatest economic factors, made after many years so extensive a change in its fiscal system, then would be the opportunity for making new and more favourable bargains, and for insisting and securing to ourselves a favourable discrimination in the tariffs of our Crown Colonies. Although I do not agree with Lord Beaverbrook in a great deal of what he does, I agree with him that the whole of our commercial relationships with the Crown Colonies and Protectorates must be placed on a new footing. Lastly, the new general tariff on foreign manufactures would, of course, in accordance with the decisions of the Imperial Conference of 1917, be the foundation for a new series of important preferences extended freely to the self-governing Dominions.

There is a very great difference of principle between taxes on imported manufactures and taxes on imported food. The modern argument for duties on imported manufactures is that the mass production of the home market will become so much more active, and that factories will run at their best economic capacity; and that, in consequence, the cost to the consumer will not be increased and may, indeed, be decreased. That, at any rate, has been the experience in regard to many of the protective duties which I imposed while I was Chancellor of the Exchequer. But in the region of food that argument no longer applies. The difficulty of the farmers in this country, and at the present time in other countries, is that they cannot get a living at the present prices. What they seek—whether here, or in Canada and Australia—is higher prices. This makes the question of food taxes very difficult and very dangerous for the Conservative Party. The food tax issue might be so mishandled as to produce great disasters. The position of the Conservative Party in England was much stronger in the days of Mr. Joseph Chamberlain than it is now. I am looking for a great Conservative victory and a strong hand and resolute action establishing the power and strength of Britain, restoring her fibre and supremacy at home and making her will respected abroad. I want to see law and order re-established in India, our fine insurance system purged of the gross abuses which are rotting the character of our people, and I am not looking for trouble or quarrelling with anyone who is going to help in these matters. The reason why Mr. Baldwin, Mr. Neville Chamberlain, and other Conservative leaders, who are all keen protectionists, have been so very backward and sluggish in accepting a policy of taxation of food is because there are scores of constituencies in the North and Midlands of England and in Scotland whence they had been advised by their agents, by their candidates, by their members, and by their newspapers that a policy of taxing the staple foods of the people would destroy or at least imperil the chances of victory and would render the task of many of their candidates, fighting the hardest seats in the darkests districts, practically impossible.

The Conservative policy on food taxes has not yet reached its final form. The Imperial Conference is not yet over. We must not lay upon the Conservative Party a burden greater than it can bear. No single party at the present time is strong enough to carry through the immense task of Imperial economic unity. It would be no service to the British Empire—indeed it would be a grave disservice—to involve the cause of Empire unity in a common electioneering dog-fight. The only basis upon which anything lasting can be built would be a national basis. There are importations which no tariff can check. Take for instance dumping of subsidized food or manufactures at prices which have no relation to the economic conditions in the country of origin. Such dumping, which is really an operation in restraint of trade, whether it be of

manufactures or of fruit and vegetables or wheat itself, can only be met by prohibition. No part of the Socialist attack upon the late Government was more sharply
stressed than the charges that bad trade and unemployment were due to expelling the
Bolshevist emissaries. This country had prostrated itself before the Bolshevist Government of Russia, and had shown them commercial favours and extended to them
credits denied to friendly, civilized Powers, and even to our own Dominions. Unemployment, however, has doubled. But much more than that is happening now. The
gang of Communist conspirators who are torturing the vast, dumb Russian people,
have now embarked upon a definite plot to disorganize the markets of capitalist
countries. They are dumping wheat, timber, and many minor commodities, the bulk of
which are produced by Communist slave-labour. Why are we afraid to deal with this?
All we have to do is to lay an embargo on Bolshevist products produced by slave-
labour, and when their ships arrive at our ports, to tell them to go back and feed their
own people first. Any Government worthy of the name of being British would do this,
and could do it easily, safely, instantaneously. The reason why this is not done is
because the strong, wise forces that made England and the British Empire, are now so
honeycombed with senseless quarrels and faction, artificially fomented for party
purposes, that the centre of the Empire is handed over to Socialist rule. It is to break
down that rule, to overthrow that feeble, subversive domination by uniting against it
all those forces in Britain which whenever they stand together are irresistible, that I
intend to devote all my strength. And in that mission I claim from my constituents not
only a wide measure of independence, but also their confidence, encouragement, and
untiring aid. (Cheers.)

In little more than a year disorder and disloyalty have reared their heads in
hundreds of districts in India which formerly were tranquil. Three grave mistakes were
made; the first, when the Indian Government allowed the Indian National Congress to
tear down and insult the British flag at Lahore; the second was to allow Gandhi's
campaign of civil disobedience; and the third was to negotiate with Gandhi in prison
instead of bringing him to trial and punishing him according to the law. They led to
some bloodshed and repressive measures which must be more severe because they were
not taken in time. The Round Table Conference has no power to frame a constitution
for India. That power rests alone with Parliament, both Houses of Parliament, for in
the House of Lords is the greatest accumulation of men who have acquired knowledge
of the problem of the East. When it is understood that the Conference has no power to
frame a constitution, I hope the Conference would do much to enlighten public
opinion and in presenting material on which Parliament would form its judgment.

I am not going to make any declaration on staple food taxes to-night. Our policy
changes so quickly almost from day to day that it is difficult to keep pace with all the
things one has to believe in and to which one has to be loyal. I intend to wait before
expressing any opinion until I know exactly where and on what we are finally going to
stake our fortunes at the coming election.

TARIFF QUESTION
October 28, 1930
Wanstead

[Extract] ... I think we should all be very careful not to lose our sense of proportion, because Conservatism and the Conservative cause, are much more important than any one particular point from which a party can fight. I have not concerned myself with any of these internal quarrels or disputes that are going on. I have saved my powder and shot for the common enemy. I have tried to direct the public censure against the unworthy occupants of the Treasury Bench.

Twenty million people have come into existence upon world food bought at a world price. If we had remained an agricultural country limited by what we raised from our own soil, we should never have been the mighty nation which carried the Allied cause triumphantly throughout the War, or have built up an Empire upon which the sun never sets. We have been able to build up higher real wages, higher standards of life, and a better temper and greater loyalty than you will see in any other country in Europe.

That is one side of the picture. At the same time we have to see every week the figures of more than 2,000,000 unemployed grow. Our great industries are depressed, and of course our agriculture has been sacrificed. We are all going through a state of world depression. The world depression will pass, but if England is the last country to come out of it we shall find the markets well webbed in and staked out against us.

We are finding increasing difficulty in placing the exports upon which our power to purchase overseas depends. Tariffs are raised against us in senseless progression. We find we are no longer in the position in which we flourished during the reign of Queen Victoria. The world of the twentieth century is not nearly as favourable to these islands as was the nineteenth. In almost every direction the changes that have taken place, new powers and forces that have arisen, have placed us in a less advantageous position than we formerly occupied. We were the world monopolist of coal in those days; now oil, which is hardly produced in the British Empire, had taken its place. The United States has towered up against us as well as other countries. Therefore, the fiscal question is a question of the most vital importance.

We have to fight these matters out as a party question, and the Conservative Party is entirely right in its view that the time has come when we should definitely establish a general tariff against foreign imported manufactured goods. Such a tariff would yield to us a valuable revenue and a relief to other forms of taxation, and the proceeds of that revenue or a part of it could be devoted to the necessary aid of agriculture.

Perhaps I go further than the official party programme for having reached the conclusion that a general tariff is necessary as a stimulus to industry and an aid to revenue. I should prefer to see it carried out at one stroke rather than to see it built up piecemeal by a number of safeguarding duties. In my judgment it is better to get clear of favouritism and lobbying by piecemeal treatment of the subject.

The question of food taxes is difficult and dangerous. We don't want fastened on us a burden at the next election that will prevent us from defeating Socialism. I don't think we should be led by the nose by the popular newspapers of the country. Although they circulate two or three million copies in the course of a day and people read them and see the news arranged to suit their point of view, they are only expressing the view of particular individuals. The policy that the Conservative Party is committed to is the real policy which the party wants. It is not forced upon us by pressure from outside, and not settled by newspapers who have candidates here and there in the constituencies. Even if the next election does not turn out well for us, at least our policy will not be dictated by some persons who on the morrow of our defeat will sail away on some new adventure of their own.

TARIFF QUESTION

November 2, 1930

Epping

A good many Conservatives seem willing to justify the campaign of detraction which had resulted in Mr. Baldwin's defeat at the General Election. I will, therefore, examine some of the charges.

First it is said that we had not economized but that we had increased the public expenditure. That is quite untrue. If allowance is made for the natural growth of the Post Office and the Road Fund, which are self-supporting, and for the increased provisions for the Sinking Fund and the relief given to the local rates by the Exchequer, there had been a substantial actual reduction of public expenditure during the 4-1/2 years.

Then it is asked why, when we had a large majority, we had not safeguarded every industry that stood in need of it, and in particular why had we not safeguarded steel. The answer is that the Conservative leaders during 1924 had given definite and repeated pledges against anything amounting to protection or a general tariff, and that at the election of 1924 at least a million Liberals and free traders had voted for Conservative candidates largely in consequence of these pledges. Throughout the last Parliament all questions of safeguarding had to be decided in accordance with the pledges which had been given by the Conservative leaders before I rejoined the Conservative Party. In the case of steel some of the strongest protectionists in the Cabinet held the view that it would be a breach of faith. I certainly think it would have been a gross breach of faith.

Quite apart from that, to put a protective duty on imported steel, which is the raw material of hundreds of industries, without making provision for the similar protection of those industries, would have been an act of folly. A protective duty on imported steel would fit quite naturally into a scientific general tariff, but as an isolated duty it is absurd and impracticable. Safeguarding of individual articles can perfectly well be applied to finished or nearly finished goods, but no important basic industries can be safeguarded apart from a general tariff. Once a general tariff on manufactures is established it is quite simple to protect alike the makers of British steel against foreign steel and the makers of British steel manufactures against the competition of foreign steel manufacturers. I have declared in favour of a tariff averaging between 10 per cent. and 15 per cent., ranging from 30 per cent. to 40 per cent. on finished articles down to 5 per cent. or 10 per cent. on those which have most labour to be done upon them after they enter the island. Within these limits I do not believe the tariff will be a serious impediment to our export trade. It will attract capital back to British industry, it will give a sense of security which will lead to enterprise, modern methods, and mass production; it will promote employment and give more bone and structure to the producing forces of the country.

The third charge against the late Government is that we established the widows' pensions and old-age pensions at 65 and that the country could not afford it. This great Act, for which I and Mr. Neville Chamberlain were directly responsible, will long be remembered in the social history of the British people. It proclaimed for all time the association between the Conservative Party with its wealthy elements on the one hand, and the interests of the working masses and of the weak and poor on the other. People forget altogether that this scheme is on a contributory basis, and that it also gathered up the immense expenses of the original old-age pensions at 70 and put them on a contributory basis, too. The youth of 16 entering insurance will pay every penny of what he receives or what his widow may receive. Every year the arrival of these reinforcements will shoulder the burden, and in less than 30 years the whole system will be completely self-supporting.

Actuaries are able to predict with virtual certainty what the population of this island will be 20 or 30 years ahead. It will be much the same in numbers as it is now, perhaps a little smaller. But it will contain a far larger proportion of old people, particularly old women, and a smaller proportion of adult male workers. These great insurance funds, which are now gathering in volume with every set of new contributors, are a system of State-aided and State-compelled thrift which will make provision in the fullness of time for the inevitable deterioration in the economic quality of the population. Another generation will recognize the Conservative Insurance Act, following as it did Mr. Lloyd George's health insurance, as one of the most far-sighted measures ever taken to promote the social and economic wellbeing of the British nation.

The task now is to help the producers. It is productive industry that is lagging behind. We must go to their aid. The late Government had already, by derating productive industry and by giving the heavier industries cheaper freight on the railways, taken an important step in this direction. The immense national electricity scheme of Mr. Baldwin's Government, now rapidly coming into play, will give our island as good an electric supply as that enjoyed even by the State of Illinois. There is another aid to production. But these are not enough. A direct and positive stimulus to production is needed. That can only be supplied by a tariff against foreign imports of manufactures. It is because this is the most necessary, urgent, practical step to be taken at this time in British housekeeping that I, who have been a lifelong free-trader, will not hesitate to vote for it and work for it. I hope that the arguments I will use to support it will commend themselves to millions of people who have hitherto been opposed to such a measure.

CONSTITUENCY ADDRESS
November 3, 1930

Epping

[Extract] ... The political situation is grave. The continuance in office of a minority Socialist Government, bankrupt in ideas and impotent in execution casts its blight on public confidence and enterprise. The menace of a general election with another Snowden Budget thrown in, hangs like a pall over all business plans. Every one feels that we are not giving ourselves the best chance to do the best for the country and for all its people.

This, above all others, is the time when the Conservative or Unionist Party, representing the most solid and strongest elements in the nation, ought to be united, courageous, and wise. Unhappily we are disturbed by faction and unrest. In the southern constituencies the Beaverbrook-Rothermere Press and in the northern con-stituencies the taxation of the staple foods, will impose an enormous handicap on our candidates. These evil tendencies are not getting better, they are getting worse. The kind of spectacle presented in South Paddington last week was calculated to repel rather than to attract the enormous unattached mass of voters without whose aid and sympathy no strong Government can be established. Unless the Conservative Party can lift its ideas to the national level and rise like a massive rock out of a sea of confusion, nothing but disaster lies ahead. That disaster, which I conceive may well be imminent, is that the general election, which may come at any time, shall result in no great change of parties, but shall leave us for a further and much longer spell of deadlock and uncertainty with another Parliament as futile, as hopeless, as born-tired, as spendthrift as this one.

With India looming up dark with storm and peril, with more than 2,000,000 unemployed stalking the streets, and British enterprise and manufacture at their lowest ebb, what are the measures of security and reinvigoration which the Government propose? The first is a Bill to amend the Trades Disputes Act. What is that but a Bill for more and better strikes? Every one knows that the Ministers of the Crown are not free agents in the matter. They had their orders from the trade unions, and against their better judgment, regardless of the reputation of their Government, they were forced to introduce this Bill. Further and better strikes. Could we have a more perfect measure of Socialist folly and British misfortune?

The second item is a Bill to raise the school age, involving heavy new burdens on the already exasperated ratepayers and taxpayers. The third remedy is at once the most ludicrous and the most discreditable of all. We have a magnificent system of unemployment insurance, but the Government are allowing it to become so overlaid with abuses that is is now a byword all over the world. The Government have admitted these abuses. They were so alarmed about them that they even went cap in hand to the other two parties and invited them to join a three-party inquiry to expose the evil and prescribe a cure. Just as this Committee were about to present their report the Socialist Government were warned by their masters behind the scenes that there must be no interference with this wholesale handing out of public money. So the Government dissolved the Committee, bringing all its work to nothing, and then declared that they were going to set up a Royal Commission to inquire into the whole matter over again. This Royal Commission has no other object than to burke the inquiry into the abuses of the dole, enabling the Government to go on ladling out borrowed public money for the abuses by which their friends and supporters benefit. Any responsible or respectable person who takes his seat on this blanketing and dilatory Commission is lending himself to a fraud and imposture on the public.

[Editor's Note: In conclusion Churchill advocated a general tariff on foreign imported manufactures and the protection of agriculture from dumping, and expressed the hope that these important objects would not be compromised by mishandling the question of taxes on wheat, beef, and mutton. Treaties with the Dominions must be made on a national and not on a party basis.]

BRITAIN AND INDIA

November 5, 1930

Loughton

[Extract] ... The letter of Sir John Simon which appeared in the Press yesterday addressed to Mr. Lloyd George, marks, I think, a certain movement of Liberal opinion in striking hostility and censure of the present Socialist Government, and, coupled with the resignation of the Chief Liberal Whip, it constitutes undoubtedly a milestone upon the road which leads to the Socialists' expulsion from power.

But you will remember that I told you at the last General Election that, if the Socialists were installed in office, very great misfortune would come to our country. The Socialist Government is formed of the men who engineered the general strike. The newspapers are full with great headlines about giant cucumbers and the Calcutta Sweep, and so on, but the general strike ought not to be forgotten as rapidly as those things are. What standards were you setting up for the guidance of British youth when you put those men in office, when you put into their hands the life of the people?

I do not blame the Socialists for the world depression. But I say that their presence in power has aggravated that depression, and their actions have tended to emphasize the evils in this country, to make our fall more rapid, more severe, and more profound, and are tending now to get us down and delay our recovery.

It is not only in these islands that the greatest danger lies. There is a great measure of well-being in the British nation. There is a great absence of the kind of suffering which exists not only in European countries but in America. The British people never ate better meals than yesterday except the meals they ate to-day. (Laughter and cheers.) Therefore, although I see a certain weakness in our producing power to which we must give our thought, I do not feel that it is at home that anything is going to happen immediately that will injure fatally or permanently the source of our economic strength.

Parliament has met again. I never saw such a Parliament. (Laughter.) It has only been in existence for about 18 months, but it is an old, decrepit creature hardly able to hear and attend to the arguments and feebly tottering its steps to what is no doubt a certain approaching dissolution.

The gravest question of all is our position in India, our relations with the Indian people, and our Oriental possessions generally. This great Indian problem is marching steadily towards us and will soon occupy the minds of men and women almost to the exclusion of all other topics. Do not let it be thought that the connexion of Great Britian with India is purely a sentimental connexion. India and Great Britain have immense mutual services to render to each other and blessings to bestow upon each other. For over 150 years we have been economically associated and united. India has been raised from barbarism and anarchy, her population increased by 100 million, her wealth multiplied, and a measure, at any rate, of sanitation, health, and science bestowed upon her people. Peace has been preserved throughout this vast region— almost a continent in herself—and Britain by that association has also gained trade facilities and great influence and prestige which her connexion with India implies.

Sever that partnership, destroy that union, let the relations of Great Britain and India sink to the level of those between Great Britain and China, let the condition of India fall to the anarchy and horror of China, and you will see in this island another million unemployed and a bona fide million unemployed. (Cheers.) We have felt it our mission to sustain India, to help her population in their march forward, and there would be an economic loss of life to this country if we severed our connexion with India that could hardly be computed.

I hope that we are going to take a firm and resolute view about India. In my opinion the British Government have been too far occupied with dealing with the aspirations of a comparatively small number of highly educated Hindus. But they have not concentrated sufficiently upon the well-being of the masses of the population, which it was their duty to do. There has been a loss of confidence in our mission in the East and a lack of the strong assertion of our duty, which is to guide, to govern, and to control.

Unless we are going to do that we had better give up our task altogether. Unless we are prepared to use our knowledge and our science faithfully in the interests of the masses of the Indian peoples and insist upon them receiving good government and some at least of the benefits of expanding scientific civilization, we have no right to preserve our connexion with the Indian Empire.

I hope myself that we shall not fail. There has been too much of that lack of confidence. We have seen it in Egypt, a country which we brought out from the worst forms of tyranny and oppression and which we have now allowed to fall away and decline because we are afraid to give the guidance and the help to the population which we ought to give.

INDIA

November 6, 1930

Woodford Bridge

The Congress Party refused to attend the Round Table Conference in London to discuss the future of India.

[Extract] ... We are a generation which lives on its newspapers just as the caterpillars feed on the green leaves in St. James's Park. It is not always possible to provide big headlines for the newspapers, but the first issue of real consequence to this country is its relations to India.

The great danger we have to face in regard to India is not in India itself, it is here. The nature of the relations between Britain and India depends almost entirely on the decisions taken in the minds of the British nation. There is a spirit of defeatism which, without any foundation in fact, without any real backing of circumstances, has affected a large and important element in the British Government and the governing classes in India, and which is represented here to an extent which is positively alarming among persons of consequence.

Let me explain the form this spirit takes. It says, "Unless you give the Hindus of India whatever they ask for they will make it impossible for you to carry on the administration of India." But that is not the sort of language that ought to be used to us. Supposing when the general strike broke out it was said, as indeed it was, "All the trade unions are coming out on strike to-morrow morning, the railways, the miners, the docks, and all the industries that can be controlled, unless you give up your Parliamentary rights and liberties, the Parliamentary system and Constitution grown up by centures or rugged tradition." What answer could we have given? We were not going to admit for one moment that resistance or obstruction would lead us to agree to terms which injured the strength of the institutions which protect British liberties.

However we may view these matters, I am inclined to think that it will be a long time before another general strike is tried in the British Isles. (Cheers.) Do not let us be shifted by threats or pressure from doing our duty in India. Let us make quite sure that in the situation that is developing the Conservative Party takes a clear, firm course and stands by the circumstances whatever they may be.

If the destinies and fortunes of the Indian people are handed over to the politically minded, highly educated Hindus, once they obtained power and control of India, they would reduce that country to the deepest depths of Oriental tyranny and despotism equal only to the anarchy now prevailing in China.

The Indian conference will be meeting in a few days. We have our representatives. They are few but gifted men and men of the highest patriotism. We look to them to make certain and sure that the resolve of Britain to do her duty unflinchingly to the masses of the Indian people will be fully and firmly expressed.

There is the uncertainty of a General Election which may occur at any moment, or may not occur for many months. No one knows, and it is evil for a community to live in such a state of uncertainty. You cannot make plans in advance, nor can investors risk their savings when they do not know what is coming. In addition, there is the uncertainty about the next Budget. We know the cruel, petty spite which animated Mr. Snowden in framing his last Budget and the blow he struck at national thrift and productive industry. Now we have to prepare for a second blow. Can you wonder that people are reducing their ventures in industries and trade? At a thousand board meetings every one is saying this is the time to take in sails. No one knows what gales are going to blow. There is an evil and real depression and lack of enterprise spreading throughout the whole world. There is world depression, but it is economic world depression. Here there is economic depression and also psychological, which strikes home to men's hearts and aggravates the world depression.

[Editor's Note: Churchill was questioned at some length by two or three people, including a woman who asked about the Education Bill.] I am going back to the House to-night to vote against it. Why stop at the age of 15? You may just as well keep people at school until they are 21 or 22.

HOME-GROWN FOOD

November 7, 1930

Harlow

[Extract] ... Shipley was the most important by-election since the General Election. It was the first by-election which really stripped the Socialist Government of its credentials. It was not only a vote of want of confidence in them given by their political opponents, but it marked a definite withdrawal of confidence in the Socialist Government by its Socialist supporters. They are without the title to decide the great affairs of State. If a General Election were to be fought on the issues that were debated at Shipley the Socialists would encounter a great political rebuke from the nation. They are a minority Government, and now the very special foundations of their own party have been overturned. They are no longer in a position to settle any decision on the great matters of the Imperial Conference or the still graver questions that will be discussed at the Indian Conference in a few days. They are a Government which has failed and which is recognized to have failed, not only by the country at large, but by their own dupes and their own ardent supporters of no more than 15 months ago.

[Editor's Note: Referring to food which could be grown in Great Britain, Churchill said]: There is the celebrated case of black currants. If British people want black currants they had better grow them in Britain, and if they canot grow them they had better do without them. I would exclude black currants coming into this country unless I am assured that there is a ring holding up prices. We cannot do the same thing with bacon without inflicting hardships upon the cottage homes of this country. There is not the slightest reason why we should not encourage the multiplication of pigs at guaranteed prices. We want to see every cottage in the country districts having its own pig.

Our policy is to give the farmer a definite share in the national life by guaranteeing that a certain quantity of British wheat shall be used in the British loaf every year. In addition, we propose to guarantee prices. We have not said what the price is to be, for obvious reasons, for the moment the figure was mentioned the National Farmers' Union would say, "What's the good of that?" (Laughter.) Even if it were a figure about that which the farmer is asking now, they would say, "Let us see how much we can get." I think this policy is far more advantageous than putting a duty on foreign wheat, because there is a difference of more than 20s. between the price at which British wheat can be produced and at which Canadian wheat can be brought into this country.

I would certainly prohibit the dumping of any commodities, food-stuffs or otherwise, in this country. By dumping I mean not commodities that are produced more cheaply outside the country than here, but goods that are brought into this country at prices below the cost of production, such as many of the goods that come from Russia.

GALLIPOLI

November 15, 1930

Royal Naval Division Reunion,
Crystal Palace, London

[Extract] . . . I have always been greatly touched by the fact that the officers and men of the Royal Navy Division have owed me no grudge for the part I played, sometimes a decisive part, in shaping your fortunes. As time passes, men's judgment alters about the episodes of the Great War; prejudices die, more knowledge comes to hand, matters are considered in their true proportion and perspective; and I for one am not at all afraid when I hear the names mentioned of Antwerp and Gallipoli. (Cheers.) If you read the Official British History of the War, prepared by highly competent and impartial officers, you will see that it is there stated that the prolongation of the resistance of Antwerp, while it did not save, and could not save, that city from capture, nevertheless gave the necessary time for the British Army to deploy before Ypres, and thus saved the Channel ports from speedy capture, at the very beginning of the War, by the German invader. (Cheers.)

The Royal Naval Division was a very young division in those days, and many were the deficiencies in training and equipment. You were sent to Antwerp because there was no one else to go, and your presence there was indispensable to the prolongation of the resistance of that fortress. From your journey to Antwerp, and your services there, there followed military events highly beneficial to the operations of ourselves and our Allies in France and Flanders, and possibly affecting in an appreciable degree the whole further course of the War in that theatre. Losses there were; a brigade was led into captivity; but we need none of us feel that those losses, painful though they were, were incurred without a sound military purpose or without a definite military result.

More sombre are our reflections about Gallipoli. The deeds of the Royal Naval Division upon the Peninsula have been well chronicled and will never be forgotten as long as deeds of valour and discipline are prized in the British Army or in the British Fleet. Now that we can survey that scene and its operations in retrospect, the number of persons who regard the enterprise of the Dardanelles as an error, as a blunder, are seen to be getting steadily fewer. In fact, only very ignorant or prejudiced persons, or persons who are guilty in some way or other of hampering or obstructing those operations, endeavour to argue that the forcing of the Straits of the Dardanelles was not a right strategic act in 1915; and the only way by which the horrors of the prolonged struggle on the Western Front and throughout the combatant world could have been avoided. The Royal Naval Division played their part well, and history would record that it was not their fault that an immense abridgement of slaughter and torment was not achieved for all nations, foes as well as friends. I say these words because of your kindness in receiving me and of your nobility in having preserved a sense of friendship towards me, although I condemned you to such frightful toils, perils, and sacrifices.

Keep together. Do not let the hands which are joined fall apart. Do not let those sacrifices and associations which grew in the white flame of the furnace of war burn out into cold embers in the years of peace. These are the deeds of history and of romance that have united you. They are among the greatest that have ever been performed. Whether in Gallipoli or in France the reputation of the Royal Naval Division was not inferior to that of any—even of the finest divisions of the British Army that were employed in the Great War. Keep the spirit of comradeship, of mutual aid and assistance alive in your hearts. Keep also the resolve that our country, which bore all the brunt of the Great War, should not be deprived in days and years of peace of her position in the world.

THE PRESS

November 15, 1930

Institute of Journalists Dinner,
Waldorf Hotel, London

[Extract] . . . Mr. Gwynne [the President of the Institute] is, upon the whole, one of those men who have added dignity and strength to journalism and have kept its standard high and clean. Times are difficult, and the burden of life weighs heavily upon the people of the British Empire. To whatever party we belong, we all feel harassed, anxious, and uncertain whether Britain is making the most she can of herself, but I am certain that the journalists belonging to the Institute will do their utmost to aid in the reinvigoration of our harassed and anxious state.

ECONOMIC SUB-PARLIAMENT PLAN

November 19, 1930

British Electrical and Allied Manufacturers'
Association Dinner, London

The electrical industries are in the range of the highly finished industries, and, consequently, protection for them will necessarily involve protection in every stage down to the crudest of the rawest raw material in all the constituent factors used in the finished product. I believe that there is an overwhelming current of opinion in these islands which would regard at this juncture of our national fortune and world fortunes a tariff, moderate and scientifically regulated, both for revenue and protective purposes, upon foreign-manufactured goods as a wise, salutary, and practical step. (Cheers.) We have a very peculiar situation here, because for the last six or seven years we have lived under an alternation of Socialist and Conservative Governments. When the Socialist Governments were in power profound disquiet and anxiety resulting in paralysis of enterprise, was felt throughout industry. When a Conservative Government was in power there were shocking strikes and troubles among the working men. Politically speaking, we have managed to get the worst of it both ways. We cannot afford to go on like this. We have not got enough in hand to play with. Our position is the most artificial of any community of our size that has ever existed in the world. There have been artificial States that have maintained themselves by all sorts of devices, but they have been comparatively small.

Are we taking the right steps as a nation? I am not speaking as a party politician. I ask myself, Are we really at the present time—Tory, Liberal, or Labour—actually doing as much as we can to get the best livelihood for the people of these islands? (Cries of "No.") We cannot but feel that there are other countries where a far greater grasp has been taken of the situation. What machinery is there in the State, what organization is there in the body politic, to weigh in the balance these matters with the patience and the sane focussing of the objectives which is necessary if you are to arrive at a sound conclusion? Our Parliament is the best in the world, but there is really no great difference to-day about political issues. They have really been quashed or squared. The differences which exist to-day are in regard to economic issues, and we have not got the machinery which can do justice to them. Can you imagine anything more foolish than to seek the verdict of this immense universal suffrage electorate upon whether tariffs on foreign manufactured articles should be imposed or not, or whether our treatment of the monetary problem has been right or wrong, upon how it would be best to cure or reform our incomparable social services, upon how a rigorous measure of public economy is to be attained? Our electorate has been expanded till it has far exceeded the bounds of the politically interested classes. (Cheers.) That is the source of many evils at the present time. While the gravest issue affecting our islands is the future of India, the subject in which our electorate has been most concerned has been the Dublin Sweepstake. Our livelihood is at stake. It is a matter of life and death. At this stage we ought to have proper machinery for considering the great economic issues. I do not think that party machinery is going to do the job well. If we have not got the machinery why should we not make it?

I offer a constructive suggestion, which will no doubt be received with the universal derision with which all constructive suggestions are usually met in a highly civilized and not yet unduly harassed country. It is that we should erect forthwith by statute an economic sub-Parliament to sit alongside of the political Parliament and to have very definite and real powers. The composition of this sub-Parliament should be mainly expert, but there should be a proportion of members of the political Parliament. (Cries of "No, no.") You would be foolish to cut yourself adrift from your masters. (Laughter.) The economic Parliament would be chosen by the party leaders in the proportion of the strength which they possess in the House of Commons. Such a body could be given powers quite different from those which are usually bestowed upon Royal Commissions and Committees, on which business men are so often invited to waste their time. It could be given power to send for persons and papers, and to debate in secret and vote by ballot. The present Parliamentary machine would be bound by law to submit measures to the economic Parliament for report, and in addition there would be power of initiative in the economic Parliament to frame Bills, and there would be stated occasions when the solutions, if any, provided in the economic Parliament would be introduced into the House of Commons irrespective of the Government of the day, and receive the judgment of Parliament and the nation as a whole. Thus the political Parliament would have constantly thrust upon them definite solutions or practical steps which they could adopt or reject. (Cheers.)

EDUCATION (SCHOOL ATTENDANCE) BILL

December 2, 1930

House of Commons

I heard the Chief Whip shouting to terminate this discussion, but I should like for a very few moments to draw the attention of the Committee to the somewhat awkward and serious character of the issue which has now been raised, which perhaps has been less raised than broken upon us. My right hon. Friend the Leader of the Opposition has asked leave to move that we report Progress and ask leave to sit again, and he has appealed to the responsible Minister in charge of our debate that he should accede to that request made in full formality. That is a matter of considerable consequence and should not be dismissed in idle levity or in rollicking and boisterous good humour or ill-humour. I do not think that the Leader of the Opposition has, in the course of the present Session at any rate, made such a Motion before. I think in all the circumstances, a minority Government in office, and the instabilities of the political situation being what they are, that a request of that kind seriously made ought not to be brushed aside or sullenly dismissed. I do not know whether it is the intention of hon. Gentlemen gathered upon the opposite benches to treat those who sit in this part of the House in a rough and bullying manner, but I am bound to say that during the time I have been sitting here I have hardly heard a single speech from this side that was not violently interrupted. It is in the interests of Parliamentary tradition that arbitrary action should be resisted by every measure at the command of an Opposition.

It is not my intention, however, to raise the temperature of the debate. On the contrary, it seems to me that the Government would be unwise not to consider the fact that the Leader of the Opposition was himself moved to report Progress and wise to give that respect to a party, which numbers almost as many members in this House as their own, and to their wishes in the conduct of the debate, which is customary. As has been referred to by my hon. Friend, the Government bench is ill-garnished with persons of responsibility. In the broad courtesies and decorum of the House of Commons a Motion to report Progress made by the Leader of the Opposition ought to be answered either by the Prime Minister or by a deputy-Leader of the House. Not one of those high officers is here. I hope the Minister of Education and the Chief Whip will not press this matter now. I do not believe it will facilitate their business. It is quite true we may have a very uncomfortable night. We may go on traipsing through the Lobbies and cheering our passage through them with laughter and with song, but it will not be a help to the administration at the present time nor to the progress of their business. There has not been much ill-feeling or ill-temper during the present Session.

Hon. Members: You have not been here.

Mr. Churchill: I am all the more an impartial judge. Not only do I appeal to the Government, but I request them not to ignore the serious consequences of neglecting the Motion which has been made. After all, we are not without resources, and, if ill-treatment is meted out, I for my part would gladly join with those who would carry their resistance to it to all lengths.

INDIA AND EGYPT

December 3, 1930

*Essex Provisional Division of the National
Unionist Association Luncheon, London*

[Extract] ... It is in the great external affairs of the Empire that irreparable harm is likely to be done if the present Government remain in power. Egypt has for the moment passed out of the critical stage, but at any moment the Socialist Government might resume its policy of withdrawing British troops from Cairo, where they are an effective guarantee of peace and where they are the sole means by which Britain can discharge her responsibilities. A growing sense of anxiety is felt for India. The spirit of defeatism, encouraged by the mere presence of a Socialist Government at the head of affairs, is spreading far and wide. While nothing has changed in the facts and truths of the Indian situation, great changes have taken place in superficial opinion. Some people are much too ready to suppose that our connexion with India is a matter merely of sentiment and convenience. It is indeed a matter of the most inspiring sentiment; but if, through weak policy, the condition of India is reduced to that of China—as well it might be—there will not only be a reproach of desertion from duty, but a bona fide million would be added to the figures of unemployment when the whole commercial relationship between Great Britain and India was sunk.

Looking at the position both in England and abroad we must see how important it is that the Conservative Party should be united and strong. It takes a great party to govern Great Britain and the British Empire. No clique or section can fulfil that task. Only a great party, with broad tolerance and a solidly established and widely spread organization, can afford the foundation upon which Ministers can discharge the momentous functions of the State. The Conservative Party must advance in one solid formation when the battle is joined at the next General Election.

INDIA (THE ROUND TABLE CONFERENCE)

December 11, 1930

Cannon Street Hotel, London

This was the first meeting organised by the Indian Empire Society. The Round Table Conference had ceased its open sittings, and was divided into Committees engaged in examining a Federal constitution.

We have thought it our duty to hold this meeting in order, so far as we can, to draw the attention of the country to the altogether unwarrantable change in the estimation of the facts and values of the Indian problem which has marked the last disastrous twelve months. From many quarters we hear statements that opinion in India has advanced with violent speed. Full Dominion status with the right to secede from the British Empire and responsible control of the executive Government are clamoured for by even the moderates represented at the Round Table Conference. The extremists who are, and will remain, the dominant force among the Indian political classes have in their turn moved their goal forward to absolute independence, and picture to themselves an early date when they will obtain complete control of the whole of Hindustan, when the British will be no more to them than any other European nation, when white people will be in India only upon sufference, when debts and obligations of all kinds will be repudiated and when an army of white janissaries, officered if necessary from Germany, will be hired to secure the armed ascendancy of the Hindu. All these absurd and dangerous pretensions have so far been met in speech with nothing but soft deprecatory and placatory words by the British Government in India, or at home. Vague high-sounding phrases about 'full Dominion status'; 'India a great world power' have filled the air. British-owned newspapers in India—of which there are still some—have been forced to the conclusion that Parliament will agree to anything that Indians can agree upon among themselves, provided that India remains nominally at least a part of the King's dominions. The effect of the speeches delivered during the five days' open session of the Conference has certainly been to give the impression that a vast extension of self-government is immediately contemplated and that all that remains is to settle the detail and method of the transference of powers, and to make some provision for the protection of minorities.

It has therefore become necessary, in order that this landslide of opinion should not lead to undue disappointment, that the basic facts should be restated in unmistakable terms. The British nation has we believe no intention whatever of relinquishing effectual control of Indian life and progress. The Round Table Conference now sitting has no power to frame a constitution for India. No agreement reached at the Conference will be binding in any degree, morally or legally, upon Parliament. No agreement of the Conference is necessary to authorise the framing of a new Government of India Act. The responsibility for framing such an Act will rest entirely with the British Government, and the decision upon their proposals will rest with the House of Commons and the House of Lords, which for this purpose must be considered a body of at least equal authority. Even in the present House of Commons with its Socialist minority Government, there is a substantial majority against the extension, in any period which it is profitable to consider, of anything like Dominion status. It seems certain that a new House of Commons will have come into existence before a Government of India Act can be introduced, and it is highly probable that that new House of Commons will be far more representative of the strong, patriotic elements of our country than the present. Therefore the persistent attempts to avoid stating unpalatable truths, and to shirk facing the stern facts of the situation, can only excite false hopes which may afterwards lead to strife and suffering.

So much for the facts in England! What are the facts in India? We are told that the opinion of India has changed. But the facts of India have not changed. They are immemorial. The political classes of India are a mere handful compared to the population. The Western ideas they have gathered and reproduced have no relation whatever to the life and thought of India. The vast majority can neither read nor write. There are at least seventy different races and even more numerous religions and sects in India, many of them in a state of antagonism.

> Our rule in India [said Lord Randolph Churchill] is as it were a sheet of oil spread out over and keeping free from storms a vast and profound ocean of humanity.

The withdrawal or suspension of British control means either a Hindu despotism supported by an army of European mercenaries or a renewal of those ferocious internal wars which tortured the Indian masses for thousands of years before the

British flag was hoisted in Calcutta. Left to herself, India would rapidly degenerate to the condition of China at the cost of measureless suffering among three hundred and fifty million people. I do not believe there is any responsible and independent man among the thousands in this country who are well acquainted with India, who will dispute these facts.

Yet we are told Indian opinion has changed so rapidly. India has found her soul at last. Classes, races, creeds, opposed for centuries, are now uniting in a common desire to terminate the British connection. What is the cause of this change? We certainly should not blame our Indian fellow-subjects for it. It is the weak-minded and defeatist tendency of our present politics which must bear the main responsibility. In one way or another in the last few years the impression has been spread far and wide throughout India that the British regime is coming to an end and that a new regime and authority are soon going to be erected. On the one hand, you have had the ever-mounting demands; on the other, the ever more apologetic responses.

Our defeatists eagerly point to the changed attitude of the princes, so long our faithful allies—not feudatories, but allies—joined to us by Treaties. The princes, we are told, are all now in favour of a vast change. But surely the explanation is simple! Once it is believed that British authority is about to be replaced by something new, that the Great Power which has hitherto ruled with irresistible force all over India and kept it quiet and safe from harm is about to wind up its affairs and depart, naturally, even its most loyal adherents must address themselves to a new situation, must prepare themselves for a new system. If the British Raj is to be replaced by the Gandhi Raj, the rulers of the native states must prepare themselves for a relationship with the new power at least as intimate as that which they have had with the old. The same is true of the Moslems. Why, even the representative of the depressed classes at the Round Table Conference, the representative of sixty million persons denied by the Hindu religion even the semblance of human rights, has spoken in favour of a responsible self-governing constitution. Naturally, all have to consider what will happen when we are gone or have ceased to function. Once the signal of retreat and departure has been given, all who are left behind must make terms with the new power. The next to be affected will be the Indian officials of the Civil Service, hitherto so skilful and loyal. After them will be affected that admirable police, who, amid every discouragement and in the face of every menace or temptation, have done their duty and kept order with hardly any loss of life except their own. And lastly, there will be the native army, who, when their allegiance is disowned by Great Britain, will be forced to transfer it to another centre, with consequences so horrible that we hardly care to dwell on them to-day.

The cause of all this change in Indian opinion is not a change of facts in the problem of India. It is the apparent lack of will-power and self-confidence exhibited by the representatives of Great Britain. I warn our Indian fellow-subjects and honoured friends not to be deceived by these superficial appearances. Underneath the smooth platitudes and euphemisms of Western democratic politics and all this airy Round Table talk, the actual process of governing India has been tardily but rigorously carried on. Twenty-four thousand Indian politicians or their dupes are in gaol. Everywhere disorder has been repressed. The Gandhi Movement, which measured its strength with the Government of India, has been for the moment, to a large extent, mastered, even by the most long-suffering of administrations—I thank God, with hardly any bloodshed and almost without the employment, except on the frontier, of any British troops! I invite the British nation to realise their own undoubted power of giving wise and good government to India. That power is overwhelming, until it is cast away. The shame is that our moral and intellectual guidance should not have been exerted as firmly as our material power. It is the contrast between the vague and soothing political sentiments on the one hand, and the rough, practical measures which have to be taken, and have been taken, in emergencies, on the other, which has produced a volume of avoidable punishment and suffering.

If the British Government and its servant and projection, the Government of India, had maintained a true contact with realities, three-quarters of the distress caused to the politically-minded classes in India could have been avoided. If, instead of raising alluring hopes of speedy Dominion status, we had concentrated upon practical steps to advance the material condition of the Indian masses; if the Congress at Lahore which burnt the Union Jack had been broken up forthwith and its leaders deported; if Gandhi had been arrested and tried as soon as he broke the law; if the will to rule had been firmly asserted, there would have been no necessity for the immense series of penal measures which have, in fact, been taken. Again, I appeal for confirmation to all those in England who really know India. Even now, at any time, the plain assertion of the resolve of Parliament to govern and to guide the destinies of the Indian people in faithful loyalty to Indian interests would in a few years—it might even be in a few months—bring this period of tantalised turmoil to an end.

Where, then, do we stand? The word of the King-Emperor is inviolable. We are pledged not only to labour for the welfare of India, but perseveringly to associate Indians of every race and creed with the processes of their own development. The Act of 1919 is a rock which cannot be removed. By that Act we conferred great and new constitutional powers upon the Indian political classes and we pledged ourselves to extend those constitutional powers honourably and perseveringly. We have assigned no theoretical limit to the extension of Indian constitutional development within the Empire. But by that same Act we reserved to ourselves an equal right to restrict, delay, or, if need be, for a spell to reverse that process. So far as there exists any contract between a people conquered by force in former times, and the modern Parliament of a benevolent nation vowed to promote their welfare, that is the contract, and there is no other.

Let us examine the problem upon this basis and in the light of practical events. The far-reaching extensions of self-government with which Mr. Montagu's name is associated were a bold experiment. They have not succeeded. The ten years which have passed have been years of failure. Every service which has been handed over to Indian administration has deteriorated; in particular, Indian agriculture, the sole prop of the life of hundreds of millions, has certainly not advanced in accordance with the ever-growing science and organisation of the modern world. The Indian political classes have not accepted the Montagu constitution. Even those for whose especial benefit and pleasure that constitution was devised have derived no satisfaction from it. Either they have refused to co-operate, or they have used the liberties which it conferred not for the purpose of improving the well-being of India, but merely as convenient tools and processes for political agitation and even sedition. There has resulted unrest, improverishment and discontent, drawing with them repressive measures and curtailments of civil liberties, which did not exist before the political liberties were widened.

In these circumstances, a new Parliament will have to decide what is now to be done. Our right and our power to restrict Indian constitutional liberties are unchallengeable. Our obligation to persevere in associating the peoples of India with their own government is undoubted. We are free to call a halt. We are free, for the time being, to retrace our steps, to retire in order to advance again. So long as the continuous purpose is sincerely and unswervingly pursued, Parliament has entire discretion. It is evident that our first efforts to create an all-India constitution have been ill-conceived. It may well be that our duty and our course now lie in curtailing the functions of an all-India body and in building up in each province more real, more intimate, more representative organisms of self-government. It may well be that these organisms, when developed and established, will form a surer foundation for an all-India Government than the present crude and unduly Westernised conception.

But here I must draw attention to a very grave danger. The Indian gentlemen and notabilities who are attending the Round Table Conference are in no way representative of the real forces which challenge British rule in India. It is true that, drifting with the tide, many of them have become the mouthpiece of extreme demands, but they have no power to pledge the Indian Congress Party to sincere acceptance of any agreement that may be outlined. The danger is that in an unwise endeavour to reach an agreement here in London, the Socialist Government will commit itself to concessions and extensions of self-government which will weaken our hands in the future, without in any way procuring the assent of the ruthless forces of sedition and outrage. Our concessions will, therefore, only be used as the starting-point for new demands by revolutionaries, while the loyal elements and the masses of the people will be the more unsettled by further evidences of British weakness. The truth is that Gandhi-ism and all it stands for will, sooner or later, have to be grappled with and finally crushed. It is no use trying to satisfy a tiger by feeding him with cat's-meat. The sooner this is realised, the less trouble and misfortune will there be for all concerned.

Above all, it must be made plain that the British nation has no intention of relinquishing its mission in India, or of failing in its duty to the Indian masses, or of parting with its supreme control in any of the essentials of peace, order and good government. We have no intention of casting away that most truly bright and precious jewel in the crown of the King, which more than all our other Dominions and Dependencies constitutes the glory and strength of the British Empire. The loss of India would mark and consummate the downfall of the British Empire. That great organism would pass at a stroke out of life into history. From such a catastrophe there could be no recovery. But we have yet to learn that the race and nation which have achieved so many prodigies and have faithfully discharged so many difficult tasks, and come safely and invincibly through all the perils of the centuries, will now fall a victim to their own lack of self-confidence and moral strength.

UNEMPLOYMENT

December 16, 1930

House of Commons

Sir Oswald Mosley's proposals to curb unemployment, which included credit for expansion and public direction of industry, appalled the Labour leaders. Mosley resigned from the Government, and carried on the battle in the Parliamentary Party and at the annual conference. In December he published a manifesto embracing his proposals.

I have been asked to make a few remarks in the course of this debate. It has been a typical debate upon the problem of unemployment. Certainly I cannot express any surprise at the indignation of the hon. Member for West Wolverhampton (Mr. W. J. Brown) and his obvious disillusionment and disappointment with the policy and performances of His Majesty's Government, or with the speech of the Minister of Transport, which everyone who heard it must feel was an extraordinary speech in these circumstances. The hon. Member who, on behalf of the Liberal party, opened the debate on a Motion which unhappily prevents the House from taking any effective action upon the speech of the Minister of Transport, put a very strong case, and made an impassioned appeal. The Minister replied with the usual officialese, the usual jargon and platitudes which, I must say, he and his friends have found themselves very ready to learn. He gave practically no sort of satisfaction to the request of the Liberal party. He rehearsed a number of statements supplied to him by other Departments, went over again the tally of the various public works which have been set on foot, and generally gave the House the feeling that there was no real attempt to grapple with the problem; but in face of this the only proposal which the right hon. Gentleman who opened the debate has to make is that we should adjourn. That, of course, is something of an anti-climax, and I think we cannot help feeling depressed at such a conclusion to a Motion so earnestly pressed by the Liberal party.

Usually, this is a depressing subject and discussed under depressing circumstances. The Government of the day lie under what is, no doubt, a death sentence. The date of their execution is uncertain. I am reminded of a well-known prison in the United States given over entirely to persons awaiting, amid the many delays of American justice, the execution of the capital penalty—the Sing Sing prison. These men do not know when their turn will come—whether it will be in three months, six months, or 12 months, or one month. It all depends upon what is done by their attorney—unscrupulous sometimes, ingenious and undeniably clever—who understand how to wring from the courts a respite or a new trial or some further delay. I ask myself: is not that really very suggestive of the position occupied by His Majesty's Government at the present time? Dr. Johnson has said that if a man is going to be hanged in a fortnight, it concentrates his mind wonderfully. That does not seem to have resulted in the case of the present Government. We know that their Attorney has visited them on several occasions in their cells or departments, and he has reported to the world the results of his examination of their condition. He tells us they have gone completely to pieces, mentally and morally. He says they are merely "footling" and, with his complete command of trans-Atlantic and London slang, "toddling" and jibbering, though perhaps I am going beyond him when I say that.

That is all they are doing, but we must not be surprised when we reflect on the strain to which these unhappy men are subjected. Naturally, their Attorney wishes to make quite sure that if they have any testimentary dispositions to make, if they can do anything to help him before their hour comes, he does not miss his opportunity. Equally naturally, he is in a position to put considerable pressure upon them, and they in their condition, are perfectly ready to hand over anything of value which they may possess or which they may be able to lay their hands upon, to stimulate his efforts to prolong an existence which has long ceased to be useful, honourable, or agreeable. But here is the real strain upon the Government. Unluckily, some of the assets of the band are not entirely in their custody. Some of the band are still at large roaming in the mountains, and they are by no means inclined to allow these gentlemen to secure a prolongation of their tenure of existence at the expense of the permanent electoral interests of their party. I venture to say that the situation is certainly depressing when a Government in this condition is called upon to face so grave a problem.

But Parliament itself and this House of Commons is also under a sentence of death. It is almost dead already. I have never seen a Parliament which lost so rapidly its resilience and vitality as this unhappy House. We have had about 20 days of these unemployment debates in the present year. I have not counted them up, but I cannot put them at very much less than 20. They have produced no results—not one of them has reached any effective conclusion at all. In fact, the only general results of the 20 days' debates have been the certainty—which I am sure will be concurred in by Members in every quarter of the House, above and below the Gangway on this side—that nothing effective will be done in the present Parliament. That is the one solid conclusion which emerges from all the debates.

Our ancestors would not have used so much Parliamentary time on a single topic in this sporadic and ineffectual manner. Undoubtedly, if there had been a subject 100 years ago which occupied so much of the nation's interest as this question of unemployment, about which so much has been said and so many suggestions and different points of view have to be explored, our ancestors would not have had a string of debates on single days taking place at odd occasions during the Session. They would have pursued the topic with continuous persistence and with resolutions, descending from the general to the particular and throwing out at each stage those who disagreed with what was proposed so as to build up the main theme of House of Commons opinion. That is how the matter would have been dealt with in the Parliaments of 100 or 150 years ago.

The attitude that this House has adopted, not only on this question of unemployment, but on the question of public economy, is one which arises from our not pursuing from day to day particular themes and insisting upon reaching some solid agreement or issue of difference. It shows, as has been observed on all sides, an element of decay in our Parliamentary system. The machinery, as the last hon.

Member has truly said, though well adapted for political issues, is not adapted for the treatment of economic problems, which are the only domestic ones in this country in which people are deeply interested at present. There is no country in the world whose economic and social structure is so intricate and precarious as our own, or which is showing less mental grip at the present time of its vital affairs or sinking more rapidly in the scale of nations. There never was a time when there was less care and thought bestowed upon public affairs.

I cannot say that we have got very much enlightenment from the Liberal party. Perhaps when the right hon. Member for Carnarvon Boroughs (Mr. Lloyd George) speaks, he will add to our information. As far as we have been able to follow the policy he is now pursuing, he seems to rest himself on three propositions. His first proposition is that unemployment is a great, vital, urgent evil and danger which we have to face; the second proposition is that he has a real cure and will borrow a large sum of money and spend it on houses, roads or telephones; and the third proposition is that the Government will not look at his scheme or carry it out in any effectual manner. What is his conclusion? It is that, therefore, he will keep them in office for a year or it may be two years in order to obtain the alternative vote. Certainly this is not a very helpful contribution to the difficulties in which we all find ourselves involved. It is interesting as showing the importance which the right hon. Gentleman attaches to the alternative vote, because he obviously rates it higher than an effectual and speedy solution of the problem of unemployment. His attitude towards the Government is expressed in the old saying: "A poor thing, but mine own." One can understand such sentiments are gratifying to him and that a sense of patronage is agreeable to him, but it astonishes me that the Government should be willing to put up with and subsist upon such insulting protection. We may well inquire, as the country is inquiring, how a Government, thus humiliated and thus sustained, can attempt to discharge all the immense functions of the British realm and Empire?

Various remedies are suggested. There are remedies put forward by the right hon. Member for Smethwick (Sir O. Mosley), who has taken up his abode in the fastnesses below the Gangway on the other side. I need scarcely say that we on this side cannot agree with his proposals for import boards and the placing in the hands of officials of the whole machinery, marvellous and intricate, by which the supplies of grain are brought to these islands and have been brought for many years so success-fully that bread is cheaper here than even in the great countries where wheat is grown. Neither could any business man or manufacturer accept Protection for industry upon the terms which those gentlemen advocate, by which industry shall be handcuffed at the same time as it is protected. It is a policy of Protection plus Socialism, the two hand-in-hand, which would neutralise any of the beneficial and stimulating effects to industry which might follow from a tariff and speedily lead us along that path which the great boundless, undeveloped comtinent of Australia has found leads, if not to disaster, at any rate to immense disappointment and contraction, and which, if it were applied to the complicated conditions of this highly artificial community here, could only lead us to measureless trouble and disaster.

There is one aspect in which I entirely agree with some of the remarks which have fallen from the hon. Gentleman opposite. I agree with him that the existing Parliamentary machinery is not adequate or adapted to cope with economic problems, and, if Parliament is not willing to devise some method by which a persistent and effectual study, with action resulting from that study, either by some subordinate body of this House of some special selection of Members from this House—unless Parliament is prepared to devise some method of that kind, undoubtedly the House of Commons will cease to be able to deal effectually with questions with which, I entirely agree, it is indispensable to the vitality of our Parliamentary institutions that we should be able to cope.

We are not called upon to reply particularly to the speeches made by or on behalf of the hon. Member for Smethwick, because he has met his match in the Chancellor of the Exchequer. The Chancellor of the Exchequer, who, I much regret to hear, is temporarily incapacitated, affords a very peculiar spectacle during his present tenure of office. Usually a Department is supposed to correct the idiosyncracies of the Minister and the Minister is supposed to correct the idiosyncracies of the Department. But when the right hon. Gentleman the Member for Colne Valley, (Mr. P. Snowden) went to the Treasury, then the idiosyncracies of the Department and of the Minister multiplied themselves together, and such elements of rigid pedantry as there are in the Treasury and the Bank of England were embraced and greeted by all the rigid pedantry of the Chancellor of the Exchequer himself.

Let us just see what are the main propositions of the Chancellor of the Exchequer: Free imports, irrespective of what other countries may do; ruthless direct taxation for Debt repayment, heedless of the consequences to enterprise and industry; rigorous economy, not only in social but in military matters; profound distrust of State-aided enterprise of all kinds, and absolute reliance upon private enterprise. Those are the broad outlines of the Treasury doctrines, so valiantly defended by the Chancellor of the Exchequer. Whatever we may think of these doctrines, they are certainly not what is going on now. There is not one of them which is not challenged by the practice of Parliament and of the nation, and which has not had great inroads made upon it. Where we are suffering is that, while the old structure built up by our ancestors is everywhere being largely discarded, no adequate effort is being made to supply a connected scheme of thought in its place.

We have on several occasions stated such remedies as we would propose from this side of the House. No one imagines that any single remedy is a complete cure, but there are many remedies which, applied together, might be effective. There are remedies which would be helpful and give a stimulus to productive industry such as would follow by the imposition of a tariff on imported manufactured articles. Undoubtedly a stimulus would be given which would attract capital into industry and give a new spirit, a psychological stimulus, to industry. The revenue from these would be applicable to reduction of burdens, for instance, on the reserves of industry which were even more heavily burdened by the Chancellor of the Exchequer in his late Budget. I have always believed that the reduction of freights would be found a more helpful way of getting a forward movement in the heavy basic industries than many of these direct schemes of giving work to the unemployed. At any rate, the comparatively small sums of money which we were able to devote to the reduction of freights would produce extremely satisfactory and sweeping results. Such are some of the proposals which have been put forward. Moreover, it is essential that the Government should not neglect its duty to reform the unemployment insurance system, as they have repeatedly promised to do, and take the necessary steps to purge it of the grave abuses which have grown up in it.

These are practical and reasonable steps which can be taken. But the greatest of all things is the restoration of confidence. The right hon. Gentleman appealed to manufacturers and business men to have hope and determination and not to lose heart, but they can surely not be blamed for losing heart in the circumstances of the present time. We are approaching Britain's second Christmas under the Socialists. What lies before us? Another Budget of the Chancellor of the Exchequer, another General Election with all its disorganisation. A double uncertainty hangs over trade and enterprise, business falters and enterprise flags. How can a recovery be expected in these conditions? Exactly a year ago I predicted that a cheerless period lay before us. Little did I or anyone here know what lay in store for us, or how disastrous this year was to prove, in every branch of our economic and social life. Many of the highest authorities agree that only worse is to follow, and worse will certainly follow unless or until we are free from a Government which, in its weakness and in its pretensions, in its incapacity and in its conceit, cumbers the ground.

1931

THE INDIAN CONFERENCE
January 20, 1931
London

The eloquent and well-meant speeches which closed the Round Table Conference do not represent a very large body of British opinion and Conservative opinion, particularly among those throughout the country who are well acquainted or in contact with the facts of modern India. The only possible conclusion which a stranger would draw from reading these speeches was that the British people were anxious to wind up their connexion with India as soon as possible, and for that purpose were endeavouring to bring all races and creeds in India together in order that the business of government may be finally handed over to them. I do not believe that is what the British nation wishes or means. If it be so, then the day of its power and greatness in the world has set for ever.

I regret very much that throughout the Round Table Conference no positive statement of the rights and will of the British nation has been set forth. One would have expected that each side would state clearly the essentials of its case, and certainly the Indians have not been backward in pressing their claims. The Hindus have spoken. And so have the Mohammedans. The Sikhs have been heard, and the Depressed Classes. But no one has even mentioned the fact that British people have some right and interests in India of their own. They have duties to perform and long built-up establishments to guard. Their case has not been stated.

On the contrary, the British Government and their representatives have sedulously endeavoured to conduct the discussion in a manner most calculated to soothe Indian susceptibilities by coming as near as possible to their claims in agreeable but vague terms. All unpalatable truths about safeguards have been left unspoken or touched upon lightly as necessary evils appropriate to a period of transition. If the safeguards are real and effective, "Dominion status" and "responsible government" are not the terms to apply to the Constitution which has been outlined.

Even in matters not governed by any safeguards the proposals to which the Conference has lent its favour would be disastrous, assuming they were not unworkable. The entrusting of the maintenance of law and order to what may well be a thoroughly hostile Indian Ministry, the handing over of that admirable police which has hitherto stood every test to the control of those whose purpose may well be to drive the British out of the country, could only expose the lives and property of Europeans throughout India to frightful hazards. The introduction of the vicious principle of dyarchy at the centre of the Indian Executive must exercise a paralysing effect upon the whole process of good government for the Indian masses.

The intervention of the Viceroy [Lord Irwin] with over-riding power if things go wrong pre-supposes, first, considerable misfortune having occurred, and, secondly, a race of supermen as Viceroys, such as we certainly have not been fortunate to command in recent times. Lastly, the alienation of the police will bring the British Army into that direct contact with Indian disorders which it has long been the settled policy of every British administration to avoid.

All this has already apparently to be conceded should Parliament approve the forthcoming Government of India Bill whenever it is framed. It has all to be conceded, not as a final settlement between the ruling forces on both sides, but as a mere transitional procedure to enable the British to wind up their affairs and quit the sub-continent they have raised from the chaos of China to a system of civilization incomparably superior to anything previously developed in the Orient.

However, there is one consolation which we may draw from the proceedings of this melancholy Conference. It is not yet too late. Those fatal words have not yet been graven on the stones of history. The key to Indian government is still in our hands. The Prime Minister, in concluding the Conference, declared that he must appeal to British opinion. Matters cannot stop where they are. In a few months fresh conferences and negotiations will begin. It is the duty of those who care for the endurance of the British Empire and who believe that that supreme fact is intimately connected with our ability to discharge our mission in India to rouse and organize public opinion in the short breathing space now accorded us.

EDUCATION (SCHOOL ATTENDANCE) BILL

January 21, 1931

House of Commons

My right hon. Friend the member for Hastings (Lord E. Percy), in moving that the House should now adjourn, had two perfectly clear objects in view. The first was to give the Government an opportunity to reconsider the position so far as it affects the actual legislation, and to enable them to address themselves to the new situation which was created. But the second object of my right hon. Friend, which was also aimed at by the Leader of the Opposition when he pointedly asked the Prime Minister his intentions, was to emphasise and make abundantly plain the humiliation of His Majesty's Government and the extremely loose and inconsequent manner in which they are conducting the business of the country. I heard the speech of the right hon. Gentleman just before the Division. Then, this was an Amendment of real consequence. Then, it was one of the gravest issues which could possibly affect the whole course of this Bill. The Government placed their Whips on in the Lobbies. They summoned their supporters from all parts of the country for the Division which they knew was to take place, I agree, not on party lines, and yet it is a Division which has in it a measure of direct censure, because, as we have been told, the situation created this afternoon is the result of 18 months of complete failure to deal in a straightforward or in a direct manner with this particular religious difficulty. The Government face the Division, they are defeated by over 30 votes, and then the Prime Minister rises in his place utterly unabashed, the greatest living master of falling without hurting himself, and airily assures us that nothing has happened. The Government, it appears, are delighted to fall in with the wishes of the House. Their only regret is that the House has not conveyed its opinion to them in a somewhat less forcible manner. So we are to go on with the discussions on the Bill, although undoubtedly a first-class impediment has been placed upon its further progress by the vote which the House has given in such surprising numbers. We may go on with the Bill, and the right hon. Gentleman will continue leading this House—we admit, of course, the difficulties in which a minority Government finds itself—and it will continue to afford precedents which will certainly enable Administrations in the future, if they choose, to proceed week after week and month after month without one scrap of credit or reputation or consistency. My right hon. Friend was actuated by these objects in moving that we should adjourn. The objects have been fully attained now, and, if the Government say that all is exactly the same, that nothing has happened, that they are perfectly prepared to accept the affront, that they do not even wish a breathing space, an interlude in order to re-examine the position—if they choose to say that, now that we have effectively made our point from this side of the House, we shall not trouble to set them right, and shall leave them effectively to stew in their own juice.

INDIA—"A FRIGHTFUL PROSPECT"

January 26, 1931

House of Commons

On January 25 Lord Irwin released Gandhi and his chief colleagues from detention and removed the proscription on the Congress Working Committee. When Baldwin supported this action, as Churchill later wrote, "I reached my breaking-point in my relations with Mr. Baldwin." In reply to this speech Baldwin pledged himself and the Conservative Party to "try to implement" the Constitution outlined by the Round Table Conference.

I desire, if the House will permit me, to approach this question from a different angle from that which is now fashionable and from a somewhat different angle even from that which guided the right hon. and learned Member for Spen Valley (Sir John Simon), in his impressive and instructive speech. But first, I should like to pay a tribute to the Conservative delegates upon the Round Table Conference for the skill, patience, and tact with which they extricated themselves from an exceedingly difficult situation, and for the manner in which they have preserved our party free to use its judgment upon future events. Although my language would not be theirs, nor theirs mine, I thank them for the care they have taken to safeguard our liberty of action. I must, of course, first of all make it quite clear that I do not speak for the official Opposition nor for my right hon. Friend the Leader of the Opposition. I speak solely as a Member of Parliament, of some service in this House, who holds views upon this matter which ought not to go unrepresented in this discussion.

I hold that the handling of Indian affairs during the last eighteen months has been most unfortunate and has led already to results which will be long lamented. I will make the briefest review which is necessary. Lord Birkenhead, with foresight and with wisdom, antedated by two years the setting up of the Commission laid down in the Act of 1919 for the reviewing of the Montagu-Chelmsford reforms. The Commission was set up by Act of Parliament, all the three parties co-operated in its setting up, and all three were represented on the Commission. The Commission, after immense labours, journeys, and studies, presented a report which was unanimous, and it presented that report to the Houses of Parliament which had called it into being. What has happened to that report of our Commission? Why has it been thrust altogether— though compliments have been paid to it—out of the sequence of events?

One would have thought that that report would have been debated by Parliament, probably on a series of Resolutions; that we should have heard, not for the first time, as we have done to-day, but repeatedly, the advice of the distinguished men of all parties who contributed to that report; and that the Government would then, guided by the Resolutions of the House and by the advice of those whom the House had charged, and whom the Act of 1919 indicates should be charged, with the duty of advising Parliament, have framed a Bill. It was also contemplated and generally agreed that this Bill, after being presented to Parliament and read a Second time, should be the subject of a Joint Committee of both Houses, to which Indian representatives of every shade of opinion should be invited to have recourse; and, finally, the Bill would have been passed through its stages and presented for the Royal Assent.

Such was the procedure marked out, coolly, calmly, and far in advance, and marked out by general assent. Why is it that we have departed from it? It is, I suppose, because the Viceroy, moved or influenced by His Majesty's Government—I do not know, I cannot tell—determined to make a pronouncement in the winter of 1929, opening up in general, guarded, but still spacious terms the idea of Dominion status. I hold that this pronouncement—I am afraid I must ask the House to permit me to state, with the candour which we have been invited to adopt my point of view—was uncalled for, that it was an interruption of the procedure prescribed by law, and that it was an intervention between Parliament and their Commission. Everyone had agreed to await the Report of the Commission, and it is most regrettable that Parliament and Indian opinion also were not permitted to receive that Report unprejudiced by prior declarations. For this, the accountable responsibility rests with the Government of the day; but as the result, see what happened.

The Report was profoundly prejudiced before its publication, and when it was seen that the Commissioners had deliberately and unanimously excluded the expression 'Dominion status' from their Report, a very painful difference was disclosed between the Viceroy and the Government of India on the one hand and our Statutory Commission on the other. At the same time, there was an enormous leap forward in the demands of the Indian political classes. What had been accepted before was now brushed aside. Moderate men adopted opinions which hitherto had been considered extreme. Outbreaks of disorder and lawlessness occurred in many parts of India, culminating in the Nationalist Congress at Lahore, at which the British flag was insulted with every circumstance of formality and publicity and, I may add, insulted with impunity.

Some time before, when it had been made a grievance that Indians were not represented upon the Simon Commission—if I may be permitted to use that term—the Commissioners themselves suggested a Conference in London as a preliminary to a Bill, and that all sections of Indian opinion should be invited thereto. That Conference has eventually assembled, but under very different conditions from anything foreseen by the Statutory Commission. Not only was the Report, with all its thought and study and with all its strong, bold, practical plan of constructive advance, going further than many of us would care to go in some respects—not only was the Report completely shelved, but the right hon. and learned Member and his colleagues, who sit about on various benches, were invidiously excluded from the whole of the Conference proceedings. This was done, as we all know, in the hopes of persuading the representatives of the Indian Congress and other extremists to attend. Our trusted friends and lawful, formal and authoritative advisers were set aside in order to placate those who are the bitterest opponents of British rule in India. Nevertheless, they would not come. The Congress Party refused to attend the Conference even though it was mutilated as I have described to suit their prejudices.

What happened then? The Government of India thereupon collected a number of notables as representative as possible of all the various phases of Indian life, but with no delegated authority, so far as the forces with which we have to deal are concerned, no power to conclude an agreement, and still less any power to enforce it. These representatives, together with the Indian princes, met in London. This body, thus composed, without any representative authority from the Indian Congress, without advice from the Statutory Commission, without any guidance in the first instance and even without any effective agenda from His Majesty's Government, proceeded rapidly and almost unconsciously to form itself into what I can only call a would-be and wholly unauthorised Constituent Assembly. Quite true it was not to frame a constitution in every detail, but this document here, which is its work, cannot be considered as anything else but the work of a would-be and unauthorised Constituent Assembly; and His Majesty's Government, eagerly catching their mood, set to work without more ado to frame a federal constitution for all India, embodying the principle of a responsible Indian Ministry at the summit and centre of Indian affairs, the whole leading up speedily to that full Dominion status with all that it entails, including—as one of the members of the Conference, Mr. Sastri, was careful to remind us—as one of its most important features, the right to secede from the British Empire. While all the world wondered, the Sovereign Power which had created modern India and which was still its sole support and defence, smilingly, blandly and no doubt in most statesmanlike language, engaged in unlimited hypothetical discussions about how to unite all the existing forces of Indian life, so as to be able to hand over to them the executive powers of the central Government and the title-deeds of the British position in India. It was even pretended, or at any rate allowed to appear, that Indian disunity was the only or main obstacle to our speedy departure.

Such proceedings, such conclusions were utterly unforeseen only a year ago in almost any quarter of the House. They would have been scouted and condemned by almost all classes of British opinion only a few months ago. The principle of responsible Government, involving all the proved disadvantages of Dyarchy at the centre, is, of course, contrary to the recommendations of the Commission. It is applied by an entirely different method in this Blue Book, and carried to a further point than was recommended in the alternative scheme submitted by the Viceroy and Government of India. We have, first of all, an immense body of knowledge represented by the Simon Commission and its Report, and, secondly, that great body of reason and authority represented by the Government of India, all set aside after a few weeks, almost a few days, of discussions and orations at the London Conference, until finally we are confronted with the constitution outlined in this Blue Book. In this hysterical landslide of opinion, the Conservative delegates almost alone kept their heads. I must admit that the Prime Minister showed a measure of deep foreboding in some of his utterances, although, of course, thickly veiled in flowery language. It is quite true that the acceptance by His Majesty's Government and by Lord Reading, representing the Liberal party, of these proposals and all their implications of speedy Dominion status and full responsible Government, was accompanied by a host of important reservations and is contingent upon many conditions some of which are unlikely to be fulfilled.

Could there be a worse way of dealing with so grave a problem? Here for weeks all the foundations of British power in India have been laid bare, and every principle has been treated as an open question. The orb of power has been dangled before the gleaming eyes of excitable millions and before the powerful forces of implacable hostility with whom we have, as is well known, to cope in India, while at the same time in the background, treated as if they were matters of machinery, are a whole series of formidable reservations and conditions. Thus, on the one hand the claims and expectancy of those in India have been raised to the highest pitch by sweeping concessions on general questions of principle, while on the other the rugged facts which have emerged in the speech of my right hon. and learned Friend (Sir John Simon) who preceded me, have all been kept in the shade by clouds of ceremonious and benevolent generalities. Meanwhile, the rapid landslide in British opinion and policy at home has been accompanied in India by a steady development of unrest, disorder, disloyalty and assassination. The well-meaning and high-minded Viceroy has had to couple with his kindly speeches and sentiments a succession of repressive measures and of restrictions on civil liberty without precedent in India since the Mutiny, except in some days of the Great War. Many of thousands of Indians are in prison in connection with political agitation. The world depression which has reached

India is accentuated by the prolonged uncertainty, by the growing disaffection, by the widespread feeling that all the things which they have known for generations are about to be thrown into the melting pot, by the feeling that some enormous change is impending and that violent times are ahead. The result has been suffering and misfortune on a very large scale and as a prelude, as I fear, to even greater troubles, because this uncertainty about all the foundations of social and political life is not over. It is going to be prolonged indefinitely. This constitution, this Blue Book is now going to be paraded round India and discussed there. All the promises and concessions will be set at their maximum; all the safeguards narrowly canvassed with a view to demanding their diminution. All this uncertainty and agitation is going to continue not for months only, but possibly for years.

I have now completed my recital of the catalogue of errors and disasters which have brought us to our present position. Here I must make it perfectly clear that I accept not only the preamble of the Act of 1919, but also Section 41 of that Act. The preamble shows the ultimate goal to which we declare that India may aspire, and Section 41 shows precisely the full and uncompromised right of Parliament to advance or to divert or, if necessary, to restrict this forward movement in the development of constitutional government. Let us take the two together. I am quite willing fully to accept the implications of both. Of course, we assign no limits to the future potential development of our Indian fellow-subjects. We enlist their co-operation—have we not been doing so continuously?—in every branch of Indian administration and of Indian life. It all depends on time and on facts. My submission to the House to-night is that the time for this extension is premature, and that the facts are adverse.

In the upshot, let us see what it is that the Indian Nationalists are expecting to receive. I take from *The Times* of two days ago a quotation from a manifesto of the Indian Nationalist members of the Legislative Assembly. This is the conclusion which they have drawn from the proceedings here. They welcome the policy which the Government propose to adopt of giving effect to their views:

> in establishing a new constitution which will advance India to full re-
> sponsibility for her own government and give her the equal status of a
> dominion among the British Commonwealth of Nations. . . . It is also
> pleasing to note that His Majesty's Government recognise that the reserva-
> tions which are to be placed upon the full powers of the Legislature are
> not only to be transitory but are to be so framed and exercised as not to
> prejudice the advance of India to true responsibility for her own govern-
> ment. In particular, we are emphatically of opinion that the reservations in
> the matter of financial adjustment must not in the least degree hamper the
> effective control of Indian Ministers over the finances of India. . . . While
> welcoming the declaration of policy, we trust its realisation will be
> immediate, which alone can really satisfy.

These are the opinions of the more moderate representatives of the Indian Nationalists. Now that Mr. Gandhi is again at large, no doubt he will contribute a further
gloss upon the Government's proposals. Anything which falls short in time or in fact

of these expectations will be a cause of fierce reproaches. I remember the right hon. Member for Carnarvon Boroughs (Mr. Lloyd George) in November 1929 warning the House and the Government of the dangers of charges of breaches of faith and of perfidy, and he said that nothing could be worse than that in our relations with India. If that were the danger then, how much more is it a danger now, when you contrast this kind of expectation entertained by the Indian Nationalists with the immense catalogue of important safeguards cited to by the right hon. Member for Chelsea (Sir Samuel Hoare), and consider them in the light of the unsolved difficulties enumerated by the right hon. and learned Member for Spen Valley (Sir John Simon). The right hon. Member for Carnarvon Boroughs dilated then upon the dangers of Dominion status and vague talk about it. Of course, we have always contemplated it as an ultimate goal, but no one has supposed that, except in a purely ceremonial sense, in the way in which representatives of India attended conferences during the War, that principle and policy for India would be carried into effect in any time which it is reasonable or useful for us to foresee. The right hon. Member for Carnarvon Boroughs wrote an article a year ago in the *Daily Mail* entitled—the phrase was taken from his own text—'Jerrybuilding for a crash in India.'

It is no good the right hon. Gentleman shaking his head, for I have already armed myself with the article for greater accuracy. When I heard the concluding portion of the speech of the right hon. and learned Member for Spen Valley, I could not help feeling how very apt was the title his leader and colleague chose for his article in the *Daily Mail*. The right hon. Gentleman a year ago poured his scorn upon the Leader of the Opposition (Mr. Baldwin), because he alleged he had gone too far in lending countenance to the idea of Dominion status, which in a particular sense has always been commonly agreed to be the final goal of Indian relationships. A year has passed. I have always cherished the hope that the right hon. Member for Carnarvon Boroughs would on this Indian matter come to the rescue of the country as he did in war-time days; but politics exercise a bewitching fascination upon him, and when politics come in at the door, his zeal for the retention of India flies out by the window. He is now actually supporting Lord Reading's proposals, which go further than those to which the Conservative delegation . . . [Mr. Lloyd George dissented.] Certainly, they go further in several respects than the Conservative delegation or the Leader of the Opposition is prepared to go.

What reason is assigned for the sudden downward lurch in British opinion? It is, as we all know, the action of the Indian Princes at the Conference. Of course, I must not seek unduly to impute or assign motives, but is that a reassuring action? Is it a sign that our position is better in India, and that our dangers in that country are less? It strikes me as being the most disquieting feature of all. The action of the Princes may well be due to the belief, now spreading so widely throughout the masses of India, that the British Raj will shortly cease to function, and that it will be succeeded by the Congress Raj or the Gandhi Raj or some other form, and that Great Britain under the Socialists and under universal suffrage, if pressed enough, if squeezed enough, if kicked enough, if worried enough, will acquiesce in such a revolution. In face of this, having to provide for themselves and for their States under the new regime, they have expressed their willingness to enter a federal parliament, and this is paraded as a justification for a new and sudden departure. No greater proof, in my judgment, could be shown of the increasing degeneration of our affairs. So far from justifying a greater confidence, it ought to reveal to us how very near the precipice we have already come.

Will these proposals, after they have been subjected to prolonged discussion, be accepted by the Indian political classes? I read a very remarkable account by the *Manchester Guardian* correspondent who was at the Conference, and I will read one most illuminating passage:

> The attitude of the older Congress leaders is the least part of the danger. Young India, including the women newly come into politics, is not in a mood to be reasoned with. It regards the Conference simply as a conspiracy of four devils—the devil of British Imperialism, the devil of the States' mediaeval autocracy, the devil of Moslem separation, and, worst of all, the devil of reason and moderation. It will listen to no proposals coming from this quarter. It has acquired the true war mentality, and the unexpected concessions made by Lord Reading—

I commend this to the Liberal party, because it is taken from the *Manchester Guardian*, the most distinguished and consistent advocate of Liberal opinion—

> are merely taken by it as an indication of weakness and fear, and will serve to inflate young India's pretensions and confirm its determination to insist on the enemy's unconditional surrender.

He says later on:

> To put the whole position briefly, we have to remember that we are now retreating in the face of an active and elated enemy. Before abandoning any position we should be careful to put our Allies firmly in possession of it.

What then will be the answer? Will it be an acceptance or a rejection? I apprehend that it will be neither the one nor the other. I apprehend that it will be a dusty answer. Some will accept, and some will reject these proposals. Those who accept them will take them as a means of helping them towards their goal, and those who do not accept them will be busy in seeing that those who have accepted them do not flag in their efforts. Great Britain will be committed and weakened, and the Indian Nationalists will be reinforced, armed with new weapons and free to use them.

Parenthetically, let me address myself to the party opposite. No one can pretend that this draft of a constitution is based upon any democratic conception, or that the Indian Executive and Assembly will in any way represent the masses of India. These masses will be delivered to the mercies of a well-organised, narrowly elected, political and religious oligarchy and caucus. Those 300,000,000 people who are our duty and trust are often forgotten in these political discussions. Those 300,000,000 people, who depend for their humble and narrowly-scraped livelihood upon the peace and order which Britain has brought in the years that are past and upon British justice, will be largely removed from our impartial protection, and they will be utterly powerless themselves to control or to make their wishes felt by their new rulers. Already the Montagu-Chelmsford reforms have produce a deterioration in every service which has been transferred. They have produced increasing irritation and unrest, and, of course, they have produced an acute revival of the quarrels and rivalries of Moslem and Hindu. This process must continue, and for all the resulting discontents the Viceroy, and the safeguards, and the British officials will get the blame.

It will be so easy for these future rulers or part rulers of India to represent all the inevitable evils and unpopularity of carrying on the Government as due to the slow rate at which the British officials and British Government are removing themselves from the country. It is upon them that the odium and onus will fall in the future. The Viceroy is contemplated here as a sort of figure far uplifted above the ordinary range of human capacity, foresight and intelligence, as someone who knows exactly when and how to act, who never acts too soon or too late. He holds enormous powers in his hands. Month after month, it may be year after year, the Viceroy will be exposed to all the inevitable unpopularity which attaches to the process of governing, and he will be in the position in which the French revolutionists in 1792 placed the King, 'Monsieur Veto,' directing upon him all the popular displeasure and odium when he resisted, as he was constitutionally charged to do, measures which were injurious.

Sir, I am no stranger to these problems of self-government: I was the Minister in charge in this House of the Transvaal Constitution Act in 1906, and I happened also to be the Minister in charge of the Irish Free State Act in 1922. I was also directly concerned in the administrative processes and executive steps necessary to bring both those most remarkable departures in self-government into operation. Of course, there are no parallels between South Africa and Ireland on the one hand and India on the other. No one has pointed that out more clearly and forcibly than the right hon. Member for Carnarvon Boroughs. But there are two lessons which I, personally, think my experience enables me to draw. The first is, as has been emphasised from many quarters to-day, the importance of blunt candour in dealing with those to whom the powers are being transferred, of knowing exactly how far you mean to go and knowing, also, exactly where you intend to stop. The other lesson which has been impressed upon me has been that, once the principle is conceded, safeguards and reservations very often prove of no lasting value. I remember the nominated second chamber for the Transvaal. What labour we expended in building that up! I remember some of my most distinguished Liberal colleagues comfortably persuading themselves, on a nice calculation of electoral possibilities, that a non-Boer Government in the first instance would be returned. All those calculations and devices were swept away. Similarly, in Ireland, once we had decided to place the responsibility on Mr. Griffiths and Mr. Collins we could not be too quick in withdrawing our police and military and leaving the new Authority to bear the whole force and burden of the task they had assumed.

Nothing of this sort is possible in India; nothing of this kind is contemplated in India, not even by the most forward Member of the present Government. We are not relieving ourselves of burdens and responsibilities in India. We are merely setting the scene for a more complicated controversy, merely creating agencies which will make it more difficult for us to discharge our task. On the one hand, there will be the all-India Parliament, which may well be dominated by forces intent on driving us out of the country as quickly as possible. There will be a Ministry charged with such grave matters *inter alia* as the maintenance of law and order and control of the police. There will be that Ministry, responsible to this all-India Parliament and dependent upon its vote. You hug to yourselves the assurance that there must be a two-thirds majority before the Government can be turned out. How long will that last? It is perfectly clear that even if the Government does not resign because there is not a two-thirds majority, nevertheless a hostile majority can make the course of business in all other matters virtually impracticable.

Simultaneously with these tremendous steps at the centre, full responsible Government, in accordance with the recommendations of the Simon Commission, is to be conferred upon the provinces. So you will have what many of the wisest judges thought should be avoided, a double concurrent convulsion. It might have been thought well to build up those organisms in the provinces, before at the same time undertaking this higher and further organisation at the summit. You will have that on the one side; and on the other hand you will have the Viceroy with the Army and with the finance of the Army, which, I am told, may well involve 80 per cent. of the whole expenditure; a Viceroy largely deprived of the machinery and sources of information which now enable him to forestall crime and unrest, and to smooth away difficulties before they come to a head; a Viceroy disembodied and divorced from many vital and intimate functions, but armed, nevertheless—of course, in the last resort—with that overwhelming physical force of the Army which it should be the care and thought of every man wherever he sits not to employ against the natives of India. The one great aim and object of every Indian administration has been to prevent the British Army being brought into direct contact with Indian disorders.

Undoubtedly this scheme is no solution, and it affords the prospect of no solution, it is no resting-place, it is no settlement. The clash and agitation in India will continue, but they will no longer be confined to rioting in the streets or demonstrations in the Legislature. They will invade the heart and the brain of the Government of India. There, at the summit of this wonderful creation, an instrument which, with all its shortcomings, has given peace and progress to nations more varied than the nations of Europe and populations in the aggregate almost as large as China—there, at the summit, by constitutional and Parliamentary weapons now, the process of gnawing and cutting down the safeguards will proceed, stimulated, perhaps, from outside by a continuance of lawlessness and rioting and of worse crimes, for the prevention of which you will no longer have the primary responsibility. What, may I ask, will be your line of moral and logical resistance then? You have declared that the safeguards are only transitory, they are temporary expedients, apologetically adopted pending what to anyone who reads this Blue Book, and notes the emphasis assigned to its various parts, can only mean the rapid and speedy realisation of full Dominion status. The struggle will go on; it will only be aggravated; it will proceed under conditions in which British rule will be shorn of all its argument and of half its apparatus. It will proceed steadily towards the goal which those who are driving this policy forward, both here in this country and in India, no longer hesitate to avow, namely, the goal of complete severance between Great Britain and India of every tie except tradition, which in India is adverse, and sentiment, which in India is hostile. Sir, I say that is a frightful prospect to have opened up so wantonly, so recklessly, so incontinently and in so short a time.

How will the British nation feel about all this? I am told that they do not care. I am told that from one quarter or another. They are all worried by unemployment or taxation or absorbed in sport and crime news. The great liner is sinking in a calm sea. One bulkhead after another gives way; one compartment after another is bilged; the list increases; she is sinking; but the captain and the officers and the crew are all in the saloon dancing to the jazz band. But wait till the passengers find out what is their position! For thirty years I have watched from a central position the manifestations of the will power of Great Britain, and I do not believe our people will consent to be edged, pushed, talked and cozened out of India. No nation of which I am aware, great or small, has ever voluntarily or tamely suffered such an overwhelming injury to its interests or such a harsh abrogation of its rights. After all, there are British rights and interests in India. Two centuries of effort and achievement, lives given on a hundred fields, far more lives given and consumed in faithful and devoted service to the Indian people themselves! All this has earned us rights of our own in India. When the nation finds that our whole position is in jeopardy, that her whole work and duty in India is being brought to a standstill, when the nation sees our individual fellow-countrymen scattered about, with their women and children, throughout this enormous land, in hourly peril amidst the Indian multitudes, when, at any moment, this may produce shocking scenes, then I think there will be a sharp awakening, then, I am sure, that a reaction of the most vehement character will sweep this country and its unmeasured strength will once more be used. That, Sir, is an ending which I trust and pray we may avoid, but it is an ending to which step by step and day by day, we are being remorselessly and fatuously conducted.

"CUT ITS DIRTY THROAT"—
TRADE DISPUTES AND TRADE UNIONS
(AMENDMENT) BILL

January 28, 1931

House of Commons

The hon. Member for West Wolverhampton (Mr. W. J. Brown) always has about his speeches the merit of endeavouring to pursue a more or less connected argument, but that is the only compliment which I can bestow upon him this afternoon, because, in regard to the Measure which he is seeking to support, nothing could be more unfortunate than the speech which he has just delivered. In regard to the particular question with which the hon. Member was mainly concerned, namely, the participation of civil servants in general strikes, or their participation in party politics, we could not have had a better living example of what ought not to be the spirit of the Civil Service of any civilised country than the case which the hon. Member has so clearly and so fully laid before us to-day.

I propose this afternoon, if the House will permit me, to approach the discussion of this important question by taking one of those retrospects into the past which are often useful in judging and in facing the issues of the moment. [An Hon. Member: "1906!"] As time passes the relative values and proportions of all things change, and, when trade unions were solely concerned with industrial matters and with the interests of their members, when they were faced with many powerful political and economic forces, they seemed to have great claims for special consideration and for the favour of Parliament. No page in the history of the Conservative party is more honourable than that on which Mr. Disraeli inscribed the Act of 1875. Then in later years a series of judicial decisions seemed to alter by judge-made law the purpose which Parliament had pursued, and there was a general feeling, not by any means confined to one side, that trade unions should still be helped and should be maintained in all that was necessary to enable them effectively to conduct strikes and collective bargaining, and to do this without their funds being endangered. I well remember those days, and I expected that I should have been reminded of them. I remember how we pored over cases like Lyons *v*. Wilkins, Quinn *v*. Leatham, the Mogul Shipping Company, and finally the Taff Vale case. In those days it seemed not only wise but chivalrous to secure for the then weaker side what may be said to be reasonable and effective facilities for presenting their special points of view even in the teeth of the most powerful opposition.

It is quite true that the legislative steps which were taken by pre-War Parliaments introduced several extremely questionable and invidious principles into our law, and conferred upon British trade unionists privileges under the law which are unique. Those invidious features, vicious though they may be accused of being by purists and extreme logicians, were tolerated, because Parliament, in which organised Labour was scarcely represented at all, felt that the trade unions must have a fair chance and a square deal, and that errors, if any, within certain limits, might well be on the side of generosity. I think that is wise and right, because, in those days, trade union funds were the sole provision against unemployment. The vacancy books of the trade unions were the only apparatus for finding jobs for men out of work, and the trade unions also discharged the function of friendly and benefit societies in respect to sickness and other calamaties which, apart from voluntary agencies, were at that time entirely neglected by the State.

Mr. Thorne: So they do now.

Mr. Churchill: That is quite true, but they are now on a national scale. Trade unionism in its day discharged all those functions. But the situation now is very different from the situation in 1926 and 1927 when the legislation which it is now proposed to repeal was passed. By legislation the whole scene was transformed and the State has largely relieved trade unions of a very large part of their responsibilities for unemployment and sickness benefit and has provided for these matters by national insurance. Trade unionism which before the War still seemed to be in a position of what we call the underdog, has grown into a vast and enormously powerful national organism on a scale and with a strength not equalled in the social structure of any large civilised country. Meanwhile, our industries began to flag under many heavy burdens, and our industrial supremacy which we relied upon with such overweening confidence has already passed away. I submit that these were rather important alterations in values and proportions, and Parliament in any case, whatever else had happened, would have been bound in time to have taken into consideration all those changes.

A far greater change than any of those has also taken place. The trade unions have become political organisations of the highest consequence, and they have formed the basis of a great new political party which has been erected upon them, which develops its own views on every aspect of public affairs, which formulates its own foreign and Imperial policy, and which embraces in its scope every subject of interest to the country. Finally, in devouring the Liberal party this new party founded upon trade unionism—[An Hon. Member: "You had the first bite!"]—in devouring the Liberal party this new party became the only foundation for alternative government. This bringing of trade unions directly into politics is one of the most remarkable evolutions we have seen in our social and domestic life in our own time. It is not for me to say that it is wholly bad. This is still a free country, and everyone is entitled to do what he chooses under our justly framed laws.

The introduction of trade unionism into the very centre of party politics has certainly produced a very great change in the relations between our Parliamentary institutions taken as a whole and trade unionism. So far as trade unionism is concerned, the results, I think, have been, very largely, unfortunate. So far as the State is concerned, it obviously requires a complete review of the position of trade unions and of the privileges—not the rights, but the privileges—accorded to them. Their privileged position under the law, which was accorded to them for the sake of the industrial functions which they discharged, obviously required to be re-examined in the light of their immense political activity. It was gravely injurious to the State and to the nation that party politics—not general politics, but party politics, and the special partisanship and prejudice which they necessarily entail—should be intermingled with industrial matters. It was bad for politics, it was worse for industry. That was the change which had taken place, and of which we were bound to take notice.

Privileges in this country are always liable to be called in question— [*Interruption.*] Perhaps, if they are used with discretion, they may long be allowed to survive, but when privileges indulgently accorded to the weak are violently and overbearingly exploited by the strong—[*Interruption*]—and when those privileges come into collision, not only with the rights of the individual, but with the interests of the State—[*Interruption*]—then it becomes necessary that Parliament should recur to the rights, and not to the privileges, of individuals and make laws which define the relationship of one class to another. [*Interruption.*] I am not in the least perturbed by this uneasy clamour by which hon. Gentlemen opposite seek to conceal the fact that they are accorded privileges under the law—[*Interruption*]—which have no parallel in the Constitution of this or of scarcely any other country. By all means let them give their loud cheers, because they will have every need to derive what encouragement they can during the progress of this Debate.

All these matters were brought to a head by the General Strike of 1926. A trade dispute was in progress—[An Hon. Member: "Which you provoked!"]. I am going to follow out my argument, and, like the hon. Member for West Wolverhampton, to pursue the methods of connected argument. With regard to the General Strike, which arose out of a trade dispute in the coal industry, and was espoused by the whole trade union organisation throughout the land, a document was published, to which reference was made by the right hon. and learned Member for Spen Valley (Sir J. Simon), under the authority of the Trade Union Congress, stating, in effect, that, unless the Government came to terms with the miners, a general strike would be declared in, I think, 48 hours. Every industry, every form of communication, nearly every public service and convenience, including the supply and distribution of food, was to be paralysed.

Enormous injury and suffering was threatened to the whole population. London was to be made to walk. The light was to be cut off. The docks, shipping, and even the newspapers, were to be laid under the ban of what was called The General Staff of Labour. Infected by a militarism which I cannot too greatly deplore, they explained in their document how the different waves of workers in the various industries were to be mobilised and flung in calculated succession, in well-considered sequence, against the fabric of the Government and the State. First, the larger and heavier unions were to come forward, and afterwards, when, as it were, everything was rocking and shaking, a whole host of complicated secondary trades were to be thrown in. All this was laid down with carefully calculated efficiency and forethought, and presented to the public as an ultimatum, as a challenge to the Government of the day, but also to much more than the Government of the day—to the Constitution of this country. Either the Government would be forced by this process to surrender or to give place to another Administration which could claim that it alone could supply the necessary services and food to the people and carry on the existence of the nation, or else the demands that were pressed forward on behalf of the miners would have to be conceded.

This extraordinary event was only the culmination of nearly 10 years of threats of a general strike, or a strike of a similar character, which had overhung the nation ever since the Great War. Of course, if such a challenge had been successful, it would have altered completely the constitutional Parliamentary system of this country. I admit, naturally, that many of the leaders of the trade unions, and also many of the leaders of the Parliamentary party, were deeply alarmed and distressed at the formidable and even disgraceful character of the enterprise on which they saw themselves embarked. They would gladly have accepted a modified surrender of the Government of the day which would have left them with the tremendous weapon of a general strike unused, intact, mysterious, hanging always over us as the supreme threat in the background. It was obvious, to me at any rate, and I make no secret of it, that from the moment when that document was issued there ought to be no further negotiations of any kind until it was unconditionally withdrawn. [*Interruption.*] I argued consistently in that sense. What followed is still so fresh in the memory of the House that I do not think I need hurt the feelings of hon. Gentlemen opposite by further dwelling upon it.

It was upon the morrow of this cataclysm that the Government of the day began to consider the necessary curtailment of trade union privileges—not rights—which bitter experience had shown to be imperative. My right hon. Friend the Leader of the Opposition, in moving the rejection of this Bill last week in a speech of characteristic moderation and sagacity, explained how careful he had been not to act in haste or resentment, and how he had waited for nearly a whole year so that opinion should cool down and the Measure presented to Parliament should bear no element or traces of the fierce contention through which all parties in this country had passed. It was not until 1927 that our Bill was introduced. The House is familiar with all its provisions, but they cannot be too often repeated in their simplicity. I hope they are going to be repeated on every platform in the country. We thought that a general strike such as that of 1926 should be proclaimed an illegal conspiracy. Intimidation, particularly in the home, was not only declared to be a departure from the existing law, but, as has been well said, was for general information declared to be specifically illegal; thirdly, it was declared that Conservative and Liberal trade unionists would not be compelled to pay for Socialist Cabinets in Parliament, and would be freed from the invidious position of having to contract out of the so-called political levy. Lastly, on the point which was dealt with by the hon. Member for West Wolverhampton in his speech, civil servants were enjoined to give undivided allegiance to the State. These important principles which were then proclaimed in that Measure carried with them at the time, and, I belive, carry with them to this moment, the overwhelming allegiance of the mass of the nation. [*Interruption.*] It is those principles that this Bill, which the Attorney-General has introduced, seeks to subvert.

No one can pretend—let me make this point clear at the outset of this passage in my remarks—no one can pretend that the Labour party have any grievance under the Constitution. On the contrary, they are the pampered pets, the spoiled darlings of the Constitution. The representatives of the most extreme opinions come into this Parliament with fewer votes behind them than any other class of Members who sit in this House. The Liberals might have a grievance, but the Labour party has no grievance under the Constitution. When they come into Parliament, they are treated with an indulgence and a consideration that no other party receives. They are enabled to form Governments one after another although they are in a minority. They are enabled to retain power in spite of mismanagement and incapacity—[*Interruption*]—which would have shattered half-a-dozen Administrations of the Liberal or the Conservative parties. What, I should like to know, would happen to a Conservative or Liberal Government if we had seen unemployment rise by 1,500,000 in a year—[*Interruption*]—while the Government of the day sat helpless without bringing forward one single illuminating or constructive idea?

So far from having a grievance, this new party, founded on the trade unions, have, under the Constitution of this country, been treated with exceptional indulgence and consideration. Do they bear their advantages with modesty? Listen to the Secretary of State for War, speaking in the debate last week. His attitude was an example, if I may say so, of very unseemly arrogance. [*Interruption.*]

Our party—

he said, and I thoroughly agree with him here—

Our party has got beyond the point when it is to be patronised.

Then why are they claiming these privileges?

> It has got to the point where it demands—not asks, but demands—the
> right to work through its organisation in the way it wishes.

Their wish is to be our law.

> If you want to prevent revolution—

language so suited to the position he occupies as the head of a great disciplined
force—[*Interruption*.] That again is language which I do not think ought to be used on
his behalf in this or in any other connection.

> If you desire to have discontent, if you desire that the country should
> be upset, then try to stop us from doing our own work in our own
> way.—[Official Report, 22nd January, 1931; col. 498, Vol. 247.]

That is the whole claim that we who oppose this Measure make. You are asking to set
up a power within a power, a separate force within the State claiming to be immune
from the ordinary restraints of law which the Constitution imposes on all other
citizens. It has been said, "It is an assured sign of a noble and worthy spirit whom
power amends." I do not think there is a very general feeling in the House that power
has greatly amended the Secretary of State for War. The quotation which seems much
more accurately to apply to him is taken from the Bible "But Jeshurun waxed fat, and
kicked." Of the many points in this Bill, I propose to touch upon two only. The first is
the political levy. It was quite inevitable, as those who have followed the historical
retrospect that I have imposed on the House will see, that the change in the character
of trade unions should bring about a change in the law affecting the political levy. As
long as trade unions were non-party, looking after the interests of their members,
absorbed in what they called bread and butter politics, no member of a trade union
was seriously injured by subscribing as a matter of course to the so-called political
levy. But from the moment when trade unions became an active weapon of party
warfare, directly identified with one particular set of political opinions, identified with
one party competing in the ordinary business of our elections, it became intolerable
that Conservative or Liberal working men should be forced by undue pressure, if there
was undue pressure, to pay for the expenses of candidates against whom they were
going to vote. It is an insult to the whole status of the manual labourer and to the
whole conception of equal citizenship that Liberals should be forced to pay for
Socialism, or that patriotic Conservative workmen should be forced to pay for the
election—[*Interruption*.] Allow me to make my point. If you obstruct my making it,
they will only think you are afraid of it. An hon. Member opposite said fear was the
sign of a guilty conscience. To make a patriotic Conservative pay for the expenses of a
cosmopolitan pacifist, to make a Roman Catholic, or a devout Anglican, or a Noncon-
formist pay a political levy in order that a secularist or an atheist should be returned to
Parliament, to compel all these things upon the members of the trade union, I do not

care how few they may be—[*Interruption*.] I am in favour of toleration, and toleration itself is invaded when even a farthing is taken from a deeply religious working man and used to support candidates of a different belief.

Mr. Speaker: The Debate will not be enhanced by unnecessary interruptions.

Mr. McKinley: On a point of Order. My point is that hon. Members opposite have asked for it. They interrupted the Lord Advocate.

Mr. Churchill: I have not the slightest intention of offending hon. Members. I am putting this abstract point. I will put it in a way which perhaps will not irritate. For instance, the subscription of a Roman Catholic working man ought not to be taken, not even a farthing, to support the kind of Bill which was so violently opposed by Roman Catholics, among others, brought into the House last week. If hon. Members do not like these comparatively mild and conciliatory remarks, I do not know how they will feel before I have finished. It is altogether a wrong point of view to assume that the moral and political feelings of working men can be treated with a spirit of rough and ready indifference and that you can say, "Oh well, it does not matter. Let them subscribe to the union. That is the most important thing they have to do." It is not true. They feel intensely on these matters, and they have an absolute right to be protected, even meticulously, against being enlisted against their consciences in any way.

We have repeatedly heard the argument that there never was any compulsion, that all a man had to do was to sign a paper saying he did not wish to subscribe, and that this perfectly simple easy action on his part was not the slightest burden and enabled him to contract out of the political levy. Then we are told that there is this inertia, that trade unions will be unfairly depleted in their funds if the fact that people have to take the positive step of saying they will contract in is imposed upon them. I agree with the hon. and learned Gentleman the Member for East Nottingham (Mr. Birkett) that the figures quoted by the Attorney-General on this subject completely sweep away this inertia argument. He showed quite plainly that, in trade unions where there is at present an ardent desire to contribute, or a general desire to contribute, the fact that they have to contract in has been no impediment, not only to the maintenance, but to a large increase of membership, and he quoted in particular the Durham miners. Those men wished to contribute to the union and the union, after our Bill was passed in 1927, largely increased its membership. Why? Because these men have done what they choose. That is just what they ought to be allowed to do. But there are other unions in the figures he quoted where there has been a very large decline in membership, and that, I think, is equally justified, and shows that there again individuals are not so united in one party. There are more Conservative or Liberal trade unionists in these other unions, and they do not wish to be involved in the funds or the party business of the Socialist party. There, again, they have been allowed to exercise a perfectly natural, healthy and honest decision.

The inertia argument has been completely disposed of by the figures of the Durham miners given by the Attorney-General, and the allegation that there was no grievance is overwhelmingly contradicted by the large decline that has taken place in the membership of many unions and in the political levies of many unions since this new liberty has been accorded to the working-class. I do not wish to be unfair. I quite admit that there are many important unions where a man would have contracted out of the political levy under the old system and would have never heard a word about it again, but there are also a number of unions where you would have heard about it. After all, to make a man write a letter, or fill in a form, contracting out is to require from him an act of exceptional initiative, an overt act which many men are reluctant to take. They do not wish to come into prominence, to put themselves against the general scheme of opinion among their mates. Why should they not be free even from the slightest sign of an invidious pressure?

Compare the act of contracting out of a trade union with the important act of voting at a Parliamentary election. Voting at a Parliamentary election nowadays, when the universal character of the suffrage has so greatly diminished the consequence of each individual voter's vote, I should have thought was a far easier test of civic virility, or courage, than contracting out of a trade union, and yet observe with what care Parliament has surrounded this act of putting a cross on a piece of paper against the name of one of two or three gentlemen none of whom is particularly attractive to the voter, guarding the secrecy of the ballot so effectively that the voter, when he enters the booth, is absolutely alone with himself and his maker. If it were sought to make the slightest intrusion upon the secrecy of the ballot, all parties in the House would be up in arms, and none more than the party opposite.

Just because in this far more invidious case of contracting in or contracting out of the trade union levy they have an interest which is not a trade union interest, which is not an industrial interest, which is a party political interest, just because of their party political interest they are determined to exact from the individual that he shall take the positive, overt act unless his money is to be taken for a policy which he detests. I was very glad to hear from the speech of the hon. and learned Member for East Nottingham that this feature of the Measure would, at any rate, receive careful attention from the Liberal party in what I am afraid I shall have to call another place. After all, this political levy question is not the most important, and it is the one on which there is a general agreement that the Goverment's proposals cannot be accepted.

The main feature of the Bill is the legislation legalising the General Strike. I must ask the House for great indulgence if I trench at all upon the legal aspects, but I am only a layman, and I can rely upon the many distinguished lawyers who are present to assist me if I should trip in any particular phrase. I thought that the speech of my right hon. and learned Friend the Member for Spen Valley (Sir J. Simon) made matters so plain that even as a layman I could quite easily comprehend them. As far as I can make out, what has happened is this. The Attorney-General received instructions from the Trade Union Congress to legalise what happened in 1926. The Attorney-General, having to win his footing and work his passage, addressed himself to his task with praiseworthy diligence. The question raised by the right hon. and learned Member for Spen Valley, which is of great interest and of great complexity, is this: Has he succeeded in his purpose or not? Let me remind the House of the question of the right hon. and learned Gentleman. "If," he said, "the circumstances of 1926 recurred, and this Bill were law, does the Attorney-General hold that the strike of 1926 would be legal, or not?" That is the question.

I am sure that the Attorney-General has the matter at his fingers' ends, and, as our greatest authority at the moment on this question, I am sure he will not leave the House in any doubt on the matter, and I will gladly give place to him if he will answer.

[Hon. Members: "Answer!"] Is the Attorney-General going to leave a point of pure technical legality which concerns him in his professional capacity to be dealt with by the breezy eloquence of the Dominions Secretary when the House wants the opinion of the Attorney-General. I want to know the opinion of the Attorney-General. There is really no need for the hon. and learned Gentleman to have such a scared outlook on affairs. The House is very generous. It is quite prepared to let bygones be bygones. Let him get up like a man and give us the answer. I have done all I can do to compel the hon. and learned Gentleman. I am left to draw my own conclusion, which is, that he has tried his best, and is not absolutely sure that he has succeeded. But here is where the trade unions, I think, owe the hon. and learned Gentleman a tribute of regard and of respect, because he has a second string.

He has not risked the legalising of the event of 1926 merely upon the Amendments to Sub-section (1) of the previous Act. He has reinforced this with a second line of defence. He has a second barrel in the shape of the Amendments to Sub-section (2). This is a most ingenious provision, for which, I am sure, his trade union supporters, or perhaps I should say masters, will be deeply grateful to him. It is a simple provision, a simple, ingenious, dilatory provision, which gives immunity to persons engaged in any strike, whether legal or not legal, whether revolutionary or industrial, whether against the State or against society, or merely against the local employer. It does not matter what the strike is, you need not worry about any of these legal subtleties and trouble about interpretation in Courts of law. The Attorney-General has given an immunity by a dilatory process, which, at any rate, I am assured, will last for three weeks—a fortnight or three weeks at the very least—before the necessary declaration of the High Court can be given. If that be so, I think that the trade unions owe him a great debt of gratitude. If he is called in question, if, being a newcomer in the party, they have any doubts about him, he is entitled to say to them, "I cannot be sure about making the event of 1926 legal if it should recur again, but, whether it is legal or not, it will take three weeks to get a decision from the High Court which will sweep away your immunity for anything you may do meanwhile, and that ought to be good enough."

There is great practical weight and reason behind the Attorney-General when he says that. After all, three weeks of a general strike—even a fortnight of making London walk, would wear out their shoe leather—if in three weeks of a general strike you are not able to knock out the nation, do not be too sure the nation will not have knocked you out. The hon. and learned Gentleman discharged his task with great thoroughness, and he fully deserved the loud and prolonged cheers which his lengthy but admirable introductory speech won from his party, and I do not understand that he denies a single one of these points. There never was such a Bill as this, a Bill to give immunity, three weeks "cut and run" at the nation without any chance of being called in question—absolute immunity for everything.

I must say a word about the procedure which we have to adopt. I am a little sorry not to see the right hon. Member for Carnarvon Boroughs (Mr. Lloyd George) in his place. Looking upon the Liberal party without him is always to be conscious of a very serious gap. I understand from what the Prime Minister said at Question time that this Bill is to be taken away from the House of Commons. After the Division to-night, if the Bill should pass, it is to go upstairs and there, in all probability, it is to be subject to the activities of the Kangaroo Closure, and the Liberal party have decided to support this. It is a parliamentary outrage of the first order. I have had nearly 30 years experience in this House, and I have never seen a like abuse of the procedure of Grand Committees. This is a Bill, not one of meticulous detail, but a Bill which raises at every point very large, broad, simple principles which are particularly suited to discussion on the Floor of the House, and about which the nation has every right to be permitted to hear.

Here are the Liberal party! I do not blame them for doing what they think is right with their votes on these Measures. One sees the great difficulty of their position—I may say, the great and increasing difficulty of their position, but I say that for a minority party, for a party with the traditions of the Liberal party, for a party having the greatest interest—[An Hon. Member: "You are one of the traditions!"] I am reminding them of them. The party have great and responsible interests in protecting the rights of minorities. They have a further interest—the greatest interest—in safeguarding Parliamentary procedure, and the means by which due public discussion is secured about questions on which there is a great deal of feeling. All those are not merely their traditions but their special care and their direct interest, and that they should, by their decision, take this Bill away from the Floor of the House of Commons and put it upstairs, and deny the great mass of Members of Parliament, with all their constituents the opportunity of taking part in these Debates, is an astounding act.

The right hon. Gentleman the Member for Carnarvon Boroughs told us the other day, on a question of the same kind on another Measure, what were his doctrines on Procedure. They were very remarkable. They were expressed with his usual candour. "It all depends," he said, "on these questions of procedure whether you like the Bill or not." If you like the Bill—I am not quoting him any more—then, of course, away with Parliamentary forms and cumbersome debate, slap it through by the quickest and most expeditious method possible. If you do not like it, then out will come all the constitutional arguments about the rights of Parliament and the interests of minorities, of which the Liberal party have always been the champions. Then will be the time for the peroration about the cause "for which Hampden died in the field and Sidney on the scaffold." Those are the ethics of Parliamentary procedure as expounded by the leader of the Liberal party. No one can deny that the right hon. Gentleman the Member for Carnarvon Boroughs and the party which he leads take infinite pains in coming to a decision whether they like or dislike any particular Measure. Although we are not permitted to take part in their discussions, we are interested in their decisions, and the House has resounded with the echoes of their conclaves and perturbations. Once they have decided to like a Bill, that is the end of Parliamentary procedure so far as the minority in the House of Commons is concerned. But, in this case, the Liberal party and their leader seemed to have very great difficulty in deciding whether they like or dislike their Bill, so they came to a compromise by agreeing, as far as I can make out, not to dislike it too much here, but to hate it like poison hereafter. The hon. and learned Member for East Nottingham was deputed to explain what was to be done to the Bill. The execution is to be in private and it is to be ruthless. After I had listened to his account, which is fresh in the minds of those who have followed these Debates, I could not see that anything was left of the Bill, except possibly the Title. That is the procedure they have decided upon.

What are the Government and the Labour party going to do about it, and what is the Prime Minister going to do? I spoke the other day, after he had been defeated in an important Division, about his wonderful skill in falling without hurting himself. He falls, but up he comes again, smiling, a little dishevelled, but still smiling. But this is a juncture, a situation, which will try to the very fullest the peculiar arts in which he excels. I remember, when I was a child, being taken to the celebrated Barnum's circus, which contained an exhibition of freaks and monstrosities, but the exhibit on the programme which I most desired to see was the one described as "The Boneless Wonder." My parents judged that that spectacle would be too revolting and demoralising for my youthful eyes, and I have waited 50 years to see the boneless wonder sitting on the Treasury Bench.

We have made our protest against this Bill. We have made our protest also against a procedure for which the Liberal party bear a keen responsibility, but it seems to me that the real grievance lies with the trade unions. They seem to me, after all has been said and done, the parties who are being deceived in this matter. I was not invited to the conference that took place last week in Downing Street between the Prime Minister and the leader of the Liberal party, but "my hon. friend the Member for Treorchy" gave me a very shrewd account of the interview between the two party leaders. After the usual compliments, the Prime Minister said, "We have never been colleagues, we have never been friends—at least, not what you would call holiday friends—but we have both been Prime Minister, and dog don't eat dog. Just look at the monstrous Bill the trade unions and our wild fellows have foisted on me. Do me a service, and I will never forget it. Take it upstairs and cut its dirty throat."

INDIA

January 30, 1931

Free Trade Hall, Manchester

On January 28 Churchill resigned from the Opposition Business Committee and ceased to be a member of the Front Opposition Bench. Until September 1939 he spoke from the back benches as an independent Conservative.

This speech was made at the second meeting held under the auspices of the Indian Empire Society.

We have come here to Manchester to utter our solemn warning against the policy which the Socialist Government has pursued in India. It is our conviction that unless this policy is arrested it will bring a fatal disaster upon the British Empire and entail endless misery to hundreds of millions of harmless Indian subjects of the King. I feel obliged to claim complete party independence upon the Indian crisis, and I come here, where so much of my political work has been done, to ask for your earnest attention upon matters which are the deep concern of the nation. . . .

A draft federal Constitution for India with Dyarchy and responsible Government at the centre has been framed. In the words of the Socialist Lord Chancellor, 'the responsibility for the Federal Government of India will in future'—mark the words 'in future'—'rest on Indians themselves.' This Constitution was very loosely put together. Not one of the thorny problems of Indian life or the real difficulties of machinery was settled. The gaps and faults in the structure were covered up with clouds of perorations and pious platitudes, and the result, embodied in a small Blue Book, is now to be hawked around India, already in a dangerously excited condition, in the hopes of winning more acceptance. It is this scheme which we are told the Conservative party will have to implement when it comes back into office. Of course, we are assured there are all kinds of safeguards. What is given in the word is taken back in the fact; what is given with one hand is taken away with the other. Sir Samuel Hoare, speaking with great ability in the House of Commons, laid down a list of safeguards and reservations which if they were made effective would reduce responsible government of India by Indians and early Dominion status for all India to very small dimensions. We are told to rely upon these safeguards, and that we shall all fight solidly together for them. I hope it may be so, but the Prime Minister is already apologising to the Indian newspapers for the safeguards, and the Secretary of State for India (Mr. Wedgwood Benn) says that we shall be 'compelled' to give full self-government to India.

It is also argued that we cannot afford to have party divisions in this country about India, because then the Socialist party will when in Opposition make the government of India impossible. This is a very grave argument, and everyone should give full weight to it. Nevertheless, I do not think we can accept it, because it means that the Socialist party in practice will be the final deciding factor in the whole of our policy towards India, and the Conservative party will be simply tied to its tail. I think upon this supreme question of India, which is no ordinary question of politics but involves the life of the British Empire, we ought to stand up for what we believe and face the consequences, whatever they may be. If the worst comes upon England and her Empire, let us make sure, above all things, that it does not come through us. Moreover, experience shows that the only safe plan for human action is to act with great simplicity, and give judgment on the merits of questions at each particular stage. I fear very greatly, if we continue to drift and jog along with the Socialists in their Indian policy, that when the time comes and we can go no further, our resisting power will be gone, and they will drag us all over the precipice with them.

But now let us see what has been happening in India. The Viceroy, a well-meaning man of the highest personal character, has had to cope with steadily increasing disorder. He put off arresting Mr. Gandhi as long as possible. Eight months ago, however, Gandhi's lawlessness became so flagrant that Lord Irwin was forced to lock him up. Instead of bringing him to trial and punishing him according to law, he locked him up as a State prisoner, and then tried to negotiate with him while he was in gaol. Gandhi, who is a fanatic and an ascetic of the fakir type well known in the East, rejected these overtures with contempt. But you can imagine how his prestige throughout India was raised by the fact that the mighty Indian Government first made him a martyr in the eyes of his fellows, and then, while he was actually their captive, solicited his aid. Now that the Round Table Constitution has been drafted and sent out to India 'on approval,' Gandhi and thirty of his leading fellow-conspirators and revolutionaries have been set at liberty, unconditionally, in the hopes that they will at any rate say some kind words about the scheme.

As might have been expected, Gandhi was received rapturously by his followers. He has been made a martyr under very comfortable conditions, and a national hero without running any risk, and he now emerges on the scene a triumphant victor. It did not take him long to launch his new defiance at the Government of India. Nearly 25,000 of his followers had already been imprisoned under the Socialist policy of conciliation. Gandhi, of course, demands that they shall be released. He insists that the picketing of British shops and factories, the breaking of the law about salt, the boycotting of foreign cloth—you in Lancashire have something to do with that, I believe—and civil disobedience generally must continue. If the Government of India accept this and withdraw all the ordinances they have had to pass to keep the peace, then he will, perhaps, be graciously pleased to examine how far the new Constitution falls short of his declared aim of absolute and speedy independence for India. We have yet to learn what the answer of his Majesty's Government and the Government of India will be to these demands and to this situation. Surely the situation ought to have been expected. In fact, if the Viceroy and the Socialist Government had wished to manufacture and foment disorder instead of hoping to quiet it, they could hardly have acted otherwise than they have done.

The reason why, in my judgment, Lord Irwin, for all his virtue and courage, has not succeeded in India as he deserved to, is that he has been proceeding upon a wrong mental theme. His attitude towards India has throughout been an apology. He has not shown sufficient confidence in the indispensable work which our country has done, and is doing, for India, or in British resolution that it shall not be interrupted or destroyed. That is the sole foundation upon which the peaceful and successful administration of India can be based. It is never possible to make concessions to Orientals when they think you are weak or are afraid of them. If they once think they have got you at a disadvantage all their moods become violent, concessions are treated as valueless, and necessary acts of civil represion often only add fuel to the flames. This Viceroy, who meant so well and tried so hard, and has always been perfectly fearless where he himself was concerned, has had to enact more repressive measures and inflict more punishments and make greater curtailments of liberty and imprison more thousands of people than has ever happened before in India. And yet all these severities have been no more effective than his concessions and kindly words. Things have gone from bad to worse, and they are now all to be aggravated again.

What is wanted at this moment in India is not more repression or more concession. It is a fundamental change in the intellectual and moral attitude of Great Britain and of the Government of India, which is a reflection of Great Britain. Instead of proclaiming, as this unwise Constitutional Blue Book does, that our object is to wind up our affairs and hand over the government of India to the tiny oligarchy of Indian politicians who have raised this agitation, we ought to begin now by making it perfectly clear that we intend to remain the effective rulers of India in every essential for a very long and indefinite period, and that though we welcome co-operation in every branch of government from loyal and faithful Indians, we will have no truck with lawlessness or treason, and will, if necessary, suspend even the most moderate Constitutional changes while there is a bad spirit abroad.

Now you will rightly say to me, 'Is this not contrary to all our experience of the self-governing Dominions of the British Empire, and is it not contrary to what you did yourself in South Africa and in Ireland?' I answer, 'Yes, it is contrary.' The problem of Indian government is entirely different from any of the problems we have hitherto faced in any part of the world. India is a continent nearly as large as Europe, and, like Europe, it has now between three and four hundred millions of people. There are scores of nations and races in India and hundreds of religions and sects. Out of the three hundred and fifty millions of Indians only a very few millions can read or write, and of these only a fraction are interested in politics and Western ideas. The rest are primitive people absorbed in the hard struggle for life. They are dependent for their livelihood and for the happiness and peace of their humble homes upon the rule of a very small number of white officials who have no personal interests of their own to serve, who are quite impartial between race and race, and who have built up in 150 years an organisation which has given these enormous masses peace, justice, and a substantial increase in material well-being, which would have been even greater except for the vast increase in their numbers. This organisation and the great services by which it operates depends for its efficiency, and indeed for its existence, upon its authority. If that authority is weakened, or discredited, or loses confidence in itself, or is hampered and broken up, measureless disasters will descend upon these three hundred and fifty million perfectly helpless poor folk. They will soon be reduced to the miserable condition of the people of China, where anarchy has now reigned for many years and tyranny for ages.

We have, therefore, a supreme moral duty to discharge to the Indian people. We have no right whatever to hand them over to a comparatively small and utterly unrepresentative political faction, to be the prey of misgovernment, of deterioration in every public service, of religious bigotry of a kind not dreamed of for generations in the West, and finally of civil war. While we have strength we must discharge our duty. Neither taunts nor blandishments should move us from it. When we can no longer discharge our duty, then our reign in India is done, and many other great things in the history of the British Empire will come to their close at the same time.

But I shall be asked, 'Have we the strength to carry out our task? Will not great numbers of soldiers be required and terrible events take place?' I reply it is not a case for warlike force. Do not allow yourselves to be frightened from your duty by language of that kind. In all the disasters that have occurred in the last eighteen months hardly a single British battalion has been used in India and not a shot has been fired, except on the frontier, by British troops. The admirable Indian police, for whose fidelity and restraint no praise is too great, has been quite sufficient to cope with every disorder, and hardly any life has been lost or blood shed in the almost ceaseless mob tumult which has occurred in so many places. Confidence in ourselves and in our mission, and firm support of our faithful agents and officials, patience and perseverance, have only to be displayed—and displayed upon the theme that Britain intends to govern India for many years to come—to save reinforcements of troops or serious bloodshed. In fact, this will be the only way by which such evils can be averted.

If, however, you continue to spread far and wide throughout the vast plains and cities of India the doctrine that the British are handing over their power to some new regime as a preliminary to clearing out of the country, and as part of the decline and fall of the British Empire, then, indeed, you may have upon your hands a situation of the most terrible kind. Then, indeed, you may find your police, hitherto so loyal and trustworthy, and your native Army thrown into a profound state of perturbation, asking one another what their future is to be, and how their new masters will view their actions, and then at any moment you may find yourself in a catastrophe of a character more horrible than anything we have experienced even in the awful times through which we have lived.

Finally, you will ask me what, then, are we to make of our promises of Dominion status and responsible government. Surely we cannot break our word! There I agree. The formal, plighted word of the King-Emperor is inviolable. It does not follow, however, that every Socialist jack-in-office can commit this great country by his perorations. In the very Act of Parliament in 1919 where responsible government is mentioned in the preamble there is also a special clause, Clause 41, which makes it plain that all progress towards responsible government must only be at the discretion of the British Parliament, and that Parliament can, if it chooses, stop the progress, or slow it down, or turn it into another channel, or even retrace our path if that were necessary. Therefore, until another Act of Parliament receives the Royal assent, there is no ground whatever on which we are committed to any particular step at any particular time.

As for this expression 'Dominion status,' about which there has been so much misunderstanding: the abstraction called India, composed of so many different nations and States, is in a ceremonial sense a Dominion already. Indian representatives sit on the Imperial Conferences; they participated in the Imperial War Cabinet, and are represented in the British delegation of the League of Nations. With every mark of honour and dignity we have welcomed the aid and co-operation of eminent men among our Indian fellow-subjects. But except as an ultimate visionary goal, Dominion status like that of Canada or Australia is not going to happen in India in any period which we can even remotely foresee. It certainly could never happen until the mass of the Indian people were as well able to look after their own interests as are the Australians and Canadians of today. It is most dangerous and improvident of British political leaders of any party to try to smooth difficulties over in India by making believe that full Dominion status can possibly come to India in our time.

On the contrary, it is their duty now, while time remains, to make it clear that these ideas play no part in the important practical steps which should now be taken in constitutional reform. We should immediately proceed to build up in the provinces of India organisations of local government which will be truly related to the populations they represent and seek to serve. That is the task which, if it should succeed, will perhaps at a later stage enable another step to be taken with sureness and safety. And if it fails, if any disorders and collapses occur, the Central Government, having preserved its authority intact, will be able to come to the rescue and tow the ship off the shoals again. We should be wrong to complicate this hopeful task by trying at the same time to set up a make-believe responsible Government at the centre and summit of Indian affairs, and still more by using loose and vague language in this critical year about Dominion status. Lord Birkenhead said: 'Tell the truth to India.' Yes, indeed, tell her no more than the truth.

The loss of India, however arising, would be final and fatal to us. It could not fail to be part of a process which would reduce us to the scale of a minor Power. Holland, once our equal, was outmatched in the world in spite of all her sturdy domestic strength, and became a small continental state. But Holland suffered this eclipse without having acquired the population of a modern first-class State. We have forty-five millions in this island, a very large proportion of whom are in existence because of our world position, economic, political, imperial. If, guided by counsels of madness and cowardice disguised as false benevolence, you troop home from India, you will leave behind you what John Morley called 'a bloody chaos,' and you will find famine to greet you on the horizon on your return.

"A DISEASE OF WILL POWER"

February 2, 1931

Philharmonic Hall, Liverpool

A certain school of historians argue that some of the great events of history have been caused by disease. They attribute the decline and fall of the Roman Empire to malaria. What is the disease we are suffering from now in this island? It is a disease much more dangerous than malaria. It is a disease of the will power.

We have carried the franchise to limits far beyond those who are interested in politics. Our Parliamentary institutions are in a state of decay. Our party system which worked as well with two parties is for the time being paralysed by three. Our problems are far graver and more delicate than those of any other Great Power. We are passing through a definitely dangerous period in our history.

Is there any real attempt to think out our economic, trade, finance, and currency problems as they ought to be thought out? Are we addressing ourselves to our difficulties with the mental energy of our forefathers? Are we not just drifting along, slipping and sliding down the slope which it will be very hard to climb up again? Are we losing the art of Government in Oriental countries? Are we losing confidence in ourselves and in our mission?

All these haunting questions force themselves upon us as we contemplate the present political situation. Is there any other country in the world which would submit to have its vital business affairs, on which the livelihood of its crowded population depends, or the Government of its great Empire entrusted to a minority of Socialist incompetents who no longer represent even those who returned them to Westminster?

Is there any other country in the world which would tamely submit to being pushed out of its rights and duties in the East? Would France be chattered out of Syria or Indo-China? Would Italy relinquish her North African possessions? Would the United States be hustled out of the Philippines? All these countries assert themselves and their rights with the greatest vigour. They are all determined to make their rights and wishes in their own sphere respected. We alone seem to be afraid of our own shadow. The British lion, so fierce and valiant in bygone days, so unconquerable through all the agony of Armageddon, can now be chased by rabbits from the fields and forests of his former glory.

It is not that our strength is yet seriously impaired. We are suffering from a psychological collapse. We have only to stand erect and face our difficulties as in the days of yore, for these same difficulties to be halved. We have got to stimulate and revivify our industry and agriculture. We have got to bring our finance under a tighter control. We have got to discharge unflinchingly our duty of giving just and impartial protection to the primitive millions of India. We have got to foster and develop, not only the morale, but the economic unity of our Empire. And as an indisputable preliminary to all those heavy tasks we have got to throw this wretched, spendthrift, intriguing, grovelling Government into the street.

Twenty months ago I warned the nation of the evil that would come upon this country if a Socialist Government arrived at the summit of power. I must confess to-night that I never dreamed that it would have been possible for so much misfortune to come upon this country or for such a decline in its strength and prosperity to have occurred in the space of 20 months. We have been galloping downhill. At this moment the conjunction of bad times with the arrival of a Socialist Government seems to have taken the heart out of the country.

The present Administration have a record for failure almost unrelieved by any single event. What are they doing now? They have no idea, no inspiration, no remedy, and no plans. They have no majority in Parliament except what they can beg, borrow, barter, or steal from the Liberals from day to day. (Loud laughter and cheers.)

All is lost but office. They are afraid to resign. Perhaps it is because they are so worried by unemployment that they do not wish by giving up their jobs to add to those weekly tables which are a big national concern. (Laughter.) There is a broad general conviction throughout this country that the Socialist Government has let the working classes down, that they have lowered our strength at home and our prestige and authority abroad.

[Editor's Note: Referring to Socialist pledges regarding unemployment at the last General Election he said] : Rarely has nemesis appeared on the scene so swiftly—in 20 months. Our first remedy and an indispensable one is the restoration of public confidence. How can business enterprise revive while we are under the vulture-like menace of another Snowden Budget with its malicious turns and twists and the political uncertainty as to when a General Election will occur? But neither can be long delayed.

There is another partial but substantial remedy in the establishing of a general tariff on foreign imported manufactured articles. I have reluctantly come to believe that this is necessary. I believe that the inauguration of this tariff properly applied will give us the first chance we have had for generations for a thorough resettlement of tariff issues between us and other countries.

[Editor's Note: Alluding to the Russian Five-Year Plan he said]: To-day the Bolshevist Government was only dumping wheat, timber, and raw materials which helped some industries in this country while they harmed others. But that is only the beginning. They are engaged in a colossal scheme to turn Russia into a vast manufacturing country. Their Five-Year Plan will largely fail through inefficiency and Socialist corruption, but if only 60 per cent. of the plan reaches full fruition a new economic event of the first magnitude to the world will have occurred.

Russia will barge into the already overcrowded markets of the world with a mass of manufactured goods made by slave labour, and the Bolshevist Government will not care what price they throw them down at in the markets of other countries. Hellish deeds are being done in Russia to-day. Hundreds of thousands of people are being toiled to death with a callousness and cruelty that has never occurred since the time of the Roman Empire. People are being clubbed and tortured to death, and yet certain classes of people in this country and the Labour Government eagerly stretch forth their hands to take tainted goods produced by cruel methods. Where has the old spirit of Britain gone? (Cheers.)

APPEAL TO LIBERALS ON FISCAL QUESTION

February 3, 1931

East Toxteth Division, Liverpool

It is astute party management which brought the ex-Liberal Conservative ex-Chancellor of the Exchequer to Liverpool to appeal to the middle-class Liberals of one of the city's principal residential areas for votes for a Conservative. East Toxteth Liberals are in a position of greater simplicity than their party occupies in the House of Commons, not being hampered with the responsibility of provoking a General Election if they give too free an expression to their dislike of the Socialist Government's misdoings. Principle clearly forbids them to vote for any Socialist candidate, but I ask you to consider that party interest, self-respect, and solid conviction equally forbid their abstention from the poll on Thursday. Without injuring our own party, without diverging from the declared policy of our leaders, we can by voting for Mr. Buchan-Hepburn exercise the true function of a by-election as distinct from a General Election, which is to use it to express the view of the whole country upon the Government of the day and upon the measures of importance which it is actually trying to pass at the time of the by-election. No Liberal who votes for Mr. Buchan-Hepburn on Thursday will be compromised in his action at the General Election, when he or she will be perfectly free to make a new choice on the new situation then. In his letter to Mr. Burden, Mr. MacDonald declared that the Bill to promote further and better strikes, the Trade Disputes Bill, is the one vital issue of the election. Such a Bill must surely be more fundamentally abhorrent to Liberals than that reorientation of traditional English fiscal policy which the world situation has forced upon the consideration of English statesmen, financiers, and economists alike.

Mr. Buchan-Hepburn's attractive personality, too, is a factor that must not be lost sight of. He is a young man of independent circumstances who has resolved to devote his leisure to the service of his country in Parliament and in politics. He has trained himself for the part he aspires to play by living for years in an industrial town, and his speeches show him to possess a competent knowledge of political questions and their bearing on the lives of the electors. He has made many friends in Liverpool already and no enemies, and he has, unlike Mr. Burden, no political past to live down.

Mr. Burden's close connexion with the Liverpool police strike of 1919 is being remembered against him at almost every Conservative meeting. That police strike is said to have cost the city £100,000, and, besides that injury to the pockets of the ratepayers, it has left among a thousand men who lost their jobs a rankling sense of desertion of their cause by two Labour Administrations, while, of the two most prominent leaders of the pre-strike police union, one has long enjoyed the honour and the salary of an M.P. for a Liverpool division, while the other is now seeking election in another division. Mr. MacDonald's singling out of the Strikes Bill as the leading issue of this by-election is denounced for its humbug, because the Prime Minister knows very well that his Bill is going to be emasculated in Committee, but there is certainly a serious problem for East Toxteth Liberals to consider when they are asked to vote for one of the authors of the Liverpool police strike and at the same time for a Bill to absolve Civil servants, including the police, in certain circumstances from their allegiance to the Government of the country.

GOVERNMENT SECURITIES

February 5, 1931

House of Commons

I ventured to send a note to the Chancellor of the Exchequer that I desired to raise a question of finance upon the Adjournment this evening, and I should like to express to the right hon. Gentleman the Chancellor of the Exchequer my sense, and also the sense of hon. Members on this side of the House, at his courtesy in being present at, I believe, some personal inconvenience. I wish to ask the right hon. Gentleman a question in regard to the rumours which have been circulated to-day of an impending Development Loan. The right hon. Gentleman is no doubt aware of some considerable depreciation in the gilt-edged market, which is no doubt of a temporary character, but it has led to the belief that the issue of a somewhat considerable Development Loan is imminent. This has a very important financial bearing. Obviously, it is a competing factor with any prospect of conversion, but it also has a political significance which will excite interest in all parts of the House, and in no part more than in the quarter, or rather the octave, which is represented on the benches below the Gangway. We are all most interested to know whether there is any foundation in these rumours or not.

For my part, I have very little doubt that the Chancellor of the Exchequer has stood to his guns, and that he has repulsed all inroads upon his financial impregnability, and is still standing firm on all those principles of Treasury orthodoxy which have been inculcated upon many occupants of his office, but have never been received with more native enthusiasm than by himself. But I do not want to stand between the House and the Chancellor of the Exchequer. Can he tell us exactly what has happened? It is not for us to judge, still less to pre-judge, the event, but it is for us to ask whether at this moment he has any statement to make to the House.

UNEMPLOYMENT INSURANCE (NO. 2) BILL

February 18, 1931

House of Commons

The right hon. Member for Penryn (Sir J. Tudor Walters) always speaks so agreeably and weaves his details together in so harmonious a fashion that everyone has greatly enjoyed the feat of prestidigitation to which we have just been treated. How the right hon. Gentleman managed, with that £30,000,000 to build 100,000 houses and keep 500,000 men all the time those houses were being built, paying them, no doubt, the proper rates of wages appropriate to their skilled trades, and at the end find the £30,000,000 has been saved from money that would otherwise have gone out in unemployment benefit, so that we kept all those men in employment and had 100,000 beautiful cottages for labourers for nothing, filled us with admiration. It occurred to me while he was speaking, and putting all these things in such an attractive way, what a very salutory rule of Parliament it is that no formal Motion involving expenditure can be submitted in this House without the assent of some responsible Minister of the Crown. Otherwise, carried away by these rosy schemes and pictures, we should soon find ourselves voting £30,000,000 for housing on Monday, £30,000,000 for roads on Tuesday, £30,000,000 for telephone extensions on Wednesday, and so on, until finally, on Saturday, when the House was sitting no longer, the Liberal party would be able to adjourn and hold a meeting in favour of economy.

It seems to me that two sets of questions are involved in this Debate on the Second Reading of this Bill. The first is a very simple question to answer. Everyone knows the answer. There would be an overwhelming measure of agreement upon the answer. Some, no doubt, would be afraid of blurting the answer out, but on the whole, I believe, everyone knows what the answer ought to be. That question is, What ought to be done about the Unemployment Insurance Fund? There is another question which is the riddle of the Sphinx—what are the causes and what are the remedies for the present world collapse in enterprise and industry? I am going to touch upon both those points, and, if the House will permit me, I will take the first one first, in order to clear the ground. All, or at any rate the great majority, agree that the insurance scheme should be placed upon a sound actuarial basis, that the abuses, what the right hon. Member for Carnarvon Boroughs (Mr. Lloyd George) called "cadging on the dole," which are legal, should be purged, and that all those who have run through their benefits—the benefits for which they have paid—should pass out of insurance altogether and should receive aid from the Exchequer through other agencies. Everyone knows there was little or no need for a Royal Commission to give us information on these points. Too well does the party opposite know what they ought to do about the Unemployment Insurance Fund. They do not want the Royal Commission to tell them. They want the Royal Commission not to tell them.

I am bound to say that I think my hon. and right hon. Friends on this bench, and also the Liberal representatives on the joint committee, were very much ill-treated. Let us see what happened about this joint committee. The Government got into office by reviling their predecessors, and by boasting that they could cure or deal with unemployment. After a while we found that, instead of unemployment being cured it was doubled, and more than doubled, and then the Government appealed to their political opponents for aid, and the joint committee was set up. It laboured during the months of the summer holidays. What happened then? Of course, a veil of secrecy has been thrown over its proceedings, and I have not been apprised of what passed behind that veil, but I have a fairly shrewd suspicion of what was afoot. The joint committee was getting too near the meat. They began to see unitedly and quite clearly what ought to be done. The Prime Minister and his Government were alarmed at this deadly danger. I do not blame the Prime Minister; I pity him. I do not blame any man for not committing suicide. But everyone knows perfectly well what to do about the Unemployment Insurance Fund, and everyone also knows that the Labour party is incapable of doing it.

So the Prime Minister acted. He broke up the committee, and the Chancellor of the Exchequer unchivalrously, ungenerously, unscrupulously and inaccurately spread the tale that it was all because the Conservative and Liberal representatives had got no ideas of any value to contribute, whereas the actual case was the exact reverse, that the members of the committee began to see their duty staring them in the face, and that duty was one the Socialist party could never discharge. Then the Prime Minister broke up the committee and established this Royal Commission, in order to stave off the whole matter as long as possible. At the time he did it he felt that he might very soon be dismissed from power. However, he was not dismissed, and the weeks have passed and are growing into months, and, meanwhile, the Royal Commission goes padding along and begins to browse up the same road that the committee took. Hanging over the heads of the Government is the report of this Royal Commission, which will tell them to do things which, whatever their wishes, whatever their convictions, they have not got the civic strength and political virtue to accomplish. Nevertheless, one cannot deny that the evil day has been postponed, and, of course, something may always turn up to change the situation.

Meanwhile, I do not think the extreme Members of the party opposite ought to be too hard on the Government. Undoubtedly, the Government can meanwhile truly and honestly proclaim in their party meetings, and to their supporters about the country, that by every device and by every dodge, by every shift and, almost, by every turpitude, they have managed to keep on paying for the longest time in the loosest fashion the largest doles to the largest number. They have something to show for being Socialists. The Prime Minister and the Chancellor of the Exchequer are quite entitled to say to their friends, "It is true we had no remedies, no plans, no ideas and no energy, but, anyhow, show us any Government in the civilised world which could have shovelled out so much money to the unemployed in an equal time." That is a proud boast.

The Chancellor of the Exchequer has been a party to all this, perhaps an unwilling party. I can imagine his difficulties, probably, better than anyone in the House, because he has been one against many. The right hon. Gentleman cannot dictate to the Cabinet, and no Chancellor of the Exchequer ought to dictate to the Cabinet, but he can of course resign. Any Chancellor of the Exchequer can do that, and have his place filled by a worse man. Nevertheless, the Chancellor of the Exchequer has been a compulsory conniver in these scandals, but he is a conniver none the less. The Minister of Labour said the other day that the abuses of the dole were only a very small part of the problem. That is not true from the point of view of the Chancellor of the Exchequer, because he is the guardian of the public purse. He has to raise harsh taxes; he has to demand sacrifices; he has to practise and try to prove his zeal for economy, and all this depends to a very considerable extent upon the good will and confidence of the taxpaying class; but he is hopelessly weakened and stultified when he himself becomes a party to gross waste and abuse, and when he is in the swim with those who are pouring out the money he cannot check them and dare not reprove abuses. In those circumstances, to the burden of high taxation is added the bitterness and resentment in the breasts of the taxpayers when they see their own affairs crippled for the sake, not of real need, but of real need vitiated by an admixture of waste, folly and fraud.

That is why the admitted abuses, while they remain unremedied, constitute a vast problem, far more serious even than the heavy financial waste which is attached to them would warrant. It is plain that in these circumstances the Chancellor of the Exchequer will preach in vain financial virtues and sacrifices all round and the formation of a sort of sacred union of all parties to meet a great emergency. It is useless for the right hon. Gentleman to suggest, as an example of economy, a reduction of 20 per cent. in Ministerial salaries. Cynical people will feel that action of that kind is like a man with five children in a sledge, who, when pursued by wolves, throws out one of the children in order that he may run on a little longer with the other four. I am sorry for the Chancellor of the Exchequer, and I must say that I feel differently about him this year from what I did last year. Last year the Chancellor of the Exchequer seemed to be going on triumphantly, confidently, and even arrogantly, sometimes. He claimed that all the finances were in pretty good order, that he was rectifying all the evil which had been done by his predecessors, and that everything was going to turn out satisfactorily. Where is the right hon. Gentleman now? I feel like the judges sometimes do when they say, "Unhappy man; I will not add by any word of mine to the pangs and poignancy of your position."

If anything could add to those pangs, it would be the contribution which has been made to the solution of our unemployment problem and the financial crisis by the right hon. Gentleman the Member for Carnarvon Boroughs. As far as I can make out, the right hon. Gentleman has deliberately set himself to make as difficult as possible the task of the Chancellor of the Exchequer in discharging his duty. Here they are, old friends, near neighbours, both residing in the breezy uplands of Surrey, both land taxers, both Radicals, both Cobdenites—the one by conviction and the other by profession; and now they have fallen out because the schemes of the right hon. Gentleman the Member for Carnarvon Boroughs have not been accepted. Now the right hon. Gentleman may console himself by exclaiming with Congreve:

> "Heaven has no rage like love to hatred turned,
> Nor hell a fury like a 'wizard' scorned."

It seems to me that no man in this House is less entitled to be indignant at the result of the election than the right hon. Gentleman the Member for Carnarvon Boroughs, who tried to win on the cry, "We can conquer unemployment," which was broadcast through the country. The right hon. Gentleman's scheme to spend £250,000,000 of borrowed money in order to find employment for 600,000 men was put before the country. Everyone knows that that scheme has been rejected and spat upon by every expert who has studied this question, and by every responsible Minister who has considered it. Suppose that the right hon. Gentleman had been taken at his word, and suppose—I admit it is a very wild supposition—that his scheme had worked out exactly as he said it would, and that the results which he claimed had flowed from it, where would he have been to-day? The unemployment figure to-day is 2,600,000, and if the right hon. Gentleman had spent £250,000,000 of borrowed money to provide employment for 600,000 men, instead of having conquered unemployment, he would have doubled it, in spite of the expenditure of this vast sum of money, and in spite of all the schemes initiated by the Government to provide employment. No man ought to be more modest, more subdued, and more thankful than the right hon. Gentleman.

I would prescribe for him an exercise of piety. I suggest that he should make a pilgrimage to the Arch-Druid somewhere in the remote recesses of the Welsh mountains and there with alms, ablations and burnt offerings he should offer his profound thanksgiving for his deliverance from a miserable exposure. On this important occasion this great crowning mercy which has been vouchsafed to him would even justify the most extreme measures; he might even sacrifice one of his flock, and I have no doubt that he would have no difficulty in finding a suitable victim. The right hon. Gentleman rarely acts without a purpose, and we have been watching day by day his steady campaign to gain the confidence of what is called the extreme left in British politics. Last year the right hon. Gentleman made a very unkind remark about the Attorney-General. He said that when a man was genuinely seeking work he must not discriminate in regard to the task that was set him. I though that was a very unkind remark. We laughed but wondered at its bitterness. Now we know why the right hon. Gentleman showed such extraordinary anger and irritation with the Attorney-General in that case. We know now that the Attorney-General had forestalled him and got there first. It must be very annoying to arrive at the head of an angry band of excursionists on a railway platform and find the only saloon reserved for a gentleman whom you expected to be in your personally conducted party.

I sympathise with the position of the right hon. Gentleman. He spoke the other day of the "money barons." I think it is pertinent to inquire, "Who made them barons?" [*Interruption.*] The industry of my hon. Friend the Member for North Paddington (Mr. Bracken) has unearthed some interesting statistics upon this subject, which, perhaps, I may append to those which have been given in such profusion by the right hon. Gentleman who has just sat down. On the board of every joint stock bank except the Westminster Bank there is a Lloyd Georgian peer. On the board of the Westminster Bank there are two Lloyd Georgian "money barons," while there have been added by the right hon. Gentleman to the Court of the Bank of England two peerages—the only ones of which in recent times there are records—those of Lord Cunliffe and Lord Cullen. The name of Lord Cunliffe is familiar in connection with the committee that recommended the restoration of the gold standard. Here the right hon. Gentleman has been pressing coronets upon the brows of these false guides, these men who misled him so shamefully, who led him to adopt the conclusions of the Cunliffe Committee, to carry out the severe deflation of the year 1920, to take every step during his time of responsibility, as both his Chancellors of the Exchequer can testify, in order at the proper time to re-establish the gold standard. These men misled him with their sordid veto. They stopped all his schemes for saving the country. And yet he clothed them in ermine and scarlet robes, and added, to the sordid veto that they had in the City, the suspensory veto which is still enjoyed by the House of Lords.

The purpose of the right hon. Gentleman's speech was obvious. The results, unfortunately, are obvious also. A loss of £70,000,000 or £80,000,000 has been inflicted upon British funds at a time which, though I would not for a moment say it was critical, is at any rate a time which requires delicate handling by all those who are responsible. Look at the effect produced by such a speech, say, in Australia. In that great Dominion a tremendous struggle is going forward, in which the whole country is taking part, for sound and honest methods of finance; and yet at that very moment the war-time Prime Minister of this country—a man whose name is a household word, and rightly a household word, throughout the land—sends forth a lot of loose and wild suggestions to excite the cheers of hon. Members below the Gangway, which, if they were followed in Australia, would only mean the downfall of those Socialist Ministers who are fighting for financial probity. [*Interruption.*] Look at the effect— [*Interruption.*] Really, the right hon. Gentleman is quite able to look after himself.

Mr. McGovern: On a point of Order. I want to know your Ruling on this question—if we are to sit here all night listening to this dialectical oratory— [*Interruption.*]

Mr. Speaker: That is not a point of Order.

Mr. McGovern: Is this relevant to the subject under discussion?

Mr. Speaker: Earlier this afternoon I was asked to give my Ruling as to how far this Debate should be allowed to range, and I think I had the general approval of the House in saying that it should take a very wide range.

Mr. McGovern: I want to protest—

Hon. Members: Name!

Mr. McGovern: I want to protest against our having to listen to comedians of this type when the working-class are starving.

Mr. Speaker: Mr. Churchill.

Mr. Churchill: The hon. Gentleman might really leave it to his Leader to deal with this matter.

Mr. McGovern: I would rather have him as my Leader than—[*Interruption.*]

Mr. Churchill: The people in countries abroad do not understand the context of these speeches, or the atmosphere in which they are delivered; nor do they understand the position of the party which sometimes dictates action. [*Interruption.*] I have no doubt that in many countries people have drawn in their minds a picture of the right hon. Gentleman leading a band of Cobdenites and Clydesiders to the sack of Lombard Street. [*Interruption.*] That is not going to happen. I hope that in this matter I may speak for the Conservative party represented on these benches when I say that the position of British finance is solid and will not be easily overthrown. There are forces resident in this country which will rally to the defence of British credit, and which will be strong enough, even at the detriment of party advantage, to support a Chancellor of the Exchequer in doing his duty.

I now turn, if the House will bear with me for a few moments longer, to a much more difficult side of this question, namely, the causes of the great economic collapse in values. I quite understand that the right hon. Gentleman is glad that I have left this to the last; he seems to have manifested a great deal of relief. It is my belief that the United States, before the crash of October, 1929, had come nearer to achieving the joint ideals of capital and labour than any community at any time. There we had the inhabitants of 20,000,000 or 25,000,000 homes making, by mass production under private enterprise, under ruthless Free Trade within a vast protected Empire, a couple of hundred standardised articles which were consumed by those very same 25,000,000 households whose members produced them. There we had Capital interested in high wages and short hours for the workers, and there we had workmen vigilantly guarding the interests of the industries with which they felt themselves identified. It is my belief that this process in the United States came nearer to bridging what I have called the mischievous gap between producing and the consuming power than anything we have seen. In striving to climb the perilous ascent, they seemed to have got their elbows on the ledge. They fell off—they were pushed off—and for the moment, but only for the moment, they are in great disorder. Why did they slip off? The immediate cause, beyond all doubt, was what the Chancellor of the Exchequer very properly stigmatised as an orgy of speculation. While this healthy development was taking place, they sought to push it too far, and, by methods of deflation, hire purchase, and so forth, they forestalled the steady growth of wealth accumulation in their country. They will come up again before long, and, with them, a large part of the world.

But I think that the orgy of speculation is not the only cause. There was a vital weakness in the economic structure of the world. What is that weakness? It is not war; it is not pestilence; there is no great cataclysm of nature. On the contrary, peace has reigned for 12 years over the world, and I, for one, believe that the desire for peace is growing stronger year by year. Science and invention have marched forward; bounteous harvests have rewarded the efforts of man. What, then, is this profound weakness? I will try to answer that question in a single word—Asia. That is what is wrong with the world. In China, in India, in Russia, to count only those three countries, you have populations which aggregate to nearly 1,000,000,000 human beings—probably nearly two-thirds of the entire human race. What is their plight? China is plunged in anarchy. India is shaking in unrest and insecurity. Russia, whatever view you take of its politics, constitutes to-day an economic factor more strange and more menacing than anything we have witnessed even in the times through which we have recently passed. Once the World War was over, we might have looked for a rapid and steady expansion in the consuming power of these three great regions and their 1,000,000,000 inhabitants. What have we seen? Just at the moment when Europe and the United States stood ready to supply, from plants which had been brought to the highest efficiency, abundant quantities of all kinds of desirable commodities—just at that very moment we have seen an actual decrease in the consuming power of two-thirds of the human race. It has contracted, taking these three countries together, and making proper allowance for changed values, from £355,000,000 of imports in 1913 to £309,000,000 in 1929. There lies the weakness, and we cannot discern any prospect of speedy improvement.

The welter in China bids fair to continue. The Indian political classes, if power is given to them, have made it perfectly clear that they intend to exclude foreign goods. As regards Russia, consider the bearing of the five-years plan upon our employment. The five-years plan in Russia, no doubt, will fail, but nothing will prevent it from succeeding, we will say, to the extent of 60 per cent. of that ambitious scheme. It will fail in all that makes for the economic well-being of its own people; it will succeed in all that makes for the economic ill-usage of other people. The dumping, not only of food but of raw materials, which is now in progress, will be followed—indeed, the process has already begun—by the dumping of all kinds of special manufactures, which will dislocate in turn every industry to which it is applied. Nothing can stand against exportations by Governments, by whole States, not for trade, not for profit, but for cash and for the accumulation of credits in foreign lands. Nothing can stand against exportations which are set on foot irrespective of profit and of the cost of production. In this case, we are obviously coming increasingly into the presence of facts and processes in the face of which the old-fashioned doctrines of Free Traders and the old-fashioned doctrined of Protectionists are equally obsolete. Among the already vast surpluses of manufacturing capacity of the present time, an enormous new productivity will barge in, which has no relation on any side to economic facts or processes or to commercial values, nor, I would add, to moral facts or values.

I was brought up under orthodox Free Trade and Treasury teachers. I have known all the great officials of the Treasury from Sir Francis Mowatt downwards. Always it was preached to me that a progressive reduction of the cost of living should have a place in the minds of public men, that that would make amends for all, that on that foundation the people would be content, exports would be invincible and enterprise would be buoyant. Obviously, that doctrine is no longer a complete practical view. It is only a partial truth which, applied in isolation, may well lead to actual error. When producers of primary products do not receive the payment or the profit which they require for their commodities, they cannot buy our manufactures. When importers refuse on a gigantic scale to accept the normal payment in export, when reductions in the prices of primary products do not reach the consumer except tardily and partially, none of those fruitful, fertile reactions on which the old economists relied to restore the equilibrium will take place. When that is what is happening now all over the world—we all know it; there is no one to challenge it anywhere—it forms one of the chief reasons why this country is bound to review fundamentally its old-established commercial and fiscal policy.

Do not let us at this juncture lose our heads. Do not let us get into a panic, or throw others into a panic. Do not let us be misled by those who wish to fish in troubled waters. Do not let us add political chaos to economic tribulation. Do not let us aggravate industrial depression by the undermining of credit. In this island there are resources and reserves of energy, sanity, strength, courage and comradeship which are unsurpassed, if indeed they are equalled, in any other great State. Many of the difficulties with which we have to contend are admittedly beyond our control. Much will have to be endured, but we have ridden through many a gale before, and, in the main, our safety and our fortune lie in our own hands. We must study ceaselessly every means, even artificial means, of making this island the best place for carrying on every form of manufacture. We must give our industry and enterprise the stimulus of a tariff and we must relieve it, as far as possible, from every burden, such as high freights, taxes upon its reserves and other burdens, and, above all, as soon as possible relieve it from the burden of political uncertainty. The Government should take counsel betimes with friendly Powers for the international treatment of the problems of currency and trade and concert joint action against the uneconomic exportations which are in increasing measure to be apprehended from Russia. We must reach out our hands in special co-operation to our kith and kin throughout the Empire. All those are courses which lie before us. When the economic revival of the western world comes, as come it will in spite of Asia, we shall be borne forward in its forefront, and normal industry, by reabsorbing into itself a very large proportion of our 2,500,000 unemployed, will reduce that problem once again to manageable dimensions.

"A SEDITIOUS MIDDLE TEMPLE LAWYER"

February 23, 1931

Winchester House, Epping

The Council of the West Essex Conservative Association was called together to receive the explanation of their representative on his attitude towards Indian matters and on his resignation from the Front Bench. This speech was the most violent and memorable delivered by Churchill on the Indian question to date. In particular, the passage on Gandhi made an immense impression on opinion—not least in India, where it has never been forgotten or forgiven.

You have been called together at my desire in order that I may lay before you the reasons why I have felt it my duty to take an independent line about India and to withdraw from the Business Committee of the Conservative party of which I had the honour to be a member. The Business Committee is a very sensible name for the small group of those members of both Houses with whom Mr. Baldwin is accustomed to consult on the general policy of the party and its conduct in Parliament. I valued highly the privilege of being included in it, and also it gave an opportunity of continuing in close, confidential touch with several of my principal colleagues and personal friends in the late Conservative Government. I was therefore very sorry to have to cut myself off from this interesting and agreeable work, and I can assure you I should not have done so without due cause. I still propose, if that is desired, to remain Chairman of the Conservative Finance Committee and to conduct the criticism of the Budget and other financial measures of the Socialist Government. I need scarcely say that I intend to do my utmost to assist our leader in the opposition to the Government in the House of Commons. I shall do my utmost to turn them out at the earliest opportunity, and procure their condign punishment and defeat at the general election, and to bring about by every means in my power a decisive victory for a united Conservative party. I found, however, that while I remained a member of this small inner circle I could not give full effect to my convictions about India. Naturally when men sit round a table and discuss political matters in intimate confidence they are largely bound by the decisions which are taken, and although there is more latitude out of office than in a Cabinet, nevertheless it is most undesirable that differences should appear among those who are thus associated.

Now let us see what these differences are. I agreed to our Conservative delegates taking part in the Round Table Conference, as I thought they would keep the Socialist Government from committing us to any dangerous or unwise departure. This our delegates tell us they have done, and I agree with them that they may justly claim that we are not committed by any action of theirs to the scheme of a new constitution for India which emerged from the Round Table Conference. I was however surprised and alarmed at the sudden landslide of opinion which took place upon that Conference and at the impression which was created throughout this country and in India that all the three parties were in agreement in principle to set up a federal constitution under Indian ministers responsible to an all-India Assembly. Still more was I alarmed when this enormous departure was itself presented as only a temporary and transitory arrangement soon to give place to what is called 'full Dominion status' for India carrying with it the control not only of law and order and of finance, but of the Army, and the right to secede from the British Empire. I do not think it is wise to hold out any hopes of any such position being reached for many generations to come. At any rate, I hold it of the utmost importance that we should make it clear that there is no chance of such a goal being reached in our lifetime, or in any period which it is profitable for us to consider. Secondly, I much regret to have to state that I disapprove altogether of the policy pursued by the present Viceroy of India, which as I shall show you presently has been attended by results already disastrous and threatening greater evils in the future.

These difficulties came to a head when Mr. Baldwin expressed his complete disagreement with the speech I made in the House of Commons at the end of last month, and when he said that it would be the duty of the Conservative party if returned to power to try to 'implement' the scheme put forward by the Round Table Conference. It was quite evident to everyone after that speech that the differences between us upon India were not merely matters of emphasis or procedure, but that they were profound and practical differences covering the whole field of Indian Policy and affecting the whole mood and spirit in which we discharge our duty to India. In the words which Lord Hartington, afterwards Duke of Devonshire, used to Mr. Gladstone in 1886 about Ireland, I can only say that upon India Mr. Baldwin and I 'do not mean the same thing.' I am sure you will agree that in these circumstances I had no choice but to separate myself upon this single question in the most friendly manner from a leader for whom I entertain both high respect and regard.

Having taken up this position in public about India I must inform you that it is my intention to go through with it. I shall endeavour to marshal British opinion against a course of action which would bring in my judgment the greatest evils upon the people of India, upon the people of Great Britain, and upon the structure of the British Empire itself. It follows therefore of course that I should not be able to serve in any Administration about whose Indian policy I was not reassured. I would far rather be a loyal private member of the Conservative party than bear official responsibility for actions and events which might well involve a mortal injury to the greatness and cohesion of our Empire. I invite you to endorse this attitude on my part, and I hope you will find yourselves able to give me your full approval and even encouragement in acting in this matter in accordance with my convictions.

The Indian problem at the present time divides itself into two parts. There is the question of a new constitution for India, and there is the question of the day-to-day administration of that country and the proper maintenance of British authority. If you will permit me, I will say a few words on both these matters. In dealing with Oriental races for whose well-being you are responsible it is a mistake to try to gloss over grave differences, to try to dress up proposals in an unwarrantably favourable guise, to ignore or conceal or put in the background rugged but unpleasant facts. The right course on the contrary is to state soberly and firmly what the British position is, and not be afraid to say 'this would not suit us,' 'that would not be good for you,' 'there is no chance of this coming to pass,' 'we shall not agree to that being done.' All these firm negatives ought to be stated frankly and plainly so that false hopes are not excited unduly and lead to disappointment and reproaches. We should always try to be better than our word and let any concessions we make be real and true. The Socialist Government on the other hand has been trying to deal with the Indian Nationalist politicians by the same sort of blarney and palaver which sometimes passes muster in Parliament or on British political platforms. I do not want to see the Conservative party, which is the main instrument by which the British Empire can be defended, dragged any further in their wake. I do not want to see the Indian politicians misled as to what our real intentions are.

Now you will observe that statements have been made within the last few days upon Mr. Baldwin's authority that we are not committed to anything except to give fair consideration to any proposals that may be made. I was very glad to hear those statements. After all, it is everybody's duty to give fair consideration to any proposals on any subject which are sincerely advanced. But that is very different from the impression which the country has sustained, and it is very different from the impression conveyed to the Indian politicians. Our leader's phrase about 'implementing' the constitution prepared by the Round Table Conference and the whole purport of his speech were cabled to the Indian delegates on the ship by which they were returning to India. We are told that they were overjoyed at what they read, and naturally they assumed that the great Conservative party was in agreement with the Socialist and Liberal parties and was prepared to implement a federal constitution with responsible government at the centre. On the strength of this they proceeded to draft a manifesto to the Indian Congress, and have ever since been labouring to persuade the more extreme elements to come and join them in a further conference to be held in India. They ought to be told, as we are told, that the Conservative party is wholly uncommitted, and that they have been unintentionally misled. But Mr. Ramsay MacDonald, the Prime Minister, is also evidently under a misapprehension; because he said in answer to a question which I put to him in the House of Commons last week that on the subject of India the Government considered that they 'had got their marching orders from the House': meaning thereby that all parties were agreed. It seems to me important that these misapprehensions, if such they be, about the official attitude of the Conservative party, should be corrected both here and in India on the highest authority and with the least delay.

The proper constitutional course for Parliament to adopt is to proceed to consider the Simon Report which was signed by the representatives of all parties. There are no doubt many things in that report which would have to be very carefully examined, some of which are no longer applicable; nevertheless it forms the only proper constitutional basis upon which discussion of the reform of Indian government should proceed by the joint action of all parties. The Round Table Conference may have thrown some new and interesting light upon Indian affairs of which of course full notice should be taken. But the whole foundation for the joint treatment of the Indian problem by the three British parties is the Simon Report, and once that report has been put on one side, as it has been almost contemptuously by the Socialist Government, it is imperative that the Conservative party should recover the fullest possible liberty of judgment. So much for the constitutional aspect.

Now I come to the administration of India. In my opinion we ought to dissociate ourselves in the most public and formal manner from any complicity in the weak, wrong-headed and most unfortunate administration of India by the Socialists and by the Viceroy acting upon their responsibility. It is alarming and also nauseating to see Mr. Gandhi, a seditious Middle Temple lawyer, now posing as a fakir of a type well-known in the East, striding half-naked up the steps of the Vice-regal palace, while he is still organising and conducting a defiant campaign of civil disobedience, to parley on equal terms with the representative of the King-Emperor. Such a spectacle can only increase the unrest in India and the danger to which white people there are exposed. It can only encourage all the forces which are hostile to British authority. What good can possibly come of such extraordinary negotiations? Gandhi has said within the last few weeks that he demands the substance of independence, though he kindly adds that the British may keep the shadow. He declares that the boycott of foreign cloth must be continued until either prohibition or a prohibitive tariff can be put up against it by an Indian national Parliament. This, if accepted, would entail the final ruin of Lancashire. He has also pressed for the repudiation of the Indian loans, and has laid claim to the control of the Army and foreign affairs. These are his well-known aims. Surely they form a strange basis for heart-to-heart discussions—'sweet' we are told they were—between this malignant subversive fanatic and the Viceroy of India.

All this is intended by the Socialists to be the preliminary to another Round Table Conference in India to which it is hoped to persuade the extremists to come. At this new gathering the far-reaching and half-baked recommendations of the Round Table Conference will be taken only as a starting-point. From this starting-point will begin the attack upon the safeguards which have hitherto been kept apologetically in the background. I think it vital that the Conservative party should without delay get itself into a strong position of resistance, and should begin to arouse public opinion throughout the country against these most unwise and dangerous proceedings. I intend at any rate to do my best, and I shall be much strengthened if you put your whole weight behind me. India is no ordinary question of party politics. It is one of those supreme issues which come upon us from time to time. When they arise the men and women who faithfully guard the life of Britain and her Empire in every rank and employment, in every part of the country, feel the same vibration. They felt it on August 4, 1914. They felt it in the General Strike. They feel it now.

Our responsibility in India has grown up over the last 150 years. It is a responsibility for giving the best possible chance for peaceful existence and progress to about three hundred and fifty millions of helpless primitive people who are separated by an almost measureless gulf from the ideas and institutions of the Western world. We now look after them by means of British Officials on fixed salaries who have no axe to grind, who make no profit out of their duties, who are incorruptible, who are impartial between races, creeds and classes, and who are directed by a central Government which in its turn is controlled by the British Parliament based on twenty-nine million electors. It is now proposed to transfer these British responsbilities to an electorate comparatively small and almost entirely illiterate. The Indian Congress and other elements in this agitation represent neither the numbers, the strength nor the virtue of the Indian people. They merely represent those Indians who have acquired a veneer of Western civilisation, and have read all those books about democracy which Europe is now beginning increasingly to discard. There are among them many estimable and clever people, and it has always been and always must be our policy to associate them as much as we possibly can with the machinery of Indian Government. But it would be altogether wrong to entrust the welfare of the great masses to the Indian political classes. That would not be 'India for the Indians'; that would only be India for some Indians, and would only be India for a very few Indians. Undoubtedly any such abrogation on our part of our duty would mean that the Indian peoples would be exploited, oppressed and cast down in the scale of the world's affairs as the proletariat of China is cast down in misery to-day. At present the Government of India is responsible to the British Parliament, which is the oldest, the least unwise and the most democratic parliament in the world. To transfer that responsibility to this highly artificial and restricted oligarchy of Indian politicians would be a retrograde act. It would be a shameful act. It would bring grave material evils, both upon India and Great Britain; but it would bring upon Great Britain a moral shame which would challenge for ever the reputation of the British Empire as a valiant and benignant force in the history of mankind.

The faithful discharge of our duty in India is not only a cause, but a symbol. It is the touchstone of our fortunes in the present difficult time. If we cannot do our duty in India, be sure we shall have shown ourselves unworthy to preserve the vast Empire which still centres upon this small island. The same spirit of unimaginative incompetence and weak compromise and supine drift will paralyse trade and business and prevent either financial reorganisation or economic resurgence. What we require to do now is to stand erect and look the world in the face, and do our duty without fear or favour. A decisive opportunity may soon be at hand. Victory may once again reward the Conservative party. Let it be a victory with a real meaning behind it. Let it be a victory which proclaims to all the world that the heart of the Empire is true and that its hand is just—and strong.

[Editor's Note: A motion of confidence and approval in their Member was carried unanimously.]

INDIA (CONSERVATIVE PARTY RESOLUTION)

February 24, 1931

Conservative Party Central Council Meeting,
Kingsway Hall, London

[Extract] ... The British rule in India is being rapidly ruined by the Labour and Liberal parties and it is the duty of Conservatives to save the situation. I protest against having any further negotiations with Mahatma Gandhi.

"THE PRESENT DECLINE OF PARLIAMENTARY GOVERNMENT IN GREAT BRITAIN"

March 5, 1931

Rectorial Address, Edinburgh University

The House of Commons as a vehicle of the popular will has gradually become the repository of almost all the power in the State, yet at the same time it is steadily declined in public repute and shows itself increasingly inadequate to deal with the real topics of public interest. It was always suggested that, as the franchise was extended and the ever-new millions were added to the electoral rolls, so the dignity and authority of the assembly would expand and consolidate. The exact reverse has happened. The broader the basis the less it has been revered, and the less its members have been respected even by the working classes. Democracy seems inclined to mock and disdain the institutions to which its rights and liberties are due.

This is a truth which would have startled the Victorians. It is a truism which hardly causes the twentieth century to blink an eyelid. Many of the Parliaments so hopefully erected all over Europe in the nineteenth century have already disappeared, or have been put in cold storage. Almost the only great real living popular chamber functioning in full power at the present time is the British House of Commons. What was the cradle of free institutions throughout the world is still their citadel. I am deeply anxious that its walls shall not be undermined by slow decay or overthrown by violent battering-rams. I believe that Parliamentary institutions are, upon the whole, the most tolerable form of government for men—and, of course, women—and I am animated solely by the desire to discover how the ancient institutions in our island can be given a new lease of life by being rendered capable of discharging effectually the duties they have claimed.

Not only is the assembly declining, but the foundation on which it stands has degenerated. When the vote was given to a few, all coveted it; when it was given to many, some coveted it; now that it is given to all, you can hardly get them to go to the poll. The sustained discussion of great public questions of vital concern to our national fame and security does not proceed as it used to do. A sort of universal mush and sloppiness has descended upon us, and issues are not brought to the clear-cut cleavages of former times. In fact, we feel we are drifting and in a sense dissolving as we drift. The time has come when we should endeavour to put more bone and structure into our political organism and to make it more truly responsive to the national need.

The vacuum formed by the shrinkage of our Parliamentary institutions has been imperfectly filled by a Press, unquestionably superior in every standard of strength, quality, probity, and decency to The Press in any other country in the world. But these British newspapers for all their growing strength are increasingly abandoning the political theme. I have been told that nothing will kill a newspaper so quickly as too much politics. The readers of the newspapers are not worrying much about politics. They take it for granted that they will be very unsatisfactory, but will not do any serious harm. The Press, except at election times, is no longer, as it used to be, the forum of continuous political discussion. It has not filled in any effective manner the gap caused by the shrinkage in the repute of the Parliamentary machinery.

But now there has appeared a wonderful new facility for public discussion which seemed exactly adapted to fill, or help to fill, the void. I mean the broadcast. But if I were to seek to use that instrument to discuss any of the grave questions touching the endurance of our Empire or the welfare of the people I should be barred. One would have thought that here was a great new facility which would have been placed at the service of the British democracy and of all those whose duty it is to guide their affairs. Not at all. It is all ruled out and vetoed.

When I first went into politics a member could easily address every person who meant to vote and wished to hear him. But that is a thing of the past. A very large proportion of the electors in every constituency will never be able to listen to the discussion of public questions by their responsible representatives or those who seek to become their representatives.

All these facts and causes show only too clearly the reasons why the foundations of the Parliamentary institution are being impaired, and how there is no real forum for the severe thrashing out of national affairs. At the same time these national affairs, so far from diminishing in importance, have greatly increased both in magnitude and in complexity. If ever the British people ought to be thinking hard about their collective life-future, it is now in this present age. Never before was so great a community in so precarious a situation. We are in the van and the forefront of the human race, but at the same time we are the most artificial, the most delicately established, the most fundamentally insecure of all great nations.

We are elevated on a high platform with enormous advantages and hopes, with a far-ranging vision, and, if we chose to use them, many hopeful opportunities for the future. But there we are perched aloft, and the structure itself is degenerating, loosening, crumbling—and what are we going to do about it?

There is one national need which Parliament, as at present constituted, is not able to meet—the consideration of economic questions. Yet these are questions which above all others occupy men's minds, for many time-honoured doctrines have been proved not to meet the new problems, or to meet them only partially. The will of the people afforded no solution to an economic problem. I have proposed that the House of Commons should associate with itself an economic sub-Parliament, free from party bias, containing commercial men, financial experts, and responsible trade union leaders, for the purposes of economic advice and guidance. The more I think upon the subject, the more convinced I am that the machinery of government should be enriched by the creation of a permanent body of that kind.

We require more bone and structure in our Parliamentary system. Can any sincere and thoughtful man believe that the House of Commons, elected as it is, composed as it is, burdened as it is, biased as it is, changing its colour with every General Election and always living in trepidation of the next, is capable of affording our vast Empire a sure centre? Can this unstable body form the sole pivot upon which the interests and the hopes of so many peoples and States may rely? The decline in the reputation of the House of Commons among our own people has been attended by at least an equal decline in the eyes of all the component parts of the British Empire. The House of Lords, in its present unreformed and restricted condition, lacks the authority which is needed at the centre and at the summit.

Other great States, our rivals in the world, though with less difficult problems than ours, have far more confident, tenacious, and thorough machinery. There is no great country in the world at the present time whose governing organism is in such a fluid state, and which has less effective machinery for thinking out its own problems. There is no country which is less capable of pursuing a steady, sober, and far-sighted policy over a long period of years. We cannot afford to go on like this. I have wondered whether the establishment of a reformed and strengthened Second Chamber, as fore-shadowed in the preamble of the Parliament Act, would not be most surely and easily achieved if it were founded in the main upon larger organs of local government than our county and municipal institutions.

Modern Germany expresses itself through nearly 30 separate Governments. The United States comprises more than 50 sovereign States within the American Union. We have in Great Britain only two bodies which are even remotely comparable in scale and importance with the individual Governments of Germany and America—Ulster and the

London County Council. Supposing that other bodies—deeply rooted in history and tradition, harmoniously adapted to local requirements, larger and more powerful than county councils or any of the existing local institutions—were to come into being naturally throughout the United Kingdom, might that not be an immense advantage both for progress and for security?

Could not the House of Commons be relieved of a mass of controversial business which could far better be fought out within a national framework in extensive local areas? Should we not draw to these new centres fresh streams of public and political capacity to enrich and nourish our very attenuated and largely worn-out Parliamentary *personnel*, and might not these bodies form, by the election of their own members, the main part at least of a Senate worthy to sustain the Imperial cause?

The evils and dangers of which I speak are of slow growth, and their cure can only be gradual. Unless Great Britain is able by a united and well-instructed effort to grapple with her economic problems, and unless she is worthy to be the heart of her world-wide establishment, you here in this hall to-day will live long enough to lose not only your inheritance, but your livelihood. The continuance of our present confusion and disintegration will reduce us within a generation, and perhaps sooner, to the degree of States like Holland and Portugal, which nursed valiant races and held great possessions, but were stripped of them in the crush and competition of the world. That would be a melancholy end to all the old glories and recent triumphs.

If Great Britain loses her Empire and India and her share in world trade and her sea power, she would be like a vast whale stranded in one of your Scottish bays, which swam in upon the tide and then was left to choke and rot upon the sands. We should be like a great shop or emporium in a district from which prosperity has for ever departed. We least of all peoples and races can afford to fail. Failure to us does not mean merely that we shall not improve. It means that we shall be ruined and frozen out.

SOVIET UNION (FORCED AND CONVICT LABOUR)

March 6, 1931

Protest Meeting, Trade Defence Union,
Albert Hall, London

You have seen the carefully prepared organization which is in action to prevent us holding our meeting and making our protest. Here are miserable hirelings, poor wretched people paid with roubles for making trouble, brought here and forced to do their bit or they do not get their cash. (Cheers.) Cannot you see far better than any words we could put to you by this carefully staged demonstration that there are force and money behind this opposition? (Cheers.) But we shall succeed in this country in maintaining free speech and the rights of citizens to congregate together and express their opinions on great public issues. This issue is surely one which should claim the allegiance and accord of those who agree about the decencies of civilization. We have heard some amount of detail of the horrible conditions which prevail in the Russian timber camps.

[Editor's Note: In all parts of the galleries there were processions of both men and women disturbers being escorted from the hall.] We must make allowance for those who are earning their pay. They get a bonus for being thrown out. (Cheers and laughter.)

Look at the impudence of it, coming here and interfering with our rights. Why don't they go to their Utopia in Russia? The conditions there are tantamount to slavery. That Government possesses despotic power, and uses that power against their political opponents, and sends them in scores of thousands to those hideous places of punishment. Then we are told that in England we ought to receive the produce of their sweated labour because some persons or other here might grease their fingers with commission. That is a matter that has got to be dealt with according to the heart and conscience of the nation. (Cheers.)

If we find to-day the Government of the day apologizing for these villanies in Russia, and patting on the backs those who greased their paws—(cheers)—if to-day we find that situation in our life, that is because we are for the moment—let us frankly admit it—in a period of collapse; we are for a moment passing under a cloud of weakness and confusion; but behind it the strength and power of the British nation is gathering. (Cheers.)

I know well the English people, and I have never seen them fail when great issues are put to the test. They are gathering their strength day by day. This meeting, filling this vast hall, of men and women who knew they would have to face opposition, is only one sign of the revival of a national strength and affection which, when it has reached its full vigour will sweep away and drive away before it all who commit offences against the freedom and the dignity of man. (Cheers.)

By voting for the resolution which has been proposed, those present will record their definite protest against a system of convict and forced labour in Russia, which, to quote a phrase of Mr. Gladstone, "Scarcely finds its equal in the dark and melancholy catalogue of human crime." (Loud cheers.)

INDIA

March 12, 1931

House of Commons

In this debate Baldwin turned on Churchill and made a devastating attack on his India policy, making considerable play with Churchill's speech on General Dyer. One observer noted: "Churchill, seated, with flushed features and twitching hands, looked as though about to spring; Baldwin, on his feet, gave that impression of a passion frozen into obedience, which is his trump card" (Hugh Martin, Battle, *229).*

This debate was a turning-point for Baldwin and Churchill, and the leader's policy was overwhelmingly approved by the Parliamentary Party. Baldwin removed Churchill from the post of chairman of the Conservative Finance group and appointed Neville Chamberlain in his place. Henceforth Churchill held no senior post in the Conservative Party until he became it's leader in October 1940.

I am afraid that I must make a demand upon the attention of the Committee while I go somewhat more fully into detail on the various aspects of the Indian question than the hon. Lady [Miss Picton-Tubervill] who preceded me has done. I must also ask for the indulgence of the Committee, because the extreme inclemency of the weather has left me with only a severely regulated ration of voice. Much has happened although only a bare six weeks have passed since we last debated the Indian question in the House of Commons. I must admit that there is some cause for congratulation among those who are eager to establish an all-India Federation, under responsible government, as the precursor of full Dominion status. I must admit that they have some grounds for self-congratulation at the progress made. Much less enthusiasm may perhaps be felt by those who view these processes as premature, dangerous, and ill-thought out, and that they are likely at an early date to lead to confusion and even disaster.

I will, if the Committee will permit me, briefly survey the sequence of events during the last six weeks: not a lengthy period. The sequence is what is important, because we must not forget that one step leads to another, and each step can only be appreciated in its proper order. The Round Table Conference had ended, and in order to facilitate a free discussion of the wishes of the Round Table Conference, in order to, what is called, carry on the work of the Round Table Conference, the Viceroy released Mr. Gandhi and his principal associates from prison. That was the first event in the last six weeks. After I had spoken on 26th January, my right hon. Friend the Leader of the Opposition felt it his duty to express in most courteous and kindly terms a very serious difference from my view, and he made that memorable statement in which he said that the one duty of the Conservative party, if returned to power, would be to try to implement the work of the Round Table Conference. I am sure that my right hon. Friend will not object to my referring to that speech, delivered only six weeks ago, since he has done me the compliment of referring to one delivered by me 11 years ago.

The speech of my right hon. Friend was one of memorable importance. It was an event in the chain which is unfolding. It was telegraphed all over India. It was sent by wireless to the ship upon which the Indian delegates to the London Conference were returning to their homes. Everywhere it was accepted as a proof that the Conservative party was in line with the Socialist and Liberal parties, and that, apart from a few die-hards and reactionaries, and other untouchables, Great Britain was united upon a policy of framing and bringing into being the constitution outlined, perhaps it would be fairer to say adumbrated, at the Round Table Conference. The Indian delegates on board their ship were greatly encouraged by the tidings they received. They drafted a manifesto, sinking some differences among themselves, appealing to the extremists and the Congress party that all should join together in further discussions in India in order to frame the constitution which had been outlined. Then there followed the conversations between Gandhi and the Viceroy, the result of which was announced last Thursday. That is the sequence of events of the last six weeks.

Let me come to the agreement reached in the Gandhi-Irwin conversations. In order to appreciate this agreement, it is necessary to consider both its objects and its terms. The object is quite clear; it is to bring about such conditions in India, such conditions of truce and armistice between the Government of India and the law-breakers, as will enable all sections to sit down amicably at the Conference table in India. That was the object—so that they could proceed to frame the constitution which I have described, of an All-India Federation, responsible government at the centre, the whole as a precursor to full Dominion status, or, as Mr. Gandhi prefers to call it, "independence." There is the object, and those who believe that it is a most desirable object and ought to be achieved as soon as possible will naturally be prepared to pay the necessary price, even a high price, for securing so great an advantage as the continuance and reopening of such discussions.

There was, I believe, a general feeling of satisfaction, or, at any rate of relief, in this House when the terms of the White Paper were read out on Thursday last—I had not the good fortune to be present, having an engagement elsewhere—by the Secretary of State for India. There was admiration for the statesmanship of Mr. Gandhi and his patriotism in calling off the movement of civil disobedience which he launched a year ago, and which the Government had vainly attempted to quell. A hope was entertained that now that the boycott of British goods is not to be political but only economic, that picketing is only to be peaceful, that there would be some recovery in our Lancashire trade, certainly a matter for general satisfaction. There was a feeling that the settlement of the Salt Law question was in the nature of a compromise and, lastly, there was great relief, even enthusiasm, when it was known that although the Viceroy had been forced to let the rioters out of prison, he had firmly and successfully resisted the proposal to lock up the police in their place. [*Interruption.*] Nothing could more painfully, and, I may say, more pitifully, illustrate the ceaseless landslide in British Parliamentary opinion than that these modest achievements should give so much pleasure, that they should even be hailed as a miracle of statecraft. It only shows that we are becoming accustomed to be thankful for small mercies and glad when anything is saved from the wreck of our great estates.

I am not particularly concerned to-day to cavil at the details of the terms to which the Viceroy has agreed. Once it is judged an aim of high policy to persuade the extremists to come to a Conference, and in view of the fact that they demurred strongly, once it is considered necessary that they should come, of course the necessary price has to be paid. I daresay, having regard to the objects in view and to the policy he is pursuing, Lord Irwin made the best bargain he could in the circum-stances. The price, however, is heavy, and it must be examined. Although the boycott and civil disobedience have been partially called off, they remain suspended over us and can be loosed at any moment by the mere lifting of Mr. Gandhi's little finger. The violation of the Salt Law was specially selected by Mr. Gandhi a year ago as the means of defying the Government of India, as the one means of defying the Government of India which would be most deeply and widely comprehended throughout the land. His lawless act has now been made lawful. Anyone may now make salt from the sea.

[*Interruption.*] Any dweller by the sea may now make salt—I agree there is very little material importance in this point. Its effect upon the revenue cannot be at all serious. I am told that salt which is made in this way is unpalatable, and even makes people ill, and so no serious loss to the revenue need be expected. At any rate, the Government of India have increased the duties on Europeans, and put up Lancashire cotton duties by 5 per cent., so no doubt they are in a good position to meet any slight loss that may occur from the salt concession.

But neither can it be pretended that this concession is of the slightest benefit to the people of India, the working masses of India. It was never intended to be. When Mr. Gandhi went to the seashore a year ago to make salt he was not looking for salt, he was looking for trouble. He was looking for a means of flouting the Government and compelling them to arrest him. Now he has compelled to Government to recognise the propriety of his action. He has elevated his deliberately selected breach of the law into a trophy of victory, the significance of which, believe me, will be appreciated from the Himalayas to Ceylon. Though I approach this question from a different angle from that of my right hon. Friend the Leader of the Opposition, so far as the practical steps which we should now take are concerned we are in entire agreement—[*Interruption*]—and I am a cordial supporter of the decision to which he has come. My right hon. Friend said that these terms, this White Paper, was a triumph of moderation over extremism, a victory for moderation over extremism. It was, at any rate, a Pyrrhic victory. It was a victory for breaches of the law against the Government responsible for enforcing the law. It was a victory of lawbreakers, who consented for the time being partially to lay aside their lawbreaking because hopes had been held out that before very long they will be law-makers.

Mr. O'Connor: May I interrupt the right hon. Gentleman—

Mr. Churchill: My hon. and learned Friend will have an opportunity of replying in the course of the Debate, and I have no doubt he will then be able to tell us all that is in his mind. I have noticed that he is prone to interrupt the thread of other people's arguments and it is a tendency which, at the outset of his career, he should endeavour to repress. As for this victory of moderation over extremism let us see what is said by a member of the Council whose position in Indian Liberal circles is unique as the only non-Swarajist mayor of Calcutta. I notice that the hon. Member for Orkney and Shetland (Sir R. Hamilton) dwelt on the victory for moderation over extremism. This is what a Liberal leader and the only non-Swarajist mayor of Calcutta has to say about it. After complimenting the Viceroy and Mr. Gandhi, he says:

> In this settlement, however, the outstanding fact remains that the Liberals in the future will be wiped out, and from now onwards no Indian will think it worth while to have any faith in constitutional agitation. I am afraid that the process of arriving at this settlement is such as to undermine in the minds of the masses respect for authority.

That can hardly mean that he thinks that this has been a notable victory for moderation over extremism. I consider, however, that Mr. Gandhi and the Congress party were well advised to come to terms. I think they have played their cards singularly well. They have secured, I am told, substantially and almost exactly the very terms demanded by the Congress as a condition of their coming to the London Conference—terms which were then pointedly and unquestionably refused. They have secured in this victory for moderation the whole of the terms which they demanded as a condition of their coming to the London Conference, and now they will go to discussions in India or a further conference in London—if they are generally satisfied— they will go to these further discussions, in which, at any rate, they have everything to gain and nothing to lose. I think that they were very well advised.

I notice that Mr. Gandhi speaks of Lord Irwin in terms of strong approbation. It is no more than just. In the course of this year the Viceroy has fostered the growth of Mr. Gandhi's power to an extent almost inconceivable, first, by neglecting to arrest him until his breaches of the law had gradually attracted and rivetted the attention of all India; secondly, by arresting him when they did for his breaches of the law; thirdly, by not trying him upon any known charge or proceeding against him by any recognised process of the law but confining him under some old Statute as a prisoner of State; fourthly, by attempting to negotiate with him when he was still in prison; fifthly, by releasing him unconditionally; sixthly, by negotiating with him as an equal and as if he were the victor in some warlike encounter; seventhly, by conceding to him as a permanent emblem of triumph the legalisation of the very practice which he had selected for the purpose of affronting the Government.

This series of steps ought to be preserved as a patent prescription for building up the reputation of a political opponent, or rather of a revolutionary leader. By this most elaborate process, undertaken, no doubt, at each stage, from the highest and most well-meaning motives, Mr. Gandhi and Congress have been raised before the eyes of hundreds of millions as the champions of Indian nationalism against the white intruder, and, henceforward, they are the dominant and recognised power with whom we have immediately to deal. They have been raised to a towering pedestal of fame and eminence in the eyes of all disloyal elements in India as having inflicted upon the mighty Government, on whose functioning the safety of the whole country depends, such humiliation and defiance as has not been known since the British first trod the soil of India. They have been lifted to a position far above the Moslems and other religions and classes in the East. Gandhi has become the symbol and the almost godlike champion of all those forces which are now working for our exclusion from India.

That is not, I think, a very satisfactory series of events which I have had to record in their sequence, and I am glad I have not to stop here. There is one event which makes amends for much. The Conservative party is not to be represented at any Round Table Conference in India. The continuance of the Round Table Conference in India was the next step in the contemplation of His Majesty's Government, and it was strongly urged by those in India who are pushing forward this policy that it was for this—to facilitate such a Conference and the discussions incidental thereto—that Mr. Gandhi was released and that the Gandhi-Irwin miracle was performed. Now, my right hon. Friend the Leader of the Opposition has decided that the Conservative party cannot participate in such a Conference. We had the usual exegesis by my right hon. Friend the Member for Chelsea (Sir S. Hoare) of that pronouncement, in a statement in which he conveyed the impression that this was not a decision of very great

Speeches of Winston Churchill

importance, but a mere matter of procedure, of convenience of method. I cannot understand how anyone who is looking at the facts of this question can for a moment be blind to the great importance of the decision which my right hon. Friend has taken. It can only show a lack of grasp of the whole situation both in India and in this country not to regard it as a matter of the greatest importance.

It has, in fact, reversed the whole programme upon which the Government and the Government of India has set their minds. The crystal palace which they were erecting has been shivered and shattered. Anyone who reads the telegrams flowing in from India can see how gravely they have been disconcerted by this pronouncement, which we are assured is a matter of no particular consequence.

Major Graham Pole: It was a misunderstanding!

Mr. Churchill: Anyhow, they are not going. There is no misunderstanding about that. Out of many confusing matters there are some few points which emerge from time to time with clarity. I agree that my right hon. Friend's decision does not decide finally the question of whether the Conservative party should participate in any further Conference which may be held in London. I, certainly, would not suggest for one moment that such a decision of that kind should be taken now.

I may, perhaps, say that I myself, with my own hand, in the Resolution which was moved at a private Committee upstairs wrote in these words "in India." My hon. Friend the Member for Kidderminster (Mr. Wardlaw-Milne) had the draft in my own hand-writing and I wrote the words in myself, for the very reason that it would, obviously, be rash to prejudge now what we should do many months hence in circumstances which we cannot possibly judge at the present time. I think we are in substantial agreement on both sides of the House, and in all parties, that the Conference in India should be dropped and that inquiries and discussions of a less formal character should precede it. No one can possibly reproach my right hon. Friend the Leader of the Opposition for his decision. It has been endorsed not only by the Conservative party in the House, but still more, I venture to say, by the party throughout the country. His Majesty's Government might very easily have inveigled the Opposition into an entanglement where, if they had agreed to the many concessions pressed upon them, they would have compromised their party or perhaps been disavowed by their party, and, if they had not agreed, the blame for breaking up the Conference in India would have been saddled upon their backs. It is just in time that my right hon. Friend has rescued us from that great danger.

I should like to say a word about this question of three-party action and of the unity of all parties. The unity of all parties upon a policy dictated by the Socialist Government would, in my opinion, be worse even than the disunity of parties upon the Indian question. The foundation of three-party unity on the question of India is the report of the Statutory Commission. Together we joined hands to create that Commission. Together we appointed our representatives and those representatives, working together, unanimously arrived at a common report. There is the basis on which your three-party unity was founded but, from the moment the Government side-tracked the Statutory report, the original basis of the three-party action ended, and I submit that the Conservative party is entitled to regain its unfettered freedom of judgment upon events as they arise. That does not mean that we shall not give a loyal and fair consideration to any proposal that the Government may put forward, or that may emerge from any inquiries or discussions which they may conduct, but it does mean, I trust, that the Opposition will not continue any longer to be burdened with the responsibilities of the executive Government. Too long have the Conservative party been exploited and carried on from point to point by hon. Gentlemen opposite.

Too long have they been made responsible for unfolding events in the shaping of which they have absolutely no control. Too long have they been prevented from exercising that proper restraint which belongs to a powerful Opposition which is probably at no great distance of time about to assume power. I will say to any of my hon. Friends who may have some doubt upon the position in which we now find ourselves, not to be alarmed if the Government say, "Very well, things will be decided without you." Nothing can be decided without Parliament. As long as the Conservative party are independent and free, their wishes will carry weight both in this Parliament and also, perhaps, in the next. There will be plenty of opportunities to make our view effective, or to give way and to make necessary concessions, or to arrive at any general agreed solution. That can be done at any time. After the discussions which are to take place in India, and after the further conference which, I understand, is now to be held in London, will come the regular constitutional process of drafting and presenting the Government of India Bill. Then there will be its passage through all the stages in both Houses possibly—[*Interruption.*] The other place have as good a right to give their opinions from the point of knowledge and authority as hon. Gentlemen below the Gangway. It will be possible, if desired, to have the joint committee of both Houses which was part of the original agreed procedure between the parties, before whom the different sections of Indian opinion can send their representatives. There will be plenty of time, at least two years—and here I am in agreement with the spokesman of the Liberal party, because I gather that he thought five years—

Sir R. Hamilton: I said that even five years would be better than making a mistake.

Mr. Churchill: I will not go any further, but, at any rate, we are in agreement that there will be plenty of time, and there ought to be plenty of time, for the full and careful discussion of this matter. It will be found, I predict, that from the moment the Conservative party have regained their freedom they will also have regained their influence upon affairs. Some regard will be paid to the views which are held by large sections of people in this country, and those people will not be denied reasonable opportunities of expressing their views. I do not consider that the Government are really hampered in the practical steps which they have to take by what has occurred. I agree with the views which have been put forward by my right hon. Friend and which are held, I believe, by his principal colleagues upon this bench.

The next task of the Government is to clear up some of the principal questions which were left over from the Round Table Conference. Not one single difficulty was solved by the Round Table Conference. No difficult clash was adjusted, and no really difficult constructive matter was solved. Take the safeguards. They certainly should form a subject of discussion in India now, and let us not forget the words of wisdom which Lord Birkenhead used when he said, "Tell India the truth." My right hon. Friend said that we ought to tell the truth upon these matters, and I say that now is the time. Take the question of the financial safeguards. We had a speech from Sir George Schuster, the Finance Member, in which he said in effect, that we were winding up our affairs and handing them over to new proprietors, and he hoped they would be indulgent to their predecessors, and so forth. But he did not make it clear to the Assembly that in the proposals which were discussed at the Round Table Conference, 80 per cent. of the finances will rest under the sign manual of the authority of the Viceroy. No conference is needed to explain that to Mr. Gandhi. It can be done by a few friendly talks, but it ought to be explained. It is no use misleading people and covering it all up with vague phrases.

Then take the question of the two-thirds majority. [*Interruption.*] You do not wish me to make these points. I do not propose to elaborate them at all; I will merely enumerate them. I am entitled to enumerate them, because they have been enumerated in this White Paper, and the hon. Lady who preceded me has already read out some of them from paragraph 2, in which these safeguards are enumerated. Certainly I am entitled to mention them if they have already been brought into the Debate. There is the question of the two-thirds majority, and the calculations which are possible as to the power of removing Ministers. Mr. Gandhi may not take quite the same view of the advantage of these proposals as the Government. Then there is my right hon. Friend's declaration about trade—a most robust declaration which he made at Newton Abbot, and which I read with the greatest satisfaction. It is a very far-reaching declaration; it certainly is not inconsistent with anything which exists in the Dominions which enjoy full Dominion status, though I agree that in every respect it is necessary. Then there is the question of the Viceroy's power. As a matter of sensible, wise and far-seeing administration, the right hon. Gentleman should begin to discuss this with Mr. Gandhi and his associates. The powers are enormous, and, as has been pointed out, they will be quite inoperative unless with the powers are given the apparatus necessary to enable their exercise. None of these points want a conference; they are far better approached in private. Then there are all those other questions, not in the nature of safeguards, but questions left over—the franchise, communal representation of Hindus and Mohammedans, the representations of the native States and a whole host—[*Interruption*]

The Deputy-Chairman (Mr. Dunrico): I hear comments that the right hon. Gentleman is not in order, and I rise to make it clear that as long as the right hon. Gentleman does not discuss those matters requiring legislation he is in order. He is entitled to indicate the grave and serious nature of the problems that have to be confronted, but not to discuss them—

Mr. Churchill: I am obliged to you for your Ruling. I do not intend to do more than cite these points as matters which, in the course of wise administration, the Government would proceed to discuss with Mr. Ghandi and the Indian Congress. Whatever view we take, there is no use drifting on without any clear idea and concealing awkward facts from the other side, and hoping something will turn up if we only go on making flowery speeches. The Indian revolutionaries, with whom the right hon. Gentleman has now to deal, will invite British representatives to quit the cloud of platitudes and perorations in which they have hitherto lain concealed, and give further and better particulars of what they really mean by responsible government, by a transition period, and by full Dominion status. Of course, that will be their smallest demand. Their smallest demand will be for concessions on safeguards. As to their full demands, they leave us in no doubt about them. I see that Mr. Jawaharlal Nehru and Mr. Gandhi have both made statements since the publications of the Viceroy's agreement. One made it clear that it is to be absolute independence that they require, and the other that complete internal autonomy—

The Deputy-Chairman: The right hon. Gentleman is now going beyond what is permissible. What I tried to make clear was that as long as he simply indicates the seriousness and gravity of the problems that have to be confronted, he is entitled to name them.

Mr. Churchill: Though the rules of Order hamper a full discussion, it only make it all the more necessary that another occasion on which to have a fuller discussion must take place. Of course, I submit to the Ruling of the Chair, but it must not be imagined for a moment that the Government and their supporters have it in their power to prevent a full discussion of these matters. When these matters come to be discussed in India, it seems that Mr. Gandhi will be in a strong argumentative position. He will be able to say when the safeguards are under discussion, "Do you not trust us? Have you lost your faith in the virtues of responsibility? Where is that sweet co-operation in your leaving the country which we had been led to expect? We have come here, not at our wish, but at your request, and if we think you are not sincere, well, we shall have to begin to use again those methods which were found so unsatisfactory in the last year." It is far better that this kind of discussion of your pourparlers should take place in private rather than that they should be the subject of a conference. Therefore, I am in agreement with the position of the Government and that of my right hon. Friend which compelled that position from the Government.

The chances of an agreement which will unite all sections in India, and which will be ratified by the British Parliament, are remote and slight. The probabilities of a breakdown are enormous. One has only to read the latest dispatches to see how true that is. Meanwhile, all over India, expectations, aspirations and appetites have been excited and are mounting. Already Mr. Gandhi moves about—so I read in the "Times" newspaper—surrounded by a circle of wealthy men, who see at their finger tips the acquisition of the resources of an Empire on cheaper terms than were ever yet offered in the world. I was reading of the Roman senator, Didius Julianus, who was dining at a restaurant when they told him that the Praetorian guard had put the Empire up to auction and were selling it in the ditch of their camp; he ran out, and bought it for £200 sterling per soldier—according to Gibbon. That was fairly cheap, but upon my word I believe the terms upon which the Empire is being offered to this group surrounding Mr. Gandhi, are cheaper still.

Now I must ask a question not entirely directed to those upon the Government side of the Committee, but to some of my own friends and colleagues, for whose opinion I have the greatest regard. I would ask them to consider, in the months that lie before us, was it worth while to throw all those issues open on the chance of an agreement being reached, was it worth while to throw all those issues of the Round Table Conference open in the hope of getting, in a Diet of Notables, rather a more convenient Parliament at the centre of the Indian Government than at present? No, sir, we have been most imprudent to depart from the prescribed constitutional course which has been marked out and laid down, upon which all parties had agreed and to which they were faithfully addicted. We have been most unwise to depart from that procedure, which I have already unfolded to the House once this Session and which will, I believe, be the final procedure which it will be forced to adopt before we come safely and honourably out of this Indian difficulty. Here let me say, and I must say it, the responsibility for what is going to happen rests with those who are having their way, it rests with those who are having their policy tried out, it does not rest with those who vainly protest against the course of events. The responsibility rests on those who are having their way; on them alone descends the reckoning which is gathering.

The right hon. Gentleman the Secretary of State for India has been in the habit of charging me with being an advocate of violent repression. He says that my policy is the lathi, the bayonet, the machine-gun and artillery, and, apparently, those words have been received with more respect and agreement upon this subject than utterances from the Government Bench usually command. It is easy to say such things, and easy to cheer them when they are repeated, but they are not true, and they are not just. The quotations which my right hon. Friend did me the honour to read from the speech I made in the Dyer Debate might at least have been borne in mind in this matter. I am no advocate of brutal force in India; indeed, I hold that no more physical force is needed in the solution of the Indian question. A tithe of the force and the punitive measures which the Socialist Government and the present Viceroy have vainly employed would have sufficed if they had been part of a firm and coherent policy, the simple maintenance of law and order; if they had not been accompanied by the disturbing of the minds of the masses by the belief that all the institutions and the whole world around them was to be thrown into the melting-pot; if they had not been accompanied by the building up of a belief in the minds of the masses that the Government of India, and the Socialist Government here, were squeezable, and that enough pressure would make them give way stage after stage. A tithe of those measures would have had their effect, a tithe of the suffering and of the police charges which the right hon. Gentleman has been pouring out and launching all this year would have had their effect if they had been accompanied by a coherent and sober policy. [*Interruption.*] Hon. Members had better hear what I have to say, because then they will know the arguments which they will have to meet and which, no doubt, with their superior skill, they will easily be able to overcome. After charges like that, surely I am entitled to reply.

The Indian problem does not require more force. May I take as an example two teams of coach horses? Under one driver they go along beautifully, happily and in a most elegant manner. Under another, who perhaps uses more force and strength, the horses are driven mad and gallop round the streets causing a disaster. [An Hon. Member: "Men are not horses!"] No, I am illustrating a point. If the hon. Gentleman does not like that illustration, let me take the illustration of two ships in the Royal Navy. In one ship there is a strict discipline, and yet everyone is happy and smiling and everything is all right. In another ship the punishment book is loaded with cases of men punished in every way, and yet the crew is driven almost into mutiny. Obviously, we need something more than the mere use of force. But who are the users of force?

No Government for generations have used the force in India which the Socialist Government have used.

Let me illustrate this point by comparing the conditions in Calcutta and in Bombay. In Calcutta there is a very active seditious movement, a great deal of revolutionary feeling, a great deal of anti-British feeling. It is a centre which might, easily become a most dangerous centre, and yet there has not been there, I think I can say with safety, a tithe of the police charges, arrests, Indians committed to prison and Indians bruised by the blows of the police that have taken place in Bombay. Why is that? In Calcutta we have had a man, Sir Charles Tegart, as Chief of the Police—only Chief of the Police, but he has nevertheless been able to give firm, steady guidance to the masses and has prevented matters from getting into a shocking state of disorder. In Bombay, under the weakest possible control at the summit, a policy has been pursued of pandering to disorder and sedition, alternating with knocking people about on a very considerable scale, and then going round and pandering to them again. The result is that the amount of misery and suffering inflicted upon the Indians in Bombay is 10 times as great as it has been in Calcutta. It is my abhorrence of the use of physical force which leads me to resist a policy which will gradually reproduce over large parts of India the lamentable conditions of Bombay, and I say it is not I, but the Secretary of State and those who think with him, who are bringing bloodshed and confusion ever nearer to the masses of Hindustan.

I have only one more word to say. [Hon. Members: "Hear, hear!"] I never expected that what I said would be agreeable to hon. Gentlemen below the Gangway on the opposite side, and I am afraid I cannot make my views upon this subject agreeable to them, but if they think those views are very wrong their interest would be to allow a full expression of them in order that the good sense of the nation may be manifested against them. It is not true, I think, to say that those who do not like the way in which the constitutional problem is being handled administratively at the present time by the Government have no constructive policy. We take our stand upon the views almost universally accepted before the present Socialist Government came into office. We take as our point of departure the report of the Statutory Commission. Why is that so very shocking? On the one hand we assign no potential limits to the ultimate progress of Indians in every form of civilisation and self-government.

Mr. Marley: I do not want to interrupt, but I would like to draw attention to the suffocating condition of the atmosphere and to ask whether anything can be done about it.

Mr. Churchill: On the one hand, we prescribe no theoretical limits to the ultimate potential progress of India and self-government. On the other hand, we hold that the responsibility for the well-being of the Indian masses rests here, with this Parliament, and that it is for all practical purposes inalienable. We hold that any constitutional changes which Parliament may decide to make do not depend upon procuring the agreement of the extreme sections of Indian opinion, or, indeed, of any section, although their agreement would be welcome. They only depend upon our right discharge of our mission to the Indian masses. If further discretionary power is to be given, as no doubt it should be given, and pretty soon, to Indians, it should be delegated power experimentally bestowed, capable of continual supervision and capable of effective recall if that power is abused or misapplied. We hold that it is futile and most hampering both to constitutional changes and to administration to talk about independence and full Dominion status at the present time.

Meanwhile, we take stock of the position. The Montagu-Chelmsford reforms have largely failed. It was a mistake in those reforms to emphasise unduly the wholly artificial and visionary conception of all India as a political entity. Clause 41 of the Act of 1919 gives us the right to vary or moderate the direction and the progress of Indian self-government. That was the general message of the Statutory Commission's Report, it is also the main purport which emerges from the alternative scheme presented by the Viceroy. The whole purpose of those documents is to show that the line on which we should now advance is in the development of Indian responsibility in the provincial Governments of India, that efforts should be made to make these Governments more truly representative of the real needs and feelings of the Indian people, giving Indians the fullest opportunity of trying their hands at all the great questions—

The Deputy-Chairman: The right hon. Gentleman is travelling far beyond the Rules of Order.

Mr. Churchill: I must submit to your Ruling, but I regret that it is impossible for me to add the absolutely necessary section of my argument. I find myself repeatedly reproached by those who say, "What is your constructive policy?" and in a few short sentences I was about to indicate, in general terms, in terms as general as those of my right hon. Friend the line along which a safe and sure advance might now be made. If I cannot do so, I will easily find ample opportunity on other occasions. With the permission of the Committee, I may say, to conclude these few general observations, and to justify our position—if any there be who share my views—that we hold that the line of advance now is in the development of provincial responsibility, and that meanwhile the Imperial executive, which is the sole guarantee of impartiality between races and creeds—

Mr. Maclean: I wish to raise a point of Order. While I have no objection to the right hon. Gentleman proceeding along the lines he has adopted, I would like to know if other hon. Members will also be permitted to proceed on the same lines and indicate their ideas?

The Deputy-Chairman: I did not hear the speech made by the right hon. Gentleman the Member for Bewdley (Mr. S. Baldwin) and did not know that he had outlined any policy. I simply lay it down, that it is not in order to discuss the details of anticipated or prospective legislation. We must confine ourselves to the administrative action of the Government.

Mr. Churchill: In the circumstances, I will not attempt to make the point to which I attach considerable importance, and, no doubt, the Government will afford another opportunity when I shall be able to discuss these matters in full. I will only say that the views which I shall not express now ought not to be described as "diehardism," because they are by no means reactionary, and they are the views expressed in the Statutory Commission's report, which is the sole foundation of the three-party action. We are encouraging hopes in India which cannot be realised, we are assigning exaggerated importance to individuals in India with whom we shall never be able to agree and we are injuring the prestige and strength of British Government in India for dealing with all these problems. We are lending ourselves and allowing the minds of millions of people in India to be attracted to all sorts of vague and specious ideas which are not going to be realised, and cannot, in fact, be given by legislation or by agreement between the British and the Indian people. Hitherto all these absurdities so airily and facilely entertained are approaching their inevitable collision with reality, and the first contact of reality upon the Indian question was manifested when the right hon. Gentleman published his decision on Monday night not to allow the Conservative delegates to take part in the Conference in India. Many more contacts with reality will be made as the weeks go by and it is for these impending shocks that I am anxious that opinion both in Great Britain and in India should be thoroughly prepared.

OUR DUTY IN INDIA

March 18, 1931

Albert Hall, London

At this moment of crisis for Baldwin, a by-election was taking place in St. George's, Westminster. At one point Baldwin considered resigning his seat and standing as a candidate, but in the event the pro-Baldwin banner was carried by Duff Cooper against an anti-Baldwin candidate vigorously supported by Beaverbrook and Rother-mere. The impact of this meeting at the Albert Hall—just outside the constituency— was overshadowed by Baldwin's attack the same evening on the "Press Lords," whom he condemned as seeking "power without responsibility—the prerogative of the harlot throughout the ages." The phrase came from Baldwin's cousin, Rudyard Kipling. It was devastating. Duff Cooper won easily and Baldwin's leadership was preserved.

I think it hard that the burden of holding and organising this immense meeting should be thrown upon the Indian Empire Society. One would have thought that if there was one cause in the world which the Conservative party would have hastened to defend, it would be the cause of the British Empire in India. One would have expected that the whole force of the Conservative party machine would have been employed for months past in building up a robust, educated opinion throughout the country, and in rallying all its strongest forces to guard our vital interests. Unhappily all that influence, and it is an enormous influence, has been cast the other way. The Conservative leaders have decided that we are to work with the Socialists, and that we must make our action conform with theirs. We therefore have against us at the present time the official machinery of all the three great parties in the State. We meet under a ban. Every Member of Parliament or Peer who comes here must face the displeasure of the party Whips. Mr. Baldwin has declared that the three-party collusion must continue, and in support of that decision he has appealed to all those sentiments of personal loyalty and partisan feeling which a leader can command. Is it not wonderful in these circumstances, with all this against us, that a few of us should manage to get together here in this hall to-night? [Editor's Note: An allusion to the great numbers who filled the building.]

Our fight is hard. It will also be long. We must not expect early success. The forces marshalled against us are too strong. But win or lose, we must do our duty. If the British people are to lose their Indian Empire, they shall do so with their eyes open, and not be led blindfold into a trap. Already in our campaign we have had a measure of success. The movement and awakening of opinion in the Conservative party have already caused concern to our leaders. They feel they have to reckon with resolute forces in the party and far beyond it, who will not be easily quelled. Already they have rejected the plan of sending a three-party delegation out to India for which Lord Irwin pleaded so earnestly. For the moment, therefore, we have a breathing space. The Socialist and subversive enemy have been thrown into disarray by the breakdown of their scheme to entice the Conservatives out to India. They are arranging their forces for a renewed attack. Mr. Gandhi, their supreme hope, is to come to London, as soon as they can persuade him to come, and here in the centre of the Empire he will discuss with British ministers and politicians the best means for breaking it up. But by that time we shall be ready too. We shall not be taken by surprise, as the country was during the Round Table Conference. We are not entirely defenceless or without means of expression. We have behind us the growing strength of Conservative opinion. We have the prospect at no great distance of a Conservative victory. Nothing will turn us from our path, or discourage us from our efforts; and by the time Mr. Gandhi has arrived here to receive the surrender of our Indian Empire, the Conservative party will not be so ready to have its name taken in vain.

What spectacle could be more sorrowful than that of this powerful country casting away with both hands, and up till now almost by general acquiescence, the great inheritance which centuries have gathered? What spectacle could be more strange, more monstrous in its perversity, than to see the Viceroy and the high officials and agents of the Crown in India labouring with all their influence and authority to unite and weave together into a confederacy all the forces adverse and hostile to our rule in India? One after another our friends and the elements on which we ought to rely in India are chilled, baffled and dismissed, and finally even encouraged to band themselves together with those who wish to drive us out of the country. It is a hideous act of self-mutiliation, astounding to every nation in the world. The princes, the Europeans, the Moslems, the Depressed classes, the Anglo-Indians—none of them know what to do nor where to turn in the face of their apparent desertion by Great Britain. Can you wonder that they try in desperation to make what terms are possible with the triumphant Brahmin oligarchy?

I am against this surrender to Gandhi. I am against these conversations and agreements between Lord Irwin and Mr. Gandhi. Gandhi stands for the expulsion of Britain from India. Gandhi stands for the permanent exclusion of British trade from India. Gandhi stands for the substitution of Brahmin domination for British rule in India. You will never be able to come to terms with Gandhi. You have only to read his latest declarations, and compare them with the safeguards for which we are assured the official Conservatives will fight to the end, to see how utterly impossible agreement is. But let me tell you this. If at the sacrifice of every British interest and of all the necessary safeguards and means of preserving peace and progress in India, you come to terms with Gandhi, Gandhi would at that self-same moment cease to count any more in the Indian situation. Already Nehru, his young rival in the Indian Congress, is preparing to supersede him the moment that he has squeezed his last drop from the British lemon. In running after Gandhi and trying to build on Gandhi, in imagining that Mr. Ramsay MacDonald and Mr. Gandhi and Lord Irwin are going to bestow peace and progress upon India, we should be committing ourselves to a crazy dream, with a terrible awakening.

No! Come back from these perilous paths while time and strength remain. Study the report of your own statutory commission headed by Sir John Simon and signed unanimously by the representatives of all the three parties in the State. Let us take that as our starting-point for any extensions we may make of self-government in India. It is very wrong that the vast majority of Conservative electors throughout the country, and the vast majority of all those who are acquainted with and have practical experience of India, and of that enormous mass of patriotic people not attached to any party, should have these vital questions settled over their heads by an agreement or an understanding between the two front benches in the House of Commons, and have their future settled as if they were a lot of sheep. We are told that three-party unity must be preserved at all costs. What does that mean? Up to the present it has only meant one thing, namely, that the Conservative party has had to toe the Socialist line, and has been dragged at the Socialist tail. Here are these Socialists, maintained in office only on sufferance or by intrigue, expecting all other parties to serve them, and to dance to their tune. We are here to-night to say 'No, that shall not be.' We have a right to our own convictions; we are entitled to act in accordance with them. We will certainly make our faith apparent by every means in our power, and in every quarter of the land.

I repudiate the calumny which our opponents level at us that we have no policy for India but repression and force. Do not be deceived by these untruths. Do not be disquieted by exaggerations of the difficulty of maintaining order in India which are spread about for interested motives by the Socialist ministers and their allies. In the whole of the disturbances of the last year—except on the frontier—scarcely a British soldier has been required. Very few people have been killed or severely wounded in the rioting. But how did the most of them get hurt? They got hurt not by the Indian police, but in religious fights between Moslems and Hindus. The great body of expert opinion which is represented upon the Indian Empire Society will support me when I say that a calm, capable, determined Viceroy properly supported from home could maintain peace and tranquillity in India year after year with a tenth of the repressive measures which Lord Irwin in his misguided benevolence has been compelled to employ.

Neither is it true that we have no constructive policy. We take our stand upon views almost universally accepted until a few months ago. We believe that the next forward step is the development of Indian responsibility in the provincial governments of India. Efforts should be made to make them more truly representative of the real needs of the people. Indians should be given ample opportunities to try their hand at giving capable government in the provinces; and meanwhile the central Imperial executive, which is the sole guarantee of impartiality between races, creeds and classes, should preserve its sovereign power intact, and allow no derogation from its responsibility to Parliament. Is that Diehardism? That is the message of the Simon report, unanimously signed by the representatives of the three parties. That is the purport of the alternative scheme submitted a few months ago by the Viceroy himself.

After all, it opens immediately an immense and fertile field for Indian self-government. The provinces of India are great states and separate nations comparable in magnitude and in numbers with the leading powers of Europe. The responsible government of territories and populations as large as Germany, France, Poland, Italy or Spain is not a task unworthy of Indian capacity for self-government, so far as it has yet been displayed. It is a task the successful discharge of which would certainly not conflict with the ultimate creation of a federal system. On the contrary it is the indispensable preliminary without which no federation, desirable or undesirable, is possible. Why, the very word 'federal' signifies a *foedus* or treaty made between hitherto sovereign or autonomous states. All federations have arisen thus. In the United States of America, in Canada, in Australia, in South Africa, in every case the units have first been created. Why should these unpractised, unproved, unrepresentative, self-chosen groups of Indian politicians disdain the immense possibilities offered within the limits of the Statutory Commission's report, and demand an immediate setting up of an United States of India, with themselves in control, and the British army at their orders? Before a Federal system for India could be set up there must be first the self-governing constituent provinces; and secondly, far greater, more real, more representative contact between the Indian political classes and the vast proletariat they aspire to rule. Even Europe cannot achieve such a united organisation. But what would be said of a scheme which handed the federal government of the United States of Europe over to political classes proportionately no larger than the inhabitants of Portugal, and no more representative of the needs and passions of a mighty continent than the inhabitants of a single city like Rome? Such are the follies we are forced to expose. We therefore resist upon the highest experience and authority the viewy hysterical megalomania of the Round Table Conference.

Why is it that the principles of Government and lessons of history which we have learnt in our experience with the great self-governing dominions, which we have learnt in Canada, in South Africa and in Ireland, apply only in a limited degree to India? It is because the problem of Indian government is primarily a technical one. In India far more than in any other community in the world moral, political and economic considerations are outweighed by the importance of technical and administrative apparatus. Here you have nearly three hundred and fifty millions of people, lifted to a civilisation and to a level of peace, order, sanitation and progress far above anything they could possibly have achieved themselves or could maintain. This wonderful fact is due to the guidance and authority of a few thousands of British officials responsible to Parliament who have for generations presided over the development of India. If that authority is injured or destroyed, the whole efficiency of the services, defensive, administrative, medical, hygienic, judicial; railway, irrigation, public works and famine prevention, upon which the Indian masses depend for their culture and progress, will perish with it. India will fall back quite rapidly through the centuries into the barbarism and privations of the Middle Ages. The question at stake is not therefore the gratification of the political aspirations towards self-government of a small number of intellectuals. It is, on the contrary, the practical, technical task of maintaining the peace and life of India by artificial means upon a much higher standard than would otherwise be possible. To let the Indian people fall, as they would, to the level of China, would be a desertion of duty on the part of Great Britain.

But that is not all. To abandon India to the rule of the Brahmins would be an act of cruel and wicked negligence. It would shame for ever those who bore its guilt. These Brahmins who mouth and patter the principles of Western Liberalism, and pose as philosophic and democratic politicians, are the same Brahmins who deny the primary rights of existence to nearly sixty millions of their own fellow countrymen whom they call 'untouchable,' and whom they have by thousands of years of oppression actually taught to accept this sad position. They will not eat with these sixty millions, nor drink with them, nor treat them as human beings. They consider themselves contaminated even by their approach. And then in a moment they turn round and begin chopping logic with John Stuart Mill, or pleading the rights of man with Jean Jacques Rousseau.

While any community, social or religious, endorses such practices and asserts itself resolved to keep sixty millions of fellow countrymen perpetually and eternally in a state of sub-human bondage, we cannot recognise their claim to the title-deeds of democracy. Still less can we hand over to their unfettered sway those helpless millions they despise. Side by side with this Brahmin theocracy and the immense Hindu population—angelic and untouchable castes alike—there dwell in India seventy millions of Moslems, a race of far greater physical vigour and fierceness, armed with a religion which lends itself only too readily to war and conquest. While the Hindu elaborates his argument, the Moslem sharpens his sword. Between these two races and creeds, containing as they do so many gifted and charming beings in all the glory of youth, there is no intermarriage. The gulf is impassable. If you took the antagonisms of France and Germany, and the antagonisms of Catholics and Protestants, and compounded them and multiplied them ten-fold, you would not equal the division which separates these two races intermingled by scores of millions in the cities and plains of India. But over both of them the impartial rule of Britain has hitherto lifted its appeasing sceptre. Until the Montagu-Chelmsford reforms began to raise the question of local sovereignty and domination, they had got used to dwelling side by side in comparative toleration. But step by step, as it is believed we are going to clear out or be thrust out of India, so this tremendous rivalry and hatred of races springs into life again. It is becoming more acute every day. Were we to wash our hands of all responsibility and divest ourselves of all our powers, as our sentimentalists desire, ferocious civil wars would speedily break out between the Moslems and the Hindus. No one who knows India will dispute this.

But that is not the end. The Brahmins know well that they cannot defend themselves against the Moslems. The Hindus do not possess among their many virtues that of being a fighting race. The whole south of India is peopled with races deserving all earnest solicitude and regard, but incapable of self-defence. It is in the north alone that the fighting races dwell. Bengal, for instance, does not send from her forty-five million inhabitants any soldiers to the native army. The Punjab is [a place where fighting races dwell], on the other hand, and the Pathans, together with the Ghurkas and the Sikhs, who are entirely exceptional sects of Hindus, all dwelling in the north, furnish three-quarters of the entire army in the time of peace, and furnished more than three-quarters of it in time of war. There can be no doubt therefore that the departure of the British from India, which Mr. Gandhi advocates, and which Mr. Nehru demands, would be followed first by a struggle in the North and thereafter by a reconquest of the South by the North, and of the Hindus by the Moslems. This danger has not escaped the crafty foresight of the Brahmins. It is for that reason that they wish to have the control of a British army, or failing that, a white army of janissaries officered, as Mr. Gandhi has suggested, by Germans or other Europeans. They wish to have an effective foreign army, or foreign-organised army, in order to preserve their dominance over the Moslems and their tyranny over their own untouchables. There, is the open plot of which we are in danger of becoming the dupes, and the luckless millions of Indians the victims.

It is our duty to guard those millions from that fate.

Let me just direct your attention once more upon these untouchables, fifty or sixty millions of them, that is to say more than the whole population of the British Isles; all living their lives in acceptance of the validity of the awful curse pronounced upon them by the Brahmins. A multitude as big as a nation, men, women and children deprived of hope and of the status of humanity. Their plight is worse than that of slaves, because they have been taught to consent not only to a physical but to a psychic servitude and prostration.

I have asked myself whether if Christ came again into this world, it would not be to the untouchables of India that he would first go, to give them the tidings that not only are all men equal in the sight of God, but that for the weak and poor and downtrodden a double blessing is reserved. Certainly the success of Christianity and missionary enterprise has been greater among the untouchables than among any other class of the Indian population. The very act of accepting Christianity by one of these poor creatures involves a spiritual liberation from this obession of being unclean; and the curse falls from their minds as by a miracle. They stand erect, captains of their fate in the broad sunlight of the world. There are also nearly five million Indian Christians in India, a large proportion of whom can read and write, and some of whom have shown themselves exceptionally gifted. It will be a sorry day when the arm of Britain can no longer offer them the protection of an equal law.

There is a more squalid aspect. Hitherto for generations it has been the British policy that no white official should have any interest or profit other than his salary and pension out of Indian administration. All concession-hunters and European adventurers, company-promoters and profit-seekers have been rigorously barred and banned. But now that there is spread through India the belief that we are a broken, bankrupt, played-out power, and that our rule is going to pass away and be transferred in the name of the majority to the Brahmin sect, all sorts of greedy appetites have been excited, and many itching fingers are stretching and scratching at the vast pillage of a derelict Empire. I read in the *Times* newspaper, in the *Times* mind you, only last week of the crowd of rich Bombay merchants and millionaire millowners, millionaires on sweated labour, who surround Mr. Gandhi, the saint, the lawyer, Lord Irwin's dear colleague and companion. What are they doing there, these men, and what is he doing in their houses? They are making arrangements that the greatest bluff, the greatest humbug and the greatest betrayal shall be followed by the greatest ramp. Nepotism, back-scratching, graft and corruption in every form will be the handmaidens of a Brahmin domination. Far rather would I see every Englishman quit the country, every soldier, every civil servant embark at Bombay, than that we should remain clutching on to the control of foreign relations and begging for trading facilities, while all the time we were the mere cloak of dishonour and oppression.

If you were to put these facts, hard, solid indigestible facts, before Mr. Ramsay MacDonald or Mr. Wedgwood Benn, or Sir Herbert Samuel, they would probably reply by pointing to the follies of Lord North in the American revolution, to the achievements of Lord Durham in Canada, or to what has happened in South Africa or in Ireland. All the Socialists and some of the Liberals, together with, I am sorry to say, the official Conservatives, have got these arguments on the tip of their tongue. They represent all of us and the millions who think with us, and the instructed Anglo-Indian administrators on whose advice we rely, as being mere dullards and reactionaries who have never been able to move with the age, or understand modern ideas. *We* are a sort of inferior race mentally deficient, composed principally of colonels and other undesirables who have fought for Britain. *They* are the sole possessors and monopolists of the spirit and of the message of our generation. But we do not depend on colonels—though why Conservatives should sneer at an honoured rank in the British army I cannot tell—we depend on facts. We depend on the private soldiers of the British democracy. We place our trust in the loyal heart of Britain. Our faith is founded upon the rock of the wage-earning population of this island which has never yet been appealed to, by duty and chivalry, in vain.

These great issues which arise from time to time in our history are never decided by the party caucuses. They are decided by the conscience and the spirit of the mass of the British people. It is upon the simple faith and profound unerring instinct of the British people, never yet found wanting in a crisis, that we must put our trust. We are deliberately trying to tell our story to the British masses, to the plain and simple folk to whom the fame of the British Empire is ever dear. In assailing the moral duty of Great Britain in India, the Socialist Government and all who aid and abet Mr. Ramsay Macdonald and his Socialist Government, or make their path smooth, will find they have stumbled upon a sleeping giant who, when he arises, will tread with dauntless steps the path of justice and of honour.

"THE MARCH OF EVENTS"

March 26, 1931

Constitutional Club, London

Following his crushing defeat at St. George's, Westminster, Beaverbrook called off his anti-Baldwin campaign. In India, Gandhi stopped the civil disobedience campaign and entered into serious negotiations with Irwin. Meanwhile, the Labour Government was at the beginning of the "economic blizzard" which eventually brought it down.

Things are not going well. We have had two shameful and disastrous years. They have been years in which we have not merely been standing still; we have been galloping down the slope. They have been years in which even deeper anxieties have entered our hearts than we felt in the darkest days of the Great War. No great country is maltreating itself as we are and doing less justice to itself. Look where you will, on the continent of Europe or across the Atlantic, you will see our competitors, some ready to be our successors, in many of the great fields in which we have shone, concentrated upon the problems of marshalling their strength and defending with vigour their national interests. Here a sort of moral palsy seems to have descended upon us. We seem to be afraid to call our souls our own. The Socialist minority Government is only kept in being by all kinds of weaknesses and divergences among the strong forces which have hitherto maintained the life of the country.

But, wherever you may look, the worst scene of Socialist mismanagement and depredation is in their conduct and administration of our Indian Empire. There is the great target which Conservatives all over the country should steadily and remorselessly fire upon. I cannot accept the suggestion that we ought to keep India out of party politics, if it only means we are going to lose India with decorum and dignity. To lose India would be far worse than to bring it into party politics. How else are those who do not agree with what has been done by the Socialist Government in India to make their point of view effective except by public speech and action? I do not intend to mince my words. I wish to make it perfectly clear I am going to attack the Socialist record and policy in India. Nothing will turn me from it, and I have cheerfully and gladly put out of my mind all idea of public office. I intend to fight this question during the next two or three years, in which it will be the culminating issue in British politics, without regard to any aspect but the merits.

I am told I am alone among men who have held high public office in this country in the view I take about the Indian policy. If that were so it would be a great honour for me, because I should be left alone to plead a majestic cause, and I should be left alone to represent the opinions of many millions of British men and women in every party who are deeply concerned at the trend of events in the East. If I am alone I am going to receive shortly an ally—a very powerful ally—an ally whom I dread—an ally with a sombre title—his title is *THE MARCH OF EVENTS*. The march of events in

India will be grim and may possibly be rapid. You have only to read your papers to-day to see how the situation there is steadily darkening.

Where was it that we went wrong in our treatment of the Indian question? In my judgment it was when we abandoned the principle of the Simon Statutory Commission Report, and when we allowed the Round Table Conference, which was set up merely for consultative purposes, to convert itself quite improperly and wholly without authorisation into a kind of Constituent Assembly. It is the commonest fallacy of present discussions to speak of India as if it were the home of a strongly coherent united race. It makes me sick when I hear the Secretary of State saying of India, '*She* will do this and *she* will do that.' India is an abstraction, represented by a handful of politically-minded classes who have no means of intercourse with each other except in the English language, who have no real contact with the masses, who are incapable of giving them the guidance they require, and are animated in the main by very great hostility to this country. India is no more a political personality than Europe. India is a geographical term. It is no more a united nation than the Equator.

The great error was made when, almost unperceived, the process of extending reform and self-government to India by Parliament was converted into a will-o'-the-wisp search after this abstraction called India and an attempt to negotiate with the various agitated figures who are cast up from the Indian Congress and the various Indian revolutionary or political organisations. That has changed the whole centre of gravity of the discussion. It was a frightful injury both to British and to Indian interests.

I have been blamed for saying that the three-party co-operation has simply meant that we have been made to toe the Socialist line. But lately we have had a revelation. Mr. Malcolm MacDonald, the son of the Prime Minister, attached in a secretarial capacity to the Round Table Conference, has written articles for the newspapers of his constituency in which he lays bare how the whole Conference was manipulated and manoeuvred by the Socialist party so as to achieve the result they had set before themselves from the beginning—namely, the conferring of responsible Government at the centre upon Indians.

Let me quote you his words:

How accurate was (the Government's) calculation of what would be the ultimate conclusions of the Conference, and of what policy it would finally be able to announce with the approval of all delegations, is illustrated by an interesting fact. The drafting of the Prime Minister's concluding statement of the Government's policy, actually delivered on January 19, was already in hand before Christmas. The text of the statement was completed during two all-day conferences between the Prime Minister and his principal Government advisers, which I attended at Chequers on December 27 and 28. This was several days before the Conference itself began to consider the all-important question of Indian responsibility in the Central Government. It was before the Indians themselves had stated their ideas in detail, before Lord Reading had made his famous speech announcing the Liberal Party's support of the Indian claims, and before the Conservatives' definition of their policy. Yet only minor alterations had to be made in the Government's statement as a result of these events following its original drafting. So much for the tactics of the Government.

See what happens when you get upon the slippery slope, when instead of the Conservative party putting its hand on the brake, it puts its foot on the accelerator.

We are told we are not committed to anything. But events are moving on and each week it is assumed that we are committed to more. Mr. Benn, in the House of Commons yesterday, treated the question as one that was settled, and said there would soon be a responsible Indian Minister to deal with the Customs. Thus, while the Conservative leaders remain tongue-tied, the whole position is being transformed.

The Gandhi-Irwin agreement was the natural and logical outcome of the Round Table Conference. Gandhi, with deep knowledge of the Indian peoples, by the dress he wore—or did not wear, by the way in which his food was brought him at the Viceregal Palace, deliberately insulted, in a manner which he knew everyone in India would appreciate, the majesty of the King's representative. These are not trifles in the East. Thereby our power to maintain peace and order among the immense masses of India has been sensibly impaired. As a part of the agreement made in these circumstances we have legalised the boycotting for economic pretexts, as apart from political pretexts, of Lancashire cotton goods. That is an astounding thing for us to have had to do. We have legalised it, and it is more effective than ever, now that it is legal and pursued for economic purposes. I have no doubt that this process of boycotting Lancashire cotton goods is a criminal conspiracy in restraint of trade, and ought never to be accepted or legalised. A company has even been formed at Gandhi's instigation to help the merchants to get rid of British merchandise already landed in India and cast it down in East Africa or elsewhere, provided the merchants sign an undertaking that in no circumstances will they import any British goods again. Are we going to put up with that? Or are we going to use every resource of influence and policy to make sure we are are allowed fair intercourse in trade and commerce in India?

But that is only the beginning. These are the first drops of the storm. Gandhi has resolved, and those who work behind him and through him are still more resolved, to bring practically all British importations, certainly all Lancashire importations, to an absolute end. That spells the doom of Lancashire. The coastwise trade, the great enterprises and business institutions which we have founded in India, are all in succession to be swept away. As for the hundreds of millions of loans which we have advanced to create the railways and irrigation services and public works of India, in consequence of which the Indian population has increased by 30,000,000 in the last twenty years, all this is in jeopardy. Unless you are prepared to defend your rights and interests in India, you will be stripped of every vestige you possess and expelled with ignominy from its shores.

Wednesday's massacres at Cawnpore, a name of evil import, are a portent. Because it is believed that we are about to leave the country, the struggle for power is now beginning between the Moslems and Hindus. A bloody riot broke out in which more than two hundred people lost their lives with many hundreds wounded, in which women and children were butchered in circumstances of bestial barbarity, their mutilated violated bodies strewing the streets for days. The British troops are now pacifying and calming the terrified and infuriated populace. But the feud is only at its beginning.

Let the Conservative party regain its freedom. Let there be no more co-operation with the Socialists. First of all I am asking that we should regain our full discretionary power. We must be free to rouse the people of our country to the approaching peril and to get our own forces into line.

You are in favour of tariffs. They are necessary on economic and financial grounds. But still more are they necessary as a part of a reassertion of our will to live and reign in the modern world. They are only a part. There is no use in uniting the Empire by trade preferences and losing India. The loss of India would destroy all that we have built up. Surely our generation which sent its brothers and sons and watched its fathers march to France and Flanders should be the last to be guilty of such a failure. We must weave together the strong forces in our island which have carried us through the tribulations of the past and which united are invincible.

A venerable member of the Conservative Party, one of my father's friends—in fact at one dramatic moment his only friend, Mr. Arthur Baumann—penned the other day some sentences with which I will now end. 'Surely,' he wrote, 'an effort should be made to save his kingdom for the Emperor of India. Let us set up a standard around which the brave and the loyal can rally. More than that we cannot do. The rest is in the hands of God.'

INDIA

April 22, 1931

Junior Imperial League Rally,
Chingford

Whoever is going to win the next election, and we have our own ideas about that—(cheers)—the Liberals are going to lose it, and they are going to lose it because they have forsaken policy for tactics and principle for manoeuvre. It is refreshing to see men like Sir John Simon separate themselves from these misguided courses and take the simple, manly course of voting according to their faith and conscience. I am glad to see that one of the Conservative leaders the other day welcomed the accession of these true Liberals and true conservatives of all that was best in this country to their ranks in the coming battle.

Also I observe that Lord Beaverbrook and his Crusaders have marched up into line. Only a few weeks ago we were told it was our duty as loyal party men to regard him with the utmost aversion—I could not repeat to you the things it was our duty to say about him. But all that is past and we are now all happily reunited. I am sure we shall all congratulate the late chairman of the party, Mr. Neville Chamberlain, upon the happy marriage he has made and earnestly hope that it will be both lasting and fruitful. We shall no doubt learn more about the marriage settlement when Mr. Baldwin makes his next speech.

[Editor's Note: Referring to the "shameful maladministration of India and fatuous mismanagement of our India policy" he said]: In no other sphere of government have our Labour leaders let Britain down so badly. Nowhere else have they done such lasting harm, no, not in their malevolent class, spiteful taxation, not in their sloppy soup-kitchen conceptions of the economic life of a modern community; no, not in their wasteful expenditure, nor even in their sheer vacuity and utter emptiness of thought on social problems. Surely the Conservative Party ought to have a policy of its own about India. Surely the time has come when it should occupy an independent position and be allowed to speak its own mind freely, like I do, about India. Surely we ought not to allow ourselves to be entangled in the disaster which is coming steadily towards us from India.

It gives me encouragement to feel that though I might be for the time being separated upon a single question from some of my friends and colleagues, yet somehow or other I seem to be more in harmony with the thought and conviction of my constituency than ever before. Lord Irwin is coming home and Mr. Gandhi is said to have booked his own passage. I suppose these two will soon be engaged in further sweet discussion in London. I see Lord Irwin wrote to a Socialist M.P. that the atmosphere in India was sweeter. It was not very sweet during the massacre of Cawnpore, where the babies and mutilated, violated women were thrown into the sewers. But perhaps it will be sweeter here. Let me tell you what will cleanse the Indian atmosphere, the one sovereign carbolic lotion which will restore the health of the British Empire in India. It is the Conservative Party standing up boldly and declaring its own faith and convictions upon the Indian question. When the Conservative Party wrenches itself away from the Socialists' slippery slope to ruin and bloodshed in India, then you will see quickly a remarkable change for the better in all our affairs.

It is quite true that we shall not at this stage be helped by the Liberals, but if we take up our own true position the Liberals will be helped by us to do their duty in saving these great regions of the Empire, with their vast populations, from the miseries into which they are being muddled and hurried. I am not responsible for the situation that has been created, but like all of you I have to bear its consequences and face its facts. What ought we to do now? We ought not to allow any Conservative delegation to enter into conference with Mr. Gandhi or sit at the same table with him unless or until he has definitely accepted all the safeguards and conditions which were prescribed at the Round Table Conference. Until he does so there is no basis for a conference.

We have so mishandled our affairs and ravaged our interests in India that the great victorious British Empire is now reduced to trying to make a treaty with Mr. Gandhi upon the terms on which the King's authority is to continue in India. That is the plight to which our wiseacres have led us. That is the result of our following humbly at the Socialists' coat-tail. Let us, at any rate, insist, if we are to be involved in this conference, that Mr. Gandhi accepts the fundamental basis of the discussion; and if he refuses, let the Conservative Party, at any rate, be free from the responsibilities of any further parley with him.

I thought the Simon Report went much too far, but the Simon Report has long been left behind. I thought the Round Table Conference was a landslide of British rights and interest, but now it is the conclusions of the Round Table Conference which are to be swept away. There is no end to the misfortunes, shame, and impoverishment which you will suffer if you show yourselves incapable, nay, if you declare yourselves incapable of offering any resistance. I do wish indeed that our leaders would address themselves earnestly and faithfully to our rights and duty in India. It is no use trying to unite the Empire by trade preferences if in the meanwhile you let India slide into anarchy. The loss of India will be the death blow of the British Empire, and every one of our foreign rivals is waiting to see that hideous signal hoisted.

Mr. Snowden, by his attitude in regard to the National Debt and by the squalid administration of the Unemployment Insurance Fund, for which he was no doubt unwillingly responsible, has created many of the difficulties which he has to meet. All the Chancellor has to do, however, is to propose and carry through a general tariff for revenue purposes on foreign imported manufactured articles.

[Editor's Note: Speaking of the conditions in Russia, he said]: We must have the power to place embargoes, not merely a tariff, upon product of slave labour sent here at prices which bear no relation to any commercial or economic operations.

I am afraid I shall have to change my metaphor before I can deal with Lord Rothermere, because, after all, this is a strictly monogamous country—(laughter)—so let me say that I hope Mr. Neville Chamberlain's successor, Lord Stonehaven, will not leave any stone unturned in order to bring Lord Rothermere also into the fold. It makes a most enormous difference to our flights throughout the London and suburban areas if we have these, our great daily papers, on our side. I call them our papers, not because they belong to us, but because nearly all our own friends and supporters read them. For the Conservative Party in and around London and the Home Counties to go into an electoral battle without the support of their popular Press is like asking British infantry to attack a position without any artillery bombardment. Their help would halve the losses and double the gains.

[Editor's Note: After referring to the recent censure motion on "this wretched Socialist Government," he said]: I am afraid that the Government's position is even strengthened for the time being. There does not seem to be much chance of an election just yet.

But I must say that there is one vote of censure which I should rejoice above all things to take part in, and that is a vote of censure upon the Socialist Government for their vain and disastrous policy in India. We see how they have cut down our Navy and tied us up in unfair international agreements, which enable every other nation to strengthen its fleet, but make us, who alone depend upon sea power, continually weaken ours. We see how they have solved the problem of unemployment—by undermining confidence and enterprise, by paralysing business, by pouring out their doles without even daring to correct the gross abuses which prevail. We see how they tried to legalize another general strike and secure to themselves by an Act of Parliament the right to 'Make London walk,' and throw the whole country into confusion. I am glad they had their dirty throats cut over that. I am glad that they have shown their own insincerity by the resignation—no not resignation, that is the last word to use—by the abject complacency with which they have accepted that supreme affront.

THE BUDGET

April 29, 1931

House of Commons

I shall not attempt to follow the right hon. Gentleman [Sir Herbert Samuel] into the two topics to which his speech was mainly devoted, namely, a well-rehearsed lecture on the advantages of Free Trade, and a somewhat laboured exposition of the rather delicate tactics which he and his friends found it necessary to pursue in pressing the Government for the relief of taxation of company reserves. I shall deal with the general question of the Budget, and the House will, naturally, not be astonished if I say that I listened to the Budget speech with amusement, which almost rose into hilarity. I could hardly believe my ears as I heard the Chancellor of the Exchequer unfold a long series of proposals which were virtually an acceptance, in fact and in form, of the financial measures and expedients which I devised and practised, and which he derided and condemned. As one by one those familiar shapes arose from the other side of the Table, and as I recalled to memory all the criticisms and scathing censures he had lavished upon each of them, I wondered whether I had not, perhaps, left behind some of my old Budget notes, and that one of his able secretaries had, by mistake, put them into the Chancellor's famous red box. Certainly, no Minister I have heard has ever given the House such an example of self-stultification. The opinions which he expressed were so recent, their form was so violent, the pattern of their reversal was so symmetrical and perfect, that whatever may or may not be said about his Budget speech, it will certainly abide for generations as a unique curiosity in Parliamentary annals.

Like his predecessor, the right hon. Gentleman was confronted with a financial emergency which he hoped would be of short duration. Like his predecessor, he was precluded from raising a large revenue by the easy and comparatively painless method of a general tariff for revenue. Like his predecessor, he recoiled from imposing further heavy direct taxation. Like his predecessor, he hoped for better times. Like his predecessor, he took capital assets to tide over what he believed was a temporary emergency. Like his predecessor, he adopted a fixed Debt charge of £355,000,000 in satisfaction of all services and claims upon the Debt and the amortisation fund. Like his predecessor, he excluded from his calculations of the net sinking fund all borrowing by the Unemployment Insurance Fund. Like his predecessor, he called in aid a reserve—and it is a reserve—by expediting instalments on various Schedules of the

Income Tax. Like his predecessor, he utilised a duty upon oil to meet, but, like him, only partially to meet, the expense of providing relief on rates to manufactures and agriculture.

Even the very form in which these accounts are now presented to Parliament in the exclusion of the self-balancing revenue and expenditure, in the separation of the Sinking Fund from the ordinary expenditure of the year, even down to the intensified blue colour paper for the Financial Statement—in every step the right hon. Gentleman has followed meekly, and, I might almost say, reverently, those very footprints which the last four or five years of his life have been spent in abominating. To-day I do not have to say "Ditto to Mr. Burke." I am even more fortunate. Mr. Burke has said "Ditto" to me, and I need not at the outset confess that these spontaneous tributes are gratifying to me in my present loneliness. I did not expect them so soon. But this is an age of speed. Every year the pace of life and the pace of motion increase, and so, I suppose, time's revenges have gone in for record-breaking.

The right hon. Gentleman's acceptance and endorsement of my financial administration has entailed, I gather, a similar conversion in the Liberal party. No critics were more severe or more unfair in the last Parliament than my Liberal critics of finance. Their authority on financial questions is great, and they do not proceed except upon the basis of life-long established principles. They have followed out all the doctrinaire and orthodox theories of finance to their logical conclusion, and, consequently, when they have given their impartial opinion, not mixed up with the struggle between Conservatives and Socialists, it naturally carries special weight in the minds of the public generally. But what has happened to all those opinions now? I gather that they have all now become, in the main, favourable or, at any rate, instead of denouncing these practices of the Chancellor of the Exchequer as the worst violation of every principle of sound finance, the right hon. Gentleman passed them off airily as ingenious and convenient temporary expedients.

What is the explanation? What process of ratiocination has been at work? I do not see the right hon. Member for Carnarvon Boroughs (Mr. Lloyd George) here to-day, but it is clear that what has happened is that "When father turns, all turn." I accept their tributes, belated though they be, for what they are worth. I suppose a favourable verdict is always to be valued, even if it comes from an unjust judge or a nobbled umpire. The Committee will see that it would be somewhat difficult for me, in all the circumstances, to take a highly controversial line, and I am, therefore, sincerely grateful to my right hon. Friend the Member for Edgbaston (Mr. Chamberlain) for coming forward with what I must regard as prophetic magnanimity to relieve me from a long-drawn task of criticism and opposition to this Budget which it is, undoubtedly, the duty of those who sit on this side of the House to fulfil. It falls to me only to make from time to time a few comments upon the strange scene of our finance this year, and I am very glad to be able to do so with complete freedom from all considerations except the merits and demerits of the case.

I shall set myself to test this Budget upon two main questions: first, how far are these proposals in themselves sound or unsound, wrong or right; and, secondly, how far is the Budget, taken as a whole, appropriate to the serious situation in which we stand? Upon the first question, I have already recapitulated the extraordinary re-

semblance and continuity of method and of outlook between the financial policy of
the present Socialist Administration and the financial policy of the late Conservative
Government. I use the word "Government" advisedly, because the Chancellor of the
Exchequer does not produce the Budget in the name of a great party without having
carefully submitted it to the principal colleagues on whom that party relies. In the late
Cabinet I had the very great advantage of the presence of no fewer than three
ex-Chancellors of the Exchequer—an unpopular breed, no doubt, but none the less
powerful for that. And it was my custom and my duty, not only to secure the assent
of the Cabinet to the annual Budgets, but to discuss their details long in advance with
the Prime Minister and with my two eminent and fraternally united colleagues. I do
not recall any differences that developed between us upon the many difficult decisions
with which we were confronted.

Therefore, I say that in all the resemblances which this Budget bears to previous
Conservative Budgets, the Chancellor of the Exchequer, at a cost, no doubt, of a
complete personal tergiversation, has at any rate placed himself upon solid ground and
ranged himself with most respectable authority. But there are not only resemblances in
this Budget; there are differences upon which a considerable structure of legitimate
and consistent criticism ought to be founded. Some of these differences I shall
endeavour to explain. Like the Chancellor I shall begin with the fixed Debt charge. We
thought in 1928 that the reinstitution of the fixed Debt charge, which was sanctified
by principles avowed and practised by Mr. Gladstone and Sir Stafford Northcote—we
thought that the reinstitution of the fixed Debt charge to cover the interest, the
sinking fund and the detachment of savings certificates, was a far better way of dealing
with this oppressive problem of the Debt than by making a provision from year to year
of such sums as were actually needed on these Debts. The fixed Debt charge removes
from national finance a whole series of erratic and uncontrollable fluctuations which
in one year give an appearance of a false economy and in another year the appearance
of an equally false extravagance.

We preferred as far as possible to separate controllable from uncontrollable or
partially controllable expense, and we established a fixed Debt charge of
£355,000,000 which, if it was adhered to for 47 years more, would completely
extinguish our National Debt. This method, no doubt, deprived the base and ignorant
of a certain number of cheap scores from time to time upon the fluctuation in the
total of our expenditure, but it had the great advantage of focusing before the eyes of
the House and the country the preventible and optional expenditure of the Government in any year, free from the confusing external facts. The right hon. Gentleman
was not content with this provision of £355,000,000, and on his assumption of office
he set himself a far higher standard; he went out of his way, and needlessly, as we told
him at the time, to add the deficit of the 1929 Budget, to add his deficit of my 1929
Budget—I think he had as much almost to do with the deficit as I had with the
Budget—he went out of his way needlessly to add that deficit to the Debt provision of
the next three years; and in a frenzy of self-righteous animadversion he actually set a
Clause in the Finance Bill, to act for all time as a warning to Chancellors of the
Exchequer, whereby automatically, unless the House intervenes, the whole deficit of
any year would be added to the Debt provision for the next year. I was rude enough in

the Debate last year to describe this Clause as mere eye-wash. Looking back I cannot feel that that term erred at all, except, no doubt, in lack of ceremony. The first and only Chancellor of the Exchequer to fall under the ban—for it is now to be removed by the hand that set it up only a year ago—is the right hon. Gentleman himself. We have all heard of how Dr. Guillotine was executed by the instrument that he invented.

Sir H. Samuel: He was not!

Mr. Churchill: Well, he ought to have been. We know of the engineer who was hoist by his own petard, the stricken eagle which nursed the pinion that impelled the steel, and we see a much more perfect example in the right hon. Gentleman sitting in his place to-day. Being of an amiable disposition I will forbear further to aggravate the wound which he has himself inflicted. I will content myself with recording the important fact that this fixed Debt charge of £355,000,000, in the setting up of which I was greatly aided by my right hon. Friend the Member for West Birmingham (Sir A. Chamberlain), pursued over the years across all their varying conditions, taking the rough with the smooth and the good years with the bad years, is in fact recognised by all parties as an adequate provision for our release from the frightful burden of the National Debt.

It has never been the custom for the borrowings for the Unemployment Insurance Fund to be set off against the net sinking fund. The Chancellor of the Exchequer has taken to this somewhat devious and questionable practice like a duck to water. Not the slightest difficulty this year in getting him to keep these two ideas in quite separate compartments in his mind. But surely the figures involved alter the case? I have always held the view that the Unemployment Insurance Fund, resting as it does upon important revenues of its own, could carry within certain limits a reasonable loan account of its own, and that was the position in our time. But when, either through grave national depression or partly through lax administration, the loan charges rise to £70,000,000 or £80,000,000 or perhaps £100,000,000 in a very short time, it is perfectly evident either that the cause of the expenditure must be curbed by economy, or that some entirely new provision for funding this ever-growing debt will have to be brought into effect.

Next I come to the Oil Duty. I may claim this Duty as being a great success. It has produced, up to the present, practically no increase in the price of petrol. All that it has done is to intercept for the Exchequer the relief which would otherwise have come to the motoring public from the fall in price. All the administrative difficulties were surmounted in the original tax. There is nothing to be said against the tax, except that all taxes are bad. There is nothing to be said against the tax half as bad or a quarter as bad as what the Chancellor himself said yesterday. I think he is justified, before all tribunals except his own, in increasing this Duty upon this occasion. We shall now be deriving more than £25,000,000 of revenue from the Petrol Tax, and that is a very fair set off—it comes within £10,000,000 of the total expense of all the rating reliefs which the right hon. Gentleman inherited. He is getting from this tax alone £25,000,000, towards the £35,000,000 that he had to provide. There is a certain gap, I agree. After this year, when the £4,000,000 in reserve are used up, there will be this gap of £10,000,000; but in the main the cost of that immense relief of transference of expenditure from the most invidious form of taxation upon industry to the Exchequer, has practically been borne and sustained by the Petrol Tax. So I hope that any future howlings on the subject will be kept within the reduced limits within which they would be proper.

Then there is the provision for expediting the instalments under the various Schedules of the Income Tax. When we applied this principle to Schedule A it yielded £17,000,000 in the single year, as against the £14,000,000 which I estimated. I am sure that it was the right thing to do at the time, and I was not aware, while the process of collecting it was going on, that any exceptional hardship was being inflicted. At any rate, there were hardly any complaints, hardly any difficulty in collecting it. For two successive Budgets I looked hungrily at the other Schedules. The right hon. Gentleman must not suppose that I did not, with appetite in my eyes, examine all these possibilities. Why did I not avail myself of them? It was because I was warned of the very serious differences which existed between applying this principle to Schedule A and applying it to the other Schedules. My advisers who first made me aware of the possibilities of Schedule A, when I discussed the other Schedules produced arguments which alarmed me so much that I left them severely alone. It was pointed out that there were great numbers of small people who could not get the same accommodation from their banks for the six months that the majority of Schedule A taxpayers are able to secure, and that the payments would come in just at Christmas time, when so many heavy charges fall upon the small householder.

We had last night from my hon. and gallant Friend the Member for Kelvingrove (Major Elliot) some figures of great interest upon this point, and I think it would be a very good thing if the Chancellor of the Exchequer and some of his advisers had the opportunity of looking at those figures, which perhaps are not fully found in the report. Only very serious reasons deter me from availing myself of this method, and those serious reasons confront the Chancellor to-day. He has rushed in where I feared to tread, and I have no doubt that he will encounter a very keen and considerable outcry and resistance, and that there will be many cases of real hardship and embarrassment resulting from this, the necessary treatment and mitigation of which may affect to some extent the yield of the tax this year.

With regard to the £20,000,000 of transfer from the exchange account, I agree that the establishment of the International Bank and the arrangements for the payment of contributions which constitute the wealth of that bank in dollars, render this sum of money available. But that this money, originally borrowed money, the produce of an unbalanced War-time Budget, should be used to defray current expenditure instead of being devoted to the cancellation of Debt, even beyond the limits of the fixed Debt charge, will be held in all quarters to be a violation of the canons of sound finance, and it strips the Chancellor of the Exchequer of every vestige of financial orthodoxy.

There remain only the land taxes about which we are to hear to-morrow or Monday. Until we know precisely what those taxes are it is of course impossible to discuss them, but I hope that the right hon. Gentleman is not going to throw out a complicated scheme, in a speech or in a paper, and expect the House to form its judgment and opinion upon that without some reasonable interval for the study and examination by experts and actuaries and accountants of these highly complicated and technical projects. I shall not attempt to discuss the matter this afternoon, because it has, of course, nothing whatever to do with this Budget, or the next Budget or any Budget for which the right hon. Gentleman is likely to be responsible. If these land valuation proposals are empty of money they are quite full of politics, and I only express the hope that their political aspects will be studied with as much care on this side of the Committee, as they have evidently been studied on the other side.

When we saw with what interest and stress and eagerness the right hon. Gentleman fastened upon these proposals, and how he saved them up for the end as the rare and refreshing fruit, the dessert that was to conclude the somewhat restricted meal which he provided—when we saw that, it was made quite clear that he is using these taxes, not for any fiscal or financial purpose, but as a means of arrangement and negotiation with the party below the Gangway on this side and in the vain hope of satisfying hon. Members on the benches below the Gangway opposite. Of course, these are very old ideas. I think that the right hon. Gentleman below the Gangway told us what Mr. Gladstone said in 1891 upon this subject, and we have all seen for 50 years their merits and demerits canvassed. Well, that is all that Socialism gets out of it. The right hon. Gentleman used these taxes as a means to show that, if he had ceased to be a Socialist, at any rate he was a good old-fashioned Radical. Poor unlucky I.L.P.! Forlorn New Party men! Socialism in our time as dead as mutton! But, never mind. Radicalism, not in the Chancellor of the Exchequer's time but some time or other, may, perhaps, hold out some glittering possibility. There is their consolation prize. If they are content with that, if they are satisfied with that, if that is all they are requiring now, then all I can say is that the influence of the Parliamentary atmosphere must be of a most potent character.

In the short time that I propose to trespass further upon the indulgence of the Committee I come to the second inquiry and the larger aspect of the Budget, namely, its wisdom and opportuneness as a whole. The task of a Chancellor of the Exchequer is always thankless. If he taxes he is abused by the victims. If he fails to tax he is insulted by the pedants. If he is simple, he is clumsy; if he is ingenious he is tricky. If he spends it is a rake's progress, and he can only save by dismissing persons from their employment. Whatever course he takes he must encounter not only fierce criticisms but valid criticisms, and no course which he can take can possibly avoid those criticisms. It is only upon very broad lines that the action which he takes can be fairly judged.

How, then, stands the Budget as a whole? There is a unity of conception about this Budget. The note which it strikes is clear. Its simplicity has not been obscured to any serious extent—apart from these land tax proposals which are not really a part of the Budget—by the kind of spiteful partisanship to which sometimes I have had to draw the right hon. Gentleman's attention as being a disfigurement upon his attractive public career. Its purpose is modest. Its purpose is none the less sensible. I do not think myself, and I am giving my personal opinion, that the Inland Revenue estimates, apart perhaps from stamps, are inflated. The Income Tax estimate is not a guess. Samples of 30,000 firms are passed under review. The most elaborate logarithms and curves are drawn to show all the different results of varying rates of collection and so forth. The officials are of the highest competence and their estimates hardly ever err, except on the side of safety, and I do not believe that the right hon. Gentleman is the kind of Chancellor who would screw up the figures without the most careful regard to the facts.

There are, no doubt, great uncertainties overhanging some of our external receipts. I do not dwell upon those uncertainties partly because of their gravity and also because I hope that they will clear themselves up in a satisfactory fashion. If they do not, then they will entail an entire recasting of our present financial affairs, but there is, undoubtedly, in the proposals of this Budget a gap between permanent revenue and permanent expenditure of anything from £30,000,000 to £40,000,000. At present that gap is filled only with hope and good resolutions. But one thing is vital to the right hon. Gentleman's policy this year and to the Budget which he has introduced, and that is resolute economy. The right hon. Gentleman owes it to Parliament and owes it to himself to vindicate this daring Budget—and I do not say that it is a wrongfully daring Budget because I think that he has dared in the public interest and not in any personal or party interest—by effecting the reductions in expenditure upon which alone its solvency depends. In this he should be aided, and will, I am sure, be aided by all parties in the House.

The Budget marks a very great decision. It is not the decision which the right hon. Gentleman paraded so eagerly on Monday. This Budget will not be memorable for the political manoeuvres connected with land taxation proposals or land valuation proposals. It will be memorable for the fact that the Socialist Chancellor of the Exchequer, in spite of party pressure, in the teeth of the whole doctrines of his life, has declared by action, which is louder than words, that in the present circumstances the limits of direct taxation have been reached. There is the message in the Budget imparted to us by lips whose reluctance to utter it is the measure of its irresistible force. There is the bleak revelation, thrust silently but brutally before British Socialism. That is the all-important recognition which the Chancellor of the Exchequer has made of facts and of his contact with realities, and it is a recognition, made not only by the Government, but, as I gather, by their Liberal allies. We do not know all the reasons by which the Chancellor of the Exchequer has been actuated, but we can judge from his action how grave and urgent some of those reasons must have been. Looking out behind the scenes upon the whole field and structure of British trade and industry, he has come to the conclusion, greatly against his party interests and feelings, that the most burdened and most loyal class of taxpayers in the whole world have reached or nearly reached their breaking point—

Mr. Hoffman: In present circumstances.

Mr. Churchill: All right, in present circumstances—and that further pressure, at this juncture, would result possibly in an even more widespread collapse of enterprise than that which we are now confronted with and would possibly be coupled with an actual diminution and would certainly not be attended by any proportionate increase in the yield of the taxes themselves. He has had the courage—and he has never wanted any kind of courage as we have seen—he has had the courage, and, I will add, the public spirit, to set aside his own convictions, to defy his party's pressures, and to do what he deems to be his duty to the country.

Very far-reaching conclusions can be drawn from that decision of the Chancellor of the Exchequer. It spells the doom of all those airy, visionary Socialist programmes of creating some new Utopia through the agency of the tax-collector. It reveals the bankruptcy of the Socialist programme. It reveals more than that. If the social services of this country, freed from abuses as they ought to be, are to progress, as I trust they will, in the immediate future, it can only be through the institution of systems of indirect taxation on a far greater scale and in a far higher proportion than anything that has yet been contemplated. I agree with my right hon. Friend the Member for Edgbaston in what he said yesterday. The compulsive need for revenue must bring the tariff. The tariff brought, by the need of revenue, must become the agency by which the growing importance of the home market will be emphasised. The institution of the tariff will afford occasion for striking those new bargains with foreign countries which are necessary and which, wisely handled, may play an important part in welding together the production and consumption of our Empire, before the present process of dispersal and disintegration has reached its fatal end.

When we survey the various alternatives which were before the right hon. Gentleman, I cannot myself say that he has not judged rightly. Suppose that he had put £20,000,000 or £30,000,000 on the direct taxpayer—he could have used the plausible argument of the Revenue returns of last year—he would have had loud cheers of triumph and of appetite from the benches behind him; he could have used this sum of money to gain the encomiums—I believe that is a word—of the financial purists for the great provision which he had made for the Debt, but he might well have struck a deadly and possibly a fatal blow, at a most critical moment, at the whole trade and business life of our country.

He has taken the right course; he has rejected that alternative; he has endeavoured to nurse the country round a most dangerous crisis in its illness. I cannot regard his action as other than a friendly and responsible gesture. He has sought to gain a breathing space. Do not let us throw that breathing space away. Precious, fleeting months must not be wasted by British industries. Often we have heard them say, "Leave us alone." Well, anyhow for a space, they are left alone. The cloud of the Budget which overhung all business affairs for the last few months is lifting. The arrangements and the policies adopted by or forced upon the various party leaders have apparently removed the probability of a general election. There is no power behind this Government to carry any serious legislative projects of a revolutionary or injurious or violent character into law. They have lost confidence in themselves, and, however wisely guided they have been, they have abandoned contact with all those distinctive, characteristic themes to which the birth and vitality of their party have been due.

Party politics, pushed to extremes, seem for the time being to have reduced themselves to something very like deadlock and equipoise on all sides. The State, for good or ill, in the next 12 months will have little to contribute, in national guidance or misguidance, to industry. One can certainly say of such a situation as one can say generally of the Budget, "It might well be worse." Let us make sure that the strength and resourcefulness of all our citizens is exerted in that interest while they are, at any rate for a space, freed from uncertainty, and, while British politics are coming to their senses, let us see what British industry can do for itself.

This is no time for complacency, nor is it a time for despair. I am deeply concerned, not only about our world position, but about the continuing ability of this island to afford the means of expanding livelihood for its immense population. Never, even in the darkest days of the War, except perhaps in April, 1917, during the culmination of the submarine crisis, have I personally felt so much anxiety about public affairs, but my faith is also strong that we shall recover, that we shall not be the last of the nations to find our way through the perils and perplexities of the present world situation, that the resources and resiliency of our Empire will not be unequal to our trials, that faction will fade as difficulties deepen, that unity and design will emerge from confusion and futility, and that we shall not be deprived, at any rate through our own fault, of our future and of our inheritance.

THE PRESS

April 29, 1931

*Newspaper Press Fund Dinner,
May Fair Hotel, London*

[Extract] . . . No institution has gained more in power in the twentieth century than the Press. No institution has woven itself more closely into the life of the people of all classes. While Parliamentary institutions have grown steadily weaker, the newspapers have become stronger and the Press has blithely consented to fill the gap caused by the subsidence of the House of Commons and the euthanasia of the House of Lords. It is extremely important that the profession of journalism should be strongly conscious of its corporate life and held together by firm bonds so that its members may always preserve the highest possible standard of duty and responsibility. Being a member of the Institute of Journalists myself, I can give the assurance that I have always done my best to set the highest example in all these respects. (Laughter.) I have been asking myself whether the Press, which is undoubtedly a stabilizing factor in this country, might not obliterate or overshadow the growth of individual opinion and of individual personality. All goes well so long as this great machine of public opinion is not broken or injured in any way. But supposing something happened which broke it, are you sure that there are existing in all their stations all over the land men and women with the force of character and grit to mobilize the ideas necessary to maintain the life and to be the pillars of our civilization? That is a thing to think about.

[Editor's Note: Referring to the remarkable developments in the production of newspapers, Churchill said]: A newspaper office with its printing machines at work suggests to me a combination of a first-class battleship and a first-class general election. No Press in the world has the incorruptibility of the British Press, and none is so fair and decent towards the private life of individuals. Nor is there any Press in the world in which public men who are interviewed by newspaper men can more confidently rely on being treated honourably and not misrepresented or betrayed in the matter of personal confidences. (Cheers.)

INDIA OFFICE

May 13, 1931

House of Commons

Churchill's fondness for the Latin phrase parcere subjectis, et debellare superbos *("spare the conquered, and war down the proud") led him to repeat it on many occasions. This appears to be the first use of it.*

I rise for the purpose of supporting the cogent and cumulative arguments which the late President of the Board of Trade has addressed to the Committee. He certainly did not indulge in that kind of rhetoric which excites the criticism of the right hon. Gentleman the Member for Darwen (Sir H. Samuel), but he confined himself to pile-driving by means of the assembly of substantial facts. Those facts have not been challenged in any quarter of the Committee, and they were, to a very large extent, supported by the right hon. Gentleman the Member for Darwen. The right hon. Gentleman, however, was oscillating between the making out of as good a case as he possibly could for Lancashire in the interests of a somewhat shaky seat, and a proper supply of the more simple forms of platitudes which he hoped would give satisfaction to and increase his influence with the party opposite.

Then we had the speech of the Secretary of State for India. I ask the Committee, I ask any of those who have been deeply concerned by the condition of Lancashire or by the state of India, whether it would have been possible to have had a more inadequate contribution to the solution of the problem. All that the Secretary of State for India did say simply minimised the evil by certain perfectly valid arguments so far as they went, but the right hon. Gentleman closed his eyes to the rest of the evil, and suggested that all our difficulties in India would be solved, and a remedy for our trade would be procured, merely by pursuing the policy of the Round Table Conference. The same argument was used by the right hon. Gentleman the Member for Darwen. I cannot see what good that is going to do for Lancashire, because, as we well know, the policy of Mr. Gandhi and the Indian Congress is the permanent exclusion of British goods in one way or another from India, either by a boycott or by a prohibitive tariff. The Secretary of State for India, on a recent occasion, did not use the argument which he has used to-day when he was asked what was the remedy for the difficulties of Lancashire, because he said that in a short time there will be an Indian Minister of Commerce responsible to an Indian legislature. Supposing this Indian Minister of Commerce proposed an embargo on British and foreign imports, and supposing he was supported in that policy by the Indian legislature, how is that going to help Lancashire? The Secretary of State will no doubt say that that is the way the constitution works, and that is how our principles work out when they are carried to their logical conclusion. The right hon. Gentleman will probably say, "India does not want our goods, and that is the end of it; Lancashire is ruined, and there is nothing more to be said about it." I think there is a very great deal more to be said about this matter.

Is it really our duty as British Members of Parliament to let things drift supinely into a position like that, and then turn round with a grin and say to a whole country which has been thrown into impoverishment, "We are sorry you are ruined and starving, but it all worked out quite logically and in accordance with our well-known principles and declarations. Our motives have been purely disinterested, and if you have been ruined, you must bear it"? Is that the whole duty of the House of Commons? Is that really the whole duty of the 40 Socialist Members of Parliament who sit for Lancashire? I think they will be expected by their constituents to do a little bit more than that. I say that it is our duty even to make some mental and moral exertion on this question, and not be content with the kind of answer which we have received. We must examine searchingly this logic and these principles which, by impeccable steps are, in fact, leading us to hideous disaster, involving cruel suffering to a great number of our people.

That is what, I consider, we have to do this afternoon, and I will try to face the difficulty. I regret the letter which has been published from the Leader of the Opposition in which he declares in the name of his party

> that the Conservative party intended to use its fullest influence in support of British traders, and to insist that in any future settlement of the Indian Constitution there should be a fundamental provision prohibiting unfair discrimination against British trade.

I must, however, point out that that principle and declaration—on which on this side of the House there is universal agreement—conflicts with the principle of full dominion status. It should be carefully borne in mind that in this Conference it is most important that hopes must not be excited which it may afterwards be found impossible to realise. At the present moment India has not got dominion status, and has not got responsible government. Parliament is responsible for the welfare, both of the people of India and the people of Great Britain. The Imperial Parliament has the whole responsibility at the present time, and, until we part with it, we have the power and the lawful right to act and work in the interests of both countries, and we are responsible for so doing.

Let me ask, is this boycott, or is a prohibitive tariff, in the interests of India, and are these things good for the Indian people? We know that they are not good for Lancashire, that they spell the doom of Lancashire, but would they be good for the Indian people? The Secretary of State for India is an inveterate Free Trader and one of the most able exponents of Free Trade. We know that the right hon. Gentleman cannot argue in favour of a tariff which goes to the extent of prohibition or a boycott, because he believes that that cannot possibly be for the benefit of the Indian masses. I feel certain that the right hon. Gentleman would be entitled to argue that this would be the exploitation of the many by the few, and would cause a rise in prices which the poor people would have to pay. What help is all this going to be to the poverty of the Indian people if they are made to pay higher prices? What help is Mr. Gandhi's idealism going to be to the Indian people, and how is it going to lift them from their poverty? All this is no remedy at all for the poverty of the Indian people.

The right hon. Gentleman knows perfectly well that this boycott and this attempt to inflict a prohibitive tariff is something which is directly injurious to the well-being of the majority of the people of India. Even Protectionists are not logically compelled to dissent from that doctrine, because the incidence of a duty notoriously depends upon the relations between the importer and the home supply. Therefore, there is not in this particular instance any difference between the views of the Protectionists and Free Traders, and all the cheap scores and debating points made by the Secretary of State are only introduced for the purpose of saving his own face and darkening the counsels of Parliament. I have no hesitation in saying that there is scarcely any commodity whose exclusion from India would inflict more material injury on the Indian masses, or give more unjust favours to the Bombay merchants and mill owners, than cotton cloth. That would be a ramp, a swindle and a hold-up of the most cruel and scandalous character.

What ought we to do? Ought we to allow it? Ought we, while we remain responsible, to acquiesce in, to connive at, nay, to bring about, such an evil result to the Indian people? Ought we to divest ourselves of responsibility in order that such a result may be brought about? That is the question which is before the Committee. Many have pointed out the evil, but we have to address ourselves to what is our duty in the face of it. We have not heard this afternoon, but perhaps we shall hear, of the extraordinary profits of these Indian mill-owners. I believe that no class of capitalists in the world, in this present year of disgrace, of economic misfortune, has made such vast profits. I was sent a whole list from Lancashire of the profits of some of these Indian mills. [*Interruption.*] They are most staggering figures. And when we consider that these staggering figures for the profits of the mill-owners are coupled with conditions in the mills of India, at Bombay and Ahmedabad, which, it is common ground between all parties, are lamentably below the conditions which ought to prevail—when we put in juxtaposition the vast profits and the grinding conditions, the harsh and wrongful conditions, and when we see that a monopoly is to be given to these people, I do say that we have a right to plead that it is an Indian interest that should be prevented from doing this.

These Indian mill-owners who have made these great profits, and who have such unsatisfactory conditions in their factories, are the great financial supporters of Mr. Gandhi; they are the money power behind the boycott. When a man is paid weekly wages, as the hon. Member for Bolton mentioned in public the other day, to lie down on the pavement in front of a shop in order to prevent goods being sold, the money that pays those wages comes from those very mill-owners who have an immense interest in bringing about a cessation of the traffic. It is a Hindu and Brahmin movement, where superstition and greed are marching hand in hand to the spoliation of millions of people.

I should like to know what is the position of the Moslems in this matter. There are 70,000,000 Moslems. I am told—perhaps I may be corrected, but I was told on high authority that the individual Moslem, man or woman, class for class, on the whole, wears more garments than the individual Hindu. That is their habit and custom. Consequently, the Moslem is a greater individual consumer of cotton cloth than the Hindu, and all this boycotting process is being conducted in the main by the Hindus. What are we to think of a proposal which places 70,000,000 Moslems where they will be bled and exploited and made to pay through the nose by this group of Hindu capitalists who are the chief subscribers to Mr. Gandhi's party fund? [*Interruption.*] Surely, we have come in contact with another of our principles and safeguards in our duty to protect minorities. Nothing could be more likely to lead to communal strife than for the warlike Moslems of India to feel that they are being made to pay for the garments that they wear in order to make vast fortunes for Hindu speculators and politicians, and that out of those vast fortunes, again, the funds are being provided to establish the political domination of their rivals in India. Therefore, I say that the safeguards which they have asserted, and our duty at the present time to minorities, oblige us to forbid and prevent such perilous exploitation, and the bloodshed and hatred which will follow from it.

I am speaking now of the effects in India, but surely we may say a word here for Lancashire, too. The Lancashire outlook is not a selfish one. Let me remind the Committee of the attitude of Lancashire in the American Civil War. There you had what was then the most prosperous part of our Islands reduced to living upon the charity of the rest, because the Northern cruisers were blockading the Confederate States; but all the time that Lancashire was suffering these evils, her fidelity to the cause of the North was never changed. That is not a community who judge of these matters entirely by their self-interest, and I have no doubt that if it could be proved to be, and was obviously for the good of India, for the well-being of all those enormous masses of very poor people there, Lancashire, whatever her suffering, would make no complaint. But when it is clearly for the harm of India, as well as for her own harm, surely she is entitled to expect her representatives to bring the matter to the attention of the House of Commons.

So far my argument has applied equally to both Mr. Gandhi's alternatives, the prohibitive tariff or the boycott. But, surely, the boycott has additional vices of its own. It is a tyranny; it is a tyranny outside the law; it is a form of unofficial bullying of a very odious kind. The boycott is an essentially malevolent action. It is an action animated by a desire to injure, proceeding to a goal which injures, by steps which at every stage injure. The Hindu religion, with its thousands of castes and social gradations, has powers of compulsion over its votaries which can find no parallel outside Asia, or, perhaps, Africa. A man's whole life can be made intolerable, and his whole hopes of future life can be cut off, if he does not conform to the policy of his spiritual guardians, who are also his political guardians. The Congress party can put pressures upon their members, and not only upon their members but upon any Hindu who does not march with them—pressures which are almost inconceivable to us in the West and to Europeans; and they use these pressures to enforce a boycott which grinds the Indian population, which enriches their wealthy friends, and which ruins Lancashire; and then we are told, "Oh, well, there is nothing wrong in it." I see that the hon. Member for Oldham (Mr. J. Wilson)—I used to know something about Oldham, and I have a great regard for Oldham, more regard than for its representatives—the hon. Member for Oldham said at the Textile Conference:

> They had as much right—

that is to say, the Indians—

> to the slogan "Buy Indian Goods," as the Conservatives of this country had to say "Buy British Goods."

Mr. James Wilson: On a point of Order. It was the hon. Member for the Sowerby Division (Mr. Tout), not the Member for Oldham.

Mr. Lang: I wish to make the same explanation. I never made those remarks at the conference.

Mr. Tout: On a point of Order. I did make that statement.

Mr. Churchill: It is quite right for the hon. Member to make a clean breast of it. Just let us look into this argument, which I have heard used in other quarters besides the one I have mentioned. How can you pretend that this Indian boycott has any resemblance at all to the "Buy British Goods" campaign? [*Interruption.*] If a number of people in this country choose to band themselves together and to agitate to purchase British goods or Empire goods, there is no objection to that; but if they band themselves together to prevent the sale of foreign goods—[*Interruption*]—if they band themselves together to obstruct customers from approaching shops, and to forbid shopkeepers to sell, their action becomes illegal, and can immediately be put down by the law. That anyone should pretend that there is the slightest resemblance between these innocent methods of encouraging the sale of home-produced commodities in this country or in India, and the kind of ruinous and cruel boycott which is being enforced in India, is most discreditable to those who do so. I really wonder that they can use such arguments.

What ought we to do? I submit that the policy which is being pursued is injurious to the people of India and ruinous to the people of Lancashire, and that we are responsible until we hand over our responsibility. What ought we to do? I say that we should do our duty. We should proclaim—[An Hon. Member: "Shoot them!"] No, I did not say that. I will come to the shedding of blood and the responsibility of the Government. [*Interruption.*] We ought to proclaim that, whether the boycott is economic or political in intention, it is illegal and wrong. We ought to make sure that the ordinances and laws of India are capable of dealing with this illegal and wrongful thing. We should enforce the law and those ordinances without fear or favour, not so much against the individuals who are hired for this purpose, who are paid weekly wages, as the hon. Member said, for this purpose, but against those who organise them—the ringleaders. We ought to take this course, and we ought also to carry out the policy which my right hon. Friend has laid down in his letter, and make sure that we do not vitiate that policy in any way by loose talk about full Dominion status, which is wholly incompatible with it.

I do not believe that there would be any serious difficulty if the matter were resolutely and patiently and calmly faced. I do not believe that there would be any grave or serious difficulty in altering this boycott in India. I have heard it said that it was rapidly breaking down when the negotiations with Mr. Gandhi were entered upon, but, at any rate, we owe it to all the parties concerned to discharge our duty. These self-imposed inhibitions and pedantries from which we are suffering, this long tangle of disingenuous formulas, have no reality except in our own minds. The problem would present no difficulties to any Frenchman, or any Dutchman, or any German, or any Italian, or any American, in dealing with a similar situation in one of their dependencies. We, in our helplessness and fatuity, are the laughing-stock of the world. [*Interruption.*] We are alone in our silliness, and Lancashire will be alone in her suffering.

Let me widen the scope of these discussions. The helplessness of the Government! I should like to know what are the principles that animate them in their maintenance of public order. I read in a Reuter telegram published in several of the newspapers a few days ago the following from Rangoon, dated 9th May:

> Fifteen rebels were sentenced to death and 56 to transportation for life to-day when the Pyapon Special Tribunal passed judgment on the 95 persons charged with waging war against the King last January or with abetting such a war. The remaining 24 were acquitted.

The judge having referred to the fact that the tribunal imposed a lesser sentence in the majority of cases added that

> strong intimidation had undoubtedly been used by the leaders towards the rank and file, whose cruelty and ignorance had been abominably exploited.

As I read those words, I wondered whether these 15 men who are to suffer the extreme penalty of the law are the only ones in India to whom such a censure would apply. The same paper in which you read this tells us of the great dilemma which is occupying the minds of the authorities at Simla, whether Mr. Gandhi should be allowed the special privilege of driving to Simla in a motor car, a privilege which has been denied and refused to all the greatest reigning princes of India. There seems to be a considerable contrast between the methods with which the humbler followers and agents of rebellion are dealt with and the treatment that is meted out to successful and triumphant leaders. The Romans had a maxim in their great days which I have several times quoted:

Parcere subjectis, et debellare superbos,

which I will translate for the benefit of some of my friends on this bench: "Spare the conquered, and war down the proud." As far as I can see, the attitude of His Majesty's Government is exactly the opposite. A successful leader of revolt whose aim is to drive you out of the country you treat almost with servility. I need not comment on this action, but, at any rate, it removes from hon. Members opposite any right to throw taunts at me of seeking by acts of terror to enforce order in India. I hold His Majesty's Government responsible for the miseries which the last two years have brought upon the people of India. The right hon. Gentleman pretended that great advantages had been gained—that there was a sullen mood when he came in and that, now they were all smiles. What a shameless misrepresentation! The boycott, and the scale that it has attained, is the fruit of weakness, the fruit of lack of confidence in our mission and in our duty, and in our power to execute that duty. It is only one of the fruits of all that evil policy of seeking peace. You have sought it perhaps in your hearts, but by your actions you have produced misery such as India has not seen for half a century. All your arrangements are steadily on the way to magnify and multiply that misery in the future.

This boycott is only one of the fruits. You have poisoned the relations between the Mohammedans and the Hindus. [*Interruption.*] Words will not do it. It is actions or inactions which produce these cleavages between these great communities of scores of millions. We are going shortly, I hope, to have a Debate on the massacre at Cawnpore. The right hon. Gentleman gave assurances, I understand, which I am sure he will act up to, that not a moment is to be lost in presenting the House with the results of the Commission of Inquiry which is sitting there. I do not wish to anticipate that Debate, which certainly will deal with one of the gravest and most horrible events that have ever happened. [*Interruption.*] I think there is no doubt that the events of Cawnpore far exceeded in horror anything that happened in the Mutiny if you take the treachery of old friends and neighbours killing each other, the atrocities, the outrages, the butcheries, the mutilations, the violations—all the photographs that have been sent to me, taken on the spot, are so revolting that no paper would be able to publish them. That was a most fearful event, and that is the first fruits of Gandhism and of surrender to Gandhism. But that is nothing to what is coming. These great rabbit-warren cities, with streets two or three feet wide in some cases, and high houses in which enormous numbers of people live—if these primordial hatreds as between tribes of insects break out there, there will be scenes and events which the world has really passed long away from in its slow progress.

It is Mr. Gandhi who says in effect, "If England will not let me have a mercenary army who obey my orders, we shall have to fight it out and it will be a good thing that Indians should fight their own battles." He says one of these races will exhaust or destroy the other. This is the man—see what he has said about the missionaries—that you have by your policy made the one outstanding figure with whom you are now to negotiate the future. Where are you leading us now? You are leading us to an absolute deadlock. You have excited hopes and fears and passions in India which years of steady government will neither satisfy nor allay. You are seeking desperately to renew this parley with Mr. Gandhi and the Congress party in order to ascertain the terms on which you will be allowed to remain in India. We know what Mr. Gandhi's demand will be. Meanwhile opinion here, too, is hardening. Even in the speeches that have been made from the Liberal bench to-day there is a very definite recognition of the grave aspect of affairs in India. Lord Reading's speech in the House of Lords the other day was a speech which certainly constituted an almost complete bar to any further surrender in Indian politics. Here is Mr. Gandhi making his demand, and here is opinion hardening, and you have so stage-managed this, that you have made this man appear to be the sole representative and champion of India. You are trying to bring him here, and to bring him here with no common basis out of which an agreement is likely to emerge. If no sincere agreement emerges, and if there is a breakdown, you will then be faced, hampered by admissions, with your authority weakened, with all those difficulties now grown monstrous from which you recoiled while they were still small.

COMMUNIST PROPAGANDA

May 18, 1931

House of Commons

The principal interest in the harangue to which we have just listened from the hon. Member for Salford, West (Mr. Haycock) is the insight it affords us into a peculiar type of mentality found here and there throughout this country, a type of mentality which received a great deal more acclamation from Ministerial supporters before they were rendered tame and respectable, to some extent, by Office. I do not intend to follow the hon. Member into all his wild and woolly words, but there is one question which I must answer, and that is why it is that I have not been tried for the private war I waged in Russia. One of the reasons is that I did nothing that was not approved by the Cabinet of the day, which was headed by the right hon. Member for Carnarvon Boroughs (Mr. Lloyd George) or that did not receive the full approval and endorsement of the House of Commons by enormous majorities, or which was not fully in accord with the published decisions of the Inter-Allied Conference, upon which President Wilson, amongst others, was a representative. The dock, if I am to be tried, must therefore be made ample enough to contain quite a large company.

There are two points in the speech of the hon. Member which, I think, call for some notice on the part of the Government. In the first place, there is the allegation that Scotland Yard has been deliberately forging documents. The Home Secretary is not in his place at the moment, but I am not aware that the right hon. Gentleman is ready to admit that he presides over a nest of forgers and that those confident officials and responsible persons who come to him every day, and with whom he has these relations, are in fact guilty of an odious and dishonest transaction of this character. If it is so, then the Government could inform us on the point when the time comes. As a matter of fact, I was not quite clear as to the date on which this alleged crime is said to have been committed; but it appears that it was committed at any time during the last five or six years. In that case the Prime Minister and his colleagues would have had cognisance of it, and would have been responsible for working with those who were connected with it. The charge, I need not say, is so absurd that it will not bear investigation, and I need not bother about it.

Mr. Haycock: Has the right hon. Member never heard of the important and unprecedented happening of eight years ago? I am much surprised.

Mr. Churchill: I never heard of such a thing, and I am not at all acquainted with it. The other point to which I invite the attention of the Prime Minister is the statement which the hon. Member made about the Secretary of the Soviet Embassy having visited the House of Commons and addressed a party meeting of the supporters of the Government. If that is so, I think it is altogether a novel departure in the relationships and actions which are appropriate to the representative of a foreign State in our midst. Very often those who are connected with foreign embassies visit chambers of commerce or make speeches of a non-controversial character to non-party meetings, but I should have thought it was altogether undesirable that a representative of a foreign nation should visit the House of Commons and harangue supporters of the Government. I had no intention or expectation of taking any part in this Debate, and it is only the extraordinary speech, to which we listened with increasing amazement, from the Prime Minister that has forced me to do so. The Prime Minister began by instituting a comparison between the speeches which I and others have made about India, and the Communist propaganda to create a revolution in India.

The Prime Minister *indicated dissent*.

Mr. Churchill: I heard the right hon. Gentleman. I do not say that he tried to make this comparison apply in all respects, but he used this in order to lead up to a conclusion in which he pointed at me and said, "If mischief is caused by Communists, it is also caused by your speeches." I think we may examine the basis of such a serious charge. I suggest that in all questions of speech or action the character of the speech or action must be considered. Before you can judge its consequence, if its character is lawful and proper, then it may well be that some anger is caused to other persons by it, but if the speech in itself and the doctrines in themselves are lawful and consonant with public order, there is no ground why silence should be maintained on public matters. Therefore, there is no comparison to be drawn between such doctrines and speeches and deliberate attempts to throw the whole country into a state of revolutionary disorder. There is this difference, I may point out, between the kind of speech which I make to one set of people and the kind of Communist propaganda handed out to another. But the people who are angered by the speeches which I make are the enemies of this country, and those who are angered by the Communist propaganda are its friends. [*Interruption*.]

Mr. Townend: On a point of Order. Will the right hon. Gentleman say—

The Deputy-Chairman: That is not a point of Order.

Mr. Townend: On a point of Order. Is the right hon. Gentleman entitled to imply that the operatives of Lancashire, who were angered by his Indian speech, are enemies of the country?

The Deputy-Chairman: The Chair can take no responsibility for the opinions of right hon. or hon. Members.

Mr. Churchill: I cannot understand all this touchiness. Rather more than normal interest is being taken in the topic that we are discussing this afternoon. I cannot understand why we cannot be allowed to debate this matter without individual Members jumping up here and there and taking points of Order which they well know are an abuse of the rule which entitles a Member to interrupt a speech. But let me say, since the Prime Minister has referred to me so pointedly, and I think wrongfully, that I am not at all prepared to accept from him guidance in public matters as to what is right and patriotic. [*Interruption*.] I am sorry to have to say that, because I have a respect and admiration for the right hon. Gentleman, and, naturally, a respect for the great office which he holds; but of this I am sure, that he has never allowed himself to be hampered in what he thought was his public duty by the kind of taunts which he was good enough to fling at me across the Floor, and at any rate that is a matter to which I think I was entitled to refer. But I will not labour that particular point.

Mr. James Hudson: Who is touchy now?

Mr. Churchill: The hon. Gentleman, who is a very perfervid partisan, and very properly, of his leaders, must recognise that in all these questions it may be asked, who began it? [*Interruption*.] The right hon. Gentleman made an unjustifiable and unjust comparison for the purposes of a small debating point, and I have answered him as he deserves. But I sympathise very much with the right hon. Gentleman none the less, because his position to-day is one of great embarrassment, and he has, with his usual deftness and skill, attempted to conceal the awkward feelings and reflections which are filling his mind. No one has laid down the law about the behaviour of the Socialist Government more clearly than the right hon. Gentleman himself. I have here a copy of a letter, his own dispatch, in connection with the man Zinovieff:

> No one who understands the constitution and the relationships of the Communist International will doubt its intimate connection and contact with the Soviet Government. No Government will ever tolerate an arrangement with a foreign Government by which the latter is in formal diplomatic relations of a correct kind with it, whilst at the same time a propagandist body organically connected with that foreign Government encourages and even orders subjects of the former to plot and plan revolutions for its overthrow.

That is the doctrine which the right hon. Gentleman has laid down, and it has been supported in much more recent times, as late as 1929, when the right hon. Gentleman said:

> Our conditions are laid down in a public dispatch. Everyone who has read the dispatch knows what they are. My colleagues know; my opponents know; and the representatives of Soviet Government know. We stand by them. Of course we do.

I have quotations from the Foreign Secretary, but I need not trouble the Committee with them, because they are beyond dispute. There are the declarations which the Government have made, which they have repeated and renewed, and which constitute the settled basis of their policy. The whole of these declarations are being flouted and mocked every day that passes. No one has talked more bold and brave than the Prime Minister, except the Foreign Secretary, on this subject of what he would stand and what he would not, what he would tolerate and what he would not. Why, he would tolerate anything! I have yet to see the dose or pill that he would not swallow if it came from Russia. The right hon. Gentleman is treated with open defiance and ridicule. I see that a gentleman named Menjinksy, Chief of the Ogpu, has said—I must say that the Russians are exceedingly frank—

> As long as there are idiots to take our signature seriously, and to put their trust in it, we must promise everything that is being asked, and as much as one likes, if we can only get something tangible in exchange.

Let me read to the Prime Minister what is published in the official Press of Russia about India, in view of his attempt to make comparisons with speeches made by people who are endeavouring to advocate a steadier policy. This is what is said by the International Press Correspondence, the organ of the Communist International, and it is dated 26th February, 1931:

> We need in India to build class proletarian trade unions at a feverish pace, intensely, every day and under all circumstances. . . . The preparations for a general political strike must be brought to the front. . . . We must rouse the masses. . . . We must inspire them with the spirit of war to the bitter end, and the spirit of struggle for India in which there will be no place for British Imperialism.

These things are published under the full authority of the Government of the day in a country where, as we have been reminded by the Prime Minister, no newspaper opinion is allowed to be expressed which is not in accord with the opinions of the Government of the day. And then you have to read these incitements, this deliberate avowal of attempts to cause revolution in India, side by side with the declarations which the Prime Minister made and which he told us he stands by. It is a case of contradiction of the most flagrant kind. I am astonished that the Prime Minister has attempted even to cover up this change of front of his with a certain veneer of smooth words. He stands more stultified by it than any man I have seen, on this Russian question. Here he is sitting, having deliberately devoured with apparent gusto every word on this subject which he has ever spoken.

Then the right hon. Gentleman, trying to make a cheap point across the Floor of the House, quoted some of the speeches of my right hon. Friend the late Foreign Secretary. Our policy was to pursue with great patience the relationships which we found to exist when we came into office in 1924. Some of us would have liked to have seen them terminated sooner. Certainly there was no lack of provocation, as was so very well stated by my right hon. Friend, but it was thought that with the Government of Russia relations had been resumed, and that as long as we could endure the arrangement we must go on patiently year after year until they became intolerable. The arguments which were appropriate to that condition of affairs are in no way stultified now, because the moment when patience became exhausted the Soviet representatives were requested to withdraw from this country and the agreement between the two countries lapsed.

Why, then, did the right hon. Gentleman attempt to charge my right hon. Friend with inconsistency? We gave a patient trial to a policy of which we did not approve and which we were not anxious to reverse, but in the end found the situation intolerable and we turned them out. The present Prime Minister has brought them back. He and his friends ran about the country telling the electors at the last election, that when the Russians were brought back trade would be so great that unemployment would be cured, and having deluded large numbers of working men with the idea that their misfortunes would be healed if only we brought back the Russian representatives, the right hon. Gentleman obtained a majority. And the people have seen the consequences which have followed from it. Our policy in this matter has been reversed. We turned the Soviet representatives out and the present Government have brought them back.

I say to the Government, for the consequences in every sphere you are responsible. You cannot go harking back upon the previous period. You are responsible for the great spread of their propaganda in India. You are responsible for their increasing hostility to this country. You are responsible for the lamentable failure of the trade between the two countries; and you are responsible for securing them special favour of funds which are indirectly used for buying armaments that may be used in the event of war.

Mr. Haycock: On a point of Order. Once or twice, Mr. Dunnico, you have pulled me up on the ground that I was out of order, and I wish to know if the right hon. Gentleman is in order in that observation.

Mr. Churchill *rose*—

Mr. Townend: On a point of Order. Is the right hon. Gentleman entitled to resume his place at the Box before you, Mr. Dunnico, have had an opportunity of replying to the point of Order raised by the hon. Member for West Salford (Mr. Haycock)?

The Deputy-Chairman: I have been following the speech of the right hon. Gentleman and its bearing upon the point which is before the Committee, and as long as he keeps within a reasonable distance of that point I do not propose to intervene, but I think that he is now getting rather too far away from the issue before the Committee.

Mr. Churchill: I have said all that I have to say. When one looks back on the long past history of our relations with Russia, since the Great War and its subsidiary conflicts were brought to a close, one sees at a glance how very much more successful the United States have been in their relations with Russia than we have been in our relations with Russia. The United States have done far more trade and a more profitable trade. They have sold a much larger quantity of goods, and have a much more favourable record in that respect, but the United States have never done what we have done, and what we are continuing to do, namely to falsify the foundations of our own system of society by giving greater favours to a Communist, revolutionary Government than we give to other friendly countries or even to our own Dominions. That is the policy which the right hon. Gentleman is enforcing to-day and his responsibility is there. I agree with him that there is no great danger of Communist propaganda in this country. There may be danger to the Communists but there is no danger to the country. This country is safe and sure and strong in itself. It is healthy and I believe will easily throw off the attempts which are being made to undermine it.

But, if the country is safe and secure, that is no reason why it should be made ridiculous by the antics of this Government or the disgraceful tergiversation of the Prime Minister.

REPRESENTATION OF THE PEOPLE (NO. 2) BILL

June 2, 1931

House of Commons

In the 1930s Churchill argued frequently for a second vote for every householder—"The man or woman who pays the rent and the rates of any dwelling in which more than two persons habitually reside," as he put it in a newspaper article in 1934. This solution to the hazards of "one man, one vote" was generally derided, and it would certainly have been rough on property-owning bachelors, spinsters and widows, not to mention property-owning childless couples. But it signified his increasing conservatism, and his belief that when "what is called full democracy has been achieved, the whole [political] system is very speedily broken up and swept away" (Evening Standard, *January 24, 1934).*

I thought that I might, perhaps, be allowed take part in this Third Reading Debate, if only because of the fact that I enjoy, I believe, the melancholy distinction of having fought more contested Parliamentary elections than anyone else alive, and that I have had to fight an election, on an average, every two years out of the 28 years that I have actually sat in this assembly and offered to the House the benefit of my guidance and assistance. I feel, therefore, that I have a very special association with the subject of electoral reform.

To-day we have listened to the Home Secretary making a more-dead-than-alive speech upon the Third Reading of a Bill into whose conception and composition no thought of the public interest has at any stage entered. At this time, when of all others there is need for a more stable and earnest political foundation, for more structure and substance and gravity in our electoral system, we have a Bill which by all accounts, from the testimony of all sides, merely accentuates the existing formlessness of our political institutions, which aggravates the fluidity of the electorate, and which adds new features of caprice and uncertainty to the conduct of each individual election.

The right hon. Gentleman the Member for Darwen (Sir H. Samuel) has referred to an article which I wrote nearly two years ago, after the General Election, pointing out that the subject of a reform of the electoral law must necessarily become a vital issue. I have in no way receded from that opinion. The motive power which has brought this Bill before the House is, of course, the Liberal grievance. It is impossible not to recognise that grievance. It is not only a Liberal grievance, for there is a constitutional defect which is before us as well. I am told, and the figures are well known, that 20,000 votes elect a Socialist, and 23,000 elect a Conservative, while 100,000 are required to elect a Liberal. There is something to be said for and against that calculation, but in principle we have so shaped our affairs that it is actually easier for the most extreme opinion to obtain representation in this House than for Conservative or Liberal opinions to be represented. In addition to that, there is the great difficulty of 4,000,000 or 5,000,000 active citizens who feel that they have not received proper and fair treatment from the Constitution. It is quite impossible to make long plans for the Government of this country on such a basis. The denial of the redress of real grievances always breeds evils, and we are suffering now from the evil of an irresponsible Liberal party. We are suffering from the evil of a party which, necessarily perhaps, is concerned at the present time with little else but preserving its own existence. I think it is time, from every point of view, that some effort was made to remedy that evil.

No Conservative can afford to be indifferent to the fate of the Liberal party. If that party disappears, if it is liquidated or broken up, where will those 4,000,000 or 5,000,000 voters go? It may be that their ultimate destination will decide the foundations of political power in Great Britain, perhaps for a generation. People say there is the swing of the pendulum, but the pendulum does not always swing. For 30 years after the repeal of the Corn Laws, the Conservative party hardly ever held office, and when they did it was only precariously. For 20 years after the Home Rule Bill, the Liberal party only held office very rarely, and then precariously. We are now at a time when the metal of politics is fluid, is molten. The various moulds are ready, and we have now, perhaps, a chance in this next year or two to decide into which moulds that metal shall be guided.

I would earnestly appeal to the members of the Conservative party, to my right hon. Friends on this bench, as I have done from the beginning of this Parliament, not to disinterest themselves in a just reform of our electoral law. You cannot, I believe, make any sound plans, as long as democracy endures in Great Britain—and that will be for a good long time yet—upon any other basis than that a majority in the House of Commons should be based upon an intrinsic superiority of strength, I do not say always of numerical strength, in the country. No Government which is in a large minority in the country, even though it possess a working majority in the House of Commons, can have the necessary power to cope with real problems. People unfairly criticise the late Government and my right hon. Friend because, they say, that Government was not sufficiently robust, sufficiently full-blooded, sufficiently vigorous in its action. They underrate altogether the immense sub-conscious force of public opinion in this country, and the pressure that it brings to bear upon a constitutional administration in time of peace if that administration is not based upon clear majority decisions, and has not behind it a definite preponderance of the national will. For these and many other reasons a wise and faithful reform of the electoral law ought to hold a key position in our minds.

I am, indeed, glad that in the conduct of this measure my right hon. Friend the Member for Chelsea (Sir Samuel Hoare) has shown that the Conservative party, the strongest individual party in the country, has a constructive view upon this subject. Merely to say that we do not like this, and we do not like that, and we will not have the other, is a policy which certainly will not succeed in the long run. Therefore, I was especially interested and glad to find that the Conservative delegates to the Three

Party Conference agreed with the Liberal party representatives that, if a change had to be made—for which, of course, we are not pleading at the moment—proportional representation in the great cities was the least objectionable way of meeting the Liberal grievance and the constitutional defect. I have always disliked proportional representation on account of its complications, and I have not infrequently spoken of it in contemptuous terms, but I accept this view of the Conservative delegates upon the Three Party Conference. Having to choose, as we shall have to choose if we are to redress the constitutional injustice, between the Alternative Vote, the Second Ballot and Proportional Representation in the cities, I have no doubt whatever that the last is incomparably the fairest, the most scientific and, on the whole, the best in the public interest.

I return to the need for more strength and structure in our Parliamentary life. A phrase of Mr. Gladstone's was used by my hon. Friend who has just spoken. The "civic entity" of great cities or, as I should call it, the collective personality of great cities, is an important factor. Manchester, Birmingham, Leeds, Liverpool, Glasgow, Edinburgh, Bristol—names which Tory democracy in the eighties used to conjure with—what effective expression have they now of their collective intellectual force? When they had, in the days before the great Reform Bill, perhaps only a couple of members apiece, they had a greater influence upon our affairs than eight or ten members representing carved up communities of no integral strength. They have far less weight than one or two men would have who spoke with the collective authority of these centres of British progress and culture. Under the Proportional Representation scheme, which the Government, in spite of protests, have rejected, with all its inconveniences, these cities would regain their collective personality and their members, of every hue, Liberal, Conservative or Socialist, would speak for the opinions of very large numbers of people forming an integral society. The leading figures in our political life would find at the summit of these great cities far more secure and independent seats than is possible to-day. Our cities would become centres where keen and powerful political debates would proceed, and the public thrashing out of great questions, such as is almost impracticable now, would proceed again before an increasingly attentive audience, and the formation of new opinion in these centres would influence thought in the surrounding districts. For these reasons, I should greatly have preferred the method of Proportional Representation to the method of the Bill. If the framers of this Measure had been faithfully and nationally minded in their work they would, I think, have striven, first of all, to add more weight and fibre to the franchise and, secondly, to remedy the Liberal grievance in the most logical and scientific manner. By so doing, they would have achieved an enhancement of the repute and power of the House upon which, after all, most of our fortunes still depend.

The Government have done the exact opposite. In purely party and political manoeuvres, in a deal for a further tenure of office, they have swept away the second vote for business premises and they have tried, vainly even in this Parliament to destroy university representation. It would have been much better, on the contrary, to add enormously to the plural vote so as to increase the strength and vigour of the franchise. Suppose, for instance, a second vote had been given to every householder or breadwinner at the head of a family, the man or woman who pays the rent or the rates, 7,000,000 or 8,000,000 additional votes would have been given. That, in my opinion, would have restored something of the quality of the old electorate. It would have drawn the true distinction which should be drawn between those wage earners who are really bearing the burden and their grown-up children or dependants who live in the same dwelling. It would have called back into being that specially responsible political democracy to whose exertions and keen discussions the health and the fame of our pre-War Parliamentary institutions were largely due. The additional 7,000,000 or 8,000,000 of extra votes would have removed all need of legislating against the handful of plural votes which still survives. It would have swamped them in a much larger mass of responsible citizenship, and would have reduced their privilege to virtual nullity. Such a plan would not have drawn any distinction between one citizen and another on the ground of age, sex, wealth, class, education, or even intelligence. It would discriminate solely on the ground of responsibility and burden borne. It would take no existing right from anyone, but it would confer a new authority upon many millions of men and women, wage-earners and salary-earners, upon those who are, as it were, in harness, drawing the family waggon, and all together drawing the coach of State.

Mr. McKinlay: On a point of Order. Is the right hon. Gentleman in order in discussing something which is not contained in the Bill?

Mr. Speaker: The rule is that on the Third Reading only what is in the Bill can be discussed. On an occasion of this kind I think the right hon. Gentleman is in order in using arguments against the Bill.

Mr. Churchill: Needless to say, I do not intend to go into the positive advocacy of any alternatives. I am only contrasting the proposals of the Bill with proposals which should play a part in any Bill for a true and better representation of the people. If the Government reject Proportional Representation, I think—here I am giving only a personal opinion—the next best method is the second ballot. Compared with the Alternative Vote, it is far better, it is perfectly simple, a clear issue is presented to the electors and there is a straight fight, man for man, for the candidates. There is no serious disadvantage in having 100 or 150 second ballot elections a few days or a week after the main part of the General Election is decided. On the contrary, there is a real advantage in enabling a portion of the electors to correct, if they choose, an undue landslide in either direction. In the old days before the War, a General Election was spread over five or six weeks, and a far more closely reasoned decision was reached than is reached at present. I was never an admirer of all elections on one day. The deliberate verdict of the country plainly manifesting itself after prolonged discussion is a considerable safeguard against incontinent decisions and the mere elaboration of the process is a check upon too frequent recourse to the tremendous political weapon of a General Election.

One of the most alarming features of our present system is that the nation goes to bed on the night of the poll and wakes up to find that an irrevocable decision has been taken. No one knows what has been done until all has been done. It would have been a wise and prudent feature in our constitution if a substantial proportion of the constituencies voted a few days later in the light of the situation resulting from the first ballots. All the more is this true when such enormous masses of voters are attached to no particular party, and when vast numbers of electors take little or no interest in public affairs, when they have to be almost dragged out of their houses to poll, when millions of people treat the whole process on which the Government of the country rests with indifference or, again, may vote on some sudden wave of prejudice. [*Interruption.*] I am not couching my argument in party terms. I am couching it in national terms, as this Bill should have been drawn. In these circumstances, to have second ballots in 100 or 150 constituencies would be a powerful insurance against a too violent lurch in either direction. I should not be at all afraid of the extra trouble involved in these second ballots. I believe it would be well worth while, and it would make for continuity and stability. Nor do I admit the validity of the arguments used on the Second Reading by my right hon. and gallant Friend the Member for Ripon (Major Hills), that it would lead to bargaining and huckstering between the first and second ballots. There is always a certain amount of bargaining and huckstering in human and political affairs. The same bargaining and huckstering will go on about the Alternative Vote, but then it will all be done individually, in holes and corners, whereas the declarations by leaders of parties after the first ballot, as well as the declarations of Members presenting themselves in each of the constituencies for the second ballots, would all be done on the public platform.

The Government have, as it seems to me, rejected without reasonable consideration both the method of Proportional Representation and this method of the second ballot. The plan that they have adopted is the worst of all possible plans. It is the stupidest, the least scientific and the most unreal that the Government have embodied in their Bill. The decision of 100 or more constituencies, perhaps 200, is to be determined by the most worthless votes given for the most worthless candidates. That is what the Home Secretary told us to-day was "establishing democracy on a broader and surer basis." Imagine making the representation of great constituencies dependent on the second preferences of the hindmost candidates. The hindmost candidate would become a personage of considerable importance, and the old phrase, "Devil take the hindmost," will acquire a new significance. I do not believe it will be beyond the resources of astute wire-pullers to secure the right kind of hindmost candidates to be broken up in their party interests. There may well be a multiplicity of weak and fictitious candidates in order to make sure that the differences between No. 1 and No. 2 shall be settled, not by the second votes of No. 3, but by the second votes of No. 4 or No. 5, who may, presumably give a more favourable turn to the party concerned. This method is surely the child of folly, and will become the parent of fraud. Neither the voters nor the candidates will be dealing with realities. An element of blind chance and accident will enter far more largely into our electoral decisions than even before, and respect for Parliament and Parliamentary processes will decline lower than it is at present.

Luckily we have not seen the last of this Bill. There is the House of Lords. The Parliament Act, which the Prime Minister and his principal colleagues, which the Leader of the Liberal party and his principal colleagues, and which I, myself, in a small way helped to make the law of the land, conferred a charter of new and modern powers upon the House of Lords. These powers are limited, but they are all the more effective for that very reason and, if they are used wisely, prudently and reasonably in a spirit of the national interest, they are tremendous powers. Never would such powers be exerted more potently or more beneficially than in the treatment of the further stages of this Bill. The House of Lords will render immense service to the House of Commons, to all political parties, and to the nation by giving further opportunities for considering this Bill in one form or another.

I see the right hon. Gentleman the Member for Carnarvon Boroughs (Mr. Lloyd George) in his place. He and his party seem to be in a very awkward situation, alternating between hope and fear. They are, as it were, standing on a trap door with the halter of public displeasure round their necks. The man who holds the lever, the Prime Minister, is the man they have disparaged and derided with every epithet which our printable vocabulary contains. The man who holds the lever is the leader of a party which can grow great or greater only by devouring them, and which is actually in the process of devouring them from hour to hour. They are going to stand on this trap door, according to the programme, according to the compact, perhaps for two long years. What is to happen to them and their Electoral Reform Bill if the Prime Minister pulls the lever before the Bill is passed? What is to prevent him from doing so? No contract, no deal or gentleman's agreement, no unspoken unity or concord of action, nothing of that kind can prevent such a result. At any moment in these two years, when the country is a little more favourable, when trade begins to mend a bit, when some issue rises good to carry with hot prejudice to an election, the Government can have themselves defeated. The whole interest of the Socialist party is against this Alternative Vote. There must be 50 Members, many of them sitting opposite now, whom we shall not see in Parliament again if it is carried. They might so easily become at some time in the near future slack in their attendance. At any time during these two years the Government might say to the right hon. Gentleman and his colleagues, "We are so sorry, we did so want to carry your Electoral Reform Bill; we are longing to put the Alternative Vote on the Statute Book, yet here we are defeated in the House of Commons on a major question. It would not be consonant with our dignity or our honour"—that would certainly come out then—"to continue in office. So we must have a General Election, and we must have it on the old basis."

Mr. Lees: I am very glad you have got some colours on that bench.

Hon. Members: Translate!

Mr. Churchill: There are some interruptions which are protected from repartee by their irrelevance. There is a terrible risk for the Liberal party and for the right hon. Gentleman. He is playing now for high stakes and long odds. Talking of gambling, where is the Home Secretary, who is always running about so busily in these matters? Yet he is here conniving at one of the greatest gambling episodes and transactions that I can ever remember having heard or seen, conniving at a disreputable and demoralising spectacle. I am really quite anxious about the right hon. Member for Carnarvon Boroughs and I am advising him for his own good. I suggest to him across the Gangway, even though it has grown broader than the Floor, that perhaps a study of these questions on their merits, and with a paramount purpose of improving and strengthening Parliamentary Government in this island, might afford him a less bleak and hazardous prospect than that which he has found it necessary at present to embrace. Perhaps the right hon. Gentleman, if he should speak in the Debate, will consider what I have ventured to say.

The co-operation of all parties in the improvement of our parliamentary institutions is what is needed. It is our duty to strengthen the House of Commons. Parliament is all we have, and the House of Commons is the main part of it. We have no fixed constitution, no supreme court as in America. We have no elaborately built-up and strongly independent Senate as in France. We have no great organisation of state and provincial governments as in Germany and United States. In the main, we are just this assembly in this small Chamber based on universal suffrage, and with our party machinery in disarray. Upon us have come economic problems with which many of us feel ourselves little qualified to deal, and upon us rests always the responsibility for a large part of the world and for the peace and progress of its peoples. We have responsibility concentrated upon us for the past and responsibility for the future. Surely the care of this central instrument ought to be a sacred trust? Surely the building up of practical, trustworthy, living organs of government ought to be one of our chief cares? The House of Commons a generation ago was honoured, a generation ago it was regarded almost as ideal for its purpose. Now it is a threatened institution, and even a despised institution. Great popular audiences listen with approval, and have recently listened at by-elections with approval, to proposals to injure or fundamentally alter the House of Commons and to obliterate very largely parliamentary government, as we have known it, and to establish new governments in new forms—either from the right or from the left—new governments vaunting an altogether unproved efficiency, but governments fatal to our long-renowned freedom.

There is this thoughtless, careless section of our people—millions of them— charged with the direct responsibility for the fortunes of this country, who would not take a tithe of the trouble to find out the rights and wrongs of grave political questions or even to cast a vote that they would take to buy a ticket in the Irish sweepstake. Look at the papers to-day! Look even at the "Times" newspaper to-day! Are they not a spectacle of immense democratic irresponsibility? I am pleading for structure in defence of our parliamentary institutions. I still believe in a great Empire united and guided by a great House of Commons and a teeming population of free citizens in this island, whose welfare does not decline. But, when I see this Bill and know, as I do perfectly well, all the forces, all the misunderstanding, all the stupidity, all the cunning, all the desperation, which have brought it about, it is impossible not to feel profoundly anxious.

Let us look at it quite nakedly. The Liberals have a grave constitutional grievance. Until that is rectified, they are fighting for their lives by weapons of faction and intrigue. No man, no party struggling for life, according to my experience, will stick at anything. There is the Government, on the other hand, a minority Government astonished to have lived so long, staggered by the blizzard they have encountered, astounded that they should have survived thus far in the teeth of it. There is this Government clinging to office by tooth and claw. There is the Prime Minister, not at the head of a majority in Parliament, not at the head of a majority in the country, making no secret of the fact to his followers that, if he were to appeal to the electorate now, he would be swept away. There is a hope that things will mend. Like an aeroplane pilot forced to come down in a short time, the Prime Minister hopes to find some better landing ground a little further on before the petrol is exhausted. Anything to keep going, anything to make it fly a little longer, anything to postpone, even if it cannot avert, the threatening crash. So, in desperation, these two parties come together and they make a bargain, in which no thoughts of the public merits, no thoughts of the well-being of the Commonwealth have played their part. Just a Bill called the Representation of the People Bill, some sort of botch, something to get through the Session, something to square the Liberals, something to stave off the evil day. It is a Bill which will weaken the structure of Parliament and vitiate electoral procedure. Great sacrifices may be demanded of us for great causes, but rarely has so great a sacrifice been demanded of our country for so petty a cause as this, when the fabric of the House of Commons is rotted and popular elections are confused, in order to secure a few more months' experience of the bitter sweets of office to this dismal, fatuous and impotent Administration.

INDIA (GOVERNMENT POLICY)

June 10, 1931

Folkestone, Kent

[Editor's Note: Referring to the Gateshead by-election, Churchill said]: Colonel Headlam pulled the Socialist majority down from 17,000 to 1,300, and carried with him practically the whole mass of the Conservative and Liberal Parties. Let that spirit spread abroad throughout our island, and we will soon be singing, "Now we shan't be long." (Cheers.) The wise policy for the Conservative Party is to get every one to close up in a general line and crush the Socialists.

I was distressed to read the highly unsatisfactory answer about India which the Prime Minister wrote to Mr. Baldwin. Mr. Baldwin asked Mr. MacDonald whether, at the resumed Round Table Conference, all the safeguards prescribed by the British delegates at the earlier Conference would be accepted as a basis by the Indians who came to it. To this the Prime Minister made a most cunning reply. He said that the safeguards in the interest of India which the Round Table Conference had prescribed must be accepted for the basis of the resumption of the Conference. Let us just look at that swindle laid out in the open for all to see! Let us look at the words "in the interests of India." Those are the words inserted by Lord Irwin and Mr. Gandhi in the Irwin-Gandhi compact in order to conceal a formula which can be read in two ways. Naturally no Indian extremist or subversive would find any difficulty in agreeing to safeguards "in the interests of India." While those words "in the interests of India" stand, Gandhi or any one else who wishes to turn us out of India can come to the Conference and argue that any particular safeguards are not "in the interests of India." Consequently every safeguard can be called in question.

Those words "in the interest of India" are a mere dodge to make believe there is an agreement when there is none. What is the use of going on with these shams?

(Cheers.) Is it not far better, in the celebrated words of Lord Birkenhead, to "tell India the truth." Why should there be safeguards only "in the interests of India"? What about the British in India? Has Britain no interest in India? (Cheers.) Has the British nation, who have lifted the population in India several hundreds of years above their level in peace, justice, and sanitation, no right to have their interests considered? Is not the interest of Lancashire a British interest, and ought it not to have fair treatment in any settlement? Are not the lives and securities of British residents in India of British interest? Are not the authority and efficiency of the great Civil Services, judicial, hygienic, scientific, by which we sustained India, a matter which touches not only British interest, but British honour? Sentiments, perorations, humbug, and double-faced talk of all kinds have had their day.

The Conservative Party must be on their guard. We must not be taken in by Mr. MacDonald's dodges. We ought to have a mind of our own upon the Indian question. We ought to make it clear that we are determined to discharge our duty to the vast masses of the Indian peoples, and not let them be handed over to greedy, fanatical politicans who, if they ever gained control of India, would immediately reduce that vast sub-continent to chaos and carnage. Look at what happened at Cawnpore. There are the fruits of lack of candour, a hideous primordial massacre has been perpetrated by the Hindus on the Moslems because the Moslems refused to join in the glorification of the murderer of a British policeman. The most horrible event which has ever occurred since the Mutiny has been the direct outcome of the Irwin-Gandhi Pact, with its smooth, ambiguous, equivocal formulas. Worse is in store, and will speedily come, unless the British nation is prepared to deal with the Indian problem in terms of manly truth. Let us look at the report about the Cawnpore massacre. They are trying to throw all the blame upon the wretched local British officer. The only person censured was the British officer on the spot—one white man amid scores of thousands of infuriated natives! From the day when we punished weakness in humble subordinates, and glorified it in those of high station, we should have declared ourselves unworthy and unfit to discharge our mission in the East.

I hope that Mr. Baldwin will take advantage of the Prime Minister's wholly disingenuous reply to his letter to free the Conservative Party from its entanglement with the Indian policy of the Socialist Government. The constitutional responsibility rests upon the Socialist Government of the day; and my appeal to the Conservative leaders is that we should leave it there, and let Conservatives make sure that they at least do not share in the guilt.

UNEMPLOYMENT INSURANCE (NO. 4) BILL

June 26, 1931

House of Commons

I rise to support the Amendment which has been moved by my right hon. Friend the Member for Stafford (Mr. Ormsby-Gore) to the effect:

That this House declines to authorise such extensive further borrowing for the purpose of making up a continually recurring deficit in the Unemployment Fund, in view of the refusal of the Government to take any adequate steps to carry out its declared policy of making the unemployment insurance scheme solvent and self-supporting.

I, like my right hon. Friend, was surprised to hear at an earlier stage the tirade and complaint of the Minister of Labour, that such an Amendment had been put upon the Paper by the Opposition. But my right hon. Friend pointed out with acumen that the words of the Amendment are taken almost textually from the terms of reference to the Royal Commission to the drafting of which the Minister of Labour herself was a party. It seems hard that the Oppostion should be censured. In fact, almost the only part of the right hon. Member's speech in which she developed any warmth, or, indeed, any vigour, was in censuring my right hon. Friend. It seems hard that he should be censured for reproducing in the form of an Amendment almost the actual words which the Government themselves had drafted weeks ago for the guidance of their Royal Commission. We have had a great many debates on unemployment insurance. I cannot remember how many times I have spoken in the lifetime of the present Parliament. [An Hon. Member: "It is the same old story."] That is one of the difficulties with which I find myself confronted. It is not quite the same story, because the tale is getting much worse and the difficulty is in finding a variant of words and of ideas which will cope with the increasing gravity of the situation and the increasing failure of the Government.

This Bill represents the financial collapse of His Majesty's Government. I do not see any representative of the Treasury here. Although this is a scheme which is destroying the whole solvency of the Chancellor of the Exchequer's finances, neither he nor his Financial Secretary has honoured us with his presence to-day. The Chancellor of the Exchequer said in the City:

I have to find this year £21,000,000 to finance a large class of unemployed persons who have no insurable qualification. I think it is the duty of Parliament now to face up to this problem and to put the Insurance Fund upon an insurance basis.

[An Hon. Member: "That has been quoted before!"] Is it not right that it should be quoted when it has never been answered? We quote, we argue, and we ask questions, and no reply is given. Instead of making replies and instead of entering the debates upon these matters, the representatives of the Government spend their time in reading out rigmaroles about some French economist and toiling laboriously through the charts published by the "Times" newspaper.

Mr. Logan: Tell us what you would do?

Mr. Churchill: The hon. Gentleman is afraid that I may say something— [Interruption].

Mr. Logan: Will the right hon. Gentleman tell us what he would do?

Mr. Churchill: The hon. Gentleman not only has a guilty conscience and is afraid that I am going to say something which is not in the interests of his party, but has abrogated to himself a function which did not belong to him, namely, to make my speech instead of letting me make it. [*Interruption.*]

Mr. Logan: If the right hon. Gentleman will sit down, I will get up.

Mr. Churchill: I am sure that the hon. Gentleman must recognise—

Mr. Logan: I am one of the bantams.

Mr. Churchill: I think that the hon. Gentleman will recognise that this bantam, at any rate, has had all the notice it deserves. [*Interruption.*] The Chancellor of the Exchequer said he was basing the whole of his Budget scheme upon the economies that would be effected on unemployment insurance. Now he has abandoned all that. He faces now a certain deficit. He has accepted the position of having an unbalanced Budget. Every principle of finance which the Chancellor of the Exchequer professed. [*Interruption.*] All these sporadic interruptions are signs of a guilty conscience. Never do I see the Government's supporters deny full hearing even to arguments which they dislike, except on those questions where they know that they have an indefensible position, where they know that they have something to conceal and where they know that they have a case of which they are ashamed. No doubt I am going to be perpetually interrupted from this quarter or that. I am quite content. I can make my point just as well by the practical demonstration as by any words that I can say. The Chancellor of the Exchequer has abandoned all those principles which he used to profess so loudly, so austerely, and which he condemned with so little consideration when they were broken by others. He has cast aside the reins and thrown them on the horses neck. He has abandoned the helm. [*Laughter.*] Will hon. Members allow me to make my point? [*Interruption.*] We are going to listen to the right hon. Gentleman opposite and I hope that we shall give him a fair hearing. The Chancellor of the Exchequer has thrown the reigns round the horse's neck. He has abandoned the helm. [*Interruption.*] He has released his control of the brakes. [*Interruption.*]

Mr. Speaker: I hope that we shall conduct this Debate in an orderly manner.

Mr. Churchill: Hon. Members opposite who are laughing at what they supposed is a mixed metaphor, are only showing their mixed methods of thought. All hopes of establishing financial equilibrium; all efforts to establish it, even the pretence of trying to do so, have now been abandoned by the Chancellor of the Exchequer. But that is not the worst. It is not only a collapse of our finance that we are witnessing, but it is the mental and moral collapse of His Majesty's government, and also, to some extent, I must admit, the collapse of our Parliamentary system. There are many subjects about which we are puzzled in this House, grave economic, currency and other issues, which baffle and puzzle men of every side, apart from Party, but this is not a subject about which we are puzzled or in bewilderment. It is not a subject where there is any difficulty in the House in arriving at definite conclusions. There is no subject upon which the vast majority of Members of Parliament are more accurately informed and more generally agreed than on this question of what to do about the Unemployment Insurance Fund.

Three out of every four Members in the House this afternoon know exactly what ought to be done in the interests of the country, taking a far reaching view, and in the permanent interests of the wage earners. They do not require commissions or committees, or even three-party conferences, to find out what to do. The light shines clear. All see it; none follow it. The hon. Member for Gorbals (Mr. Buchanan) whose speeches on this subject are a contribution which ought never to be lacking from a discussion of this kind, asked a very pointed question of the Government. He said:

> The Government set up a three-party committee. . . . It has been said that the three parties—the Tory party, the Labour party and the Liberal party—agreed to a means test. Is that true?—[Official Report, 22nd June, 1931; col. 109; Vol. 254.]

That is the question which the hon. Member asked. What was the answer? I did not see the right hon. Lady the Minister of Labour leaping to her feet to respond to that direct question.

Miss Bondfield: I did, and I said that it was not true.

Mr. Churchill: I had a copy of the Official Report with me.

Miss Bondfield: I answered it today.

Mr. Churchill: I am not referring to what happened to-day, and the right hon. Lady with all due respect knows that I was not referring to to-day. The hon. Member for Gorbals has not spoken to-day and therefore it could not have been in reply to him. The question asked by the hon. Member ought to be answered by His Majesty's Government. Is it true that Ministers of the Crown, Socialist Ministers, have committed themselves in any way to the idea of imposing a means test on those unqualified for insurance? Surely we are going to get an answer! Not one of them dare answer; not even the exuberant Lord Privy Seal. No, I mean the Minister for the Dominions, or is the right hon. Gentleman the Chancellor of the Exchequer—I do not know what he is, he passes so rapidly from one triumph to another. Is it a fact that there is not a single Minister on the Bench who dare answer the question put by their own supporter below the Gangway? Why is it that they do not give an answer? We are not obstructing a reply. Those who were invited by the Government to join in the three-party conference, this embryo of a Council of State, they are making no objection to the question being answered. Why is it not answered?

Miss Bondfield: The right hon. Member evidently was not in the House when his colleague made the statement this morning and when I pointed out that I did not accept the statement as correct, but obviously I could not discuss the matter.

Hon. Members: Why not?

Mr. Churchill: I was present and I heard the right hon. Lady say that she entered a caveat. That is a sort of parry to a perfectly direct question. She said that she entered a caveat. Why cannot she say Yes or No? Why all this secret diplomacy? It is because the right hon. Lady knows perfectly well that there is a general agreement amongst responsible people in regard to what ought to be done on this subject and that the only thing that is stopping action is the Government's fear of electioneering consequences. Of course, I do not pretend that under our present condition of parties, this three-party system or catch-as-catch-can, on the eve of an election—I do not pretend that bad electioneering is not an important argument. But it is weighing with the Government in contradiction to their obvious and recognised and well understood duty. That places the Government, who are after all responsible, in a very discreditable position. Of course it would be affectation to pretend that this question does not affect all parties. Where it depends upon the votes of millions of working men and women, and rather more millions than the party opposite and an increasing number of millions, judging by recent results—

Hon. Members: Mostly fools.

Mr. Churchill: That is a strange remark for a Labour representative to make, to describe as fools millions of his own class, millions of people who choose to exercise their undoubted rights by voting for someone a little different from him.

Hon. Members: Those who vote Tory.

Mr. Churchill: There has come into existence a new vested interest, a dole vested interest, and behind it is enforced by the dole vote. In our present Parliamentary system we have not yet shown ourselves capable of resisting pressures of that kind. That is the gravest thing in the situation which is disclosed by these repeated debates. The Parliamentary system, the structure and virtue of the Government, is not capable of taking what is thought to be an unpopular course, however necessary, however salutary, however right it may be. Such symptoms are dangerous to institutions. Not to know is bad, but to know and not to be able to act is fatal. So we are led by His Majesty's Government through these tedious and interminable labyrinths of deception and delay, round and round the maze, from committee to conference, from conference to commission, from commission to personal inquiry by this or that Minister, and then back again to committee, always with a few months delay, and each time "wait for the interim report," "hurry up the interim report," and when it comes "wait for the main report," and so on—all with the object of gaining time, while Ministers of the Crown continue to shovel out the dole, let deficits accumulate in the finances, let confusion deepen and let abuses rip. That is the position. No one has spoken so vehemently and so pitilessly as she has upon this question. It is quite true that the quotation which I am about to give has been read before, but I read it again because at the close of this Debate the House ought to have the salient facts before it. She said:

> If you came forward and wiped out the limit of borrowing powers at £40,000,000 and went on borrowing to £50,000,000 or £60,000,000, it would be a dishonest course, because it would be contracting a debt that you saw no possible way of paying off. Therefore, I have dismissed definitely from my consideration any question of increasing the borrowing powers of the fund.—[Official Report, 25th November, 1929; col. 1103, Vol. 252.]

How far we have travelled from the days when the right hon. Member said that. That was when the Fund was only £37,000,000 in debt; now it is £115,000,000, and soon it will be £130,000,000 or £150,000,000. It is said, if I quote correctly, that the road to hell is paved with Money Resolutions. At first the right hon. Member was noble and impeccable and self-righteous at the expense of her predecessors. She has now flung away every vestige of political decorum. Not only has she broken consistency with the past but at this very moment she is acting out of harmony with her declared convictions only a little while ago. At the present moment she is defending and aggravating the very system which she declared was dishonest and improper.

I deplore sincerely the downfall of the right hon. Member. I know her as an able and earnest social reformer, as a would-be statesmanlike administrator, as the first woman to be called to Cabinet rank and, bearing a great sense of responsibility in that respect, she is now revealing to the whole world that she is unequal to the task of doing her duty as she sees it. Somebody has talked about "The Rake's Progress," and we have all heard of "Eric, or Little by Little" and I used to be much affected by a popular drama called "The Girl Who Took the Wrong Turning," but these demoralisations come on so gradually, step by step, that it is difficult to resist them. If the Minister of Labour could only transport herself back to 29th November, 1929, and if she had then been confronted with a demand to raise the borrowing powers to £115,000,000, without any reform of the abuses in the system, which were well known to her then and are better known to her now—if she could then have been confronted with such a proposal she would rather have left her office than have been responsible for it. But, bit by bit, she has been drawn into this position. I am impelled to quote from a poet because he has expressed so well the process by which the Government and the supporters of the Government were insensibly drawn to their present position upon this unemployment insurance question and the borrowing by which it is financed:

> "Vice is a monster of so frightful mien,
> As, to be hated, needs but to be seen;
> Yet seen too oft, familiar with her face
> We first endure, then pity, then embrace."

I do not hesitate to say, at any rate—I speak only for myself, and for those who agree with me—what ought to be done. I have no sympathy with the proposals of the Royal Commission. It was a Socialist Commission, set up by a Socialist Government. They picked the members with full knowledge of their attainments and outlook. They set the reference, they asked the very question to which a Report like this could, I believe, be the only possible answer, and they ordered the interim Report to be presented to them. They are responsible for the Commission. Throughout the country it must be made clear that it is their Commission, that it was their method of dealing with this problem, and that we were not consulted in that matter at all. His Majesty's Government alone are responsible. They have drawn from this Commission, by the questions which they asked, what I can only describe as clumsy, crude, unscientific and unhelpful recommendations. We know the way that hair is cut in some places. You put a bowl on the child's head and cut off all that showed round the edges.

This Report seems to me to miss the whole vital point of principle at stake in this question. It proposes to cut down the benefits and increase the contributions throughout the whole insurance area; it makes no distinction between the insured and the uninsured; it adds to the burdens of the insured wage-earners and reduces the rights for which they have paid; and it leaves insured wage-earners hopelessly intermingled with the non-self-supporting element. All are lumped together under the generic disparaging term of the dole. Thus the self-respect of the great majority of working men who have ever used insurance is affronted, and the whole structure, the whole character, of these great social institutions like unemployment and other forms of insurance is brought into disrepute and contempt in all parts of the world.

We are certainly not bound by the Commission's Report, neither ought we to fail to proclaim, in my judgment, a clear view. I hold most strongly that a line must be drawn without delay, clear and unmistakable, between insurance and assistance. The insured pay for themselves; let them draw the benefits they have purchased by State organised thrift. The assisted stand in another category; they must be provided for according to their needs. The aid which is accorded to them must be measured by the policy of the State, but it should not be pretended for one moment that that aid is a kind of right, an actuarial right, arising from any process of insurance. I repudiate the suggestions of an inhumanitarian position on this side of the House or certainly among a great many of its Members altogether. All my life I have been engaged at frequent intervals, short intervals, in dealing with great schemes of insurance. I am the original author of the first Unemployment Insurance scheme by trades that was introduced in this House, now nearly a quarter of a century ago, and the labour exchange system I brought into being and set up.

All these great schemes, which were largely copied from Germany and which derived inspiration from that great Empire built by Bismarck, who saw and understood how a nation could be made strong and its people united—all these schemes, which the hon. Members and the party opposite would have been incapable of devising, and not had the wit or the patience to devise or the power to execute, now constitute the characteristic social bulwark of the British working classes—[An Hon. Member: "What about the right hon. Member for Carnarvon Boroughs (Mr. Lloyd George)?"]—I followed with him in many of these matters. I only say that I have been associated with the whole of this great structure and I stand here, not to assail it, but to defend it, and to urge that it shall be purged of abuses. It is, indeed, a shame to see these schemes vitiated and exploited, sinking into insolvency and disrepute.

The Government, which knows quite well what is happening, and what ought to be done, refuses to do its duty, nay, is incapable of doing its duty, and falls back into a jungle of prevarication, obstruction and delay, which these debates have revealed with unprecedented ingenuity. It is lamentable. It is our duty to rescue the Insurance Fund, which, in the main, is working well, and better than any other system devised. Hundreds and thousands of men and women are having the resources, just at the time they need them, out of the contributions they have paid. They are having no more than their right. They can look every man in the face. They are dependent on the State in no way except under the covenant they have entered into, and they are getting the aid which enables them to avoid selling their household goods, and enables them to carry on until a new opening occurs. All this great scheme, which is the glory of our country, properly understood, is being vitiated by the abuses that you are allowing to creep into it, and in not drawing the line which separates the self-supporting element in the community from those who are compelled to incur the bounty of their fellow subjects.

That is the position as I see it. But there is one more stage, and it is the least satisfactory of all that we have to consider. The Ministerial speeches show that the Government are now playing for the dole vote. It has become a definite part of their plan of campaign. Very large numbers are involved when 2,600,000 are upon the register, and before Christmas the number will probably be 3,000,000, and next year probably still larger. Not only those who are on the register at any given moment, or who may have recourse to it at any time throughout the year, but their dependants, constitute an appreciable part of the electorate. The dole vote, the dole-vested interests—that is what, in default of all other foundations of respect in the country, His Majesty's Government are increasingly relying upon. They are trying to marshal this vote by representing out of doors and here in this House that they are the party who will extract larger sums from the Exchequer, and will distribute them more loosely to larger numbers than any other party in the State.

Mr. Mills: It is not true.

Mr. Churchill: That is why the Minister of Labour and the Chancellor of the Exchequer have been made to eat their words, have been made to consent to a policy which they have publicly denounced. I say undoubtedly that the speeches which were delivered from that Bench on the last occasion show every desire to turn this great public disaster into a means of gathering support for the party which at the present time has control of the public purse.

Our duty is plain. We have to proclaim the principles of correct finance and of sound and scientific administration of the Insurance Fund. We have to separate insurance from assistance, if it costs us votes. Indeed, I believe that a party in the present political situation which adopted a sound and scientific policy on this subject, even if it looked at first sight as though it would cast them votes, would gain very quickly an enormous measure of support from that central and untouched mass of voters who are not now taking part in politics, but who are seeking amid their fog and confusion for something that they can trust and something that they can respect.

WAR DEBTS

June 27, 1931

*Chancellor's Address, Degree Conferment Ceremony,
Bristol University*

[Extract] . . . The decision and inspiration, the wisdom and the comprehension which led President Hoover and the United States of America to proclaim a general moratorium for a year in the payment of War Debts and indemnities has, I feel sure, been received by all members of the university with sincere acclaim.

The unwholesome accumulation of gold in the only two countries which benefit from those uneconomic and non-commercial payments has largely paralysed world credit, checked the flow of trade, paralysed prices, especially the prices of prime commodities, and has made it impossible for millions of workers on both sides of the Atlantic to earn their daily bread. Although it is by no means the only evil cause which is at work, unquestionably it is a potent contributory factor. Germany has been reduced to desperate straits, and without a prosperous Germany, Europe can never be once again a healthy family of nations.

Collapse and default were perhaps not far distant, when suddenly the whole prospect of the world was changed by an act of courage and statecraft almost unsurpassed in living memory. Had it been done in good times, times of wealth and prosperity, it would have been wise. Done as it has been in times of adversity and financial pressure, it is not only wise, but acquires the character of nobility.

DISARMAMENT AND EUROPE

June 29, 1931

House of Commons

No one can say that the Committee this afternoon has not been occupied with matters of the gravest consequence. The statement made to us by the Prime Minister is one of the most important that I have heard for some years in this House, and I would crave indulgence to express some comments and opinions upon these great questions, to which I have given very long reflection and about which I am, perhaps for the first time for many years, able to speak in entire independence. I take this statement of the Prime Minister and the series of figures which he has had drawn up with so much care by the technical departments. What did it prove, in the first instance? It proved, quite clearly, the failure of all the Disarmament Conferences which have been held up to the present time. It was not only a confession, but a declaration, a proclamation, of the failure of these conferences. We all respect the motives and the movements which have promoted these conferences, and we all admire the sentiments which have been expressed at them, but up to the present they have not done any good at all. On the contrary, they have been a positive cause of friction and ill-will, and have given an undue advertisement to naval and military affairs. They have concentrated the attention of Governments in all countries, many of them without the slightest reason for apprehension about or dispute with each other, upon all sorts of hypothetical wars which certainly will never take place. The reason why these Disarmament Conferences are so fertile in provoking and promoting misunderstandings is because everyone pushes his own national point of view; everyone adopts a rather hypocritical formula of words to cover the national point of view while taking advantage of any criticisms to which the others are open. It is the habit of nations represented at these conferences to:

> "Compound for sins they are inclined to,
> By damning those they have no mind to."

Nations which have conscription point in astonishment to the very heavy cost of the British and American defence services. Britain and America in their turn criticise the growth of those very large reserves of man-power which are obtained by nations having compulsory service, practically at no serious charge at all. The naval Powers take a serious view of land armaments, and the military Powers are of opinion that there ought not to be naval organisations, and that the freedom of the seas is what should be aimed at. The nations which have battle fleets regard the submarine as a most

improper weapon of war. The nations which cannot afford battle fleets regard it as a
highly convenient discovery. And so on. Every country champions its own special
interest at these conferences, and all together proclaim their high ideals. I am of
opinion that up-to-date, whatever may happen in the future, nothing has been
achieved by all these conferences that have been held, and by all the immense amount
of pressures of argument and eloquence which has been applied. I believe that the
armaments of the world to-day would be positively even smaller, certainly no greater,
if none of these discussions had taken place at Geneva. [An Hon. Member: "What
about Washington?"] I will deal with Washington in its proper place. I am talking now
about the International Conferences at Geneva. The pressure of expense in hard times,
the growing confidence which comes from a long peace, and the removal of specific
causes of danger—these are the forces on which you must rely, in the long run, to
promote a general diminution of armaments.

There has been one result of this great and beneficent movement for Disarmament. One nation has disarmed. One nation has disarmed to such an extent—it is
admitted on both sides—that she has become extremely and dangerously vulnerable.
We alone have disarmed. The figures which the Prime Minister recited to-day—an
enormous structure of figures—show not only the passing of British sea power, but
they show the descent of this country into a condition of unpreparedness, and but for
political considerations of insecurity, such as we have never previously experienced.
We have abandoned our naval supremacy. We have abandoned parity with the next
strongest Power. We are, as I shall try very briefly to indicate to the Committee,
incapable of maintaining our food supply and our oil supply in certain contingencies.
Our Air Force is vastly inferior to that of our nearest neighbour—luckily a good friend
of ours. Our Army was never measured against the armies of the Continent. Our Army
was never more than a glorified police force to aid in preserving the tranquility of
one-fifth of the human race, and as such it has been cut to the bone.

I frankly admit that what has been stated in this Debate is correct, that the
diminution in the power and strength of our military forces is far greater than the
reduction in their expense. The Navy was certainly in 1914 in size far greater in
proportion to the expense than it is at the present time. The staffs have been increased
while the fighting force has diminished, and the same is true of the Army and the
Expeditionary Force. As for the Air Service, that is a new and an additional expense
very necessary for security. Everything has been reduced except the cost. Expenditure
is undoubtedly heavy on armaments, and that is one of the counter-criticisms used by
other countries when they attend Disarmament Conferences.

I shall say only a word or so about the disclosure of our naval weakness which
has been made by the Prime Minister to-day. I accept unreservedly the exclusion of the
United States altogether from our calculations. I think that is the decision of the
country as a whole, and if it is accepted it should be accepted with the full courage of
conviction. If the United States Navy is equal to, or weaker or stronger than ours, that
is a matter with which we need not concern ourselves at all. But I must draw the
attention of the Committee to the evil consequences which have followed the negotiations and treaties of Washington and of London. The Prime Minister spoke of the
Treaty of London as a potent step in the direction of peace. I do not at all deny that it

has been productive of very great benefits in the relations between Great Britain and the United States, and that is an enormous advantage, but the inconvenience and injury to our Navy and our naval policy are most grave, taken, as they must be, in conjuction with the diminution of our naval strength.

I have no intention of doing more than mentioning the facts. We have lost our freedom of design and all that power of initiation in which we were the leaders of the world. We are being condemned to building a long series of artificial treaty ships, ships not built to conform to the highest conception of naval architecture for war purposes, but to fit in with the clauses and limitations of Treaties. We have been compelled, and are still compelled, to go on scrapping valuable vessels, with many years' good service in them, while out of the small remaining money we have had to build new ships in their place. The worst feature that has followed from this policy of endeavouring to regulate armaments by means of artificial agreements and conventions has been that we have become so involved in Treaty specifications that we no longer study the naval problem with that precision and intensity which it requires. For instance, we are always engaged in matching and examining the strength of our Navy on the basis of parity with the fleets of the United States, which has nothing to do with our problems.

We spend an enormous proportion of our naval effort upon maintaining battle fleets at parity with countries we have long ago ruled out of all military consideration—thus depriving ourselves of the power of making provision against the real dangers which are advancing upon us in the narrow seas. Our flotillas are becoming altogether inadequate to the task of protecting our food supplies in the narrow seas. I yield to no one in my genuine friendship for our neighbour France, but I say to the Committee that our flotillas will soon be inadequate to meet and afford protection against the rapid and formidable growth of the weapon of the French submarine. In the Debate last year I stated that never since the days of Charles II have we been less able to assert an independent view against our French neighbours. That is a very formidable fact. I have meditated a great deal since I spoke, and I find that my view has been confirmed by further reflection, and I consider that is a most grave and serious thing.

If the French Minister for War were asked about the various military problems which he might be called upon to face; if he were asked questions on that subject in a Committee of the Chamber, he would no doubt have an answer ready for almost every case. He would, for instance, be able to point to arrangements in case of certain events happening in Germany, or with other countries, and, in case trouble with this country were suggested, he would be able to show certain precautions. If he thought that trouble would arise by Poland being invaded by Russia, he would be able to point to the network of treaties which are supposed to guarantee freedom in that quarter. To every one of those questions in the French Committee of Defence there would be an effective answer to be made. There are three or four questions for us going to the root of matters to which the representatives of the great Services in this House, and still more their officials and experts, would not be able to provide coherent or effective answers.

I have often wondered since the Great War whether it could not have been prevented by more frank and open exposures of the real dangers which were largely apparent to many of those who knew what was passing. We were restrained in those days by the fact that merely to talk about such matters created alarm and exitement. This is undoubtedly a disadvantage, but it must be faced. Before the War, silence was preserved under thick layers of civility and discretion, padded quilts of aggreeably embroidered diplomacy, and these were used to muffle all sinister or discordant sounds until in quick succession there came crisis, clamour, mobilisation, censorship, cannonade, and our lives were wrecked. Surely it ought to be our uncreasing thought and effort not by any means to allow such a surprise to fall upon the populations of great countries again.

Of course, I understand that the Prime Minister is bound to cover up everything he says with a canopy of smooth-sounding and comfortable phrases and generalities, but I feel entitled to probe a little more precisely into the causes of the failure of these Disarmament Conferences, and, if the Committee will permit me, I will try to do so. The foundations of world peace are strengthening among all the civilised countries of the world. That is my firm belief, but there is one country that is outside the scope of these considerations, and that is Russia. [*Interruption.*] Russia is incalculable, aloof and malevolent. I want to call attention to this aspect of the question. The importation of the war metals—antimony, tungsten nickel and vanadium—there are others—which are used for the purposes of hardening steel or for other instruments of war—into Germany in 1914, exceeded five times the average for the three or four years which preceded. That is a very remarkable fact. I do not say it for a moment to suggest that the German Government were planning the War. What they were doing was putting themselves in a position of special preparation. Exactly the same phenomenon, according to my information, is repeating itself to-day in regard to Russia.

Mr. Kirkwood: Who is selling it to them? [Hon. Members: "You are giving them credits!"] They are not getting it from France or from Germany. They are getting it from us.

Mr. Churchill: I am not concerned with that at the moment. My argument is a connected argument from beginning to end, and if I can have the courtesy of the Committee to follow it, they will see that it is a connected argument. I say that, according to information which I do not believe will be challenged from the Treasury Bench, the importation of these special war metals which are required for the hardening of steel and other purposes is proceeding in Russia at an altogether unexampled and unprecedented rate. Of course, there is a very good explanation. It is that the Five-year plan is making Russia into a great manufacturing nation, and that, naturally, she requires exceptional supplies of these metals for the high-speed machinery which, for the first time, she is installing in her factories. I hope it is a true explanation. But this Five-year plan may be a cause of very considerable disturbance. If it breaks down, the Government of Russia will need to put some new theme before the minds of their people. They have introduced in a time of peace the mentality of war. Even the ordinary processes of trade and industry are presented in the language of battle—"shock troops," and so forth. If a failure takes place in this great plan, for which the whole people are making sacrifices usually made only in time of war, then it is certain that some other theme may be required to engage the efforts of these great numbers of human beings. If such another theme were required, then the special importation of war metals would be available for the alternative.

Then there is the possibility, which we cannot exclude from our thoughts, that this scheme may succeed, or that it may succeed to 60 per cent. of its strength, and then one country after another in Europe may find itself upset by importations of a wholly uneconomic character. Suppose these nations proceed in concert against importations of this kind, and the Russian experiment is thrown back on itself, might not that also be a moment of great tension and great danger? Certainly it will be a moment of great danger for all those border States which lie on the Russian frontier. It is true such dangers do not involve us directly or immediately. They are distant, and do not immediately concern us. But they may spread—as things have spread before, from evil causes—very rapidly from nation to nation, in defiance of human reason and until the most unexpected conclusion has been reached.

These are the circumstances in which the Disarmament Conference of 1932 is to be held. The Foreign Secretary will be there, no doubt, a very competent chairman, unless any local troubles should rob Europe of his services in the interval, but his task will indeed be attended, as my hon. Friend who spoke from these benches has said, by difficulty and delicacy. All that line of small new States from the Baltic to the Black Sea are in lively apprehension of Russia. Finland, Estonia, Lithuania, Latvia, Poland and Rumania—every one is in great fear and anxiety about its neighbour. All of them have been carved in whole or in part out of the Russia of the Tsars. They have won their independence at the conclusion of the War, or they have won territory at the conclusion of the War. All are in fear of Russian propaganda or of Russian military force. All are strongly anti-Communist. They have gone through great internal stress and tension, and they have built themselves up on a Radical, democratic antithesis to Communism. As such, they are specially obnoxious to the ideals and interests of the mighty Power which lies to the eastward. All these States have universal military service; they are all heavily armed, so far as they can afford to pay for it. They all look to each other for mutual aid. They all look to France for guidance, and they all consider—I am bound to state these facts to the Committee, and I have many years of thought and study behind me—the French Army their ultimate guarantee. You may say, in fact, that the French Army to all these small States and their independence and liberty, plays the same sort of part that the British Navy in the days of its power did to the small countries and liberties of Europe. Sermons addressed to these States at the conference will no doubt be received with politeness when they come from people whom one knows to be entirely well-meaning.

But Communism and Russia are not to these countries the kind of topics they are to us, where they can be made a matter of mockery. The whole structure of these States is rent with a conflict that is proceeding, persecution of Communism and counter-attacks on all these Governments, and beyond the frontier there is always the sense of this enormous mass which may at any time be set against them. [An Hon. Member: "What about the White Army?"] That is not, I think, a very fertile contribution. Sermons and exhortations are all very well, but I was very glad to hear from various speakers this afternoon that it is realised this kind of advice and moral lecture may be pushed too far when it comes from countries not in anything like the same danger as those to whom the exhortation is addressed. Coming from England, we at least can say—as has been proved to-day—that we are setting an example, that we have exposed ourselves to real danger, that we are in a position of insecurity, and that we have done that in our desire to set an example. But, still, our dangers are very far off. Coming from the United States, such lectures would not, I think, be well received, because she is not only protected by two great oceans, but, since the War, has increased her armaments more than any other country. I am very glad the gist and tone of the Prime Minister's speech were such as to indicate we were not going to press our views unduly upon this very delicate combination of countries with which we shall be brought in contact next year.

I was, indeed, delighted to hear the Prime Minister making an appeal, addressed to his own party, to be fair to France. The Prime Minister, naturally, has to veil everything he says, but the significance of the few words he dropped during the latter part of his speech in regard to recognising the anxieties and position of France were, I venture to think, much more important than all those well-turned phrases which expressed sentiments which will never miss their proper reception of cheers in this Island. That is the most important part in the concluding portion of the Prime Minister's speech. It is not in the immediate interest of European peace that the French army should be seriously weakened. It is certainly not in British interests to antagonise France, or all these small States associated with France, by pressing unreasonably for its reduction. We may well think France is over-insured, but it is certain that if we press at this conference too heavily in that direction, we shall not succeed in improving the relations between the countries. I must say that the French Army at the present moment is a stabilising factor, and one of the strongest, apart from the general hatred and fear of war. We should beware of deranging the situation which exists. It is not satisfactory, but it is one that might easily be replaced by a worse situation. The sudden disappearance or weakening of that factor of stability, the unquestioned superiority of French military power, might open floodgates of measureless consequence in Europe at the present time, might break the dyke and

> "Let the boundless deep
> Down upon far-off cities while they dance—
> Or dream."

Apart from that, it would be the highest imprudence for our Government to cast reflections or disturb the good relations which prevail between us and the French.

I have ventured to lay these reflections before the Committee while there is plenty of time and while there is calm. I think we ought to recognise that the dangers which come from Russia are at the root of the failure of Disarmament in Europe. This mighty Power, outside the family of nations, outside the concert of Christendom, proclaiming a creed destructive of all existing civilisation, pursuing an economic policy fundamentally disturbing to industry, not influenced by any consideration of morals or of humanity, with many lost provinces to retrieve, possessed of unlimited manpower, and rapidly equipping itself with all the most frightful and devastating instrumentalities of modern war—there you find a reason why you are not making the progress in your Disarmament Conferences that you had a right to hope for—there, and not in the undue nationalism of particular countries. It is in the perfectly comprehensible and very valid fear of all these small nations in contact with the power of Russia that you find the obstacle which has delayed your progress. That is the first thing that we ought to recognise.

Secondly, I venture to submit to the Committee that in my judgment, whatever these dangers may be, whether you rate them high or low, they will be seriously aggravated if at any time there should be any approximation of military strength between Germany and France. In this connection we must not forget that the man-power of Germany, the contingent of youth arriving at the military age each year, is at the present moment double that of France. I am quite certain that the whole situation would become infinitely more critical if there were at any time an approximation of military power between those two countries. Thirdly, there is our own influence that we have to consider. We must use of our influence to modify the age-long antagonisms, as we have done, between Germany and France. We may have to use our authority in the discharge of our obligations under the Locarno Treaty, and our power to play our part will be deeply, and perhaps fatally, affected if we have not a sense of safety and security in regard to our naval defence and in regard to the supplies on which we live and which must come in through the narrow seas.

Those are the three considerations which I would venture to put before the Committee. I would not wish it to be supposed that I am an alarmist, or foresee another great war in our lifetime. I am as anxious as any Member in this House to work my utmost to keep us out of war, and, even if the peace should be broken by others, to prevent our being involved in the struggle, and I do not believe that, if we act with wisdom and prudence, we need be drawn into another war. But, believe me, much more is required than good will and fine sentiments to put us in a satisfactory position. We must be safe, as we are not safe now. England's hour of weakness is Europe's hour of danger. It was so in 1914, and it may be so again. Therefore, I recommend to the Committee, first of all, that we regain at the earliest moment our naval freedom to secure our food supplies in the narrow seas, and, consequently, regain our independence from European entanglements and our free judgment in regard to any issue which may arise and which may be inseparable from the secure position of our vital food supplies. Secondly, I greatly welcome the statement of the Prime Minister that we shall not seek to weaken unduly the power of France on land, and thus expose ourselves to a dangerous rebuff. Lastly, we must, simultaneously with these other two processes, ceaselessly endeavour to bring France and Germany together for a settlement of outstanding disputes and grievances. If all of these three policies—not any one of them will suffice, but, if all of these three policies are pursued at the same time, soberly, sincerely and skilfully, then we shall have done our best to contribute towards the maintenance of the peace of the world, and there is as yet no reason why we should not succeed.

INDIA (CAWNPORE RIOTS)

July 9, 1931

House of Commons

My Noble Friend the late Under-Secretary of State for India [Lord Winterton] delivered a speech which covered the whole field of Indian administration, and, although it was couched in the most modest terms and in that restrained language which we are all urged to use upon this subject at all times, it amounted none the less to a severe indictment of the policy of His Majesty's Government and of the Secretary of State for India. My right hon. and learned Friend the Member for Spen Valley (Sir J. Simon) spoke of his sympathy for the great difficulties with which the Secretary of State has had to grapple. I do not feel the same as he. I think that many of those difficulties are of his own manufacture and are the manufacture of his friends. The right hon. and learned Gentleman for Spen Valley paid compliments in various directions. I am very glad he has not paid a compliment to me. After compliment there comes a pretty fierce thrust, to which the compliment is but an introduction.

I shall not take up any of the time of the Committee this afternoon upon compliments in any quarter. I am anxious to carry on the discussion from the point to which it was brought by my right hon. and learned Friend the Member for Spen Valley. He devoted the whole of his powerful and impressive speech, the most damaging speech, if you look beneath the compliments and all the safeguarding sentences, that has been delivered in this Parliament against the policy of the Secretary of State, primarily to the question of the Cawnpore report which we have before us this afternoon, and I think he was quite right to do so, because without this Cawnpore tragedy there would have been no Debate this afternoon. This was the starting point and main impulsion upon which this Debate was asked for. Although I intend, not at any length, to survey the general field of Indian life and Government, I shall begin by asking the Committee to follow the significance of the Cawnpore report in the same manner as the right hon. and learned Gentleman has done.

Let us look at the chain of causation; let us remount it link by link. First of all, about these massacres in Cawnpore. What is the cause of the massacres? I am going to say in the simplest terms. The cause of the massacres is the tension and hostility between the Hindus and the Moslems. They have been inflamed against one another. Why have they been inflamed? Why were they inflamed at this juncture? Here, again, there is no doubt whatever, if one studies the report before us, that they have been inflamed in Cawnpore by the action prolonged of the Hindus and Congress Party in the civil disobedience movement, and matters were brought to a head by the pact between Lord Irwin and Mr. Gandhi, and the release of prisoners in large numbers which accompanied that agreement. That brought the matter to a head.

I was never one who thought that the Gandhi-Irwin pact was a wise or prudent or statesmanlike measure. I considered that it was a very grave perilous error in thought and in Government, and bitterly have we paid for it even in the short time which has elapsed. The right hon. Gentleman says that although it may have led to massacres here and there, or words to that effect, it has given peace over the greater part of India. It has not given peace. I will quote him an authority which he will accept, no less an authority than Mr. Gandhi himself. I am not quoting any British officials. Here is the highest authority of all, Mr. Gandhi. Let us see what Mr. Gandhi said about this pact which has brought peace.

> The Gandhi-Irwin arrangement is a pact or truce

said Mr. Gandhi:

> It can never be a peace.

That is Mr. Gandhi. This meeting and making of an agreement between His Majesty's chief representatives in India and the leader of a movement of civil disobedience was a direct precursor, and, as I assert, a recognisable and principal cause of the massacres which took place in Cawnpore. But let us look behind. Let us follow this chain up, in the reverse order in which events have taken place. What was the cause of the Irwin-Gandhi pact? There you come to the Round Table Conference which was a direct cause of the Gandhi-Irwin pact. I do not see how Lord Irwin could have given effect to the sentimental expectation excited by the foolish outpourings of the Round Table Conference, unless he proceeded to release all the prisoners and to endeavour to come to some terms with Mr. Gandhi and the Congress Party and to erect them into a body with whom he might have a negotiation. I criticise the Act, but I quite understand that the Viceroy, following on all that had happened here, was bound to make some arrangements of this kind. Therefore, I say you need to see the cause of the massacre of Cawnpore, and you have to look at this other blunder of the Round Table Conference which raised all those hopes of responsible government as a mere interlude to Dominion status and seemed to infer that there could be no difficulty in giving effect to all those hopes in a very short time. Here are the two: This is the ancestor, the Round Table Conference; and here is the descendant, the lineal descendant, the report of the Cawnpore massacre.

Let us look at this report of the Cawnpore massacre. It is a working model of the kind of situation in which you are going to move generally in India. It is what you might call a cameo of disintegration. First of all, there is the atmosphere, this atmosphere where the high Government makes terms with lawlessness and disorder, this atmosphere where hopes are excited which cannot be fulfilled; this atmosphere where all the foundations of Indian life are unsettled by the suggestion that follows, that the great power which has given peace to India for two centuries is winding up its affairs, and is going to withdraw its governing, guiding, and protecting hand. That is the first fact and the first feature, which comes out of this report.

What is the next feature? It is the harassed British civil servant no longer sure of himself, no longer sure of his superiors. This civil servant, taught not to enforce the law evenly or fearlessly; taught that he must not interfere with Congress volunteers because they are covered by some agreement made on high; the harassed civil servant, I have no doubt typical of many hundreds of those who have hitherto upheld with so much success our name and authority in India, but now weakened, his prestige weakened, his confidence in himself undermined. That is the second feature which comes to our eyes in reading this report.

Then there is the hideous outbreak of horrible massacre. My right hon. and learned Friend the Member for Spen Valley spoke in terms which cannot be reproved about that; the treachery to which old friends and neighbours were exposed; asked into their neighbours' houses for safety and then butchered, women and children, in the most horrible fashion; an outbreak of primordial fury and savagery and of all those animal and bestial instincts. I should like the Committee to note the attitude of the British military authorities. British troops reside in a city of 54,000 inhabitants, and there are 66 men who march out in the first instance. More troops are gradually brought to the scene, but what is the atttitude of the military authorities? They do not allow—and very properly so—their men to be split up into little detachments and spread about in the streets of the city. They feel they must keep them concentrated until at any rate theyare quite sure it is not the white inhabitants who are likely to be the victims of mob fury. That is a most significant fact. The difference between the military authorities on the spot and the civil authorities which is referred to in this report is representative of the different point of view between the military and civil authorities throughout India—the civil authorities being involved in a continuous series of compromises and arrangements, which I have already described, with the forces of disorder, and the military authorities holding themselves as far as they can aloof and keeping the troops out of contact with the Indian mob or crowd in the streets, and their forces intact, in case a very much graver emergency arises. That is most instructive, and it comes from the pages of the report.

What is another feature of the report? There are the attempts to conceal the facts which were made by the Secretary of State. The account he gave of the casualties was intended to minimise the whole affair, and to-day he has endeavoured to minimise it by saying there had been other horrible occurrences of this kind. The report says that 400 or 500 persons were killed, but there are a great many authorities and persons in India who hold that is it much more like 1,000 persons who lost their lives in the streets and alleys of Cawnpore. Lastly, following the report, we see the Commission of Inquiry set up by the Government of India, which, after surveying the scene and writing a most able report, selects for blame and punishment, Mr. Sale, a British civil servant, who was in charge of the city—one white man almost alone with all responsibility. He is selected and held up for public censure which, I have no doubt, in one form or another, will mean the ruin of his career. What is his crime? His crime is that he has followed the example—perhaps a little too literally—set him from on high. It is very difficult for civil servants in India at present to act with the confidence of a Clive or Warren Hastings when all the time from above arrangements are being made with the forces of disorder to render the authority of those civil servants and their prestige alike enormously lessened. What has happened at Cawnpore, as set down in the Blue Book, is only what will happen throughout India on a far larger scale if British authority should be withdrawn. Language has been used—and most wrongfully and most deceitfully used—to suggest British authority is going to be withdrawn. The Lord Chancellor said:

> India will in future be governed by Indians

not "in the future" mark you, but "in future." There alone you have a statement which is likely to cause every form of despondency and alarm. Mr. Gandhi has expressed his views on this question of communal strife—a saintly figure, as we are told by my hon. and gallant Friend to whose speech we listened with so much pleasure, who has devoted his life to assuaging communal differences—Mr. Gandhi, expressing his view on this question, said that if the British troops were withdrawn no doubt there might be trouble, but why should not Indians fight their own battles—their own battles, that is, against each other—which might end in the exhaustion or destruction of one or the other race? Can you wonder that the minorities are alarmed? This episode of Cawnpore is a shameful failure on the part of His Majesty's Government to protect the minorities. It is a shameful failure to give the ordinary primary protection to individuals and to minorities. Who are the minorities? We hear a lot about minorities. One of the minorities consists of 70,000,000 Moslems, another of the 60,000,000 Untouchables, and another of the 5,000,000 or 6,000,000 Christians. There are several smaller minorities. There are the Eurasians, or Anglo-Indians, in a most pitiful plight, and, last of all, but not least, there are the British and their wives and children. Those are the minorities, and I say every one of them, from one end of India to the other, is at this moment quaking with fear or anxiety. I do not wonder at it.

The Secretary of State to-day tried to use words of reassurance. He read out a statement made by the Prime Minister saying that minorities would be protected by such guarantees as might be necessary. When any of us at any time in these long discussions has felt anxious and disturbed and has put queries to those who are conducting this policy, the only answer that has been given is "Oh, well, the case of minorities will all be carefully provided for and be entrusted to the supreme powers reserved to the Viceroy." I have said in this House that to put such burdens as are contemplated upon the Viceroy is to go beyond the limits of the capacity of the greatest men that we have known in this country, but that is always the stock answer to any misgivings which are put forward on behalf of the minorities. What does the present Viceroy say about his duties? I must read this quotation to the House. Lord Willingdon at Simla on 29th June:

> I am quite clear that the work the Viceroy has to do is much too heavy for a gentleman of my mature years, and I venture to hope that all those concerned, when they get over to London in the near future, will hurry on towards the completion of their labours in regard to constitutional reforms so that my life may more closely approximate to the four happy years I spent in Canada as a constitutional Governor-General and in order that I may be relieved of many of my constitutional duties.

That is a very extraordinary speech to have been made and it is only following up, I admit—

Mr. Benn: On a point of Order. May I draw attention to the fact that under the Standing Orders criticism of the Viceroy is forbidden except on a substantive Motion? Criticism of policy is, of course, natural and permitted.

The Chairman: I understood the right hon. Gentleman was quoting a speech. In so far as his quotation was concerned, I think it was in order.

Mr. Churchill: Far from criticising, I was proceeding to defend, because the Viceroy was only following the example which was set by the right hon. Gentleman. He was following accurately the line taken by his official superiors. Here is the right hon. Gentleman who two months ago in one of the Debates on India, when dealing with the question of the boycott of Lancashire trade and the constant suffering caused in Lancashire, said—I am not quoting his exact words—"Well, in a short time there will be an Indian Minister of Trade with whom all these matters can be satisfactorily arranged." Can you wonder that the Viceroy, therefore, is entirely justified in following up the line set by his official superior on the Treasury Bench? Then there is the Finance Member, Sir George Schuster, who, speaking on the Budget, said:

> In conclusion, he need only add that the present Government of India were in the position of managers of a business. A change in management was under discussion. In the case of a business, if he might continue the analogy, the parties concerned, if upright and sensible men, would surely say "We must co-operate during the period of preparation." He could hardly imagine that in such circumstances the new proprietors would say, "Those whom we are succeeding are our enemies and we will try to trip them up at every turn."

Let me point out that every one of these statements—the last two are the only ones I am referring to now, and I am not referring to the Viceroy's statement except to read it—go far beyond any measure of agreement that has been reached between the two parties, and anything which Lord Reading has committed himself to on the constitutional question. I need not go into the safeguards and conditions which Lord Reading prescribed, but they were most elaborate and he has taken a subsequent occasion in the most public manner to reaffirm all those points and conditions, as the right hon. Gentleman knows. What right has the Secretary of State, or anyone serving under him, to use language putting possibilities which presuppose that all these difficulties will be surmounted and that before very long there will be a Dominion status or responsible Government in India? I do not at all wonder that the minorities are alarmed when they hear of all this, and still less do I wonder that British investors are alarmed when they hear the Finance Minister speaking at Simla in these terms about a change of management and proprietorship at the same time that Mr. Gandhi and Congress are insisting upon repudiation at any rate of a large portion of the debt.

Can you wonder that the Government have been compelled to go forward and do what no other Government which has watched over the affairs of India has ever done, namely, to pledge British credit to sustain the credit of our great dependency? In bygone years, the credit of India was as good as that of Great Britain, and now at this overburdened moment we have to face another assumption of responsibility and new liabilities have to be put upon our finances. I should like to know what is the sense of talking from that bench almost in the same breath about Dominion status and guaranteed finance. The two terms are identically contradictory—responsible government and guaranteeing finance. There is no meaning whatever in such statements. [An Hon. Member: "What about Australia?"] We have not guaranteed there, and it is a remarkable case in point—the case of Australia which is tied to us by ties at least as close as those which bind us to the Indian dependency. How unfair it is of the right hon. Gentleman, and of those who speak in this sense, to Members of the Conservative and Liberal parties who have gone so far to help him on his path, to take this advantage and make declarations of this kind which are altogether premature.

There is a third feature of Indian administration to which I am bound to refer before I sit down. Since this process which has been called Indianisation has been proceeding, there has been a marked deterioration in the efficiency of the great Services. I am not going into them in detail, but in the great Services of forestry, agriculture, and so on, there has been a marked deterioration, which is very serious and grave, I am told, in some cases. It is quite certain that you will not get the same class of British Civil Servants to serve under natives in all these employments as you have hitherto been fortunate in obtaining. You may, indeed, get many British officers who will serve, but I doubt very much whether they will uphold the same high traditions upon which the whole efficiency of our rule is based.

This Indian question is not primarily a constitutional question. It is a question, as I have said, of apparatus, of machinery. Upon the efficiency of these great Services depends our power to lift the whole of this vast mass of helpless people in India above their present level, or above the level to which they would certainly sink if they were left to their own unaided care, and that deterioration is of the utmost gravity and consequence. We have had the Report of the Commission which has examined into the state of labour in India—the Whitley Commission. Certainly, that Report should be read by Members of this House with the same attention with which they have read these other publications. The shocking conditions which are revealed to exist in the mills throughout India—[Interruption]—are indeed most painful, and I am not at all surprised that hon. Gentleman should be eager to say that this disgraceful condition has occurred under British rule. Why did it occur under British rule? Because British rule has not been exercised with that thoroughness—[Interruption.] If the Viceroys and Governments of India in the past had given half as much attention to dealing with the social conditions of the masses of the Indian people, as they have to busying themselves with negotiating with unrepresentative leaders of the political classes for constitutional changes, if they had really addressed themselves to the moral and material problems which are at the root of Indian life, I think it would have been very much better for the working folk both of Burnley and of Bombay, of Oldham and of Ahmedabad, there would have been better conditions in India, and there would not have been the distress and misfortune that there is in Lancashire through competition based upon a labour status which is absolutely indefensible.

I am not going to depart from an attitude of hostility to the Secretary of State. I consider that the two years for which he has been responsible are two years of the greatest misfortune and retrogression that India has ever suffered in the lifetime of living man. The right hon. Gentleman has been treated with the greatest indulgence and consideration—too much, I hold. He has been denied nothing in the support given to him by other parties in the House, whether in regard to concession or in regard to repression. In every way he has been supported. I say that he and those who are acting with him are responsible for what is going on, and for what is going to happen. The responsibility rests with those who are having their way on this matter. It does not rest with those who consider that, in spite of every warning, we are advancing upon a fatal path.

The right hon. Gentleman is having his way; he is carrying all before him. By the fruits of his policy he must be judged. What are the fruits that are now apparent? There is the big injury to Lancashire, which is not in the slightest degree affected by any arrangement come to between the Viceroy and Mr. Gandhi. The boycott continues; trade is flagging, and the distress throughout Lancashire is aggravated. In the second place, there is the broken credit of India, requiring this House to undertake to take upon its shoulders this enormous new burden. Thirdly, as set forth in this Blue Book, there are the horrors of Cawnpore. Those are the results of your policy to-day. They are only an instalment, only a payment on account, a mere earnest of what is to come if you persist in pursuing this fatal path.

Where, may I ask, are we going? Where are we being led? Where are we drifting? Make no mistake about it; we are drifting towards a violent collision; we are drifting towards an utter deadlock in a few months' time. Mr. Gandhi and the Congress have made it perfectly clear that they will not regard even Dominion status as adequate. They seek, in one form or another, absolute, complete independence. They have been erected by the Government into a treaty-making power, quite unnecessarily and needlessly. You have brought these persons up and made them a power with whom you now have to negotiate, but who cannot guarantee the execution of any instrument which may be arrived at and by which you will be bound. On the other hand, opinion in the Conservative party and in the Liberal party—I do not care what is said in dispute of it—is steadily stiffening. I feel a very different atmosphere now from what there was in the days of the Round Table Conference. [*Interruption.*] I will continue to do my utmost to sustain that stronger and saner opinion. I was delighted to see the speech made by my right hon. Friend the Member for Chelsea (Sir. S. Hoare) the other day in the country, using language of extreme, uncompromising firmness in regard to the maintenance of the safeguards which are so important and far-reaching; and the speech of the late Under-Secretary to-day was in the same key.

You have on both sides two parties, two forces, both poles apart and without really any adequate or hopeful basis on which they can sit at the same council board. The Hindus and Mohammedans have been inflamed against one another, not intentionally, but as the inevitable consequence of the steps that have been taken. As to the loyalty of the Princes, it has been distracted and confused by the spectacle of indecision which this great centre of the Empire has exhibited. You have settled nothing; you have unsettled everything. You have faced no difficulties; you have solved no problems. The right hon. and learned Member for Spen Valley could have cited 20 points of cardinal importance in the proposals for a Federal Constitution, none of which has ever been faced. Where there have been differences between Indians and Great Britain, some adjustment has been made by Great Britain giving way; but as to differences between Indians themselves there has not been one concession, not one difficulty has been solved or surmounted. Nevertheless, on we go, moving slowly, in a leisurely manner, jerkily onwards towards an unworkable conclusion, crawling methodically towards the abyss which we shall reach in due course.

There is the position, there is the result of your three-party co-operation, there is the result of what is called keeping India out of party politics; there is the result to which we have been led by all the wiseacres and all the leading articles—vague, sentimental declarations of equivocal character, meant to mean one thing to Indians and another thing to Great Britain; disquietude caused throughout the Indian masses; the usual interminable delays which beset all Indian party deliberations; progressive degeneration of our authority throughout India; financial decline—all leading up at no great distance to a complete political deadlock. That, I say, is the position that is before us to-night; and remember that, when that deadlock is reached, you will have to begin all over again to rebuild in suffering all that you have cast away in folly.

INDIA (CONSERVATIVE POLICY)

July 11, 1931

Chingford

[Extract] ... I have acted in complete loyalty to the Conservative Party, and am going to work with all my strength to secure the downfall of the present Administration at the earliest moment, and the return to power of a Conservative Government. There is no part of our work in the world which more entitles us to look back with pride and gratitude than the acquisition and development of our Indian Empire. It would be a shame if we were to weary in our task and allow the reins of authority to fall from our relaxing fingers and leave India to fall back into bloody chaos and anarchy.

In dealing with India we come up very quickly against realities. One of these is the broken credit of India which has necessitated the British Government coming to the rescue of Indian finance and doing what has never been needed before, giving a vague and general guarantee at a time when our own are heavily pressed, in order to assist Indian credit. That reality was produced directly by the maladministration of Mr. Wedgwood Benn and his Socialist colleagues. The second reality is the paralysed trade of Lancashire, and the third the massacre at Cawnpore, where we saw Hindus and Moslems at each other's throats because of all this unwise talk and vague promises that Great Britain is going to relinquish her authority.

I am glad to think the views I have been putting forward since this question became acute are daily gaining support throughout the Conservative Party. You may be quite sure that I will take no factional attitude. My only desire is to see the Conservative Party play its true part in this Indian controversy.

THE FINANCIAL SITUATION

September 8, 1931

House of Commons

In August 1931 the Labour Government, in complex circumstances which have been often described but which still remain incomprehensible, broke asunder on the issue of the resolution of the urgent economic crisis. Ramsay MacDonald formed a National Government with Baldwin. Churchill was excluded from the new Administration. It was curious that it was Churchill who made the first public appeal for a General Election to strengthen the National Government and introduce Protection, but it was a curious period.

It is so many years since I have had to make a speech in this House without the support of that Box, that I feel almost entitled to demand a measure of that indulgence which the House is accustomed to give to new Members. Moreover, I must frankly admit that I am unused to the dizzy heights of the back bench and altogether uncertain whether I have gone up or down. I must also confess that during the last speech I felt at times quite shy; I felt as if I were listening to a family quarrel, to a bitter dispute which was going to break up a happy home, and I am bound to say that I do not think it ended on a very high note with those tearful measurements of the relative pecuniary losses involved in the grave constitutional cataclysm which has just taken place. The speech of the right hon. Gentleman the Leader of the Opposition was mainly formed of his complaints against his late colleagues in the Socialist Administration. They are apparently serious; they are certainly appalling; and I have no doubt that they will one day form the subject of very attentive historical investigation. But we who have crossed the Floor of the House at the call of our leaders have little or no concern with those complaints. Our part has been to come to the rescue of a Socialist Government reduced to loggerheads and impotence and to do what we can to help the country through its difficulties.

We have our own complaints against the right hon. Gentleman and the party opposite which has now adhered to his leadership, and they are very grievous complaints. There has been some historical recital of the past, and we cannot forget that the right hon. Gentleman and those who sit with him obtained Office by treating in the most unfair and merciless manner their predecessors, who were confronted also in their task with grave difficulties. We cannot forget that they made promises of the wildest character and indulged in measureless boastings. Then, as this year began to unfold, the late Government took a series of steps which greatly aggravated the crisis so far as we are concerned, and which tended to diminish public confidence. It was in January that the Chancellor of the Exchequer sent Sir Richard Hopkins to give his evidence before the Royal Commission on Unemployment Insurance in which he declared that our Budget was unbalanced. It was in February that the Chancellor made his most solemn warning statement to the House, but nothing was done. Our credit suffered the injury of the warning but our practice was in no respect amended. Matters drifted on; more expenditure was incurred; further obligations were accepted by the Treasury; and all through June there was no whisper or suggestion for dealing with the situation. The Budget which the right hon. Gentleman produced bore no trace of the alarmist declaration he had made beforehand and made no provision to restore the situation.

Then we got to July. In July the German crisis came, and it was apparent that our trade balance was adverse. Gold began to leave the country at an alarming rate. It was in July that the first rumours of the proposed formation of a National Government became rife. They then got into the newspapers. No doubt we shall hear from my right hon. Friend the Lord President of the Council a somewhat fuller account of all the important conversations which lead up to this suprising though no doubt necessary change. I mention this fact for a particular reason. If the leaders of the late Government were so clear in July that a great financial crisis was approaching that they were already considering the possible political reactions which would follow from it, why did they not take some financial precautions then? Surely there was a good opportunity then. Here was our great London money market, with all its delicacy and great value to the country and the Exchequer—one of the great assets which we possess in the world—here it was obviously in a difficult situation with the world becoming very chaotic all round it, and here were the Government seeing that a crisis was impending and even discussing matters with other parties. Why did they not take some financial precuations?

I am assured that it would have been possible to take financial precautions. Our credit at that time was such that we could easily have obtained an ample trans-Atlantic credit which we would probably never have had to use, but which by its amplitude would have made it quite clear that there would be no challenge to sterling. With our position, with our foreign investments and great industrial aptitude and capacity, what a shame it is that we have come down to this humiliation! Nothing at all was done on the financial side. The right hon. Gentleman, who was the second or third Member of the Government, bore a great load of responsibility, and the more so because when the crisis came he and nine-tenths of the Government and his party quitted their responsibility. He objected to "ran away," so I choose the word "quitted." He quitted his responsibility and gathered all his forces together; then, declaring themselves a hostile Opposition, they set themselves in speeches and declarations to make the task of their successors as difficult as possible.

In this, the right hon. Gentleman has had an undeniable measure of success. The action which he has taken has blighted to a considerable extent the hopes which were associated with the formation of a national Government. Now that the largest party in the House is in irreconcilable opposition, it is true that the term "national Government" can no longer be properly used, but the hopes formed upon that Government have also been weakened, and I am told that adverse monetary currents are still flowing and even in some respects accentuated. With the whole Socialist party gone into Opposition resisting the policy of the Government, resisting the effort to deal with the situation, of course confidence will not return and judgment is suspended.

Everyone feels that the battle is still to be fought. The right hon. Gentleman, who a fortnight ago was treated with so much consideration and honour as our Foreign Secretary, has played a recognisable part in bringing about this public misfortune. In these circumstances, the moderation and restraint which I recognised in his speech are no more than were becoming.

It is of the future rather than of the past that I wish to speak in the short time that I shall trespass upon this exceptional measure of indulgence which I am to receive from the House. The crisis is not over—neither the political nor the financial crisis. On the contrary, it is beginning and will be prolonged. The position which was taken up by the leader of the Conservative party is one of immense consequence, and we cannot at this time measure exactly how far this consequence will carry us. It certainly involves a very great sacrifice of the purely party interest for which he was responsible, but that was made in the hope of rendering an indispensable service to the country at a moment of extreme urgency. Whether that historical action was wise or unwise, only time can prove. Some may think that it would have been better to have given the most complete assurances of support to the Socialist Administration in respect of all the economies and financial measures that they were willing to take. After all, they were prepared to commit themselves to £56,000,000 of the most unpopular economies, economies which, no doubt, they are going to try to denounce us for carrying into effect. They were committed to that £56,000,000 of economies, and I am not at all sure that if they had received full assurances of support from both the other parties they might not have got through their own difficulties themselves, without bringing this extraordinary political disturbance upon the country. However, the deed is done. It was done from high motives, disinterested motives, and we have got to make the best of it.

I must admit that my first reaction on reading—abroad, on my holidays—of the formation of this new Government was that it should stay in office for a good long time. I hoped to see this Government, a National Government as I then thought it was, including the whole three parties, deal effectually, upon an agreed basis, with the Tariff Question, and to deal with it not as a matter of party scores but as it should be dealt with, as a vital question of business and economics in which the whole country is interested. I hoped to see it deal with the Gold Standard, to see it review and examine that position, taking as its starting point the resolutions of the Genoa Conference of 1922 about the economy and the utilisation of the available stores of gold, and being guided at every stage by the evident hoarding of gold on a gigantic scale which has been proceeding ever since 1925, especially in the two countries which have benefited from reparation payments. I thought also, and hoped, that this Government might achieve the conversion which would be such a great easement to our affairs. And there were other important things. But then, in a few days, or in a day or two, we learnt that it was not a National Government at all. It soon appeared that, through no fault of its own, it could rely only upon two out of the three parties in the House. We saw the whole Socialist party cross the Floor and resolve themselves into opposition, and from that moment it seemed to me—and I would like my friends on this side to consider this with care—that a challenge was open, that a definite challenge was open to the fundamental interests of the State, and that, in the famous phrase of Mr. Gladstone, such a challenge once thrown down must be taken up and events must go forward to an issue.

Everyone can see the dangers and disadvantages of a General Election in the next few months, but the question we have to ask ourselves is whether those dangers and disadvantages will be lessened by putting it off. The late President of the Board of Trade told us very candidly, and even brazenly, how great are the benefits which he expects the Socialist party will reap from delay. They are, indeed, obvious. A fortnight ago the party opposite were held responsible throughout the world for the conduct of events, for acts of omission and commission which had reduced this rich country to its present plight; but with a few honourable exceptions they have shifted the burden, as it is vulgarly called, they have "passed the buck." That burden is now borne by His Majesty's Government, that is to say, by an administration supported by, roughly speaking, 250 Conservatives, 50 Liberals and 10 or a dozen Labour men. I am sorry to have to recount those figures, but, after all, they constitute one of the underlying facts of the Parliamentary situation. With every day that passes the short, shifting memories of our electorate will fade. A vast, unorganised electorate will have new discontents and new disappointments, and they will assign to the Conservative party, which, after all, is the main and dominant force in this Government, an increasing measure of the weight and burden of affairs.

In six months' time, it will not be the Socialist Govenrment that will be in the dock, but the Government of the day; and those whom I shall never cease to declare have very largely brought these misfortunes upon us will once again be the airy and irresponsible critics of the administration, will once again be promising galore, will once again be boasting of all they could do if only they came back into power. I believe that, with truth, a very unpleasant truth, the right hon. Gentleman the Leader of the Opposition might say, in words with which Dr. Coué familiarised us, "Every day and in every way I shall get better and better." I hope that that also will be borne in mind. It may be said that this is only a party argument, but let us look at the national side. One of the great causes, as I have always held, that has weakened and quenched our trade and industrial activity in this recent depression has been the uncertainty which has overhung the whole political field. In the board rooms of a thousand companies men have said to one another, "No one knows when the General Election will come; no one knows how it will end. We would do much better not to embark on new enterprises and on expenditure to replenish plant until we know a little more as to where we are." No country in the world makes its people and its business live in such a continuous condition of uncertainty as we do. In France, America and other countries the people know there will not be a General Election or a change; but we here have been for two years under the perpetual threat of a General Election, and I say that while this uncertainty continues indefinitely it will be the very greatest handicap upon the revival of our business. Moreover, we have, probably, a modest majority, and inside that majority there are strong currents. The position of the Government must be precarious if their tasks and labours are prolonged. From every point of view the business of this country will be prejudiced until we reach some finality.

Further, there are two very great questions either or both of which might expose His Majesty's Government to the greatest danger. The first is India. This Government, in my judgment—I submit it respectfully to the opinion of the House—is not in a position to make any large departure in Indian policy. It would not be fair to ask the assent of Parliament to some great surrender of its powers at a time when ordinary political activities are suspended. I hope that we shall have an assurance—I ask it amicably, but pointedly, of my right hon. Friend the Lord President of the Council—that there is no immediate question of any substantial or new departure in Indian policy, that the exploratory work upon which the Conference is engaged will carry us on for some time to come, and that before any serious decision is taken full normal political conditions will have been restored. That is the first point; but there is another and greater question which overhangs our situation. It is the question of Protection, the establishment of a protective tariff, and other measures connected with the control of dumped imports and with the fostering of British agriculture.

Lieut.-Commander Kenworthy: Ask the Home Secretary!

Mr. Churchill: I am of opinion that, whatever views may be held in this House, the nation is now ripe to adopt that policy. Three-quarters of the late Labour Cabinet, lifelong Free Traders, or at any rate a very large proportion, were prepared, we are told, in this crisis to adopt or approve a tariff for revenue, which, since it would have had no countervailing excise, would unquestionably be the establishment of a general protective tariff. And in what other way, I ask, can the vast sums of money which are lying idle in the banks—[Hon. Members: "Oh!"]—be made available—[An Hon. Member: "Why go to France or America for money?"] The hon. Gentleman is forgetting that our trouble was over the exchange—[*Interruption*]. You might be more grateful than that when the matter is explained to you. In what other way can these great sums of money be voluntarily attracted to support British industry, and in what better way can industry and employment be increased and the cost of unemployment be reduced, unless we are to confine ourselves simply to these hard cuts in benefits?

No, Sir, it seems to me that the position of Conservative Ministers, who have so often declared in the plainest possible manner their faith and belief that a great mitigation of unemployment can only be achieved by the adoption of a system of Protection and Imperial Preference, will become almost intolerable if they continue month after month, for a very long period, confining their efforts altogether to enforcing unpopular economies, and levying new and burdensome taxes without being permitted to bring forward a constructive and remedial measure. Anyhow, I submit to the judgment of the House, and especially those sitting on this side, that there will be no revival of British industry in the circumstances to which we have come until a tariff is proclaimed. I go further and say that there will be no restoration of confidence at home or abroad until the Socialist party has been again decisively defeated at the poll. If there is a large measure of agreement upon the argument which I have ventured to put forward, then clearly the task before us is to use this precious interval, which may not be very lengthy, to endeavour to frame and formulate a national policy and programme gathering together and marshalling around that policy the greatest and strongest support from men of good will in all parties.

I am anxious that the Conservative party should co-operate in this work. I rejoiced, when I came into the House this afternoon and witnessed this great scene, to notice that indubitably the Floor was broader than the Gangway, and long may it remain so. The main cause of our exceptional misfortunes in these times of world stress has been that there has been a confusion, a paralysis of the Government instrument through the turmoil and intrigue of three parties, and one of the consequences arising out of that has been a minority Government which did not represent the strength or will-power of this powerful country, but an unexpected convulsion has achieved what no Government could have accomplished. Now we are all together. Now we see our common opponents arrayed against us, but I earnestly hope that we are not going back to the dark days which have led us to this pitch of confusion. We need a Government instrument commanding not only the support of a majority in this House, but commanding the support of the majority of people of this country. Such an instrument alone can restore that grip and focus of affairs which has enabled weaker countries than ours to recover and escape continued decline and humiliation.

I will conclude by making an appeal to the Liberal party, and I will address myself particularly to my right hon. and gallant Friend the Secretary of State for Scotland. He is a friend in form now as well as having long been a friend in fact. I do not suppose that there was any appointment to the new Government, so well chosen as many of them have been, which gave more satisfaction in all quarters of the House than the choice of my right hon. and gallant Friend for a position which is suited to his gifts and qualities, and that satisfaction was nowhere stronger than in his native land, over whose administration he now presides. I single him out not because of that fact, but particularly because he does not belong to the old, vicious, bitter, obsolete past of the fiscal controversy, but he belongs to a period in which fair and unprejudiced views may be taken. My right hon. and gallant Friend belongs to a generation which takes a fair and unprejudiced view on these matters and I appeal to him to discard pedantry and to seek a true sense of proportion, having regard to the position in which our country stands to-day. If it were possible for those who have now come together—or the best of them—to reach an agreement upon a truly national programme covering the whole field, we might speedily escape from our present welter and bring our country back to its old strength and prosperity.

I was brought up in my father's house upon such watchwords as "Trust the people" and "Never fear the British democracy," and I do not think we need fear them now. They are a great people, and they are at their best on great occasions. They rise to emergencies when there are real emergencies to face, and they know quite well that there is more freedom here than in many foreign countries. They know quite well that the rich in this country are more heavily taxed than anywhere else, and they also know that poverty and misfortune are more liberally and compassionately dealt with in this country than anywhere else, and better than they are dealt with even in great countries like the United States which were unsmitten by the War. Those people are proud of their country, and they will never forgive the men of any party who took part in allowing this country to fall behind in the march of nations which has reduced us to our present position in the world. I say to the Government and to those who are going to support them in their difficult task that we need not be afraid of the British democracy in the grim struggle which lies ahead of us. Give them a fair chance and a good plan, give them fidelity and courage, and then you may go to them in good heart.

THE BUDGET

September 11, 1931

Constituency Meeting, Chingford

Snowden's emergency Budget increased income tax to five shillings on the pound, and made economies in government expenditure of £70 million. All state employees had their salaries reduced, including the armed services.

[Extract] . . . Three quarters of the members of the House of Commons are in favour of a measure of Protection, and it must be brought in during the life of the Parliament. The Budget deliberately follows the most vexatious and irritating paths. We have very heavy troubles to bear and a very heavy hill to climb, but we need not make the troubles heavier or the hill steeper.

Moreover Mr. Snowden's proposals do not face the basic problems that lie at the root of the present crisis. The first of these is the fall in prices all over the world through the hoarding of gold by France and America. The second is the balance of trade through the decay of our industries and the excessive importation of unnecessary goods which we are taking from abroad. The third is the balance of the Budget by taxation and economy. All three must be dealt with and not merely the last. This Budget represents the last expiring convulsion of Treasury Cobdenism. I have thrown that off for ever. Everyone knows that the Budget proposals to deal with this emergency ought to contain a substantial measure of protection which would restore the trade balance by restricting imports, and would stimulate and hearten British industry. At least three-quarters of the present House of Commons are in favour of this and know that it is necessary.

Mr. Runciman, the life-long Liberal free-trader, has urged the Government to limit imports. Mr. Henderson, the leader of the Socialist Party, has declared in favour of a general tariff for revenue. The greater part of the Liberals recognize the gravity of the crisis and the immense changes which have taken place in our economic situation. The whole Conservative Party are united breasthigh for the great step. It must be taken, and it must be taken now. It must be taken in and by this present Parliament.

The Budget, as it stands will be an injury to the nation. It will largely increase unemployment, and further depress trade. It might be that the Budget must be voted as it stands. It may be that a protective tariff can not come into operation quickly enough to meet the immediate need. All right, whatever happens, at whatever cost, we are going to meet that need. There will be no weakness shown by Britain. But instantly there must be set on foot the larger measures which will overtake and mitigate the needless severities and supplement with constructive action the deficiencies of Mr. Snowden's present proposals.

REVISED BUDGET PROPOSALS

September 15, 1931

House of Commons

I do not know what the experience of other hon. Members may have been, but, for my part, whenever I have the good fortune to listen to a discourse by the right hon. Gentleman the Member for Central Edinburgh (Mr. W. Graham), I always have the feeling that the right hon. Gentleman knows all about everything and could go on expounding it for ever. After listening to his capacious harangue and its immaculate delivery, one would never have thought that the speaker was the representative of an Administration which, having reduced this country almost to beggary, had fled from their posts in terror of the consequences which were approaching them.

A great part of the right hon. Gentleman's speech was divided between reproaches of his former colleagues and of the Chancellor of the Exchquer [Mr. Snowden] for their lack of foresight in dealing with the approaching crisis, and a very interesting disquisition upon the root causes of our present misfortune. I am not in marked disagreement with the right hon. Gentleman in a great deal of what he has said—[*Interruption.*] I am most anxious to be as brief as possible, because there are so many Members who want to speak. Already large inroads upon our time have been made, and I propose to curtail my remarks, if hon. Gentlemen will help me as much as possible. I agree with the right hon. Gentleman that the root cause of our troubles is the unnatural accumulation of gold in the two countries which have alone benefited from the payment, across tariff barriers, of these accursed War Debts and reparations. I agree with him in that respect.

Up to the summer of 1929, the swift accumulation of gold in France and America had not become apparent; it had been masked by the great American lendings to Europe. But since that time the United States have added £170,000,000 to their reserve, and France has added £183,000,000, while at the same time the stocks of the rest of the world have been diminished by over £130,000,000, and at this present moment the position, as the right hon. Gentleman said, is that, out of £2,275,000,000 worth of gold, France and the United States together hold £1,350,000,000, or two-thirds of the whole gold of the world. And observe that not only is this immense sum held by these two States, but a very large portion of it, amounting probably to one-third of the whole visible gold of the world, is held sterilised, that is to say, it plays no more part in the operations of the world than it did when it lay in the virgin rock of the Rand. It has been dug up out of a hole in Africa, and put down in another hole that is even more inaccessible in Europe and in America.

Gold, as I see it, is the accepted measure of human effort, which enables the services, the exertions, and the fruits of the toil of the coolie in Japan or the coffee planter in Brazil to be exchanged against the work of a London cabman. If all things are to be measured against one another, before they can be measured they must be

referred to this standard of gold. Let me take a couple of simple analogies—
[*Interruption*] —if I may with the courtesy of hon. Gentlemen. Suppose that a great
bridge were being built—[*Interruption.*] I am sure the hon. Member for Plaistow (Mr.
Thorne) will not deny courtesy to a brother private Member. [*Interruption.*] Suppose
that a great bridge were being built, or a great modern building, requiring accurate
measurements at every stage, and that three-quarters of the foot rules required were
locked up in one or two of the foremen's offices. Imagine how the work would slow
down, and finally be brought to a standstill. To take another similitude, which may
well appeal to hon. Gentlemen opposite, who are so well acquainted with the
workshops of this country, suppose that a great factory were full of the most
wonderful machinery—full of the most perfect modern machinery—and all the lubri-
cating oil, or practically all of it, were monopolised by a couple of departments, while
all the other splendid machines, finer than had ever yet been seen in the world, were
left to heat, and grind, and rack, and shatter themselves to pieces. That is the situation
which, it seems to me, is undoubtedly being created by this altogether abnormal and
artificial abstraction of gold from its honourable and hitherto indispensable function
as a measure of human effort.

Nothing in what I have said in any way conflicts with the advocacy or adoption
of the gold standard. It fell to my lot to take the final steps of seven or eight years of
policy in that respect, and there is not a person in this House, wherever you look—and
there are six or seven ex-Chancellors of the Exchequer—who has the slightest ground of
reproach against me for that. Do not let it be thought that, in adopting the gold
standard, we were seeking simply to bolster up the rentier interest. The whole essence
of the gold standard is that it secures, or was intended to secure, a stable return for the
wages of labour, and to promote the continued cheapening of living. If the fight which
is now being waged on this side of the House to preserve the pound sterling—a most
difficult task—should be lost, it will not be necessary to debate in this House the cuts
that are to be made in the livelihood of this country; they will be imposed automatically by irresistible price movements over which you will have no more control
than you have over the weather.

This abstraction of gold, which is a quite recent feature, having, as I have said,
only come into naked publicity in the last 2-1/2 years, has raised an entirely new
position. There is nothing wrong with the gold standard, but how could the gold
standard be enforced if there were no gold? The standard may be all right, but
two-thirds of the gold has been impounded, and we are, therefore, reduced to a
position where an enormous reduction has been made in the vital output of the world,
and where a great part of the life-blood of the world has been frozen. As gold becomes
scarce, it becomes dear, and, as it becomes dear, everything measured against it falls in
price, and so you have this hideous, purposeless, unreal uneconomic, ceaseless fall in
prices, which, in its first stage, one might have deluded oneself into acclaiming as a
cheapening of the cost of living, but which is now clearly at a level that was never
foreseen by any of the old economists. It goes on and on, downwards, until the credit
of one institution after another is affected, and all the pillars of the structure of our
civilised life are one by one successively undermined. That is the position.

If I may continue my argument on this point, I want to know what would
happen supposing that what has been going on for the last three years went on for the

next five without interruption, and the acquisition of gold by these two countries—I am not blaming them; there is nothing malevolent in ther action; it has happened simply by certain rules working out—supposing that in the next five years they acquired all the gold in the world, what would happen then? Are we really to assume that all the rest of the world would be valueless—[*Interruption*]—that there would be no means of exchanging the fruits of toil, that all human exertion would be at a standstill? No. That is a point which we are rapidly and steadily approaching. Of course, the impounding or sterilisation of a great part of this dispensable medium, or vehicle, of commerce and of exchange, must lead to the breaking out of barter. You have already had barter, and you have had it in the most unlikely place. You have had it already in the United States—barter between the United States and Brazil for coffee—coffee against wheat; so that the United States are not only on a gold standard, but on a coffee standard too. Could there be clearer proof that the whole world is off the track in this matter of the relation of gold in world prices? I have no hesitation in saying that, unless all the countries of the world can either utilise the gold for the function which it has hitherto discharged, and make it available for that function, or can devise among themselves some new index of exchange—those which are not gold-possessing countries—the continued fall in prices and the continued destruction of credit will reduce our civilisation surely, and in no very great interval of time, to a bleak and ferocious barbarism.

It is curious that my right hon. Friend the Member for St. Ives (Mr. Runciman), who made from this bench a speech which interested us so much the other day, did not appear to be at all conscious, though of course he knows it perfectly well, of the great change which has taken place in the handling of gold, in the monetary situation; and I must say that up to the present the Chancellor of the Exchequer has not shown us what place these considerations occupy in his general scheme of thought. All these arguments about orthodox finance, the sanctity of contract, austere and rigorous economy, fine bills of exchange on which everyone wrote their names as they went round the world—all these arguments, which are perfectly sound, have a completely new and decisive factor rupturing them when the supplies of gold are, to the extent of one-third, actually rendered beyond the reach of man. At the very time when science was about to offer us the facilities for the making and exchange of all kinds of delectable goods, the vehicle which should have transported those goods, the indispensable measure, has been reduced by nearly one-half. That is the evil from which we were suffering. It rests entirely with the Government to devise the method, but I hope and trust that they will, without a moment's needless delay, place themselves in contact with the other Powers in order to convene the most powerful conference or assembly of nations which it is possible to bring together, in whatever place that is best suited for their deliberations, and to take the resolutions of the Genoa Conference of 1922 as their foundation and proceed immediately to enter upon the grand inquest of mankind into the loss and abstraction of gold and the consequent fall in prices.

Let me say that our position is not so weak as would be supposed. It must not be imagined that the two countries which have the gold are entirely contented with their lot. The United States may reach £1,000,000,000 as its gold reserve at almost the same time that its unemployment figure reaches 12,000,000 or 14,000,000; and France, a country for which I have the greatest regard and admiration in so many ways, has, I say without hesitation, heavy troubles ahead if the present cracking of the whole economic system continues from artifical causes. Therefore, I say to the Government, do not suppose that you are powerless in discussing these matters with other nations. They may not see it in the same light as you. They have problems of their own of a most grave kind and nothing would suit them less than if events were forced to their logical conclusion and those nations which did not possess gold had to establish some separate and independent means of interchange among themselves. You may be sure that nothing I am saying would weaken the hands of His Majesty's Government to deal with the matter. On the contrary, the facts are inherent in the situation. I hope and trust that, when this Conference meets, it will not only deal with the fall in prices and the gold question, but that out of its deliberations in some form or another a final quietus will be administered to the payment of War debts and reparations.

The second great question which governs the Budget is, of course, the balance of trade, which was referred to by the right hon. Gentleman in the closing portion of his speech. We owe it to the right hon. Gentleman the Member for St. Ives that practically complete agreement has broken out in the House on one particular step, namely, the curtailment of a particular class of luxury imports. I welcome the announcement that has been made that the Government are inquiring into this matter, with the intention of acting forthwith. Treaty obligations do not apply to tariffs which are raised to prohibitive levels but only to direct prohibition, or so I have always been informed. I should like to point out that a tariff which is prohibitive on luxuries in no way excludes a tariff which on other parts of the list is both protective and revenue in its effect. A large majority of the House knows, as the speech of the right hon. Gentleman clearly accepted, that such a tariff ought to be an integral part of the main proposals of any British Government to deal with the present emergency. [Hon. Members: "No!"] I wonder if, after Prayers one day, when everyone is at his best, we had to vote by ballot, how large the majority would be of those who would feel that without this element in our policy at present we cannot treat our problem in a complete or comprehensive way. I do not press that, because obviously there is a growing measure of agreement, and obviously that question, even in the life of this Parliament, is going to come increasingly and irresistibly to the front and to claim its logical place in all the measures necessary to restore confidence abroad and a revival of trade at home.

Mr. MacLaren: Another step in the madness!

Mr. Churchill: We ought to have regard to the hon. Member, and we make allowances for the peculiar mental disposition which always throws him off his balance when land values are mentioned.

It is only in the third place that I come to the immediate and imperative task of balancing the Budget of 1932. I am only dealing in what I say with the Budget of 1932. The right hon. Gentleman's proposals can only be judged in their true perspective in relation to this arrest and fall of world prices and in relation to measures to correct the adverse trade balance. No discussion of the method of balancing the Budget would be intelligible except on the foundation of these two primary tasks and I shall, therefore, have to take up some of the time of the House in dealing with that. But the balancing of the Budget is a matter of purely domestic finance. We are all agreeing that it must be balanced. Both sides, and all parties, are pledged to that, and the only question is the method, and on this we are entitled to have our opinion. It has often been complained that under our franchise British Ministers are prone to take the line of least resistance. Certainly, no one could accuse my right hon. Friend of having been guilty of that weakness on this occasion. I desire to make any criticisms on his proposals in a spirit of entire goodwill. He is in the position, very common nowadays in the great capitals of the world, of a very big firm which has got into a very bad strait and has to be held up at all costs by everyone else. I can assure him that, although I did not in my day get treated with very much consideration from him, when I had my difficulties, like the general strike, nevertheless, I am of a generous and forgiving disposition and I will treat him with consistent mercy, tempered only here and there with justice. I cannot, however, pretend that his solution of our difficulty of balancing the Budget, apart altogether from tariffs, is what I should myself have proposed. I am supporting his scheme, and I am going to vote for it steadily on every occasion. I have no difficulty or doubt about that. If we do not support that, what have we got? It is all that stands between us and collapse Therefore, I am supporting his scheme and, of course, any criticism which I should make is only minor and subsidiary and I trust may be found practically helpful.

There are, however, some criticisms which I must make. The first is a very small one, though not so small as it looks. I think it is an abuse of language to speak of the prospective deficit of 1932 as £170,000,000 and not to mention that it includes £52,000,000 of Sinking Fund. It is an abuse of language to speak of a deficit or to talk about an unbalanced Budget when you are in fact paying your way and also providing large sums for the amortisation of debt. I am not blaming the right hon. Gentleman, because he has followed a precedent which many Chancellors have set in speaking of it in that way but, when we have to consider the effect on public opinion all over the world, there is no need to make our case out worse than it is. The actual statement should, therefore, be that the prospective deficit is £117,000,000 with a surplus of £53,000,000, out of which £52,000,000 is available for debt redemption. The right hon. Gentleman says at this juncture that the Sinking Fund ought to have been suspended altogether. There are, of course, respectable authorities, although I am bound to say I have not been able to find the references in Sir Michael Hicks-Beach's speeches which I have been looking for, which favour and justify suspension of the Sinking Fund in times of great public emergency or acute trade depression. But with the hope of conversion, to which the whole country must lend its efforts, I consider that the right hon. Gentleman is fully justified in maintaining the Sinking Fund at the reduced figure he has done, although the fact of raising taxation to a ruinous level will itself entail a very serious evil. But I cannot feel that this argument applies to the £9,000,000 which was going to be borrowed by the Road Fund, but which the right hon. Gentleman is now going to pay out of taxes. The Road Fund has large and increasing revenues. [Interruption.] Perhaps I have not properly understood the proposal. The right hon. Gentleman is cutting down expenditure, but not to any great extent. I understood that the £9,000,000 which would have been borrowed by the Road Fund out of its own resources is now to be found out of taxation. Is that so or not? There is no addition to expenditure in that respect. I listened very carefully to

the right hon. Gentleman's Budget speech and I thought he included it among the
additions which he was making—I am not sure that I am not right after all—to the
burdens that he had to bear. It was one of the constituent factors in this deficit of
£17,000,000.

The Chancellor of the Exchequer (Mr. Philip Snowden): I will explain.

Mr. Churchill: We all very much admire the right hon. Gentleman and his work,
especially the latter part of it, and we wish to know exactly what form that work is
taking in order that we may render him his due need of approbation. But I hope that
this suspension of the borrowing power of the Road Fund is not going to indicate an
undue curtailment of telephone and telegraphic extension work throughout the
country and public works of all kind, national and municipal, because, if that were to
be so, the financial gain would emerge immediately on the other side of the ledger in a
heavy increase of unemployment. We cannot conceive a more violent reversal of policy
than would be involved in the virtual cessation or drastic curtailment of all borrowing
on capital account for development purposes. I remember the late Government being
attacked for not borrowing more. I remember having to stand at that Box and show at
length all that we were doing and why we could not do more. Since then others have
been responsible and borrowing has been increased and boasted of. Only a few months
ago the Prime Minister was reading out a long catalogue of all the measures that were
being taken to increase loan expenditure in order to deal with the unemployed during
the winter. As for my friends on these benches, the echoes of their perorations still
linger in our ears. Certainly a corrective should be administered to extravagance in
every form. But surely such a change in outlook, so sudden a reversal of policy,
deserves profound consideration. It is contrary to all the processes of thought to which
all parties in this House have become accustomed, and until it is fully explained it will
leave Parliament devoid of any coherent theme which they could present to an anxious
and a bewildered public.

Apart from the question of the confidence of foreign Powers in our management
of our affairs and our credit, which must not be under-rated, but which must not be
over-rated, because nothing will save us except right action, we shall not be saved
because of what others think of us, but because we handle our national affairs in a
right and proper manner, so that, apart from foreign opinion, there is nothing in this
policy of internal deflation which is in any way relevant to our economic problems.
There are immense sums lying, not idle but on deposit, in the banks. I was given a
figure of over £2,000,000,000, and really at a time like that, it seems to me that to
place upon the taxpayers—for that is what is being done—a charge of £39,000,000 to
be raised by taxation at these destructive levels instead of allowing the Road Fund to
borrow, if the Road Fund is solvent in relation to its revenue, is carrying the financial
burden higher than practical wisdom would justify. The policy of further severe internal
deflation added to the necessarily high extra taxation may easily defeat the right hon.
Gentleman's own purposes. If, for instance, 200,000, 300,000 or 400,000 additional
persons are thrown out of employment, the expenditure of keeping these persons,
however it may be reduced, will again destroy that very balance of the Budget for
which all our sacrifices have been made. Therefore, I hope and trust that the right hon.
Gentleman will review with great care all these questions of borrowing on capital

account by solvent bodies or solvent funds for the purposes of constructive development during the forthcoming winter. Do not let your panic lead you into further trouble. We may have gone far in one direction, but let us get back to the high road, and not simply plunge into the ditch on the opposite side.

I have a great difficulty this afternoon in criticising the economies and the taxes. I know their ugly faces one by one The various taxation problems of the country have been brought before me in the last five years in the most direct form. I feel a great difficulty in criticising individual economies, cuts and taxes, because I do not want in any way to break the solidarity of the national effort to place its housekeeping on a far stricter and more secure foundation. I do not want to do that at a time when a great party and its Leader have shown such inconceivable meanness—I can use no other word. It is surprising that men we have known all our lives in the House of Commons should dissociate themselves from all their declarations and the responsibilities they had undertaken, and devote themselves generally to manufacture the utmost party capital out of the tribulations of the country at the present time. Therefore, I, for one, will not attempt to examine, as I would otherwise have liked to do, all the relative hardships imposed by the different cuts and taxes, but generally I should like to say that I am very much surprised that my right hon. Friend has forgotten that Tea Duty which Mr. Churchill so mistakenly took off three or four years ago. He has forgotten all about it. I took it off, and there is no reason why he should not put it on. If it had not been taken off, it could not be put on. One might almost say that it was foresight on my part to prepare this reserve for this occasion. A tax remitted is a tax in reserve. Most certainly an old, well-tried tax should be a tax which should be brought in to meet an emergency. It would be possible, I am told—private Members have great difficulty in getting accurate figures, but I give them to the best of my ability—that the Tea Duty should have been imposed yielding £6,000,000. I suppose that the coffee and chicory group would have added another £500,000 to that. It could have been reimposed without raising the price of tea above what it was in 1928. Surely that might have played some part in the right hon. Gentleman's proposals. But the sugar story is more remarkable still.

Mr. George Hardie: The sugar subsidy is still more remarkable.

Mr. Churchill: But this story is surprising, as the hon. Gentleman will see. Sugar at present is 2-1/2d. a lb. The additon of 1-1/2d. a lb. would raise sugar to 4d. a lb. That would give the Exchequer nearly £20,000,000, and it would leave the price of sugar substantially lower than it was after the great and memorable remission which the right hon. Gentleman made in 1924. That appears to me to be a very striking fact. Not only is this £18,000,000 for the revenue, but the subsidy ceases to be paid. Really, when we consider all that is being done and all that we are going to support, I think that the right hon. Gentleman might have weighed and balanced these duties against some of the other steps he has found it his duty to take. But I am not, as I say, going further into these matters. The right hon. Gentleman has appealed for sacrifices from all, and I suggest that he should participate in this general process by making from time to time some sacrifices of his own pet idiosyncrasies. Although I have criticised the right hon. Gentleman's Budget, I am, as I said, going to vote for it in all its stages, and even if it were much worse than it is, I, and I think everyone on this side, would still unquestionably support him in this Budget and the same attitude will, in spite of any misgivings, be followed, in my belief, throughout the country as a whole.

But we cannot stop here. Surely there ought to come behind this Budget a larger and more carefully considered constructive and remedial plan, overtaking, overriding and mitigating the effects of this Budget, a plan which will deal with causes as well as with effects, and which will be constructive as well as merely disciplinary. This is the question I ask in conclusion. Can this Parliament achieve such a task? The situation changes from day to day. It is extremely uncertain and difficult to judge, but if this Parliament were able to make a contribution of this kind, it would be a very great advantage. Joint action in the first stages of a great change of policy would command a far higher degree of national unity than would ever be won in the fiercest and most successful electoral contest. Anxious as I am on party grounds, I admit, for a General Election, I am sure that Parliament, this Parliament, ought to try to discharge its full duty, and the instrument ought not to be broken and placed aside until it is definitely proved incapable of rendering the essential services required from it. A declaration by a majority of this House upon the principle of immediate Protection for industry and, as the right hon. Gentleman so rightly pointed out, for agriculture too, would fortify and consolidate our whole position, would give encouragement where it was most needed and would draw, clearly and plainly, the lines of battle between friend and foe. We should see the next step quite plainly, and those who had agreed to the first step would be able to take other steps together in loyalty and comradeship.

THE FINANCIAL SITUATION

September 29, 1931

Liverpool

On September 15 there occurred the so-called "Invergordon Mutiny," when the sailors of the Atlantic fleet, based at Invergordon, refused duty in protest against the loss of pay. The matter was resolved, but on September 21 the Gold Standard was suspended.

[Extract] . . . No Government can exist without a purpose and a plan. When the present Government was formed it had a purpose—to preserve the gold standard—and it had a plan—to balance the Budget; but the gold standard has gone and the balancing of the Budget will be finished next week. After that the Government have neither purpose nor plan, and a Government without purpose or plan is a dead thing.

The question of the moment is whether this Parliament and Government can find a new purpose and a new plan to give it a new lease of life, or must it die and must we out of new birth throes find new agencies to serve our bitter, grave, and urgent needs. There is no escape from this question, however unwelcome it may be. No vain regrets, no shrinking from the ordeal, no loud trumpeting will avail. This

Parliament must act or go. Is there, then, any new purpose or plan upon which this Parliament can act unitedly, with sincerity and vigour?

There is assuredly a purpose, a policy, a plan which is in all your minds. If pursued soberly and earnestly, without personal prejudice or party bias, it would give an honourable span of life to the present House of Commons. I mean, of course, a measure of protection for British industry and agriculture.

A tariff is not a quick or quack remedy for all our ills. It is only one part of a national policy; but presented as a necessary step in national self-regeneration, as a practical business measure, as a measure of Imperial reconstruction, it may become a bond of union for all the strongest forces in the country.

There is a need to find new revenue to mitigate the effect of the Budget. There is a need to balance healthily our exports and imports. There is a need to stimulate our flagging industries. Most of all, there is a need to rouse the spirit of Britain, to restore her self-confidence and resolution, to assert her authority and rights among the nations, to regather around the Mother Island the power and resources of the Empire. If this Parliament is incapable of giving any satisfaction to these needs, the sooner it is gone the better. (Loud cheers.)

I was brought up in the days of Queen Victoria. I saw our country at the head of the world; leader in so many spheres of social, industrial, and Imperial progress, sedate, serene, envied and honoured by all. I cannot bear now to see those standards dimmed. When I think of what we did in the Great War I ask myself, with millions of English folk: what have we done to lose our glories, and what can we do to bring them back? (Cheers.)

The greatness and prosperity of Britain has depended on three great glories and breadwinners—the Navy and Mercantile Marine, the Empire of India and the East, and the City of London. Without those it would have been impossible to maintain those superior standards of life and labour which have so long raised this country above all others in the world. The Socialist movement, which has grown so powerful in this century, attacked all three policies. It menaces our sea power, it undermines our Indian Empire, it has sapped the confidence of the world in the City of London.

If an election should come upon us, the duty of every loyal-hearted man and woman is plain—namely, to root out from Parliament all those subversive forces which have worn down the strength of Britain.

The responsibility for driving us off the gold standard rests mainly on the countries which have impounded the gold. They have no right to reproach this country. We have always done our duty; we have tried to maintain the standards of sound finance in the world, which was taking every advantage of our high conduct. We have done all we could to promote the rebuilding of Europe after the War, and we have laboured our utmost to fulfil our obligations in the strictest manner. But the burden that has been thrown upon us by world causes and the action of other Governments has proved beyond our strength to bear.

It may be that the pound sterling apart from gold would become a new international medium. If so, England would be the leader of a society of nations embracing a large part of the world, all perhaps except France and America, who would increasingly trade with one another on the basis of a stabilized pound sterling.

If that position were reached the two gold-hoarding countries would have to come to terms and make common cause with us and mankind. Therein lies the solution of our difficulties. If we are to reach this conclusion we must put British grit and character behind the pound sterling.

We must rebuild, consolidate. We must join hands with one another in comradeship and effort to improve our position and even to hold what is left. We must be strong and self-reliant, and we must have a stronger system of government.

We must have a Parliament containing a large majority of members united in a resolve to lift our country from the ruts and quagmires into which it has fallen. I have asked myself, as you may have done no doubt, whether the present Parliament can achieve such a task, and whether the present National Government would be strong enough to take the necessary measures.

ELECTION ADDRESS

October 10, 1931

Grove Hall, Wanstead

Churchill's arguments for an immediate General Election were shared by the leading Conservatives. Parliament was dissolved on October 7, and MacDonald and Baldwin appealed for "a doctor's mandate." With Labour in chaos and the Liberals in shambles, the result was not difficult to foresee.

[Extract] . . . There has been no more ignominious or abject exhibition than was made by Mr. Henderson and his friends when they fled from their duty and prevented every other person from doing his best to pull the country out of the mess they had got it into.

The Conservative Party has put country before party. Is that spirit of putting country before party being shown by all who are playing, or seeking to play, the part? What is the National Liberal candidate going to do in the Epping Division? I see it has been reported that Mr. Comyns Carr is going to come forward as National Liberal candidate in support of the Prime Minister's policy of a free hand to deal with the economic question. I presume Mr. Comyns Carr is what you would call a Samuelite. There are other Liberalites, Simonites, Lloyd Georgeites, and there may be some others. (Laughter.) What is Mr. Comyns Carr doing here? I put this question direct to Sir Herbert Samuel—Does he approve of Mr. Comyns Carr's hostile candidature to me in this constituency, or does he not? Whatever is his opinion, let him declare it. If he says that he approves of Mr. Comyns Carr's candidature, then how can he complain that the Conservatives are attacking him in his own seat at Darwen. If he disapproves of it, then it is clear that all we have to deal with is an unofficial interloper with wrecking propensities. Mr. Baldwin at Birmingham last night deprecated Conservative opposition to Sir Herbert Samuel. I, too, would share in that expression of opinion, but surely if such a doctrine is put forward by the leader of the Conservative Party the leader of the Samuelite Party should also speak in his turn and enjoin the same forbearance.

In my judgment going off the gold standard was a grievous and lamentable event, but every effort was made to avert it. No foreigner can say that we did not make every effort to avert that step. We at any rate have conducted our national finance and international finance upon a sounder basis than many of the foreign countries who have recently seen fit to read us lectures. The pound is worth whatever British grit and energy can make it, and that is no mean asset. I see no reason why the pound sterling, although divorced from gold, should not become itself a medium of exchange between all those countries except the two who have gathered and hoarded the gold. I suggest an international conference should be called to deal with the fall in prices, but to support our recommendations there we must do our utmost to establish sterling as a medium of exchange between the largest number of countries in the world. All will depend upon the establishment of a Government which is known to have nothing to do with Socialism in any shape or form.

THE NEW PARLIAMENT

October 11, 1931

Epping

[Extract] ... You need not fear to give plenary powers to a constitutional administration. A patriotic Parliament and an active public opinion will control or guide their use. But after all we have been through, and are going through, we must have a long spell of steady government under men who have a fair chance and a free hand to revive the greatness of Britain, restore unity to her Empire, and bestow prosperity upon all its peoples.

The new Parliament must govern our fiscal policy. As Conservatives we are convinced that an effective measure of protection for British industry and British agriculture must hold a leading place in any scheme of national self-regeneration. . . .

The doubting, incoherent policy of the Socialists in India has not only brought discord and suffering upon that large proportion of the human race who dwell in India, but has impaired our own position in the eyes of the world. . . . I hold now as always that the report of the Simon Commission should be the starting point from which we should approach the Indian problem. But law and order must be firmly and impartially maintained throughout the Indian Empire, and no constitutional experiment must challenge the ultimate responsibility of any organism of Indian administration to the British Crown and Parliament.

ELECTION ADDRESS

October 12, 1931

Epping

[Extract] ... The Liberal Party is split into at least three well-marked divisions. There are the Simonites, who have thrown in their lot boldly with the national cause; the Samuelites, about whom I am unable to give any correct information; and the Lloyd Georgeites, the most united party in this country—small, but united by bonds far above the ordinary connexions and associations of political life. (Laughter.) I may fairly ask Mr. Comyns Carr to which of these three groups he belongs. The first great object before us is clear, plain, almost brutal—it is to inflict a decisive defeat on Socialism, to let the whole world see that the democracy of Great Britain has put aside those false guides who have steadily but remorselessly led us to the edge of catastrophe. We have to beat them out of Parliament; to reduce their representation in Parliament to an absolute minimum. The second object is to get as many Conservatives into the new House of Commons as possible. We seek and welcome allies, but must be the main front of the whole of the forces which are fighting for the salvation of the country. I hope this great movement will mean one more spring from the old lion, one more attempt on the part of Great Britain to hold her own and assert her authority in every quarter of the globe. Foreigners have come to think that we are demoralized by Socialism. I hope that the new Government will mean good-bye to all that.

ELECTION BROADCASTS

October 13, 1931

Epping

[Extract] ... There could be no better example of the excessive claims and pretensions of other parties and groups at the present time than is afforded by the list of speakers who are to be allowed to use the broadcast during the election. Out of nine voices which are to be heard there is only one Conservative. Mr. Baldwin is the sole Conservative speaker who is to be allowed to use this marvellous new facility for addressing the people. The rest of the programme is made up of five members of the late Socialist Government and three Liberals. This is carrying the suppression of Conservative opinion beyond the bounds of reason and fair play. It is not fair to the electors as it gives them an altogether false impression of the forces at work in the nation to-day. The Conservative Party welcomes the aid of sincere allies from the Labour and Liberal Parties in order that a decisive condemnation of Socialism should be pronounced by the nation at this grievous juncture. Great sacrifices have been made by the Conservative Party for that purpose. No similar sacrifices have been made by their Liberal and Labour allies. All that the Samuelite Liberals have done is to withdraw a number of mad-dogging candidates who had no chance of victory, and were in many cases without the necessary funds to fight.

"A POSITION OF IGNOMINY"

October 16, 1931

Epping

[Extract] ... Two and a half years of Socialist government has reduced the country to a position of ignominy. When the crisis came some of the Socialist leaders stood to their guns and faced the music, but the great bulk of them simply ran away. They became the Opposition, and tried to make capital out of those very cuts, nine-tenths of which they had themselves approved before their Cabinet broke up. In a very rough and stern manner the National Government has balanced the Budget. Now they have to balance trade. That can be done by increasing exports and decreasing imports. If we are to win back our position in the world it is absolutely necessary to call in without delay a new patriotic Parliament which is not unduly hampered by party cries and pledged only to do its best for the general good.

THE "CALLOW, HALF-BAKED, HALF-FLEDGED SOCIALIST PARTY"

October 19, 1931

Burnley, Lancashire

[Extract] ... The main issue is the defeat and condemnation of the Socialist Party. That party has with base ingratitude broken and devoured the Liberal Party and has put in their place a far feebler representation of democratic and progressive thought. They have proved the feeblest champions of democracy and the working class the country has ever seen. The rise of that party has also been a public misfortune to trade unionism. Far more than that, the Socialist Party has been directly detrimental to the best interests of the country.

No country can less afford the rash experiment of putting a callow, half-baked, half-fledged Socialist Party in power. We have world depression and at home we have a Socialist Government. Those two together have created the present situation.

LABOUR UNFIT TO GOVERN
October 23, 1931
Forest Gate

[Extract] ... The behaviour of the Socialist Ministers in the crisis showed more clearly than anything else that the Socialist Party at this stage of their development is unfitted to govern. But let me do them justice. They have a new plan now. They have a sort of feeling that if they got hold of the banks they could make things much better for themselves and their friends. These men, who admit that they were incapable of carrying out their duty and could not even conduct a general strike so as to make a fight of it, now want to thrust their butterfingers into managing the banks. I always wanted to see Conservatives and Liberals working together against the common opponent, and I am delighted that in so many parts of the country they are working together. They are not doing so in my division. I have got a Liberal opponent, but I do not let a little thing like that influence me at all. ("What about Lloyd George?") I am sorry that we have not got Mr. Lloyd George with us. I did my best to bring him along. I am sorry indeed that the great wartime Prime Minister should not be with his country in the perils of peace as he was in the perils of war. However, the country will not run short of stout fellows to defend her interests in the hour of need.

ELECTION ADDRESS
October 24, 1931
Theydon Bois

[Extract] ... I think the National Government is quite right in asking for a free hand. We are not asking Liberals to commit themselves to any scheme. In fact one has not been drawn up and many disagreements will have to be surmounted before it is produced. Giving the Government a free hand does not mean that they are going to act like Tsars of Russia, Lenins, or Mussolinis. Parliament will be there. I will be there. I will not hesitate to criticize anything which I believe is not for the good of the country. I believe that we can bring more prosperity to our people if we modify our policy in the direction of a tariff, even a tariff designed to enable us to grow more of our food. If such a tariff is framed skilfully and managed scientifically I do not think it will add to the cost of living.

THE NEW PARLIAMENT

October 30, 1931

Constituency Meeting, Chingford

The General Election was a landslide for the Conservatives and their Labour and Liberal allies, winning 521 seats. Labour was reduced to 52; the Liberals to 33. Lloyd George's "party" now consisted of 4. Of the former Labour Cabinet only Lansbury retained his seat.

[Extract] ... The election result is a marvellous expression of the love which the British people have for their country, and for its fame and power. The condemnation of the foreign-made doctrines of Socialism is overwhelming. Foreign nations who thought our day was done have now their answer.

Universal suffrage has sent the largest majority of Tory members to Parliament which has ever been dreamed of. It is our national well-being and our ancient power which the nation wishes to see restored, and the electors have called into being a free Parliament to do it. The new Parliament is free as no Parliament for generations has been free. The members have appealed to their constituents for a free hand. They have been granted it in overflowing measure.

I hope that the new Parliament will be a true Council of State and that it will take broad and long views of the public interest. Opinion must be freely and fearlessly expressed, and the conclusions of the majority of the House, at every stage, must rule the policy of the State. The responsibilities which weigh upon the Government are even more intense than those which rest upon the House of Commons. They must be a Government of action and of clear-cut policies. They must pronounce without hesitation upon the fiscal problem, the currency problem, the Indian problem, and the Imperial problem. Upon the true solution of these high matters the future of Great Britain depends.

This is no time for weak compromises or ambiguous formulas designed to promote a semblance of unity among individual politicians. An integrity of thought and policy should inspire the Government and sustain the new House of Commons if we are to be worthy of your trust. If this is not forthcoming and a mere amalgam of irreconcilable opinions is produced, the House will have to take charge of the situation itself and produce harmonious and effective combinations.

The Conservative Party has made great sacrifices. It would be well advised at this juncture to encourage its allies to set their feet firmly on the path of national and Imperial regeneration. It would be far better if the measures which we all know are requisite to revive our national strength could be taken upon an authority greater than that of any single party. If they are not taken, then the inalienable responsibilities of the majority of the new Parliament will have to be asserted, and that Parliament will continue to enjoy its plenary powers.

It would be very wrong to put the country to the expense and uncertainty of another election. I disagreed entirely with Sir Herbert Samuel when he said that before a tariff could be imposed—a permanent general tariff—it would be necessary to have another General Election. How much longer are we to go on with that process, and how many more times is the nation to assert its will? We can halt between two opinions no longer. There can be no revival of trade until this matter is settled.

ACTION ON TARIFF

November 11, 1931

House of Commons

I do not think that I need quarrel with the temper of the speech which has just been delivered from the Front Opposition Bench by one of its surviving occupants, and, in so far as I refer to it at all, it must be to confirm the general accuracy of the statement which he made to us about the Savings Bank. It is perfectly true that under legislation which goes back, I believe, to 1861 but which was renewed in 1921, there is power to draw upon Savings Bank deposits for national and other funds, the whole, of course, being based upon the security of the Consolidated Fund and, as a matter of fact every Chancellor in the last 10 years, I myself included, used such methods. When the late Chancellor of the Exchequer adopted this process last year—I admit to a much larger extent than it had previously been adopted—the matter was raised in the Public Accounts Committee of which my hon. Friend the Member for Farnham (Mr. A. M. Samuel) was chairman, and the proceedings were approved by the Public Accounts Committee. I am bound to confirm that statement, as it has been made and as the Leader of the Opposition specially appealed to me upon the subject. I do not believe that it played the remotest part in determining the decision of the electorate, but still the facts are as I have stated.

I should like, before embarking upon serious argument, to explain briefly my personal position in relation to His Majesty's Government and to the new triumvirate which rules over our fortunes. I had to sever myself from my right hon. Friend the Lord President of the Council in the last Parliament on the question of India—on the question of holding out hopes of Dominion status to India, and responsible government at the centre and, generally the policy of the Gandhi-Irwin Pact. I made my differences public and they still continue. The Prime Minister at the Election went out of his way to attack me and my finance although of course the Government of the day, which contained many of those who are now his principal colleagues was collectively responsible with me for it. I had some acrimonious correspondence with the Prime Minister upon the subject. Lastly, there was the Home Secretary, who, when he was quite sure that the Conservative voters in Darwen were going to play the game, sent, on the eve of the poll, a message urging that my opponent should be elected and that I should be excluded from this House. I am not making much of this because I have got through. [Hon. Members: "Where is he?"] Here we both are, but I do say that all these matters which were before my constituents at the time when they voted, entitle me to claim an attitude of perfect independence so far as the triumvirate is concerned. However, I am glad to be able to announce to the House that, if I may without disrespect borrow a phrase from the Gracious Speech: "My relations with foreign Powers continue to be friendly." I shall not withhold from my right hon. Friends my advice and counsel. My attitude will be one of discriminating benevolence, but I shall not fail to warn them, in good time and quite plainly, upon any occasion when I see them falling short, either by neglect or by action, of the course which is appointed for them. I shall do my best in that way to contribute to what we all hope will be their successful conduct of affairs.

I must say that, coming into this House after having sat in previous Parliaments, one sees many strange sights and many surprises. Little did I expect to see the right hon. Gentleman the Member for Bow and Bromley (Mr. Lansbury) the Leader of the Labour party in this House. I do not throw any reflection upon his ability or his good fellowship, which entitle him to that office, but I thought he was too low down in the hierarchy. However, there is at any rate one Front Bench from which "the old gang" has been cleared off, so young blood has its turn. But, Mr. Speaker, it is not inappropriate that the right hon. Gentleman should lead what is left of the Parliamentary representation of the Labour party. More than anyone else he has, I think, stood for the policy of what I would call the dole, the whole dole, and nothing but the dole. He has, with perfect sincerity and with many agreeable turns of phrase and fancy, held up to us always that dim Utopia which would reduce our civilisation to one vast national soup kitchen, surrounded by innumerable municipal bathing pools. But the working-classes of this country wanted more than that. They wanted to see capital and credit, science and organisation, devoted to the elevation of the material welfare of their class and of the Commonwealth as a whole, and they have voted as we have seen. Therefore, it is not unfitting that the right hon. Gentleman should now be left to champion as well as he can the cause of Socialism amid ruins which are very largely of his own creation.

I now come to my right hon. Friend the Lord President, and there also I can find great matter for surprise. During the years when I worked so closely with the right hon. Gentleman—almost a pair of brothers working together—I always was alert to catch his inspiration and to profit by the sterling qualities for which he is renowned, and, if there was one doctrine that my right hon. Friend inculcated upon me more than any other, it was his abhorrence of coalitions. Why, Sir, he even spoke in public rebuking some of the younger Members of this House, warning them of the dangers of hunting with other packs beside their own, and therefore it is certainly surprising to find him now the champion coalitionist, though doubtless for a very good reason. I am sure no one is more aware of the dangers of such a course than my right hon. Friend, and I am sure he will be reminded of those dangers whenever he should chance to walk across the portals of the Carlton Club.

Lastly, I come to the Prime Minister. I am sorry he is not here, because I would rather say what I have to say in his presence, but I quite understand the work he has to do outside. It is less than nine months ago that I listened to the Prime Minister, standing at that Box, urging us all to vote for a Bill re-legalising the general strike and re-imposing the political levy, and I remember that on that occasion I was so indiscreet, as it now turns out, as to describe him as "the boneless wonder." It is surprising now to see that he has become the main, if not the sole, prop of our harassed State, to see him the saviour of the Gold Standard—no, I beg pardon, of the pound sterling—to see him at the head of a Ministry of all the talents—well, I suppose I ought to say "nearly all the talents," as I want to be respectful to my right hon. Friends behind me—and to see him leading a House which contains the largest majority of Conservatives and of Protectionists which has ever sat here.

I pay my tribute to the inestimable service which the country has received at the hands of the Prime Minister. All my life I have opposed the growth of Socialism. He has done more to check it, and for the time being to destroy it, than any other man could have done. I have seen the Socialist party in this House grow from its smallest beginnings. A group of miners' Members and a handful of so-called intellectuals were all there were a few years ago, and from that it rose till it was a party which afforded a foundation for Government and finally became the largest party in this House. The wheel has turned full circle, and there is the Labour party back where it started from 20 years ago.

I cannot pretend to be sorry. In all that period they have done no good; they have devoured the Liberal party and supplanted it, and have shown themselves the feeblest champions of the democracy they claim to represent; they have misled the trade unions into party politics; they have not contributed a single helpful scheme, they have set no great Measure, produced no great policy, which has been serviceable to the Commonwealth or even to those whose interests they claim specially to represent. I cannot help feeling that they led the country to the verge of a catastrophe, and for my part I am exceedingly glad to see that the Prime Minister has had the courage to set aside his life's work and to free our country at this critical time, for a long spell of years at any rate, from the incubus and dangers which have brought us so much evil.

All these matters belong to the past. They form a theme for satire, the material for history, but they belong to the past. "The tumult and the shouting" of the Election have died away; the excitements of the formation or the re-formation of the Government are over. All that the people can give with their votes has been given; all that the newspapers can give with their powerful articles and headlines has been given. That phase is over, and the Prime Minister and those associated with him are fairly and squarely up against the job, the task which is before them, a task superlatively difficult, grim and grave, not only because it is difficult, but because also of the expectations aroused, but a task splendid, inspiring, in the rewards which would attend its successful discharge, a task which carries with it in its accomplishment the wishes of everyone who cares about this country.

I am not expecting the Government, as the hon. Gentleman opposite rather complained, to confront us at this juncture with a cut-and-dried solution of all the great national issues which are pending. I should think that was most unreasonable. They are themselves exhausted by the Election, which was most strenuous. They have only just come together. I do not believe they have ever yet sat as a Cabinet in their new form, and it would be absurd to expect them and unfair to press them to come forward with plain, clear-cut decisions on these grave and thorny issues. But there are, I think, three questions on which I invite the House this afternoon to ask for some further and better particulars.

The right hon. Gentleman the Leader of the Opposition asked whether we could be given more information about India, either by a speech or in some other way, and of course it rests with him to ask for the facilities of Debate. The handful of gentlemen there who hold the official authority are almost the only channel by which, so far as I know at present, the arrangements of Debate can be made. But I am not sure whether a Debate on India at this juncture would necessarily be very opportune, and if whoever speaks for the Government can give us a reasonable assurance that no far-reaching commitments or treaties will be entered into or made without this House having in the first instance had an opportunity of understanding the issues involved, and of discussing them, I for one shall be quite content that this matter of India shall stand over for the present.

Then the Prime Minister referred, in his speech at the Guildhall, to the stabilisation of sterling. His words were judiciously vague on this matter, but still they had a quality of definiteness about them which I believe was undesigned. I did not gather that the Government have taken the decision to stabilise sterling at any fixed parity or at any fixed date. Our plight and the world plight is due to many adverse factors, to high tariffs, which have obstructed the free flow of trade between nations, to Asiatic disorder, to wild speculation, to War debts and reparations; and there are some who say that we are still living beyond our means. All these are adverse factors, but one fact stands forth, in my opinion, more clear-cut and precise and obvious than any of these. I mean the fact that one-third of the whole gold supply of the world—that is to say, I suppose, 15 years of the annual gold production—has been impounded and buried and sterilised in the last two or three years and is, for all intents and purposes, entirely removed from any part in our affairs.

There may be other things. You may say that all our troubles should not be put on to that, but I do not seek to do so; I do not put the whole of our troubles on to the sequestration of gold. There may be other matters, but here is a perfectly definite point to make for, and I trust and hope that the Government will take international action by means of a conference and use the whole influence that we possess to induce the countries which have hoarded gold to make it again serviceable for its function as a standard of value. [An Hon. Member: "How?"] There are many ways. If that cannot be done, they should endeavour to establish what I venture to call a kind of Esperanto currency on the basis of sterling with the friends of sterling. I agree very much with what was said by my right hon. Friend the Member for Hillhead (Sir R. Horne) in the speech which he made out of doors the other day, in which he urged that the inconvenience of a non-fixed pound sterling should be faced for some time longer until we have had the opportunity of negotiating in international conference with those other countries and know where we are about the hoarded stores of gold.

There is a third matter which, like the working classes, must not be overlooked—Protection and this controversy about whether we shall go on being Free Trade or shall become a Protectionist country. Quite a lot of candidates at the

Election were very excited about it as far as I could see—Conservative candidates—and I believe that judging from the state of the House, quite a large number have survived and are here. I hope that His Majesty's Government are going to be sensible about Protection. In my view, this Parliament has the fullest mandate to apply any measure of Protection which it deems wise. The circumstances of the General Election were such that they do not leave the Prime Minister and the two party leaders associated with him the sole or final judges of what the nation voted for. The House, too, shares the free hand for which they appealed. The Election, as it proceeded, largely shaped itself and took its own irresistible course. Every Member of this House knows what his declarations were to his constituents and what his answers to questions were. He knows what he put in his election address; he knows what his relations with his constituency became and were during the course of the Election, and what constitutes good faith as between him and his constituents. Every Member, therefore, in my submission to the House, is a judge of the mandate which he has individually received, and the sum of those individual mandates constitutes the effective mandate of the House of Commons.

I do not presume to speak for anybody but myself. I am sure that the overwhelming wish and intention of the electorate was that we should now definitely abandon our Free Trade system and make a substantial and scientific experiment in general Protection. Others may hold a different view, but my belief is that a very large majority of the House would feel fully authorised by their constituents to give a decision upon the matter of a decisive and fundamental change in our fiscal policy. The country expects it; the world expects it; and a Parliament has assembled which in its lifetime will assuredly enforce it. I cannot see the need for an inquiry into the principles of Protection and Free Trade. We have been debating this topic for the best part of a hundred years. It is not a matter which requires consideration, because every politician must have been considering it all his life. I, for one, accept the fact that the nation has decided in favour of a real and great change in our fiscal policy.

I hope that the Prime Minister will not fall into the error of adopting inquiries as a means of delay. Those of my colleagues who were present in the last House of Commons will remember the lamentable story of the inquiries into the dole scandal. There were three successive inquiries, not because the Government did not know about the scandal and what ought to be done to put it right; they knew perfectly well; the inquiries were to put off the evil day of having to decide something. The Government waited about in the hope that something would turn up, and in the end it did turn up with a vengeance. I cannot see the necessity of an inquiry as to whether we should have Free Trade or Protection, and it would in the nature of things be absurd.

There is, however, a series of inquiries which could indeed absorb all the attention to His Majesty's Government, inquiries not into the principle of Protection, but how to apply that principle to the vastly complicated industrial system of these islands, and to the industries which have grown up tier upon tier during a century of Free Trade, which have grown up on the basis of free imports, buying them from wherever they can regardless of whether they are dumped or not. To apply Protection to that system is certainly a matter which requires delicate handling and planning. The application of such a system, also, must be considered in relation to our shipping and our vital export trade. All this is a subject for inquiry. Lastly, you have, of course, to consider the application of this principle in regard to the special circumstances of the time, such as the devaluation of the pound sterling. We all agree that these matters must engage the attention of the Government. These are not inquiries of a formal character; they are only part of the ordinary work and duty of the Ministers of the day. They are not inquiries from which any reports would emerge; we do not expect them to present us with reports; we expect them to present us with legislation.

Then there is the case of agriculture. When I went about the country at the last Election, I found a universal feeling among urban dwellers that we are far too dependent upon foreign food. It is necessary that we should be dependent upon overseas staple foods because without overseas supplies of cereals and meat we could never have produced or maintained the population of a first-class Power. We are, however, dependent to an extent which is injurious upon foreign fruit, vegetables, bacon and dairy produce, which could be grown quite as well here if satisfactory organisation were made, and which would be an enormous source of help and employment to the people of this country. How to organise this so that abundant supplies of home produce will be available step by step in proportion as the foreign produce is restricted or excluded, is indeed a subject which should absorb the attention, not only of the Minister of Agriculture, but of his principal colleagues. If the purpose is achieved, I do not expect that the House will quarrel as to the methods; the end is what we have in view. That the nation contemplates a profound regeneration of its agriculture, I have no doubt, and, as the Mover of the Address in his most charming speech yesterday pointed out, the town populations have given their assent to the favourable consideration of this problem.

No post in the Government is more important than the one held by my right hon. Friend the Minister of Agriculture. It is a key position. It is, I believe, well known that the right hon. Member for Carnarvon Boroughs (Mr. Lloyd George), whose absence we all deplore, or ought to deplore, said that if he had joined the first National Government, he would himself have asked for the post of Minister of Agriculture. That is certainly an indication of the immense significance and importance attached to that position. I earnestly hope that the right hon. Gentleman will be sustained and supported by his colleagues in organising the whole of this vast business, and that he will at an early date, not give us his plans—that we do not expect—but show us the direction in which he is advancing and convince us of the resolution which inspires him.

No one will grudge the necessary time to prepare these projects. The matter is in one respect, however, very urgent indeed. This mighty country, living by exports and by world connections, cannot afford to remain long in uncertainty about what its fiscal policy is to be. Nations have prospered under Free Trade and nations have prospered under Protection, but no great complicated community has or ever could prosper standing about marking time in No Man's Land, unable to declare whether it is proceeding under the Free Trade or the Protectionist hypothesis because difficulties have arisen which prevent a coherent view from being expressed. There are endless arguments on either side and both Free Trade and Protection have their advantages and disadvantages, but to go on halting between two opinions will be to combine the disadvantages of both and the benefits of neither. All British industry is waiting tip toe at the present time to know under what conditions it is to carry on its work. A thousand enterprises hang poised upon the Government's signal. We dare not allow the whole main block of British industry to be left needlessly—I recognise the necessity for a period of delay—in the same position of harassing uncertainty, of cruel wanton uncertainty in which the safeguarded industries were left during the whole of the last Parliament, when they became the object of the formidable hatred of the late Chancellor of the Exchequer. Above all, I hope that our fiscal system will not become the sport of personal differences, however conscientious, within the organism of the Government. We must have a theme in its integrity. A tariff which is a result of careful and patient adjustment of personal differences may have some merits as an historical document, but it is probably quite unrelated to our fiscal requirements at any point. I have been a Free Trader all my life, but I have been forced during recent years to abandon that system, and I am very grateful to constituents and colleagues who have put no pressure upon me to go faster at any stage than I felt personally inclined to go, and to go in mental comfort. As I have been forced to abandon that position, all the more do I desire, now that one great scheme of thought has been discarded, that we should adopt the other in its integrity, give it a fair chance, and bring it into operation in accordance with all that modern experience and modern industry can show us on the subject. If a National Government means anything, it should be capable of solutions like that, solutions which, as I say, arise from the cold and scientific study of the actual facts and figures of the case. We admit that there may be delay during preparation, but in the course of this Debate we hope to hear other Ministers explaining further the statement of the Prime Minister that the general position will not be prejudiced at all during the period of delay.

The Prime Minister spoke yesterday about dumping. He said it was a tendentious expression. I never knew there was any great doubt about what we mean by dumping. I always understood that dumping was the sale in this country of articles at a price below either the price at which they are sold or the cost of production in the country of origin, whichever is the greater. That has always been the definition upon which Free Traders and Protectionists have been agreed. But I rather gathered, though perhaps I may be corrected later, that the Prime Minister was not contemplating preventing that kind of dumping in the interval, but was only contemplating the limiting of imports during this period when he is preparing his plans to what those imports were in the corresponding months of last year, that there was to be a kind of quota, which was not to be exceeded. Well, I should like to know what is the purpose of the Government, because last year there was a great deal of dumping, and of Russian dumping, far below the cost of production or the price in the country of origin, and great injury was done; and, if we admit that injury was done, surely we ought not to insist that a similar measure of injury should be done again in the interval to which I have referred.

I thank the House for having given me so much attention, but let me say that I do not envy the Ministers their office. I have held high office for nearly a quarter of a century, and I know how many thorns there are to all those brilliant roses. Moreover, in this Government many have taken offices lower than those to which their rank and position in politics might justly have entitled them, and have made sacrifices in that way. I doubt if there is anybody—the number would be very few—who has not made heavy pecuniary sacrifices and sacrifices of leisure to undertake his duty. I do not envy them at all; I respect them. I do not envy them their offices, but I do envy them their opportunities. Those may be envied by anyone, wherever he sits.

But if their opportunity is great so is their responsibility. It is only one step from the sublime to the ridiculous. The question which we have to ask ourselves continually is this: Is the National Government going to be above party Government or below party Government? The nation voted for a National Government believing that it was some form of Government which would provide a superior solution of our problems, lift our affairs to a higher plane, and that is still their hope. Have we found, or are we going to find, those superior advantages, or have we merely transferred the ordinary party Debates which in bygone days have blown themselves out harmlessly in the proper place, the debating chamber, to the secret, vital, inmost recesses of the executive councils. If that were the case, as I hope it is not, then I think we should have lost more than we have gained.

The Government must have a soul—even a party soul is better than no soul at all—and paralysis which invaded the supreme centre of action would leave us with rulers—who, with every credential and all the power in their hands, found themselves without a message, without a theme, without a plan. If the National Government were to lead to national impotence there would be a terrible disappointment, with a terrible reckoning to follow. But, happily, to-day we are not called upon to lend ourselves to such sombre alternatives or possibilities. We have every right to believe that when the Government have got together they will choose together, and that from their speedy and early action a definite coherent policy will emerge. If the National Government can lift our affairs to a higher plane of efficiency and action, if they can revive our prosperity, if they can raise again our fame and power throughout the world, then those who have taken part in creating it will have a shining page in British history. As they march forward on that path they are entitled to the support of every one of us here, and all and everyone, wherever they sit, will wish them heartily Godspeed.

STATUTE OF WESTMINSTER BILL

November 20, 1931

House of Commons

The Secretary of State for Dominion affairs and his late colleague in the Socialist Administration have laid before us the case for this Bill in very learned and worthy addresses. They no doubt concocted the Measure together when they were members of the same Administration, and it is a happy conjunction of events that they should be able to present it this morning in unison, simultaneously and concurrently, from both Front Benches. I hope the House, with its usual courtesy to minorities, will be willing to tolerate an expression of opinion from a Conservative quarter, not indeed of opposition, but rather of caution and restraint. I hope the House will also endorse the assertion of one or two fixed, unyielding points. It is high time that we had some fixed unyielding points in our political philosophy. For a good many years we have proceeded complacently upon an ebbing tide and few there are who have not yielded to the easy going sentiment and lassitude of the age. Now we are called upon to express all the general conclusions of the Imperial Conference, and all the good-natured emotion which sustains them, in the hard language of statute law which has resulted in the introduction of this Bill.

The Secretary of State for Dominion Affairs congratulated himself upon this Measure, but I cannot congratulate His Majesty's Government on this occasion. They have constituted themselves the heirs, they are the representatives, of the most splendid expression of the love and loyalty of the British people for their country and for the cohesion of the Empire of which our records bear witness. They possess a greater majority than dreamland ever portrayed. This majority has been largely produced by the votes and by the heart-felt patriotism of many millions of very poor people. It is, I think, bad luck—I say it sincerely, because it is a coincidence—it is bad luck that the very first and almost the sole Measure of the Gracious Speech should happen to be the Bill which we are asked to read a Second time to-day. When all the generous sentiments in which all parties have bathed themselves during recent years have to be reduced to the language of Acts of Parliament, the result is not only pedantic, it is painful, and, to some at any rate, it will almost be repellent. Anyone who likes to read the Clauses of the Bill will understand quite well the aspect that I am expressing.

I wish to divide my examination of this Measure this morning into three parts—its effect upon the Empire, its effect upon Ireland, and its potential effect upon India. Like everybody else in the late Conservative Administration, I was involved in and am responsible for the Imperial Conference declarations of 1926. In all our self-governing Dominions there have been for many years two parties on Imperial questions. One party has set the Imperial connection at its highest; the other has set it at the minimum; and these two parties have disputed against each other in Canada, in Australia, in New Zealand and in South Africa. The declarations of 1926 have removed this issue altogether from the arena of Dominion politics. We accepted in this Motherland the view of those who wish to state the Imperial obligation and Imperial ties at their minimum; we abandoned the whole apparatus of sovereignty and constitutional law to which our ancestors, and even the later Victorians, had attached the greatest importance. Remembering that, and remembering the atmosphere of those days, not long gone, and the spirit of those days, I cannot think that we were wrong, and I do not think that we are wrong now. I feel that we are bound, where the great self-governing Dominions of the Crown are concerned, boldly to grasp the larger hope, and to believe, in spite of anything that may be written in Acts of Parliament, that all will come right, nay, all will go better and better between Great Britain and her offspring.

I had, however, misgivings at the time, in 1926. I had misgivings that we were needlessly obliterating old, famous landmarks and signposts, which, although archaic, have a historic importance and value. I remember that that great statesman, the late Lord Balfour, with whom I talked this matter over very often, answered me, and to some extent re-assured me, by saying, "I do not believe in wooden guns." I thought that a very pregnant remark. He saw no advantage in preserving an assertion of rights and powers on which, in practice, we should not find it possible effectively to base ourselves. I still repose faith in the calm, lambent wisdom of that great man in his later years.

It follows from this acceptance, as I am bound to accept responsibility, among others, for the conclusions of 1926, that I am bound also to face the ordeal of seeing them embodied, with all the awkwardness of the process, in practical legislation. The legislation, however—and this is a question which the House is free to resolve—the legislation to fulfil the purpose may be well-conceived or it may be ill-conceived. It may easily give an untoward bias in interpretation upon many points, and that is certainly a matter which we must examine. I could, indeed, wish that it were possible to remit this Measure to a Joint Committee of both Houses of Parliament, where all the unequalled legal authority and constitutional knowledge of the House of Lords could contribute its constructive touch to the shaping of this most important and memorable Statute.

The Attorney-General is not with us. He, I understand, presided over a committee of lawyers who actually drafted this Bill. The Attorney-General at that time, when he was drafting the Bill, was in the full flush of his ardent enthusiasm at having newly embraced the Socialist ideal. He had cast aside his Liberalism and had seen the light, and he was, perhaps, hardly in a normal condition. It may well be that, if the Attorney-General, now that he has leisure and now that he is in a different political environment and atmosphere, might easily, in reviewing his work of last year, be more fortunate in the phraseology and terms in which he expressed the purposes to which we were committed by the Conference of 1926. But, when all is said and done, I should not be prepared myself, nor would, I dare say, a good many of my friends who take an interest in these matters, to vote against the principle of this Measure in its Second Reading stage. I see that some of my hon. Friends have on the Paper a proposal to move the rejection of the Bill. I hope that they will not carry that through to its extreme conclusion, because I think it would only create a false issue in the minds of the public. If large numbers of our fellow-subjects in the Dominions like to think, and like to see it in print, that the bonds of Empire rest only upon tradition, good will and good sense, it is not our policy—except as I shall hereafter mention—it is not our policy or our interest to gainsay them.

But there I think we must call a halt. At this point we enter the region of special obligations. These special obligations, entered into between the Mother-country and the various Dominions, have been strongly affirmed by all the great self-governing Dominions of the Crown, and we see the results of their inclinations and wishes on the text of this Statute. We see them in Clauses 7 and 8. Canada, for instance, stipulates that nothing in this Act shall be deemed to apply to the repeal, amendment, or alteration of the various British North America Acts from 1867 to 1930. The Commonwealth of Australia and the Dominion of New Zealand stipulate that nothing in the Act shall be deemed to alter their constitutions under the Imperial Acts which have called them into being. They assert the inviolability, so far as they are concerned, of the Imperial Statutes upon which their houses are founded. It has not been left for us to make these claims. It is the Dominions who have made them for themselves.

But in the case of the Irish Free State there is also a special obligation which does not find its reservation within the corners of this Statute. It is a special obligation to which, I think, we are bound to pay the greatest attention. I mean, of course, the Irish Treaty of 1922, or the Articles of Agreement as it is sometimes called. I am well acquainted with this. Curiously enough, it has been my duty not only to have charge in this House of the Transvaal Constitution Act of 1906, which was the parent and forerunner of the Act of Union of South Africa of 1909, but also I was the Minister in charge of the Irish Free State Constitution Act of 1922, and it is of that Act in its relation to this Treaty that I wish particularly to speak.

I regard the Irish Treaty, in spite of all its terrible surroundings, as a great pact and symbol of peace between the British and Irish peoples after 700 years of reciprocal maltreatment and misunderstanding. I am one of the surviving signatories of that Treaty. I remember vividly the circumstances in which it was made. Both sides were strained to their utmost limits. Every one of us British delegates realised the measureless danger to an Imperial power of surrender to the kind of violence to which we had been subjected. The Irishmen whom we faced knew that they took their lives in their hands for their part, and nearly all of them have given their lives for the fulfilment of the Treaty obligations. I do not wish to labour details, but the names of Arthur Griffiths, Michael Collins, and, though he was a signatory of the Agreement, Kevin O'Higgins ought not to fade from our memories, because they gave their lives for the maintenance of the instrument called the Irish Treaty or the Articles of Agreement. They had pledged their faith to Englishmen whom they met for the first time, with whom they had previously warred, but of whose fidelity they were now assured, and they marched in that faith steadfastly on their path to the end which was not delayed.

I cannot believe that such an instrument thus defended should be lightly set aside or that we should create a situation in which it should be lightly set aside. I know that we are told it will make no difference, that if it was the will of the people of Southern Ireland to repudiate their Treaty obligations, what we write in this Statute or leave unwritten would make no difference. I do not agree. The Irish Treaty constitutes the title deeds of the new Irish Free State. We never considered hypothetical contingencies, or what sanctions might be invoked in particular cases of repudiation of solemn treaties and agreements. But, if the Irish Treaty were illegally or violently repudiated, the Irish Free State would have lost its title deeds. That certainly would happen. In the common law of Europe, in the jurisprudence of the world, the Irish Free State would have lost its foundations. It would have become a mere inexpressible anomaly. That would be a great disaster to them and a great weakening of their position in the whole world which they have so carefully endeavoured to defend and build up. Therefore, it is the interest of Nationalist Ireland, and of Sinn Fein Ireland, no less than of this House, to preserve the sanctity of that memorable Treaty between these two proud parent races from whose loins so much of the British Empire has sprung.

I am advised on high technical authority that this Bill confers upon the Irish Free State full legal power to abolish the Irish Treaty at any time when the Irish

Legislature may think fit. Doubtless we shall hear the opinion of my right hon. and learned Friend who is the surviving Law Officer of the Crown upon this question, and well I know the force and power of the legal arguments which the Law Officers, with their great erudition and commanding professional skill, are always able to assemble in support of Government policy. I cannot pit my own knowledge as a layman against such authority, but I am advised by extremely high and weighty legal luminaries that the effect of this Bill passing in its present form would be to make it perfectly legal and perfectly simple for the Imperial Act which embodied the Articles of Agreement to be repealed by the Irish Free State. The Irish Treaty rests on and is embodied in the Irish Free State Constitution Act, 1922. Clause 2 of the Statute of Westminster which the Dominion Secretary has already read, reads in terms which no one can have the slightest doubt about. No one can say it is obscure or cryptic. It is the plainest Act of Parliament that I have ever read.

> No law and no provision of any law made after the commencement of this Act by the Parliament of a Dominion shall be void or inoperative on the ground that it is repugnant to the law of England, or to the provisions of any existing or future Act of Parliament of the United Kingdom, and the powers of the Parliament of a Dominion shall include the power to repeal or amend any such Act, order, rule, or regulation insofar as the same is part of the law of the Dominion.

What can be plainer than that? It would be open under this Bill to the Dail at any time to repudiate legally—that is the point—with the full sanction of law and Parliamentary procedure, every provision of the Articles of Agreement. They could repeal the Irish Free State Constitution Act in every respect. It would be absurd to argue that, when they had repealed the Irish Free State Constitution Act, an Imperial Act, they would be inhibited from further action by the fact that they themselves passed through the Dail their own replica of the Imperial Act. If the parent Act were destroyed, everything else would perish with it, and at this point we must look at the Irish Free State Constitution Act and its Schedules in which the Articles of Agreement are embodied. Anyone who likes to read the Articles of Agreement will see how very important are some of their provisions.

Mr. Healy: Read Article 12.

Mr. Churchill: May I not choose which Article I shall read? It would be open to the Dail if they were so minded—and there is no reason why we should not find them so minded in the future—to repudiate the Oath of Allegiance which is embodied in Article 4 and which is the great guarantee while it stands against a great many unfortunate departures. They could certainly abolish and decide for themselves this question, which, I admit, is a delicate one, of the right of appeal to the Privy Council. It is a matter upon which both sides should be consulted, but, once the Statute of Westminster is passed in its present form, it would be open to them, without even consultation, to settle that disputed issue in their own way and on their own terms.

An Hon. Member: They can do it now.

Mr. Thomas: I said that they have nullified it on several occasions up to now.

An Hon. Member: Illegally.

Mr. Churchill: That is the whole point. We are entitled to adhere to and to press peacefully and patiently our view of those things. By this Bill in its present form we shall have placed it out of our power to continue to hold our view of the case, because we shall have provided an absolutely legal method by which the matter can be settled in an adverse sense to that which we hold. They could repudiate the right of the Imperial Government to utilise, for instance, the harbour facilities at Berehaven and Queenstown which are contained in those Acts and other Articles of Agreement. They could repudiate the right of facilities for aviation and oil fuel storage to which great importance was attached by the country at the time this Treaty was negotiated. They could repudiate the limitation upon the size of the Army of the Irish Free State, which is now restricted to the same proportion of the Irish population as the military establishments in the United Kingdom bear to the population of the United Kingdom—a very fair and reasonable proposition, and one which still bears the test of time. I do not say that they would do so, but they would have a perfect right to do so once they had repealed the application to the Dominions of the Irish Free State (Agreement) Act of 1922. There are other various provisions with which I will not trouble the House.

We are asked by the Dominions Secretary to look at the Preamble to this Act. Some language is used in the Preamble about the Crown which, I am assured, does less than justice to the ancient constitutional doctrines which exist, but the proposal that secession from the Commonwealth of Nations should require to be, or that the questions affecting the Crown should require to be, dealt with by all the parties to the British Commonwealth of Nations, is, of course, very valuable, but it is perfectly worthless in its present form. It has absolutely no validity at all as a Preamble. The Preamble is nothing. It has no legal force. Judges, I am told, do not read the Preamble. They look at the Clauses. There is no meaning attaching to it at all. But we had a Preamble to the Parliament Act:

Whereas it is expedient without delay to set up a new and reformed Second Chamber.

Twenty years have passed. What is the use of the preamble being there. It may well be, therefore, that in the long run, perhaps in this Parliament, we may read again that Preamble. It will at any rate show that there is no legal force in the Preamble. There are other various provisions with which I will not trouble the House, but in essence under this Act, if it is passed in its present form, the whole structure of the Irish Treaty can be destroyed, not by illegal repudiation, but by the mere passing of a law through the Irish Free State Parliament, which this Bill declares they have plenary powers to pass if they think fit. I think that that is a very wrong thing and one to which we ought not to lend ourselves, especially at the outset of a new, and what we may all hope may be, a famous Parliament.

Great anxiety has been caused in Northern Ireland by the position which will be created when this Bill is passed and needless anxiety, because, if we mean the same thing, there is no difficulty in giving effect to the purposes of the House. Moreover, the remedy is so obvious and so simple that I am most hopeful that His Majesty's

Government, with all their power, will be willing to adopt it. An Amendment will be moved in the Committee stage by my right hon. Friend the Member for Burton (Colonel Gretton) which will seek to introduce into Clause 7 after the words:

> Nothing in this Act shall be deemed to apply to the repeal, amendment or alteration of the British North America Acts, 1867 to 1930.

the words which are incorporated in the text of the Bill—the words:

> or to the Irish Free State Constitution Act, 1922.

I trust that His Majesty's Government will accept the Amendment in the sense that it is moved, and I hope that the Solicitor-General will be able to tell us straight away that they will do so. I must point out how strictly the Amendment conforms to the spirit and the principle of the Irish Free State Constitution Act and the Articles of Agreement. Section 2 of the Irish Free State Constitution Act says, and I ask the House to notice these words:

> Subject to the provisions hereinafter set out the position of the Irish Free State in relation to the Imperial Parliament and Government and otherwise shall be that of the Dominion of Canada, and the law, practice and constitutional usage, governing the relationship of the Crown or the representative of the Crown and of the Imperial Parliament to the Dominion of Canada shall govern their relationship to the Irish Free State.

Subject to the provisions set out, the relationship shall be that of the Dominion of Canada, and here in Clause 7 of the Statute of Westminster Bill, my right hon. Friend will in due course propose to safeguard the special obligations entered into between Great Britain and the Irish Free State in the same Clause and immediately after the provisions which by the wish of the Dominion of Canada safeguard the British North America Acts from 1867 to 1930. You could not have a closer concordance either with the Irish Treaty or with the constitutional arrangements which Canada desires. His Majesty's Government are now at the beginning of what we all hope will be a prosperous and even a glorious tenure of power. They will do well not to set aside lightly the representations which are made to them in all good faith and in all good will by many who sit in their support upon these benches.

There is no violent hurry about this matter. The Government have introduced the Bill and in that way they have kept their pledge, but Parliament is in control, and no one can limit in any way the power of Parliament to deal with this Bill. As has been pointed out, some of the Dominions themselves have amended it. In other cases they have passed Resolutions. We, for the first time as a Parliament, have to go through the process of examining and studying carefully all the concrete and definite proposals in the form of the Statute, and certainly we should not be hurried. I hope and trust that it is not intended to bring this Debate to a premature conclusion this afternoon.

I have only one more topic to deal with. This Bill does not, of course, deal with India, but it naturally, and I think inevitably, must govern our thoughts in relation to the Indian situation which may some day arise. For the first time, we see set out in cold legal language what Dominion status means. Let anyone who reads these Clauses contemplate the frightful disaster which would be brought upon India if the full Dominion status as set out here became the law governing India. For India we have inalienable responsibilities and adequate and necessary powers to maintain them. We are going to have a debate in a few days on India; therefore I will not dwell upon that topic, but when we have before us the actual legal provisions of Dominion status, is there anyone who does not see the folly and the wrong of the declarations which excited the hopes of the Indian political classes that, after a brief period of transition, full Dominion status would be conferred upon the Indian central Legislature. The gravamen of the charge which I bring against those who have made improvement declarations upon these matters is shown by the presentation of this Bill to-day.

The declarations in favour of Dominion status which were made a year or two ago took no account of the fundamental change between the time of the Montagu reforms and the Irwin declarations in the meaning of Dominion status. The term is the same; it is printed in the same letters; it is pronounced with the same accents, but it means, after this Statute has been passed and after the declarations of the 1926 Conference, something fundamentally different from what it was in the days of the Government of India Act, 1919. No one can doubt that Dominion status as defined in this Bill would be incompatible with the slightest semblance of Imperial authority over the races, the peoples and the States of the vast sub-continent of India.

Could we ever see more clearly than we do in this debate the valuelessness of paper safeguards? It would be even an argument of the Government: "It does not matter what you do or you do not do; the safeguards are valueless." I do not think that we should throw away any safeguards which are necessary or proper. The valuelessness of paper safeguards is one of the painful conclusions driven in upon all our minds. In the fullness of time and in the nick of time a Parliament has arrived which is capable of calling a halt in these matters. It is a Parliament which is bound by the obligations of the past. It is a Parliament which is willing to face realities both in Ireland and in India. It is a Parliament resolute to preserve the lawful, practical essentials of Imperial structure, and I trust that His Majesty's Government will prove themselves, at the beginning of their work and of their career, in sympathy and in harmony with the wishes and feelings of this Parliament.

STATUTE OF WESTMINSTER BILL

November 24, 1931

House of Commons

I had a full opportunity on Friday of stating the misgivings, and indeed, the objections, which I personally entertain to this Measure in its present unamended form, and as I listened this afternoon, first of all to the long and discursive Debate upon various constitutional points, and, secondly, to the Debate on this Amendment, I am bound to say that my opposition to the Bill was not in any way mitigated. I shall not repeat the arguments which I submitted to the House last week, but as I listened to the speech of the Secretary of State for Dominion Affairs I could not help feeling that it put the case on a false and disproportioned basis. We see defects in the Statute. We wish that its legal form and shape could have been more in harmony with the traditions, at least, of the British Constitution, but we are committed to the Statute and we do not see how in this House and at this time we have the power to re-shape that Statute in detail.

If only this Measure had been committed to a Joint Committee of both Houses, on which the great lawyers of the House of Lords, whose names and legal authority are respected in all the Dominions, could in perfect frankness and sincerity have examined this matter, and smoothed off the unfortunate terms of phrase and of provisions which are in it, I am certain it would have been possible to present this matter again to the Dominions—there being no hurry for it—and to obtain from them some reconsideration of certain points. While we show every respect and attention to the wishes and views of the Dominions, and are always anxious to defer to their desires, still, the Mother Country must sometimes have a wish or a point of view of its own, and I cannot believe that that wish, that point of view, when strongly and reasonably felt, might not be accepted in the family circle of the British Empire or, if you are afraid of the word "Empire," as you seem to be, in the family circle of the British Commonwealth of Nations—with at least as much good will as we have shown towards the wishes which the Dominions have expressed to us. So much for the present Statute.

The Secretary of State for Dominion Affairs argued as if those who had expressed misgivings about these proposals were opposed to the resolutions of 1926 out of which this Statute has been born. That is not the position. There has been no attack on the main principles of the Bill, and there has been no opposition to the Statute as a whole. There is only one important point of principle at issue at the present time, and that is whether the Statute of Westminster should include a saving Clause for the Irish Treaty Act. That is the sole question before us. The Secretary of State made an impassioned speech, which seemed to imply that the relations between Great Britain and Ireland, now so much improved, would be fatally thrown back if we were to insert in the text of the Bill the words which have been proposed by my right hon. and gallant Friend. I do not think that it is an unjustified demand that we should insert those words. What has astonished me is that the Government have never disputed the principle that Clause 2 of the Statute gives legal power to the Irish Parliament to repeal the application to Ireland of the Irish Free State Act of 1922. I imagined that we should hear this disputed by legal authorities. We have heard other legal authorities on the subject, but it has not been disputed by the Government. If, for instance, the Solicitor-General had said, "Your fears are groundless, and nothing in this Act will give power to repeal the Act on which the Treaty rests," then I should have said, "We are friends, because, if our objects are the same, you cannot object to words being inserted which secure your purpose and ours as well."

The Solicitor-General: I did not wish to interrupt the right hon. Gentleman, but he has made a statement which I desire to say is not quite in accordance with the facts. The right hon. Gentleman says that no dispute has been raised as to the unqualified power, if this Bill is passed, of the Irish Free State to abrogate or to abolish the Treaty. That was certainly challenged in the speech of my hon. Friend the Member for Crewe (Mr. Somervell), and I repeated that challenge in my speech, and said that in my humble judgment the Constitution could not be amended, having regard to Article 50 of the Treaty, except in accordance with the Treaty.

Mr. Churchill: I fully apprehend the very important statement which the Solicitor-General has just made. Apparently, there is a doubt as to whether this Act does or does not give power to repeal the Treaty. The Solicitor-General reassures the House that, in his opinion, it gives no such power. On the other hand, we have had legal authorities expressing an opinion to the contrary. If the Government think that the Act will not throw any strain upon the Irish Free State, and we hope so too, why cannot we be united in inserting words which put this matter beyond doubt. If it be true that this Statute invalidates the Treaty Act, and the supporters of the Bill hope that it will not do so, let us make our hopes secure by putting in the simple words which my right hon. and gallant Friend seeks to introduce in the Bill.

I listened with great attention to the letter from President Cosgrave which was read in order to influence our decision. I have great admiration for President Cosgrave, and I know how faithfully he has stood by all the obligations entered into by his late colleagues who were signatories of the Treaty, and I have known this for many years. I do feel, however, that this is a matter which ought not to be decided upon personal assurances by individuals. We have to consider what should be the settled legal foundation to put our Constitution right. President Cosgrave is the most long-lived Prime Minister of any of the Dominions, but to say that the Irish Free State Government is the most stable of Dominion Governments is to ignore the fact that the Irish Government have been forced to adopt extreme powers unknown to ordinary law, and almost amounting to martial law, in order to protect the people against lawless acts of terrorism and outrage. The Government in Ireland, which is now ruling the country by exceptional legislation far exceeding the drastic powers of any Coercion Act passed by this House, is possessed of a majority varying between three or four, and which has sometimes risen to five or six. A general election is approaching in Ireland, and I cannot feel that we shall be held up to reproach and censure in this House because we are insisting on our rights and upon our legal claims. Having received an assurance from President Cosgrave which does him honour, and which I am sure he would make good with his last drop of blood, I ask why the insertion of the words of this Amendment is held to be derogatory to us.

We may consider ourselves bound, as far as possible, by the Treaty Act. When the Treaty was passing through this House I said that we had no right to sanction the conditions of that Treaty. An hon. Member has mentioned Australia, New Zealand, and Canada, and every one of those Dominions have insisted upon having the Foundation Act made immune from the new powers of repeal which are accorded by this Statute. Some hon. Members say what about South Africa? The Solicitor-General, in his speech on Friday, made a great point of South Africa. When I came to study the matter more at leisure than was possible in the course of that Debate, I was very much shocked to see how hurriedly the hon. and learned Gentleman must have had to get up his brief in this question. He said, referring to what I had said:

If the Treaty of the Constitution of the Irish Free State is, against her expressed wish, to be put into this Bill, a similar course will presumably have to be taken with regard to the Constitution of South Africa, and I do not know whether my right hon. Friend—

that is me—

would think it was consistent with the dignity of that Dominion, which he did so much to set on its way, to put into this Bill a provision that its Constitution shall not be broken and its entrenchment Clauses shall not be repealed contrary to every good faith and sense of honour....—[Official Report, 20th November, 1931; col. 1247, Vol. 259.]

His argument is that to put this saving for the Irish Treaty into the Statute of Westminster in respect of Ireland would be derogatory to Ireland, and a great reflection upon Ireland which we should not care to see the Dominions Secretary apply to South Africa. I will read the Resolution which the South African Parliament passed after considering the provisions of this very Statute of Westminster Bill:

That, on the understanding that the proposed legislation will in no way derogate from the entrenched provisions of the South Africa Act, this House, having taken cognisance of the draft Clauses and recitals which it was proposed by the Imperial Conference of 1930 should—

and so on. Here, therefore, is South Africa itself by resolution approving of the insertion of the very same provision that we ask should now be inserted in respect of the Irish Treaty. The Irish Treaty finds no counterpart in the relations between us and any of our Dominions. It is at once more recent, more tragical and more solemn than any other instrument that exists, going even as far back as the Articles of the Treaty of Vereeniging. But this Irish Treaty, may at no distant date become a matter of grave, real, practical politics. Suppose that a change of Government should occur in Ireland, you will be immediately confronted with a very grave crisis on this Treaty, and will be held responsible if you weaken in any way the moral—and in the moral I include the legal—rights of this country to defend the Treaty. We are in such a pusillanimous mood, apparently, that it almost has to be made a matter of apology, almost regarded as an act of impropriety, for any British representative to put forward modestly and politely, with studious and calculated courtesy, claims which are indefeasible in law. This Irish Treaty represented only what could be saved from the wrecks of great Imperial authorities, but, such as they were, they were of the greatest value, and they were fought for in the controversies between the two countries. We ask that the same saving shall be given with regard to this Treaty as is given in this Measure to every other one of the Dominions in respect of their fundamental laws, and which South Africa itself sought in its resolution to impose upon itself.

I am not going to keep the Committee any longer. The right hon. Gentleman is about to address us, and we must listen with the very greatest respect to all that he says, not only because I know it will be heartfelt and sincere, and will aim at helping the House out of its difficulties and offering to it assurance and comfort, but also because my right hon. Friend is the lord of legions. If Providence is on the side of the big battalions, he, no doubt, has the Divine blessing resting upon him to-night. Not only has he this magnificent majority with which the nation has provided him on this occasion, but he will also have the assistance, should this matter go to a Division, of the defeated army. The Socialists will be able to march into line, and the Dominions Secretary and the Prime Minister will be able to make that reunion to which they assure us they are looking forward. I say to them, "You will have your way, and you will have the responsibility. We have found it to be our duty to protest. We have made our protest. We are satisfied, after all that has been said in this Debate, that, in asking that this safeguard and provision should be inserted in the Statute, we have done no unworthy thing."

Mr. Devlin: I do not think that, during an experience of 30 years in this House, I have ever witnessed so extraordinary an exhibition as I have just seen, nor have I ever listened to a more mischievous speech than that of the right hon. Gentleman. He concluded his speech with an attack on his Leader. Since this new National Parliament was elected, the right hon. Gentleman has made many interventions into our Debates. I would like to ask him what precisely is his position in the public life of England; whom does he represent; what principles does he hold; and who is his Leader? [Hon. Members: "Who is yours?"] I am my own leader, and I differ from the right hon. Gentleman in this, that I am probably a solitary Member in this House, because I have never departed from my principles. The right hon. Gentleman has had a varied career. No one in this House has a more profound personal regard for him than I have; no one listens to him with such intellectual delight as I do; I think that this House and the public life of this country are enriched by the magnificent talents which he possesses. But, if there is one thing that I could never conceive myself doing in any circumstances, it is following the guidance of the right hon. Gentleman. I came into this House 30 years ago. The right hon. Gentleman was then a Unionist. He was not only a Unionist, but he was a Free Trader. I was very young and very unenlightened, but I was modest enough to hope that I might be like him. I sat at his feet and listened to his magnificent speeches on behalf of Free Trade. Because he became a Free Trader, he transferred himself to these benches. He was a Unionist, and he became a Home Ruler. He joined the Coalition Cabinet, and he remained in that Cabinet and, as a Coalitionist Minister, he carried the Treaty. I do not know precisely where he stands to-day, what are his principles or—

Mr. Churchill: I stand for the enforcement of the Treaty.

INDIA (GOVERNMENT POLICY)

December 3, 1931

House of Commons

Order read for resuming Adjourned Debate on Question [*2nd December*] :

That this House approves the India Policy of His Majesty's Government as set out in Command Paper, No. 3972 (Indian Round Table Conference), presented to Parliament on 1st December, 1931.–[*The Prime Minister.*]

Question again proposed.

Mr. Churchill: I beg to move, in line 3, at the end, to add the words:

Provided that nothing in the said policy shall commit this House to the establishment in India of a Dominion constitution as defined by the Statute of Westminster; provided also that the said policy shall effectively safeguard British trade in and with India from adverse or prejudicial discrimination; and provided further that no extensions of self-government in India at this juncture shall impair the ultimate responsibility of Parliament for the peace, order, and good government of the Indian Empire.

I cordially agree with what was said by my right hon. Friend the Prime Minister and echoed by the Secretary of State for India yesterday about the disadvantage of phrases and generalities upon the Indian problem. I would almost say it is a pity that this observation was not made before, because I am sure that many of the generalities and wide, loose, equivocal statements which have been made from time to time during the Indian Conference must have been very galling to the Prime Minister who is a master of terse and pithy statements. However, I gladly agree with him that both here and in India we have become at times the victims of phrases, and we have been obsessed by and entangled in our own terminology. Take the hackneyed phrase "Dominion status." During the Great War India obtained Dominion status so far as rank, honour and ceremony were concerned. The representatives of the Government of India attended the Imperial War Conference, they attended the Peace Conference, and they are included among the British Dominions who serve on the League of Nations.

Most of the leading public men–of whom I was one in those days–made speeches–I certainly did–about Dominion status, but I did not contemplate India having the same constitutional rights and system as Canada in any period which we could foresee. I did, and I do, contemplate our Indian fellow countrymen as fellow subjects enjoying equal rank with us and all other subjects of His Majesty's Government without distinction of race, creed or colour. Moreover, it was obviously inherent in the nature of things that we could not carry on the Government of India for a day except through the administrative abilities and the co-operation of very large and increasing numbers of educated Indians rising steadily to positions of greater responsibility and discretion. Therefore, I accept the statement made by the Secretary of State for India in his admirable speech last night in which he said:

> We have to reconcile the obligations of this long British partnership with India with the legitimate aspirations of Indians to take a greater part in their own Government—[Official Report, 2nd December, 1931; col. 1209, Vol. 260.]

I accept that, and I think that the right hon. Gentleman has stated accurately the problem which is before us. All this is common ground. I am tired of it being suggested that those who differ in this or that from the policy of His Majesty's Government are mere obscurantists and obstructionists who have no idea or policy but the denial of all progress in India and the arrest of constitutional development. I do not admit that the sense in which the expression "Dominion status" was used 10 or 15 years ago implied Dominion structure or Dominion rights. I looked up the word "status" in the dictionary, as you would say, Sir, for greater accuracy. I do not admit that it means structure or rights. The word "status" means rank—not necessarily rights or structure. Let me take an instance which will be familiar to everyone. Take the Privy Council. There are a large number of Privy Councillors who are all of equal rank and some are privy to all the secrets of the State, and actually conduct the Government of the country. Others are not privy to any of the secrets of the State, and have only a remote chance of conducting the Government of the country, but there is no legal bar to their doing so, and all are equal. As Mr. Fox once said in a Debate on property and the inequalities of property: "Men have equal rights to unequal things." I think that that is a very profound observation upon the actual state of the world in which we live, and it has its bearings upon the question of Dominion status. Ten or 15 years ago there was a great deal of talk of the offence caused to Indians by the idea that they occupied a lower rank and status than the people of this island. We were assured that once this slur was cleared away, once there was no further suggestion of what they call in India "Nordic superiority" an immense boon would be afforded to our brave Indian fellow-soldiers who fought in the War and to Indian collaborators in building up the British Empire, that it would afford a sensible relief and encouragement and an enhanced sense of dignity, and no practical or serious difficulties would arise. We were told that what India wanted was a recognition and the form of equality of status. No one ever suggested then even in the most haggard moments of the War or the most expansive hours of victory that the Indian proletariat with its vast masses, its almost innumerable peoples of India would be likely to live in peace, happiness and decency under the same polity, and the same forms of government which prevail among the British, Canadian or Australian democracies. The idea is preposterous, and is well known to be preposterous. It is not preposterous, assuredly, because the natives of

India are inherently incapable of working modern democratic institutions, or that they are inherently unfit to enjoy any form of autonomy. It is impossible because the conditions of India, of the country in which they live, the political, social, cultural, racial, religious conditions of that country are such that any attempt to apply the democratic institutions of Australia and Canada rigidly and pedantically to India, would produce measureless tyranny and misery, ending in bloodshed and probably utter confusion. That is why it is our duty at once to concede status as we have conceded it, and to reserve and withhold structure in our dealings with the Indian problem.

I have given, I think, a very fair account of the opinion in governing dominant circles in this country at the time of the Montagu reforms on this point. Certainly, I have stated my own recollections. I was not directly brought into these matters, but I have stated my own recollection of what the general view was. Side by side with this desire to confer equality of rank upon our Indian fellow-subjects, there were earnest and practical efforts to associate Indians even more directly with the responsibilities of Government and administration. But the whole position was defined and set out with the utmost clarity in the Preamble and in the Sections of the Act of 1919. The Prime Minister referred to the Preamble yesterday, but he did not refer to Section 41, which must be read with the Preamble. That Section is the one which gives us the power to regulate, limit or restrict the pace at which the constitutional reforms should proceed in India, and the two must be read in conjunction, one with the other. Read together they proclaim at once the sincerity of our purpose, and the plenary, and, as I hold, inalienable authority of Parliament to control, regulate, restrict or alter the character, extent and direction of Indian constitutional progress. I take my stand upon that Act of Parliament. Until it is superseded by another Act of Parliament, it embodies and expresses the whole constitutional relation between Great Britain and all the nations, races and tribes of India.

There are many who hold that the Statute of 1919 went too far. I sometimes meet people who have given up all hope or interest in the Indian situation, and when they are invited to consider a new and dangerous position, they merely say, "Oh, well, all that was settled in 1919." There are many who contend that serious evils flowed from the Act of 1919, and certainly that no good was done either to the wellbeing of the people of India or to their loyalty to the King-Emperor. These critics point to the increasingly vociferous discontent of the Indian political classes for which this Act was largely passed, and the increasing administrative deterioration of all the scientific and cultural departments which have been handed over, or, as I would prefer to say, experimentally delegated to Indian control. I must admit the force of these assertions, but I say, nevertheless, let us take our stand upon the Government of India Act, 1919. That is our only starting point for any new departure or advance in the Indian problem which is now, or may now be open to us. I do not recognise the validity of some of the declarations which have been made in the interval. I may deplore their consequences, but I do not recognise the validity of individual declarations. Here is the Statute, the Act of 1919, and here is the Parliament which can alone, when it chooses, alter it in any direction it pleases.

The Statutory Commission arose directly out of the 1919 Act. I am going to make some demand upon the good will of the House, and, basing myself on the gravity of the problem, I am going to follow for a few minutes the Prime Minister in his historical review, but I shall, perhaps, touch on some points which he omitted, no doubt through want of time, and perhaps I shall place my emphasis with different weight upon others. The Statutory Commission, as I said, arose out of the Act of 1919. Lord Birkenhead, taking time by the forelock, not waiting until the 10 years period had run out, anticipated the date prescribed in the Act for a Commission to review the workings of the Montagu reforms, and he set up the Commission known in history as the Simon Commission. That Commission was set up, I must remind the House, with the utmost formality. No simple Order brought it into being. It was based upon a special Act of Parliament passed through this House with the names of the Commissioners duly chosen from the three political parties.

The Commission presented their report. All—Liberals, Conservatives and Socialists—were unanimously agreed. I do not pretend—I have never pretended—that every word of that report was right, or that all its recommendations are applicable. Obviously, they are not. But I have always ventured to urge that here was the true Parliamentary foundation for action, and here should have been the basis upon which all our discussions should have begun. I must say that a grave responsibility at the bar of history rests upon those who have incontinently, and with much presumption and levity, cast aside the recommendations of this Commission, and have departed from the orderly, recognised, constitutional procedure which had been prescribed by law, and, having done that, having brushed aside the whole of the plan on which the three parties were proceeding in unison, have embarked, almost at a night's notice, upon all kinds of airy and adventurous excursions of their own.

Ten years pass rapidly. I have several times been connected with public matters where all difficulties have been satisfied by saying, "Oh, well, let this be reviewed in 10 years." I have lived long enough to sit in a Government which found that 10 years' period come to an end, and saw the evil of putting off difficulties merely by so brief a term as 10 years. But before the 10 years' period prescribed in the 1919 Act was completed, it was clear to almost everyone who knew India that this idea of Dominion status, into which had been read the idea of a Dominion constitution, could not be helpful in any way to any British or to any Indian interest. The Statutory Commission, after a profound study—two years of their lives they gave up to the matter; no one knows a quarter about the subject that these men know from their vast work—the Statutory Commission, after their profound study, deliberately excluded the expression "Dominion status" from their unanimous report—a tremendous fact, when you remember the atmosphere at the time; a great august decision, which has never received the weight and attention which it deserves from Parliament.

Nowadays everyone, I suppose, can see how unwise it was of the late Government and of their Viceroy to revive and renew the idea of Dominion status at a time when such a declaration could only prejudice the Report of the Statutory Commission for which Parliament was waiting, and also at a time when this idea had received a new connotation, and had become a symbol of hostile propaganda. Moreover, as we have been pertinently, and even pointedly reminded in the last few weeks, the whole character and definition of Dominion status has been fundamentally altered by the declarations of the Imperial Conference of 1926. Read now your Statute of Westminster when it comes to you from another place, and let any man, I do not care where he sits, ask himself whether he would take the personal responsibility of extending the rights and authorities conferred and described in that Act to the peoples of India in any period which can be foreseen. I call to account those who were responsible, first, for the departure from constitutional procedure as prescribed by law, and, secondly, for this declaration of the Viceroy, which prejudiced, and, indeed, destroyed, the whole vast work of the Simon Commission. Other grave mistakes have no doubt been committed in Indian affairs, but these are the parent mistakes—these are the parents of all the evils which have flowed upon us since, and are still flowing upon us in a rising tide.

The Prime Minister yesterday spoke to us about the origin of the Round Table Conference. I do not quarrel with his description. There were no Indian representatives on the Statutory Commission. Discontent was caused; the Indians demanded admission; they were refused admission. To satisfy them it was proposed by the Foreign Secretary himself that there should be a Consultative Conference, a kind of collateral consultative conference. So, when the time came for this conference to meet—it was a very sensible thing to do—the question was, who should be the British representative? One would have imagined from the speech of the Prime Minister that he was most eager to carry all parties with him in the matter. I am afraid his historical recollection is at fault in that respect. As a matter of fact, great concern was caused among Conservatives, for fear that a declaration would be made at this consultative conference by the Socialist Government of the day which would have a binding effect and tie the hands of Parliament in the future.

The Conservatives accordingly demanded, and so did the Liberals, who at that time were working in accord upon this question—it was one of those periods when the right hon. Gentleman the Member for Carnarvon Boroughs (Mr. Lloyd George) was in a highly patriotic mood; unhappily, the mood did not last very long on that occasion—the Conservatives and the Liberals demanded representation. The Government resisted. They objected, and so did the Indian Congress. They thought it would alter the whole character, and so did the other people who were likely to be invited. They objected. However, in the end a joint representation was insisted upon, and a joint representation was effected. I am bound to say that I do not think the Indian Congress and the others need have worried very much about it, because there is no doubt that the fact that the representatives of all these three parties were gathered there has enabled this conference to play a vast, and it may well be a fatal, part in the whole of the development of our Indian policy.

When the Conference met, in view of the Viceroy's declaration, in view of a great many foolish speeches which were being made, and in view of the general feeling of weakness and despondency which spreads throughout the British Empire when a minority Government, and a Socialist minority Government, is in power, the Indian Princes, not knowing where to turn, came forward and offered to join in a federal system. Immediately there followed this landslide to which I have always drawn attention. In a night, in a day, the whole situation was transformed. The Consultative Conference, which was to lie alongside the Statutory Report, converted itself into a quite unauthorised kind of informal constituent assembly, and immediately set to work to fabricate and manufacture federal constitutions of every kind in every direction. This process was accompanied by speeches and perorations which might well have justified the assumption that the United States of India and full Dominion status were actually at hand, or very close to our hands. I do not at all wonder that great hopes and expectations were excited over India, and great disappointment, naturally, has followed as those expectations have gradually, but steadily and remorselessly, been contracted.

The Conference, I say, went on its path, and, when it separated in January, the Prime Minister made the declaration which is repeated in Paragraph 2 of the White Paper which is now before us. The House is familiar with it, and has read it with attention, and, therefore, I will not re-read it. There was the new declaration—there was the declaration which side-tracked the Simon Commission, which committed us to an altogether different departure and different mode of action. I, from the very first, have protested against this violent change, but hitherto I have never been asked by the Leaders of my party to become committed to it in any way. This is the first time we are asked to take upon ourselves responsibility for the declaration made by the Prime Minister at the head of the Socialist Government in January last. Otherwise we have been free. I will return to that in a minute.

The consequence of these events was, of course, an attempt to procure the assent of the Indian Congress. Mr. Gandhi and other leaders were all in prison. They had to be released to induce them to take part in this great new settlement. Then followed their release, and immediately upon that we saw the spectacle of Mr. Gandhi and some of his leading lieutenants negotiating almost on equal terms with the Viceroy and arranging the celebrated Gandhi-Irwin Pact. There followed upon that the attempt to set up two parallel Governments in India—a Government of the Congress, which was to be in close, harmonious touch with His Majesty's Imperial Government, and was to be, as it were, an agent and a co-operator in the work of governing India. I say that that was a most profoundly injurious blow struck at British authority, not only in India, but throughout the globe.

My right hon. Friend the Lord President of the Council said before the General Election that he and the Prime Minister were a pair of brothers. The discovery of their brotherhood dates from an earlier period than the difficulties of the pound sterling. They came together upon this Indian matter. The close association between the Prime Minister and the Lord President of the Council, and the great friendship which my right hon. Friend has for Lord Irwin, led to all the forces of the Conservative party machine, all the enormous influence which they possess throughout the country, in this House and in the Press, and all the loyalties of a great party looking forward to a victorious General Election, being turned against those who protested against this sudden, unconstitutional and novel twist that had been given to Indian affairs. The result of this has been that no fair or adequate expression has been given to the deep sense of alarm and of repulsion, I may say, felt throughout the country, and especially by all those British folk who have a real knowledge of India and are brought in actual contact with Indian affairs. Their alarm at these events was completely overlaid, and they were virtually extinguished as a political force. There seemed to be no Conservative point of view; there seemed to be no resistance at all to this swift drift of events, heedless, almost, of the direction in which it was going.

That was harmful to our world reputation. All that the world could see was an apparent complete absence of backbone in our Imperial affairs. It was freely said on the Continent, "England will always give way to whoever shouts the loudest." It was said, that England had lost her capacity for leading, guiding, and, I would add, ruling Oriental countries; that, just as she gave up her naval rights without any real need, so she would give up her rights and her enormous interests in India if pressed far enough. Invoke certain principles, it was said, repeat certain formulas and phrases, and England will submit as if she were under a spell of wichcraft. That is what was said, and believed almost universally throughout the world. Believe me, Mr. Speaker, this had as much to do with the collapse of British credit as any speculations of acceptance houses in the City of London. England, apart from her Empire in India, ceases for ever to exist as a Great Power. Strip this Island of her appanage of interest and sovereignty in tropical lands, and you would indeed have a plain explanation of the collapse of the pound sterling.

The pound sterling is based on many things, but among them, indispensable and almost prime, is the gigantic historical position of Britain in the East; and when it was widely believed, and when it was actually part of the British Government's policy not to deny, that in a time which might be short or long, but whether long or short we did not dare to say—it could not be stated—that in a time which might be short or long we should be ready, if the Indians wished, to evacuate India; when that was the world opinion, which we did not contradict, and could not, in virtue of the argumentative position taken up by the Government, contradict, naturally the confidence of the world in our general strength was undermined.

The negotiations with Mr. Gandhi, coupled with all the flowery speeches about the United States of India and the currency of this phrase "Dominion status," together with the new definitions which were being imparted to it—the whole of these things were interpreted, by people who do not understand our ways or our resources, or our power of recovery, as a complete collapse in national and Imperial morale. Foreign countries could not understand it at all. They could not understand it any more than the Germans could understand that England might become a great military Power. They could not understand that England is much stronger than she looks. They did not, do not, and will not believe what we cannot bring ourselves to doubt, namely, that we have only to make a sustained effort of national will-power to recover our entire position.

The results were disastrous in India, as well as to our position here. British authority was for a time brought into unparalleled contempt. All classes in this teeming population who had the slightest capacity for thought above their homes, their daily bread, and their religion, were led to expect some vast impending, gleaming change in the whole foundation of life and Government. That was a terribly unsettling element to bring about, working its way in tremors through these enormous, vast populations, carried from mouth to mouth—"The British Raj is going to depart; there will be a new Raj to take its place before long." All classes to India were feeling this unsettling, undermining, shattering influence in their lives. In India, constitutional and political matters affect only a tithe, perhaps, of the people. The great mass are interested in the technical apparatus of government, which secures them some protection of health and some of the facilities of science, but 999 out of every 1,000 at least are absorbed in the struggle for life in this world or the next. All are being unsettled, all are being taught to regard the proceedings of the ruling power as a mere winding up of their affairs, as a preliminary to abdication and exit. Naturally they look about. Who would not be unsettled? Naturally, in the face of this astonishing threatened desertion, they look out for something to take hold of. They turn from side to side seeking an anchor that will hold. As the British authority passed for a time into collapse, the old hatred between the Moslems and the Hindus revived and acquired new life and malignity. We cannot easily conceive what these hatreds are. There are mobs of neighbours, people who have dwelt together in the closest propinquity all their lives, who, when held and dominated by these passions, will tear each other to pieces, men, women and children, with their fingers. Not for a hundred years have the relations between Moslems and Hindus been so poisoned as they have been since England was deemed to be losing her grip and was believed to be ready to quit the scene if told to go.

I make some apology to the House for this historical survey. Others may state it in a different way, but that is the sequence of events which, in my judgment, has led us to the present position, and you cannot discuss the present position without comprehending the chain of causation by which we have reached it. I now come to immediate history. I listened yesterday to the speeches of the Prime Minister and the Secretary of State, and I must confess that I am completely mystified about the policy of the Government. The Secretary of State, addressing me amicably but pointedly, said, "Do we mean the same thing?" I was very tempted to say, "Do he and the Prime Minister mean the same thing?" At any rate, I would gladly answer this question when I could get a satisfactory answer to mine. No one would be more pleased than I should be to feel that he and I were agreed. It has been very painful to me to separate myself from friends and colleagues with whom I have had much pleasure in working and with whom it was most agreeable to discuss the common action that we could take in political affairs. Glad should I be indeed if we mean the same thing. I must try, therefore, to clarify the position a little, and I will do so before I sit down.

Let me say, however, in the first place that there are serious objections in my opinion to making a speech delivered on a valedictory occasion, with all the generalities and civilities appropriate to speeding the parting guest and with all the agreeable sentiments naturally aroused in the breast of the host when he takes leave of those with whom he has long collaborated, the right hon. Gentleman bidding farewell to "My dear Mahatma." A speech delivered in these circumstances may well play its part in the regular and agreeable and decorous conduct of administration, but it does not and ought not to serve as the foundation for a solemn declaration of policy by the House of Commons. However, the speech has been elevated into a State paper. Obviously, it is a report of a speech largely extempore, with all the loosenesses of phrase and unprecision of sentences which unhappily we are all led into when we are speaking in these conditions. This is a State paper which has superseded the massive report of the Statutory Commission. This is a State paper which is now the foundation of our future action, and we are to give a vote of confidence, a vote of approval, to this speech whatever it may mean, and I conceive it to be designed to mean different things to different people.

There is one part of the paper, however, which is certainly not at all ambiguous, and that is paragraph 2. That is the vital, operative part. There is the new declaration, and that is what we are now asked to make ourselves responsible for. That is a grave and far-reaching decision for us to be asked to take. In January, when this statement of the Prime Minister was made at the Round Table Conference, it was only a statement of a Socialist minority Government. The Conservative party was repeatedly assured that it was wholly uncommitted. Most important deputations visited the party leader and received from him an assurance, and my right hon. Friend dropped the word "implement" into which by his enthusiasm he had been incautiously betrayed. In December the Conservative party is invited to bind itself to the acceptance, not only of the provincial autonomy recommended by the Simon Commission, but to responsible government at the centre and the establishment of a federal system. The whole of these changes are only the preliminaries which, after a transitional period, are to give way to what I presume must be what is called full responsibility for her own Government, what I presume must be Dominion status or Dominion constitution as now defined by the Statute of Westminster.

What has happened to induce us to make this change? What has happened in the interval to induce us to make this tremendous advance in Conservative opinion? What has happened to make us commit ourselves to the full Socialist policy as formerly promulgated by the Prime Minister and Mr. Wedgwood Benn? Certainly not any agreement that has been reached at the Round Table Conference. On no one single disputed point has there been any agreement. Public order, defence, trade, finance, representation of States, protection of minorities—on none of these topics has there been any agreement. There have been some advances towards agreement in matters in which Indians have united to demand concessions and the British have conceded, not as much, but a good deal of what they asked, but there has been absolutely no agreement of any kind in the differences between one set of Indians and another except these various minority agreements which are largely in the nature of mutual protection. On the contrary, there has been marked sharpening and hardening of all these during the progress of this Conference.

Last January Lord Reading postulated a number of conditions without which he declared he would not support a responsible federal Government. I remember well that his speech was at that time thought to be extreme by the Conservative delegates on the Conference. Yet, now that there is no agreement on any of the disputed points, both he and the Conservative delegates are ready to go the whole way together, and we are to be compelled to accompany them on that perilous voyage. Last January it was urged that much larger concessions as to self-government might well be made to India for the sake of getting, and on the basis of, an agreed settlement; that you could make much larger concessions than could be given in a scheme which was simply imposed by the spontaneous act of the Imperial Parliament. Good will, we were told—the assent of the Indian political classes, the co-operation of Congress and of Mr. Gandhi—would make a basis upon which we would go much further than if we had to act alone. In the last Parliament, as I must remind my friends here, it was part of the innocent Lobby propaganda of the Conservative Whips that there was no need for Conservative apprehension about the Prime Minister's declaration or about the Round Table Conference proceedings, because, it was said, all depended on agreement between Indians themselves and this agreement would certainly not be obtained. It has not been obtained, but the policy that was dependent upon agreement is now to go forward in the teeth of disagreement, and the Conservative party, which was not committed even on the basis of agreement, is now to be committed on the basis of disagreement.

That is what has happened, and again I ask what is it that has occurred in the interval to produce this surprising change that we are now going to be compelled to make? Consider what has happened in India. There has been the massacre of Cawnpore, the most terrible episode that has happened since the mutiny, there has been a long and increasing succession of assassinations, there has been a movement of boycott which has largely ruined the trade of Lancashire. We had only the other day Lord Lothian's speech showing that the lives of officials and Europeans in Bengal are held only on tenure from minute to minute. There have been the stern ordinances which the Government have thought it their duty to impose. There is nothing in the state of India which justifies the Conservative party in committing itself to-day to a position in this matter that it was not asked to commit itself to, that it was solemnly free from responsibility for, in the beginning of the present year.

Mr. W. Thorne: National Government.

Mr. Churchill: Although it is a National Government, Conservatives still exist. They may be proud to serve, but still they live, and have a right to live. I think I have thus shown that there has been an immense change in the position of the Conservative party, involving the whole of this new Parliament. All are being committed to the Socialist policy of the Prime Minister and the late Secretary of State, without even that measure of agreement or acceptance on behalf of the Indian political classes which less than a year ago the Socialist leaders themselves thought indispensable to this scheme. This step we are asked to take irrevocably at 48 hours' notice without the slightest examination worthy of the name by Parliament of the merits and character of the Round Table Conference scheme or still less of the scheme of the Statutory Commission. Those who were in the last Parliament will remember how rigorously the provisions of constitutional change were always excluded from our Debates. I was myself on several occasions prevented from making even an indirect reference to them—a reference necessary to render the discussion intelligible—because it was said, "No, we are only on the administrative points upon the Secretary of State's salary."

The whole of these matters were ruled out of the last Parliament, and this is the first opportunity upon which the House of Commons has ever been allowed to discuss questions like, well, say, whether it is a good thing—I do not say it may not be—at this juncture to make a federal system before the communities out of which it is to be made have been created? That is an absolute departure from all that has ever been known of Imperial construction. Another question is whether it is wise to merge the fortunes of the Indian States with those of British India? It may be, I do not say it is not, but it is the first opportunity that it has been possible for us to mention that since the 26th January last. We might also discuss whether 450 roadless constituencies as large as Scotland, each containing half-a-million illiterate voters, can be a satisfactory basis for what the Prime Minister in his speech calls: the democratic principle expressing itself solely through majority power. We might discuss whether it is prudent to hand over—if this is what we are going to do, and I confess I do not know whether it is so or not—the responsibility for law and order, that is to say, the police and secret services, shall we say, in Bengal, Bombay, the North-West Provinces, the Frontier Provinces, to hand over those responsibilities to Indian provincial cabinets enjoying plenary authority and elected upon a franchise whose working no human being can value or measure. We might discuss whether it is prudent at the same time and by the same operation to create a brand new federal system for a continent nearly as large as Europe, inhabited by nearly as many human beings, the vast majority of whom are in a primitive state, with more national, racial and religious divisions than Europe, and far more bitter and far more bloody feuds rampant and rife within it. And having created this United States of India you endow this federal system with the responsible powers or a large measure of the responsible powers hitherto exercised by Parliament. That is a tremendous issue to which, surely, some time and thought might be given by Parliament to consider before it takes a decision to which you will for ever afterwards be told "you are bound irrevocably."

There was much in the Simon scheme—I know my right hon. Friend will forgive me mentioning his name in this way; that is the penalty of being an historical person—there was much in the Simon scheme which caused anxiety. The full provincial autonomy of countries as large as France and Germany, including peace and order, was to be confided to utterly unproved men upon what I believe to be an utterly unrepresentative basis and chosen by methods unnatural in the East. That was a most audacious and temerarious departure recommended by the Simon scheme. That was supposed to be so reactionary that no one dare even mention it since it was penned and signed. At any rate, the Simon scheme proceeded upon a practical argument. It strove to get rid of diarchy and dualism in the provinces. It took the line of making a bold experiment in the provinces, giving self-government in its integrity with full responsibility, but keeping the supreme control, the supreme central organism of government and the ultimate authority of Parliament integral, intact and inviolate. If anything went wrong in the provinces, if abuses, disasters, confusion, retrogression, massacre and pillage occurred in the provinces, then there would be an organism of supreme power, absolutely integral, one unbroken unit which could come to the rescue of the province which had gone into disorder or confusion, could put the coaches on the line again, and come to the aid of, and give peace and order again to a population which was suffering the horrors of anarchy. That is the Simon scheme in a nutshell, if I am not taking his name in vain. That was a plan and a policy.

But what have we got now? When loyalty and order in India have sunk far lower than when the Simon Commission penned their report, we are to undermine simultaneously by a double convulsion all the local foundations of British rule and many of the central foundations as well. I am not saying I refuse to associate myself with such a policy, but to say that without discussion we should be committed to it is a terrible abuse to be imposed by a Government of the House of Commons. I can conceive variants of this scheme which might be an improvement of what is put forward in the Simon Report, but it is a risky thing. These are matters of enormous consequences and complications, and at the very moment when the aid and action of the central Power may be more needed than ever before on account of the provincial experiments and on account of the state of the country, the central Power is to be hampered by that very diarchy which has already been found so injurious in the provinces to good government that the Statutory Commission advised its abandonment even at a great risk of having to hand over law and order to the provinces. All this scheme is inherent in paragraph 2. Paragraph 2 is the operative part of this document which sets out and commits us to that scheme.

All that is but the prelude, is but a period of transition which nobody dare say will be a long one. It is against your policy to say it is a long one. It is a mere prelude before the inauguration of full Dominion status as defined by the Statute of Westminster, with control by an Indian Legislature of police, army and finance, and power to abrogate any Imperial law, even the law which calls it into being, power to discriminate against British trade, the right to which Privy Councillor Sastri has attached so much importance, to secede from the British Empire, and by an effort of volition to cast off the sovereignty of the King-Emperor. I have not over-stated by one hair's breadth the issues hanging upon the decision to which we are now asked to commit ourselves, and which we never knew anything about until the day before yesterday.

What did the Government want to demand this vote of confidence for? We were perfectly content to have a Debate on the Motion for the Adjournment. Why did they wish to seize this vote of confidence from the House at this juncture on a policy which they admit themselves is all in a state of flux? We have to commit ourselves to-night within six or seven hours from now, without examining these proposals in detail, without giving them a tithe of the time and attention which are given to the most ordinary Acts of domestic legislation. I say that it is astounding that we should be placed in that position. We shall be told that nothing can be done without the Act of Parliament, and that all the reserves and defences of Parliamentary procedure—the First Reading, Second Reading, Committee, Report, Third Reading—all these will be at our disposal when the time comes. Several years must pass before such an Act can even be introduced. Why worry? Let us get rapidly on to other business and pass the vote of confidence in the Prime Minister's Indian scheme for which he now asks.

We have only to look back to last week. Short as memories are nowadays, we have not yet forgotten the arguments by which His Majesty's Government—I do not blame them; they were the arguments which were alone available—secured the passage of the Statute of Westminster Bill. We had committed ourselves, we were bound in honour. We had committed ourselves by the decisions of 1926. We had no choice but to ratify them and to implement them, heavy as our hearts might be, and as their hearts were as they told us. Still, we all had to go through with it. That is your Protection of an Act of Parliament when you have already committed yourselves in advance to some vague affirmation of principle. Now we are being drawn and entangled in the same kind of gradual, imperceptible procedure. We might almost say that the operation is proceeding according to plan. In a few years these vague, indefinite and obscurely stated principles in the speech of the Prime Minister, with all their ambiguity, and whatever they may mean or may not mean, may come before us in a Statute, and we shall be told, "You have already bound yourselves. Read the Prime Minister's speech. Read your own solemn affirmation of it given on the third day of December, 1931. You have no choice." We are giving ourselves over bound hand and foot, without knowing in the least what concession may be made.

I would sit down at once if the Government would be content with the adjournment of the Debate. While we are asked at this juncture to take this decision, I am bound to press my case to a conclusion. I say that it is not fair to the House, and may be woefully injurious to the State. Can you wonder that some of us who do not agree with the general tendency of Socialist policy in India feel that we must make some rugged affirmations of our own such as are contained in the Amendment we have thought it our duty to put upon the Paper before we can assent to a vote of approval of the general policy of the Government? I say that I would not vote against the Government at this stage on the difference between a whole-hearted measure of autonomy in the Provinces on the one hand, or some compromise between autonomy in the Provinces and central autonomy. I would like to see the scheme and consider it. My prepossession is against the latter scheme. At any rate, it is a matter we should consider at leisure and with precise information before us, but that we should now have to commit ourselves to the whole of this policy without being permitted to assert some of the indispensible requirements to which the British Government are entitled to attach importance is most oppressive.

We have postulated in this Amendment three conditions. I hoped that it might be accepted by His Majesty's Government. The Prime Minister's speech showed me, at any rate, one thing. I was very sorry to see it. It showed me that the Amendment would not be accepted, but I was left in doubt whether it would not be accepted because he did not agree with it, or because he agreed with it so much that he considered it superfluous. It was not clear whether he regarded it as an honest assertion of British requirements, or whether he regarded it merely as an effort on my part to gild refined gold and paint the lily. Then, late at night, there came the speech of my right hon. Friend the Secretary of State of India, our Secretary of State for the Department which is charged with these events, the responsible Secretary of State upon this subject. There was no equivocation about that. I sat here and listened without the slightest difficulty in deciding what was the intention and purpose of the Secretary of State's speech, for my right hon. Friend said, quoting my reference to the Statute of Westminster, that the Government policy has no more to do with the Statute of Westminster than the man in the moon. The Statute of Westminster, at any rate, defines the present position of Dominion status. Therefore, Dominion status, apparently, has no more to do with the policy of His Majesty's Government than the man in the moon. Certainly, there is no difference between what we have put in our Amendment and the excellent and clear-cut statement of the responsible Secretary of State. My right hon. Friend went on to detail safeguards, and not for the first time. It has always fallen to his lot to dwell upon the safeguards,and he has always done so very faithfully. He carries a great measure of confidence, even from those who have not agreed with him, because of his inflexible adherence to certain positions which he outlined at the outset. I hope the House will read that speech; it is most important. He spoke of the Army. That must be reserved. Foreign affairs must be reserved. Financial stability, that is to say, the balancing of the Budget, currency, the banking system—all these must be reserved. Not much will be left for the Chancellor of the Exchequer when all these subjects have been reserved. Internal order and police must be reserved, in the ultimate issue.

The Secretary of State for India (Sir Samuel Hoare): The phrase that I used was "internal security." I said nothing about the police.

Mr. Churchill: I beg my right hon. Friend's pardon. Internal security, in the ultimate issue, must be reserved. The protection of minorities must be reserved. The minorities in India, added together, are majorities, substantial majorities. They are entangled at every stage with the Hindus. There is to be no discrimination against British trade, and the interests of the Services are to be properly safeguarded. Here, instead of the three points which we have put forward in our Amendment, the Secretary of State has put forward eight points, including the three which have been mentioned by us. I will not take up the time of the House in arguing how much will be left of responsible Government, or what will be the meaning attached to the phrase "responsible Government" when all these safeguards have been given full and loyal effect to. The Secretary of State quarrelled, in the most courteous manner, with my Amendment only on one ground: it does not go far enough. It only states three desiderata of the eight or nine which my right hon. Friend put forward with so much force to the House. If that is the only dispute and difference between us, I will gladly do my best to remove the difference that is outstanding. If that is the only difference, I am sure that it can easily be got rid of. I told my right hon. Friend this morning that I should be quite willing to withdraw the Amendment. I have been in consultation with hon. Friends associated with me, and we should be quite willing to withdraw our Amendment if the Government would agree to substitute for certain words at the end of the Motion:

That this House approves the India policy of His Majesty's Government as set out in Command Paper, No. 3972 presented to Parliament on 1st

December, 1931, and also in the speech of the Secretary of State for India
of the 2nd December.

Now I address myself to the Prime Minister, and I ask him publicly a question. I am
authorised by those who are associated with me, no doubt, a forlorn and scanty band,
to withdraw the Amendment if the Government will merely add to their Motion the
speech of their own Secretary of State—the statement of policy made by him, not
merely an enumeration of the safeguards but the whole of the statement he made,
including his resolve to persevere with the policy of self-government and with the
erection of a federal system. If he will include that speech in the Motion which he is
asking us to pass this evening, he will have a unanimous vote so far as his supporters
are concerned. I pause for a reply.

The Prime Minister (Mr. Ramsay MacDonald): It is perfectly plain that everything that was in the secretary of State's speech is in the White Paper.

Mr. Churchill: Then I take it that the offer is refused. The Government,
supported by the Liberal party—[Hon. Members: "And the Conservative party!"] —
will use their Whips against the incorporation in the Resolution of Confidence to them
of the speech delivered by their own Secretary of State on this subject last night. I say
that that is an oppressive use of the machinery of Parliament. I would like to know the
explanation. I can see perfectly well the explanation. The right hon. Gentleman is
wishing to speak with two voices to two audiences. Here is what he has said to the
Indian delegates, which they have taken away with them to encourage them, honeyed
words, only saying the things that please them, leaving out a firm insistence on British
rights and a blunt expression of what belongs to us, and merely dwelling on what we
wish to give to them. They are to take that away with them, to be encouraged by false
hopes and to be misled by a wrong impression of the actualities and the verities of
British opinion. There are verities and resistances in British opinion.

We in this House are to be induced to consent to a policy and a White Paper by the
speech—the most reassuring speech—which the Secretary of State for India made to us
for domestic consumption, which is not to be incorporated in the Resolution which
we are to pass, and when legislation is presented to us, a few years hence, that will be
the only operative fact of which the House will be able to take cognisance. When the
Resolution comes forward and we say: "Look at what the Secretary of State said in
regard to safeguards," it will be said to us that what we voted on was the Prime
Minister's statement. When we say that there are some things in that statement which
show that he bore those safeguards in mind, we shall be told: "The operative thing is
the solemn declaration made by the Prime Minister in January, 1931; from which he
has never swerved and which we are carrying into force to-day." That is the condition
in which we find ourselves. What is the value of the declarations made by the Secretary
of State if they are not to play their full part in the decision to which the House is to
come? The Government Whips are to be put on to resist the application of the
Government's own policy in order that a false impression may be given in India, or
that we may ourselves be entrapped into a loss of our liberties and discretion at some
future date.

This shows that the Government, with all their able men, with all the good wishes and the good will which they command have been paralysed from birth by internal weaknesses. They have lost in height what they have gained in breadth, they have lost in stature what they have gained in girth and they have lost in fibre what they have gained in bulk. That is what the people are saying all over the country. Things of this kind are more likely to injure the Administration than the most firm action, even if in some respects it were mistaken action in the handling of a great public problem. What are we to do? We are to send out committees to India. They are to roam around India, large parts of which may be under something like martial law. They will roam around India in places where the ordinary constitutional rights are superseded by measures of enforced protection. They are to be subjected to the same sort of ill-usage as that to which the Simon Commission were subjected by the adherents of the Congress party. India is to be kept in this state of unsettlement, perhaps for two or three years, with these hopes and fears of some great change that is going to take place.

Five years have passed since we began unsettling the pathetic content of the people of India. It is five years since the Simon Commission was appointed, and three years since it reported. All the time there has been change, perpetual friction and disturbances, raising every kind of grave question and every type of discussion. That is to go on for another two or three years *pari passu* with the repressive measures, the stern repressive measures, which, I believe, have largely arisen out of our foolish policy of fermenting this feeling of unsettlement. All the time our officials in India, officers of all kinds, will have to go on with their enormously difficult work, with this haunting feeling behind them that nothing is settled, that there is nothing to stand on. Meanwhile the committees will be roaming up and down the country. There will be the feeling all the time that some great development is sure to occur, and there will be this horrible undermining impression that they are the representatives only of a rearguard which is edging off, shuffling off responsibilities and ultimately out of the country altogether. The people of India as well as the people of Great Britain are entitled to better treatment than that.

I have finished, and I am most grateful to the House for permitting me to intrude for so long upon their attention. What can we do but persevere with our Amendment? It is not a vote of want of confidence in His Majesty's Government. On the contrary, it merely asserts the principles which they themselves affirm, and which both the Prime Minister and the Secretary of State have affirmed. It can only be made a Vote of want of confidence by what I think is the abusive action on the part of the Whips, to which the leader of the Conservative party had no right to lend himself. Let me tell the House, seeing that there are so many new Members, how this matter will be put first as a positive Motion, the Question being,

That the words proposed to be added stand part.

Therefore , the House will vote upon the words of the Amendment:

Provided that nothing in the said policy shall commit this House to the establishment in India of a Dominion Constitution as defined by the Statute of Westminster, etc.

The House will vote upon that for or against the Amendment, and hon. Members will consider the implication of voting against. It would mean a reversal of these proposals. If they put it in that way, hon. Members will be able to see what it is they are asked to vote against. If the Amendment be defeated, it will still be open to any hon. Member who has voted for it to vote for a general Vote of Confidence in the Government. There is no inconsistency in that; because any hon. Member may say that he would rather have the Government Motion with the Amendment, but that if he cannot get it with the Amendment, nevertheless he must go on. There is no reason why we should not have a free vote on the Amendment, and afterwards a Vote of Confidence in the Government can be given. The Amendment affords the one sure foundation upon which those who believe it is their duty not only to advance the cause of Indian self-government but to uphold the rights of Britain and tell the truth to India can take their stand.

PRESS INTERVIEW

December 11, 1931

Aboard the Europa, *New York City*

At the end of 1931 Churchill went on a lecture tour in the United States.

How are conditions in England?

Well, we had an election. A very good one. It was the most remarkable election that I have read or heard of in England. Hundreds of thousands from the poorest districts voted for a government to take office and cut their own dole when they realized that their country was in danger.

The result of this election has put the political situation on a sound basis and I believe the National Government will stand for several years. It was a fine proof of the stability of our political institutions in Great Britain. I never had any doubt about it, but considerable doubt has been expressed by foreign countries. It is a proof that the social legislation which we have created this century and which many people have mocked at has established a genuine loyalty in the hearts of the people.

Will Great Britain enact tariff laws?

After having kept the free trade flag flying since 1846 Great Britain now is going to become a full-fledged protectionist country. It is not going to be proposed immediately—we very rarely do anything with a sweep. But practically all the parties in the new government have abandoned the free trade theory.

We are beginning to realize that we have an enormous home market which we must hold to ourselves. If we are being shut out of foreign markets we must secure a larger share of our own. The new British tariff won't help the world, but it will help Great Britain. It will be a scientific tariff adapted to every purpose, protection, negotiation, imperial preference.

Of course a general lowering of tariffs would be much better for the world, but that isn't going to happen.

I think the situation in Germany serious, but that if payment of reparations ceases England will still do her best to continue to pay her war debts.

Do you believe the British Empire is going down, as certain visiting Englishmen have said?

There are many new forces in the world now which did not exist in the palmy days of Queen Victoria. And, of course, we are an easygoing people. As a result of the war there is an exhaustion which is not merely economic, but psychic, moral and mental. But, after all, the crisis that afflicts us is not political. After the last election we can say that that question is settled.

It is an economic condition that is gripping us, and I've even heard that you have got some echoes of it over here. The situation is really very serious. The continued fall of the price of everything in relation to gold means an immense deflation, a drying up of world values. We are writing ourselves down every day.

How do you see the international situation?

There will not be another war, at least in Europe, for many years. I think the League of Nations has done good even in the present imbroglio in the Far East.

All the nations are reducing their navies with the exception of the United States which has now a larger Navy than before the war. But we agreed to it, and there it is.

ANGLO-AMERICAN CO-OPERATION

December 11, 1931

*Economic Club, Worcester,
Massachusetts*

[Extract] . . . Cooperation of the two great English speaking nations is the only hope to bring the world back to the pathway of peace and prosperity.

If ever we should help, it is now, when the world is off the track and the pathway of peace and prosperity seems lost. The leading men of all countries do not seem to have a clear idea of the situation nor the steps to take to bring us out of the chaos. However, there is one thing that we can be sure of: that wherever the pathway may lead, we shall travel more securely if we do it together like good companions.

1932

DEMOCRACY NEEDS IMPROVEMENTS

January 25, 1932

Interview, Waldorf-Astoria Hotel,
New York City

The world today is ruled by harassed politicians, absorbed in getting into office or turning out the other man, so that not much room is left for determining great issues on their merits. Democracy may therefore be persuaded that individuals be entrusted with these great issues. [The appointment by President Hoover of Charles G. Dawes to head the Reconstruction Finance Corporation is] a remarkable and very hopeful step in this general direction.

The progress of the world is dependent on eminent individuals. It has never been ground out by political machines. It is a great delusion to think that the people have the kind of government that they want in any country in the world now. They have got the kind of government they vote for and are told they want.

[Editor's Note: Referring to the coming disarmament conference, he said] : I have always relied on time, returning confidence, taxation and want of money as the surest means by which the burden of armaments will be reduced.

"THE PATHWAY OF THE ENGLISH-SPEAKING PEOPLES"

January 28, 1931

Brooklyn Academy of Music,
New York City

[Extract] . . . England and America are going in the same direction. They have the same outlook and no common discords. Why, then do we not act together more effectively? Why do we stand gaping at each other in this helpless way, ashamed that it be said that America and England are working together, as if that were a crime? We must be the strong central nucleus at the council board of the nations.

[Editor's Note: Churchill said he did not approve of the London Naval Treaty] because it weakens us not in respect to America, but in respect to the European powers and to that great Asiatic power [Japan], with whom, of course, we are very friendly.

[Editor's Note: Referring to Prohibition, Churchill said Britain had been more successful than the United States in attacking the frightful social evils of intemperance.] Like you, we attacked those evils by state interference with the liberty of the citizen, but we used the two sharp weapons of taxation and regulation. We treated the problem as a disease rather than a moral issue.

INTERNATIONAL FINANCE

February 3, 1932

Public Music Hall, Cleveland, Ohio

[Extract] All that is necessary [to regain world prosperity] for the two or three principal governments of the world is to proclaim their desire to revalue commodities and services up to the level of 1927, then—call in their experts and order them to devise the methods and details.

[Editor's Note: Referring to the theory that over-production was to blame for the Depression, Churchill said]: We are stripped bare by the curse of plenty.

[Editor's Note: On tariff barriers and on the fact that large debts between nations were payable only in goods he said]: But when Germany attempted to pay back the war debts in reparations and goods, the other nations refused to take the goods, building tariff frontiers to protect their own industrial organizations.

And when Germany offered to pay France by sending workmen to help rebuild the devastated areas, France refused in horror at the threatened taking of jobs from her own workmen.

The problem was solved up until 1929 by the creditor nations lending back to Germany the money she paid. But when the 1929 crash came, the United States and others stopped lending back. The result was that Germany could pay only in gold.

... Unless Germany can pay her creditors in goods, or unless there is a great increase in prices, there is no hope of collecting the war's debts. ...

The deflation now in progress is the greatest danger to capitalism, ... deflation, if continued will isolate the nations completely, will bring repudiation of debts, will reduce the whole world to barbarism and barter of the Dark Ages.

Debts between nations can be paid only in goods but the victor nations did not want goods. Germany, for instance, offered to pay with workmen to rebuild the destroyed buildings but France indignantly cried, 'We saw enough of your men in the war.' Thus, there was only the process of paying in gold.

If the gold in France and the United States were put into circulation, instead of kept sterile in vaults, it would have driven prices up, ... the high prices would make the tariff ineffective, and goods would pour in until the whole situation had resumed its economic balance.

The United States in 1928 was closer to bridging the gap between the consumer and the producer, which is what all economic systems have aimed at, and I propose that the two English-speaking nations of the world order their government experts to revalue commodities at the 1928 level and devise methods and details to keep the situation pliable.

It is the function of government to provide authority, it is for the government to declare what must be done, and the function of experts to provide the necessary steps. In this role it is not impossible that experts could devise the steps to revalue commodities and provide a stabilizer.

[Editor's Note: On reparations he said] : Germany is not being bled white by the reparations demands . . . the United States did not bleed the world.

The United States immediately relent all she got as payment on war debts . . . Germany really has received a bonus. She has had an infusion of credits and commodities which she needed and desires and enjoys. She was in the position of the debtor who owes so much that he can see no other way but to go out and borrow more.

The system of war reparations was foolish, but I am not ready to believe yet that Germany cannot pay. Unquestionably she cannot pay now, but let us reserve judgment. Just now reparations are down to such a scale that they may not be beyond her power.

"THE PATHWAY OF THE ENGLISH-SPEAKING PEOPLES"

February 7, 1932

Orchestra Hall, Chicago

[Extract] . . . We hear always when we draw closer together in international affairs the whisper, (and sometimes the cry) 'Ah, look! The English and Americans are working together!'

Well, why should we be ashamed of that? Why should we not frankly recognize that there must be some source of doctrine and authority to rescue the nations from confusion?

Remember, I beg of you, that, vast as our resources are, there is another power coming into being which makes its appeal to certain classes in all countries and which has its agents in all countries. I mean the force of international communism.

I see two imminent forces that will be brought to bear in the shaping of mankind's destiny—the armed Asiatic conception of communism and the English-speaking ideal of individualism. Our disunion may make the struggle end the wrong way.

May it therefore not be our time now to raise together, with our united hands, the standards of the home, of the family, of individualism, of God? This we can do, not with our hands raised against the rest of mankind but with our hands clasped.

Moving in harmony with that spirit, we of the English-speaking lands will travel more prosperously and travel further if we tread the path together, like good companions.

[Editor's Note: Churchill closed his talk with an appeal for a closer union of the English-speaking peoples against Communism and the disintegrating forces of a disunited Europe.]

DEFLATION AND WAR DEBTS

February 8, 1932

Economic Club Meeting, Hotel Astor,
New York City

[Extract] [Editor's Note: Rejecting the idea of a repudiation of debts by European nations, Churchill said] : Great Britain and the United States are the greatest creditor nations. We cannot afford to countenance repudiation, still less encourage a situation in which it will occur, by slapdash phrases. With care and patience many frozen assets may be thawed and many values re-created. I am not prepared to accept the idea that Germany can never pay anything for war damage. I am sure she cannot pay anything now, and I do not see why at this moment we are called upon to go further than that.

There is no room either for false indignation against the United States or for false pity for Germany. . . . [Editor's Note: Referring to the process of deflation Churchill warned that if it continued it would isolate nations as they were in medieval times and would reduce] this fair modern world with all its knowledge and science and measureless possibilities to the barbarism and barter of the Dark Ages.

Happily, the remedy is in our hands. There is still time to arrest and reverse this hateful process, to restore a fair standard of values throughout the world, and to bring back again the sunshine which has been darkened by clouds of human folly.

In my opinion, it would be sufficient at this stage if two or three of the principal governments of the world were to proclaim their intention of revaluating commodities and services upon, let us say, the 1927 or 1928 level; and then if sufficient financial experts were selected and told to devise steps by which this should be done and the form of international currency that would be required to keep a stable standard of value thereafter, I do not think you would be setting them an impossible task. I expect they would find that there were several ways of accomplishing this purpose once it was clearly defined and authoritatively set forth.

Neither do I think there would be great difficulty in procuring the agreement of a sufficient number of powerful nations to a workable plan.

I expect that if once the English-speaking peoples made up their minds and were agreed between themselves upon a practical plan, there would not be very great difficulty in getting one or two of the others to come in too. In fact, it seems to me there would be a rush to join the board. At any rate, there is where I would begin.

I would like to see the governments of the United States and Great Britain, through their agents, the Federal Reserve and the Bank of England, come to the definite conclusion that commodities must be revaluated up to the 1927 or 1928 level, and that thereafter sufficient currency must be available to provide a stable measure for prices.

You cannot waste time going around to persuade everybody. If these two were agreed, it would not be long before the Bank of France would wish to be included in their consortium. But, anyhow, our two nations in accord would be quite powerful enough to restore to human society the enormous benefits of which it is now deprived.

These are surely the times when the English-speaking peoples should keep closely together. On the whole, they mean the same thing. Why, then, do we not act together more, make more plans in common? Why do we stand gaping at one another? If the world is to escape its miseries there must be some strong central nucleus of agreed and recognized authority at the council board of nations to which, while it acts unselfishly, due deference is shown.

There is, remember, another world force, international communism, centred— the armed and arming strength of Russia. Is it not the duty, nay, the appointed task of the English-speaking peoples to stand between Europe and Asia and the new tyranny? To raise again the standards of personal liberty, of enlightened liberalism, of family home, faith in God upon which the glory of mankind has been erected? If so, the task is surely not beyond our united strength.

Above all, let us have good courage. Do not add to monetary deflation the further hideous deflation of panic and despair.

My confidence in the British Empire is only equaled by my confidence in the United States. All the world looks to the English-speaking peoples, for example, guidance, valued leadership. They must not look in vain. Let us be unconquerable. Remember 'the earth is a good mother.'

ANGLO-AMERICAN RELATIONS

March 8, 1931

Westchester County Centre,
White Plains, New York

[Extract] . . . Aristide Briand took great pains to organise the "United States of Europe." Joint action should be taken by the United States and Great Britain to oppose any dangers which might result from a union of the nations of Europe. Neither the United States nor England can alone afford to adopt an antagonistic attitude toward any continent; the two nations together could protect their own interests against any other combination of nations and maintain peace in the world. Let us have no fear of the United States of Europe as long as the United States and England grow together. Any sinister results could then be properly dealt with.

[Editor's Note: Comparing the destinies of Great Britain and the United States, Churchill said] : What business has gained in America, politics has lost. The flower of American manhood does not go into politics but chooses industry instead. In England just the reverse is true, and very frequently English young men devote their lives unselfishly to improving the state of the nation.

I think an interchange might work out very nicely. Let your young men run our business and we might lend you some of ours to run your government. I think I might make a present of this idea to the League of Nations.

[Editor's Note: Replying to a question asking whether in his opinion Russia had contributed anything to world progress, he said]: Not half as much as to world disaster.

[Editor's Note: Commenting that he had regretted that Great Britain had been the first to recognise the Soviet Government, he continued]: I thoroughly approve of the American position, that of not lowering its own standards to gain Russia trade.

THE IRISH SITUATION

March 17, 1932

Plymouth, on Return from the United States

During his visit to the United States Churchill was knocked down by a taxi in New York and narrowly escaped serious injury.

[Editor's Note: Referring to the declaration of the new Government of Ireland, Churchill said]: The land grants were part of the agreement. In 1926 the Irish asked for a modification. We agreed, and Mr. Cosgrave and his colleagues declared that they had been treated with the utmost generosity. To go back on that and repudiate these solemnly agreed obligations would be an act of perfidy. Still more would it be an act of bad faith to repudiate the Oath of Allegiance which was the central point around which all the discussions on the Irish Treaty focussed. It is impossible that England should ever lend the slightest countenance to such violation of a solemn agreement between the British and Irish peoples. We stand absolutely on the Treaty. If Mr. de Valera and his Government will repudiate the Treaty they repudiate the title deeds of the Irish Free State, which becomes an anomalous body without a status at all, either in or out of the Empire.

THE BUDGET

April 21, 1932

House of Commons

I do not share the mild but general disappointment with which the main facts of the Budget have been received. I did not expect much, and I am readily resigned to receive nothing. I wish, of course, that my right hon. Friend [Mr. Neville Chamberlain,

Chancellor of the Exchequer], before restoring the Tea Duty and according so important a preference as 50 per cent., could have been in a position to assure us that a counter preference would be afforded to us by India and Ceylon. But, no doubt, he will be pursuing that important aspect. I wish, of course, there could have been some relief upon the allowances of the smaller class of Income Tax payers, the black-coated working men, who were so seriously affected by the venomous provisions of the October Budget. I should have been glad to hear in his speech some greater encouragement that there was a prospect of a conversion operation in the present year, but perhaps there are good reasons against his enlightening us on that matter.

Of course, above all, I regret very much that he has not found himself in a position, for one reason or another, to remit the additional duty on beer. I must in that respect claim full liberty to associate myself with any view that the House may take in favour of a mitigation of the present position. It seems to me that the Chancellor of the Exchequer could easily make such a concession without altering the Budget. There is this exchange stabilisation fund for which he is claiming, very rightly, borrowing powers up to £150,000,000, and in which there is a nucleus composed of money similar to that which has been used in the past year to the extent of £10,000,000 to defray current expenditure. Therefore, there is no insuperable reason why the matter should not be reconsidered, and I would earnestly ask my hon. Friend if he will not reconsider it between now and the concluding stages of the Budget.

When I have said that, looking at the position as a whole, I cannot reproach him for not having divested himself of reserves and resources at a time like this. I cannot reproach him for having given us a Budget of marking time, and, although we are all, alas, crunching the gravel of the barrack square for another 12 months, he has probably been wise and prudent in what he has done. I have heard it said, and from my own personal experience I have found the observation just, that every Chancellor of the Exchequer makes his first Budget. All the rest make themselves. It seems to me that my right hon. Friend has been wise to postpone the making of his first Budget till a more genial season, to another year, and it is to that Budget that we shall look forward with hope and eagerness.

Further, we do not know all the difficulties of the Chancellor of the Exchequer. In this House party is dead and Debate is reduced to very modest proportions, but the old struggles of party are proceeding within the bosom of the Cabinet, and it may well be that, if my right hon. Friend had begun to make remissions when he necessarily had few remissions to give, all sorts of stresses would have arisen inside the Executive itself. It might well be that the celebrated agreement to differ might have degenerated into an agreement to part, and our famous National Government, the star team as its co-parent has so proudly dubbed it, our sole defence, under Providence, at the present time, as we are so often assured by Ministers themselves, might have passed in a flash, untimely, from life into history. A great many of us would regard such a step as premature at present. I, therefore, do not intend to criticise in any hostile spirit the policy that my right hon. Friend has announced. I treat it as an interim policy dictated not only by financial but by political considerations.

But I cannot follow with the same docility the Chancellor of the Exchequer in the account he has given of the transactions of the past. He spoke on Tuesday in terms of warm eulogy of Viscount Snowden's courage and determination in October last.

But that is not all the story. The contributions to our affairs by the Noble Viscount did not begin in October last. I think we must look back a little further. Here I hope I shall not embarrass my right hon. Friend the Lord President of the Council, the leader of the Conservative party [Mr. Stanley Baldwin], if I say a few words in defence of the record of the Conservative Administration over which he presided. I do not want to put him in a difficulty now that he has developed, late in life, such a keen relish for hunting with other packs than his own, but I think he need not feel unduly ashamed of what took place in those days.

There is a good deal to be said on behalf of that Administration. At any rate, they had great difficulties, not in all respects as great, or perhaps not so incessant, as the difficulties which confront the Government of to-day, but nevertheless they had their difficulties. The political opponents of that Government used methods to attack them which were most injurious, most devastating to finance. The general strike and the prolonged coal stoppage which the Socialist leaders organised or fomented cost the Treasury, directly in revenue or in expenditure, upwards of £80,000,000, of which I gave full details to the House, which affected the Budgets of three succeeding years. That was a very heavy blow to us. It reduced the provision for the repayment of Debt to an enormous extent; it disappointed our hopes and intentions in that respect; it forced us to maintain direct taxation at levels which were directly hampering to trade, and it weakened the strength of our country in a great many ways which cannot be brought into arithmetical account.

In those days economy was also very difficult. It got a good cheer on Tuesday last. It always will get a good cheer. But it was even more difficult then than it is to-day. I remember—and I am sure my right hon. Friend the Chancellor of the Exchequer remembers too—our poor little Economy Bill of 1926. It only tried to save a small £17,000,000, but what a hullabaloo was raised. Not only Socialists but Liberals, and we expect much better of Liberals—joined in this cacophony of abuse. I made a calculation that the word robbery was used 87 times, confiscation, 10; plunder, 10; steal, 3; raid, 11; theft, 2; filch, 1; grab, 1; cheat, 1—the present Foreign Secretary [Sir John Simon] contributed that particular word—breach of faith, 19; betrayal, 5; outrage, 1; infamy, 1; rascality, 1; perfidy, 1; mean, 15; paltry, 1; despicable, 1; shabby, 1; and dastardly, 3. That gives an idea of the sort of difficulty with which we were confronted in endeavouring to secure a very moderate economy, and, of course, when the General Election came, every effort was made to rouse prejudice upon the economies which we had made. We had stolen the soldiers' money, we had filched the money of the friendly societies, and my right hon. Friend the Chancellor of the Exchequer was specially pilloried for having pinched the babies' milk. It was a propaganda vile and unscrupulous, but at the same time undoubtedly effective and profitable.

I hate to be in disagreement with my right hon. Friend, but I am sorry to say that no one was more forward in this work than the late Chancellor of the Exchequer. No one showed more courage and determination in putting this point of view. He revelled in the trials of His Majesty's Government in making good the losses of the general strike. He obstructed all economy except, of course, cutting down the Navy, which goes without saying. He also at the same time presented himself as the champion of financial orthodoxy and was always very strict, stern and punctual to mark the slightest shortcoming in those who then held the responsibility for our finances. Notwithstanding this fact, from time to time he promised the abolition of almost all the indirect taxes, except, of course, the taxes on liquor. Tea, sugar, silk, petrol, and, of course, all the wicked McKenna and Safeguarding Duties, all were to be swept away, and he extolled the salutary effects of ever-increasing direct taxation in toning up the efforts of the producing and capitalist classes. Thus did the Noble Viscount prepare himself for the responsibilities which he was eagerly seeking and which he was soon fated to assume.

I have always regarded the Socialist assumption of office in 1929, after the General Election, as an event very damaging to our national repute and prosperity. The spectacle of a body of men so newly engaged in organising a general strike, and containing leaders in police strikes and other subversive movements, the spectacle of such a body of men being placed in plenary command of the whole Government, dividing among themselves all the offices of honour in the State—I cannot expect them to cheer—such a spectacle, was one which was not compatible with any steady or intelligible standard of personal conduct or civic duty among public men. To foreign countries, of course, it was incomprehensible. They at once predicted the disasters which so speedily ensued. The confidence in Great Britain was profoundly shaken, and it was profoundly shaken at the very time when it was perhaps most necessary that our prestige and authority should stand high. We must be thankful indeed that those days are ended. I am thankful with others that they are ended.

I have always been able to keep my enthusiasms for the present National Government within the bounds of decorum, but now I am going to pay them a compliment, and, as far as it goes, a sincere compliment. I say that they are far more imposing and impressive—perhaps I had better not do it by halves—I will say that they are even more imposing and impressive abroad than they are at home. Here we know too much about them, or about some of them. Here the details of their performances can be observed at close quarters, but distance lends enchantment to the view, and certainly, with all their faults—and they are neither few or small—they are an enormous improvement upon their predecessors.

I was much refreshed during my travels in the United States by the contrast in the repute and prestige of Britain and of the British Empire now than when I went there two or three years ago. In 1929 you could not persuade Americans that we were not a declining or a decaying Power. I did what I could. I said that the English Socialists were not like the Continental Socialists, and not like the Russian Socialists. I said that their leaders had a bourgeois outlook, or else they were political careerists. I said that they would never try to carry into effect, in office, their crazy doctrines and the crazy pledges which they had given to gain office. I said that I was always sure that if things came to the pinch they would far rather betray their party than betray their country. I did all that I could for them, but it was not much good. How different is the position to-day. To-day, we are looked up to—I can say it after travelling through most of the great cities in the middle, west and eastern parts of the United States—with admiration, and with admiration tinged with outspoken envy. We must all rejoice unfeignedly at such a transformation, such a material transformation, in our affairs, so necessary to our credit and our power to cope with the difficulties which are upon us. There, I think, I have paid my compliment to the Government.

Let me, after what I think is an agreeable interlude, return to the late Chancellor of the Exchequer. I come directly to his Budget of April last. Here I must be very careful of the Rules of Order. The late Chancellor of the Exchequer is now a Viscount. He is a peer of Parliament. He has marketed what I might call the surrender value of his life policy in Socialism on terms happily advantageous both to his country and himself. He has been translated from these spheres to those dim splendours at the end of the corridor which are the goal of so many rising demagogues, where he is protected from any comment that is not strictly governed by gravity and restraint. In my historic retrospect I have to deal not only with the Budget of October last, but with the Budget of April of last year, and I will couch my remarks as far as possible in an impersonal form. I will speak, not of the late Chancellor of the Exchequer, but of the "late Financial Administration." I think that will be satisfactory to the most tender susceptibilities.

We can all see now that the April Budget was a gross deception. The figures given to Parliament by the late Financial Administration were figures and estimates which could have had no warrant in the facts as they were then known to the Treasury. I must admit, less sceptical as I am than the present Chancellor of the Exchequer, that I accepted the assurances that were offered to us from the Treasury Bench. I know well the care with which the Treasury officials prepare their Estimates. I know well the elaborate, the minute, and the intricate processes of experience and calculation which take place before the forecasts of the forthcoming year are made. I know that 40,000 accounts are searched through, codified and classified, before a forward estimate of Income Tax is made in any one year, and that is one branch alone. It seemed to me incredible that the Chancellor of the Exchequer's figures, even if they were a little over sanguine—many people may be over sanguine—were not substantially true. I could understand if it had been a few millions out one way or the other; but what happened? Five months later the late Chancellor of the Exchequer had to produce the courage and the determination to confess that his Estimates were wrong by £75,000,000.

Of course, he did right to bring those facts to the mind of Parliament and the country. Observe that in the interval no sudden new catastrophe had occurred—no war, no earthquake, no pestilence, no general strike, nothing out of the ordinary, except the great world depression which, indeed, had become more acute. Unemployment had grown and its cost had grown. But all these were tendencies which were gradual, which were progressive and which, I say without fear of contradiction, were plainly apparent at the time of framing the April Budget. They were apparent even to outsiders. Members of the Opposition, without any secret sources of information, were able, and foreign countries no doubt were able, to form their own judgment. The Committee will remember the last speech of our charming friend and colleague, the late Sir Laming Worthington-Evans, whose loss we feel so much and whom we miss so much. Only three days before his death, in a speech which I think was the best I ever heard him make, he gave a most true and careful analysis of the financial position and showed that the statements that were being made to us were almost certainly false. Such views were also taken in other quarters of the House. If ordinary Members of

Parliament were able to detect what was taking place, how much more must the true facts have been apparent to those who possessed day by day official information and who had only to look at the grim figures placed before them each week by their subordinates to see exactly how matters stood.

What did the late Financial Administration do? He I beg pardon—it breathed no whisper of its guilty secret. The summer months were occupied in the futile follies of land taxes, or in unwholesome intrigues—if I may say it without abusing the hospitality of this bench—about electoral reform. So the summer slipped away. So the precious weeks were wasted, one by one, until, finally, the exposure could be staved off no longer, until foreign nations saw quite clearly what our position was, until panic broke out among foreign investors in London, until the flight from the pound began, until this rich country and Empire, with its measureless resources, was reduced to quivering on the verge of bankruptcy and repudiation, and until the late financial administration had no resources but to throw itself upon the patriotism of the Conservative Opposition it had so harshly, so deceitfully, and so wrongfully misused.

"Betwixt the stirrup and the ground,
Mercy I askt, mercy I found."

So much for the April Budget. Now I come to the October Budget, which is very important, because it governs our affairs to-day. We are back upon the October Budget. My right hon. Friend—I do not blame him—has not made, I think, any alteration. I do not say that it was within his power. This is a prolongation of the October Budget. He said that the late financial administration showed great courage and determination in that Budget. That may be true. I do not wish to detract from that, but there was very little skill or wisdom, if I may say so, in the construction of that Budget. It was a bad, clumsy, vicious, partisan Budget, which cast our finances in an awkward mould, and a mould from which it will be extremely difficult to extricate them. I say that the late financial administration took the fullest advantage of the crisis which it had so largely created, and used and exploited the loyalty and patriotism of the Conservative party, in order to give effect to its narrowest prejudices.

It was very difficult to bring any effective criticism to bear in the national circumstances which prevailed. After all, we all felt that any Budget that was balanced was better than no Budget at all. We could not consider the details; the House simply refused to consider them. The worse they were, the more ready it was to accept the position because of the greater issues involved. But I must remind the Committee that I pointed out from this bench, that if the remissions which Viscount Snowden and I, in our tenures as Chancellors of the Exchequer, made in tea and sugar from 1924 onwards had been put back in the taxation, we should get a revenue from tea and sugar of £20,000,000 a year, if my memory serves me aright, and that the price of tea and sugar would still have remained lower than in 1928, when people were quite pleased at the price prevailing. It would have been quite easy and, in my judgment, only common justice to have restored those remissions when, for the second time, the direct taxpayer was meeting an avalanche of £50,000,000 or £60,000,000 of additional taxation. Had that course been taken, there would have been no need to strip the small Income Tax payers of their much-needed allowances, and no need to lay a foolish, excessive, uneconomic, improvident, unprofitable and unfair tax on beer, and there would have been no need to propose cuts of such rigour that we were drawn into that series of disgraceful incidents which occurred in the Fleet. So much for the Budget of October.

Now let us consider the late Financial Administration's outlook upon finance, the question of currency upon finance, the question of currency and the monetary problem. Let us see what happened. One example will suffice. He borrowed, I think, £120,000,000 upon very costly terms to keep us on the Gold Standard, and to prevent the exchange from going down; whereas a few months later his successor and colleague, with his assent, and, I think, with general assent, is now taking power to borrow £150,000,000, not entirely in a comparable manner, in order to make sure, not that the exchange does not go down, but that it does not go up. We live in times when very few people who take a prominent part in public affairs will not find themselves confounded from time to time by events, and from time to time forced to take a new view, but I venture to think that never has stultification—and self-stultification—been more swift and perfect than in the case of the monetary outlook of the late Financial Administration. In those days we were led to believe it was about to retire from public life, and such a prospect naturally excited widespread sympathy, but, after the election, in which it so distinguished itself, it was announced that we were still to have the advantage of its able services, and it may well be that Viscount Snowden—I may safely refer to that now—is now exercising a control upon our policy for which, I venture to think, the character and the composition of the House of Commons afford him little justification.

To complete my right hon. Friend's eulogy of his predecessor, I have ventured to look back at some length into the past, but now I have done with yesterday—only yesterday—and I come to the politics of to-day. I have been away for some time, and an extraordinary change has occurred since I left this country. I left a Free Trade country. I come back to find full-blooded Protection, tariffs of all kinds, revenue tariffs, retaliatory tariffs, bargaining tariffs and definitely protective tariffs in actual working, or being rapidly and ardently erected. It seems to me that the Government have very properly deferred to the will and the weight of the new Parliament, the representatives of the people, as I predicted, before I went away, they would have to do, and it seems to have proved as easy to effect this fiscal revolution as—what shall I say?—as it was to keep order in India once you made up your mind to do so. I come back to find a vast, far-reaching, and, for a generation at least, irrevocable change already accomplished, and I ask you, Sir Dennis [Herbert, Ways and Means Committee Chairman], what must I do in this new situation? I must do my duty, and I see my duty clear. I must accept this new situation with good will. I must accommodate myself to the decision which I had for some time regarded as necessary and inevitable, to which my fellowcountrymen have come, and I must labour loyally, whatever my views might have been in the past, to make our new protectionist system a real success. It is absolutely necessary that the fiscal policy of Great Britain, be it Free Trade or be it Protection, should be sincerely and faithfully applied in all its scientific integrity. It is necessary to all of us, whatever our views might have been, that the fiscal policy of our country, Protection, should now be given as fair and as good a chance as Free Trade was given in bygone days.

It is very fortunate that this memorable and historic departure, this solemn abandonment of Free Trade, this casting down of so much of the teaching of Mr. Cobden and of Mr. Bright after 70 years, should have been effected with so great a measure of consent among all parties in the State. It is a public advantage that our fiscal policy should stand not on a party but on a national foundation, built by a National Government. I did not see the Home Secretary [Sir Herbert Samuel]. I know that some of the Ministers have made speeches or given votes against it, and I am told that we are to be treated to further exhibitions of the same kind in the future. But what does all that matter except to the individuals concerned, as long as these Ministers are willing to remain an inseparable part of the great political engine which is so swiftly carrying these remarkable changes into law? Speeches may be irritating, they may have to be answered, but speeches are soon forgotten. Actions speak louder than words. The solid, over-powering fact remains that Protection has been carried by a united National Government, and that all Free Trade resistance has been effectually crushed by its combined strength. If the deed were to be done, surely it were better done in this way than by a party majority, and I think that, in a peculiar manner, no man has helped this more than the Home Secretary by the assiduity with which he has discharged his function of a quacking decoy duck.

Protection having been resolved upon, I hope it will be carried out wholeheartedly. Obviously, we must not overlook the interests of our shipping industry. We must not overlook, in anything we do, the exporting capacity we have developed in the higher ranges of manufacture. We must not overlook our need to receive from abroad the goods the interest upon our vast foreign investments. Above all, we must not inflict hardship upon the mass of our people. But those are considerations of which every Government dependent upon universal suffrage would be mindful and bound to study, and which none would dare ignore. These considerations—here I have a word of comfort for my Free Trade friends—will impose certain natural limits upon the new policy, and will, I firmly believe keep our British tariffs at a reasonable and salutary level. Therefore, even the Free Traders of Clacton need not be unduly alarmed. The facts of our island situation are their ultimate guarantee against anything like too excessive tariffs which have injured so many foreign States, and are, we all know, so great a curse in the modern world. I look forward with keen interest to the future development of this new system. We must all wish that its success will fulfil the highest hopes of those responsible for it.

As I left the politics of yesterday for those of to-day, I now leave the politics of to-day for those of to-morrow. Whatever be the success of our British tariffs, I do not believe that they alone will solve our social and economic problems. Still less will they alone solve the world problems, or end the awful and deepening economic depression of mankind. Those problems, that depression, industrial, agricultural, maritime, still confront us, as they confront all other countries. We are in a far better position to address ourselves to these problems than we were last year, and than we were six months ago. We have gained an immense threefold advantage. We have in this new House of Commons, and, mark you, it is this new House of Commons which is the real dominating and decisive factor in our politics at the present time, a guarantee of political stability. We have in this Budget, I know my right hon. Friend will forgive me, this bleak Budget, at any rate the assurance of financial solvency, and we have a weapon of unequalled, almost unprecedented, power in a country like ours which is quitting Free Trade after so many generations—the weapon of fiscal freedom. With these three advantages we had not got last year, advantages which no other nation has in the same way—political stability, financial solvency and fiscal freedom—surely, thus armed and equipped we can march forward against the main causes of world misfortunes with good hopes that we may solve them, and certainly with the assurance that no one will fight a more valiant battle than the people of this island to find a way through their difficulties.

Many diseases are more easy to diagnose than they are to cure, but it is something, at any rate, to diagnose an evil, even if you cannot immediately prescribe remedy. Fortunately, there is a very general agreement in this country among thinking men upon the evil. No one who heard the speech of my right hon. Friend the Member for Hillhead (Sir R. Horne) yesterday, or observed its reception in all parts of the House, can doubt how wide is the measure of prudent and general agreement gathering upon the monetary question. It is accepted almost without dispute in England that the prime cause of all our troubles is the attempt to pay these huge sterile War Debts and Reparations across high tariff boundaries that will not receive goods, and thus payment has to be made in gold. The small and limited supplies of gold, which have hitherto served as a foot-rule or measure in our affairs, have been purloined and misappropriated for a purpose for which they are wholly unequal, for liquidating these gigantic debts.

This it is which has led in three short years, very suddenly and very swiftly, upon America stopping relending to the unhealthy engorgement of gold by particular countries, which have a special benefit from Reparations and War Debts. It is this which has led to the consequent sterilisation of large portions of gold and the consequent enhancement in the price of gold, and to the automatic and simultaneous diminution in the value of everything else which is made to-day or can be made by our efforts to-morrow. There is the root evil. Out of all the tangles and clouds of argument we can see quite plainly this knobbly point projecting: the artificial enhancement in the price of gold and the consequent fall in the price of everything that is measured by it. Gold is a measure. It is a measure between the efforts of one country and another, between man and man, between class and class, between the past and present; but I regret and grieve that it is a measure which has played the traitor. Poor devil; it may not be its fault; but that is the fact.

When I was moved by many arguments and forces in 1925 to return to the Gold Standard I was assured by the highest experts, and our experts are men of great ability and of indisputable integrity and sincerity—

Mr. Wallhead: And they are always wrong.

Mr. Churchill: The hon. Member is not always right—that we were anchoring ourselves to reality and stability; and I accepted their advice. I take for myself and my colleagues of other days whatever degree of blame and burden there may be for having accepted their advice. But what has happened? We have had no reality, no stability. The price of gold has risen since then by more than 70 per cent. That is as if a 12-inch footrule had suddenly been stretched to 19 or 20 inches; as if the pound, avoirdupois, had suddenly become 23 or 24 ounces instead of—how much is it?—16. Look at what this has meant to everybody who has been compelled to execute their contracts upon this irrationally enhanced scale. Look at the gross unfairness of such a distortion to all producers of new wealth, and to all that labour and science and enterprise can give us. Look at the enormously increased volume of commodities which have to be created in order to pay off the same mortgage debt or loan. Minor fluctuations might well be ignored, but I say quite seriously that this monetary convulsion has now reached a pitch where I am persuaded that the producers of new wealth will not tolerate indefinitely so hideous an oppression.

Are we really going to accept the position that the whole future development of science, our organisation, our increasing co-operation, and the fruitful era of peace and good will among men and nations; are all these developments to be arbitrarily barred by the price of gold? Is the progress of the human race in this age of almost terrifying expansion to be arbitrarily barred and regulated by fortuitous discoveries of gold mines here and there or by the extent to which we can persuade the existing cornerers and hoarders of gold to put their hoards again into the common stock? Are we to be told that human civilisation and society would have been impossible if gold had not happened to be an element in the composition of the globe? These are absurdities; but they are becoming dangerous and deadly absurdities. They have only to be asserted long enough, they have only to be left ungrappled with long enough, to endanger that capitalist and credit system upon which the liberties and enjoyments and prosperity, in my belief, of the vast masses depend. I therefore point to this evil and to the search for the methods of remedying it, as the first, the second and the third of all the problems which should command and rivet our thoughts.

This new House of Commons contains a great number of new and young legislators. I commend this problem to them as the supreme topic of the age. You may ask me for a remedy; what would I do? I am not going to be led into that intricate domain in which experts differ fundamentally upon questions to which they have given a lifelong study, but I do see two practical forward steps which we may take, and which we ought to take. A major step if possible; a minor step if the major is denied to us. What is the major step? Here I am going to be quite precise. The major step is obviously the close and effectual comradeship of this country and the United States of America, the two great creditor nations of the world, the two great English-speaking nations, in an agreed purpose to deflate and revaluate commodities in relation to gold up to, let us say, the 1928 level; that is to say, up to a level which affords the producer of prime commodities and raw materials, the industrialist or the agriculturist, a reasonable reward for his toil, and which by affording him a reasonable reward will enable these prime producers to buy again the manufactures of the cities and workshops of the world.

Therefore, I say His Majesty's Government should address themselves urgently to the Government of the United States, and they need not be afraid in so worthy a cause of encountering a rebuff. If to-morrow the English-speaking people were agreed upon the main purpose, if they were agreed upon a policy, France, in spite of her hoarded gold, would have to seek admission to our councils the next morning, and these three Powers, together with others, would be able to give guidance and chairmanship and primacy to the councils of nations, without which all may speedily degenerate into chaos or a melancholy low level of misfortune. I may be told that we cannot talk to the United States of America because they are busy about their election; that we do not know who is going to govern the United States; that we do not know whether they have at this moment the inherent capacity to make an arrangement and carry it through. We may have to wait for many critical months, and we may find after that that no agreement is possible. All right, do your best, but, if nothing can be done there, let us fall back in the meanwhile upon what I must regard as the minor step, the second best, which, nevertheless, may prove a highly practical policy and may become the means of our economic salvation. Let us fall back, as his Majesty's Government, as far as I understand their policy, seem most wisely disposed to do, upon what I will call the magnificent congregation of sterling communities. Let us make the best of that in default of a better. We can live on that, even if we may not thrive.

I read a speech last week by the Norwegian Minister of France, delivered in the Norwegian House of Commons upon the sterling policy of Norway, and he said: "Do not let us quit the convoy" or words to that effect. It is a curious similitude; it is an echo of the last years of the War, when Scandinavian convoys were conducted to and fro across the North Sea in the teeth of every menace by hostile fleets and submarines by the power of the Royal Navy. "Do not let us quit the convoy." In this case, instead of the Royal Navy, it is the power and virtue of Britain which guards the sterling convoy and brings the good ships safely across the ocean into port. Great responsibility falls upon us at the present time. We have to steam a steady pace. We have to consider the slower and weaker ships. We have to adapt ourselves to circumstances, and be vigilant to ward off dangers; and we have to gather an ever-increasing company of vessels within the protection of the sterling convoy.

We shall have other opportunities, in the successive Debates upon the Finance Bill, of returning to these all-important monetary questions. Meanwhile, the measures of the Chancellor of the Exchequer give a greater steadiness to sterling, to fit it for its duties, without depriving it of that element of flexibility which the confused conditions of the world require. They ought to claim our hearty accord. It is for these causes, among several other, that I will certainly give my general support to the Budget which the Chancellor of the Exchequer has just opened.

IMPORT DUTIES BILL AND INDIA

April 27, 1932

House of Commons

The Import Duties Bill provided for a general tariff of 10 percent on imported goods, with the exclusion of Empire products, raw materials and most foodstuffs. As has been rightly said: "Forty or fifty years before, the change to Protection would have been sensational, almost revolutionary. . . . Now . . . there were no victory rallies by triumphant Protectionists, no demonstrations of protest by indignant Free Traders. The heart had gone out of the quarrel" (A.J.P. Taylor, English History, 1914-1945, 330).

Everyone will agree with the tribute which the Lord President of the Council [Mr. Baldwin] has paid to the Financial Secretary to the Treasury. It has frequently occurred in our Parliamentary history that the Chancellor of the Exchequer has had to fall out of the line temporarily and then is the chance of the Financial Secretary to the Treasury. Everyone in every part of the House will feel that he has stepped into the breach in the most effective fashion. The great majority of the House will agree with the Lord President of the Council in all that he has said about the importance of keeping the details of tariff arrangements clear and free from the day-to-day work of the House of Commons and administered by an independent and impartial tariff commission. We are all agreed on that, and the right hon. Gentleman was only forcing an open door in the stress that he put upon that aspect of the topic now under discussion.

What is that topic? The point in question is whether, for the purpose of getting this particular Import Duties Bill through, we may not be permanently limiting and compromising those principles of the House of Commons by which, after all, we have not done so badly, by which in this period of the world's history we have arrived at a position about which we are not concerned, and by which we have a great Conservative majority engaged in carrying through a great Conservative programme. Do not let us, because to-day we hold the power, be in too much of a hurry to sweep away those liberties and principles and even those technicalities of procedure, which perhaps have been the unseen contributory cause of the growth of a structure of political society in this island which has withstood many stresses and many assaults. I was relieved to hear from the Lord President of the Council that he denied the statement of my right hon. Friend the Member for Sparkbrook (Mr. Amery) when the right hon. Member for Sparkbrook said, "Is it true that for the rest of this Parliament tariff policy is entirely removed from the House of Commons?" As far as I could gather, the Lord President of the Council said no, that nothing we were doing now could affect any future year.

Mr. Baldwin: Yes. That is with regard to this Resolution on the Paper. I said that, whatever might be done in future years, might have to be most carefully considered in the future. We shall have to consider carefully how to manage a discussion of tariffs in the House of Commons.

Mr. Churchill: Suppose that this Resolution is passed to-night and nothing further is done, no reversing Resolution is passed, then during the entire life of this Parliament there will be no means of discussing this matter?

Major Elliot: This is an annual matter.

Mr. Churchill: Then it is quite clear from the answer to the right hon. Member for Sparkbrook that we are in no danger of parting with any liberties of the House of Commons for more than the currency of the present year. If that is so, I am greatly relieved to hear it. I am obliged to the Lord President of the Council for having made it quite clear. I was also gratified to hear from him that he is prepared to accept the suggestion of the hon. and gallant Member for Gainsborough (Captain Crookshank), namely, that this question of the method by which the Import Duties are placed in an exceptional category of procedure shall be brought under effective review, and that he is prepared to refer that to the Committee on Procedure. Is that so? Is the right hon. Gentleman willing to refer to the Committee on Procedure, our own Committee which is now sitting, the question of how the future discussion of Import Duties is to be conducted? I understood from his speech that he was.

Mr. Baldwin: I think, speaking from recollection, that what I said was that I was perfectly willing to consider either with them or in consultation with my colleagues in what way this could be done.

Mr. Churchill: Then considerable relief will be given to those Members of the House who fear that, for the sake of the convenience this year of the Chancellor of the Exchequer [Mr. Neville Chamberlain] in attending the Lausanne Conference, which I hope will be more successful than some other conferences, and of some other matters which are special to this year, we might be parting with some of the broad general liberties of the House of Commons. We have a definite understanding that the right hon. Gentleman is going to consult with the Committee on Procedure and not deny them the opportunity of expressing their opinion on these matters, and that, failing agreement between the right hon. Gentleman and the Committee on Procedure, the Government will make some further positive statement on the matter after they have consulted among themselves. I am therefore of opinion that we should support the Government and not hamper them in getting through this Resolution. I agree with what the Lord President of the Council has said. It is an extraordinary situation. We are carrying through an immense fiscal revolution, and we should not hamper the administration at the present time. Therefore, I wish to support the Government on the definite assurances which have been given.

INDIA

April 29, 1932

House of Commons

I shall not follow my hon. Friend the Member for Whitehaven (Mr. Nunn) so far back into the past as he has seen fit to go in the most admirable speech, both in matter as well as in manner, which he has delivered to the House. I shall, however, have to go back some way into the more modern history of India. Only six months have passed since I had the opportunity of taking part in an Indian Debate in this House, and a great change in policy and in the scene we survey has taken place in that recent period. From the date of Lord Irwin's unfortunate declaration about Dominion status in October, 1929, down to January of the present year the policy which had been declared and consistently pursued by the Socialist Government and the two National Governments which succeeded it was consistently based upon the hope of co-opera-tion with Mr. Gandhi and the Indian Congress. Not merely Dominion status but a Dominion constitution was in contemplation for all India, and in that Congress was to play a vital part.

There followed from this all the visionary speeches and perorations which characterised the first Round Table Conference. There followed the landslide of

British political opinion of 1930 and a newspaper propaganda of the type of which the "Manchester Guardian" was the most distinguished contributor. That paper declared that we were the rear guard retreating in the face of a victorious and aggressive enemy and we must lose no time in putting such friends as we have in India in positions where they could cover our further withdrawal. There followed the release of Mr. Gandhi from prison and then came the Gandhi-Irwin Pact. That Pact was foolishly cheered by a number of Conservatives, some of whom may be sitting on any bench in the House, and whose memories no doubt prick their conscience now. Then there followed widespread disorders in India and hideous massacres of Moslems by Hindus and severe reprisals by Moslems upon Hindus. Then came the second Round Table Conference at which Mr. Gandhi was treated with exceptional ceremony, and he was even permitted to visit Buckingham Palace in an attire so scanty that it excluded him from the Vatican. I am only showing how far we went in these matters. The second Round Table Conference, like its predecessor, was remarkable for all kinds of platitudes and flowery speeches, none of which had any relation to the realities of Indian Government or to the true needs or loyalties of the mass of the Indian people. "Mr. Dear Mahatma," was the way in which Mr. Gandhi was addressed by the Prime Minister when he was returning to India to resume his agitation. We found the National Government using all the pressure of its party Whips to compel the House of Commons to endorse the loosely-phrased and far-reaching commitments of the Prime Minister's valedictory speech.

Such was the situation when I last addressed the House, but in January there came a great change. Then the new Viceroy, Lord Willingdon, supported, and I have no doubt inspired by my right hon. Friend the Secretary of State for India, and, feeling that he had behind him the life and strength of the new House of Commons, resolved to arrest Mr. Gandhi and the Congress leaders, and, by enforcing a series of most drastic Ordinances, to restore law and order firmly throughout India. This decision, so courageously and soberly carried out, makes a great difference in my attitude towards the Indian policy of His Majesty's Government. When I spoke at a meeting at the Cannon Street Hotel in January, 1930, I said:

> Sooner or later you will have to crush Gandhi and the Indian Congress and all they stand for.

That statement of mine was more censured than any other that I made and more condemned by those politicians who were at that time controlling Indian affairs. It was thought to be a shocking thing to say, but see what happened? I and those who thought as I did in both Houses of Parliament, including the high experts of the Indian Empire society which contains many experts thoroughly acquainted with the conditions not only of India but of the East, were condemned as men who wished to plunge India into a welter of bloodshed, using machine guns and artillery upon unarmed mobs, and as people desirous of exposing this country to the risk of having to send several divisions of troops in order to dragoon the people of India. It was in vain that we declared on every occasion that there would be no need for any serious use of force, and that a firm policy of maintaining law and order in India would not be attended by serious bloodshed or serious risk. What has happened? The Government of India, and the National Government at home, have adopted this very policy of crushing Gandhi and the Indian Congress. For nearly four months, Mr. Gandhi and his principal lieutenants, together with many thousands of his followers, have been in gaol; the Indian Congress has been proclaimed as an illegal organisation—[Hon. Members: "No!"]

Mr. Morgan Jones: May I ask the Secretary of State if that is so?

Sir S. Hoare: No, it is not.

Mr. Churchill: Put it as you will; the Indian Congress has been proclaimed in many of its branches—[Interruption]—I am very glad to accept that correction—as an illegal organisation; its meeting at Delhi has been prevented, and those who sought to attend it have been arrested. The Red Shirt movement on the Frontier, which was for so long a time a bugbear, has been suppressed, apparently without serious difficulty. And through all this, as I used to point out in my travels in America, probably fewer people have been killed by Government bullets in India than have been killed by gangster bullets in the same period in the United States. Except on the North-West Frontier, where our troops shield the defenceless and helpless millions of India from the incursions of formidable warrior Pathan tribes, there has not, I believe, been any need to use a single company, or even a platoon, of British soldiers for the maintenance of internal order. The Indian Policy, that admirable and devoted force, under their handful of British sergeants and inspectors, have been able to assert the Imperial authority with ease and with sureness, and, I thank God, with hardly any loss of life. Certainly not a tithe as many Indians have been killed or injured in the various sporadic riots which have occurred this year as were massacred by their own fellow-countrymen at Cawnpore and other places in the year 1931.

We must consider these events as most important, and, in view of the immense, inalienable responsibility that we have for the welfare of the people of India, we must consider them encouraging and satisfactory. This afternoon I should like to congratulate, first of all, Lord Willingdon and his Council; secondly, and not less, my right hon. Friend the Secretary of State; and, not least, this new House of Commons, whose resolute and patriotic spirit makes itself increasingly manifest throughout all quarters of our reviving Empire. To have achieved so great a measure of re-establishment of law and order by methods which have involved so little violence, is a signal example of what may be done by coolness and sagacity. I abhor terrorism in every form, as my record in Indian Debates will show. Most of all do I abhor it in a Government so powerful as is the British Government in India. That nothing of this kind has occurred, that no grievous or frightful incidents have happened up to the present, is a very powerful tribute to the patience, tact, and slow endurance with which situations of the utmost difficulty have been handled, and it should secure gratitude for those responsible for it, not only from their fellow-countrymen at home but from the large and overwhelming majority of law-abiding people throughout India.

At the same time, I cannot help regretting the weakness and pusillanimity, the poor and low view taken of our rights and duties in India, which has caused so much needless suffering. While I approve of the measures now taken by His Majesty's Government, and rejoice in their success, I cannot but regret that a sound and straightforward policy was not adopted sooner. There are, no doubt, a great many difficulties confronting the Indian Administration; we are not by any means out of our difficulties yet; but those difficulties are, very largely, the price of previous unwisdom. My right hon. Friend told us to-day that 26,600 persons were interned or imprisoned for seditious or riotous conduct. I believe, and I think there are others who share my view, that if, when Mr. Gandhi first began his campaign of salt making in open defiance of the law, he had been promptly arrested and brought to trial in the ordinary way; if the Lahore Congress in the Spring of 1930 had been broken up after it had publicly insulted the British flag; if there had not been that tendency to share the Government of India with the Congress through the pact between Lord Irwin and Mr. Gandhi, and if the whole of India had not been profoundly disturbed, distressed and excited by widespread rumors that the end of British authority was approaching, and that England was exhausted and impotent under the rule of the Socialists—I believe that, if all that had not been going forward, it is probable that three-quarters of those who are in gaol to-day in India would be peacefully pursuing their daily avocations; and that applies still more to the very much larger number of persons whom the Socialists Government locked up as a result of throwing the country into a condition of instability and disorder.

Never have we witnessed such a spectacle of an Imperial Government undermining the foundations of its own authority, sapping its own prestige and reputation, spreading rumours and imparting an ever-rising sense of some great change among enormous masses of primitive people, as we saw in those evil years—violent, audacious defiance on the one hand, matched by needlessly dangerous surrenders on the other. It is a remarkable proof of the stability and solidity of British rule throughout India, and of the great measure of acquiescence which it receives in the fundamental loyalty of the Indian peoples, that the whole Peninsula, as large and as populous as Europe, was not thrown into a frightful convulsion by this method of handling the situation. We survey to-day a situation incomparably better both for England and for India, a situation far better from every point of view, than that which gripped and almost seemed to paralyse us at this time last year.

Here let me say without hesitation that I do not feel that this reassertion of law and order closes, or ought to close, the door upon Indian constitutional advance. On the contrary, I think that from some points of view it clears the air. I think that we are moving towards conditions which make it possible for us to presume our settled policy of bringing the strong, loyal, able elements in Indian life ever more closely and more directly into responsible association with Indian affairs. To make or promise constitutional changes while we seem to be incapable of preserving law and order, to buy off dangers which we have not the strength or the resolution to meet, would assuredly lead by the shortest road to anarchy and revolution. But once the Imperial Government is, beyond all doubt and question, master of the situation, then wise constitutional improvements stand on a healthy and honourable foundation, conferring benefits alike on those who give and on those who receive. Therefore, I certainly do not ask—I have never have, but certainly not to-day do I ask the Government to close the door upon sane and well-conceived constitutional reform in India.

I should be out of order, under the somewhat awkward rules of these Supply Debates, if I were to enter upon any detailed discussion of the alternative constitutional methods which lie before us. I am only going to deal with the problem as it affects administration. I will say to my right hon. Friend, first of all, that I hope and trust he will not descend again into the dark places from which we have been to an important extent extricated by the belated but salutary action of the Viceroy and himself. As I have said so often, do not go on raising expectations which you know are not going to be fulfilled. I believe that, in dealing with Oriental people, it is a great mistake to overpraise what you are yourself intending to do. I believe we should state what we are giving at its minimum in words, and let it be at its maximum in fact and in deed. Let us reverse the process of the last few years.

Instead of making all these vague and general commitments, let us take quite soon and quite swiftly the necessary precise executive action to make an advance as soon as an opportunity occurs. Let us freely give all that can be given, and let us bluntly and frankly refuse anything which would not suit us, would not suit British interests, or would not be good for Indian interests. Let us, in the late Lord Birkenhead's words, tell the truth to India. That is, I am sure, the keynote to which we ought to have been attuned throughout the last few years, whereas, on the contrary, the whole endeavour has been to wrap up the ugly facts of the situation in smooth words. There is the Secretary of State for Scotland. He is not here, but I have his speech in mind. He said he was remaining in the Government in spite of differences on Free Trade because he wished to support the policy of appeasement which we were carrying out in India. 26,600 people have been sentenced to various terms of appeasement. How characteristic it is of our method of handling these questions. You have to find some word which is smooth and which veils the actual truth. I believe we do not gain in our relations with the Indian people by adopting these rather smooth forms of speech which are sometimes helpful at political or party gatherings.

I know many of the difficulties of the Secretary of State, but they are not by any means all in India. It is possible that the greatest difficulties that he has to cope with are the obligations which have been entered into on this side of the ocean. I am very much afraid of the danger that India will be again thrown into a state of trepidation, palpitation and perturbation by the continued, gratuitous, vexatious stirring of the deep pools of Indian life, not because of any Indian needs, but because of British party or British political needs. I am in favour of a constitutional advance in India, but it ought to be a point of honour with us so to shape the advance that it is solely conceived upon its merits according to India's needs. We ought to do what we have to do entirely from the point of view of the well-being of India, and we ought not to shape our policy in order to save the face of someone or other in a high position over here. What India needs for her welfare is what ought to rule us and not what British politicians, who have so often been wrong, need in order to make a show of consistence and continuity of policy for their themselves. India has suffered a great deal in the past through their ignorance and through their foolish habit of imagining that the ideas and processes of democracy, to which Western nations are attaching less faith year after year, are the sole means by which the welfare of the Indian people can be secured. I hope that that, at any rate, will be borne in mind.

There are also, undoubtedly, great difficulties on the spot. We must remember that not one of the real obstacles that brought the Round Table Conference to failure has been removed. The agreement among the Princes has not advanced from where it was 18 months ago, and it is still veiled in clouds of generality which surround the serious differences which undoubtedly exist. The differences between Moslems and Hindus, Untouchables and Sikhs have been sadly exacerbated. They may be calming a little now, when there is a feeling of greater assurance beginning to spread over the face of India, but they have undoubtedly become much more acute than in former years. The elections for the Frontier Province have been, I am informed, a dangerous and a scandalous farce. Violence of every kind has been threatened. A very small percentage of the electors have voted. Those electors themselves are a tiny proportion of the population, and yet the body so resulting is to be entrusted with the widest powers of administration of that province, of all the provinces in India the most susceptible to explosions of violence. The condition of Bombay is still discreditable to the administration. The boycott has not yet been effectively broken. Our three committees, which have been peregrinating, are now returning to us bearing with them, no doubt, their bulky and indigestible sheaves of reports. As to the safeguards, upon which we are told we must put so much reliance, what is happening on the other side of the St. George's Channel should surely be deeply instructive on that point.

All these difficulties stand in the way, and I think we run a great risk of overemphasizing the importance of political change in India as contrasted with material and moral advance. I will borrow, if I may, a phrase Sovietic in its origin and therefore likely to gladden the heart of the Leader of the Opposition. I say that we ought to look at the broad proletarian masses. We ought to see that their well-being is our supreme care and our noblest duty. What do we care in this House of Commons for all the feuds which surround the life of Hindu and Moslem in India? We are not concerned with the theocratic ambitions of the Hindus. We are not concerned with the old traditions of class and of sovereignty which belong to the Moslems. We are apart from these and above these, and we have no interest in supporting harsh usurers and pitiless landlords against the unprotected humble masses, nor have any of our officers or agents. What do we care for the monopolist intrigues of the wealthy cotton spinners and manufacturers of Ahmedabad or the speculators of Bombay? Our concern, and our ruthless concern, must be, as my hon. Friend said in his speech, the greatest good of the greatest number of the people of India. If ever a British interest clashes with the greatest good of the greatest number, then I say without hesitation that the British interest in question should be properly subordinated. I believe that the interests of the Indian proletariat and the interests of Great Britain are in absolute harmony. The clashes which take place are only in the political classes which stand between us and the great masses of the people. Impartial justice, increasing care for the weak and the poor, the upholding of able and honest officials whose lives are devoted to the land of their services, the scientific organisation and apparatus of modern life—all these are alike needs of India and the duties of Britain.

I hope and trust—and it will be the point on which I shall close—that we are not going to dissociate ourselves at all from this prime duty of sustaining the welfare of the great mass of the Indian people. When I moved an Amendment six months ago asking to add the words, "peace, order and good government in India," to the Resolution, the Prime Minister said that "peace, order," was quite all right, but "good government"— and there he hesitated, and I felt that the door was being opened to what I can only consider would be the most humiliating and unpleasant situation. I cannot agree that we ought to abandon in any constitution which we may give our ultimate responsibility for the welfare of the masses, and, in the cheap and specious guise of giving what is called "more freedom to India," it would be monstrous if we were to hand over these hundreds of millions of human beings to be exploited and harried by small, bitter and unrepresentative groups, gangs and cliques. It would be a moral degradation for England to say that we are not concerned with domestic misgovernment, domestic tyranny or injustice. So long as we have equal trading rights and the control of foreign relations and our ultimate military ascendancy, we are not concerned with what goes on within the ambit of self-government. That is not a scheme in which the glory of Britain and the genius of India could ever be partners. I say without hesitation that it would be better by far that we should quit for ever the soil of India than that we should take by armed force such profit as can be made out of association with India and shamelessly ignore our duties to its innumerable peoples.

What an ignominy it would be to us if we built a kind of hard shell or crust of British interests, exclusively reserved around India, within which every kind of native oppression and misgovernment would flourish and sat there mouthing the formulas of an inapplicable Liberalism or invoking the name of self-government. The task which we have to do in India is by no means ended as some people seem to think. The task is to raise the material and cultural level of the great masses. The right hon. Gentleman opened his speech to-day—and I was glad to hear him do it—and dwelt at some length upon the great public works now coming into full activity in India. There is Lord Lloyd whose views are very old-fashioned compared with the more enlightened sections of the Socialist and Conservative parties. Yet I expect that the Lloyd barrage with its opportunities of cultivable land and hearth and home to literally millions of Indians—3,000,000, I think—will be found to have done far more good and will be far more honoured in Indian history than all the constitution mongering upon which for the last ten years Governments of India have been unduly engaged, that it will do far more good than all the Montagu-Chelmsford reforms put together, and that it will even outweigh the perorations of Lord Lothian, Lord Sankey, and Lord Snell.

If we feel that the task of guiding and leading forward the masses of India to a wider and more rich material prosperity, if we feel that that is beyond our strength, if we feel compelled to renounce them altogether, then I say indeed our day in the Orient is done, and we had better quit a scene of faded splendours. We had better divest ourselves of associations which, once our duty to the Indian peoples are ignored, would become not honourable, but degrading. But if we are still capable of making exertions in a worthy cause and still have confidence in our mission and in ourselves, then the case for perseverance, as the Secretary of State has put it to us to-day, holds the field.

The Leader of the Opposition at the close of his interesting and discursive oration dwelt with relish upon the frequent and inevitable fall of Empires and the effacement of their civilisations. He even seemed to me to represent the fall of the Roman Empire as a most fortunate and auspicious episode in the history of mankind. He gleefully prophesied that if and when we were driven out of India the Indians would soon make short work of any vestiges of modern civilisation or improvement which we had imparted to them. He may be right. I think that it may well be so. It may well be that the departure of Great Britain from India would be followed by something very like the dark ages which succeeded the fall of the Roman Empire. Some of us on this side of the Committee at any rate think that it is our duty to labour long and to labour earnestly and to stand between the peoples of India and so lamentable a fate.

POLITICAL PAINTERS

April 30, 1932

Royal Academy Banquet, Burlington House,
London

It is very characteristic of the chivalry of the Royal Academy that you should, on this occasion, have picked out among all the politicians who were at your choice for the places of honour at your gathering the Home Secretary [Sir Herbert Samuel] and myself, two of the least understood politicians outside that festive scene. (Laughter.) Here we find sanctuary. I would not dream of lecturing the Royal Academicians on your art. Outsiders might do that, but as a humble amateur, I treat with the greatest possible disciplinary respect the eminent leaders of the profession. I will tell you something about another "Academy" not only a "Royal Academy," but at the present time a "National Academy," and it resides at Westminister, from which quite a number of the guests have come tonight.

The National Government has a great deal in common with the Royal Academy. It is not so ancient, and it may not live so long—(laughter)—but it meets an indubitable public need, and it embraces—I am not quite sure that the word "embrace" was well chosen, but I will let it pass—every style and every shade of political artistry.

I must tell you about some of the leading political painters. First of all there is the Prime Minister. How glad we all were to learn that his health is so much better. (Cheers.) His works are well known. We all regret that they are not more frequently visible at home. He has been exhibiting so much in foreign countries lately that we rather missed his productions here. (Laughter.) I believe that on the Continent he has several most important masterpieces still unhappily in an unfinished condition—(Laughter)—and we look forward hopefully to their arrival and to his return.

I have watched for many years the Prime Minister's style and methods, and for a long time, I do not mind saying, I thought there was a good deal too much vermilion in his pictures. (Laughter.) All those lurid sunsets of capitalist civilization began rather to pall upon me, and I am glad to see he has altered his style so fundamentally. In all his new pictures we see the use of cobalt, of French ultramarine, of Prussian blue, and all the other blues—(laughter)—not excluding, I am glad to say, the British true blue—(laughter)—that cerulean, that heavenly colour we all admire so much. I think the Prime Minister in his pictures uses blue very much like the late John Sargent, not only for atmosphere but for foundation, and I personally like his modern style very much better than the earlier method.

Then there is the Lord President of the Council [Mr. Baldwin], who, I can assure you, is still quite a distinguished painter in our Academy. If I were to criticize him at all, I would say that his work lacks a little in colour and also is a little lacking in the precise definition of objects in the foreground. (Laughter.) He, too, has changed in his later life not only his style but also his subject. We all miss very much the jolly old English pictures which he used to paint—"The Worcestershire Farm," "Pigs in Clover"—(laughter)—and "Broccoli in Autumn." Above all, we miss just now that subject which no pencil could have done more justice to than Mr. Baldwin's—"Brewing the Audit Ale." (Laughter.) Making a fair criticism, I must admit that there is something very reposeful about the half-tones of Mr. Baldwin's studies. (Laughter.)

Then we have in our Academy the Dominions' Secretary [Mr. J. H. Thomas], who represents what I might call a very fruity type of cubism. (Laughter.) Some people think it shocking; others say it lacks conviction. That is a very serious criticism, is it not? Nevertheless, it is certainly a most interesting contribution to our national show.

I trust you will want to ask me how it is that I am not exhibiting these days. (Laughter.) Why is it I have not got a row of important pictures on the line at my Academy. I will be perfectly frank with you. I make no concealment; I have had some difference with the committee—(laughter)—the hanging committee. Luckily their powers are limited so far as I am concerned, and I am not submitting any of my works for their approval this year. (Laughter.)

I have joined the teaching profession. We have a sort of Slade School at Westminister. They are a fine lot of young students, most ardent and with much before them—to learn (Laughter.) I am endeavouring to assist them in acquiring a knowledge of Parliamentary technique. I have a few things on the easel of my own which I hope some day to present to the public. After telling you these few things about our political academy I am sure the company will join with me in drinking the toast of your own.

IMPORT DUTIES BILL

May 4, 1932

House of Commons

We have listened to a very able speech, and a speech which would have been very appropriate had it been delivered from any other place than that which my right hon. Friend [Sir Herbert Samuel, Home Secretary] occupies. In the conditions in which it was spoken, I cannot help being reminded of what was said a good many years ago about the late Duke of Orleans, at the time when he issued some manifesto affecting French Royalism: "He has missed a very fine occasion of keeping quiet." Let me borrow the language of my right hon. Friend which he applied to me interrogatively—accusatively. Let me ask him, what national purpose is served by the speech which he has just delivered? Will it save Free Trade? Will it help to make Protection come into working more smoothly? Will it comfort the Free Trade Liberals? Does it tell us anything that we did not know before? Will it strengthen the National Government? Will it improve our constitutional procedure? And, last, but not least, will it relieve my right hon. Friend himself of any burden of responsibility?

When I first heard about this agreement to differ, I did not condemn it; I thought it was a tolerable expedient in all the circumstances. Free Trade is almost a religious doctrine with many people. The Government was formed on an all-party basis. The Liberals reserved their rights in this matter at the election. They can plead a conscientious difference. The Government was admittedly formed to embrace these different points of view, and, therefore, it did not seem impossible, although it was obviously undesirable, for the Free Trade Ministers to say, "Our opinions on the main economic issue are unchanged; we cannot advise the country to go in for Protection; but there are larger things at stake at the present time than the issue of Free Trade and Protection. Our colleagues have asked us to remain; they have accorded us full liberty to dissociate ourselves from their main policy, and, therefore, we are here on those terms." I think, stretching a point or two, that that might have been put up with. But I am bound to say that, when I went to Ottawa, I was disconcerted to find how strong was the opinion among leading men of both parties there that something had happened over here which had effected a grave and permanent alteration, and possibly injury, in the system of Cabinet Government throughout the Empire. We must not forget that, although we have no authority over the great Dominions of the Crown and the many Governments which have imitated and modelled themselves upon us, what we do exercises an enormous influence upon them, and, therefore, I say I was disconcerted when I went to Ottawa. But I never imagined then that we were to be confronted repeatedly with what I can only say is the indecent, and even scandalous, spectacle of Ministers wrangling upon the Treasury Bench, and of important officers of State doing their utmost to discredit, impede and undermine the main policy of the Government of the day.

I think my right hon. Friend's position is uncomfortable from many points of view, and I sympathise with him, apart from politics, very much indeed. His position is not secure even in logic. I understood his view to be that, although Protection was wrong, once he had made that clear, the importance of the National Government at this time was so great, and his contribution to it was so indispensable, that he must nevertheless continue as a Minister. Therefore, it seemed to me that his view was that preserving the National Government was more important than preserving Free Trade. That is a perfectly tenable and a perfectly respectable view. But it surely follows that he should not weaken the Government by any action which he takes on behalf of Free Trade. He has decided between these two propositions, and, at the summit of things, nearly all questions are fairly evenly balanced; there are great perplexities on either side. My right hon. Friend has decided which is his major and which is his minor proposition, and I think the speech that we have heard from him to-day shows an illogicality and an inconsistency. It goes back on his decision that preserving the power and efficiency of the National Government is more important at this juncture than preserving the Free Trade system.

No doubt my right hon. Friend desires to escape responsibility. But can he escape responsibility while he is a Minister? Can any speech that he makes, however able—and, as I said the other day, speeches are not so important in a controversy of this kind as action—can any speech relieve him of his responsibility? Of course, he can declare that he did not advise Protection, but he cannot discharge himself from his responsibility in carrying Protection, any more than Pontius Pilate, washing his hands in public, could escape from his responsibility while he remained a high functionary of the Roman Empire. My right hon. Friend is actually driving forward Protection with all the force of His Majesty's Government, and all that his speeches, like the one that he has just delivered, tell us, is that he does not believe in what he is sharing in doing, and that he thinks it economically unsound and socially unjust. If my right hon. Friend really feels so strongly about the question, if his sense of proportion has changed, and he no longer thinks that the National Government is more important than Free Trade, I am afraid I cannot help him any further. If that be the conclusion which he has reached in his breast, only one course, only one step is open to him.

But let me see if, searching in the past, we can find some incidents for his guidance and assistance. Very often in history eminent men have been placed in false situations by the force of events. Study their conduct. There was Naaman, who had to bow the knee in the Temple of Rimmon when he went there in connection with his duties at the Syrian Court. His position has been quite well understood in history; he has not been stigmatised for it; but I expect that if Naaman, when he went into the Temple of Rimmon, had perpetually interrupted the service, there would have been a good deal of ill feeling among the congregation. Henry of Navarre said that Paris was worth a mass. Perhaps it was; perhaps the peace and unity of France was worth a mass to him; and history has certainly, despite the lamentable cynicism of his remark, not dealt unkindly with Henry of Navarre. But imagine the situation if, when he was at the altar at this ceremony, he had felt it his duty on every occasion to announce that he regarded the whole thing as blasphemous and idolatrous. I am quite sure that his action would have been robbed of much of its grace and all its efficacy. I hope that these historical examples may be of some service to my right hon. Friend and to those who are acting with him.

Very high claims are made on behalf of His Majesty's present Government. A supreme crisis arose, and it still continues. The efforts of all well-meaning men are required. They have to combine together. They have to lay aside every impediment to stop the pound sterling from falling—no, I beg pardon, from rising—[*Interruption.*] With all this language my right hon. Friend is identified. He has now added another reason for his support of the Administration in all these difficulties and compromises, namely, a Conversion Loan in the future. I should never have thought, myself, that the Home Secretary would have been consulted on such a matter; I should have thought that it was really a question which did not require his special assistance; and I cannot believe that the Liberal party would sabotage a national Conversion Loan, or would not give it loyal support, merely because he severed his connection with His Majesty's

Government. But it is the Conversion Loan, which is in the future, for which my right hon. Friend has to wait, although he is unconverted to the main policy of the Government, and probably also is wholly inconvertible.

It is sometimes stated that the situation in which we find ourselves is similar to that in which we were during the War—that we have our backs to the wall. I have never quite agreed with that view. I thought, myself, that there was a good deal of exaggeration about the crisis which arose last August and September—and a certain amount of manipulation. Anyhow, my view has not prevailed. The foundation on which the Government rests is that a great and supreme crisis is running in full career at the present time, and the Home Secretary owes not only his Ministerial office—I do not put that too high, because, after all, an office is not a sugar-plum in this country; it is a sacrifice, a service, a burden—he owes not only his Ministerial office, but his seat in Parliament, to the fact that very large numbers of Conservatives took the view that individual opinions must be subordinated, that party colours must be suppressed, in the interests of a national attempt to deal with our affairs.

Together with the Prime Minister and my right hon. Friend the Lord President of the Council, the Home Secretary has invoked all the highest obligations of patriotism upon all of us. They have raised the signal "Country in danger," and, as always in this island, the country has responded to such a call. If this be true—and much of it is undoubtedly true—does it not demand service and sacrifice in a very special degree from Ministers and leaders themselves? Is it not imperative for them to set an example? Ought not the conduct and the behaviour of a National Government to be upon a higher plane, and not upon a lower plane than that of an ordinary Government? Is it not an offence, even I think I might say a flagrant offence, in a Minister in a high position to lower the repute and weaken the actions of the Government—[An Hon. Member: "Which Minister?"] I am addressing myself to any Minister who should take such action, but in the main the target of my observations is the Home Secretary. I want to ask this question. Are only the common electors and the private Members to make sacrifices, while the generals are free to frolic and rollick as they please? We all know the quotation from "Measure for Measure." I took the trouble to verify it a few minutes ago.

"That in the captain's but a choleric word
Which in the soldier is flat blasphemy."

Surely aristocratic privilege can be pushed too far—this doctrine of one law for the rich and another for the poor being so crudely and stridently proclaimed. Discipline, yes, but discipline only for the rank and file! I remember how the Party Whips were used, for instance, on the Statute of Westminster Bill, and we know they will be used when the Beer Duty comes up for consideration. The right hon. Gentleman takes part in all this. He is a consenting party, nay, a part of the contributory energy which drives this process forward, and yet, when he himself is dissatisfied, he is ready again and again to defy all tradition and all convention. I must labour, with the aid of the House, to bring home to the right hon. Gentleman, for whom I have the highest esteem, the enormity of the course of action that he is following. The Government asked for a doctor's mandate. Doctors sometimes differ. They differ on a particular case, they may differ very strongly, but they do not go alarming the patient and alarming his relations by brawling in public. Still less do they try to interrupt and impede a critical operation. Such conduct would be judged unprofessional, and there are very good reasons, both to the patient and to the doctors, why it should be judged unprofessional.

Take another example. In war there are often differences between high commanders—terrible differences. They see themselves ordered to carry out attacks which they are sure will fail, and sometimes they are tragically vindicated. But I always understood that it was a point of honour that such differences, however forcibly expressed in the council of war, should not reach the troops or reach the enemy. Anyhow, it is always the duty of every man whole-heartedly, whatever his personal interest or his personal fortune may be, to hope and wish for the success of the national arms and the national cause. When we entered the Great War, there were many who disapproved, and some who expressed their disapproval, but there were very few who carried that expression of disapproval so far as to hamper the national defence. [*Interruption*.] I never made such a charge against the Prime Minister.

Mr. Buchanan: The Workers' and Soldiers' council.

Mr. Churchill: I know far more about what happened at that time than the hon. Member ever had an opportunity of learning. What I was going to ask my right hon. Friend, speaking as an old Liberal, addressing a Liberal, was why he does not try to model his conduct in this difficult time more upon the lines of the late Lord Morley and Mr. John Burns? They differed very strongly, but they made their protest and, after that, remained wrapped in impenetrable silence. I should have thought that my right hon. Friend would follow their course. It is true that they resigned. No one is asking him to resign. On the contrary, I think the House as a whole wishes him to stay. He has shown that he is a courageous, efficient and upright Minister. The House as a whole is in favour of the continuance of the present regime, and we should be very sorry to see the simultaneous disappearance of the four satellites of Jupiter. The right hon. Gentleman has made his own position clear, but he need not make it clear *ad nauseam*, and he has no right to do it if it weakens the efficiency and humiliates the prestige of a Government whose creation and whose continuance he has repeatedly declared to be vital to our interests.

The inauguration of Protection itself is a tremendous and an intricate operation. Very high hopes are set upon its success. I think that something very like a wave of despair would pass across millions of our fellow-countrymen if this great new experiment and departure were to fail. If, for instance, prices rose and profiteering grew, if there was very little diminution in unemployment, if agriculture languished, if Ottawa faded, some of the stoutest and most energetic and active forces which have carried our country through many stormy years would suffer, almost heartbreak. Therefore, whatever views we have, or have had, we must hope for the success of this great national movement. Even the most bigoted Free Trader can have no other wish than that success will attend the policy that has been declared, and certainly no one in a high official position ought to keep on nagging and niggling and crabbing and clutching at those who are actually in charge of a policy of this kind. The right hon. Gentleman had much better recognise that we are definitely committed to a policy of Protection.

Never has there been so great a change, certainly not in my experience, which has been made with the overwhelming assent and acceptance of the country in so unstinted a degree. Nothing now can stop us becoming a Protectionist country. All those reasoned doctrines and philosophies of Free Trade have been discarded by universal suffrage by the whole stream of opinion, from the poorest up to the most intelligent and powerful people in the land. They have been discarded in favour of Protection. The decision has been taken. What, then, when this experiment has begun, can be the usefulness of such a speech as that which we have just heard? It can only spread doubt and alarm and hamper the execution of the policy. I hope, now that that speech is over, that it is the last of these exhibitions which, though they do not in the least alter the course of events, are an offence against Cabinet Government and are an affront to Parliament. I see the Minister of Education, and far away in the corner the Secretary of State for Scotland. I appeal to them, at any rate, to leave it where it is now. Do not let them renew to-morrow the deplorable incident that we have been forced to witness today. If they care at all for the continuance of the National Government, do not let them make it a by-word and a laughing stock. Let them rest upon their unmistakably plain declarations and provoke no further the patience of this friendly House of Commons.

Upon this issue which is before us to-night I am a supporter of the Government. I cannot claim, of course, to rival my right hon. Friend the President of the Board of Trade in his Free Trade record. He has been a vestal virgin of Free Trade. It is true that he had a past. It is true that during the Great War he engaged in flirtations, like the Paris resolutions and the McKenna Duties. Still, a lot of things happened in the Great War that we cannot look too closely into after the event, and thereafter the right hon. Gentleman repented of his conduct and by many years of absolutely impeccable behaviour succeeded in living it down. Only a year ago he was the most complete, unimpeachable Free Trade purist in the House of Commons. I, on the other hand, cannot compete with him. I admit that I have been led further and further astray ever since 1920, when I had to vote for the Safeguarding Duties and for the key industries duties, and I am, I believe, the author of more Protectionist duties in my five Budgets than any other man until, of course, the present tariff.

But, although I cannot rival my right hon. Friend in his fiscal record, at any rate I like very much the way he is addressing himself to this new problem. I am very glad that he has not allowed himself to be led into what I might call compromise Protection. I was afraid we should see a number of half-hearted expedients which would rupture Free Trade without giving Protection a fair chance. The country does not want compromise Protection. It wants scientific Protection. I mean the adoption of such a fiscal system as shall be adapted, on a Protectionist hypothesis, to the peculiar needs and requirements of our island and of our Empire. We do not want to have any more of these attempts, not only in the fiscal but in so many, fields of politics, to bridge a 12-foot stream with a six-foot plank, and then for the sake of good feeling and party loyalty make it a seven-foot plank. We do not want any more of that.

We want this policy, now that it has been definitely and irrevocably adopted, to be tried out in its full integrity. Therefore I am going to support the whole of the

Schedule of duties which are now the subject of our Debate. No doubt there are serious mistakes in it, but the wonder is not that there are mistakes in it, but that they are so few. The wonder is that this enormous change, this revolution, is being brought into operation so smoothly with so little real divergence of opinion and with so little effective outcry from the trades and industries concerned. Some of these matters we can discuss on the Budget. Silk, for instance, is more appropriate upon the Budget than to this discussion. There are the questions of the textiles and so forth, but, of course, those representations must be attended to by the Commission. I am not going to worry about those matters or aspects now.

I am not at all alarmed by the speech of the right hon. Gentleman. On the details the decision has been taken. I am content to ask, Has the Schedule of Duties been framed by clean hands? Has it been framed by competent people? Has it been framed by men with sincere convictions? Has it been framed by men who have no axe to grind, personal, party or political? The answer to all those questions seems to be sound and satisfactory. The advisory committee may be wrong, but they are much more likely to be right than wrong, and I should leave them to do their work. I do not think that we could have had a better, more competent, more honourable or more disinterested committee than the one which has been set up. Every interest can have access to that tribunal. But look at all those arguments, that enormous area of arguments, which used to be used against Protection—which I used with others—completely swept away by the procedure which the Government have adopted. They have been completely swept away. All those arguments about improper political pressure! There has been none. There has been no scramble of great interests, no log-rolling, bribery or corruption, none! And it may well be that this country, with its long-developed civilisation and Parliamentary institutions, will be able to gather the benefits which protectionist countries have reaped without incurring at the same time those grave maladies which have so often accompanied them in other countries. This policy has been decided by the great mass of national opinion and of intellectual opinion in the country. I believe that the execution of it has been done in the right way and in the best way, and, as far as I am concerned, at every stage I shall give it God speed.

INTERNATIONAL MONETARY POLICY

May 8, 1932

Broadcast to the United States, London

[Extract] . . . I believe something has gone wrong with the monetary system. It no longer affords men and nations an adequate means of exchanging what they are capable of producing. Gold, having been cornered and hoarded, has gone up 70 per cent. in value in the last five years, and the price of everything else, measured by gold, has fallen.

See what that means. The farmer has to plough a 1,700-yard furrow in order to pay off as much mortgage or overdraft to the bank as he could have paid by ploughing a

1,000-yard furrow only five years ago. All debts have nearly doubled and yet creditors feel as badly off as debtors.

Among all other commodities silver has fallen to a miserable level. I am not going to plunge into the thorny jungles of currency, but surely the fact that silver is denied all rank or recognition, the fact that the difference in price between silver and gold is greater than it has ever been, the fact that less silver was produced last year than for centuries, ought to excite the concern of world statesmen.

Silver is the money of all Asia. Silver is the money of a billion human beings, and it ought not to be treated with as little regard as if it were a sack of potatoes. Silver has always been the comrade and ally of gold. Surely we would do well to consider more carefully the part it has to play in our world housekeeping.

It is the hideous process of deflation which is the main cause of our troubles. It has filled the cities with unemployment, has frozen the railways and workshops, has threatened every debtor with insolvency and every creditor with default. What are we going to do about it. Are we going on gaping at each other in this helpless way while every morning the efforts of all the producers of new wealth are written down remorselessly and every day sees a narrowing prospect of life and labor for mankind?

I ask, as I have asked on so many American and British platforms, why do our two countries not take counsel together? Why do they not try to reach a common understanding about the money policy of the world? Why do they not try to arrest this remorseless and destructive deflation? Why do they not try to revaluate commodities to the level of, say, 1928, and secure a price level which would give a fair return to the prime producer and thus enable him to buy again the manufactures of our cities and workshops? No one country, however powerful, can stop this evil alone. The fall of prices and the weakness and want of confidence which follow from it making things still worse, and can be controlled only by the common action of the leading nations. And what two nations of all others should take the first steps, if it be not the two great world creditor nations, the two great English-speaking nations, Britain and the United States? Divided all our efforts would be in vain. United in sentiment and policy we can lead the whole world back out of these gloomy caverns into the broad sunlight of activity and progress.

Let us strengthen ourselves for that task by strictly balancing our budgets and facing responsibilities like men. Why shouldn't we put our heads together in matters of common concern, nay, universal concern?

[Editor's Note: Turning to tariffs Churchill said]: Nations are walling themselves up in different pens. Even we in England have been forced to do that at last. Well, we have got a pretty good pen in the British Empire when we have organized it as we are going to do, and so have you in the United States. Whatever happens, we can both stand a lot of punishment. But why do we have to have the punishment? The world is tormenting itself largely without cause.

FINANCE BILL (MONETARY POLICY)

May 10, 1932

House of Commons

After the solemn speeches, so faultless in tone and so compulsive in their appeals to our feelings, to which we have just listened, it will not, perhaps, be without an effort that the House will recall itself to the ordinary business of the day. We have to carry on as our brave French comrades have also carried on in times of trouble, and the first remark I wish to make is one of thanks and gratitude to His Majesty's Government and to my right hon. Friend the Lord President of the Council [Mr. Stanley Baldwin] for having given us two days' Debate for the Second Reading of the Finance Bill. I am afraid that I was not right in my epithet "usual," and I should be still more wrong if I had used the word "invariable," which, I am afraid, was on the tip of my tongue; but, at any rate, we may agree together on the epithet "desirable."

I listened yesterday in the Debate, which certainly showed that time was not wasted, to many speeches, and I was particularly glad to notice the speech of my Noble Friend the Member for Peckham (Viscount Borodale) and the speech of the hon. Member for the Scottish Universities (Mr. John Buchan), which raised again the unfashionable subject of economy. Economy has now its chance, and never was there more need for it. Taxation has already reached, in many of its features, levels which are not merely burdensome but destructive not only of the revenue but of trade and employment. Income Tax, beer, whisky, however you may feel about the desirability of raising money from those sources, have all now reached points where the mere maintenance at the present level will gradually wear out the source from which the revenue is derived. It would be an enormous boon if £50,000,000 could be saved from our expenditure. It is no good saying to me, "Why did you not do it?" I never had the opportunity which His Majesty's Government have. We had to fight in a party atmosphere. Every Measure we proposed was stigmatised in the most wounding manner possible. But the National Government have a chance which was denied to their predecessors, and will probably also be withheld from those who come after them.

I was glad, indeed, to hear the Chancellor of the Exchequer say that later on in the year, when other and more pressing matters would be disposed of, he was going to do a bit of hard thinking on the subject of economy. I can assure my right hon. Friend that not very much hard thinking is required. All that he has got to do is to ask the officials of the Treasury to provide him with a cut of £10,000,000, £20,000,000, £30,000,000, £40,000,000 or £50,000,000. There will be no difficulty at that point. The difficulties will begin when those proposals reach the Cabinet, and the difficulties will accentuate themselves when, having passed through the Cabinet, they reach the House of Commons, and they will reach a climax when, having passed through the House of Commons, they finally reach the nation at large. However, surely now is the time, because what is the use of a National Government if it cannot do salutary, unpopular things? A National Government differs from a party Government in that it has, I will not say no soul to be damned, but it has no hope of posterity, and its body is so large that it is scarcely worth kicking. But now is the time, I do hope that my right hon. Friend will take full advantage of his opportunities of doing things which an ordinary party Government cannot do. It will be easier to do them this year than it will be next, and it will be easier to do them next year than the year after, and, therefore, no time is to be lost.

I should like to speak more about economy, and I should like to speak about debts, internal and external, and about beer, but we shall have our opportunity in due course for discussing them. The speech which was made yesterday by my right hon. Friend the Member for Hillhead (Sir. R. Horne) raised topics, not for the first time, which overshadow and overlay almost all other questions that can engage our attention. He spoke of what is called the monetary problem or the currency problem, or, as I prefer to call it for short, as we are going to hear so much about it, and it would save trouble if we chose a label—the money problem. That is the great problem. Mr. John Bright, when he was President of the Board of Trade, found it sufficient to say that he did not understand the currency problem, and that he did not believe there was anyone who did. We have got to try to understand it. Those easy and complacent gestures and attitudes, so suited to the calm Victorian times, will not suffice to meet our perplexities and embarrassments to-day.

Therefore, with every consciousness of my own infirmities in the subject, and praying for all possible indulgence, not only for my present shortcomings, but for any past record I may have, I shall endeavour to address my remarks, which I trust will not be lengthy, entirely and exclusively to this one all-pervading and all-commanding topic. Sir, what is money? It is the medium—I am not trying to give a schoolman's definition—by which we try to bridge the mysterious gulf between production and consumption. When money is scarce, that gulf is wide, and production and consumption are at a minimum. When money is plentiful, that gulf is narrowed, and production and consumption rise to their full pitch. When more money is offered than is required by production and consumption, that is inflation. When there is enough money for current requirements and none for expansion, and industry wishes to expand, then there is restriction. And when there is not enough money for expansion, and not even enough money to carry on the ordinary transactions and maintain the old and existing levels, that is deflation; and that is what we have been suffering from for the last three or four years with increasing severity.

The amount of money that can be rightly offered at any given time depends upon the conditions of credit and of confidence and upon the realities of trade throughout the world. If money is manufactured without regard to confidence or credit and without regard to the realities of the trade position, then money quickly loses its virtue, and, after various convulsions, which we have often seen exhibited in other countries, society reverts to the primitive condition of barter as the only means of relating consumption and production.

Gold is the constable who has hitherto been employed to avoid mistakes and disasters of that kind. For a great many years gold was a trustworthy and faithful servant, but in the great War he went to the front, and he got so knocked about there that in the present state of our affairs you can only say that the constable has gone mad. He has been used so much, doing all sorts of jobs for which he was never suited, and he has been so affected by his ill-usage, that he has ceased to be a currency warden and has become a commodity himself. He is not actually stopping the supply of money, not only for expansion, but for the actual carrying on of the world's business. As for further expansion, he has vetoed it altogether. The constable is no longer regulating the traffic and checking dangerous traffic here and there; he is bringing the whole of traffic to a standstill, and bringing it to a standstill just at the very moment when we all want to get on and, but for this obstruction, I believe, when we all could get on. That is the way in which I personally try to interpret these frightfully difficult and technical topics in my own mind, and I believe that they will bear some careful examination even from the high and learned authorities to whom the discussion of these matters is customarily relegated.

In the year 1919, as my right hon. Friend the Member for Hillhead told us yesterday, after the Cunliffe Committee had reported, the Bank of England was instructed by the Government of that day to work towards the re-establishment of the Gold Standard. In 1925 the Bank, after six years of labour, six years of influencing the money policy, and under, I think, three separate Governments of different complexions and parties, declared—and the Treasury agreed with them—that the moment had come to resume the Gold Standard. Until 1929, although there were murmurings, and no murmurings more audible than those which were uttered, I must in justice say, by my hon. Friend the Member for East Aberdeen (Mr. Boothby), in the main it could never be said that the attempt to lift the world back to the Gold Standard would not succeed, and, while that condition prevailed, of course, there was no real support— support is so often born of necessity—for the carrying forward of the work of the Genoa Conference, which certainly needed—and I take any blame which may rest on me—to engage the continuous attention of all the Powers that were on the Gold Standard or were interested in maintaining it. But there was nothing that really excited the entire thought of great peoples or of their leaders during that period.

It was not until the United States of America, after the market crash of October, 1929, ceased to re-lend to Europe that we saw the monstrous spectacle of gold being used, not as the balancing force or measure of human effort, but actually to pay off these enormous war debts and reparations across tariff frontiers which would not receive goods. Then, when this happened, at once the fire which had been smouldering unseen for at least two years burst forth in a destructive flame. Up till that moment, the end of 1929, the only sign that things were going wrong had been this steady fall in prices. I was always brought up, by the able men with whom I came in contact at the Treasury and elsewhere, to believe that a reduction in the cost of living was one of the safest and surest things that you could possibly aim at, that a reduction in the cost of living, diminishing, be it only by a tiny fraction, the pressure of life upon the cottage homes, would immediately find its reward in the contentment of the masses of the people and would immediately be a stimulus to business, to enterprise, and to competitive power.

Well, up to a certain point that is true, but it is clear—we know now—that beyond a certain point the fall in prices and the fall in the cost of living is attended by other reactions, which confront the masses of the people with problems and with misfortunes which are just, or almost, as trying to them as are those attendant upon a high range of the prices of the necessaries of life. It is like the suction pump, which for very many years was believed to work because nature abhorred a vacuum. That was the theory, but when they went a little deeper—I forget how many feet—than they had previously done, it worked no more, and they had to have an entirely new explanation; and new laws were discovered which were not foreseen at that time, just as there are new laws to discover now, in trade and in finance, which previously, in Victorian times, when all seemed to work within those narrow margins satisfactorily, we had not discovered or foreseen. Cheapness of living, it is perfectly clear, cannot be regarded any more as a final objective. It cannot be considered apart from the general condition of enterprise, of industry, and of employment throughout the country and throughout the world.

I say, therefore, that this money problem dominates all, and let us hope that it will not devour all, like Aaron's rod, turned into a serpent which devoured all the other serpents. Nearly all the other factors and all the other symptoms of our economic life will be found to be either comprised in the money problem or are now arising out of it. Nothing can stand against a 70 per cent. enhancement of the measure of value. It is not the slightest use pretending that that is not the dominant fact in the life of the modern world to-day—the foot-rule extended, as I said, to 20 inches, and all production to proceed upon that exaggerated, aggravated test. What a vast annihilation of wealth, other than scrip, what a vast, withering disparagement of all new effort is involved in that extension of the foot-rule from 12 to 20 inches, or of a gold price increased by nearly 70 per cent. No contracts, no exertions, no savings, no sacrifices, no loyalties, no good will are proof or can avail against such a wrongful distortion of the fundamental measure.

It is vain for us to try to shirk this question, much though we should like to do it, and it is no use for the House of Commons to allow it to be thought that it is incompetent to probe it and to discuss it. Of all men, my right hon. Friend the Chancellor of the Exchequer must face it. It has invaded us all, and we must all face it, but of all men he must face it. It will not only wreck his Budget—his Death Duties, his stamps, his Income Tax—it will not only wreck that, if these tendencies continue, but it will wreck his life work, his tariffs, his father's cause, which he has brought into actual operation with great smoothness and with great decision. But that too is prejudiced and jeopardised, or will be, by a continuance of these deflationary tendencies. I see in the papers to-day an increase of 85,000 in unemployment, not due to tariffs. You may say it is in spite of the tariffs; at least, you may argue that, but it is due—

Sir Percy Harris: It is caused by foreign coal quotas retaliating to our Import Duties.

Mr. Churchill: You have no right to say that, you have no reason or justification to say that, when you have this enormous deflationary undertow at work, which, far more than your tariffs, is affecting the entire conditions under which business is conducted.

Mr. Charles Duncan: Anyway, it is not the Labour Government.

Mr. Churchill: Well, no one was ever treated more generously than the Labour Government. Any other Government would have been lynched. I do feel that, although we are happily no longer publishing these figures every week, but only every month, a continuance of an increase in unemployment—at Whitsuntide it will very likely increase, and then there is the seasonal increase for a good many months—does affect and prejudice the successful launching of the immense fiscal scheme to which my right hon. Friend has devoted himself and for which he bears so direct but distinguished a responsibility. One can never tell at what moment the four satellites of Jupiter may not quit their orbit and leave the sun, joining in the music of the spheres with the well-known dirge, "I told you so!" No, Sir. This is a matter which affects everyone, but no one more than the Chancellor of the Exchequer himself. I was struck very much by an expression used by my right hon. Friend the Home Secretary in a speech the other day when he referred to the escalator. I think it was a very just and lively similitude. Suppose we had to do again what we did six months ago. Suppose we had to force down wages, to cut salaries, to cut the *rentier* interest, to bear more crushing taxes, to scale down debts, to make further hard economies. Suppose we put our tariffs into operation, and the next morning we wake up and find that the escalator has wound us down to the old level. It would be a most heartbreaking experience for our people. A friend of mine was reminding me of the passage in "Alice in Wonderland" describing a country in which you had to keep on running very hard merely to stand still. I have a feeling that that is the sort of position that we are in, or getting into, in regard to this money problem.

I agree with the Chancellor of the Exchequer in his general view that though we are on sterling, and though we must do all we can to make it the widest possible, the most serviceable and most convenient measure of human effort, although we must marshal the sterling countries in the sterling convoy, and steam at a pace which enables all the vessels to keep in company and keep station—although we must do all that, I agree with the Chancellor in his view that sterling is not free from the domination of gold. Sterling has a strong separate life from gold, and it has at this moment a more fertile and an easier price level, yet, nevertheless, the right hon. Gentleman is, I believe, perfectly correct and very timely in reminding us that gold rules and dictates the main level of world prices. And I agree with him that no monetary reform or good management which was confined only to sterling could liberate us entirely from the thraldom from which we are suffering; and that is the reason why, apart altogether from anything we may do for ourselves, our ceaseless endeavour must be to promote international action.

No country can tackle this money question alone. Capitalist civilisation, the sole means by which freedom and prosperity for the masses can be achieved, is adrift. There is no single Power strong enough to take the helm. No one Government has authority to lay out the course, to give the guidance. The strength of three or four of the greatest Powers in the world will be required for that. Moreover, the remedy which we have to apply can only be applied by combined action. I do not believe that individual, unrelated inflation or individual, unrelated credit expansion by various countries will solve the difficulties in which we all lie. It is not merely local credit expansion that we require, but world credit expansion. Separate simultaneous action by several countries, even in the right direction, even if they are moving on what are called parallel lines, will not suffice to arrest the evil, and it might in some circumstances, unless great precautions are taken, degenerate into even greater and more disastrous forms of economic confusion than those we are suffering from now.

Let me take an instance, purely hypothetical, supposititious. Let us suppose that the United States inflate, as some say they are doing. At the present time, in what is called balancing their budget, I believe they provide no sinking fund, I believe they credit themselves with the full payments from Europe on account of war debts and reparations; but even on this basis suppose they fail to balance their budget, and suppose they are forced to make a great internal borrowing, perhaps 1,000,000,000 dollars. Suppose confidence there is shaken, and that hoarding there is aggravated. Suppose then that France, shall we say, "bears" the dollar, and the exchange has a tendency to fall. Then my right hon. Friend the Chancellor of the Exchequer, with his fund, advances to sustain the dollar. But he may not be strong enough to do it. That fund of £150,000,000, compared to a great, unfortunate development of that kind, would be little more than Mrs. Partington's broom against the Atlantic ocean. My right hon. Friend may try to warn off panic money from this country, but the more he warns the more it will want to come here. Capital in flight does not seek interest or profit; it seeks security. It shuns all suitors, and forces itself upon those who claim that they do not require it in any way. Suppose, finally, the pound rises in price and the dollar falls, and the pound rises not, be it observed, because of any intrinsic merit in our own trading system but through the demerits of the situation of other peoples, then we shall be left with great quantities of depreciating dollars which we have paid for with great quantities of appreciating pounds. In the end we shall have a high exchange, and further depression of trading, with other evils. All this may happen, I do not say it will happen, but it may happen, and I use it as an illustration of the inadequacy of the individual action of a particular country to expand credit while other countries are waiting and watching to take any advantage which they may secure for themselves in the process.

My right hon. Friend the Member for Hillhead, in what I thought was a singularly impressive and attractive part of his courageous speech, said that a patient might be suffering from apoplexy or from anaemia. He likened our condition to that of a patient suffering from anaemia. I wish anaemia were the only disease. Now we have an aggravation, a complication; neurasthenia has been added to anaemia. After two or three years of anaemia a mind state has supervened in the patient which makes it particularly difficult to apply remedies, and which make many of the remedies which work under normal conditions no longer produce their proper reaction. Therefore, it seems to me the remedy which we apply must not only be practical and physical, but must be psychological. Even worldwide monetary reform could only be applied if there was simultaneously a restoration of confidence. It could only be applied in these circumstances: You must not merely aim at policy, but you have got to have power behind the policy.

There must be the international cooperation if there is to be a cessation of this hideous process from which we are suffering. We cannot wait until every country is persuaded. We cannot go round arguing with one country after another until every one of all the numerous countries represented at the international conferences has been persuaded to join. But if the United States and Great Britain were to be of one mind in approaching this topic—I leave out details and all methods—I am quite sure that France would have to associate herself with our action the very next day, with all her power and all the great contribution which she can make, and other powerful countries would have no choice whatever but to join in the movement. I regard international action to arrest the fall of prices as the sole hope of averting a world crash to which everything we have suffered up to the present will be a mere prelude. I begged for it in October last. I begged the Government of that day, the first National Government, to summon such a conference in October last. I beg for it now, and that is why I was so much grieved and shocked to hear my right hon. Friend the Chancellor of the Exchequer say last night:

> It must be recognised that it would be quite impossible for the representatives of this country to engage themselves in another conference at the present time.—[Official Report, 9th May, 1932; col. 1672, Vol. 265.]

He went on to say, "We have enough conferences already to keep us occupied till the end of the year. All the halls are full; all the performers are already engaged. We are stocked up with conferences"—of course in saying that I am not quoting him any more. I think that was a terrible declaration. What, Sir, even if the United States were willing to come to a conference on the fall in prices are we really to refuse and to tell them, "Oh, we are too busy to attend to you"? My right hon. Friend, who is so cool a judge of things, is surely on this occasion falling short of his usual just sense of proportion. Why, Sir, this conference which I plead for is of all other conferences the one most worth having. It is the one which will give the other conferences their best chance of success. It is the one which may be an indispensable preliminary to the success of these other conferences. It is the only conference we could call where all the parties who sat around the table would have the same objective and would gain the same advantages if the objectives were attained.

We all have high hopes of Ottawa; fine aspirations are centred upon Lausanne. In happier circumstances, what a noble opportunity would be offered to us at Ottawa to unite our Empire and make our trade flow in fertile inter-Imperial channels—if only that conference could meet in happier circumstances in an atmosphere of hope, an atmosphere of confidence and enterprise, with the upturn of the world behind it, and our Empire uniting itself, marching forward in the van. If only that could be achieved! But, now, I fear if these remorseless tides of deflation continue to ebb, ebb and ebb, and if world prices continue to sag, sag and sag, when they get to Ottawa we may find a grim gathering, and have little to do but to share miseries and face them bravely, as, no doubt, they will be bravely and loyally faced.

As for Lausanne, what good can result from holding that conference before the United States election has taken place? Any agreement which is come to between the debtors in Europe will become a platform counter in a most fierce and confused contest in the Unites States. We could not choose a worse moment for launching proposals for the mitigation of the present debts and the reparations position than at this juncture. Reason and knowledge are silent at election time to a large extent, and Democrats and Republicans will vie with each other in denouncing any proposals which may emanate from a foreign or European source, and in boasting which party will be the one that will exact the uttermost farthing. You may easily destroy by precipitate action the powerful movement in favour of debt revision which is spreading more widely all through the United States, and particularly British debt revision, which has enormous backing of its own. I trust that on no account will an agreement be reached at Lausanne in June. And poor Geneva! The conference at Geneva is proceeding while other conferences are absorbing our efforts, and at a time when the whole world is under this sinister deflationary pressure, and when no one knows where it is going to end, when trade is at a standstill, when a war of economic attrition is proceeding between all nations, when unrest and fear rule in so many lands, when communications are slowing down and when great steamships no longer cross the ocean except with a mere handful of passengers, do hon. Members think that that is a time when nations are likely to disarm, to destroy the weapons already paid for, or to reduce military forces and institutions which they feel may play a part in protecting themselves against external enemies and which may add to their internal security?

Yet we are told, and the world was told last night by the Chancellor of the Exchequer, that we shall be too busy at Lausanne and Geneva to attend a conference even if the United States were willing to come to a conference upon what is agreed on all sides is the prime cause of our misfortunes and peril. I beg the Chancellor of the Exchequer to reconsider those fateful words. A conference on stopping deflation could not interfere with any party interest, and no party would have any interest in preventing the deliberations of such an inquiry. No report of such a conference could be expected for some time, and of course it would be a conference which would primarily have to be composed of experts acting under the broad guidance of politicians, and it would not require the daily presence of our leading statesmen.

We are agreed upon the evil, we are agreed upon its gravity, and we are largely agreed upon the causes from which the evil has sprung, and we are now asked to agree to let it take its course. I have heard it said that there have always been from time to time these differences, and that there were other crises in 1848 and 1873, and they tell us that we got through them all. But those crises occurred in a far less complex world. You have never had a world like this before. It is more vast and more complex than we have ever seen at any other time. It is a time when enormous populations have been lifted by science to high economic levels, and where scores of numbers of persons have a long way to fall. We live in an island which is the heart of seaborne commerce, and we have 10,000,000 people for whom, unless and until national and Imperial arrangements are made, there would be no food apart from world commerce and world credit. I do not dissent from the specific financial proposals which have been made by His Majesty's Government, and I agree with the emphasis which the right hon. Gentleman the Member for Hillhead has imparted to those measures. I voted for the tariff, and I am sure that it is necessary, but I do not believe that all the measures and all the tariffs taken together will solve or save the situation in which we find ourselves. Only world action can cure a world evil, and no such action will be taken except through the cooperation of Great Britain and the United States, with other strong Powers hastening to rally to our joint appeal. Therefore, I counsel and I urge that we lay aside every impediment, postpone every obstructive obstacle, and that we concentrate upon the one vital, prior, paramount objective, namely, international action to arrest a fall in prices, to restore and re-open the possibilities of world trade, and to unite again the civilisation and prosperity of mankind.

DISARMAMENT

May 13, 1932

House of Commons

I could not bring myself altogether to disagree with the Leader of the Opposition when he said that he considered that the speech of my right hon. Friend the Foreign Secretary [Sir John Simon] was depressing and disappointing, certainly to those who have attached high hopes to Disarmament Conferences, and to the Conferences which are now proceeding. But when I listened to the speech of the Leader of the Opposition, to his admirable sentiments and his humane expressions, I could not see that, if he were at Geneva himself in the next few weeks, when, as the Foreign Secretary has said, these serious practical issues are going to arise, he would add any real forward impulse to the decisions on these issues. It is just because there is this very great difference—I am sorry that there should be—between the public professions, the warm sentiments which are expressed on all sides by political leaders on the one hand, and the actual forces which influence the decisions of Governments on the other—it is just because of this great gulf and division that the Conference on Disarmament has now got into a condition which I must regard as not only disappointing, but, from many points of view, discreditable.

My right hon. Friend began with an elaborate legal justification for holding the Conference at all—the Treaty of Versailles, the Treaty of Locarno, and so on. There is no need for legal justification. If by any means an abatement of the expense and sacrifice involved in maintaining large armies and navies could be achieved, we should not look back to the legal reasons which had brought the Conference into being. What we have to consider is whether any useful result is actually being obtained at the present time, or has been obtained. I confess I have always doubted the utility of these conferences on disarmament in the present condition—I say only in the present condition—of the world. I see that I said, practically a year ago:

I believe that the armaments of the world to-day would be positively even smaller, certainly no greater, if none of these discussions had taken place at Geneva.

I see that I said also:

> They have been a positive cause of friction and ill will, and have given
> an undue advertisement to naval and military affairs. They have con-
> centrated the attention of Governments in all countries, many of them
> without the slightest reason for apprehension about or dispute with each
> other, upon all sorts of hypothetical wars which certainly will never take
> place.—[Official Report, 29th June, 1931; cols. 955-6, Vol. 254.]

My right hon. Friend the Foreign Secretary, in his speech, pointed out to the House
that, when you come to discuss quantitative disarmament, every nation asks itself, not
"What is it that I am actually going to have in military instrumentalities?" but "What
is the claim that I must peg out for myself in circumstances which I cannot foresee,
and which may come upon me at any time in the next 10 years?" Consequently, the
whole tendency of these conferences, and they have been going on ceaselessly for six
or seven years in one form or another, has been to lead to the Governments of all
countries, and the military, naval and air authorities behind the Governments of all
countries, stating their demands and claims at a maximum. Undoubtedly, also, the
whole mind of the governing instruments of the different countries have been continually concentrated upon the prospects of war, and they have been invited to
consider, as I said, all sorts of conditions which may never come to pass, with the
result that you have now an organised, regimented opinion in all the Governments that
are met together at Geneva, and all are there in order to make sure that no diminution
of armaments is effected which infringes the strong position that their military and
naval experts have taken up in the internal discussion which have taken place.

So far as the Navy aspect is concerned, I have nothing to add to what I have have
said on so many previous occasions, that I believe that there has been no diminution of
naval force through any of the agreements which have been made since, possibly, the
first Treaty of Washington. Economic pressure has led to great slowings down, but, so
far as we are concerned, I still believe that we are greatly disadvantaged by the Treaty
of London which was entered into last year. We have parted with our freedom. That is,
to us, a very great disadvantage, because we had the lead in design, and could ensure
that such moneys as we could spare for naval defence should be employed to the best
possible advantage. We have parted with that; we have tied our hands with respect to
our own special dangers which may arise in the narrow seas. I still hold that it would
have been far better for us to have said to the United States, "Build whatever you will;
your Navy is absolutely ruled out of our calculations except as a potential friend.
Build whatever you will, and allow us to deal with our special problems." We have
suffered in that respect, and, more than that, I think it is possible that the world has
suffered by the great decline in the force and power of the British Navy. When I was on
the other side of the Atlantic, I used frequently to point out that American dissatisfac-
tion at events which were taking place in the Far East must to some extent be due to
the fact that it was owing to the decline of the naval power of Great Britain that an
entirely new development and balance of forces had arisen in the oceans of the world.

I come now to the proposals of qualitative disarmament about which my right hon. Friend was so very insistent. He told us that it was difficult to divide weapons into offensive and defensive categories. It certainly is, because almost every conceivable weapon may be used either in defence or offence; it all depends upon the circumstances; and every weapon, whether offensive or defensive, may be used either by an aggressor or by the innocent victim of his assault. My right hon. Friend said that he wished to make it more difficult for the invader, and for that reason, I gather, heavy guns, tanks and poison gas are to be relegated to the evil category of offensive weapons. The invasion of France by Germany in 1914 reached its climax without the employment of any of these weapons at all. The heavy gun is to be described as an offensive weapon. It is all right in a fortress; there it is virtuous and pacific in its character; but bring it out into the field—and, of course, if it were needed it would be brought out into the field—and it immediately becomes naughty, peccant, militaristic, and has to be placed under the ban of civilisation. Take the tank. The Germans, having invaded France, entrenched themselves; and in a couple of years they shot down 1,500,000 French and British soldiers who were trying to free the soil of France. The tank was invented to overcome the fire of machine guns with which the Germans were maintaining themselves in France, and it did save a lot of life in the process of eventually clearing the soil of the invader. Now, apparently, the machine gun, which was the German weapon for holding on to 13 provinces of France, is to be the virtuous, defensive machine gun, and the tank, which was the means by which these lives were saved, is to be placed again under the censure and obloquy of all just and righteous men.

There is also the question of gas. Nothing could be more repugnant to our feelings than the use of poison gas, but there is no logic at all behind the argument that suggests that it is quite proper in war to lay a man low with high explosive shell, fragments of which inflict poisonous and festering wounds, and altogether immoral to give him a burn with corrosive gas or make him cough and sneeze or otherwise suffer through his respiratory organs. There is no logical distinction between the two. A great many of our friends are here to-day because they were fired at by German gas shells, which inflicted minor injuries upon them. Had it been high explosive shell, they would in all human probability have been killed. The whole subject of war is, beyond all words, horrible, and the nations are filled with the deepest loathing of it, but, if wars are going to take place, it is by no means certain that the introduction of chemical warfare is going to make them more horrible than they have been. The attitude of the British Government has always been to abhor the employment of poison gas. As I understand it, our only procedure is to keep alive such means of steadying this subject as shall not put us at a hopeless disadvantage if, by any chance, it were used against us by other people.

Then there is the question of submarines, which I wish had never been discovered or invented. Everyone who has been connected with the Royal Navy or the Admiralty would take that view. But a small country, with seaport towns within range of bombardment from the sea, feels very differently about having two or three submarines to keep the bombarding squadrons at a respectful distance.

I have only gone into these details in order to try to show the House how very absurd is this attempt to distinguish between offensive and defensive weapons and how little prospect there is of any fruitful agreement being reached upon it. These illustrations that I have given will be multiplied a hundredfold when the naval, military and air experts on the committees to whom this subject is to be remitted get to work. I have not the slightest doubt that nothing will emerge from their deliberations, which no doubt will be prolonged, except agreements to differ in one form or another. I think a much truer line of classification might have been drawn if the Conference of all these nations at Geneva set itself to ban the use of weapons which tend to be indiscriminate in their action and whose use entails death and wounds, not merely to the combatants in the fighting zones but to the civil population, men, women and children, far removed from those areas. There, indeed, it seems to me would be a direction in which the united nations assembled at Geneva might advance with hope.

It may be said that in war no such conventions would be respected, and very few were respected in the Great War. We hope there will be no other wars, but, even if there are wars in the future, we need not assume that they will be world wars involving all the Powers of the world, with no external Powers to impose a restraint upon the passions of the belligerents or to judge of the merits of their cause. I do not at all despair of building up strong conventions and conceptions held by the great nations of the world against the use of weapons which fall upon enormous masses of non-combatant persons. Still more should I like to raise my voice in abhorrence of the idea, now almost accepted among so many leading authorities in different countries, that the bombing of open towns and the wholesale destruction of civilian life is compatible with any civilised decency. We are all allowing ourselves to be led step by step into contemplating such hideous episodes as part of the ordinary give and take of a war, should a war ever come.

I submit to the House that this attempt to employ the energies of Geneva upon discriminating between offensive and defensive weapons will only lead to rigmarole and delay and is in itself a silly expedient and that a much truer method would be to endeavour to focus and marshal opinion upon the lines of preventing the indiscriminate use of weapons upon non-combatant and civilian populations. I think the adoption of such topics for discussion really casts a certain air of insincerity over the proceedings at Geneva. I do not believe any of the naval or military experts who meet to discuss these matters will have any doubt whatever that no practical advantage can be gained. As for the French scheme of security, that certainly is a logical proposition, and I do not know whether, in a quite different world from that in which we live, the relegation of the air arm to a central police force might not conceivably be a means of providing a higher organisation of society than anything that we can achieve, but, of course, in the present circumstances it is obviously impossible that such a development should take place. Here, again, is another one of these very complicated propositions which have been put forward, the only purpose of which it would seem is to afford for those 53 nations who have arrived together to discuss Disarmament some provender upon which they could sustain themselves.

If you wish for Disarmament, it will be necessary to go to the political and economic causes which lie behind the maintenance of armies and navies. There are very serious political and economic dangers at the present time, and antagonisms which are by no means assuaged. I should very much regret to see any approximation in military strength between Germany and France. Those who speak of that as though it were right, or even a mere question of fair dealing, altogether underrate the gravity of the European situation. I would say to those who would like to see Germany and France on an equal footing in armaments: "Do you wish for war?" For my part, I earnestly hope that no such approximation will take place during my lifetime or in that of my children. To say that is not in the least to imply any want of regard or admiration for the great qualities of the German people, but I am sure that the thesis that they should be placed in an equal military position to France is one which, if it ever emerged in practice, would bring us to within practical distance of almost measureless calamity.

We must also remember that the great mass of Russia, with its enormous armies and with its schools of ardent students of chemical warfare, poison gas, its tanks and all its appliances, looms up all along the Eastern frontier of Europe and that the whole row of small States, Finland, Estonia, Latvia, Lithuania, Poland—not a small State, but for this purpose in the line—and Rumania, are under the continued preoccupation of this enormous, and to them in many ways unfriendly Russian power. It may well be that there is no danger, but I expect that if we lived there we should feel rather uncomfortable about it.

Mr. Lansbury *indicated dissent*.

Mr. Churchill: The right hon. Gentleman opposite would not feel uncomfortable about it because he has special friendships with the Soviet Government and no doubt he would make quite sure that they respected any country which he had honoured with his temporary presence. It seems to me that these grave political dangers must be faced and recognised. All these small nations look to France, and the French Army, as giving them a kind of central support.

Although I should like to see the foundation of European peace raised upon a more moral basis, I am very anxious that the present foundation should not be deranged until at any rate we have built up something satisfactory in its place. I hope and trust that the right hon. Gentleman the Foreign Secretary will continue his pious labours at Geneva, and that he will be able at some future date to give us a more favourable account of them. For my part, I shall continue to trust to the strong and ceaseless economic pressure of expense which is weighing upon all countries, to the growth of a greater confidence which a long peace must ensure, and to the patient and skilful removal of the political causes of antagonism which a wise foreign policy should eventually achieve.

Sir J. Simon: I should like to ask the right hon. Gentleman a question and to get his approval of one matter. I will read to him from the Resolution which I moved at the Conference. It begins thus, after the preliminary references:

> That as regards the question of the abolition or internationalisation, certain tests should be applied, notably, what degree of risk to innocent civilian populations was involved in the use of particular arms.

I should be greatly obliged if I could have the right hon. Gentleman's support to that matter.

Mr. Churchill: I gladly associate myself with that, and I trust that my right hon. Friend will endeavour to develop that line of argument rather than attempt to distinguish between offensive and defensive weapons.

FINANCE BILL (GOLD STANDARD)

May 25, 1932

House of Commons

The Committee, I think, will be well advised to accept in their fullest sense the assurances that have been given us by the Financial Secretary. I was, unfortunately, not in my place when he gave the specific assurance that there was no intention to return to the Gold Standard at normal parity while gold was behaving as it is. Of course, the Bill on which we are engaged is an annual Bill, and makes provision only for the year. One cannot reasonably expect that gold will once again return to propriety and normal, decent behaviour in such a short space of time and, therefore, I think the assurance he gave was one in which there was, as he said, a very great measure of solidity. When my right hon. Friend rose just now, he greatly reinforced and confirmed all these impressions and drew attention to the important character of the statement that he had made on the subject of the non-return to gold at normal parity in the immediate future or in any period which is practical and worth while considering, a statement made by him on behalf of the Government and on behalf of the Chancellor of the Exchequer, who is unhappily not with us to-day. Therefore, I think the hon. Member who moved the Amendment and my hon. Friend opposite have achieved all that they could expect to achieve, and all that a Parliamentary Debate entitles them to achieve at this stage in its influence upon the policy of the Government and in the declaration which it has evoked from the administration. There was one expression in the first speech of the Financial Secretary upon which I must comment. He said we ought to get this out of the way and pass on to more important topics. There are no more important topics. Search the world and you will not find a topic more important than this grave, grim money problem. You may not see the solution. We may not be able to propose the solution. There may be many conflicting solutions, but this is the supreme topic that concerns the whole nation. Every class is concentrating its mind and its intelligence, as far as it can comprehend it, upon it. Do not let us imagine that in dismissing this matter, we are passing to more important topics. We are passing to topics, whatever they are, incomparably petty compared with this.

FINANCE BILL (BEER DUTY)

May 26, 1932

House of Commons

I beg to move, "That the Chairman do report Progress and ask leave to sit again."

I venture to rise to move this Motion in order to elicit from the Government a statement of how they view the situation which has arisen this evening owing to the accidental non-discussion of the proposed new Clauses relating to the Beer Duty. [*Laughter.*] It is not a matter for laughter. The Government opposed these new Clauses, and I had no intention of voting against the Government, but there are enormous numbers of people, reputable and worthy people, whose trade, livelihood and interest are involved in this matter, and if by a mere accident the discussion of it was prevented, and there was, as it were, no vocal expression of the feelings that exist upon the subject, no statement of the case with all its hardships, no admonitory exposition to guide the finance for future years—if that were to take place, I venture to think that it would be deeply injurious to the Government and to the Conservative party. I know that my right hon. Friend the Leader of the House [Mr. Stanley Baldwin] is not a man to take small points or to take advantage of any accident of this kind. He has his duty not only as leader of the Conservative party, but as Leader of the House, to see that fair play and good and equal treatment are administered over the whole area of public business.

I have no complaint against the Government at all. They have done absolutely nothing wrong. The fault rests, undoubtedly, with those who were in charge of these important Amendments. I am stating the case quite fairly—the fault lies with them. My hon. Friend the Member for Canterbury (Sir W. Wayland) has been incessant in his attendance in the Chamber. [*Interruption.*] I mean it. I say he has been incessant in his attendance. [Hon. Members: "Where was he?"] If hon. Gentlemen think this is a joke they are making a very great mistake. These great industries have to suffer in these hard times, but there ought to be a full statement of their case, and, even supposing a fault or error has been committed by an individual—as a matter of fact his was an absence for only two minutes out of an hour or an hour and a half when this matter was likely to come on—it is altogether unworthy of His Majesty's Government—it would be unworthy, I do not say it is—or of the House of Commons to penalise this trade and this interest in this way. They must offer us a Debate, a reasonable opportunity of discussion. [*Interruption.*] I do not say anything that the Government have done is unworthy; on the contrary, they have done nothing. No one is in the wrong except those who now appeal to the Government, but we are quite determined, and in my judgment it rests with the Government to offer some solution of this difficulty. [Hon. Members: "Why?"] Because it will be in the general interest that that should be done. [Hon. Members: "No!"] I hear some Liberal cries of

"No"–[*Interruption*]–well, they are all mixed up with us on these benches–but I invite the Government to offer us some consideration in this matter. In any case, it would be undesirable that this subject should be discussed so late at night as this. No one is seeking to challenge the view of the Government, they are going to have their tax, but there ought to be an opportunity for the case to be stated, and the fact that it has been missed by accident will, I am sure, not be treated by my right hon. Friend in a harsh spirit, or in the unchivalrous spirit which some of the cries behind me have indicated.

FINANCE BILL (BEER DUTY)

June 8, 1932

House of Commons

I should like to join with my hon. Friend the Member for Canterbury (Sir W. Wayland) in congratulating my right hon. Friend the Chancellor of the Exchequer [Mr. Neville Chamberlain] upon his return, as we can see, in the fullest mental vigour, to the House. It must have been very disappointing to any Minister as assiduous and so keenly enveloped in political affairs to be absent while his Budget was actually under discussion. We are very glad that he has come back, and has come back to take part in a discussion of this kind. I think that my hon. Friend the Member for Canterbury was quite justified in raising the discussion, but I hope that he will not press his proposal to a Division. I have on two occasions voted against the present National Government in this Parliament, but those were great matters of permanent Imperial consequence such as the Statute of Westminster and a democratic constitution for India. This is not a matter on the same level. It is a matter of domestic housekeeping and of annual finance, and we are not, I think, at all called upon to press opinions about the expediency of a particular tax to a point where they would raise, as has been pointed out by the Chancellor of the Exchequer, all those other far greater considerations affecting the whole life and position of the country. Nevertheless I think that it is right that the case against the over-taxation of this particular commodity should have been stated, as it has been with so much moderation and force from both sides of the House. We are entitled to deal with this matter as a revenue matter primarily.

I admit the force of much of what was said by the hon. Member for West Bermondsey (Dr. Salter) on the temperance aspect, but, when you consider the progress which has been made, no doubt under the influence of high taxation in the past, in the sobriety of this country, no one can consider that the temperance aspect is an urgent aspect in the discussion at the present time. In the year 1913, the last pre-war year, there were 183,000 convictions for drunkenness, and in 1931, the last year for which we have the complete figures, they had fallen to 53,000. It is perfectly clear that the temperance aspect of the matter ought not to sway our opinions about this tax at the present time, and that we are entitled to look at it solely from the point of view of revenue. I will look at it–and I want to detain the House very briefly–only from that point of view. The question is not whether we should tax beer, but whether we should over-tax it. My right hon. Friend admitted that it was over-taxed. In the five Budgets which I opened and carried through the House I received an average of £81,000,000 a year from beer. I admit that there was a slight falling off in the last year. In the three Budgets which have been carried and proposed since the duty was raised the average, including the estimate for this year, is only £76,000,000, so that there is on the face of the figures a net and absolute loss of something like £5,000,000 attendant upon the increase of the tax. It is a very extraordinary and tremendous fact that that should be so.

I agree that it is fair to say as my right hon. Friend did that it is not all due to the tax. The bad trade, the changing habits of the people, all those have played their part, but it must be remembered that bad trade has been largely mitigated by the enormous sums contributed for the relief of unemployment and distress, and also that the progressive cheapness of living has kept pace with the depression. Therefore, I think, it is not unfair to argue that probably three-quarters of this loss of revenue has been due to over-taxation and to trying to get more from this source than it will in fact yield, copious as has been the supply which it has yielded to the revenue. Whatever the need of money may be now or in the future, it surely cannot be sound, economic or provident finance to injure and run the risk of destroying a revenue which has been one of the main, long-established, abundant sources of perennial revenue to the State, and one which, if it were to be destroyed, could not be replaced in any way that we can see at the present time.

Every commodity will bear a certain degree of taxation, and the modern view, differing altogether from the Gladstonian theory that you should have very few taxes and so on—the modern view undoubtedly of the House is that each commodity should, if necessary, and if otherwise convenient, bear its proper weight and burden of taxation, and that you should spread the taxation over a number of separate commodities rather than press unduly heavily on one particular source so as to inflict a serious permanent injury upon the trade concerned. Men can carry heavy weights if they are well distributed and well balanced. The question which we are entitled to ask when any particular tax is being considered is, Is the knapsack being well fitted upon the shoulders which have to bear it? Under the Budget of the late Chancellor of the Exchequer [Lord Snowden] in September last, I could not feel that he was adapting the national burden which the nation was ready, nay determined to assume, to the national shoulders with wisdom. It seemed to me to be most clumsily imposed, and this was one of the taxes which struck me as being not only improvident from a financial point of view but vexatious and irritating.

I hoped that my right hon. Friend, a Conservative Chancellor of the Exchequer free from the narrow prejudices which hampered his predecessor, would have seen his way to retrace the foolish step which was taken in September last under very peculiar conditions and which I do not intend now to animadvert upon at all. The right hon. Gentleman says that his remission of the revenue duty would cost him £10,000,000. Of course, the figures are highly disputable, because it was only realised in the April White Paper that the first Snowden increase of duty produced a heavy shortage. When he made an estimate for an increased yield in the year he did not mention the fact that the duty was already down on the year. So it is impossible for private Members to disentangle the effects of the first over-taxation of beer from its second and aggravated over-taxation. All is mixed up and also influenced by general causes to which reference has been made, but, however you look at it, the destruction of revenue is indisputable. There has been a destruction of revenue of perhaps £4,000,000 or £5,000,000 accompanied by a most heavy increase of the rate of the tax.

This question cannot be put forward as a matter of indulgence. This is no time for indulgence. It is simply a question of obtaining the largest possible permanent revenue not only this year but in years to come. If it be true that we have reduced our revenue by £4,000,000 or £5,000,000 through trying to get more from the tax than it can yield that is an enormous argument for stopping, if not now, at the very first available opportunity, and getting back to a degree of taxation which will safeguard the future. In his speech my right hon. Friend almost accepted the fact that injuries were being inflicted now which coupled with the habits of the country would permanently impair the revenue from this source. That will leave an increasing gap to be filled in future years, and which can only be filled by imposing other additional burdens or by making further heavy cuts. It really cannot be thrifty finance to pursue such courses.

In a House like this, with so many supporters of the Government and many friends and political associates, I agree with what has been said from various quarters, that those who suggest that any tax should be taken off are under a moral obligation to suggest some alternative, serious as are the risks to private Members who suggest possible alternatives. I proposed, when I spoke on the Second Reading of the Budget that the necessary £10,000,000 might have been taken from the moneys which are set aside to form the nucleus of the new Exchange Equalisation Fund, and, of course, I was very much denounced for that. I was accused of using a capital asset for recurrent expenditure. But this same capital asset was used last year by the late Chancellor of the Exchequer to meet recurrent expenditure, and it was used by the National Government after it came into power for recurrent expenditure, and I saw no reason at all under any canon of orthodoxy which the Government have so far erected why a similar amount from the same source should not have been taken for the assistance of the Chancellor of the Exchequer when he was framing his Budget in the first instance. It is easy to sneer at such suggestions and assume a great air of financial correctitude, but I am sure that if the Chancellor of the Exchequer, when he was framing his Budget, had wished to reduce this particular taxation, this beer taxation to its maximum economic level, he could, quite easily and without any reproach, have presented his proposals in the form in which I have suggested.

Upon this question of orthodoxy, let me ask the Government: Are you orthodox? Are you pure? Besides impairing a source of revenue, beer over-taxation causes, as we know, serious losses under other heads of revenue. I do not want to enter into an argument of detail about what those losses are. I have been given some figures which have been carefully prepared and which show that on Schedule D, on the Surtax, on the Estate and Stamp Duties, especially the junior class of securities, and ultimately on the licence duties under Schedule A, that there an additional loss of something between £5,000,000 and £6,000,000 is to be apprehended by the injury done to the beer revenue and to the beer trade. I know that those figures are disputable, but that the loss is substantial is common ground in all parts of the House. What does my right hon. Friend the Chancellor of the Exchequer say when he is confronted with that fact? He says: "Ah, loss there may be, but this loss will not fall on this year. It will only fall on next year." That may be an argument, but it is an argument fatal to financial orthodoxy, for what is that but an admission of a forestalment of revenue for next year? We are to gain £8,000,000 in our revenue this year at a cost of £5,000,000 or £6,000,000 next year. It is a forestalment that will have to be made up in a future year, and at a time when the steady, continuous impairment of revenue from beer is actually in progress. It is not only a case of devouring the seed corn but of mortgaging future reduced harvests. With all the good will in the world, one must object to the Government's right in this matter to parade with virtue, impeccable and austere, their financial orthodoxy. It is an even worse deviation from financial strictness to create this situation, this forestalment of revenue from next year, than if the right hon. Gentleman had used the £10,000,000 of the Dollar Exchange Fund, when he had it in his possession, in the same manner that it was used by his predecessor. And what about the argument that no capital asset should be used for recurrent finance? How we delude ourselves if we suppose that we can inflict, possibly, a lasting, mordant lesion upon a vital indispensable source of revenue, without committing the fault of using a capital asset for a temporary emergency, and not only a capital asset, because this is a source of continued revenue from year to year exceeding the value of any of those capital assets sometimes brought into Exchequer finance in a difficult year.

I should have thought that the fundamental change that had taken place in the country in our affairs, in our outlook upon finance, since the Budget of last September would have justified a review of this over-taxation of beer. In those days, the whole object was to maintain a high level of exchange, and for that purpose a Sinking Fund of great strength was needed, but now that we are labouring to keep our exchange down, and spending money for that purpose, it is strange that the same taxation and the same sources of revenue should be maintained. Some hon. Members have mentioned sugar as an alternative source of taxation. I raised that point in September. We could obtain £20,000,000 from sugar by merely restoring the relief given to sugar given by the late Chancellor of the Exchequer and by myself, and the cost of sugar would then be less than it was in 1928, when everybody said how cheap sugar was and how gratifying was the increase in public consumption. What does the Chancellor of the Exchequer say? What he said was most grave and alarming. He said that he could not afford in the present situation to sacrifice his reserves. If that meant anything, it meant that he cannot consider sugar as an alternative, because he may need sugar too. Am I right in that assumption? I am afraid that I am. That raises the extremely serious position that we must not use sugar as an alternative method in place of beer to raise this extra revenue, because sugar may be wanted too. Before we get to that, or to anything of that kind, it will be the duty of the Government to exercise every other alternative before they impose further taxation in relief of the present situation and to supply extra revenue to the State. The Government in such an eventuality will have to consider not only Sinking Fund needs in view of present conditions, but the question of public expenditure in all its branches will have to be considered by the House.

I see no reason why we should press this Debate to a Division. For my part, I should certainly not vote against the Government on this subject. We cannot hope to alter the finance of this year. The right hon. Gentleman declared the obvious truth, that the Government must stand or fall by a serious vote on a main item of its Budget proposals. True, His Majesty's Government have magnified this issue by posing it in this manner, but with the international conferences that are pending there are good and solid reasons why we in this country should not seem to shirk any burden, however unwisely or however unfortunately imposed upon us. We may have our own opinion about policy, and we are entitled to express it in debate. We are entitled to complain at the manner in which the pieces have been set upon the board, and it is not futile. We hope by debate to influence opinion in the future. We may have to submit and suffer, and suffer we shall, needlessly and fruitlessly, but if we can build up opinion in the House of Commons and among Ministers, then we shall make it very unlikely that this particular specimen of regrettable over-taxation will be forced upon us in the forthcoming year.

"THE MONEY PROBLEM"

June 15, 1932

Royal Empire Society Luncheon,
Cannon Street Hotel, London

[Extract] ... We are met in the City of London because our weights and measures have been tampered with. Gold has been cornered, scrambled up, and hoarded. In the last few years the price of gold has risen by nearly 70 per cent., and the value of everything else has fallen in like degree. We know that the fault lies with gold or with those who have mishandled gold. It does not lie with the many thousand other commodities measured by gold. A remarkable feature of the last 10 years has been the way in which the price of these commodities have kept a steady relation with one another. They have marched forward together in an orderly array, indeed they have closed their ranks. One commodity alone, gold, has broken from the ranks. That is what has sabotaged every form of human effort, and has depreciated every service man can render to man. All values have fallen, and, should the process continue, every institution will be, if it is not already, threatened with insolvency or repudiation.

The odd thing about the cornering of gold is that no class has benefitted from it. Every nation and every class has suffered. All creditors, whether national or individual, will, if this goes on, be faced increasingly with the insolvency of their debtors. Already the world is breaking out in moratoriums. Nations who played the principal part in cornering the gold measures of the world are suffering as much as those who had not impounded the long-accepted world currency.

We are told "You cannot manipulate yourself into prosperity by tampering with the currency." We have only to look round to see that we have been monkeyed out of prosperity because currency has been tampered with.

There never was a moment when the desire of mankind to consume and the power of mankind to produce were greater. This great gathering in the City shows the interest this money problem is exerting on the minds of men of all classes. Your presence is a signal of movement, of action, throughout Great Britain, which will insist that the topic should hold its place in the minds of those who are governing the State. Time is very short. The tension of the world increases. We can see the internal stresses of the various nations from China to Peru, or at least from Japan to Chile. (Hear, hear.)

A conference is now being held at Lausanne to put War debts and reparations in cold storage, to put them in some freezing chamber where it is trusted their sinister microbes will be killed for ever. The attempt to pay War debts and reparations across tariff frontiers which will not receive goods—the only form in which payment of international debts is possible—is the prime, direct, operative cause of the present world misfortune.

Let me tell you something which has not been said before by any of our national statesmen or capable editors. War debts caused the gold disease, but the cancellation or suspension of war debts, although obviously necessary and imperative, will not now stop the disease. You may rub a sore place till you engender a cancer. You have to leave off rubbing then, but when you do the cancer still goes on.

What we have to deal with now is the progressive devaluation of all human effort in terms of gold and scrip, and this carries with it week by week the progressive weakening and shrinkage of all the credit instruments and confidence upon which civilized society stands. The monetary system of the world is now in a state where the mere cessation of the original evil will not arrest the progress of its lamentable consequences. To find the cure we must do something quite different from the simple adjusting of war debts and reparations. That is why I am so glad the Government have favoured the plan, which I pressed upon them last September, of a world conference on the money question in order to arrest this remorseless deflation still in progress and to revaluate commodities up to the normal level of prosperity. There are two tasks before this world conference. The first is to discover the best technical method by which the devaluation of commodities can be substantially arrested, and the second is to invest that process with the authority which will command and hold the confidence of the most powerful States and communities, and of the investing classes in every land.

These two tasks cannot be separated. It is no use having a method if that method is not accepted by a sufficiently powerful league or confederation to impose itself upon the minds of men and gain their full confidence and usage. For this purpose the presence at the council board of the other great branch of the English-speaking race and the other great world-creditor nation, the United States, is, in my opinion, indispensable. We might have to try to arrive at a solution without the United States, but no solution reached without them could be comparable to those which are possible with their mighty aid. It would be a misfortune, indeed, if the world resolved itself into two groups, the sterling countries and gold countries, between which very little commerce would be possible. The United States are willing to come to a monetary conference. They have accepted the invitation of his Majesty's Government with a degree of spontaneous positive acceptance which I certainly expected, but which many people did not, and it is most hopeful. (Cheers.) I have every reason to believe that, once it is known that the British Empire and the United States are laying their heads together upon the money problem, the other great financial powers of the world will demand inclusion in their conclave.

Is it not a wonderful thing that amid so much confusion we find that all the dominant national Powers of the financial world are willing to come to London to discuss the money question? They will take their seats at a table where all have a common interest and a common need, to find a solution, if such be within the wit of men. Is it not a tribute to our country, and indeed to our National Government, that London may have the presidency of this new hope?

I deprecate raising difficulties about the agenda. The United States will not come if debts or reparations are included in the agenda. Many nations would not come if protection or the prevention of world-wide quotas and protection were included in the agenda. We should only be risking the path to safety by being too ambitious. Moreover, it is indispensable that the status of silver as a monetary factor should be included in the scope of the conference. Although War debts and reparations may not be on the agenda, they will in some measure have been disposed of for the time being. Although tariffs and new obstructions to paralyse the world trade, which are multiplying on all sides, will not be on the agenda, they cannot be absent from the minds of those who meet around the London table.

I look upon the conference on the money question as an object vital in itself and indeed the only great practical step that can now be taken. But if we could get a plan or agreement among the greatest nations to revaluate commodities, and provide a stable measure for the exchange of the services and productions of all men, surely there would have been created an atmosphere, a spirit, a situation, which would lead directly to a concerted attempt to reopen the channels of world trade. Here is the commanding pivot upon which the material fortunes of all nations now turn. Here is the brake which may arrest the reversion to primitive mercantilism and to mutually destructive commercial nationalism. I trust that this Government will grasp the larger hope with courage and simplicity, and will not be deterred from taking a first, wise, necessary step, by the fact that the whole path to recovery and world rescue cannot yet be marked out.

Through daylight saving the world got up together in truer harmony with sun time. That is what he have to do in the monetary sphere. At present we have no daylight saving there; we have only daylight losing through the unceasing enhancement of gold. There is but one salvation. This monetary lever has to be grasped in firm and trustworthy hands, grasped with the combined authority of the greatest nations of the world.

DOMINIONS OFFICE

June 17, 1932

House of Commons

It is perfectly clear that the Leader of the Opposition would not at any point resist a serious pressure or demand which was made upon this country by the Irish Free State. That has been the whole effect of the speech which he has delivered. Everything must be settled reasonably; trouble must not be made on this point or on that; we must endeavour to meet them half way. Never mind what they have done about the annuities, never mind what is the issue upon the Oath, we must continue to persist in our endeavours at conciliation and at meeting them half way.

Mr. Lansbury: Hear, hear!

Mr. Churchill: I am glad not to have misrepresented the right hon. Gentleman. But at what period does this story come? It comes after we have been for 10 years endeavouring to conciliate and meet the wishes of the Irish people. It comes 10 years after the Treaty, which was accepted by them as a full settlement, and since that Treaty we have interpreted it at every stage, on every point that has been raised, in favour of their inclinations. Their position at the Imperial Conferences enabled them to develop the whole of this trend towards the Statute of Westminster, which, I agree, appears to have been very injurious and ill-judged, but which was largely done to meet their views. And these Agreements which it is now sought to repudiate are not Agreements forced by England upon Ireland. They are the Agreements freely entered into by the accredited representatives of the Irish people, and now they are the Agreements which are to be broken, which are to be repudiated, nakedly and openly, as the Dominions Secretary has shown, and as far as I can gather, the right hon. Gentleman would not raise a hand or a finger to stop any inroad upon the rights of this country.

Mr. Lansbury: I was only doing exactly what the right hon. Gentleman himself did during the Debate on the Statute of Westminster, quoting him as an authority that the Free State has an absolute right to do what it has done.

Mr. Churchill: No. A legal right, certainly. I am afraid that that may be so, and that is why I so much regretted that His Majesty's Government did not accept the Amendment my right hon. and gallant Friend the Member for Burton (Colonel Gretton) moved. That Amendment sought no more than to impose upon the Irish Free State the same inhibitions which Canada, Australia, and New Zealand had imposed upon themselves, and I think it would have been wise and prudent to have accepted that Amendment. Indeed, I believe the fact that we did not accept it, that the power of the Government was used to vote down that proposal, greatly prejudiced the chances of Mr. Cosgrave in the election, because Mr. De Valera was able to tell his supporters that he had a legal right, and to hold the people who were rather timid but wanted to support him by the fact that he had a legal method of achieving his ends and making them believe that the British Government on the whole would not make any trouble about it. Therefore, I do adhere most strongly to the point of view which I took up when I last spoke on this subject before Christmas.

But this question is not being argued as a legal matter. The Government have—very wisely in view of the terms of the Statute of Westminster—broken away entirely from these legal aspects of the question. We are arguing it entirely as a matter of good faith. The right hon. Gentleman the Leader of the Opposition says that no one has answered his question why, if the Irish have a legal right to abolish the Oath, we should resent it if they do what is their legal right to do? We say that it is a moral offence, a breach of faith. What we propose to do is also within our full legal rights. We are perfectly entitled to judge what should be our attitude towards Powers or States, whether inside or outside the British Empire, which render nugatory all treaties or agreements which are transacted with them. Having regard to the great interest of the world at the present time in promoting a process of bargaining and agreement and having bargains made between nations upon which we can rely, we are discharging not only a national but an international duty in preventing a breach of this kind by any means within our power and within our full discretion.

The ex-Solicitor-General was put up to make what I can only describe as a loathesome speech, one which is calculated to darken counsel at every point, and to arm and inspire all those on the other side of the St. George's Channel who are endeavouring to make a solution of this question very difficult. Both he and the Leader of the Opposition have shown us that the present attitude of the truncated Socialist party is one which offers absolutely no guarantee to the people of Great Britain that any one of their interests, however vital, will, once it is disputed by the Irish Free State, ever be stood up for. So much for the right hon. Member for Poplar (Mr. Lansbury), who was so personally offensive the other night. Well, we know that in any question of this kind which arises, whether in regard to Ireland or India, his counsel and that of those in his control will always be to find this or that excuse for depriving Great Britain and the British Empire of any of the remaining safeguards and interests which we possess.

I rejoice to see my right hon. Friend the Member for Carnarvon Boroughs (Mr. Lloyd George) in his place again; I will not say in his place, because I am sorry to see the company that he has chosen, but at any rate he made it clear to us to-day that his situation is purely geographical and not political in any way. The right hon. Gentleman rendered a real service to the Committee and to the country upon this question, because he made it perfectly clear that this is no petty legal question. I agree entirely with him that if Mr. De Valera and his friends said, "We do not like this form of oath, we think it humiliating," we could say to them, "Have you anything else to suggest which will make you a loyal partner in the general scheme of the British Commonwealth of Nations?" But nothing of that kind has been put forward, and the right hon. Gentleman has reminded us forcibly and powerfully that the whole question of Imperial and national safety is involved the moment you accept or tolerate Mr. De

Valera's demand to be an independent Republic, with the right to negotiate arrangements for aerodromes or naval bases in any part of Ireland, and the right to deny their ports or their coasts to us even in time of war.

I am very glad my right hon. Friend raised that point, because there is far more behind this than the Oath. If it were the Oath only, it could be easily settled, and I think it has been very satisfactory that this Debate has enabled the House as a whole to express a very strong opinion in favour of His Majesty's Government marking by positive, overt and speedy action their sense of injury at the ill usage and breach of faith to which they had been subjected. My right hon. Friend the Secretary of State for the Dominions said that on the question of annuities they intended to deal with the matter, or words to that effect. I understood that meant that they would deal with the matter in such a way as to recover for this country what is its proper due, and, believing that to be so—and I see the right hon. Gentleman assents—I should like, as one who often criticises the Government to express my entire agreement with the course which they have adopted in this difficult matter.

INDIA

June 27, 1932

House of Commons

I wish to intervene for a few moments, but I must leave time for the Secretary of State [Sir John Simon] to clear up any points that may have been brought out in the Debate. I left my home this morning with some feelings of apprehension when I heard that a statement was to be made by the Secretary of State on a very important matter. I felt some anxiety, but I am bound to say that on the whole I feel very considerably reassured by the statement which he has made to us to-day. We know what his difficulties are, some of them left by his predecessors, but the bulk of them arising out of the incubus of the constitutional process which he has to carry out in India. He gave us an account, an encouraging account upon the whole, of the situation. He said that firm government and the assertion of law and order had succeeded in nearly every Province in India. Very good. He had stopped the no-rent campaign, and in practically every Province civil disobedience had broken down.

But my right hon. Friend then had to proceed to tell us the other side of the story. He had to go forward with his constitutional programme, and it is this constitutional programme which is adding to his difficulties, which is creating the very discontent and the very unrest which strong measures are required to allay. The constitutional programme marches forward. We have the Lothian Report. I do not know how many Members of the Committee have read that report or studied it with attention. It would not be proper to go into it in detail, but what can be a greater embarrassment to the administration in India than the bringing out of this report at this juncture? Look at the contradiction in terms presented by the policy of His

Majesty's Government. There is the re-enactment of the Ordinances, which are extreme coercive measures of restraint, and at the same time there is flung out to all parts of India a report which says that 36,000,000 people are to be enfranchised, and that they will be the foundation of the responsible authority which is to decide the future destinies of India. Imagine these two events, the one contrasted with the other. There are 31,000 people in prison in India at the present time. I do not suppose that half of them would have been there if law and order had been maintained by the right hon. Gentleman's predecessor. They include all the active politicians. There is a great deal of logic in what the Leader of the Opposition said, although I was sorry that in some of his speech he appeared to apologise for the murder of British officials by young girls.

Mr. Lansbury: The right hon. Gentleman has no right to say that. I sent a telegram to India of my own volition directly that happened, and I have done my best to say that murder and assassination are an abomination and will injure any cause for which they are used to forward. I am against not only that kind of murder, but all murder, whether it be war or anything else.

Mr. Churchill: I know that in the moral aspect no one is better than the right hon. Gentleman, and no one can make any complaint against him. I have not the slightest doubt that he is revolted by such crimes, but there were many sentences in what he said which seemed to explain the actions of these high-spirited people. I know that this interpretation will be put upon them in other quarters. I was saying that he was quite right when he said that most of the active politicians were already in prison. The right hon. Gentleman is keeping order with one hand and with the other is preparing the way for these gentlemen to come out of prison, and to go from prison into Parliament. That is a contradiction in terms, an extraordinary difficult policy which he is carrying out. Immense unrest is caused throughout India by the publication of a report like the Lothian Report. There are 450,000 villages in India, and only 11,000 odd have been able to evolve the simple organisation of a village council. Therefore, we cannot proceed on that line. Yet it is out of these people, who are not able to provide this simple homely organism in their villages, these primitive, illiterate and ignorant people—it is not their fault—that we are to try to lay the foundation of and erect, not indeed provincial government, but a united states of India—a vast structure of 40 or 50 nations, woven together, the size of Europe and practically the population of Europe. You are to try to build the kind of organisation which Europe struggles after, and will for generations struggle after in vain, upon these humble primitives who are unable in 450,000 villages even to produce the simple organisation of four or five people sitting in a hut in order to discuss their common affairs.

We cannot wonder that the country is disturbed. There is the right hon. Gentleman having to proceed with his task of keeping order on the one hand and at the same time encouraging the very subversives he has in gaol—not through his fault—by promising them that on a day which will not be distant 36,000,000 of electors are going to return the Congress party to Parliament. I cannot elaborate the arguments now, and I am sorry that I cannot, because I think this is worthy of the attention of the House—these people voting with their coloured tickets in coloured boxes, because they cannot read or write, and with every movement discerned by the eye of the only caucus in India, the machine of the Congress. All this fills the villages with apprehension.

I wish I had time to point out how many people have meddled in this Indian affair and given our interests a push downhill and then have faded out of the picture. There was Lord Reading, who made his speech at the landslide conference. He said that never would he agree to give them responsible government at the centre unless there was agreement between Hindus and Mohammedans. Where is that to-day? [*Interruption.*] There was Lord Shetland, who played a great part and who had great ideas about these village councils and so on. It is all swept away. All that has gone. We are now down to this Lothian Report, and that is nothing but the cheapest, chop-logic, crude, raw, semi-obsolete, half-distrusted principles of mid-Victorian Radicalism, dished up to serve the ends of India. At a time when all over the world, from China to Peru as they say, or from Japan to Chile, revolution and disorders are taking place, when three-quarters of the peoples of Europe are under dictatorships, these wretched people whom the right hon. Gentleman has administered and kept in order are to be disturbed by being told they are all to be plunged into an election where 36,000,000 illiterates will vote by coloured cards, and where the Indian Congress will see that they vote in the right direction. I do not wonder at the difficulties of my right hon. Friend.

I am sorry that I cannot develop the subject. [Hon. Members: "Go on!"] No, I must give the right hon. Gentleman time to reply, for he has great responsibilities, but I must just say this upon the question of procedure. The Prime Minister has decided to give the communal decision. I think it is terribly risky. In trying to please all parties he may easily please none. There is the Roman motto "Divide and rule." We have unanimously decided that that is an improper motto for us to follow, but do not let us fall into the opposite system—combine and abdicate. That, indeed, would be a great danger and a very great error into which we might very easily fall. Still, I must admit that the supreme responsibility rests upon the executive Government to pronounce in these matters finally, and therefore I am not in marked opposition to, indeed I am in considerable agreement with, my right hon. Friend and with the Government in the procedure which they have marked out. This procedure seems to me in the main to be a return to the old Birkenhead proposals, that there should be inquiries by the Government, or by a statutory commission or in any way they like, consultations with all sorts and all kinds of opinion, that at the end of those inquiries there should be a decision by the Government on the heads of their proposals and that, after that decision, those proposals should go to a Joint Committee of both Houses of Parliament. I think that constitutes a very remarkable change—I will not say "change," but a very remarkable development—in the progress of the Government. This Joint Commission of both Houses is one of the stages which was originally prescribed when the late Lord Birkenhead commenced, with the assent of all parties, his Indian policy. I hope that the Government will presume that a Joint Committee of both Houses will be fairly chosen, and that both sides will have their point of view expressed. There will be representatives of both sides in this case. The sides are united, and there are only those who differ from the Round Table policy and happen to be people who have either lived their lives in India or who know a great deal about it. I hope that all the points of view will be represented, and that the Committee will not simply be made up of the tame supporters of the Government and of would-be Ministers. [*Interruption.*] The right hon. Gentleman the Member for Bow and Bromley (Mr. Lansbury) has thrown many insults at me, and he has no right to say that I desire to be a Minister in the present Government.

I think that this Joint Committee constitutes a very great advance in the treatment of the subject. Not only does it secure the full power and the full control of Parliament, but, in addition, it removes this question from the hateful area of a negotiated treaty like the Irish Treaty, which the Round Table Conference put it into, and brings it back on to the broad platform that Parliament is responsible for the well-being of India, that nothing that Parliament has said can remove from it the responsibility for the good government and progress of India, and that we must, after all consideration has been exhausted, take our own decision and extend to the people of India such further devolutions of power from this House as we think are proper. I am grateful to the House for their great kindness, and to the right hon. Gentleman for allowing me this interlude. I am bound to say that, grievous as are the problems that confront us in regard to India, I believe that he has simplified them by the statement that he has made this afternoon.

IRISH FREE STATE
(FINANCIAL ARRANGEMENTS)

July 4, 1932

House of Commons

The hon. Member for Bridgeton (Mr. Maxton) is usually so attractive a speaker that we always await his intervention in Debate not only with interest but with pleasure. When he fails to convince, he often tries to persuade, and many are found drawn gradually into a comprehension of his point of view, if not of sympathy with him. But I must say that the speech he has made this afternoon has left a wider gap between himself and the great majority of this assembly than any speech I have every heard him deliver. A long string of errors of fact, of half-truths, of partial statements and of wrongful deductions, have been presented to us upon what is, after all, a matter almost squalidly plain and simple. The hon. Member used an argument which was put forward to some extent by the right hon. Gentlemen on the Front Opposition Bench. He says that the Irish are an independent, self-governing Dominion; that they are exercising only their constitutional right, and proceeding in a Parliamentary manner, and so forth. He says that Mr. de Valera obtained a mandate from the country to abolish the payment of the annuities; that he proposes to take office and obtain proper sanction from his own Parliament, and that, therefore, there is no ground of complaint. But where do we come in? The hon. Member talked about the will of the people. He says that the will of the Irish people must be given effect to, even if that involves an extra burden of taxation upon the people of this country.

I listened to what the hon. Member for Bridgeton said about the Land Annuities, and I thought, what a poor encouragement he gave to future statesmen and Governments in this House to make sacrifices in order to mitigate the lot of working farmers and poor people! This was the legislation of one of the greatest statesmen we have had in this House, Mr. Gladstone, and afterwards Mr. George Wyndham, who gave an amount of enthusiasm and personal effort to the framing of these Bills and carrying them through, which is not to be seen often in the conduct of our Parliamentary affairs to-day. Here is Mr. Gladstone's Measure to build up a peasant proprietary in Ireland, a thing which, as is well known, we have never been able to achieve in this country—here is his Measure spoken of with scorn and in terms which would mock and discourage the hopes of responsible reformers in every generation. I do not know how, upon the doctrines which the hon. Member put forward, any business can ever be done by any Assembly in the world, how any negotiation can ever be conducted on the basis that at any time all may be repudiated.

The right hon. Gentleman the Member for Wakefield said that there is a dispute, that the matter is very tangled. It is not tangled a bit. The right hon. Member said it is very complicated, and that much may be said of both sides. It is said, "Because there is a dispute you are to give way, or, at least, you are to make a compromise solution apart from the merits of the case at all." Where is the use of making any agreements at all, if you make an agreement and the next year or the next week up come the other side, having taken your sacrifices, after taking all they can get, and they say, "We have looked into that contract and think it is not good business, and we are not going on with it any more." What that is doing is to reduce civilisation to chaos and anarchy. I thought the hon. Member for Bridgeton was a Socialist. He must be an Anarchist. He has gone after Bakunin, and left Lenin in the lurch. "On the eve," he says, "of going to Ottawa, you behave in this manner." But it is just because we are going to Ottawa and are labouring at Lausanne for settlements by agreements that it is essential that the Government should mark with reprehension the attempts to render settlements by agreement nugatory. That is the very reason. What is the use of going to Ottawa or staying on at Lausanne if the next week or month either side were entitled to say, "We are going back on all we have signed"? The hon. Gentleman is not only destroying the generous impulse which moved Mr. Gladstone to aid the Irish peasantry, and thus darkening and narrowing the hopes and prospects of future Parliaments, but, at the same time, he is throwing a handspike into the whole machinery of international agreement.

Mr. Maxton: I was wanting to get the statesmen of the day to extend a generosity in proportion to that which Mr. Gladstone extended in his time.

Mr. Churchill: As I say, I do not think this country has been ungenerous. All the financial arrangements with the Irish people were declared by them to be most generous. I remember well. When it was found that there were some difficulties, they came over here and asked us—I was at the Exchequer at the time—to consider their position. We considered it, we made further sacrifices, considerable sacrifices, to meet them, and Mr. Cosgrave went back to Ireland and said they had met generous men who had treated them in a generous manner. But that is not the language we get now. We meet with very different treatment. Now it appears that we are Shylocks, insisting on our bond. We have made a settlement which in every way went to the utmost limit and was accepted as generous.

There was one remark made by the Dominions Secretary with which I very cordially agree. That was that if the Irish leaders, the Irish Ministers, had come to us and said, "We find the burden oppressive; it is more than we can bear. We would like to discuss it with you and ask for mitigation," and so forth, we would be bound to hear what they had to say and bound to go into the matter in a spirit of good will. We would be bound to go into it with the spirit which should distinguish one of the greatest and the wealthiest Powers in dealing with a small weak, poor, agricultrual community. I have been sometimes anxious as to whether the burden of cross-channel payments upon Ireland, however legal and however well established by agreement, was perhaps unduly severe. I have made some inquiries. I understand that the amount which is now to be withheld by Mr. de Valera amounts to £5,000,000 a year, out of a Budget of £27,000,000. It would be a very great mistake to assume that that was the end of the story. You have to look behind these figures and see what are the actual facts. First of all, there are the Land Annuities which are all paid for beneficial services, which cannot be in the slightest degree compared with War Debts or Reparations arising out of the sterile and devastating operations of war. I am bound to say that until I obtained the following figures I was not fully apprised of the facts.

Does the House realise that if there is £5,000,000 paid for Land Annuities and other matters across the Channel of St. George from Ireland to England, there is more than £3,250,000 paid back out of that very money to residents in Ireland? £2,000,000 in pensions goes back to be spent in Ireland by the brave Irish soldiers who fought for the cause of the Allies in the Great War. There is £1,250,000 for the pensions of the Royal Irish Constabulary and others, and although the money is paid under some heads to us, this vast flow goes back across the Channel, and the net balance of payments is less than the £2,000,000 a year. Payments which go out of Ireland to be spent elsewhere are less than can be accounted for by these Land Annuities, as a result of which the Irish have a peasant proprietary, which through all that country's misfortunes has enabled them to have a very great measure of happy rural life.

I felt bound to intervene for a few minutes in order to congratulate the Government not only on the course they have adopted, but upon how little there is found to be said against it by those who are its professed opponents. I consider that the Dominions Secretary has acted with extreme patience and forbearance. He has gone to the limit of courtesy and of good will, and he has not at any time allowed anger to disturb his judgment. The right hon. Gentleman used a great many homely phrases which will be echoed by the ordinary British workman in every street and village in this country. Everyone understands the simple language which the right hon. Gentleman talked, the language of ordinary honesty and fair play. I know there are some who are his critics on this and that, but in this matter it seems to me that he has trod with success a path at once of moderation and of firmness. For my part, I shall certainly give him any support that is in my power.

I agree with one thing that was said by speakers on the opposite side—that this is a serious matter. The House, I have no doubt, is convinced that it can embark upon it, and that there is no other course open, turn where you will. How could you say "All right. We will put on the extra taxes and collect this money from our own people and wait for better days, until the Irish Free State has wiser rulers"? Would that be the way to bring about, perhaps, a condition of affairs in which a more happy and more convenient relationship would be established? All we are doing is to withdraw for a time some of our custom from a shop where we have—I am abandoning the phraseology of war, and using more peaceful similes—been treated not only with great incivility but with very open and palpable dishonesty. We are withdrawing our custom for a time. We may return. It will be free to us at any time to return to our old and intimate commercial arrangements. But there are very great numbers of people in this country who have the greatest reluctance to deal with Mr. de Valera's Government.

With regard to the point that if the supplies are purchased elsewhere the tax will not be collected from Ireland, that, I do not think, corresponds at all with the facts. The commodities which will be the subject of this tax are produced in enormous quantities in many different markets, and a very great deal is produced in our own market, or is capable of being produced in our own market. I am told that if these taxes are imposed skilfully and judiciously, and careful selection is made, the supplies from many quarters will be so abundant that the price of the commodities will not be markedly raised, and if the price is not markedly raised, it will be the Irish exporter who will have to pay the tax by taking a lower price still and forgoing a share of his profits. That, I believe, is a wholly feasible and orthodox economic line of argument.

I offer my congratulations to the Government on the course which they have taken. But, do not suppose that this is a resolution to be taken to-day and forgotten to-morrow. Do not suppose that it will all be plain sailing. The Dominions Secretary pointed out the hardships and inconvenience of having to change a market with which you have dealt for long and to go to another. Undoubtedly some inconvenience is to be caused, but if it is for good reasons we ought to face it. Do not let us lose heart or patience or change our views if a few months hence we find that there are still friction and difficulty. For my part I have every sympathy with the Irish people. I know that we have millions of friends in that sister island, people who love this country although they are proud of their own. Besides those there are great numbers of Irishmen whose self-respect makes them loathe the course on which they are being led now.

I have the greatest sympathy with the Irish people. I have no anger or malignity against them, nor, I am sure, is there any on the Treasury Bench. It is our honest hope and desire that although for the time being there may be friction, after a period not too remote we may again have those close and amicable arrangements which were being built up under Mr. Cosgrave's long and memorable tenure of power. He made a Treaty and kept a Treaty. He did more. He built up the structure of the Irish nation. He made this small Free State a reality. He made it live when many people thought it had no chance of life. He made it respected in many quarters all over the world. He made it a centre chosen for conferences which appeal to all those of his communion in every land in the most intense manner. Now for the time being there is a setback. I am sure that the course we are adopting will not only give us the only means of doing justice to our own people, but I believe that, in the long run, it will do more to abridge the period of friction which must now ensue, than any other action which His Majesty's Government could take.

WEST AFRICA

July 9, 1932

Nigeria and Gold Coast Dinner Clubs,
Savoy Hotel, London

[Extract] We celebrate tonight the epic of our West African Empire. . . . I hope we are not going to pretend that the progress of West Africa will be secured by compelling masses of simple illiterate and primitive people to put coloured tickets into ballot-boxes to represent their tribal hatreds and their superstitions. By doing so we should soon cast away the work of Laird, of Goldie, and of Lugard, and we should recreate throughout West Africa the melancholy conditions that crude adaptation of Western ideas has produced in Liberia. Let our task there be to make first-class Africans, not third-class Europeans or third-class Americans. Neither do I hold with Lord Olivier that all private capitalist enterprise should necessarily be for ever excluded from the West African colonies. I think cases should be judged on their merits, and that a competent and incorruptible Civil Service would not find it impossible to weave the fertile impetus of private capitalist enterprise into the life and development of the territories we administer. West Africa is one of the most notable instances in which British commerce has followed the great rivers of the world. Let us make sure that the lifework of the West African pioneers is not unnecessarily hazarded or shamefully cast away.

REPARATIONS ABANDONED

July 11, 1932

House of Commons

The Lausanne Conference, in effect, ended the payment of German reparations. A year later Britain ended payments to the United States.

I cannot associate myself with the Socialist Opposition in applauding the settlement of Lausanne or joining in the apparent jubilation which that event has caused. Of course, anything which removes friction between Germany and France is to the good, and I congratulate the Prime Minister [Mr. J. Ramsay MacDonald] on that. But it seems to me that it is Germany which is most to be felicitated upon what has taken place. Within less than fifteen years of the Great War Germany has been virtually freed from all burden of repairing the awful injuries which she wrought upon her neighbors. True, there are 3,000,000,000 marks which are to be payable by Germany, but I notice that Herr Hitler, who is the moving impulse behind the German Government and may be more than that very soon, took occasion to state yesterday that within a few months that amount would not be worth three marks. That is an appalling statement to be made while the ink is yet damp upon the parchment of the Treaty. Therefore I say that Germany has been virtually freed from all reparations.

What, then, has become of the Carthaginian peace of which we used to hear so much? That has gone. Some of it may have been written down in the Versailles Treaty, but its clauses have never been put into operation. There has been no Carthaginian peace. Neither has there been any bleeding of Germany white by the conquerors. The exact opposite has taken place. The loans which Britain and the United States particularly, and also other countries, have poured into the lap of Germany since the firing stopped, far exceed the sum of reparations which she had paid; indeed, they have been nearly double. If the plight of Germany is hard—and the plight of every country is hard at the present time—it is not because there has been any drain of her life's blood or of valuable commodities from Germany to the victors. On the contrary, the tide has flowed the other way. It is Germany that has received an infusion of blood from the nations with whom she went to war and by whom she was decisively defeated. Even these loans, which are almost double the payments Germany has made in reparations, are now in jeopardy. They are subject to a moratorium.

Let me give one striking instance which came to my notice when I was crossing the Atlantic Ocean. We and America took under the Peace Treaty three great liners from Germany. The Germans surrendered them at a valuation and then borrowed the money to build two very much better ones. They immediately captured the Blue Riband of the Atlantic, and they have it still. Now the loans with which the Germans built these ships are subject to a moratorium, while we are unable to go on with our new Cunarder because of our financial crisis. That is typical of what I mean when I say that Germany has not nearly so much reason to complain as some people suppose.

Absolved from all the burden of reparations, with a moratorium upon all commercial debts, with her factories equipped to the very latest point of science by British and American money, freed from internal debt, mortgages, fixed charges, debentures and so forth, by the original flight from the mark, Germany only awaits trade revival to gain an immense mercantile ascendancy throughout the world. I think that we are entitled to felicitate Germany on what has taken place, and I am sorry to see, as far as any information has reached us, that her only reaction is to ask for more.

England has not done quite so well out of the whole business. As usual, it has been our part to make the sacrifices; and we seem to have done it most thoroughly and most cheerfully. Not only did we pay for every farthing of our war expenditure, but we lent £2,000,000,000 to various allies. We reduced this immense sum by a settlement, in which, when Chancellor of the Exchequer, I was much concerned, until we received £19,000,000 in reparations from Germany and £19,000,000 in war debts per annum from our allies. The principle of this settlement was the well-known principle of the Balfour Note—that we would take no more from Europe than was asked from us by those on the other side of the Atlantic. We nearly succeeded in achieving that annual balance of payments as between our debtors and creditors. There are, however,

£134,000,000 of arrears; that is, we have paid that much more to our creditors than we have received under this agreement.

I must pause to reflect on the extreme changeableness of public opinion. Where are all those who used to demand that we should extract the last penny of war debts and reparations from Germany? There still rings in my ears the abuse and criticism to which I was subjected because I did not get more out of France and Italy. The spectacle rises in my imagination of the scene at Liverpool Street Station, less than three years ago, when the then Chancellor of the Exchequer [Mr. Snowden], who was supposed to be stark and stiff in comparison with his predecessor in re-claiming war debts and reparations, was received by rapturous crowds, who saluted him with tremendous cheers as the Iron Chancellor, and how he was conducted with the Prime Minister, the same Prime Minister, to the Guildhall to receive the freedom of the City. All this was because he was supposed to have secured half a million pounds more. [Editor's Note: August 6, 1929; Hague Conference on Reparations, Mr. Snowden attacked the Young Plan and denounced the French delegate's interpretation of the Balfour Note as "grotesque and ridiculous."] I well remember the calculations which Mr. Snowden when in Opposition used to make about the burden I had placed on British shoulders by my misjudged leniency to France and Italy. I have always held the view that these war debts and reparations have been a great curse. I was a cordial supporter of the Balfour Note from its inception, and I have always held the view that the sooner we could free ourselves from them and the less we extracted, the better for the whole world, always provided that we were not left in the position of shouldering the whole burden. I have not changed my view. Now we have the act of Lausanne, we have the same Prime Minister, a similar crowd, the same cheers, a different railway station, it is true, and a policy, so far as they can tell us, which is the exact opposite of the policy of The Hague.

ANGLO-AMERICAN RELATIONS

July 12, 1932

Pilgrims' Society Dinner to George Washington,
London, and Broadcast to the United States

We all welcome Dr. Nicholas Murray Butler here this evening. We know what his life's work has been. We wish him all success in his mission of guiding and inspiring American youth. We admire, though it is not our business, his energetic warfare against drunkenness, prohibition and crime. We are grateful to him for all that he has done for Anglo-American friendship. No better name than his could be associated here with the toast of the evening, the memory of George Washington.

It is an honor to me to have been called upon to introduce him and a responsibility to be broadcast not only to the millions of American listeners, whom I have often addressed, but even on this occasion to my own fellow-countrymen.

My Lords and gentlemen, fourteen years have passed since I was last entrusted with this theme. It was in 1918 when we were moving into the final compulsion of the Great War. London was crowded with American troops on their way to the front. A week before English and American troops had for the first time in our history of 150 years advanced together as comrades in arms.

What a dismal catalogue of misunderstanding, of strife, jealousies, of hatred, what ferocious injuries, given and repaid, have filled the dark periods of the quarrels of the English-speaking people! Then there ensued this blessed interval of a hundred years of peace. But I felt as I spoke fourteen years ago the profound conviction that the times of war and the times of ordinary peace had come to an end, so far as our nations were concerned, and that from this time forward the English-speaking peoples would begin again to write their history in common.

My lords and gentleman, this conviction has not failed in the years that have followed. On the contrary, it has strengthened with nearly every event that has happened since.

Of course, in this workaday world there must be disputes and differences, there must be conflicting commercial interests, there must be tiresome arguments over money matters, and so forth, but be assured that none of these will disturb the onward march of Anglo-American friendship.

More and more, year by year, we feel the influence of our glorious joint inheritance, of our many essentially similar institutions, and above all of the unifying power of our common tongue. Lord Derby, certainly I, whose forebears fought simultaneously on both sides, in these quarrels, can feel no bitterness over the past.

But what is more remarkable is that in this island, which at one time seemed to be shorn of its greatness by the loss of the North American Colonies, all vain regrets and resentment have long since passed away. All that past is wrapped, indeed, in oblivion, but it is wrapped in calm, mellow recognition and acceptance.

Your national heroes, Dr. Butler, have their place in our Valhalla. The status of George Washington is honored in the heart of London. His civic and military virtues play their part in the education of our youth, just in the same way as the eloquence of Burke and Chatham have influenced the American mind.

The quarrels have ended. Their sting has passed away. Their scars are graven only on the monuments. Battles are remembered only to celebrate the martial virtues of the brave and faithful men who fought them, and to all this, my lords and gentlemen, there has been added in our lifetime an increasing unity of ideals of the freedom and rights of the individual, a dispassionate respect for the rights of small or weak nations, and a revulsion against communism in all its insidious forms, the firm maintenance of the lawful rights of property, as long as those rights are brought into harmony with the changing needs of the modern world, and, above all, our deep desire to see all men in all lands live together in justice and in peace.

A few months ago I stood on the banks of the Potomac in that quiet, charming home which Washington had made for himself in the New World. I could not believe that he would have regretted or resented any part of these healing processes. I believe, on the contrary, he would have welcomed this deliberate but irresistible conciliation, and I am glad that I have lived at a time when those processes have been scaled as so many of the facts of history, of the decisions of history, are scaled by common action of British and American soldiers in the field of arms.

My lords and gentlemen, those deep-lying tendencies have been registered by substantial advantage in the practical sphere. One by one the obstacles to our closer co-operation have been removed, but they have never more the power to cause friction between the British and American people.

In the Pacific Ocean we both have the same outlook and very largely the same interests. The immense growth of the American navy—pardon me for mentioning the fact, Mr. Ambassador—excites no apprehension on our part.

Now, above all, there comes the present world situation in which only by joint action of the English-speaking people can we hope for a revival of the wealth of nations by establishing stable values and regulating the commercial traffic of the world. Our troubles are not by any means ended. The economic crisis, the money crisis in which the world is engulfed, are the problems of the statesmen and the peoples of both our countries.

I believe there is one conviction shared on both sides of the Atlantic. It is this—there are two inspirations left us by Washington's memory tonight—candour and courage. Those were two of the guiding characteristics of his life. They should inspire both of our nations. Let us cherish these virtues now. Let us work together always in words of simple truth and respect, labouring to understand each other's point of view, and not being afraid, in all good neighbourliness, to expose and explain our own.

As for national courage and personal and civic fidelity which Washington showed in every situation, is it not needed as much today in the anxieties and perils of modern times as it ever was in the fires of bygone wars?

I have heard, Lord Derby, that Lord Cornwallis once observed after Yorktown that the military fame of General Washington would rest not on the Chesapeake but on the Delaware. He singled out that marvellous, bitter, nerve-racking campaign and the grim Winter at Valley Forge as the achievement which most revealed the fortitude and constancy of the American leader.

You in the United States to whom I am speaking now are now undergoing, in other ways and in different forms, a similar ordeal to that. We, too, in our country are doggedly driving forward through all our difficulties. Be sure we shall both succeed and be victorious in our separate spheres that we may join hands and give employment to others less strong or less capable. With the indomitable perseverance of Washington and the courage of ourselves, may we never fail in guiding the fortunes of mankind.

My lords and gentlemen, in memory of George Washington, let us drink a toast.

EUROPEAN DANGERS

November 23, 1932

House of Commons

The Imperial Conference of 1932 was held in Ottawa, Canada, from July 21 to August

*20. The implicit repudiation of Free Trade principles caused the resignations of Lord
Snowden and the Liberal members of the National Government.*

It is about a year now since I stood here and welcomed the National Government on its assumption of its great responsibilities. It is not quite the same Government today. Two out of the three official parties and organizations in the country are
tirelessly working against it, and, on the other hand, of course, the natural elements of
Conservative strength and tradition are not developing the same degree of partisanship
on its behalf as is usual in party government. We have had a year of conferences. There
have been quite a number when one comes to think of them: the Lausanne Conference, the Danubian States Conference (dead almost as soon as it was born), the first
Geneva Conference, the Ottawa Conference, the third Round Table Conference on
India, and now Geneva again. Very little success, I think, has attended these conferences, except, of course, Ottawa. There may be a good many people who do not
think much of Ottawa now, but perhaps their children may think more of it, and their
grandchildren more still. That, at least, is our hope, and it is in that hope that this act
of faith and Imperial consolidation has been performed. But with regard to the other
conferences I am bound to say that they all seem to me to fall under the criticism of
trying to pay off realities with words.

Everything which has happened since July last shows how unwise it was to bring
the Lausanne Conference to a conclusion, and to trumpet its results all round the
globe. If we look back on those July days, when the Prime Minister [Mr. Ramsay
MacDonald] was welcomed in triumph on his return, with all the Cabinet and
Under-Secretaries drawn up like a row of Grenadiers of varying sizes at the railway-
station, we can see how absurd were the claims which were then advanced that
Lausanne had "saved Europe," and that a "new era" had opened for the world. There
is quite a lot still to be done in Europe, and for many people it is very much the same
old era in the world.

There is no doubt whatever that harm was done to the prospect of the
settlement of the War debts by what happened at Lausanne. I ventured to warn the
Government before this happened, in May or June of last year, of the extreme
unwisdom of making the Debt Settlement an issue at the American elections. The
consequences of Lausanne have been to force all the candidates for Congress and the
Senate, on both sides of politics, to give specific pledges and to make definite
declarations upon this subject. We all know what happens at elections.

If the House will be persuaded by me they will now embark upon a short voyage
over a placid lake and come from Lausanne to Geneva. What a scene awaits them
there! They will walk through streets guarded by machine-guns, whose pavements are
newly stained with blood—I presume because of the conscientious scruples which
prevented the use of the perfectly harmless tear gas—and they will enter those halls of
debate where, with a persistency which rivals in duration the siege of Troy, the nations
are pursuing the question of disarmament. [Editor's Note: On November 9, 1932,
Swiss troops fired on Communist rioters in Geneva. Thirteen people were killed and
seventy wounded.] It is a melancholy scene. I have sympathy with, and respect for,
the well-meaning, loyal-hearted people who make up the League of Nations Union in

this country, but what impresses me most about them is their long-suffering and inexhaustible gullibility. Any scheme of any kind for disarmament put forward by any country, so long as it is surrounded by suitable phraseology, is hailed by them, and the speeches are cheered, and those who speak gain the meed of their applause. Why do they not look down beneath the surface of European affairs to the iron realities which lie beneath? They would then see that France does not stand alone in Europe. France does not speak for herself alone when she speaks at Geneva. France is the head of a system of states, some large, others minor, including Belgium, Poland, Rumania, Czechoslovakia and Yugoslavia, comprising many millions of human beings, all of whom depend for their frontiers upon the existence of the present Peace Treaties, good or bad, all of whom are armed and organized to defend themselves and to defend their rights, and all of whom look to France and the French Army in very much the same sort of way as small nations before the War used to look to the British Navy in the days of its power. That is one side of the picture.

On the other side there is Germany, the same mighty Germany which so recently withstood almost the world in arms; Germany which resisted with such formidable capacity that it took between two and three Allied lives to take one German life in the four years of the Great War; Germany which has also allies, friends and associates in her train, powerful nations, who consider their politics as associated to some extent with hers; Germany whose annual quota of youth reaching the military age is already nearly double the youth of France; Germany where the Parliamentary system and the safeguards of the Parliamentary system which we used to be taught to rely upon after the Great War are in abeyance. I do not know where Germany's Parliamentary system stands today, but certainly military men are in control of the essentials.

Germany has paid since the War an indemnity of about one thousand millions sterling, but she has borrowed in the same time about two thousand millions sterling with which to pay that indemnity and to equip her factories. Her territories have been evacuated long before the stipulated time—I rejoice in it—and now she has been by Lausanne virtually freed from all those reparations which had been claimed from her by the nations whose territories have been devastated in the War, or whose prosperity, like ours, has been gravely undermined by the War. At the same time, her commercial debts may well prove ultimately to be irrecoverable. I am making no indictment of Germany. I have respect and admiration for the Germans, and desire that we should live on terms of good feeling and fruitful relations with them; but we must look at the fact that every concession which has been made—many concessions have been made, and many more will be made and ought to be made—has been followed immediately by a fresh demand.

Now the demand is that Germany should be allowed to rearm. Do not delude yourselves. Do not let His Majesty's Government believe—I am sure they do not believe—that all that Germany is asking for is equal status. I believe the refined term now is equal qualitative status, or, as an alternative, equal quantitative status by indefinitely deferred stages. That is not what Germany is seeking. All these bands of sturdy Teutonic youths, marching through the streets and roads of Germany, with the light of desire in their eyes to suffer for their Fatherland, are not looking for status. They are looking for weapons, and, when they have the weapons, believe me they will then ask for the return of lost territories and lost colonies, and when that demand is made it cannot fail to shake and possibly shatter to their foundations every one of the countries I have mentioned, and some other countries I have not mentioned.

Besides Germany, there is Russia. Russia has made herself an Ishmael among the nations, but she is one of the most titanic factors in the economy and in the diplomacy of the world. Russia, with her enormous, rapidly increasing armaments, with her tremendous development of poison gas, aeroplanes, tanks and every kind of forbidden fruit; Russia, with her limitless man-power and her corrosive hatreds, weighs heavily upon a whole line of countries, some small, others considerable, from the Baltic to the Black Sea, all situated adjacent to Russian territory. These countries have newly gained their independence. Their independence and nationhood are sacred to them, and we must never forget that most of them have been carved, in whole or in part, out of the old Russian Empire, the Russian Empire of Peter the Great and Catherine the Great. In some cases these countries are also in deep anxiety about Germany.

I am sure that I have not overdrawn the picture. I have marshalled the facts, but I have not overdrawn the picture. Can we wonder, can any reasonable, fair-minded, peace-loving person wonder, in the circumstances, that there is fear in Europe, and, behind the fear, the precautions, perhaps in some cases exaggerated precautions, which fear excites? We in these islands, with our heavy burdens and with our wide Imperial responsibilities, ought to be very careful not to meddle improvidently or beyond our station, beyond our proportionate stake, in this tremendous European structure. If we were to derange the existing foundations, based on force though they may be, we might easily bring about the very catastrophe that most of all we desire to avert. What would happen to us then? No one can predict. But if by the part we had played in European affairs we had precipitated such a catastrophe, then I think our honour might be engaged beyond the limitations which our treaties and agreements prescribe.

We must not forget, and Europe and the United States must not forget, that we have disarmed. Alone among the nations we have disarmed while others have rearmed, and we must not be expected to undertake a part larger than it is in our capacity to make good. For that reason the Memorandum which His Majesty's Government sent to Germany a couple of months ago [September 18, 1932] was a wise, a prudent and a necessary document. I think they might have prepared the public here and in Germany a little more for the terms of that Note, but that it was absolutely necessary I have no doubt. If at that moment when General von Schleicher, one of the most powerful men in Germany, had openly said that in certain circumstances Germany would arm whatever the law and the League of Nations said, if at that moment when all parties in Germany were competing against each other as to which could put up the bravest front against the foreigner, in electioneering with foreign politics—a dangerous and delicate proceeding—if at that moment when it seemed, perhaps unwarrantably, that Italy was lending encouragement to the German view, we had added our approbation, or allowed it to be assumed that we approved of such a claim made by General von Schleicher, His Majesty's Government would have incurred the most serious responsibilities without any effective means of discharging them. I thank His Majesty's

Government for their Note, and I should regret if anything has been said since which in any way weakens its effect.

Coming more closely to Geneva, I should like to say that I have watched the Disarmament Conferences which have now been going on for many years, and I have formed certain opinions about them. Disarmament divides itself into disarmament by scale and disarmament by ratio. Disarmament by scale is not so important, but disarmament by ratio, the altering of the relative positions of nations, is the part of the problem which excites the most intense anxiety and even passion. I have formed the opinion that none of the nations concerned in the Disarmament Conferences except Great Britain has been prepared willingly to alter to its own disadvantage its ratio of armed strength. I agree that there have been diminutions of armaments, but they have largely been produced, as they always will be produced, by the pressure of economic and political facts in a time when there is peace; and I do not think that any of these nations have intended to do anything which would destroy the status quo; and certainly they are not willing to impair their factor of safety. I prefer the expression "factor of safety" to another expression which has been used—insurance. Insurance is not a good word, because it does nothing to ward off a danger, and it only compensates, or attempts to compensate, after the evil or misfortune has occurred. "Factor of safety" is the expression which I prefer, and I do not think that any nation has been willing to impair that factor. Therefore, the first phase of the Disarmament Conferences, going on for four or five years, the Preparatory Commission and so on, consisted in every one of these nations trying to disarm some other nation, and a whole array of ingenious technical schemes were put forward by military experts, each of which was perfectly fair and reasonable until it was examined by the other side. Only in one case has this first phase of altering the ratio produced a success—when the United States wished to secure complete naval equality with Great Britain, and we complied with their request. For the rest, I do not think that anything so far has been achieved by the discussions.

But for some time a second phase has supervened at Geneva. The expectation of general disarmament upon a great scale has failed; the hope of one nation being able to disarm its rival has been frustrated by the very stout and stubborn resistance which every nation makes to that process. Now I am afraid that a large part of the object of every country is to throw the blame for an impending failure upon some other country while willing, if possible, to win the Nobel Peace Prize for itself. Again, we have had an elaborate series of technical maneuvers by military experts and by Governments and their advisers. I am not going to particularize, I am not going to put too sharp a point to my remarks, because I do not like to say anything which might be offensive to great nations who have put forward schemes for disarmament which place them in such a satisfactory light and cost them so very little in convenience. But every time one of these plans is launched the poor good people of the League of Nations Union clap their hands with joy, and every time they are disappointed—nay, I must say deceived. But their hope is unfailing. The process is apparently endless, and so is the pathetic belief with which it is invariably greeted. I repeat that we alone have been found willing to alter continually our ratio of armed strength to our disadvantage. We have done it on land, on sea, and in the air. Now His Majesty's Government have said that we have reached the limit, and I think we shall all agree with them in that statement.

I am sorry to be so pessimistic, but it is absolutely a duty to put the rugged facts as I conceive them before the House. I have constantly predicted, as the Prime Minister and the Lord President will bear me out, publicly and privately, that these Disarmament Conferences would not succeed in removing the danger of war, and I doubt if they will succeed in substantially reducing the burden of armaments. Indeed, I have held the view that the holding of all these conferences over the last seven or eight or nine years has had the opposite effect, and has actually prevented the burden from being lightened as it would have been if we has trusted to the normal and powerful working of economic and financial pressures. But these conferences have focused the attention of the leading men in all nations upon the competitive aspects of armaments, and upon technical questions which they never would have heard of. This process has intensified the suspicions and the anxieties of the nations, and has brought the possibilities of war nearer to us than they were some years ago. That, I fear, startling and unpleasant as it is, cannot be disputed by anyone who looks at the facts of the European situation today.

We have steadily marched backward since Locarno. I am sorry that Sir Austen Chamberlain is not in his place. Many criticisms have been applied to him. Since the War Locarno was the high-water mark of Europe. Look what a distance we have fallen since then. Compare the state of Europe on the morrow of Locarno with its condition today. Fears are greater, rivalries are sharper, military plans are more closely concerted, military organizations are more carefully and efficiently developed, Britain is weaker: and Britain's hour of weakness is Europe's hour of danger. The war mentality is springing up again in certain countries. All over Europe, except here, there is hardly a factory which is not prepared for its alternative war service; every detail worked out for its immediate transformation upon a signal. And all this has been taking place under Governments whose statesmen and diplomatists have never ceased to utter the most noble sentiments of peace amid the cheers of the simple and the good.

These are not pleasant facts, but I believe they are facts. I am sure they must be painful to the Prime Minister. Everyone knows how ardently he desires to work for peace, and everyone knows that there are no limits to his courage in such a calling. He said last month, to a deputation from the Churches which waited upon him, "I hope you will go on pressing and pressing and pressing. Do help us to do the broad, just, fundamental, eternal thing." We all admire such sentiments. Dressed in noble, if somewhat flocculent eloquence, they obtain the allegiance of all. But let it be noticed that there is just the same vagueness in this sphere of disarmament as is complained of in many quarters in the Government's utterances upon domestic matters, and particularly unemployment. There ought to be more precision. The question is: Have we gone the right way to achieve the purpose in hand? For more than three years my right hon. Friend has been Prime Minister and largely Secretary of State for Foreign Affairs. That is the sphere which he has chosen to make peculiarly his own. It must be very depressing for him to feel that the position has definitely got worse during his stewardship, and to see how much worse it has got since Locarno. Everyone would like to do the "broad, just, fundamental, eternal thing," whatever that may be, but they would like to do it in a way which made things better and not in a way that made them worse. I will not predict that no agreement will be reached at Geneva. Indeed, it would be disastrous if no agreement were reached there. But I do not believe that what is going to be done at Geneva is going to mean any great or decisive change in the condition of the world, or any real progress towards the consolidation of European and world peace. On the contrary, it may well be that the situation will be exacerbated by the termination of the Disarmament Conference.

I remember that after the Great War had begun a complaint used to be made by very upright men and women: "Why were we not told about this before? Why did we not hear before about all that was going on?" Everyone can remember that. And when the War was over there was a strong feeling in favor of what is called open diplomacy. In my experience, and interior knowledge of the working of Governments, which extends over nearly a quarter of a century, I cannot recall any time when the gap between the kind of words which statesmen used and what was actually happening in many countries was so great as it is now. The habit of saying smooth things and uttering pious platitudes and sentiments to gain applause, without relation to the underlying facts, is more pronounced now than it has ever been in my experience. Just as the late Lord Birkenhead used to say about India—I think it the beginning and end of wisdom there—"Tell the truth to India," so I would now say, "Tell the truth to the British people." They are a tough people, a robust people. They may be a bit offended at the moment, but if you have told them exactly what is going on you have insured yourself against complaints and reproaches which are very unpleasant when they come home on the morrow of some disillusion.

There is a certain amount of exaggerated talk of what is called French ascendancy. I do not like the present situation; no one does. But there is this to be said about French ascendancy, the French system in Europe, or whatever you like to call it—it gives stability. As Lord Grey has recently reminded us, France, though armed to the teeth, is pacifist to the core. All the countries associated with France have no wish to do anything except to maintain the status quo. They only wish to keep what they have got, and no initiative in making trouble would come from them. At the present time, and until or unless Germany is rearmed, France and her associates are, I believe, quite capable of maintaining themselves, and are in no immediate danger of being challenged by countries which are dissatisfied with the status quo. There is nothing wrong in that. I am not saying that it is the last word. It could be improved, but there is nothing wrong in it from a legal or public point of view. The case of France and her associates stands on exactly the same treaty foundations as the League of Nations itself. Not only have they ample military force, as I believe, at present, but they have the public law of Europe behind them until it is changed.

I think we ought to feel assurance that there is something equally solid with which we can replace the French system before we press them unduly to weaken the military factors of safety upon which their security depends. Europe might easily go farther and fare worse. I am not saying that I am pleased with the situation as it is. I am pointing out how easily we might, in trying to improve it too rapidly or injudiciously, bring about what of all things in the world we wish to avoid. I say quite frankly, though I may shock the House, that I would rather see another ten or twenty years of one-sided armed peace than see a war between equally well-matched Powers or combinations of Powers—and that may be the choice.

That I am a realist in these matters I cannot deny, but I am not an alarmist. I do not believe in the imminence of war in Europe. I believe that with wisdom and with skill we may never see it in our time. To hold any other view would indeed be to despair. I put my confidence, first of all, upon the strength of the French Army; secondly, upon the preoccupation of Russia in the Far East, on account of the enormous increase in the armaments of Japan; and, thirdly, I put it, in the general way, upon the loathing of war which prevails among the nationals of all the countries not dissatisfied with the late peace. I believe that we have a considerable breathing-space in which to revive again those lights of goodwill and reconciliation in Europe which shone, so brightly but so briefly, on the morrow of Locarno. We shall never do that merely by haggling about cannons, tanks, aeroplanes and submarines, or measuring swords with one another, among nations already eying each other with so much vigilance.

Are there no other paths by which we may recover the spirit of Locarno? I would follow any real path, not a sham or a blind alley, which led to lasting reconciliation between Germany and her neighbors. Here at this moment, if the House will permit me, I would venture to propound a general principle which I humbly submit to the Government and the House, and which I earnestly trust they will follow. Here is my general principle. The removal of the just grievances of the vanquished ought to precede the disarmament of the victors. To bring about anything like equality of armaments [between the vanquished and the victor nations] if it were in our power to do so, which it happily is not, while those grievances remain unredressed, would be almost to appoint the day for another European war—to fix it as if it were a prize-fight. It would be far safer to reopen questions like those of the Dantzig Corridor and Transylvania, with all their delicacy and difficulty, in cold blood and in a calm atmosphere and while the victor nations still have ample superiority, than to wait and drift on, inch by inch and stage by stage, until once again vast combinations, equally matched, confront each other face to face.

There is another reason why I commend this to the House. It must be remembered that Great Britain will have more power and will run far less risk in pressing for the redress of grievances than in pressing for disarmament. We can only promote disarmament by giving further guarantees of aid. We can press for the redress of grievances by merely threatening, if our counsels are not attended to, to withdraw ourselves at the proper time from our present close entanglement in European affairs. The first road of pressing for disarmament and offering more aid only leads us deeper and deeper into the European situation. The second either removes the cause of danger or leads us out of the danger zone.

Just look to where our present policy is leading us. Look at the situation into which we are apparently marching blindly and with a sort of helpless chorus of approval. When we say to France and to Poland, "Why do you not disarm and set an example, and respond to our gesture, and so on?" they reply, "Will you then help us to defend ourselves, supposing that you are wrong in your view of what our factor of safety ought to be?" Nobody keeps armaments going for fun. They keep them going for fear. "We would gladly reduce," they say, "provided we get you in line with us for certain. If you will take some of our burden off our shoulders there will be no hesitation on our part in transferring that burden." And what they say to us they say still more to the United States—or if they do not say it, they think it. But surely this is very dangerous ground for us. We are to persuade our friends to weaken themselves as much as possible, and then we are to make it up to them by our own exertions and at our own expense.

It is as if one said, "I will go tiger-hunting with you, my friend, on the one condition that you leave your rifle at home." That is not the kind of excursion on which our old men ought to send our young men. We have, of course, serious obligations, which we have no intention of discarding, under Locarno. But under Locarno we remain the sole and free judge of the occasion and of the interpretation put upon these obligations. Without our own vote on the Council of the League of Nations, which must be unanimous, we cannot be involved in war. But see now what the French propose in this latest scheme. They propose, quite logically and naturally, in responding to the pressure of Britain and the United States on disarmament, that the decision of the Council should be by a majority. That would mean that our fate would be decided over our head. We might find ourselves pledged in honour and in law to enter a war against our will, and against our better judgment, in order to preserve those very injustices and grievances which sunder Europe today, which are the cause of present armaments and which, if not arrested, will cause another war.

These are not the days when you can order the British nation or the British Empire about as if it were a pawn on the chessboard of Europe. You cannot do it. Of course, if the United States were willing to come into the European scene as a prime factor, if they were willing to guarantee to those countries who take their advice that they would not suffer for it, then an incomparably wider and happier prospect would open to the whole world. If they were willing not only to sign, but to ratify, treaties of that kind, it would be an enormous advantage. It is quite safe for the British Empire to go as far in any guarantee in Europe as the United States is willing to go, and hardly any difficulty in the world could not be solved by the faithful co-operation of the English-speaking peoples. But that is not going to happen tomorrow. It is not in our power to anticipate our destiny. Meanwhile we ought not to take any further or closer engagements In Europe beyond those which the United States may be found willing to take.

I hope that the League of Nations is not going to be asked now to do the impossible. Those who believe, as I do sincerely, that the League of Nations is a priceless instrument of international comity, which may play as great a part as the most daring, hopeful founders ever forecast for it, should be especially careful not to put upon the League strains which in its present stage it is utterly incapable of bearing. I deprecate altogether the kind of thought that, unless the League can force a general disarmament, unless it can compel powerful nations in remote regions to comply with its decisions, it is dead—away with it. All that is as foolish as it is to grudge the small sums necessary to keep this precious international machinery in being. He is a bad friend to the League of Nations who would set its tasks beyond its compass.

There is only one thing more to say before I sit down, and it is suggested to me by the speech which the Lord President of the Council [Mr. Baldwin] delivered recently [November 10, 1932]. I did not hear it, but from all accounts it was one which profoundly impressed the House, and revealed the latent and often carefully concealed powers which reside in my right hon. Friend. But that speech, while it deeply impressed the House, I have no doubt—and I have read it with great attention—led to no practical conclusion. It created anxiety, and it created also perplexity. There was a sense of, what shall I say, fatalism, and even perhaps helplessness about it, and I take this opportunity of saying that, as far as this island is concerned, the responsibility of Ministers to guarantee the safety of the country from day to day and from hour to hour is direct and inalienable. It has always been so, and I am sure they will not differ from their predecessors in accepting that responsibility. Their duty is not only to try, within the restricted limits which, I fear, are all that is open to them, to prevent war, but to make sure that we ourselves are not involved in one, and, above all, to make sure that, if war should break out among other Powers, our country and the King's Dominions can be effectively defended, and will be able to preserve, if they desire to do so, that strong and unassailable neutrality from which we must never be drawn except by the heart and conscience of the nation.

LONDON PASSENGER TRANSPORT BILL

November 29, 1932

House of Commons

It is perfectly clear from the position that we have now reached how well advised the Minister of Transport was in moving to report Progress. Everything that has taken place in this discussion has clearly shown that that is the proper course for the Committee at this moment. The Minister of Transport got up and desired to unfold to the Committee a statement vital to their coherent and competent consideration of the Bill. For some reason or other he found himself unable to do so. Then the Attorney-General rose, with all the weight of his office behind him, to assist us, in the interests of the Committee, in the interests of discussion on this Motion, and draw our attention to three Amendments and the Government's intention in regard to those Amendments. He had information which he wished to convey to us, just as the Minister in charge of the Bill had information which he wished to convey. But we have got no information, and it is perfectly clear from the Ruling of the Chair that the information which they wished to confide can only be of a limited and restricted form and could not convey any clear or intelligent impression to those who heard it. We are discussing whether we should report Progress, and I think the Government would be very well advised to follow up that happy thought. Obviously the House ought to be in possession of this important Ministerial statement before it addresses itself to the discussion of the detailed Amendments. Obviously, it cannot be in possession of that information, owing to the Rules of Order. There must be, therefore, a great failure in our Debate to-day if we are called upon to embark upon these Amendments without having received the indispensable information which the Government wish to confide and which they have already endeavoured to confide to us.

There is really no hurry about this Bill. It would be very natural, after the long delay which has intervened in its various stages and its mixed parentage, to which my hon. Friend referred, and it would be very necessary that there should be a general Debate on the principle of the measure, its history, its position and its character, before we embark upon the long pages of Amendments, some of which are so newly printed, on the Order Paper. The Government have a hundred facilities open to them to get the Committee out of a difficulty. The difficulty is apparent; it is a patent deadlock, but the Government can easily resolve it. They can carry out what are evidently the wishes of the Minister in charge of the Bill. All they have to do is to report Progress upon this Measure, instead of using an enormous deadweight majority to carry things through whether the House likes them or not. All that they have to do is to accept the Motion which the Minister himself has made, and for which I certainly intend to vote, to proceed to other business on the Order Paper to-day, and to put down on the next occasion when this discussion is resumed some Motion or Resolution, which can quite easily be done, a simple Motion for the Adjournment, for instance, which would enable the whole question to be discussed quite freely. Then we could embark upon these pages, these folios of Amendments, with the whole matter put into its proper form and concept by the Minister in charge of the Bill, in accordance with what the Government consider is best calculated to enhance the efficiency and the dignity of our Debate.

WAR DEBTS AND REPARATIONS

December 14, 1932

House of Commons

I do not propose to follow the speech of the hon. and learned Gentleman [Sir S. Cripps] who has just addressed us, except in so far as to note with approbation the strong sentiments against repudiation which are entertained by the Socialist party as the result, I presume, of electoral tuition. My right hon. Friend the Chancellor of the Exchequer [Mr. Neville Chamberlain] gave a very broad and impressive survey of the whole past history of this subject, and I must say that I found myself in very close agreement with practically every fact with he adduced, with their sequence and, to a large extent, with the emphasis which he assigned to them. I do not propose to go back into the whole past controversy which has ranged around the original American Debt settlement. I am much more interested in what has occurred in this Parliament and during this Parliament, and I shall draw the attention of the House to aspects of the Government conduct of this matter during the present Parliament. I do not desire to dispute the historical basis; I am much more concerned with the method. One would have imagined, to hear my right hon. Friend's admirable speech, so well posed in its presentment of a great topic, that the Government management of this affair had been impeccable. I certainly do not think that is the case. I think it would tax the resources of my vocabulary to do justice to a series of wrong turns which I venture to think has characterised their conduct in this grave matter.

When we last debated this matter in July we had before us the Lausanne Agreement. That had just been signed. It was hailed as an immense personal triumph for the Prime Minister [Mr. Ramsay MacDonald]. May I say how sorry I am that he is not with us to-day, because this is, above all things, a matter on which the head of the Government would have wished to have laid his views before Parliament, and, above all things, a matter on which Parliament would have desired to hear a statement from him. Lausanne was hailed as a great triumph for the Prime Minister. We were led to believe that the whole curse and burden of War Debts and Reparations had finally been lifted from the world. It was only after some severe interrogation, in which I ventured to take part, that it was found that the cheering was premature. It was only after some considerable pressure that it leaked out that the settlement of Lausanne was no settlement at all; that it was a settlement contingent only upon satisfactory remissions being obtained from the United States. After some protest and some hard work, papers were drawn reluctantly from His Majesty's Government revealing, what everybody was bound to find out and what had already been made public in the foreign Press, that there was behind the much applauded settlement of Lausanne a so-called semi-secret Gentleman's Agreement, which took away with one hand all that had been accomplished with the other.

During this Debate my right hon. Friend the Chancellor of the Exchequer was good enough to censure me in very severe terms. I have great regard for him, and I greatly admire his conduct of his arduous office, but no one shall say what he said on that occasion without my endeavouring, amicably and at the same time pointedly, to show that there were more sides to the controversy than were represented in his censure. My right hon. Friend said:

> The Member for Epping has done no service to this country in endeavouring to undermine any confidence which may have been aroused by this settlement.

[Hon. Members: "Hear, hear."] Oh, there were many more cheers last time, I can tell you—

> and in suggesting that we have in any way made more difficult or more embarrassing the relations with our own creditors elsewhere.—[Official Report, 11th July, 1932; col. 974-5, Vol. 268.]

Of course, you may say that we ought never to criticise—a perfectly reasonable view. You may say that this House should abrogate its functions of criticism and censure, and that the only place from which words of warning and words of controversy should come is the diminutive representatives of party on the Front Opposition Bench. I would warn the House very earnestly, and, above all, the great Conservative majority which not only fills it but bears the whole brunt of responsibility, that if it were thought that we were careless of our duties and did not examine these matters with great attention; if it were thought that Members were liable to be driven this way and that by the guidance of my hon. Friend on the Front Bench and the other Whips, not only would this Parliament, from which so much was hoped by our loyal working people, pass away in derision, but the very gravest injury would have been done to the very structure of Parliamentary institutions altogether. Let us see who rendered no service when we debated this matter in July. The Chancellor of the Exchequer led the House to believe he and the other British representatives had carried the United States Government with them in their negotiations at Lausanne. I am going to read his words:

> After all, we have been in touch at Lausanne not only with European representatives, but we have had the opportunity of conversations with the representatives of the United States, and I would ask the House to believe that in this rather delicate situation we have no reason to believe that the course we have taken is one which is going to lead to any of these unfortunate results which the right hon. Member for Epping anticipates.— [Official Report, 11th July, 1932; col. 975, Vol. 268.]

I am not quarrelling about the actual words, but, if they did not mean that he hoped and believed that they were carrying the representatives of the United States with them, I do not know what they mean. The statement certainly was accepted by the House in that sense. I have no doubt whatever that when my right hon. Friend makes a statement like that he is sincere, and I have no doubt whatever that he had grounds for what he said. But whether he was wise to say it is quite another matter. I was astounded to hear him say it, because, knowing something of the feeling in the United States, having had some opportunity of seeing it, I was sure that nothing would more disturb President Hoover, when the lines of electoral battle were being drawn, than for any statement of that kind to be made. But what happened? The very next day, or the day after, President Hoover wrote to Senator Borah:

> I wish to make it absolutely clear that the United States have not been consulted regarding any agreement reported by the Press to have been concluded recently at Lausanne, and that, of course, it is not a party, nor in any way committed to any such agreement.

But look what followed, much more remarkable still. On 14th July the following communiqué was issued to the Press from the Treasury, the Chancellor's own Department:

> Misunderstanding has arisen regarding Mr. Chamberlain's reference, in his speech in the House of Commons on Monday, to conversations with representatives of the United States. He did not suggest, and, of course, had no intention of suggesting, that representatives of the United States had approved, either tacitly or explicitly, of what was done at Lausanne.

We find this Treasury communiqué served up to us as a valid retort in the communication which Mr. Stimson addressed to us the other day in response to the admirable Note setting forth the opinion of this country. Now, if it comes to a question of who did no service to this country at that moment I am prepared to stake my claim before any fair tribunal as against that of my right hon. Friend. It was a very unfortunate indiscretion on his part. I would like to say to the House that, personally, I always think it is rather shabby to criticise a Government after the event unless you have given warning somehow or other beforehand. I am in the recollection of the House, and I say that I did in May last warn the Government of the dangers of reaching a conclusion on the debt question at Lausanne. I am not going to read a quotation from my own speech, but I begged the Government not to bring this matter to a premature conclusion then. There was no need for them to do so. A simple prolongation of the Moratorium would have avoided bringing this matter into the whirlpool of American politics.

Having said that in May, I felt fully entitled in July to criticise them when they had committed this great mistake. But my friends, many of them on this side were not pleased with me, and I dare say they will not be pleased with me now. But still I shall take my course, as I think fit. I say that there were three reasons why Lausanne was a great mistake. First of all, we released our hold upon our debtors, upon our assets, before we had obtained release from our creditors. In the second place, we offended the United States and plunged this question into their electoral affairs. In the third place, we prejudiced our own British case in the United States by linking it up so much with France. Now we have reaped to some extent what we then sowed. Let me say to the House that I think there is no truth in the claim that Lausanne was necessary to save Europe, that a settlement then was indispensable to save Europe. Still less can it be claimed that it has saved Europe. Anyone can judge that. The position in Europe is worse, from many points of view, than it was in July. The efficacy of the Lausanne settlement was destroyed from the moment when it was realised that it was only contingent upon a settlement with the United States.

The immense relief which Lausanne accorded to Germany, largely on paper, the immense relief from obligations which the settlement accorded to Germany, was immediately made the starting point for fresh demands, and demands of a more disturbing character, disputes about money matters and debts, disputes about how soon that great nation was to be able to re-arm. No sooner was Germany relieved of her solemn obligations to pay Reparations to the countries devastated by the War, or countries like ours whose prosperity had been undermined by the War, than, on the very next day, the Germans, with that naivety and spontaneity which renders them so attractive, immediately exclaimed, in the presence of the whole world, "Good, I am better off now. I shall go out and buy a large cannon." So far as Austria was concerned, the loan which emerged from the settlement at Lausanne was only accepted by them after an immense internal struggle by a single vote, showing how great was the difference of opinion in that country upon the subject.

Generally, I say there has been no substantial advantage of any kind to compensate for having brought Lausanne to this premature conclusion. There was perhaps the hope that the Prime Minister would revive and strengthen his prestige by another triumph on the Continent. The Prime Minister likes very much to pose in self-admiration before the broken looking-glass of Europe. Some success, however dearly bought, it was felt necessary must be extracted from this confusion of European conferences, this labyrinth of European conferences in which he lives, moves and has his being. I will not suggest for a moment that that was the determining argument in the minds of those who signed, but it may well have had some bearing, and, if it had, all I can say is that even that gain has been found fleeting. The results of Lausanne were nugatory and illusory. They prejudiced and compromised our chances of satisfactory settlement with the United States.

But I am not going to over-state my case and argue that if there had been no settlement at Lausanne the United States would have let every one off their debts. Nor am I going to argue that, now there has been a settlement at Lausanne, the United States will not arrive at a satisfactory solution of these difficulties. All I argue is that the Government took the course which was least calculated to make our difficulties smooth, and that they have greatly aggravated our difficulties. I do not say they have ruined our prospects, but they have sensibly added to the complications which we have in any case to face. What are we now? The machine-like workings of the United States Constitution have created what is virtually a hiatus in the relations of that great country, the vast, intricate vital relations of that great country, with the outside world. Until a new Government is in power and responsible, writing Notes to the United States is like writing Notes to the Atlantic Ocean. No one feels this difficulty more than enlightened, leading Americans themselves. It is a survival from an older form of constitutional Government, very arbitrary.

In this hiatus, this interval, payment has been demanded of us, on 15th December, and, at grips with this grim situation, the right hon. Gentleman and the Government have decided to pay, and to pay in gold on that date. There is not the slightest doubt that the overwhelming majority of this House consider that they have decided rightly. I think also they have decided rightly to pay in gold. I do not intend to be dragged into the currency question to-night. I can only say that nothing is more significant of the way in which world opinion is forming on the subject of gold than that, when we had to make this payment, there was unanimity of feeling in this country that gold was the least valuable thing we had to send, and that there was apparently equal unanimity in the United States that gold was the least desirable thing they could receive. Certainly, that is the crowning insult which gold has received since it has been the great standard of measurement of values between man and man. I think the Government were right, and I still would hope that they will handle this transference of gold in such a way that there will be no deflationary effect upon our trade. But that we shall have an opportunity of considering, no doubt, at a later period.

I only wish that the Government had taken their decision to pay on the 15th, and to pay in gold, a little more promptly and a little more unitedly, with a little more conviction, and, I must say, with a little more dignity. I was very glad indeed to hear the Chancellor of the Exchequer denounce the idea of repudiation or default to-day so strongly in his speech, because it has not been at all pleasant for those of us who are his admirers to read day after day in the columns of the Press uncontradicted assertions that he had been in favour of default on this occasion, and had been overruled by his colleagues in the Cabinet. We are glad to know that there is no truth in that. Anyhow the House I am sure will support the Government in their decision to pay. I agree with a great deal of what has been said on both sides on this subject, that the whole world has an immense, vital, practical, material interest in the solvency and fidelity of Great Britain. We, ourselves, as I mentioned upstairs the other day, have only to think of Mr. de Valera in Ireland, Mr. Lang in Australia and the Shah of Persia, to realise that we have a very considerable interest in it too. Therefore, anything in the nature of default could only be justified by Great Britain when every other alternative had been exhausted and when the whole world was convinced that every other alternative had been exhausted.

I cannot feel that the situation is hopeless by any means or that we shall be driven into all those difficulties which the hon. and learned Gentleman opposite foresaw. It is our absolute duty to make a further effort, if it is in our power, to avert the catastrophe—for such it would be—to the economic, social, capitalist civilisation of mankind, of an open default by Great Britain of her contractual engagements. We ought to pay a heavy price, we are paying a heavy price, to avert that. But here let me say, in answer to a point raised by the hon. and learned Gentleman, that there are some prices which we could not pay and which we ought not even to consider paying. The hon. Gentleman said that we must disarm in order to please the United States and win their favour. I do not admit for one minute that there is the slightest connection between debts and national defence. The debts of a nation affect its credit. The defence of a nation affects its sovereignty, and sovereignty is in a different sphere altogether from anything connected with finance or credit. In the same way all suggestions of cessions of territory are covered by sovereignty. In China in former days people used to sell their children, but that is a practice which has never taken root in Western Europe. When the question is one of money and we have the money, when it is one of gold and we have the gold, it is well worth our while making this additional payment, injurious though it is to us, to make sure that we can say with the assent of all the nations that we have left nothing undone that it was in our power to do.

I am bound to say that I did not like the last Note but one which my right hon. Friend sent to the United States. Of course, repudiation or default means the refusal of one party to carry out his contractual obligation to another, and certainly my right hon. Friend has made it plain that nothing of that kind is in our minds or intentions at the present time. Still, this Note which was made public on Monday did seem to hold out a threat of an unilateral decision by this country, in certain circumstances which we trust and hope will not arise. I must say that I think there was no necessity to have made any such suggestion in the Note. When we are paying, as we are, let us have the full credit and distinction which attach to that operation. There is no need to give notice of repudiation. It is not a matter which requires notice. I hope it may never come to this country, and I wish that my right hon. Friend had reserved any suggestions or hints such as were contained in that Note until they could be exchanged in all the secrecy of an international conference.

I am not going to keep the House very long, because I know there are many who wish to speak. I have finished what I have to say about the United States and I turn to France. No one can accuse me of being unfriendly to the French people. I have always been supposed to take very much their view about the European situation, but I think that the policy of His Majesty's Government has been most mistaken in their relations with France. We ought never to have associated ourselves with France in dealing with the United States upon War Debts and we ought never to have tolerated, let alone encouraged, the idea that France might be allowed to pay the United States and not to pay us. Good news has arrived from Paris to-day which enables me very greatly to abridge the remarks which I venture to offer. But I must remind the House of the facts a little more in detail than the right hon. Gentleman dealt with them in his retrospects.

The French and Italian debt settlements, for which I was responsible, were made upon the sole credit of France and Italy. The Cabinet definitely decided that they would accept a substantially smaller sum, on the sole credit of those two countries, without reference to Reparations, than they could otherwise have obtained. One has only to read all the correspondence which was published and the statements which were made to see how completely and absolutely that was accepted by France. It is true that M. Caillaux wrote a letter suggesting, in certain circumstances, if there was a failure of German reparations of 50 per cent. or more, and if exchange difficulties were serious, that there should be reconsideration. In the answer which I sent on behalf of the Government we pointed out that in those circumstances we should also be heavy losers from the cessation of German payments, and that we also should have to consider the payments which were required from us. But nothing in the right to ask for reconsideration implies, in any way, the right of one party to decide the matter in his own sense.

Therefore, I say that our claim against France was absolutely good and valid and that there was no necessity for France, if we had enforced our claim or if we were to enforce our claim, to require payment again to be made from Germany. France was in a position quite easily to pay, for she had nearly £1,000,000,000 of sterling in the form of gold or gold equivalent, and £30,000,000 or £40,000,000 of balances here. It is idle to pretend that the payment of the £6,000,000 which has been due and has been accumulating month by month, ever since June last, could not have been transferred without the slightest disturbance to the exchange. That was the first of the conditions which the Cabinet laid down for the settlement of the French and Italian debts—that it should be on the sole credit of those countries. There was another and a very important one—the doctrine of *pari passu*. That implied that France and Italy must treat us as well as they treated any other of their creditors. Obviously debtors may not discriminate between creditors. Creditors may discriminate between debtors but the usage of every country is that payments to creditors must be made in equal proportions. I said in the House on the very first occasion that I spoke as Chancellor of the Exchequer on this subject:

> Any payments made by our debtors in Europe to their creditors in the United States should be accompanied simultaneously *pari passu* by proportionate payments to Great Britain.—[Official Report, 10th December, 1924, cols. 264-265, Vol. 179.]

A communiqué was issued on the same point from which I may read one extract: It is a very good communiqué I may say—I wrote it myself:

> His Majesty's Government have from the outset made it perfectly clear that any arrangements which they can come to with France must be

governed by the principle so often declared that they must receive from France proportionate and *pari passu* payments to any she may eventually make to the United States in settlement of her war debt. It would be no service to Europe already so grievously stricken, if the sacrifices of one creditor of France merely conduced to the advantage of another.

Why did the Government whistle all this down the wind so lightly and so easily? When I read on Friday that the Government were actually urging France to pay the United States, having cheerfully let them off the obligation to pay us, I was profoundly shocked and distressed. It seemed to me that it was hardly possible that such an inversion of good sense could have been put forward. We were actually urging the French to pay the United States at our expense. [Hon. Members: "Oh!"] Of course, if they were to pay £4,500,000 to the United States and we had forgone the £6,000,000 due to us. That is the position which still exists, I believe, in the case of Italy. If Italy pays the United States, she will pay the United States £250,000 and withhold the £2,000,000 which it is in her power and her duty to pay under the very generous settlement, the too generous settlement—[Hon. Members: "hear, hear!"] Well, no one can call it too generous now. I thought in those days that we were getting all we could, but how lucky we would be if we could get a half or a quarter of what we got in those days, under what we thought to be a generous settlement with those countries.

In the case of Italy, as I say, that situation will still obtain, but France has cut the Gordian knot. There has been, evidently, an explosion of opinion, of passion almost, which has induced them to put aside the enormously favourable opportunities which, with the assistance of the British Government, have been placed at their disposal of making a payment on this occasion and of coming to the International Conference with all the *éclat* and prestige of a solvent and paying debtor—and the whole of it would have cost them nothing because it would all have been borne on the expenses of Great Britain. The situation, however, has been changed by the French vote, and it has been changed greatly to the British advantage. I congratulate His Majesty's Government on being liberated from their own errors against their own will. We are not now going to be discriminated against. We are still the debtors of the United States but we are not going to be the debt-collectors of the United States or furnish their other debtors with the means of paying. At any rate we are treated *pari passu* by France with other countries.

There is an even greater advantage which, I think, we have derived. We are absolutely free from all contact with France in our negotiations with the United States. Do let us make sure that we begin on that basis from to-day. By that means we shall have a far better chance of reaching a solution, which is so earnestly desired. Our case with the United States is entirely different from that of France. People are sometimes inclined, and it is very natural, to feel harshly about the United States, but let me say that the treatment of France was generous. At this moment I understand that France would be paying, under her debt agreement, no more than the cost of the post-war loans. France made a very good arrangement for herself with the United States, and it is the greatest possible mistake for us to get so close to France that our just claims are, as it were, smirched and confused by that association. But it is not only a question of the actual terms of the debt settlement. There was a very strong feeling of irritation in the United States against France, which we have no need to mix ourselves up in at all. When I was in Washington in January the air was full of rumours of a flight from the dollar, and the French were withdrawing, I believe, 50 millions in gold from the United States. The greatest bitterness prevailed, and was not concealed, and especially was this bitterness felt because it was only a few years since France had received the very liberal terms, as they were thought then, from the United States in the matter of her debt.

Why should we involve ourselves again, now that we are free, in all this unpleasantness and difficulty? I say that to be forced to link our case with France would be a disaster, but to try to do it—I do not know what to call it—would be the acme of ineptitude, the quintessence of *maladresse*. It passes all understanding that we should have got ourselves into that position so lightly, and I should like to ask the Government this question: I have only the newspapers to guide me, but I read a report in the "Times" of M. Herriot's speech—a very abridged report—which contained the statement that England could easily have made better terms for herself, but would not, out of loyalty to France, or words to that effect. Is that true? If it is true, is it sane? On what grounds are we not to make the best settlement that we can for ourselves? As I say, I think His Majesty's Government have had a great deliverance by what has taken place in Paris, because, whatever may have been agreed upon, it is perfectly clear that we can now start fair, and it is because we are free and can start fair that I am hopeful.

If the House will read between the lines of Mr. Stimson's reply to the right hon. Gentleman's second Note, they will see that the greater part of that Note is addressed to other Powers, not to us to whom it is sent. A great part of it is quite inapplicable to our case. Those statements were not inserted by accident, but were inserted by friendly hands on the other side of the water which have been aiming at getting into a situation where better treatment can be given to Great Britain. Take the question of tourists. That has nothing to do with us; that is France. Take the reference to the remittances; that is Italy. The whole of that Note, although addressed to us, is conceived, I think, to hold out the prospect that the negotiations which are going to be started have at any rate some hopes attaching to them, and make it absolutely clear that we should be wrong to abandon those hopes at this stage.

There are many passages which are most favourable to an Anglo-American discussion. A distinction is drawn between war and post-war debts; a distinction is drawn between supplies which were consumed in the fighting and loans which were expended for other purposes. By all such tests, we could be judged without the slightest apprehension. I am not saying for a moment that such principles would be acceptable—that is another matter—but I do say that the whole of this Note is instinct with the possibilities of a favourable negotiation, as long as we can go there ourselves, with our gigantic case, and without mixing ourselves up in the troubles or difficulties of other people. Everyone who is in touch with American opinion knows that there is a great and growing desire to treat fairly the best customer of America, the punctilious debtor, the only debtor that has made an immense contribution in the payment of her debt.

The new men who will shortly take power in the United States and exercise influence there are animated, I believe, by warm sentiments towards this country. They reverence the memory of President Wilson. There were many points on which Europeans differed from him, but this I will say, that President Wilson was the best friend of Europe who ever sailed Eastward across the Atlantic. Our payment to-morrow, when others default, and all the more because others have defaulted, will strengthen all this friendly movement. It is much too soon to despair of a just and an honourable settlement, for the making of which the two great world-creditor nations and the two English-speaking peoples have an equal and a paramount interest.

1933

UNEMPLOYMENT

February 16, 1933

House of Commons

I will only venture to detain the House for a short time, because I had not intended to intervene at all until I heard some of the statements which fell from my right hon. Friend the Chancellor of the Exchequer [Mr. Neville Chamberlain]. I must say I think something should be done to express the feeling of disappointment, and even of hopelessness, which must have arisen in many hearts as he proceeded upon his precise, well marshalled, orderly discourse. What is the picture that he puts before the House and before the country? What is the proposition? It is that everything is being done that can be done and that all is proceeding satisfactorily and in due course, but that, in spite of all this, many years must pass before the figures of unemployment can be reduced to—I think he said—a small figure. That is a ghastly prospect for us all to have to face, and it was that phrase of the right hon. Gentleman's that induced me to trespass for this moment upon the time of the House.

Ten years! Is that the last word of His Majesty's Government? I rejoice to think that by the unexampled provision which this nation made for the relief of distress through insurance schemes and otherwise, and by the faithful performances of the taxpayer, material distress is to a very large extent withheld from our people, even in this terrible time, but material distress is not the whole evil of unemployment. There is this frightful moral agony of unemployment. Take the case of the 3,000,000 unemployed. You are not merely dealing with the weaker brethren, with men who hardly ever keep a job, but you are dealing with a couple of million men who have hardly ever been out of work in the whole of their lives. Take these men. I see the figure of the breadwinner, the father of the family, sitting in his chair in his cottage. Ten years! His wife has perhaps got a job—perhaps she has got his job—and his daughter may have got a job. His son, a young boy, may have got some blind-alley occupation. The father of the family, whose honour and faith are pledged to carry those dependants on his shoulders, sits there in his chair, a burden upon the house, helpless in the midst of those whom he had vowed himself to defend, his very right to exist challenged in the land for which, perhaps, he had been ready to sacrifice his life not many years ago. It is no good going to that man and saying: "Keep pegging away!" What has he to keep pegging away at?

I am not impressed by the argument of the Government, neither with those which were used by the Minister of Health yesterday, nor with those of my right hon. Friend the Chancellor of the Exchequer, that all measures of stimulating or subsidising production in one form or another ought to be ruled out at this time, because they have failed in the past. I do not think that it is true to say that they have failed. They may not have stemmed the enormous world tide of unemployment, but they may have mitigated it. In fact, you can show that they have to a certain extent mitigated its force. Naturally, if you have a great world tide of unemployment flowing, you will be able to show a much larger total of unemployment at the end of the year, although you may have received benefit from those measures. I deprecate altogether the *non sequitur* that because unemployment has increased while remedial measures were employed such measures should no longer be adopted. I think that the Government would have been very well advised last August in taking some steps to open up, as far as they could, the building trade and the development of public works. There are some very well-known, great public works, one of which I see was destroyed last night, and which at any rate would give us a better island to live in after they were completed.

I would not for a moment ask the Government to perform impossibilities or to reproach them, because they cannot cure unemployment, but unemployment has only increased about a quarter of a million in the last six months. It would have been quite possible, by taking prudent steps last summer or last autumn, to take that extra 250,000 off. It would not have rid us of the evil and it would not have solved the problem, but it would have given the Government the right to say that they had stemmed the tide and that there was a diminution, however small, and not an increase, in unemployment. Believe me, an event of that kind would have a far greater effect upon your credit, upon your national prestige and upon the reputation and authority of the Government, than anything you will get out of a £50,000,000 Sinking Fund, however strictly and punctually it is enforced. It would not have been a reasonable thing to embark on another large, bold programme at a time when there was public panic, as there was in 1931. Of course, you could not do it when there was a great conversion operation, but all could have been put in readiness, and I am bound to say that nothing that I have heard in this Debate has shaken my view that it would have been a wise and reasonably prudent step, justified on the highest economic and on the broadest grounds of long policy, to have set on foot a programme sufficient to have brought a quarter of a million mere men into employment at this moment.

I entirely agree that these are but palliatives. What I felt in the speech of my right hon. Friend the Chancellor of the Exchequer was the hopelessness. I greatly preferred his speech, with its carefully considered and marshalled arguments, to the Prime Minister's broadcast; that, I thought, was most deplorable. The Prime Minister likes to broadcast. He has endeavoured to secure a monopoly of it for himself, and he endeavours to exclude from the use of that great organ any opponents and any critics. I am surprised that the right hon. Gentleman did not make a better use of it. When I heard those statements about the duck pond—no, it was the paddle-pool—and the rope mats, and the renovation of the archaic Roman bridge, I thought of those men sitting in their cottages, in this distress that falls upon them, and I am bound to say that I think that that speech must have been a shock, a very great and an insulting shock to them, coming as it did from a Prime Minister who, in the first instance, led the Socialist party into office on the claim that he could cure—virtually cure—unemployment.

Then the Bethnal Green letter—the "death-knell Green letter" it might be called—which has been expanded and expatiated upon by the Chancellor of the Exchequer this afternoon, is virtually a statement that there is no immediate plan or policy which the Government are pursuing, other than allowing the great drift of world events to take their course. I do not think that it is right to condemn men because they cannot encounter the tide of world events, but you are entitled to condemn them if the spirit which they produce does not show that they are endeavouring as far as they can to do so. Immense powers reside in this Government. You compare its action with previous Governments; that is not fair. No previous Government, except in the War, has had the power which this Government has, an absolute power. In both Houses of Parliament, overwhelming majorities; a mighty Press to support them; broadcasting. You have every power at your disposal, and all that is to come is what we have heard to-day. I am sure that when the right hon. Gentlemen's speech is read it will be felt all over the country that it is very poor, thin fare for this nation, and that a far greater constructive effort, more grip, more mental energy, more resourcefulness ought to be represented by those who have those great powers, and who are in charge of our destinies. If this that we have heard to-day is the last word that the Government have to speak upon this problem, then indeed the outlook before us is grave and lamentable.

RUSSIA, JAPAN AND INDIA

February 17, 1933

*Anti-Socialist and Anti-Communist Union Meeting,
Queen's Hall, London*

When Japan invaded Manchuria in September 1931, China appealed to the League of Nations. The League set up a commission under the chairmanship of Lord Lytton. Japan was formally censured for not seeking peaceful means to redress her grievances, and Japan withdrew from the League. Churchill's sympathy for Japan was not out of line with British feeling at this time, but was contrary to the emotions of the most vigorous advocates of the League.

[Extract] ... The military and economic menace of Russia to all civilized countries is grave, but the political or moral menace has much diminished in the last 10 years.

Now, I must say something to you which is very unfashionable. I am going to say one word of sympathy for Japan, not necessarily for her policy, but for her position and her national difficulties. I do not think the League of Nations could be well advised to have a quarrel with Japan. The League has a great work to do in Europe. I value enormously that noble instrument which has been erected at Geneva, this council chamber where the leading nations of the Old World can pour out their troubles to one another. God forbid that it should collapse, and I have no patience with the penny-wise economies which grudge the English contribution to its structure. But when you come to the Far East you are asking the League of Nations to attempt a task very remote from their sphere of influence. The professed Socialists and professional pacifists would lure them on into a dispute which the League of Nations has no power to carry through.

I hope we shall try in England to understand a little the position of Japan, an ancient State, with the highest state sense of national honour and patriotism and with a teeming population and a remarkable energy. On the one side they see the dark menace of Soviet Russia. On the other the chaos of China, four or five provinces of which are now being tortured under Communist rule.

To some nearer home, the greatest immediate cause of a revival of Socialism in England in my opinion is not the spouting of street-corner orators nor even the influence of the Socialist Press. The danger is that a National Government shall declare itself incapable of vigorous action to solve the problem of the wage-earning classes, that they will show themselves neglectful of the terrible plight of those who are called "black-coated" working men, people of intelligence now thrown out of work by the thousands, for whom there is no State provision of any kind, young men educated at the universities, for whom there is no opening in life. An anti-Socialist union to be effective must revive the strong, warm sense of regard for the weak and the poor, in the Tory Party.

More dangerous is the effect of Socialist control upon the national spirit. We have all seen with a sense of nausea the abject, squalid, shameless avowal made in the Oxford Union. We are told that we ought not to treat it seriously. *The Times* talked of "the children's hour." I disagree. It is a very disquieting and disgusting symptom. One can almost feel the curl of contempt upon the lips of the manhood of Germany, Italy, and France when they read the message sent out by Oxford University in the name of Young England.

Let them be assured that it is not the last word. But before they blame, as blame they should, these callow ill-tutored youths, they must be sure that they have not been set a bad example by people much older and much higher up.

If ever there is a vote from the British people in favour of the strength of the country, for its credit and welfare, for its flag, its power, its fame, it was at the General Election of 1931. Yet upon the morrow of our great victory we find the Tory Party so cowed and muffled that is is almost afraid to mention its own name. It is hardly believable that the Tory Party, who can divide themselves into three and yet be stronger than all the other groups and parties in the House of Commons, has swallowed lock, stock and barrel the policies of the last Socialist Government about the Indian Constitution. The policy has even become in some respects more extreme. Yet three-quarters of the Conservative Party in every constituency throughout the country are opposed to the Socialist policy upon India. One deep-throated growl from the National Union of Conservative Associations would be enough to stop the fox.

BROADCASTING AND POLITICAL CONTROVERSY
February 22, 1933

House of Commons

I am so much in agreement with the speech that has just been delivered [by Mr. Lloyd George], and indeed with the speech that was delivered by my hon. Friend the Member for the Scottish Universities (Mr. John Buchan), that I shall compress my remarks, I hope, into a very short compass so as to leave time for others who wish to speak. I am not going to discuss this question at all from the point of view of the personal feelings that I may have upon the manner in which the British Broadcasting Corporation have administered their trust so far as I am concerned. I do not think the matter of individuals is at all important. There is far more of importance in this issue than that. It is one of the greatest issues that Parliment can possibly have to deal with.

We are in a period of full democracy—universal suffrage—and, as my right hon. Friend has pointed out, not only has the electorate enormously increased but the means of coming in contact with it have actually diminished in the comparatively short time that I have been in public life. I remember, as he has reminded us, the days when all the affairs of Parliament and politics were accompanied by a running commentary by the half-dozen leading men on each side, which was reported verbatim in every newspaper and which was read by all the people who governed and guided and formed political opinion throughout the island. It has gone—absolutely vanished. No newspaper can bear a verbatim report of political speeches. Although the newspapers have multiplied their circulation ten, twenty and thirty-fold, they have reached a class of readers who are much too absorbed in the ordinary toil of getting their living to be concerned in following long speeches of politicians reported verbatim. After their day's toil is done, they wish to rest, or they wish for amusement, and in their newspapers crime, frivolity, and crossword competitions are quite sufficient for them. So this platform has gone.

Then there is the report of the House of Commons. Everyone who likes to look at the reports of our proceedings of 30 years ago published in the Press and compare them with what is given now can see how all that great forum of discussion has been cut out, as it were, from the programme of national life. Lastly there is the size of the electorate in every constituency. When I was first a Member of Parliament 34 years ago, in a great constitutency you could see three-quarters of your supporters. You could perhaps see half of the whole constituency. What can you do now? In a fortnight you can only touch the fringe. All that has gone. So that at the moment when the greatest decisions in the world are confided to an electorate of 25,000,000 people, or whatever it is, you find that they are deprived even of the mechanism which has hitherto enabled political contact to be maintained. I think that is a most grievous and anxious fact to bring before the House for the attention not only of those who are interested in politics but for those who are thinking of the long future development of the country.

The world is losing faith in this democracy. It is losing faith in the methods by which it is manipulated. The stunt Press, the great caucus machinery, the stunt oratory—all these things are leading political thinkers who a hundred years ago were marching on hopefully to fuller democrary to recoil, and they have recoiled. Look at Europe. Much more than half of Europe has degenerated in this century from Parliaments so hopefully erected in the last into arbitrary or military Governments, and the movement is steady everywhere. Alone almost we here labour and strive to preserve the vitality, the authority and the glory of our Parliamentary institutions and of our free Government. I am sure that these processes which are at work nowadays have only to continue to destroy the Parliamentary institutions and the free political life under which, and with which and by which our country has grown, and grown great. At this very moment in our history. the protecting genius of Britain comes forward with his marvellous new instrument, this wonderful apparatus, which enables a continuous association to be maintained between the voting millions and the guiding authority of the State. It is a trememdous, wonderful gift, which has come to us. I am told—I must admit that it was my right hon. Friend the Postmaster-General who told me, and he will not mind my betraying confidence at his expense—it may be in a few years' time that it will be possible to invite Members to address their constituencies on a special wave length adapted to the particular areas. What a wonderful thing! It will be one of those labour-saving devices to which no one who is in the middle of a long campaign could possibly object, and what an advantage to be able to speak to the men and women you represent, not in the excited, hectic, controversial atmosphere of a public meeting with all its rowdiness and interruptions, which have grown considerably, I am bound to say, as time has gone on, but in quiet surroundings after a long day's toil.

It is a great gift which has been given to us, and, like so many of the gifts of science, we have so far neglected and almost rejected it. Just as we are told that because mankind has become so wonderfully skilled in making all the things it wants therefore we must enter upon a period of grim privation and tighten our belts, so in this field of broadcasting, when this gift has been given to us in the most critical period in our history, we find it neglected, laid aside and almost stifled. I am, of course, speaking of political controversy. I agree with all that the right hon. Gentleman said about the high quality of British broadcasting in the entertainment which is given to the public, but upon the question of political controversy, in which the House is interested to-night, turns the practical utility of this instrument for the future. Since when have the British Government shirked or been afraid of controversy? I have never heard of such a thing. Controversy has been the buoyancy of Government and the means by which they have kept themselves alive. Ministers are kept keen on the grind-stone of criticism, and very often the process of framing the answer to an attack has been the spur which has discovered the remedy for an evil. I have sat long enough in Cabinets to know how refreshing it is when the atmosphere of smug complacency and mutual admiration is broken in upon by the window being flung open and a keen, even bitter gust of fresh air comes in.

Why should this Government be afraid of controversy? I could conceive that if you had a weak Government, a Government with a lot of second-rate men, a Government which was suffering from the new disease which the Prime Minister has discovered, this "Being below par" disease; I could quite conceive that such a Government might well wish to build up any little adventitious shield or protection to keep itself in security from outside shock. But when you have a National Administration of all the choicest spirits of the age, pulsating with energy, aglow with inspiration, with an appetite for activity, such a Government has certainly no need to shrink from the sharpest contact with criticism. Indeed, it is, of all Governments, the one Government that should take the plunge and open the broadcast freely to political controversy, from every quarter and of every kind. I must admit that there are limits. Sedition and obscenity are punished by law, and no one suggests that they should be admitted to the broadcast. The violation of official secrets is protected by legislation.

I do not attach any importance to the arguments which we hear, that you must not talk about Indian or foreign affairs. Let me take Indian affairs first. I am not going into detail, but I think it has been very wrong that there has been no permission given during the whole of these last two and a-half years for a statement of views which some of those who are not represented either by the official Government or the official Opposition are able to share. I think that has been very wrong and unfair. What harm could it do in India that is not capable of being done already by a speech or article that is telegraphed out to India? Obviously, the withholding from the broadcast of Indian matters is not because of any fear of influencing the Indians, who have not these facilities in their 750,000 villages, but who receive telegraph reports. The object is to prevent the formation of British opinion. That is what I think is unfair and a fraud. It is an abuse of power and an abuse of this great institution to try to prevent our own fellow countrymen from forming an opinion.

Take foreign affairs. I remember, in bygone days, that the great men used to discuss foreign affairs with enormous latitude. I have heard them say things that, really, would make the hair of the modern, correct politician rise on end. Mr. Chamberlain, Mr. Gladstone and other statesmen habitually discussed foreign affairs with great vigour. The foreign nations did not take offence, because they said: "It is only Mr. So-and-So," or "Mr. So-and-So." Then, somebody else answered him, and one tale is good until another is told; very often only good until another is told. In the past there was a great deal of plain speaking about foreign affairs. But why was there irritation the other day in Poland? Because it was not a man's opinion that was being given, not the opinion of a public man, who could be corrected by other public men, but because it was this impersonal, sub-human or superhuman sham god that was speaking.

These well-meaning gentlemen of the British Broadcasting Corporation have absolutely no qualificiations and no claim to represent British public opinion. They have no right to say that they voice the opinions of English or British people whatever. If anyone can do that it is His Majesty's Government; and there may be two opinions about that. It would be far better to have sharply contrasted views in succession, in alternation, than to have this copious stream of pontifical anonymous mugwumpery with which we have been dosed so long. I am very much encouraged by this Debate. I think there is a general feeling in the House, even among the Liberals, a minority, and it may be an increasing minority, that I am championing fair play and free speech. This Debate, if it is properly interpreted and enforced, may mean the opening of a new, wider and freer use of this great instrument, which if it is opened to the political life of the nation can only bring enhancement to the strength of the State, and set upon more permanent foundations the institutions which this small island has evolved.

THE INDIAN QUESTION

February 23, 1933

Epping

[Extract] . . . You must not be discouraged by the large Government majority in the Indian debate on Wednesday. The Government could, of course, count upon the enthusiastic aid of the Socialists and the Samuelites in crushing the Conservative minority. But although only 42 Conservatives felt bound to testify on this occasion by voting against the Government, the Conservative vote behind the Government has fallen by nearly 100.

A very large number of Conservative members are known to have profound misgivings, and they will increase as Mr. MacDonald's true purposes in India become more plainly revealed. Sir Samuel Hoare made an announcement yesterday of the very gravest character. He said that the Government has decided that responsibility for law and order and the control of the police should be handed over to the responsible control of the Indians themselves in the different provinces.

Anyone who knows the conditions in Bengal and Bombay will realize what dire peril that will bring upon every British resident there. Never has been seen such a spectacle of a powerful country divesting itself gratuitously, wantonly, without any need or compulsion, of its duties and responsibilities and casting away the title-deeds of its power and fame.

I warn you that the fight will be long and bitter. Every effort will be made to deride and discredit me. All the resources of the Central Office and the Party Whips will no doubt be employed. I have acted entirely upon definite decisions taken at every stage by the West Essex Conservative Association. Nearly three years ago they authorized me to quit the Conservative shadow Cabinet in order to plead the cause of the British Empire in India. I shall continue to do what I believe to be my duty without the slightest regard to personal interests or private friendships.

Conservatives in the constituency and throughout the country ought to bring their influence to bear upon their members. The Epping Division has decided to persevere in the effort they are making to rouse the National Union of Conservative Associations to the danger to the Empire before it is too late.

It is shocking that the party should be manipulated and shepherded, as it is, into a course utterly opposed to its interests, its duty, or its traditions. The responsibility for the disaster into which they are being led will be upon the Conservative Party. Mr.

MacDonald and his band of National Socialists will disappear, but the injury to the British Empire may never be repaired. . . .

Mr. Chamberlain's recent statement that it may be 10 years before the unemployment figures are reduced to a comparatively small total has caused widespread despondency and alarm. If Mr. Chamberlain's statement is true. I am bound to say that the country is expecting far more resolute efforts to adapt the social and economic system to the needs of the times than anything the Government has yet proposed or seems to have in mind.

We do not ask for impossibilities. I do not criticize the Prime Minister and the Government for not having cured the evil of unemployment. I remember how harsh the present Prime Minister was in his criticism of the late Conservative Government when unemployment stood at only 1,000,000. If I criticize, it is not because they have failed to cope with unemployment, but they have not mitigated it, and they seem to have given up trying to mitigate it.

The Prime Minister's broadcast from Lossiemouth on New Year's Eve was incredible chatter on little subjects that do not matter. . . . Why hasn't the national credit been used to finance schemes of constructive work during the winter? They are still negotiating over the question of resuming work on the two giant liners. There seems to be a lack of mental energy and of mental grip throughout the administration. The Prime Minister has had a long, dull reign paved with feeble platitudes.

FOREIGN POLICY AND IRELAND

February 24, 1933

Constituency Meetings, Buckhurst Hill and Wanstead

[Extract] . . . Young people argue a great deal about whether they would fight or not if a war came. But there is no likelihood of a war in which Great Britain would be involved. Even if foreign countries go to war with one another. I know of no reason why a wise and honourable foreign policy should not enable us to stand aside and prevent the fire from spreading. The Government has very rightly refused to extend our obligation in Europe or elsewhere.

Under the present constitution of the League of Nations, we cannot be forced into war against our better judgment of what is right or wrong. I think the first duty of British statesmen is to make sure that we are not drawn into any war, and only their second duty is to try to prevent others from fighting, or to try to bring their quarrels to an end. The supreme interest of Great Britain is peace in our time. With that object our foreign policy should encourage France to keep a strong army, so that there is no danger of her being attacked by her neighbours.

Similarly British interests require us to keep out of the quarrel which has broken out in the Far East, and not wantonly throw away our old and valued friendship with Japan. It is the interest of the whole world that law and order should be established in the northern part of China.

The condition of China, plunged in a strange combination of anarchy and Communism, is the cause of boundless and inexpressible misery to her industrious people. China is in the same state that India would fall into if the guiding hand of England was withdrawn. I advise you to read a remarkable book about Chinese life called *The Good Earth*, which shows the virtues and the sufferings of hard-working Chinese cultivators of the soil, and how happy they would be if they could only have impartial justice and the security for the fruits of their toil instead of being tortured by warlords, Bolshevists, and brigands of all kinds.

Our British interest is to secure the open door and a fair chance for our trade in all parts of China. A clear-sighted policy should be able to secure this. It is no use dragging the League of Nations into the Far East, where their influence can only be very small and where they have no means whatever of controlling events.

So long as the foreign policy of his Majesty's Government continues to be guided by sagacity and good will and is careful of British interests, I will give it cordial support.

I am also in general agreement with the Irish policy of the National Government. No doubt we made a mistake at the beginning when we rejected the Conservative amendment to the Statute of Westminister, which could have excluded the Irish Treaty from its provisions. That has probably led to Mr. de Valera's assumption of power. But since then the Government has acted justly, soberly, and firmly. Mr. J. H. Thomas has shown himself steadfast, and though he has his own way of doing things, and saying things, he deserves public support and approval.

I trust that the Government will not admit any right on the part of Mr. de Valera even to raise with them the question of the incorporation of Ulster against her will in the Free State. So long as Ulster chooses to link her fortunes with Great Britain the whole power of the Empire must be used to protect her citizens in their undoubted rights and liberties.

There is no danger of the Southern Irish starving. On the contrary, they will have a glut, and if they like to live a primitive rural life instead of what is called "modern civilization" that is for them to decide. Meanwhile it is the duty of our English farmers to produce without delay the food which we used to buy from Ireland, and there is no doubt they can do it very quickly under the shelter of the present duties or higher duties if necessary.

THE FAR EAST AND UNEMPLOYMENT
AT HOME

February 27, 1933

Waltham Cross

[Extract] . . . I think it was a difficult question to decide whether to place an embargo upon the export of arms to China and Japan, but on the whole I believe you will feel with me that a wise decision has been reached. [Cheers] It should be quite impossible for us as one single nation without the aid of other countries to discriminate between the two countries which are at war. We have no means of preventing arms which were being consigned to China being captured by the Japanese Navy.

We do not intend in any way to become embroiled in the conflict which is proceeding at the other end of the world. [Cheers] We could quite easily stop the export of arms from our own port, and as I understand that all the existing contracts which have been made are to be carried out, and as we all hope that the actual fighting will not last very long. I think we have been able to adopt the correct attitude without serious loss to our own manufacturers. It seems to me that British interests require us to keep out of this quarrel and we should not wantonly throw away our old valued friendship with Japan.

It is in the interests of the whole world that law and order should be established in Northern China. Anarchy and Communism have caused widespread misery to countless Chinese people. China is in the same state that India would be if the guiding hand of British rule were withdrawn. I have no doubt whatever that the Northern Province of China, to which Japan gives a very considerable measure of orderly government, is the least unhappy of all the provinces of China at the present time. The British interests there are not to be dragged into partisanship with either side. It is necessary for us to secure an open door for our trade and a fair chance for our merchants. A clear-sighted policy should be able to secure this without any risk that would involve us.

I do not think it is any use expecting too much from the League of Nations. I have a great respect for the League and think it is a valuable instrument in Europe. I should be sorry to see its functions arrested and because I respect it, I am most anxious that it should not be dragged into this quarrel at the far end of the world where it has practically no influence and absolutely no power to be of aid.

Those who say "If the League cannot stop the war in the Far East, what is the use of it?" are poor friends of the League. I have seen much very good work done by the League in Europe and in some parts of Asia. We must not blame the League for not attempting tasks beyond its strength and absolutely outside its scope. . . .

We are spending £140,000,000 a year from the National Exchequer on relief for the unemployed, which is more than the estimates for the Army, Navy, and Air Force put together. It is a prodigious new charge to be borne by the taxpayers. We have constituted this great fund, and it has, thank God, prevented starvation or acute physical distress among the mass of people in this time, not of dearth, but, strangely, of world plenty.

Unemployment is not only a material evil; it is a moral agony. There is no longer the question of the Tired Tims and Weary Willies falling out of work: they never could hold a job. Of the 3,000,000 unemployed, at least 2,000,000 have never in their lives before been out of a job except perhaps for very short periods.

[Editor's Note: In a reference to the coming World Economic Conference Churchill said] : I was the person who suggested that nearly a year ago. The Chancellor of the Exchequer [Neville Chamberlain] was very scornful about it at the time, but ever since then the Government have taken up the idea. The Prime Minister was delighted because he loves conferences.

The conference in my opinion has been unskillfully handled. The Prime Minister said he supposed it would meet before last Christmas; we should be lucky if it met before the end of the summer.

INDIA

February 28, 1933

*National Union of Conservative Associations Meeting,
Friends' House, London*

Churchill spoke in support of a resolution proposed by the West Essex Unionist Association: "That this council is of the opinion that the setting up of a responsible Government for All India on the principles of Western democracy will be injurious at the present time to India welfare, British trade, and the strength of the Empire." This was a virtual rejection of the policy of the Government, and was only defeated by 189 votes to 165.

The first question to be considered is how far we are pledged as a nation and as a party to the principle of self-government. Clause 41 and the Preamble of the Government of India Act, 1919, laid it down that the Statutory Commission (as represented by the Simon Commission) is to "report as to whether, and to what extent, it was desirable to establish the principle of responsible government or to extend, modify, or restrict the degree of responsible government existing therein." From these words, it will be seen that if there is a pledge to go forward on the path of leading Indians into an ever-increasing control of their own affairs, there is also a pledge to Britain and the British Empire that we should be the judges of the speed at which that task is to be executed.

As regards the suggestion that the critics of the present policy accepted the Report of the Simon Commission, I admit that it was agreed to by all parties, Liberal, Socialist, and Conservative, and as it seemed to provide a solution on which the nation could agree, I myself thought that it might well serve as a basis for Parliamentary discussion. On the other hand, I have never agreed to the Commission's proposal to hand over the police even to the Provinces. What I have always felt about the Simon Report is that at least it gives to the Provinces a chance to show whether Indians are really capable of governing themselves wisely and incorruptably, and if they succeed, then will they establish their case for a further advance. If, however, they fail, the Imperial power at the centre of the Government of India, remaining intact with all its resources, will be able to come to the rescue of any Province which self-government failed and help to restore law and order.

I, for my part, warmly supported the resolution which congratulated the Secretary of State for India on the steps which he has already taken to restore law and order. Sir Samuel Hoare has performed a great work with an enormous amount of patience, force, and skill. The condition of India has improved in its credit, in the boycott, and other ways. However, that improvement was effected not by the proceedings at various Round Table Conferences, but because Mr. Gandhi and thousands of his supporters were arrested. The Socialist assertions that divisions of troops would be needed to suppress the disorders in India has been proved entirely false. The mere assertion of the will to rule justly and to enforce the law impartially has been sufficient to restore peace and order, for which the vast mass of Indians are profoundly grateful to-day. Yet the Secretary of State is now proposing to hand over the government of India to the very people who were responsible for these disorders, at the very time when we are faced with the spectre of Ireland and all our unhappy experiences in regard to that country.

Western electioneering methods can be of no help to the East. Even the West is losing faith in some of the aspects of Western democracy. Yet it is at this moment that we intend to force upon India this fragile Constitution with a make-believe democracy. To achieve it unfair pressure has been exerted upon Conservative members of Parliament, also upon the Princes in India. There is no justification for such a step from the point of view of any British or Imperial interest. The policy seems to be dictated by the desires of four or five amiable and powerful men in this country who have developed idealist conceptions, and have become profoundly interested in, and fascinated by, the noble art of constitution-mongering.

In my opinion, the present policy of the National Government is nothing but a Socialist policy, and the Conservative Party is failing to exercise its critical faculty with regard to great proposals of constitutional change. I challenged the Secretary of State to grant a free vote in the House of Commons when the White Paper comes before it, and I conclude by appealing to the Council, bypassing Resolution No. 3, to place their convictions on record and thus secure a fair representation for Conservative opinion upon the Joint Standing Committees, and influence a decision in favour of a free vote in the House of Commons.

AIR ESTIMATES

March 14, 1933

House of Commons

If our discussion this afternoon were confined solely to the topics upon which the Under-Secretary of State [Sir Philip Sassoon] thought it prudent to dwell, if, for instance, we were to go away, as we might easily go, with the idea that the Air Force exists to fight locusts and that it never drops anything but blankets, we should undoubtedly entertain incomplete impressions of some of the issues which are brought before the House when the Air Estimates for the year are introduced. I do not consider that the present state of Europe is comparable with the state of Europe in 1914. Although there is great unrest, and hatreds are as rife as ever, yet I feel that there is not the same explosive and catastrophic atmosphere as existed in 1914; and therefore we may discuss in cool blood and with calm hearts, or at any rate in tranquil circumstances, some of the technical issues which are raised by this Vote.

I must turn especially to the memorable speech which was delivered by the Lord President a few months ago. I agree with what I imagine were his feelings when he wished that neither aeroplanes nor submarines had ever been invented. I am sure they have both been deeply detrimental to the special interests and security of this island; and I agree also with his general theme that the air power may either end war or end civilization. But we are bound to examine carefully the speech of the Lord President because of the feeling that he aroused alarm without giving guidance. My right hon. Friend swept away many important things in that half-hour. He did not believe there was never to be another great war; he thought wars would come again some day, but he hoped, as we all hope, they would not come in our time. He had apparently no real faith in the sanctity of agreements, such as the Kellogg Pact; neither had he any faith in the means of defense which are open to civilized communities when confronted with dangers which they cannot avoid. He led us up to a conclusion which was no conclusion. We are greatly concerned, and yet we were afforded no solace, no solution. So far as he made an appeal to youth, it was very difficult to see what was the moral which he inculcated, and as far as I can understand, reading in the current publications, his appeal to youth has been widely misinterpreted in some of our leading universities. [Editor's Note: A reference to the Oxford Union's resolution "that this House will in no circumstances fight for its King and country."]

There is a certain helplessness and hopelessness which was spread about by his speech from which I hope the House will endeavor to shake itself free. There is the same kind of helplessness and hopelessness about dealing with this air problem as there is about dealing with the unemployment problem, or the currency question, or the question of economy. All the evils are vividly portrayed, and the most admirable sentiments are expressed, but as for a practical course of action, solid footholds on which we can tread step by step, there is in this great sphere, as in other spheres of Government activity, a gap, a hiatus, a sense that there is no message from the lips of the prophet. There is no use gaping vacuously on the problems of the air. Still less is there any use in indulging in pretense in any form.

The spokesman for the Labour Party, in a speech which certainly presented a definite point of view, spoke with much satisfaction of the proposals which the Government have been making at Geneva. The air forces of the world are all to be reduced to our level, and then we are all to take together another step down to the extent of 33-1/3 per cent. Well, is there any reality at all in a proposal of that kind? We must not allow our insular pride to blind us to the fact that some of these foreigners are quite intelligent, that they have an extraordinary knack on occasion of rising fully up to the level of British comprehension. Of course, if all the air forces of the world were to be reduced to our level, as we are only fifth in the list, that would be a great enhancement of our ratio of military strength; and the foreigners are bound to notice that. [Editor's Note: At this period the air strength of the leading Powers was as follows: France, U.S.A., Japan, Italy, and Great Britain.] So I could not help feeling that the proposals which were made, and would sound very well while they were being unfolded, would give great gratification to the League of Nations Union, who, poor things, have to content themselves with so little. They would give the same kind of warm, sentimental, generous feeling that we were doing the "broad, just, fundamental, eternal thing" that the recent arms embargo announcement [February 17] give to so wide a circle. But I do not suppose that anyone would have been more surprised than the Under-Secretary of State or his Chief [Lord Londonderry] if, when they had made these specious suggestions at Geneva, all the Powers had suddenly risen and, with loud acclamations, said, "We accept them." I am sure that even the Prime Minister would have been, at any rate momentarily, disconcerted. In fact, there was no chance of these proposals being accepted, not the faintest chance—and no one knew it better than His Majesty's Government when they made them.

We ought not to deal in humbug. There are good people in this country who care about disarmament. In many ways I think they are wrong, but I do not see why they should be tricked. I think they should have the plain truth told them, and if they disagree they have their constitutional remedy. It is no kindness to this country to stir up and pay all this lipservice in the region of unrealities, and get a cheap cheer because you have said something which has not ruffled anyone, and then meanwhile do the opposite, meanwhile proceed on entirely pre-War lines, as all the nations of Europe are proceeding today in all the practical arrangements which they are making.

Another reason why these proposals had no chance of being accepted is their effect upon France. In the present temper of Europe can you ever expect that France would halve her air force and then reduce the residue by one-third? Would you advise her to do so? If she took your advice and did it, and then trouble occurred, would you commit this country to stand by her side and make good the injury? If we proceed to argue on lines which have no connection with reality, we shall get into trouble. You talk of secret diplomacy, but let me tell you that there is a worse kind of secret diplomacy, and it is the diplomacy which spreads out hope and soothing-syrup for the good, while all the time winks are exchanged between the people who know actually what is going on. That is a far worse situation. I am as a fact a member of the League of Nations Union. If I were one of their leading authorities I should be far more irritated with people who deceived me than with persons who, supposed to be lost souls, stated the blunt truth; because, unless the people know the truth, one day they are going to have a very surprising awakening.

These proposals which have been made by the Government at Geneva are not likely to be accepted, and I do not think there is a single man in any part of the House who thinks, or who has ever thought, that they had the slightest chance of being accepted. You are not going to get an international agreement which will obviate the necessity of having your own defenses or which will remove the appalling dangers which have been so freely stated. I am most anxious that in anything that is said to France at Geneva upon air armaments or upon military armaments we should do nothing which exposes us to the French retort, "Very well; then you are involved with us." I would far rather have larger Estimates and be absolutely free and independent to choose our own course than become involved in this Continental scene by a well-meant desire to persuade them all to give up arms. There is terrible danger there.

I read in the newspapers today that the Prime Minister has been giving an ultimatum or making a strong appeal to France to disarm. Whether you deal with the Army or the Air, you are taking an altogether undue responsibliity at a time like this in tendering such advice to a friendly nation. No; I hope and trust that the French will look after their own safety, and that we shall be permitted to live our life in our island without being again drawn into the perils of the continent of Europe. But if we wish to detach ourselves and lead a life of independence from European entanglements, we have to be strong enough to defend our neutrality. We are not going to preserve neutrality if we have no technical equipment. That reason might again be urged if we are discussing Navy Votes. I am strongly of opinion that we require to strengthen our armaments in the air and upon the seas in order to make sure that we are still judges of our own fortunes, our own destinies and our own action.

I now come to the technical issue which was raised by Mr. Baldwin's speech—a famous speech, I must say, because how many speeches we make in this House and how few are remembered a week after! But here months ago my right hon. Friend made his speech and in this Air Debate it is the dominant theme. He was dealing with the bombing of open towns and the murdering of women and children as an orthodox and legitimate means of civilized war. I cannot follow him in two respects. First, he assumes that it would certainly be done. Secondly, he assumes that there is no remedy. Neither of these impressions should guide public thought upon these matters. He said, with very great truth, that the only defense is offense. That is the soundest of all military maxims. But, as can be seen from the context of the phrase, my right hon. Friend had been led to believe that the only method of offense by which you could defend your own civil population from being murdered was to murder some of the civil population on the other side. But that is nonsense. The true defense would be entirely different.

In a war between two States with equal air forces it would not pay—I put it no higher; leave out morality, humanity and the public law of Europe—it would not pay, from the military self-preservation standpoint of any Power engaged in an equal fight to waste its strength upon non-combatants and open towns. To use an expression which I have heard, they could not afford to waste their bombs on mere women and children. Essentially a struggle of this kind—which I pray as much as any man we shall never live to see, and which I am resolved to do my utmost to avert—any struggle of this kind would resolve itself into a combat between the two air forces. If all of a sudden two Powers with equal forces went to war, and one threw its bombs upon cities so as to kill as many women and children as possible, and the other threw its bombs on the aerodromes and air bases and factories and arsenals and dockyards and railway local points of the other side, can anyone doubt that next morning the one who had committed the greatest crime would not be the one who had reaped the greatest advantage?

Mr. McLean: What do you mean by that?

Mr. Churchill: What I mean is that this horrible, senseless, brutal method of warfare, which we are told is the first military step that would be taken, the killing of women and children, would not be comparable, as a military measure, to an attack upon the technical centres and air bases of an enemy Power.

Mr. Godfrey Nicholson: What about the moral effect on the people?

Mr. Churchill: The moral effect would be far greater if it were found the next day that the hostile air forces were incapable of flying at all. That would have not only a moral effect, but a physical effect of very remarkable strength. But I must say this: while in the first instance in any conflict the air forces would fight and would not be able, if equally matched, to look elsewhere, yet once one side was decidedly beaten, this process of torturing the civil population by killing the women and children might well be used in order to extort abject surrender and submission from the Power whose air defense had been broken down. Anyone can see how that might be applied. If there were any Power in the world to which it would not be applied, perhaps it would be our island, because so much easier methods would be open for reducing us to submission. If we were completely defenseless in the air, if we were reduced to a condition where we could not deal with this form of warfare, I doubt very much whether even then the victorious Power would be well advised to come and kill the women and children. By intercepting all the trade passing through the narrow seas and on the approaches to this island, they could employ the weapon of starvation which would probably lead to a peace on terms which they thought were desirable.

Therefore, it seems to me that the possession of an adequate air force is almost a complete protection for the civilian population, not indeed against injury and annoyance, but against destruction such as was portrayed by the Lord President; and that, after all, is what we have to think of first. I cannot understand why His Majesty's Government and the representatives of the Air Ministry do not inculcate these truths, for truths they are, as widely as they possibly can. The only defense is an adequate air force, and the possession of an adequate air force will relieve the civil population from this danger until that air force is victorious or is beaten. If it is victorious then the danger is removed for a long period. Therefore, I do not think that we should be led by the Lord President into supposing that no means of safety are open to a vigourous, valiant race. There is a means of safety open. While I would not abandon hope of international agreement, I would not base the life of this country upon it in their present stage, but to cut us off from that, on the one hand, and to suggest on the other that no remedy is in our hands in the region of force, is indeed to expose us to a gloomy vision.

Not to have an adequate air force in the present state of the world is to compromise the foundations of national freedom and independence. It is all very well to suppose that we are masters of our own actions in this country and that this House can assemble and vote as to whether it wishes to go to war or not. If you desire to keep that privilege, which I trust we shall never lose, it is indispensable that you should have armaments in this island which will enable you to carry on your life without regard to external pressure. I regretted very much to hear the Under-Secretary state that we were only the fifth air Power. I regretted very much to hear him say that the ten-year program was suspended for another year. I was sorry to hear him boast that they had not laid down a single new unit this year. All these ideas are being increasingly stultified by the march of events, and we should be well advised to concentrate upon our air defenses with greater vigour. Certainly it looks curious that while our Army and Navy have been increased in expenditure this year—no doubt absolutely necessarily, because we had disarmed far below what is reasonable—the Air Force, which is the most vital of all, should be the one subjected not to an increase but to an actual reduction. [Editor's Note: Army Estimates for 1933, £1,462,000 more than for 1932; Navy Estimates for 1933, £3,093,000 more than for 1932; Air Estimates for 1933, £340,000 less than for 1932, and over one million pounds less than for 1931.]

Above all, we must not be led by the Lord President into this helpless, hopeless mood. Our island is surrounded by the sea. It always has been, and, although the House may not realize it, the sea was in early times a great disadvantage because an invader could come across the sea and no one knew where he would land; very often he did not know himself. On the Continent the lines of advance are fixed by the mountain passes, the roads, and the fertile plains and rivers. We were under a great disadvantage a thousand years ago in being surrounded by the sea, and we suffered terribly from it. But we did not give up; we did not evacuate the island and say that we must live on the mainland. Not at all. We conquered the sea; we became the mistress of the sea, and the very element which had given the invader access to the heart of our country, to our hearths and homes, became its greatest protection—became, indeed, the bridge which united us to the most distant parts of our Empire throughout the world. Now there is the air. The sea perhaps is no longer complete security for our island development; it must be the air too.

Why should we fear the air? We have as good technical knowledge as any country. There is no reason to suppose that we cannot make machines as good as any country. We have—though it may be thought conceited to say so—a particular vein of talent in air piloting which is in advance of that possessed by other countries. There is not the slightest reason to suppose that we are not capable of producing as good results for money put into aviation as any other country. That being so, I ask the Government to consider profoundly and urgently the whole position of our air defense. I am not going to commit myself, without an opportunity of examining all the technical and financial details, to any particular standard, but this I say—that, in view of the significance which this subject has at the present time, in view of the state of the world, and in view of the speech of the Lord President of the Council, it is absolutely indispensable that the necessary programme of air development should be carried out, and that our defenses in this matter should be adequate to our needs.

"THANK GOD FOR THE FRENCH ARMY"

March 23, 1933

House of Commons

We all desire to see peace and goodwill established among the nations, old scores forgotten, old wounds healed, the peoples of Christendom united to rebuild their portion of the world, to solve the problem of their toiling masses, to give a higher standard of life to the harassed populations. We can all expatiate upon that. The differences which arise are those of method. They arise when our sentiments come into contact with baffling and extremely obstinate concrete obstacles.

Our first supreme object is not to go to war. To that end we must do our best to prevent others from going to war. But we must be very careful that, in so doing, we do not increase the risk to ourselves of being involved in a war if, unfortunately, our well-meant efforts fail to prevent a quarrel between other Powers. It is by this test that I wish to examine the foreign policy of the Prime Minister. During the whole of the last four years he has directed, and not only directed, but dominated, our foreign policy, and no one can pretend that the results are satisfactory. On the contrary, the state of Europe, the condition of the Far East, our relations with Japan, the authority and prestige of the League of Nations, the security of this island—all have in various degrees sensibly deteriorated. It may be that events have been too strong for the Prime Minister. There are tasks beyond the power of mortal man. It may well be so, and his friends will naturally like to adopt that view, but others may think that the course that he has adopted, from the highest motives, has actually aggravated the position.

The staple of the policy of the right hon. Gentleman has been disarmament. Of course, it is true that in that respect he was only following the policy to which all parties were committed and many nations committed by treaty. Nevertheless, the undue insistence upon disarmament, the prolonged attempts at Geneva of one nation to disarm another, and latterly of each nation to put some other nation in the wrong before public opinion—this prolonged process, which began before the Prime Minister was responsible for our affairs, but which he has impelled with all the resources at his disposal, has not had good results—in fact, it has in some respects worsened the relations between the Great Powers. I have held this view for some years, and I see it continually confirmed by events. I am very doubtful whether there is any use in pressing national disarmament to a point where nations think their safety is compromised, while the quarrels which divide them and which lead to their armaments and their fears are still unadjusted. The elaborate process of measuring swords around the table at Geneva, which has gone on for so many years, stirs all the deepest suspicions and anxieties of the various Powers, and forces all the statesmen to consider many hypothetical contingencies which but for this prolonged process perhaps would not have crossed their minds and would only have remained buried in the archives of some general staff.

I have always hoped and believed that the continuance of a long peace and the pressure of taxation would lead to a gradual, progressive neglect of armaments in all countries, as was the case after the conclusion of the great Napoleonic wars. I say nothing against private interchanges in secret diplomacy between the Foreign Offices of the different countries of a friendly character—"If you will not do this, we shall not have to do that," "If your program did not start so early, ours would begin even later," and so on—such as have always gone on, and may perfectly legitimately go on. I believe a greater advance and progress towards a diminution of expenditure on armaments might have been achieved by these methods than by the conferences and schemes of disarmament which have been put forward at Geneva. It is in this mood that I look at the Prime Minister's latest plan.

Taking a layman's view of these fact and figures, I cannot say that they are injurious to our own defensive interests, but I doubt very much indeed the wisdom of pressing this plan upon France at the present time. I do not think it is at all likely that the French will agree. They must be greatly concerned at what is taking place in Germany, as well as at the attitude of some others of their neighbors. I dare say that during this anxious month—we seem to have passed through a very anxious month—there are a good many people who have said to themselves, as I have been saying for several years, "Thank God for the French Army." When we read about Germany, when we watch with surprise and distress the tumultuous insurgency of ferocity and war spirit, the pitiless ill-treatment of minorities, the denial of the normal protections of civilized society to large numbers of individuals solely on the ground of race—when we see that occurring in one of the most gifted, learned, scientific and formidable nations in the world, one cannot help feeling glad that the fierce passions that are raging in Germany have not found, as yet, any other outlet but upon Germans. At a moment like this, to ask France to halve her army while Germany doubles hers—that is the scale of figures—to ask France to halve her air force while the German air force remains whatever it is—I am aware that there is no military air force permitted to remain—such a proposal, it seems to me, is likely to be considered by the French Government, at present at any rate, as somewhat unreasonable.

It seems unlikely, therefore, that these proposals will be found acceptable either by France or by various other countries concerned. I do not mean that they will be rejected out of hand. On the contrary, all the nations at Geneva have developed a very elaborate technique in dealing with disarmament proposals which do not suit their needs or which they think are dangerous or inconvenient. They have learned very well to talk the language which is agreeable to the League of Nations Union. They think they do it very well there. They have had a lot of practice at it. They never refuse at first sight any proposal, however injurious, visionary or foolish they may think it. On the contrary, they make praiseworthy speeches. They interchange agreeable compliments—"How interesting!" "How hopeful!" "What a meeting of our point of view is embodied in this !" "It is the first time we have really had a helping hand in this difficult situation." "What noble sentiments have inspired this theme for which we are indebted to the genius of England!" And then, having read it a second time, to use our Parliamentary forms, amid prolonged enthusiasm, they adjourn to the banqueting-hall and leave it to be killed in committee by a lot of minor objections to detail, or by putting forward counter-proposals which only make confusion worse confounded.

I understand that already there are fifty-six disarmament plans. Perhaps the Prime Minister has the right figure. It may be more now, because he has been two or three days away from Geneva. Fifty-six well-meaning plans, which certainly suited very well indeed the interests of the countries which proposed them, have already been disposed of by this machinery, and it seems not unlikely that the fifty-seventh will share the common fate. But although the plan of the Prime Minister may not be accepted, it cannot, I fear, fail to arouse distrust in the breasts of those from whom it asks the most hazardous sacrifices at the most inopportune time. Here I say very little of the Prime Minister's oratorical style. We are familiar with it here. We know that he has, more than any other man, the gift of compressing the largest number of words into the smallest amount of thought. We have heard him on so many topics, from India to unemployment, providing us, apparently, with an inexhaustible flow of vague, well-sounding exhortation, the precise purpose of which is largely wrapped in mystery, and which, as far as it can be discerned, can be understood differently in different quarters, according to taste. They only comment I would make upon his eloquent speech at Geneva is that when he said to the assembled nations that if they would not adopt the proposals they would be mannequins—the functionaries who, I believe, are employed by French dressmakers to exhibit their wares to the best advantage—they would be mannequins, and not men, I cannot help thinking that he lapsed a little from those standards of international decorum which we expect in a representative of the British Empire in such circumstances. When I think of the figures which I have just been mentioning [*Laughter*] —I was dealing with statistics, and not with fashions— when I think of the statistics, I am not at all sure that the French will find such remarks even amusing.

All these considerations lead us to a very grave matter. I think that it is undoubtedly dangerous to press France at the present juncture to disarm, because of the effect which that must necessarily have upon our own obligations and our liabilities under the Treaty of Locarno. We have serious obligations under Locarno, but they are provided with various important safeguards which insure our having a wide discretion whether we should or should not engage, on one side or the other, in a European war. I am going to mention those safeguards because they are of the utmost consequence to all of us in this country who wish to be assured that we shall never see our men dragged into another tremendous Continental struggle.

The Council of the League of Nations must be unanimous. It would probably not be unanimous. In fact, in the grouping of the Powers it could hardly be unanimous, apart from the fact that we ourselves would be an indispensable factor in that unanimity. Then there is the emergency obligation under Clause IV. This operates in the case of what is called a

> flagrant violation of peace constituting an unprovoked act of aggression, which by reason of crossing the frontier, or the outbreak of hostilities, or the assembly of armed forces in the demilitarized zone requires immediate action.

"Immediate action" means before the Council of the League of Nations can be invoked. I know that that is often mentioned, but here again I think that a considerable latitude of judgment rests in the conditions of the Treaty. The word "flagrant" in this case not only embodies the idea of a grave breach of law, but it also involves the elements of magnitude, danger and urgency. It is of the utmost importance that those elements should be read into the meaning of the word "flagrant." We should be entitled to consider all these aspects before we felt ourselves bound to join in a European war without even having the opportunity to discuss the matter upon the Council of the League of Nations.

It must always be assumed, of course, that Great Britain will stand by her obligations. Probably she will be better than her legal word, but I do not admit that the Treaty of Locarno deprives us of the right to judge the facts and circumstances, even in an emergency, according to what we think right in our interests and for our duty. But many refinements, which may be of vital consequence to the people of this island and of the British Empire, will be swept away—I warn the Government—if we press France to disarm and encourage Germany to rearm to a point where dangerous conditions are created. If you press a country to reduce its defenses beyond its better judgment, and it takes your advice, every obligation you have contracted, however carefully it has been expressed, will be multiplied in force, and you will find your position complicated by fresh obligations of comradeship, honour and compassion which will be brought very prominently to the front when a country which has taken your advice falls into grave jeopardy, perhaps as a result of what you have pressed upon it.

I remember what happened before the Great War. The growth of the German Navy obliged us to concentrate all our battleships in the North Sea, and we withdrew our squadron of battleships from the Mediterranean. The French moved all their battleships into the Mediterranean. There was no bargain. The two operations took place independently. But although there was no bargain, when the peril of war came and all Europe was seen to be rushing towards catastrophe, the Ministers of the British Government who were the most resolved against participation in the War admitted the force of the argument that, since the north coasts of France were undefended in consequence of the French having moved their battleships, we should be bound to make sure that she did not suffer for that reasons, and long before any agreement was reached as to whether we should participate in the War a general agreement was reached in the Government that the Germans should be forbidden to send any warships into the Channel. That shows the danger of pressing people to disarm beyond their better judgment, and of becoming too closely intermingled in their defensive arrangements. What terrible consequences this may have upon your freedom of choice at some future time! I am profoundly anxious that we should preserve and enjoy the full freedom to judge of our obligations under Locarno without any additional complications. Therefore, I urge the very greatest caution upon His Majesty's Government at the present time in pressing the French Government to weaken their strength relatively to Germany.

There is another and more obvious argument against our trying to weaken the armed power of France at this juncture. As long as France is strong and Germany is but inadequately armed there is no chance of France being attacked with success, and therefore no obligation will arise under Locarno for us to go to the aid of France. I am sure, on the other hand, that France, which is the most pacific nation in Europe at the present time, as she is, fortunately, the most efficiently armed, would never attempt any violation of the Treaty or commit an overt act against Germany without the sanctions of the Treaty, without reference to the Treaty, and, least of all, in opposition to the country with which she is in such amicable relations—Great Britain.

The Prime Minister spoke today of what he has put forward as the greatest effort for peace since the Great War. In this he did less than justice to the author of the Locarno Treaty, because certainly on the morrow of that we reached a position of far greater tranquility and security than we have ever been able to obtain since. How glad we should be to go back to that shining morrow of Locarno and the hopes that were expressed there! It seemed to me at that time that as long as France was armed and Germany was disarmed we ran no great risks under the Treaty of Locarno, and we had an opportunity of bringing France and Germany together in friendly intercourse.

Although bringing France and Italy together in friendly intercourse is a most important work, yet the master key of Europe is some understanding and relationship between its two greatest nations, Germany and France. If we are now going to try to establish conditions of equality—the Prime Minister used the word "equality" in a very loose way this afternoon, and I had to press him and make him add the important words "equality of status"—if we are not going to try to create conditions of equality between France and Germany in armaments, or even an approach thereto, because the potential alliances of Germany must be considered, we shall invest the whole situation under Locarno with a far graver, far more imminent and more practical character than it possesses today. If you are going to reduce the armies to the levels set out in the White Paper, then I say that before that result is achieved, Parliament ought to review the whole position of our responsibilities under the Treaty of Locarno. If the armies of Europe had been measured during the last month or the last six months, especially the last month, as they are set forth in this White Paper, those very horrors that it is our whole aim to avert from us would have leaped out upon us already. If Europe has enjoyed peace this year, it has been under the shield of France. Be careful not to break that shield. It is perhaps not the broad basis on which we should like to see the harmony of Christendom stand, but it is a shield. Beware that you do not lower it or weaken it by any action in your power before you have, at least, something which gives as good practical security erected behind it to put in its place.

Now I come to the proposals which the Prime Minister laid before us of a pact between the four Great Powers—no doubt, technically within the League of Nations—to preserve the peace and to plan a revision of the Treaties of Versailles and Trianon. I have always been attracted by this idea which Signor Mussolini has made so prominent. I have spoken for years of a pyramid of peace, which might be triangular or quadrangular—three or four great Powers shaking hands together and endeavouring to procure a rectification of some of the evils arising from the treaties made in the passion of war, which if left unredressed will bring upon us consequences we cannot name. The Prime Minister is, I think, a new convert to this idea. I have not had time to examine all his past utterances, but I had an impression that he had always condemned anything in the nature of a four-Power or a three-Power agreement and had considered that that was, as it were, inconsistent with the general authority of the League of Nations, on which so many Powers are represented. However, let that pass. Whether he was converted by the eloquence or by the strong personality of Signor Mussolini, or whether he had it in his mind before he went to Rome, are mysteries which are naturally hidden from us.

Although I have always been in favour of something of this character and have thought it the best line of approach to solid peace and to getting rid of the war peril, I am bound to say that the situation has deteriorated to such a point in the last year that such a plan is not nearly so hopeful now as it would have been some years ago, or as it might be perhaps at no distant date in the future. I am very doubtful whether the Prime Minister has been wise to launch it in the way in which he has done at the present moment. I should have thought that it was indispensable before this plan of a four-Power pact could have a fair chance to have got the Disarmament Conference laid to rest, and not to be assailing the nations involved with doubts as to their military strength and anxieties about their security at the same time that you are going to ask them to undertake the appallingly dangerous and difficult duty of endeavouring to get some revision of the peace treaties. I have always tried to urge upon the House that the redress of the grievances of the vanquished should precede the disarmament of the victors. This four-Power pact is a new idea, and you must revise your other procedure in relation to the new idea if you are to give it a chance.

The Prime Minister's interventions in foreign affairs have been—not through any fault or neglect on his part—remarkably unsuccessful. His repeated excursions have not led to any solid, good result. Where anything has been achieved it has nearly always been at British expense and to British disadvantage. On the whole, his four years of control of our foreign relations have brought us nearer to war, and have made us weaker, poorer and more defenseless. [Interruption]. Hon. Members say "No." You have only to study what is the position of Europe today. You have only to listen to what has been said from that Bench to know that we have been brought much nearer to war. [Hon. Members: "No." "By whom?"] I do not wish to place upon one man the responsibility for that, but at the same time when any one man has for four years held the whole power of this country in foreign affairs in his hands, and when he has pursued the lines of policy which I have indicated, you are making a profound mistake if you think the efficiency of our public service will be enhanced by pretending that there is no responsibility to be affixed anywhere.

I withdraw nothing. I repeat what I have said—that, with the best of endeavours, with the most praiseworthy exertions, the right hon. Gentleman's efforts have not been attended at any point with a measure of success. [Hon. Members: "Lausanne."] Lausanne. All right. Under Lausanne we have now accumulated the gold to pay an additional installment to the United States. Under Lausanne we have already told the French and the Germans that they need not pay us anything. Is that a great success? If eventually you reach good results and all War Debts and Reparations are forgiven and forgotten, then will be the time for these perfervid tributes to the Prime Minister. Then will be the time for hon. Gentlemen to range themselves up on the platforms of railway-stations, but that is not the position now. The position now is that we have let everybody off, and we are going to pay everything ourselves. [Editor's Note: The idea of repudiating Mr. Baldwin's Debt was not at that time entertained.]

Then there was the Naval Treaty of London, which I am glad to think the Conservative party voted against. It is cramping and fettering our naval development, not merely the scale but the actual form and shape of our naval expenditure, in a manner which is certainly detrimental. Then there is the Disarmament Conference at Geneva, a solemn and prolonged farce, which has undoubtedly lowered the prestige of the League of Nations and irritated many of the countries affected. Then, to come to more recent times, there is the arms embargo. So little am I prejudiced that I welcomed it in all the innocence of my heart, carried away by the excellent speech of the Foreign Secretary. I said that I thought it was the best thing to do. What happened to me? I had hardly had time to turn round when the Government themselves had abandoned this policy, which they had put forward not only on the grounds of policy and expediency, but on those higher considerations of honor and avoidance of blood-guiltiness which made such a very great appeal to their audience. Let me say that this treatment of the arms embargo has seriously affected our relations with

Japan. We have abandoned the arms embargo now. We have not the advantage of the high morality which the Foreign Secretary [Sir John Simon] preached to us, and we shall have to pay for it very considerably in after-years, if, as may well be the case, some special intimacy should grow up in trade matters in that part of the world between Japan and Germany. An hon. Member mentioned Lausanne. I have supplied him with other instances and illustrations of my theme.

Lastly, there is the visit to Rome. I do not wish to treat it too seriously. No doubt it was a pleasant expedition. No doubt it gave Signor Mussolini a great deal of pleasure; the same sort of pleasure that a thousand years ago was given to a Pope when an Emperor paid a visit to Canossa. It was certainly a striking spectacle to see these two heads of Governments, the master of sentimental words and the master of grim and rugged action, meeting together in such friendly intercourse. I associate myself with my right hon. Friend in welcoming the Prime Minister back. We have got our modern Don Quixote home again, with Sancho Panza at his tail, bearing with them these somewhat dubious trophies which they have collected amid the nervous titterings of Europe. Let us hope that now the right hon. Gentleman is safely back among us he will, first of all, take a good rest, of which I have no doubt he stands in need, and that afterwards he will devote himself to the urgent domestic tasks which await him here, in this island, and which concern the well-being of millions of his poorer fellow-subjects, and leave the conduct of foreign affairs, at any rate for a little while, to be transacted by competent ambassadors through the normal and regular diplomatic channels.

INDIA (CONSTITUTIONAL REFORM)

March 29, 1933

House of Commons

The two able and informing speeches to which we have listened are fitting elements in the introduction of the third day of this important Debate and, indeed, the whole character and quality of the Debate has shown the keen interest that the House has taken in the subject of Indian constitutional reform. That is as it should be. Our ancestors never grudged attention to Indian matters. Read the great Debates on the impeachment of Warren Hastings, or the Indian Bill of Mr. Pitt or Mr. Fox, or the Debate upon the assumption of the Imperial Crown by Queen Victoria, or the Debates of 1919. All these fill our Parliamentary records. And yet I think the Debate that we are engaged in may well be more important not only than any but perhaps than all these foregoing Debates put together. Whereas all these discussions in the past were the slow, gradual, steady building up of a great structure of peace and order in India and increasing the authority and vigilant attention of Parliament over all the Indian scene, we are now confronted with proposals which mark the definite decline, and even disappearance, of our authority in India, which proclaim our disinteresting ourselves in the welfare of its people and our readiness to hand over, after 180 years, India's fortunes to Indian hands.

We are to do this at a time in the history of the world when the processes of Parliamentary government and electioneering are becoming increasingly distrusted and discarded throughout the Western world. We are to do it at a time when the struggle for national existence and for the maintenance of secure, firmly attached markets is becoming ever more fiercely intensified and when we see the most powerful, the most civilised, and the most modernised countries resolutely seeking to hold, to acquire or to regain oversea possessions and without the slightest compunction claiming and asserting the rights of colonisation and the right of conquest. When you think of what we are discussing and of the situation of the world, surely, it is not too much to say that this Debate is fraught with memorable consequences both to the people of Great Britain and to the numberless peoples of Hindustan.

We are approaching the end of this Debate, but it is only the beginning of what may be one of the most serious controversies of British politics. It will be a painful controversy, because it must necessarily largely be conducted against friends or former friends. It will be a long controversy, because the procedure which is prescribed makes it impossible that the Bill to be founded upon the White Paper can become law for 15 or 18 months, and, as I gather, three or more years may elapse after that before the system of Federal Government responsible at the Centre of India can be brought into existence.

Let me, then, survey the whole scene, and I begin at the turning point with the Montagu-Chelmsford reforms. The Montagu-Chelmsford reforms have failed. They were an experiment, admittedly hazardous and doubtful, made in good faith, but they have failed. They have failed by every test, moral and material, which can be applied. Every service which has been transferred to Indian hands has deteriorated markedly. Nepotism, corruption, inefficiency, general slackening, a lowering down of the Services has invaded and infected all the departments which have been experimentally handed over and which, I may remind the House, are of such vital consequence to the daily life of the masses of the Indian people. Instead of increasing contentment, these reforms have aroused agitation and increased disloyalty. Instead of bringing peace between jarring races and rival religions, they have only awakened old passions which were slumbering, and slumbering profoundly, under the long Pax Britannica. These reforms have concentrated the mind of India so far as it is conscious and vocal during the whole of this period upon political and constitutional change, and diverted the energies of the country from all those important material and administrative improvement which are really the main interests of the Indian peasant and of the Indian workman. They have not even contented those political classes for whose satisfaction they were originally conceived.

I do not wish to make this statement too sweeping, because, no doubt, a lot of good work has been done, and will be done, but still, in the main, the first fact on which we should stand to-day is the failure of the Montagu-Chelmsford reforms. I say they have failed. I dare say that my Noble Friend the Member for Horsham (Earl Winterton), who I am told has a rifle carefully loaded for me, will say that I shared the responsibility for them. I will not disclaim any responsibility. I was not, in fact, a member of the War Cabinet which continued to rule until November, 1919. When the regular Cabinet was restored and for the first time I was asked, officially or un-officially, to express an opinion upon these matters, the Montagu-Chelmsford reforms had already been read a Second time in both Houses of Parliament, and had come to us with the unanimous recommendation of the Joint Committee of both Houses, or almost unanimous. But still I was a member of the Government, like my right hon. Friend the Lord President of the Council. We were both members of the Government, and, I have no doubt, made speeches in support of the Administration and its general policy, as others have done before and will perhaps do hereafter. Here I am going to defend my right hon. Friend as well as myself, and carry him along with me under my aegis. We shared our responsibility with all the Members of the House of Commons at that day.

The great scheme of Mr. Montagu and Lord Chelmsford passed through Parlia-ment without a single division. We may well ask why the Members of those days, many of whom are in the House to-day, behaved in this manner, and what were the reasons which led us to this supine neglect? I suppose that we thought, "It must be all right." We thought, "The India Office have approved the plan and all the details have been carefully discussed with the Government of India. The 'Times' newspaper writes able articles in its favour." So we thought, "No doubt the Secretary of State is a very nice fellow, has taken immense pains, and has set his heart on the scheme." No doubt we thought 10 years ago: "We must not add to the difficulties of the Prime Minister whose burdens are so heavy and who has to go abroad so often. We must back up the National Government which has just been returned by so large a majority." I suppose that we thought all those things, and with a little assistance from the able Whips the scheme was allowed to pass throught without even any serious examination by Parliament. We are all to blame.

I remember seeing—I do not think that I attended those Debates—on one occasion an elderly member of the Conservative party standing up there—Colonel Yate—apparently very excited and making frantic gestures of warning, but we all said: "Oh, he is only one of those die-hards. Some fellow who has been a lot in India and consequently cannot know anything about it." I am glad to revive his memory to-day. Although we Members of that Parliament may be all to blame, to-day we are dealing with issues which far exceed in importance the mere awarding of praise or blame to individuals. Let no one who sits here, or wherever he sits, delude himself by supposing that he can escape responsibility for what is now proposed by casting the blame on the past. Here we have to deal with the present and with the future, and every one, from the youngest Member to those who have longest borne the burden of affairs, is accountable to the nation and to history for speeches, votes, action or inaction now and in the critical months which lie before us. If mistakes were made in the past, do not repeat them now. If there are elders in this House who look back with remorse to decisions with which they have been associated in the past, let not those who are more happily situated prepare for themselves sombre self-reproaches in the afternoon or evening of their lives. Blame me if you will, blame the Parliament of those days if you will, taunt me if you will, discount my opinion, as you are entitled to do by any words I have spoken before, if you will; but in your hands, and on your heads lies the responsiblity of what you yourselves are now about to do.

The conditions of the last General Election were very exceptional; probably they were unique. Very large numbers of Members are here who have not been here before, and who did not, in many cases, expect to be called upon, and all the more credit to them for coming forward to face the task of fighting an election with no hope or ambition. It is to those Members I particularly appeal. Let them take warning from what has happened in the past. Let them be careful. Let them beware that in years to come when another House of Commons will be here and perhaps other trains of thought will rule our minds, they do not find themselves sitting by their own firesides when across the dark distances from India, to quote a celebrated phrase of John Morley, they hear "the dull roar and scream of carnage and confusion" coming back to us. Then bitter will be their feelings of responsibility and of agony when they feel that they themselves played a part in bringing about a situation of such frightful disaster. I appeal to them to discard altogether the mere recriminations about what happened in the past. They cannot throw the blame upon the past nor can they throw the blame upon the people. What more could the British democracy have done than give the majority which they gave at the last election? Never was there such a vote in favour of the greatness of Britain. Some may say mistaken in some way. I am not arguing that. But everyone knows that the impulse which brought all those millions of very poor people was the strength, honour, and endurance of our country, and its greatness among the nations. It is no good saying that democracy is doing this. If any failure occurs, it is in the representatives which democracy has chosen, or in those who have the power to direct their actions.

The first question which we should ask ourselves and which was touched upon by the right hon. Gentleman, is: Are we free to decide, are we free or are we pledged; are we free or are we bound, and to what extent are we bound? We cannot be bound by individual speeches. They may reflect upon the individuals who make them, or may not, but the policy of the State must be determined only upon legislative action and solemn delcarations made by the Soveriegn on the advice of responsible Ministers. In these days, when so many speeches are made by all people who take part in politics, it would be most dangerous to admit for a moment that speeches even of Ministers and Members of the Government can be taken as pledges and as bonds which fetter the power of Parliament and the representatives of the nation to deal with the great problems of the day as they think right and best. Happily there is no dispute whatever between me and the Government about that. I have always taken my stand on Clause 41 of the Act of 1919. My right hon. Friend the Secretary of State read out a passage, carefully prepared, every word of which had been carefully weighed, on Monday last to prove that we were not bound, or pledged, or committed in any way except in so far as you may say by way of moral obligation, the general trend of our institutions, and the growth of opinion in India. Therefore, I say that we have a right to decide.

Let me ask: have we the power? During the last Parliament, under the late Viceroy, very serious disorders broke out all over India. There were religious massacres of Moslems by Hindus, and there were reprisals. There were perpetual riots in Calcutta and Bombay. We saw the Congress burning the Union Jack at Lahore, with impunity. We saw prolonged paralysis of Government around Peshawar. We saw Lord Irwin negotiating with Mr. Gandhi. We saw the Indian Congress hoping to establish itself as a parallel Government in India and presuming almost to stand between the Government of India as an interpreter to the people of India. Side by side with all these events we had the undermining perorations of the Round Table Conferences, leading Indians to assume, without any warrant from Parliament—because we know that Parliament is free—that they would very shortly be called upon, after a brief period of transition, to assume responsible Government in India. When I protested against this state of affairs, against these tendencies, when I urged that it would be necessary, sooner or later, to break the Congress and Mr. Gandhi and all that his movement stood for, the late Secretary of State, Mr. Wedgwood Benn, and his like, were accustomed to reply that I sought a reign of blood and terror in India, that artillery and machine guns would have to be used ruthlessly, that large reinforcements of troops would have to be sent from England into the country. All these hideous nightmares were paraded for our warning and alarm.

The present Government, the present Viceroy and the Secretary of State, who both share the credit, have acted as I then advised, and what has been the result? Order has been largely restored throughout India. The Civil Disobedience Movement is broken. Mr. Gandhi, upon whom the Prime Minister and Lord Irwin lavished their caresses, has been in prison—I am sorry for it, for many reasons—for more than a year, together with a very large, but happily diminishing, number of his followers. Hardly anybody has been killed or severely hurt. Not a single British battalion has been employed except on the frontier. Very few collisions have taken place of a serious character between the police and the rioters. The decision of the Government of India to enforce the law without fear or favour has been instantly accepted throughout India by the overwhelming mass of the people. I believe, therefore, that there is no doubt of our ability to govern India justly and wisely, in our own way, and to entrust able, educated Indians, with whom alone the Government of India can be conducted, with an ever broader share of responsibility in the administration, as and when we think fit.

I reject, therefore, the defeatist argument that we have not the power. We have the power, and we have the right to decide. I know that the Secretary of State will tell me that the mere enforcement of law and order would not have produced peace unless accompanied by the kind of proceedings in which he has been indulging at the various Round Table Conferences, and that it is the hopes excited by Ministerial speeches about the advent of central responsible Government in India which have calmed the passions which had formerly been rife. There I differ from him entirely. I believe that is the reverse of the truth. Just as the disorders in India under Lord Irwin arose largely from the rumours that the British Raj—to quote a term well known now in our controversies—was coming to an end and that the Gandhi Raj, or the Congress Raj, would succeed it; just as these rumours promoted the disorders under Lord Irwin, in the same manner these same rumours have hampered the restoration of order, have delayed the revival of confidence, have made the officials less sure of themselves and have spread that feeling of unrest and approaching change among all political classes.

The achievement of my right hon. Friend and of Lord Willingdon, who both deserve credit, is remarkable, and it is the more remarkable that they should have so easily restored order in the face of all this continuous undercurrent of political and constitutional insecurity.

If, then, we have the right and power to choose freely, what should our choice be? We are often taunted by those who say: "What is your alternative?" I do not think that is a very fair question to ask. You have a great Government in power, with all the resources at their disposal, who, after these many years of labour, have produced this White Paper and their scheme of 110,000 words. Why should they say to a few poor gentlemen who represent the Conservative party—[*Interruption*.] If the Noble Lady the Member for the Sutton Division of Plymouth (Viscountess Astor) will go to her constituency, she will find out who represents it. Why should a few of us be expected to present another complete, brand-new, elaborately worked-out system? We in this matter have the great advantage that we employed a Statutory Commission, which for three years travelled about the length and breadth of India and presented a report, unanimously agreed to by all parties, and we, in our humility, think we are in the first instance entitled to rest ourselves broadly and confidingly upon that. I have never considered the Report of the Simon Commision—I do not know that I ought to call it that any more; I think I had better say the Report of the Statutory Commission, not wishing to embarrass my right hon. Friend the Foreign Secretary—I have never regarded the Report of the Statutory Commission as if it were a final revelation, sacrosanct, incapable of modification or amendment of any kind.

In particular, many of us have argued that the police should not be handed over to the provinces, and we will argue that as opportunity occurs on the Floor of this House. To do justice to the Statutory Commission, they did not say that the police should be handed over in this crude manner. They used a lot of arguments, some of which we heard yesterday, about the only way to stop the police being abused is to put them in the hands of the people who are abusing them. But when it comes to their actual recommendations there is a very hopeful and very helpful recommendation, namely, that one or more—that is better still—nominated Ministers should be attached to the Governor of every province. Obviously, if that were so, the Governor of any province where the conditions rendered it necessary could entrust the portfolio of the Home Office to one of the nominated Ministers who enjoys his confidence. I say this to show that, while we do not accept the Simon Commission as the final word, to be accepted exactly as it stands, it might well be taken as the basis for Parliamentary examination. We have contended that it should carry special weight in our debating and should have been used in all the subsequent negotiations and consultations with the Indian delegate.

That seems to be a not unreasonable position for private Members to assume in this matter, but the Secretary of State twists our attitude to suit his own contention. He made a speech the other day in which he taunted those who said that they supported the Simon Commission as a basis, with being prepared to force democratic Government in India upon the provinces. He argued, in effect, that by adopting the proposals of the Simon Commission as the basis of discussion we had stultified ourselves in opposing the application of the same principle or of the same system to the Central Government of India. That is another warning to the House of the advantage which will be taken—I am sorry to say it—by the Government, by those I will call the Round Table-ites, of every step taken by their opponents towards compromise and agreement. Only two days ago the Secretary of State said that practically everyone in the House was eager for the setting up of provincial Government in India. I will therefore declare quite plainly, speaking entirely for myself, that while for the sake of agreement between all parties I attach the greatest importance to the recommendations of the Statutory Commission, and many of us are willing to see further experiments made in the provinces, it does not follow at all that we think that that experiment will succeed.

I think that in many of the provinces responsible Government will only accentuate administrative deterioration, racial and religious unrest and political tumult, which have been the fruitful results of the Montagu-Chelmsford scheme. Far from advocating such a scheme, or forcing such a system upon the people of India, or being eager to do so, I wish sincerely that matters had not been handled in this way or had come to this pass; but for the sake of agreement, despite our misgivings—you cannot stop the progress of the world because of misgivings—I should be quite ready to make it clear, by all practical tests, that we are sincere in doing all in our power to help Indians to a greater share in the responsibilities of Government—I think we might well begin in some of the provinces, as was suggested by a Noble Lord yesterday—provided, of course, that the power which is given, the delegated power, can be resumed without serious disturbance if it is found to work to the injury of the people of India.

If we thus agree to provincial self-government, it is not because we are forcing it upon anybody, it has been forced upon us; it is not because any of us think it will succeed, it will most likely fail, but if it fails at least the disaster is local not general, it is subordinate not supreme; and, as long as the central Government of India is intact, secure, or to quote the jargon in this matter in India—unitary—it will always be possible to help a province which has fallen into disorder or in which the administration has scandalously degenerated, whose people are suffering from a failure of essential services; it will always be possible to help them back to such poor structure, poor but precious, of justice and civilised organisation which we have hitherto been able to erect in India. If, on the other hand, the provincial experiment succeeds over the whole of India or in a particular province, or in some provinces, we shall have to admit that a tremendous argument has been established, an argument of facts, not of words, an argument of achievement not of aspiration for a further advance. If we were provided after 10 or 15 years with a considerable number of prosperous, orderly, contented, loyal provincial units, nothing could stop an arrangement being made to weave these units into the higher synthesis of a Federal organisation.

There are two contentions of His Majesty's Government to which I must refer. The first is that none of the Liberal elements in India, on which they are relying, will take part in provincial autonomy unless they have the police handed over to them and unless Federal government is set up at the centre. All I can say about that is that it is not an argument which should weigh with us. We are here to give what we consider right and wise, not to give what we consider wrong and unwise because it is the minimum necessary to satisfy some not very representative Indian political groups.

The second point was contained in the speech of the Foreign Secretary yesterday. He used what I think is an even more questionable argument in his guarded, balancing, lukewarm but brilliantly ingenious speech with which he regaled us, and I could not help thinking as I listened to it of the cynical remark, "Distrust first thoughts; they are usually honest." I think we all understand, anyone who lives long enought in this House and who has experienced the vicissitudes of going in and out of Government will realise, the difficulties with which he had to contend and will admire his craftsmanship in dealing with them. On these occasions the skilful advocate will always look for a new fact. When a search is being made for reasons for a change of opinion the first thing is to search for a new fact, and the right hon. Gentleman produced a new fact; that the Princes of India offered to come into Federal government only if it was to be upon a responsible basis.

Is it possible that the right hon. Gentleman does not know, has he never heard, of what lay at the back of that extraordinary stipulation on the part of the Princes? I have heard on fairly good authority that the disappointment of the Princes, their alarm at the announcement of Lord Irwin that Dominion status was brought to the fore again, made them feel that they must look to their own future, secure their future under a totally different order of things. Then members of the Congress party discussed with some of the Princes, and an arrangement was made very much on the basis of what my right hon. Friend opposite would denounce—if you will help us to gain more power at the centre we will see that you keep your full rights over your own subjects in your States. That is the only reasonable explanation of such a stipulation on the part of the Princes.

I confess that I am not attracted by any part of that argument. I am not particularly anxious to see the Princes at this juncture brought into the Central Government of India, nor am I anxious to set up a Federal system in India. I am not at all induced by the argument which suggests that we should do something which we do not like in order to accomplish something which we like still less. In this Debate His Majesty's Government have been very apologetic. Perhaps that is too much to say; at any rate, they have been very deprecatory. The Minister of Health, who I do not see in his place, went even further in humility and moderation, in the moderation of his enthusiasm for the Government's proposals, than anything I have heard said in this House. Speaking on Saturday in his constituency, in contact with the opinion of his constituents, he said of the White Paper that

It was in the first place only a suggestion.

This product of so many conferences, inquiries, discussions, debates, the labour of the East and the West, this White Paper, for which we were told to wait and not prejudge the issue before it came out, the Minister of Health now says is "only a suggestion." I think that is going too far. We should really have a little stiffer attitude from the Government about their own proposals because they are every day engaging great masses of opinion in support of them. But they have been apologetic, and no one can say that the Motion which we are to vote upon now is not very cleverly and very adroitly framed, obviously with the intention of dodging a Division and confronting Conservative opponents of this policy with a proposition which they cannot possibly resist. Who can resist a Motion which begins by stating that no decision is to be taken by this House? Who can resist a Motion for appointing a Joint Select Committee, not in substitution for the ordinary Committee and Report stages in this House but in addition to those stages, and as preliminary to the Parliamentary procedure involved in the passing of a Bill? Certainly no one can vote against such a proposal. I think it is our duty to give the Government all possible support in repulsing the extremist Motion put forward by the official Opposition, and I shall certainly contribute my vote to what I trust will be for them a thoroughly satisfactory majority.

But do not let the House delude itself by supposing that the dangers of this question are passing away. On the contrary, this Committee which is to be appointed is appointed by a Government which will have an overwhelming majority upon the Committee and which, in addition, to its own majority will have all the support of the Socialist representatives and all the support of the Liberal representatives. The position of Conservative Members on that body, those who are not addicted to, or affected to, the Government will, indeed, be forlorn. They will sit hemmed in on all sides by men pledged to secure the triumph of the Government policy or even to carry it further, and then after prolonged discussions have taken place and these unfortunate representatives have been voted down time and again by the machine, the overwhelming machine, at the disposal of the Government, the Government will present to Parliament a Bill which they will say is based upon the report of an impartial Select Committee which they appointed for that end.

I think that the Conservative party is asked to take an immense responsibility. Every party in this country has its own function. The Labour party is concerned with the minimum standards of life and labour. The Liberal party have their liberty, and it is an honourable charge, but the Conservative party have always had the duty of holding together the strong body of constituted authority in the State and the possessions we have throughout the world. It has always been their duty to view with great caution and in a critical faculty widespread proposals for constitutional change. Now you see what happens when the Conservative party, instead of putting its hand on the brake, is led to put its foot on the accelerator—the whole balance of our public life is destroyed.

I invite hon. Members to see how events develop. The Conservative party controls this House of Commons. [Hon. Members: "Ought to do so!"] And Parliament controls the Viceroy and the Government of India. These in their turn come into play. We see the strange and unnatural spectacle of the Imperial Government turning its strength against its own interests and rebuking its own friends. We see the pressure which is put on the Princes. We read the extraordinary incident referred to by the right hon. Member for Hillhead (Sir R. Horne) of the altercation, or discussion, between the Jam Sahib and the Viceroy only the other day. We do not see so closely the pressure which is put on the officials. For five years past the high personnel of India has been arranged, continuously arranged, with a view to securing men who will give a modern and welcome reception to these sort of proposals. It is one of the greatest evils of the Montagu-Chelmsford reforms that throughout the Service the path of promotion has tended to be more easy for those who readily throw themselves into what are regarded as the irresistible moods of the British nation.

Sir John Wardlaw-Milne: Has the right hon. Gentleman any proof of that statement?

Mr. Churchill: I say that the officials ought not to have been quoted by the Secretary of State. I did not introduce this topic. The hon. Gentleman who is so ready to act the bully—[Hon. Members: "Withdraw."] I have a very difficult task. I do not wish to have any quarrel with my hon. Friend, and, if I said anything discourteous to him, I am sorry. But I am bound to say that I am stating a case with enormous forces ranged against that statement, as I see, and therefore it is not, perhaps, particularly valiant for an hon. Member to leap up in that way.

Sir J. Wardlaw-Milne: On a point of Order. Is the right hon. Gentleman entitled to make statements like that when he is asked in a very courteous way if he has any proof of his statement made against the Indian Civil Service, a most sweeping statement made against the whole of the Indian Civil Service?

Mr. Churchill: I am replying to the statement of the Secretary of State that practically all the high officials in India were in favour of this White Paper, and I think it is perfectly fair to say, in view of that, that during the last five years, and even during the last 10 years, the kind of opinion which has been promoted to leading positions throughout the Indian Civil Service has been that of people who are supposed to be modern-minded and acting in the spirit of the Montagu-Chelmsford reforms.

Sir S. Hoare: The right hon. Gentleman has no justification whatever for that statement.

Hon. Members: Withdraw.

Mr. Churchill: I will never withdraw a statement which I am certain is founded on fact. Then the Secretary of State claimed all the commercial classes. Of course, when the Conservative party of this country is known to have thrown its weight behind a scheme of this kind—this has been going on for the last three years—the commercial classes in India have despaired, and their despair is now quoted as if it was their approval. When the Prime Minister emphasises the safeguards, when the White Paper emphasises the safeguard, they are, of course, magnified for British consumption, and when it comes to India the opera glasses are turned round the other way. There are two audiences and two voices. We heard that the Government was confronted with the dilemma—either the safeguards are real, in which case responsible government is a sham; or responsible government is real, in which case the safeguards are a fraud. There is another dilemma into which we must ourselves be careful not to fall. That is, are we opposing this scheme for what it concedes or for what it withholds? Let me say that I think we ought to condemn it both for what it concedes and for what it withholds. The greatest objection to the scheme is that it neither gives nor withholds on any coherent or workable plan. On the one hand it offers autonomy in the most sweeping terms; on the other it sets up autocracy in an extreme form. It leaves these two opposite principles to struggle together within the heart and brain of the government of India.

It is a perfect plan for inaugurating an era of ceaseless strife, and the contending forces are evenly balanced. Both are armed with great power and great facilities, so that their warfare will be long, exciting, equal and calamitous; but I cannot conceive a scheme of which it could more properly be said that it comes "not to bring peace but a sword." The Viceroy or Governor-General is armed with all the powers of a Hitler or a Mussolini. There is practically nothing that he cannot do in the sphere of the Army and foreign affairs. He has the power to tax apart from the Legislature; he has the right to safeguard minorities; he has the right to safeguard the interests of the Civil Service; he has the right to safeguard the interests of the native States; he is authorised to prevent commercial discrimination. All these great powers are confided to him. By a stroke of the pen he can scatter the Constitution and decree any law he pleases, or martial law, which is no law at all. Of all these he is the sole judge.

Such a functionary is a dictator, and he has behind him a very powerful Army. Yet at the same time he is instructed to work a democratic Constitution tactfully, and to govern by consent, when consent is not forthcoming. I pause to ask, have such opposite qualities ever been united in the breast of a single human being? The phlegm of Bismarck, the energy of Mussolini, the special knowledge of Colonel Lawrence, the high ideals of Mr. Gladstone, the deft persuasiveness of the right hon. Member for Carnarvon Boroughs (Mr. Lloyd George)—all would seem to be needed in the functionary who has to discharge these opposite tasks and with so much thoroughness. The Secretary of State said yesterday that the Viceroy would have less to do than he had to do now. I should have thought that that was an absolutely absurd contention.

Let me look at the constitutional aspect. All these safeguards which are placed in the hands of the Viceroy are not new; they are not new creations of the Government. They all reside at the present moment in the structure of the Government of India, in the Viceroy and his Council, in the Secretary of State and his Council, in the great Indian Departments, and in this House. They are all there. But what we are doing now, and I think it singularly unfortunate, is to pick out all these essential safeguards and to set them out in a row, in a category, to be the target of every kind of criticism, and to place the Viceroy in a position where he, the representative of the King-Emperor, is responsible and can be made responsible and blamed for almost everything that takes place in this vast Empire.

But there is one notable omission from the Viceroy's powers. He is removed from the people he has to govern. The only functions of Government, practically, that are outside his jurisdiction, are those which concern the daily welfare of the masses, their education, justice, hospitals, their railways, their engineering works, the care of their forests and natural resources, the weight of taxation. He can, I gather, increase taxation, but not diminish it. All these things are beyond his sphere. We have a superman, not yet found, who has everything laid upon him except to mitigate the lot of the common people. That is judged unworthy of his attention; that can be safely transferred and handed over. I even heard the Secretary of State boast, glory in the fact that the affairs of 230,000,000 people were handed over freely, lock, stock and barrel, to these new legislatures, untrained and untried, which in all other respects are to be carefully controlled by safeguards.

I hope the House was stirred by the very powerful speech of my right hon. and gallant Friend the Member for Newcastle-under-Lyme (Colonel Wedgwood). He certainly struck a new note in this controversy. The powers of the Viceroy and the Governor-General, immense as they are, are counter-worked, to make things equal, by other provisions of this Consitituion. The holder of these great power is rendered virtually impotent. For his information he has to depend upon responsible Ministers; he has to work through them and the departments which they control. The police, 180,000 of them, in five years are possibly not even to be recruited by him. Even the Army is spoken of as a force which is to be transferred some day to Indian hands. All the great services which make the life of the Indian superior to the life of the Chinese have been taken from the purview of the Viceroy. The British officials are provided with an emergency exit so that they can throw up their jobs, should their condition become intolerable. The lonely Satrap has all the power, but it is blind power. He has no means of acting upon the hundreds of millions of people he controls, except by troops. His position is very similar to that occupied by the Tsar of Russia before the Revolution, with immense power, immense ceremony, mighty military forces, but no real contact with his people.

Where, I should like to know, would a general be without his staff? Where would a Member be without his local organisation? Where would a Minister be without his Department? Where would a Government be in times of distress if the police were withdrawn from the control of the Executive? Such is the position of the Governor-General. He can tax, but who is to collect the taxes? He can overrule an Act of commercial discrimination, but if there is a boycott to effect the same purpose as the Act would have done, he must go to the very Ministers he has overruled and ask for their support in controlling the boycott. He can protect the rights of the Civil Service, but their appointment, their treatment, all their daily affairs, will be in the hands of responsible Ministers, who, I cannot help feeling, will increasingly wish to get a very large reduction in the number of white officials. Why should they wish these officials gone? My right hon. Friend has made it abundantly plain. These British officials are to be the cadre, the steel framework upon which this country has to rely to enforce all the safeguards.

Of course, the position of these officials will be very invidious. You cannot consider the state of the Indian Services as they are to-day; you have to consider the state in which they will be in four or five years' time, when they have been under responsible native administration. They will be an organism of Indian life, and it is by no means to be taken for granted, indeed it is even improbable, that these great departments can be taken over at a moment's notice by the Viceroy or by the Governor-General simply by an act of power at a time when probably there is a great Nationalist movement in progress in India, and when he is overruling and dismissing the responsible Government which has been set up. Why should Indian officials risk their livelihood and their careers against their own fellow-countrymen in an emergency of this kind, for the sake of an Imperial Power—an alien Power I think the Foreign Secretary said they called it—which has declared itself in process of liquidation and is actually in train to hand over its authority to a new regime? My right hon. Friend the Member for Hillhead quoted a statement from Sir Tej Bahadur Sapru yesterday, but he left out, by accident, a very important passage which I must read to the House:

The Constitution, however, places such a powerful weapon in your
hands that if you can send into your legislatures the right sort of men, I
have not the least doubt you can achieve all you want probably much
quicker than you imagine, because the cumulative weight and effect of
these changes will be such that they dare not resist your demand for the
further expansion of the Constitution, its natural and logical evolution
being Dominion status.

A little further on he said to his colleagues:

I would advise you all to grasp power, for it is far better that you
should send those who oppose you to gaol than suffer yourself to be shut
up. I therefore say it is the duty of every one of you to capture the
machinery.

Mr. Maxton: Hear, hear!
Mr. Churchill: Yes, and that is very like the doctrine which the hon. and learned
Member for East Bristol (Sir S. Cripps) unfolded the other day. Proceed by constitutional measures until you get control of the police and the Army, and then go ahead
with your revolution. But I am bound to bring these points to the House although
they are by no means in harmony with the mellifluous language which is usually
employed on these occasions. If this is the position of the Viceroy, with all the power
and, as I say, without the executive machinery to exercise that power, look, on the
other hand, at the position of the Indian Parliament. They will be able to claim that
they are the elected representatives of the people. They will have control of the party
machine, of the organisation of elections, and so forth. They will have the great
bureaux in their hands. They are told that they are responsible for the well-being of
the nation. Endless means of friction will arise between the responsible officials and
the Government or the Governor-General and they will have a hundred means of
making their pressure constant upon those harassed functionaries. I am amazed at the
perverted ingenuity with which the Government have arranged a grievous and a certain
struggle, very similar, as my Noble Friend the Member for Aldershot (Viscount
Wolmer) has said, to that which convulsed England in the struggles between Crown
and Parliament during the whole of the 17th century.
I shall endeavour to curtail my remarks as much as possible, but I am anxious to
conclude the argument which I am putting before the House. The case of the
Governor-General will apply, on a small scale but more crudely and directly, to the
Governors of the provinces. Eleven potential dictators—11 hopeful and aspiring Parliaments! And this warfare in the provinces will proceed simultaneously with the graver
disturbances at the summit. Then, when this is occuring, you will perhaps learn the
wisdom of the Statutory Commission's remark, that unitary government at the centre
was most important during the development of the Provincial Legislatures.
I will examine only one other element in the Constitution—the Senate or upper
Chamber at the centre. A great deal of fine filigree work has been put into that. There
are Princes, Moslems, representatives of the landowners, certain official representatives
and so forth. There is some provision, I believe, for a two-thirds majority and so on,

and I am ready to admit that the character of that assembly will be such that it will have very stiff opinions about the rights of property. I have not the slightest doubt it will be very careful to protect the rights of property, the rights of the landlord, or of the moneylender, or of the Ahmedabad mill-owner, or, no doubt, of orthodox religion. In that respect it may be a highly Conservative chamber, but not in the best sense of the word. But when you come to the kind of question with which we are concerned here, issues which arise between Parliament and the Crown, issues which arise between India and Great Britain and which will be fought out, then it seems to me that you may very easily find that these forces, on which you are so trustfully relying at the present time, may be actuated by quite different motives from those which you attribute to them.

How can Hindu Princes—and are they not seven-eighths or nine-tenths of the whole—be expected to stand against the movement of Hinduism throughout the whole of India? How can they be expected to stand against that movement when Congress will have means of causing disorder in any one of their States? How can you expect Moslems to show themselves less forward in advocating what is called the national cause than their Hindu fellow-countrymen? No, Sir, it may well be that while you will have, for the purpose of the maintenance of Indian property rights, and Indian trading interests, a very strong, firm, oligarchy, there is not the slightest guarantee that the whole of them may not be ranged on nationalistic lines against the Viceroy and this country in any serious constitutional dispute.

Evidently Ministers do not believe that this situation is one that can last, and it seems they have no doubt how it will eventually resolve itself. Hence all these safeguards arranged to satisfy British opinion. But they are all placed in the Instrument of Instructions and not in the Constitution and thus can be discarded by a single resolution. [Hon. Members: "No."] Certainly, they can be discarded by simple resolution and not by the process of a Bill.

Sir. S. Hoare: In the first place, the special responsibilities will appear in the Bill itself. The Instrument of Instructions will merely be an additional guarantee.

Mr. Churchill: But those which are in the Instrument of Instructions can be varied by a simple resolution, and that is the most serious flaw in the right hon. Gentleman's elaborate scheme.

Sir. S. Hoare: I am sorry to interrupt the right hon. Gentleman again, but this is very important. The special responsibilities of which he is speaking will be in the Act itself and they will have statutory authority, in every important case, anyhow.

Mr. Churchill: I am glad of that, but I say that the Constitution itself, the bringing into power of the Federal Constitution, does not depend upon a Bill. That is to be brought into operation by a simple resolution. I should like to ask my right hon. Friend who is it, what force is it, which really welcomes the Constitution he has put forward. The Indian Congress denounce it in unmeasured terms. Indian Liberals say they will use it only as a tool to extort further favours. As to the Indian Princes, you have great doubt whether you can coax, cajole, persuade or coerce even half of them to come in. I very much doubt whether any Conservative Government could be formed which would endorse such a Constitution. The Socialist party, as the official Opposition, have shown by their Amendment that they will only take this Constitution, which you are regarding as a most audacious adventure, as a starting-point for a further departure. Nowhere, here or in India, is it a national policy, or accepted as a national settlement.

I must draw the attention of the House to the insidious way in which this Federal scheme is being brought into operation. It is to lie in the Constitution Act and to be brought into operation by resolution. There is no date assigned on which it is to be brought in and the right hon. Gentleman the Secretary of State gave a very naive reason why no date should be assigned. He said to the Round Table Conference at the end of the year:

> The machinery of the Constitution would be of a complicated nature, and Parliament, if it were confronted with a definite date, might be much more cautious in the delay and the provisions of caution that it might demand than it would be without a date.

That shows what the right hon. Gentleman thinks of us. It is as if you were to say: "The poor silly Members will not worry about it so long as there is no date, because they will say that it will not happen for some time; but if there is a date then they will boggle about it and make a lot of awkward objections." Then, the Federal Constituion will dominate Indian affairs, and to bring it into operation and at the same time to attack the safeguards will be the desire and the effort of all classes of Indians. This pressure will continue and when there is a Socialist Government in power, as there may be some day, how easy it will be to remove the safeguards which stand in the way. How easy it will be to sweep away or to slur over the conditions which you claim should be established in the setting up, say, of your Federal Bank or in other provisions of that kind.

Where will the Conservative party be then? Where will it stand then? It will not be the Government, but will it be the Opposition? It will have conceded every single principle, and stripped itself of the protection of constitutional procedure when these violent changes are to be brought into play. I can anticipate the speeches that will be made by a Labour Secretary of State in some future Parliament. Mr. Wedgwood Benn or some other able gentleman will say: "We are bringing the Federal Constitution into operation now. True, all the conditions have not been complied with, but this is a policy, in principle agreed between all parties. This is a policy which a Parliament containing an overwhelming Conservative majority approved, and we are only carrying it into effect with some minor alterations in detail. There is no serious opposition to this policy." Then you will find, in resisting that process, which can be achieved by a single simple Resolution of both Houses, that either it will have to go through and that this vast edifice can be set up without proper precautions or conditions, or else you will have to throw a burden upon the House of Lords which, in its present unreformed condition, I think would be grossly unfair and extremely unwise.

Since the year 1927, when the Simon Commission was first appointed, all India has been agitated by constitutional change. There has been no breathing space. I was hoping that the Government would find it possible to take some decisions which would give, at any rate for a spell, a pause to constitutional agitation in India. Surely the administrative apparatus, which in India is 20 times more powerful and more important to the people than these political and constitutional changes, should be given a chance to work. Surely we ought not to complicate the already hazardous departures which are proposed by the Simon Report by vague, hypothetical, and much larger departures for which the conditions have not yet been established. Surely Parliament should have the manhood to say, "We will give what we can give now, freely and boldly. We will not promise to go further until we see that the results of giving all that we now can give have been in practice." Surely that is a faithful, a sensible, and reasonable policy for our country to pursue and for an Imperial Government to advise, instead of adding, on the top of all that is now proposed, this scheme, for which you admittedly have not got the conditions yet established, and which will continue to keep India in a ferment and in a turmoil until it has eventually been achieved or until it has finally been discarded.

I thank the House very much for having listened to my statement. I have trespassed, I fear, at undue length upon it, but I have only this to say at the end. It is a tragedy that the greatest gift which Britain has given to India was not the fight that India needed most. During the last 50 years the population of India has increased by 100,000,000. The prevention of wars and famines and the control of infanticide and pestilence by British rule have brought that enormous accession to mankind. It would have been far better if the exertions of our devoted men and women in the East could have emerged, not in a mere multiplication of teeming humanity upon the very lowest level of subsistence, but in a substantial raising of the standard of life and of labour of a smaller number. But that has not been within our power. The 100,000,000 are here. The 100,000,000 new human beings are here to greet the dawn, toil upon the plains, bow before the temples of inexorable gods. They are here. You cannot desert them, you cannot abandon them. They are as much our children as any children could be. They are actually in the world as the result of what this nation and this Parliament have done. It is impossible that you should leave them to be diminished by the hideous processes of diminution which keep the population of China in check. It is impossible that you should hand them over to the oppressor and to the spoiler, and disinterest yourselves in their fortunes. By every law of God or man Parliament is responsible for them, and never could we hold an honourable name among the nations if we pretended, by any sophistry of Liberal doctrine or constitutional theory, to cast away our responsibility, so vital and grave.

But here in our own island we have a very similar situation. Our population, too, has rapidly expanded. There are perhaps 15,000,000 more people here than could exist without our enormous external connections, without our export trade, which is now halved, without our shipping, which is so largely paralysed, without the income from our foreign investments, which is taxed to sustain our social services. I suppose some 2,000,000 or 3,000,000 people in this island get their livelihood from beneficial and honourable service interchanged between us and India. We have some 3,000,000 unemployed now, and this is no time for us to divest ourselves of rights and interests, which we have lawfully acquired, and to expose our population in the years that are to come to a steady, grinding contraction in the standards of their life. I pray that the people of Britain may be awakened to a sense of their danger and to a sense of their duty before it is too late.

INDIA (CONSTITUTIONAL REFORM)

April 10, 1933

House of Commons

I shall detain the House only for a very few minutes, but I should like to say, in answer to the very excellent and clever speech just delivered by my hon. Friend [Mr. Morrison], that we have heard this tale against voting very often. Time after time we have been told that there is no real issue, and that this is only a Resolution which commits us to the spirit of the Prime Minister's speech at the farewell Round Table Conference. Then we have been told: "Wait till you see the White Paper." We have also been told: "Wait till you see the Joint Select Committee." Now my hon. Friend says the real moment will come when the Bill is presented to the House. Meanwhile, things are not standing idle. The whole force of the Government here and in India is used to drive forward their policy. Meanwhile those who, in response to appeals for party loyalty and goodwill have abstained from voting, find themselves damnified when the Select Committee is to be set up, because we are told that only 45 voted and that the others who did not vote are a quantity about which indeed arguement may be entertained but upon which no serious or solid assertion may be made. I believe it would have been far better if everyone who had doubts about this question had entered a caveat by their votes, and then they would have been in a position to acquire such representation as would have enabled this Parliament to deal adequately with so very grave a matter.

My right hon. Friend the Secretary of State for India, has, in his gay and airy way, twitted me with imitating Mr. Gandhi in a policy of non-co-operation. I do not think the House will consider that that was altogether just, but, in so far as it is witty, it is not new wit, because I have seen it many times in the public prints that support the Administration. Is it true? Is it just? The co-operation which Mr. Gandhi refused was a co-operation in administering and working the law of the land; the co-operation which Members who have declined to serve on this Joint Select Committee have refused is a co-operation in making a new law about which they have great doubts, and which they are endeavouring to oppose. There is no sort of comparison between the two cases.

The hon. Member for Tewkesbury (Mr. Morrison) has told us that in view of the refusal of some of the pronounced opponents of the Government to sit on the Committee that, as the Government were not able to get impartiality, they have fallen back on knowledge. It was with the Committee before our eyes that we refused to serve upon it. There is no question of the Government saying: "We were going to be impartial, but as some hon. Members will not serve we must make a new Committee which will not aim at impartiality; we are relieved from our pledge of impartiality, and must set up a new committee," when the Committee was set up long before. That argument is not one which should weigh with hon. Members in the Division. I should like very much to have served on the Committee and should have regarded it as an honour to have taken part in the deliberations of a body which contains so many eminent and venerable figures. I would not have allowed any personal consideration or convenience to stand in the way. I do not even say that the representation which the Committee offers to the various groups and parties in the House is in itself unevenly balanced, provided that the Committee had not been swollen to inordinate proportions. Such figures as were discussed, and as have appeared, for the minority representation would not have been, in my opinion, unfair had the Committee been limited to 22; but even then the Government would have had an effective majority. The right hon. Gentleman is not satisfied with a little of the pudding. He wants the lot. He must overload; he must pile on.

There are four, shall I call them paid officials of the Government on the Committee compared with two opponents of the Measure; and, in addition, how many more? They have been detailed by various hon. Members this afternoon, five or six, or seven or eight Members, who in one way or another have committed themselves to this policy, who have been brought into the general swim and movement of Government business because they have been openly associating themselves with this policy. The Committee will not give any fair chance of procuring a reasoned reconsideration of the question of principle. It may make improvement in details; and of the very able Members who at the desire of some of my friends are on the Committee one represents for the first time, the great commercial interests of Lancashire. They will be able to develop those points, but the Committee as constituted gives no hope of altering the general decision of the Government to set up a Federal Government in India, or what we consider to be tantamount to an abdication of power at the Centre.

The hon. and gallant Member who moved the Amendment pointed out to the Government a very reasonable course which they could have adopted. They could have placed all the Members of the Government they have on their list associated with the Committee, on the same basis as the Indian Delegation which is to come over. That would have been more convenient in the practical working of Government business, and it would have had a further advantage. I do not know whether hon. Members have thought of the enormous difficulties which will arise in regard to the method of consultation with the Indian Delegation. Very dangerous questions of status may arise, questions as to whether they are placed in a derogatory position, and which might cause unnecessary ill-will. But if Ministers of the Crown took the same treatment and were placed in the same position, that danger and difficulty would be removed, and Ministers of the Crown would not be called upon to attend more than was required by the Committee or more than they desired themselves.

I have not often heard a Debate which has been so completely one-sided as this Debate. Apart from two speeches, no hon. Member except the Secretary of State has spoken in favour of this arrangement. I feel that we are being moved steadily nearer and nearer to the verge of an irrevocable decision. With extraordinary coolness and persistency the Government, month after month and year after year—I have been resisting this now for three years, since I severed myself from my right hon. Friend and his policy—have told us that this is not the time to vote. All of a sudden the time will come when the Government will say: "Here is the report of our impartial committee, a large majority are in favour of it. Look at the expectations which you have aroused in India. You cannot go back now. You have no other course but to go on." That is to deny the House the facilities of debate; it is to deny to the Select Committee the efficacious work which they could have done. I hope that even now the Government will indicate that efforts will be made to remodel the Committee more in accordance with the wishes of the House.

[Later, on the motion "That Five be the Quorum"] I beg to move, to leave out the word "Five," and to insert instead thereof the word "Eight."

I trust that the Government will accept this Amendment. According to the precedent of the first Joint Committee, out of seven Members of the House of Commons, the quorum was four, or rather more than half—that is to say, eight out of 14 in the Joint Committee. Now the Government propose that the quorum should be five out of 16 Members of the House of Commons, or less than one-third, and a similar proportion in the case of the whole Committee; that is to say, 22 Members could be absent from the Committee at one time, and the work could be carried on by only 10. This question has to be considered in relation to the undoubted packing of the Committee, to which the House has testified so powerfully to-day. This is one of those cases in which the Government have so large a majority that they can afford to contend with the Opposition in relays. Something of this kind was done, I think, by the recent Conservative Government, which had so large a majority that only one-third of their Members need be on duty at the same time. This matter, however, is one of very great importance. We have been told that these gentlemen who have been selected have special knowledge, and are capable of giving expert attention to the subject. If only 10 out of 32 need be there at a time listening to the evidence and attending to the discussions, undoubtedly what would happen would be that, when a clash arose, the Government would send out their signals, down would march their troop of Ministers and immediate personal retainers, and the position would be reestablished. Meanwhile the Committee is to be left to chatter as long as it likes so long as no menace to the policy that the Government have in view is to be envisaged. My right hon. Friend has a chance to rid himself of such an imputation by accepting my Amendment. I am certain it is a perfectly reasonable principle to say that at least half the Members have to be there if the Committee is to do business. That is all that I am asking for this House, and the other House will probably imitate our procedure in the matter.

FOREIGN POLICY AND GERMAN
REARMAMENT

April 13, 1933

House of Commons

I have heard, as everyone has of late years, a great deal of condemnation of the treaties of peace, of the Treaties of Versailles and of Trianon. I believe that that denunciation has been very much exaggerated, and in its effect harmful. These treaties, at any rate, were founded upon the strongest principle alive in the world today, the principle of nationalism, or, as President Wilson called it, self-determination. The principle of self-determination or of nationalism was applied to all the defeated Powers over the whole area of Middle and Eastern Europe. Europe today corresponds to its ethnological groupings as it has never corresponded before. You may think that nationalism has been excessively manifested in modern times. That may well be so. It may well be that it has a dangerous side, but we must not fail to recognize that it is the strongest force now at work.

I remember, many years ago, hearing the late Mr. Tim Healy reply to a question that he put to himself, "What is nationalism?" and he said, "Something that men will die for." There is the foundation upon which we must examine the state of Europe and by which we should be guided in picking our way through its very serious dangers. Of course, in applying this principle of nationalism to the defeated States after the War it was inevitable that mistakes and some injustices should occur. There are places where the populations are inextricably intermingled. There are some countries where an island of one race is surrounded by an area inhabited by another. There were all kinds of anomalies, and it would have defied the wit of men to make an absolutely perfect solution. In fact, no complete solution on ethnographical lines would have been possible unless you had done what was done in the case of Greece and Turkey—that is, the physical disentangling of the population, the sending of the Turks back to Turkey and of the Greeks back to Greece—a practical impossibility.

I recognize the anomalies and I recognize the injustices, but they are only a tiny proportion of the great work of consolidation and appeasement which has been achieved and is represented by the Treaties that ended the War. The nationalities and races of which Europe is composed have never rested so securely in their beds in accordance with their heart's desire. It would be a blessed thing if we could mitigate these anomalies and grievances, but we can only do that if and when there has been established a strong confidence that the Treaties themselves are not going to be deranged. So long as the Treaties are in any way challenged as a whole it will be impossible to procure a patient consideration for the redress of the anomalies. The more you wish to remove the anomalies and grievances the more you should emphasize respect for the Treaties. It should be the first rule of British foreign policy to emphasize respect for these great Treaties, and to make those nations whose national existence depends upon and arises from the Treaties feel that no challenge is leveled at their security. Instead of that, for a good many years a lot of vague and general abuse has been leveled at the Treaties with the result that these powerful States, comprising enormous numbers of citizens—the Little Entente and Poland together represent 80,000,000 strongly armed—have felt that their position has been challenged and endangered by the movement to alter the Treaties. In consequence, you do not get the consideration which in other circumstances you might get for the undoubted improvements which are required in various directions.

The Prime Minister last year, in a speech at Geneva, used a very striking phrase when he described Europe as a house inhabited by ghosts. That is to misinterpret the situation. Europe is a house inhabited by fierce, strong, living entities. Poland is not a ghost: Poland is a reincarnation. I think it a wonderful thing that Polish unity should have re-emerged from long hideous eclipse and bondage, when the Poles were divided between three empires and made to fight one another in all the wars that took place. I rejoice that Poland has been reconstituted. I cannot think of any event arising out of the Great War which can be considered to be a more thoroughly righteous result of the struggle than the reunion of this people, who have preserved their national soul through all the years of oppression and division and whose reconstitution of their nationhood is one of the most striking facts in European history. Do not let us be led, because there are many aspects of Polish policy that we do not like or agree with, into dwelling upon the small points of disagreement, and forget what a very great work has been achieved, a work of liberation and of justice, in the reconstitution of Poland. I trust she will live long to enjoy the freedom of the lands which belong to her, a freedom which was gained by the swords of the victorious Allies.

We may look elsewhere. There is Bohemia, the land of Good King Wenceslas, which has emerged with its own identity re-established. There are the small countries on the Baltic, all holding tenaciously to their principles of nationhood. There are all those countries from the Baltic to the Black Sea, small individually compared to the greatest Powers, but comprising an enormous proportion of the European family. All these countries are armed and determined to defend the lands of their fathers and their new-gained independence, and it is most unwise to pursue any foreign policy which does not take account of these facts, which are not, as I have said, ghosts or memories of the past, but the living forces with which we have to cope at the present time.

New discord has arisen in Europe of late years from the fact that Germany is not satisfied with the result of the late War. I have indicated several times that Germany got off lightly after the Great War. I know that that is not always a fashionable opinion, but the facts repudiate the idea that a Carthaginian peace was in fact imposed upon Germany. No division was made of the great masses of the German people. No portion of Germany inhabited by Germans was detached, except where there was the difficulty of disentangling the population of the Silesian border. No attempt was made to divide Germany as between the northern and southern portions, which might well have tempted the conquerors at that time. No State was carved out of Germany. She underwent no serious territorial loss, except the loss of Alsace and Lorraine, which she herself had seized only fifty years before. The great mass of the Germans remained united after all that Europe had passed through, and they are more vehemently united today than ever before. We know what has happened to the War indemnity. They have lost their colonies, it is true; but these were not of great value to them, and it is not at all true for them to say that these colonies could ever have afforded any appreciable outlet for their working-class population. They are not suited for white colonization.

On the other hand, when we think of what would have happened to us, to France or to Belgium, if the Germans had won; when we think of the terms which they exacted from Rumania, or of the terms of the Treaty of Brest-Litovsk; when we remember that up to a few months from the end of the War German authorities refused to consider that Belgium could ever be liberated, but said that she should be kept in thrall for military purposes forever, I do not think that we need break our hearts in deploring the treatment that Germany is receiving now. Germany is not satisfied; but no concession which has been made has produced any very marked appearance of gratitude. Once it has been conceded it has seemed less valuable than when it was demanded. Many people would like to see, or would have liked to see a little while ago—I was one of them—the question of the Polish Corridor adjusted. For my part, I should certainly have considered that to be one of the greatest practical objectives of European peace-seeking diplomacy. There again, however, we must think of the rights of Poland. The Polish Corridor is inhabited almost entirely by Poles, and it was Polish territory before the Partition of 1772. This is a matter which in quiet times, with increasing goodwill, Europe should have set itself—and might well some day set itself—to solve.

The question of the Germans regaining their colonies is being pressed by them, and the question of their rearmament—which, personally, I consider more grave than any other question—is being brought to the front. They demand equality in weapons and equality in the organization of armies and fleets, and we have been told, "You cannot keep so great a nation in an inferior position. What others have they must have." I have never agreed. I think it is a most dangerous demand to make. Nothing in life is eternal, of course, but as surely as Germany acquires full military equality with her neighbours while her own grievances are still unredressed and while she is in the temper which we have unhappily seen, so surely should we see ourselves within a measurable distance of the renewal of general European war. If this process of rearmament or of equalization were actually to take place while the present conditions prevail, undoubtedly the nations who are neighbors of Germany and who fear Germany would ask themselves whether they would be well advised to postpone coming to a conclusion until the process of German rearmament has been completed. It is extremely dangerous for people to talk lightly about German rearmament and say that, if the Germans choose to do it, no one can stop them. I am very doubtful if Germany would rearm in defiance of the Treaty if there were a solidarity of European and world opinion that the Treaty could only be altered by discussion, and could not be altered by a violent one-sided breach. I, therefore, do not subscribe to the doctrine that we should throw up our hands and recognize the fact that Germany is going to be armed up to an equality with the neighbouring States in any period which we can immediately foresee. There may be other periods, but certainly we ought not to admit it at the moment.

I am not going to use harsh words about Germany and about the conditions there. I am addressing myself to the problem in a severely practical manner. Nevertheless, one of the things which we were told after the Great War would be a security for us was that Germany would be a democracy with Parliamentary institutions. All that has been swept away. You have dictatorship—most grim dictatorship. You have militarism and appeals to every form of fighting spirit, from the reintroduction of duelling in the colleges to the Minister of Education advising the plentiful use of the cane in the elementary schools. You have these martial or pugnacious manifestations, and also this persecution of the Jews, of which so many Members have spoken and which distresses everyone who feels that men and women have a right to live in the world where they are born, and have a right to pursue a livelihood which has hitherto been guaranteed them under the public laws of the land of their birth.

When I read of what is going on in Germany—I feel in complete agreement in this matter with hon. Gentlemen opposite—when I see the temper displayed there and read the speeches of the leading Ministers, I cannot help rejoicing that the Germans have not got the heavy cannon, the thousands of military aeroplanes and the tanks of various sizes for which they have been pressing in order that their status may be equal to that of other countries. The House has not always done justice to Sir Austen Chamberlain's conduct of foreign affairs. He was very much scolded and condemned at the close of the late Conservative Administration, but the Locarno Treaty and all that followed from it was a model of skillful peace-seeking diplomacy. Although other difficulties have come in other times, I cannot see that the handling of the Foreign Office since he left it should fill him with any particular feeling of humiliation.

I will leave Germany and turn to France. France is not only the sole great surviving democracy in Europe; she is also the strongest military Power, I am glad to say, and she is the head of a system of states and nations. France is the guarantor and protector of all these small States I mentioned a few moments ago; the whole crescent which runs right round from Belgium to Yugoslavia and Rumania. They all look to France. When any step is taken, by England or any other Power, to try to weaken the diplomatic or military security of France, all these small nations tremble with fear and anger. They fear that the central protective force will be weakened, and that then they will be at the mercy of the great Teutonic Power.

We should be very careful not to mix ourselves up too deeply in this European scene. Our desire to promote peace must not lead us to press our views beyond a point where those views are no longer compatible with the actual facts of the situation. It may be very virtuous and high-minded to press disarmament upon nations situated as these nations are, but if not done in the right way and in due season, and in moderation, with regard for other people's points of view as well as our own sentiments, it may bring war nearer rather than peace, and may lead us to be suspected and hated instead of being honoured and thanked as we should wish to be. Even more vain is it for the United States to press indiscriminate disarmament upon the European States, unless, of course the United States is prepared to say that those nations which take her advice will receive her aid if trouble should arise, and is prepared to envisage the prospect of sending millions of soldiers again across the ocean.

Our country has a very important part to play in Europe, but it is not so large a part as we have been attempting to play, and I advocate for us in future a more modest role than many of our peace-preservers and peace-lovers have sought to impose upon us. I remember when I was very young, before I came into this House, a denunciation by Dr. Spence Watson of what he called "the filthy Tory rag of a spirited foreign policy." In those days the feelings of the forerunners of those who sit opposite were directed against jingo policies of bombast and Palmerstonian vigour. But you may have another kind of spirited foreign policy which may also lead you into danger, and that is a policy in which, without duly considering the circumstances in which others are placed, you endeavour to press upon them disarmament or to weaken their security, perhaps with a view to gaining a measure of approbation from good people here who are not aware of the dangerous state of affairs in Europe. There you could have a peace policy which may be too spirited.

It is easy to talk about the moral leadership of Europe. That great prize still stands before the statesmen of all countries, but it is not to be achieved merely by making speeches of unexceptionable sentiments. If it is to be won by any nation it will only be by an immense amount of wise restraint and timely, discreet action which, over a period of years, has created a situation where speeches are not merely fine exhortations but record the unity and conciliation which have been achieved. There is the moral leadership of Europe. It is not to be won by such easy methods as merely making speeches which will arouse the applause of every good-hearted person in this country.

The Prime Minister spread on the table at Geneva a few weeks ago a vast plan for bringing all armaments down and consequently improving relatively the military strength of Germany. The right hon. Gentleman made an extraordinary admission. He said he had not gone through the figures himself. But he took responsibility for them. It was a very grave responsibility. This proposal, which was put forward with the highest motives and with many good reasons behind it, touches all the most delicate and dangerous spots in Europe. If ever there was a document upon which its author ought to have consumed his personal thought and energy, it was this scheme of disarmament, prescribing for every country, great and small, what its military, air and naval forces should be. I have not heard it said with any assurance by the Government that the Committee of Imperial Defence were consulted upon these figures. I have not heard it said that the chiefs of the Fighting Services here have been consulted upon these figures. Unknown hands have prepared these figures, and the author of the document has admitted to us that he had not himself mastered them, either in scope or in detail.

Here in this country we know that no dark designs are harbored by our Government against the peace or well-being of any country. There may be mistakes, there may be muddles; but no dark designs are harboured by any British Prime Minister or Foreign Secretary. He could not live under the conditions of British Cabinet Government if it were otherwise. But foreign countries do not always attribute to us this innocence. I have been reading some of the comments in foreign newspapers lately, and in a Liberal newspaper of good standing in Switzerland I was surprised to see the interpretation that was put upon the proposals innocently and precipitately put forward by the Prime Minister. In that paper all is calculated out and worked up to give the impression that the Prime Minister was deliberately indulging pro-German sympathies and deliberately endeavouring to weaken France, and, seeing the detail with which the argument is set out, one could not help being impressed.

But that is not by any means the whole story. No sooner had this tremendous step been taken of prescribing to every country what its defenses should be than the Prime Minister left Geneva for Rome. He arrived in Rome one day, and found himself with a new foreign policy the next. Signor Mussolini's proposal for a Four-Power pact or agreement has many arguments in its favor. I liked very much the language used by my right hon. Friend about the importance of the Great Powers who would have to bear the brunt of any serious conflict establishing good relations between themselves and being in close touch with each other, if only to enable them to spread those satisfactory relations wider among the larger number of smaller Powers. As I say, there are many arguments in favor of co-operation by the four Powers, but one does not always need to advertise the fact so very vigourously. There are many Cabinets in which an inner Cabinet grows up without any of the other members being offended, but it is only under the stress of war that we took the step of forming a War Cabinet, which definitely distinguished between those members and other persons in the Government. So it is in this European field.

As I say, there are arguments in favor of this policy, but at the present time there are two serious arguments against it. The first is this: Of all times, this was not the time to make such a proposal with any prospect of success, and, secondly, nothing could be more unsuitable than to combine this Four-Power Pact with the disarmament proposals which had been laid before Geneva only two days before. By those proposals France was asked to reduce her army from 700,000 to 400,000; and at the same moment that this very serious demand was made upon her she was also invited, as the result of the Rome Conference, to take her seat at a table of four, with Herr Hitler and Signor Mussolini, the two Dictators, and with the Prime Minister, about whom France, of course, still has memories.

Putting this double pressure upon France at this moment, both from Geneva and from Rome, was calculated to court defeat for either or both of the schemes which the Government successively and, ultimately, simultaneously advanced. Such a procedure was to doom them to failure beforehand. It could not fail to aggravate suspicion, and not only to weaken the influence of our country, but to involve us more deeply in the Continental situation; for you cannot take the lead in this remarkable manner, presenting these successive policies to Europe with such rapidity, without being entangled to a very large extent as a consequence of the proposals that you have made.

Plans for disarmament so comprehensive should not have been put forward by the Prime Minister without his having studied them most carefully with all the highest technical experts here, nor should the proposals with which Signor Mussolini confronted the Prime Minister and the Foreign Secretary when they arrived in Rome have been even entertained on the spur of the moment. There may be all sorts of proposals put forward, with great ability, by a powerful personality which sound very well and look attractive at first sight, but in matters affecting the peace of so many countries and the lives and well-being of millions of men what harm would there have been in waiting till the Cabinet Office could have examined it in all its aspects? They would not have taken very long to point out what the inevitable reactions would be. It astounds me that the Prime Minister, who has had such considerable opportunities of acquainting himself with European affairs, should not have mastered the real facts of the European situation or the articulation of the different countries which compose the system. At any rate, the results have been quickly apparent. France, confronted with this double, simultaneous demand, was deeply disturbed. But the French have learned to attune their language to the standard forms of phraseology which are highly in favour throughout the English-speaking world. They never on any account make abrupt or sharp contradictions of any proposals that are put to them. They say, "Most interesting, most helpful, and a great move forward," but they leave to their allies, the small nations—and not so small either—to say what France feels and thinks, but realizes had better be said by others.

What happened? Within one single week, if I may judge from the public prints, Poland, Czechoslovakia and Rumania at once made their appearance, and every one of them made in concert—no doubt with prearrangement—statements in which the danger of war was brutally referred to. Such a warning must never be disregarded. It is quite true that such warnings do not now bear the significance they would have borne in the days before the great struggle. But at the same time the statements made on behalf of these three Powers do constitute a definite and grave warning of the dangers of pursuing this policy. Thus all the small Powers, including the Scandinavian Powers, are making common cause in the League of Nations in order to defend themselves against what they think is a threatened overlordship of the four Great Powers. What happens then? The Pact or Agreement so incontinently accepted has to be amended, has to be modified to fit the view of the small nations in the League. It has to be modified again to meet special claims. It has to be modified again to meet the requirements of France, and it very soon reaches the point where it loses the adherence of Germany. It is no good saying it is merely "much ado about nothing." That is not so. Harm has been done, disturbance has been created, suspicion has been spread, and English influence has lost a measure of its virtue and added a measure to its responsibility. There may be days when all our influence will be required to help to keep the peace of Europe, and when all our detachment will be required to enable us to keep clear of being involved in war.

I will say one word about the Prime Minister's visit to the United States of America. It will be only a word. I do not understand how any Prime Minister could have failed to take up, in the spirit of the highest cordiality, the invitation tendered him in such striking terms by the President of the United States [President Roosevelt] at the beginning of his tenure of power, and I am very glad indeed that the Government have decided to send the Prime Minister upon this mission, described and limited as it has been. For my part, I should not like to have spoken in this Debate in a critical sense without wishing the Prime Minister, who is not here now, a pleasant holiday and an agreeable conversation, a fruitful result for his mission and a safe return to this country.

ENGLAND

April 24, 1933

Royal Society of St. George, London

I am a great admirer of the Scots. I am quite friendly with the Welsh, especially one of them. I must confess to some sentiment about Old Ireland, in spite of the ugly mask she tries to wear. But this is not their night. On this one night in the whole year we are allowed to use a forgotten, almost a forbidden word. We are allowed to mention the name of our own country, to speak of ourselves as 'Englishmen,' and we may even raise the slogan "St. George for Merrie England."

We must be careful, however. You see these microphones? They have been placed on our tables by the British Broadcasting Corporation. Think of the risk these eminent men are running. We can almost see them in our mind's eye, gathered together in that very expensive building, with the questionable statues on its front. We can picture Sir John Reith, with the perspiration mantling on his lofty brow, with his hand on the control switch, wondering, as I utter every word, whether it will not be his duty to protect his innocent subscribers from some irreverent thing I might say about Mr. Gandhi, or about the Bolsheviks, or even about our peripatetic Prime Minister. But let me reassure him. I have much more serious topics to discuss. I have to speak to you about St. George and the Dragon. I have been wondering what would happen if that legend were repeated under modern conditions.

St. George would arrive in Cappadocia, accompanied not by a horse, but by a secretariat. He would be armed not with a lance, but with several flexible formulas. He would, of course, be welcomed by the local branch of the League of Nations Union. He would propose a conference with the dragon—a Round Table Conference, no doubt—that would be more convenient for the dragon's tail. He would make a trade agreement with the dragon. He would lend the dragon a lot of money for the Cappadocian taxpayers. The maiden's release would be referred to Geneva, the dragon reserving all his rights meanwhile. Finally St. George would be photographed with the dragon (inset—the maiden).

There are a few things I will venture to mention about England. They are spoken in no invidious sense. Here it would hardly occur to anyone that the banks would close their doors against their depositors. Here no one questions the fairness of the courts of law and justice. Here no one thinks of persecuting a man on account of his religion or his race. Here everyone, except the criminals, looks on the policeman as the friend and servant of the public. Here we provide for poverty and misfortune with more compassion, in spite of all our burdens, than any other country. Here we can assert the rights of the citizen against the State, or criticize the Government of the day, without failing in our duty to the Crown or in our loyalty to the King. This ancient, mighty London in which we are gathered is still the financial center of the world. From the Admiralty building, half a mile away, orders can be sent to a Fleet which, though much smaller than it used to be, or than it ought to be, is still unsurpassed on the seas.

More than 80 per cent. of the British casualties of the Great War were English. More than 80 per cent. of the taxation is paid by the English taxpayers. We are entitled to mention these facts, and to draw authority and courage from them.

Historians have noticed, all down the centuries, one pecularity of the English people which has cost them dear. We have always thrown away after a victory the greater part of the advantages we gained in the struggle. The worst difficulties from which we suffer do not come from without. They come from within. They do not come from the cottages of the wage-earners. They come from a peculiar type of brainy people always found in our country, who, if they add something to its culture, take much from its strength.

Our difficulties come from the mood of unwarrantable self-abasement into which we have been cast by a powerful section of our own intellectuals. They come from the acceptance of defeatist doctrines by a large proportion of our politicians. But what have they to offer but a vague internationalism, a squalid materialism, and the promise of impossible Utopias?

Nothing can save England if she will not save herself. If we lose faith in ourselves, in our capacity to guide and govern, if we lose our will to live, then indeed our story is told. If, while on all sides foreign nations are every day asserting a more agressive and militant nationalism by arms and trade, we remain paralyzed by our own theoretical doctrines or plunged into the stupour of after-war exhaustion, then indeed all that the croakers predict will come true, and our ruin will be swift and final. Stripped of her Empire in the Orient, deprived of the sovereignty of the seas, loaded with debt and taxation, her commerce and carrying trade shut out by foreign tariffs and quotas, England would sink to the level of a fifth-rate Power, and nothing would remain of all her glories except a population much larger than this island can support.

Why should we break up the solid structure of British power, founded upon so much health, kindliness and freedom, for dreams which may some day come true, but are now only dreams, and some of them nightmares? We ought, as a nation and Empire, to weather any storm that blows at least as well as any other existing system of human government. We are at once more experienced and more truly united than any people in the world. It may well be that the most glorious chapters of our history are yet to be written. Indeed, the very problems and dangers that encompass us and our country ought to make English men and women of this generation glad to be here at such a time. We ought to rejoice at the responsibilities with which destiny has honoured us, and be proud that we are guardians of our country in an age when her life is at stake.

INDIA (REPLY TO MR. BALDWIN)

April 30, 1933

Westerham, Kent

Churchill made this statement to the Press Association at Westerham in reply to a speech made by Stanley Baldwin several days before at Worcester.

Mr. Baldwin accuses those who do not accept this India policy of trying to split the Conservative Party with the immediate result that the Socialists may come into office after the next election and that eventually we shall be plunged either into Bolshevism or Fascism. This is a grievous charge. But who is responsible for splitting the Conservative Party?

Surely the whole burden rests upon a leader who forces upon his party a policy on which it has never been consulted and which runs directly counter to the deepest instincts and traditions. History has always assigned the responsibility for splitting a party to the leader who proposes the departure.

Thus the reproach of splitting the Conservative Party in 1846 has always been judged to rest with Sir Robert Peel, and not with Mr. Disraeli and Lord George Bentinck. And the responsibility for splitting the Liberal Party in 1886 has always been borne by Mr. Gladstone, and not by Mr. Chamberlain and Lord Hartington.

Whether Sir Robert Peel was right or wrong about the Corn Laws or Mr. Gladstone about Home Rule for Ireland is still argued. But nothing can relieve the leader who initiates a fundamental change from all the consequences which result from it. Those who are pressing forward a policy which will not be accepted by the great mass of their party are the splitters, those who drive the wedge into the oak are accountable, and not the oak, which splits in accordance with its natural grain.

Mr. Baldwin also repeated at Worcester Sir Samuel Hoare's offence of claiming the Civil servants of India, especially the younger members, as being wholeheartedly in favour of the White Paper. It is unusual for Ministers to quote Civil servants as their supporters in political controversy. The Indian Civil Service is under the orders of his Majesty's Government. Their advancement and promotion rests on the authority of the Secretary of State. The Viceroy and all the Governors act upon the direction of the Secretary of State.

During the last four years Mr. MacDonald has been Prime Minister. He and Mr. Baldwin either in office or in so-called Opposition, have stood sponsors for the present Indian policy. Every official who has accepted appointment or preferment in India has been chosen on the basis that this policy would be carried forward and have accepted their offices in that knowledge.

Apart from this it is their bounden duty to obey the orders they receive. What would be said if high officials, or still more younger Civil servants, in India began to express individual opinions hostile to the main policy of the Government of the day? In these circumstances it is improper to cite these officials as supporters of the White Paper. Their lips are sealed; they can neither speak nor answer.

In fact, the statement is not true. A very large proportion of the officials, civil and military, in India who are carrying forward the Government's policy are doing so with serious misgivings and because, since there appeared to be no resistance to it by the Conservative Party in Great Britain, the impending disaster seems inevitable.

Here we must note the provision made to enable them to retire from their appointments on pension at discretion. Surely this is a strange manifestation of their confidence in the success of what is now proposed. The British mercantile community in India, also feeling itself without support at home, has to make the best terms it can on the spot. This applies forcibly to the Indian Princes, upon whom most unusual and peculiar pressures are being exercised.

What is the use of Mr. Baldwin citing Lord Willingdon? He was appointed by Mr. Ramsay MacDonald and Mr. Wedgwood Benn to carry through the policy of the Round Table Conference. It is true that by firm administration of the law wholly out of keeping with the policy of Lord Irwin and the Socialist Government, and by drastic repressive ordinances completely contrary to the policy of responsible self-government, he has produced an almost instantaneous improvement in the whole Indian situation. This achievement is now actually used by his superiors in justification of a policy which would make its repetition impossible.

On a minor point Mr. Baldwin inadvertently misstates the facts. He says that when the first Round Table Conference was set up Mr. MacDonald invited representatives of the Conservative and Liberal Parties to meet with the Socialists and see how far a common path could be trodden. In fact, Mr. MacDonald was very reluctant to allow either Conservative or Liberal representatives to sit upon the Round Table Conference, and it was only after the Conservatives and Liberals, who then commanded a majority in Parliament, indicated that they thought it necessary to be there that he consented.

I have said that Mr. Baldwin's Worcester speech is grievous. It is also grave. It shows once more that the leading men in the present Government, and Mr. Baldwin above all, are resolved to force the India abdication policy through at all costs and by every use of party machinery at their disposal. Those who feel that it will strike the death-knell of the greatness of the British Empire and will inflict vital injury upon the economic life of the English working classes are bound to act in accordance with their convictions. This they will certainly do.

It does not follow that their success would mean a split in the Conservative party. It might conceivably convince its present leaders thay they have no right to pervert the power and abuse the trust which have been accorded them, and may remind them that they have a representative capacity and a responsibility to those in whose name they rule.

INDIA (CONSTITUTIONAL REFORM)

May 12, 1933

*Lancashire and India Trade Preservation Society Demonstration,
Free Trade Hall, Manchester*

[Extract] . . . No one would have expected that the National Government would use the power which came to them through a great financial and political upheaval to pursue the very same Indian policy upon which the discredited Socialist Government had been engaged. Such a proceeding is an abuse of the election appeals made to Conservatives and to the nation to sink all other issues for the sake of national solvency. But now we find that the same small group of men—Mr. Baldwin, Lord Irwin, Lord Reading, Lord Lothian, and the Editor of *The Times*, with Mr. MacDonald apparently as a somewhat bewildered spectator—are driving forward the Round Table policy inherited from the Socialist Government with all the powerful machinery of the Conservative Party. Yesterday in London a far-reaching decision was taken by the women's branch of the National Union of Conservative Associations, representing the opinion of the whole Conservative Party throughout England. In view of that decision, taken against the wishes and advice of the Conservative leaders, and in spite of the strenuous use of the immense influence and sincere loyalty which they command, the question of Indian constitutional reform entered upon a new phase. We are entitled to ask our leaders to respect the convictions of the mass of the party. I earnestly hope that our leaders will not treat the wishes and feelings of their followers with neglect and indifference. Still less ought they to use the machinery of party whips and party funds on a fundamental issue in defiance of the lawfully expressed will of those to whom that machinery and those resources belong.

The Indian Constitution in the White Paper is unworkable, it will not bring peace to India, it will open an intense period of strife. It is not accepted by any body of Indian opinion, moderate or extreme, except as a means for carrying on a fierce seditious agitation. The Indian Congress Party is a thoroughly disloyal organization, whose aim is to drive us out of the country. Yet they are the only party which can work such a Constitution. The hideous principle of dyarchy is now to be introduced into the supreme government of India. A bitter constitutional struggle will be set on foot. On the one hand will be the Indian politicians with all the far-reaching powers now to be placed at their disposal and with the control of most of the great departments of State. On the other will be the Viceroy, with all his safeguards, his powers of veto, and the bayonets of the British Empire at his back. It will be exactly the same kind of struggle as was fought out in England in the seventeenth century between Parliament and the Crown. Each side will have enormous powers and rights, and their conflict, when they are pitted one against the other, will throw India into interminable tumult and light up again those ferocious fires of racial and religious hatred from which India has been rescued by British rule.

At the very centre of this struggle will be the trade of Lancashire. The new Indian Parliaments will attack British trade by a dozen means. They will give their contracts to foreign nations out of spite to us. They will harass British firms trading in India in a score of ways. The cotton trade, upon the existence of which Lancashire wage earners and employers depend, will under the White Paper become a mere pawn in a struggle for more power. The present generation may live to see a very great restriction of our trade with the Far East. Can it now afford to jeopardize our trade with India?

I contest Mr. Baldwin's claim that the Indian Civil Service is in favour of the reforms. The opinion of the Anglo-Indian community at home, of which the Anglo--Indian community in India is only a projection and an offshoot, view what is being done with the greatest alarm.

SHOP ASSISTANTS' HOURS

May 18, 1933

*Early Closing Association Meeting,
Hotel Metropole, London*

[Extract] . . . The public, instead of sprawling their hours of shopping over the greater part of the 24, have now concentrated them.

I think the Government might well be right in depreciating at this time any attempt to regulate more precisely the hours of shop assistants. I have always urged the closing of shops in accordance with the hours agreed upon. My opponents said there is no need to close the shops if the hours of the assistants are regulated. That is a wholly fallacious view and a dangerous view. To see whether shops are open or shut is pretty easy, but to ascertain whether assistants are being employed over their time or not would involve very great expenditure and multiplication of officials. When people complain to me that they cannot buy chocolates or cigarettes after a certain time, I always reply that if they cannot get their goods within the ample hours shops are open they had better practice self denial on themselves.

INDIA (CONSTITUTIONAL REFORM)

May 18, 1933

*Primrose League Meeting,
Putney*

[Extract] . . . Nations in their perlexity leaned upon England and found here a strong prop represented by a National Government. I hope the Government will not undo the good they have done by unwise action in other directions.

Sir Samuel Hoare reminds me of a cow which gives a very good pail of milk and then kicks it over. For the moment there is an enormous improvement of the administration of India, and I take some pride in the fact that I have always said it was quite easy to restore order in India without bloodshed and without the use of British troops, simply by maintaining the law firmly and impartially.

Mr. Baldwin has very strongly denied on several occasions that the proposals in the White Paper are a legacy from the Socialist Government. The first Round Table Conference was the authority which started the plan, and we have had a very revealing explanation from Mr. Malcolm MacDonald, the Prime Minister's son, who was attached to that conference as Cabinet Secretary. Mr. Malcolm MacDonald made a perfectly clear statement showing that the policy was foreseen, elaborated, and planned at Chequers in December, 1930, before the Conservative delegates had expressed their views at all. That was the policy subsequently adopted and embodied in the White Paper to-day.

There is a class of people who say, "We have pledged our word, and even if it means the ruin of India and distress in Lancashire and Britain, never mind, the Englishman's word is his bond." I do not admit for a moment that there is any pledge which prevents Parliament from now doing justice to the actual merits of the situation and giving the best solution to India and to Britain in the problems in which they are both involved. The real liberty which India enjoys is British justice, impartial administration, and security for peace and order. That liberty would be fatally destroyed if in any devolution of government we now make either the Hindus or the Mohammedans become in the ascendant and use class ratio and religious prejudice against the other.

The Simon Report and the Statutory Commission went very far—I think too far—but they are left far behind by this new landslide. They have sailed off in to this vague idea of creating a united State of India when in Europe they have never been able to reach an organism of that kind.

I am told that all the civil servants who are serving in India are in favour of this policy, but I do not believe that they are. I will give two reasons. First, the Government had to issue a statement that all civil servants under the new system would be able to retire at any time on the proportionate pension they had earned. That emergency exit offered them does not show that they are all frightfully enthusiastic about the new policy. (Laughter) Then again, only a few days ago, it was announced that this pension fund has been moved over to this country to meet the wishes of the contributors to that fund. That hardly argues the complete confidence in the new regime which one would imagine.

The Anglo-Indian community in India is only an offshoot of the great Anglo-Indian community in this country, and they know each other. I am sure that the Anglo-Indian community at home is entirely opposed to these new departures in the White Paper.

Never could we remain in India if we disinterested ourselves in the welfare of the Indian masses. I would rather see the British end their story in India, I would rather see our last battalion sail away home with clean consciences, our last official with clean hands, than that we should remain there to see the old Asiatic tyrannies resumed upon the helpless masses of those people while we remained nominally responsible without the power to save them.

INDIA (CONSTITUTIONAL REFORM)

May 23, 1933

Licensed Victuallers Protection Society Dinner,
Connaught Rooms, London

[Extract] . . . I admire your courage in including as your guests Lord Lloyd and myself. The election of 1931 was a great and loyal effort on the part of the masses of the people to vindicate the honour of Britian and restore her solvency. What the National Government has accomplished is an enjoyable contrast to the Socialist confusion that preceded it and its work deserves the respect of all parties in the State. At the same time it is more important that the conduct of our affairs should not lose that virility and force because of a pretence that all the people of this country were agreed when they are not. There ought to be a healthy antagonism in politics.

I believe that a large majority of the Conservative Party is feeling profound anxiety about Indian policy. I would not blame those who are pursuing it if they used only their own influence and their own powers of argument, but I challenge their action in presuming to use the party machinery, the Whips and the party funds, against the wish of almost every representative body of Conservatives throughout the country. There they go beyond the credentials which they hold. There they run the risk of abusing the trust confided in them.

AMERICAN WAR DEBT

June 13, 1933

House of Commons

I would like to express my sincere congratulations to my right hon. Friend the Chancellor of the Exchequer [Mr. Neville Chamberlain] and to His Majesty's Government as one who has laboured at intervals over many years in this very difficult controversial field on the splendid, albeit not final solution which they have found themselves in a position to announce this evening. I would add and it is the only other sentence I intend to utter, that I wish also to express my admiration for the great, wise, generous, comprehending, far-seeing words in which the President of the United States has given a message of peace and hope to all the nations.

INDIA (CONSTITUTIONAL REFORM)

June 25, 1933

Gloucester

We must not make India a party question. It would be disastrous if it were brought into British politics. Are we then to sit in silence and see this tremendous matter settled over our heads against our deepest convictions? Did non-party politics or national politics mean a complete suppression of the Conservative view?

We are told "But the Socialists will come into power. Settle India now lest a worse thing befall." But that argument logically would mean that there could be no Conservative policy on India or on any subject beyond what the Socialists would approve and continue. If that were true it would be better that Mr. Lansbury or Sir Stafford Cripps, or whoever is the Socialist leader, should be perpetual Prime Minister. Thus those who had the ultimate power would have the direct responsiblity. This sort of argument shows that the men behind the Indian White Paper have little confidence in the discussion of the merits of their scheme.

There will be a meeting of the Council of the National Union of Conservative Associations in London on Wednesday. At this meeting the Government does not dare to ask plainly and bluntly for approval of their Indian policy. A resolution has been put down by the Westmorland Association, claiming boldly approval for the Government's Indian policy. But the party managers made haste to "doctor" the resolution of the local association, until it meant nothing more than approval of remitting the Indian policy to the consideration of the Joint Committee of both Houses. Every one is in favour of that.

I voted for it in the House of Commons, and if the Committee had not been packed with an overwhelming majority of the partisans of the White Paper, I would gladly have served upon it. Neither in the House of Commons nor in any of the meetings of the National Union had the Government seen fit to ask for the approval of their followers even upon their Indian policy. Conservatives must not be misled by such tactics. They are all part of a deliberate plan to make the Conservative Party come along quietly till it had got so far that it could not turn back. From the beginning we have been assured that we were not committed by any of the proceedings of the Round Table Conference or by any new pronouncement. At every stage we were urged to wait for this, that, or the other. But side by side came the insidious propaganda, "after all the expectations that have been aroused in India you cannot go back on the work of the Round Table Conference."

And next week, if this colourless meaningless official resolution is unanimously carried, as no doubt it will be, if it is in order, the papers—especially *The Times*, the *News-Chronicle*, and the *Daily Herald*, a strangely, assorted trio—will immediately proclaim "Rout of the Tory Diehards. Indian Policy of the Government Decisively Approved."

Meanwhile all the time behind the scenes a small group of men in high positions who are the authors of the White Paper policy and are determined to carry Indian home rule, are driving it forward with all the immense machinery and resources at their disposal. While all the time the country is being soothed and lulled by assurances that they are quite uncommitted and that there is no need for them to express the grave anxieties they feel, every preparation is being made to carry the policy into effect.

A law has been passed empowering Indian Governors to prolong the local Legislatures pending constitutional change. Governors are appointed who are either ardent supporters of the scheme or who have taken office on that basis. To silence objections all Civil servants have been offered the right to retire at any time on proportionate pensions. The Princes are being subjected to enormous, subtle, and improper pressures. The contributors to the Indian military widows' and orphans' fund, who are also deeply alarmed, are callously told that if they like to bring their funds home they can do so, and have their pittances substantially reduced by the lower interest rates prevailing here. Plans are made—very properly in the circum-stances—to withdraw the fortress of Aden from the control of future Indian Govern-ments. Aden is to be saved from the wreck.

Can you wonder then that we feel grave anxiety? Can you wonder that the Conservative women delegates representing the whole country express their grave anxiety by an overwhelming majority? Is it wise for the Government to stifle such expressions of sincere and honest opinion? Would it not be wiser on the contrary to encourage the freest expression of opinion so that Ministers could know where they stand before they take their final decisions?

Anxieties are not lessened when they are borne in silence. Grim facts are not relieved by resolutions of confidence wrung from the loyalty for which the Conser-vative Party is justly famed. At any rate, I can assure you that those who are resisting this abdication of control in India will fight unwearied and undaunted however violent may be the pressures and however unfair may be the reproaches to which we shall be subjected.

Our position is plain and I will restate it. Every extension of Western election-eering systems in India will be accompanied by worse deterioration in the honesty and efficiency of Indian government. Further Indianization will ruin the great services without which India will fall back to the level of China and probably below it. If nevertheless you feel bound to make a further experiment in the Provinces on the lines of the Simon Report it will be all the more necessary meanwhile to keep Central Government in India strong, intact, and free from the vice of dyarchy. No federal union, no airy United States of India should be attempted until provincial units have been established and have proved themselves capable of showing loyalty to the Crown and of giving decent administration to the Indian masses.

Lastly the police and judiciary must not be handed over to Indian control now nor in any period that we can foresee. Certainly not until the hideous strife of races and religions in India has definitely ended. We cannot read the future. But this I believe is what the British nation will in the end decide.

INDIA (CONSERVATIVE POLICY)

June 28, 1933

Conservative Party Central Council Meeting,
Friends' House, London

Churchill's attempt to reverse official policy was defeated 838 votes to 316.

There was one thing which Mr. Baldwin said in his speech with which I most cordially agree, and it certainly has served as a guide to us in our discussion. He reminded us that we were meeting together in the Friends' House, and it is as friends and allies—I might almost say comrades if that noble word had not been appropriated by the Socialists—that we have met to fight out quite rigorously between ourselves this grave issue. But in our fight we must always bear in mind that after this is over and settled—as I believe it will be if we hold firmly each to his convictions—after it is over we shall have to stand in line together again.

I have been opposed to this Round Table policy since the very beginning three years ago, and my right honourable friend will remember I had to separate from his councils greatly to my disadvantage. (Laughter) This enormous gathering, representing the forces of the Conservative Party, all these and the feelings expressed in our discussions, show quite clearly the enormous progress we have made in putting the other side.

You must remember the enormous power of the Government. There they are with all the influence, social and political, which they can exert, with the stimulus of the Socialists to support and guide them farther on this course—as I look back I think it is marvellous that we have got so far and done so well.

Remember what happened with the Montagu-Chelmsford Report. You may say I did it. But what happened? There was not a single division in Parliament, there was hardly any debate, and it went through in that kind of non-party atmosphere which we are told is the solution for the India question. We know how much we have suffered by what we so prematurely did then. Whatever may happen to-day, that is not going to happen again. This matter is not going through without the most strenuous resistance and the most searching criticism and examination by those who believe that it is fraught with grave danger.

We are told that it is premature to make up our minds. The last speaker, Lady Bridgeman, in her excellent and agreeable speech, indicated that it was premature to make up our minds, but what did my right honourable friend, our leader say to us to-day? He read the words he used at the Albert Hall, and he told us that he had made up his mind about it. (Cheers.) Three years ago he considered the chief arguments we are using now and put them in their proper place. (Cries of "No." and counter-cheers.) He considered those arguments, took his own decision, and is prepared, very rightly, to abide by the consequences. If he forms his opinion with all his great responsibility as long ago as three years—

[Editor's Note: There were cries of "No" from all parts of the hall, and then Baldwin, who was sitting immediately beside Churchill, stood up and tapped him on the shoulder. Churchill turned round in surprise, and then walked to the edge of the platform, while Baldwin waited for a storm of cheering and counter-cheering to abate. When there was silence Baldwin said: "I said I took three years considering it."]

My right honourable friend certainly said that, but if you examine his actual words I do not think you will find that I have misrepresented him. [Shouts of "Withdraw."] However that may be, if my right hon. friend is no doubt still considering the matter, is not that all the more reason why we should express our real and true opinion? (Laughter.)

Is it right that a warning signal should be made? Surely the red light should flash and the danger message should be sent out before the vital points are passed and nothing remains. There is time now to alter and revise the policy when the Joint

Committee is still sitting. We have no right to intrude upon their task, but we have a right to express to our party leader and—[shouts of "You ought to have been on it," "Why aren't you on it?"]

Mark you, we are assured on the one hand that only inquiry and examination is going on, but at the same time, and almost in the same breath, we are told that after all that has been done, after all these Round Table conferences, it is impossible to go back to the previous position.

We have a bounden duty, with all the preparations that the Government are making day after day to carry the scheme into effect—we have an absolute duty to justify on this occasion our true opinions, whatever they may be for each man and woman. I do not want to stay much longer, but I will say this: This present White Paper constitution is unworkable. [A delegate: "What is your plan?"] It is not accepted by any party or representative body in India, except as a means of extorting further concessions. The Princes are reluctant to accept it. They may be forced into it, but they are reluctant to accept it. Lord Willingdon, the distinguished Viceroy, has told us the only party who could work this scheme is the Indian Congress Party. But where are the Indian Congress Party? They are in prison. They are to have placed under them that loyal police, who are to be placed under the control, as it may well turn out if this system is not changed, of the very men they have recently arrested. This is the position, and everything is moving towards it.

I have been asked what is my plan. I will answer that question if you will treat me with consideration. [Interruption.] It is easy to run propaganda to victimize a particular man. [Dissent and laughter].

I am asked this question. I think that if Mr. Baldwin could have finished up his speech (of course I know he could not really) by saying that he had thought it out very carefully and had come to the conclusion that we could not hand over the policy in the Provinces, and that no federal system should be established until the Provincial units had proved themselves real working living entities, and that in the government of the masses of India they had proved themselves capable of showing loyalty to the Crown—then indeed we should have had a plan for the better government of India in which we could all march forward together, not only with personal regard and respect for our leaders, but also knowing that we were acting in accordance with our convictions.

I have said the question of India will become a touchstone in the near future, but it is more than that. It is a symbol. The way in which this question is handled by the British nation will be proof of their resolve to defend their rights and uphold their interests in every quarter of the globe. (Loud cheers.)

ANGLO-FRENCH RELATIONS

July 3, 1933

Association France-Grande Bretagne Dinner,
Union Interalliée, Paris

[Extract] ... Great Britain and France find common ground in three great interests—peace, parliamentary government, and personal freedom. We desire peace, for we seek neither territorial expansion nor the settling of old scores; we still hold to the parliamentary system in a world which almost everywhere shows its eclipse by dictatorship, and we hold equally closely to the precious liberty of the individual, which depends upon parliamentary government.

Many people are disappointed at the future of the Geneva Conference. I personally have always felt the gravest doubts as to the wisdom of pressing disarmament upon Europe at the present time. What can be more dangerous to peace than to put Germany on an equal footing with France? I say here, as I have said more than once in the House of Commons: "Thank God for the French Army." Other countries would make a great mistake if they pressed France beyond her better judgment to weaken her army, and France would make a great mistake if she sought to rely for safety on foreign guarantees instead of on her own strength.

Nevertheless, the Disarmament Conference could still achieve a useful task, modest though it might be in comparison with its original aim. If it could induce the giving of full publicity about armaments it would at least remove the suspicion which embitters fear and makes it doubly dangerous. It is a melancholy thought that peace, after the sufferings of the world, should still be largely based on physical force. But it would be unwise to dispense with that basis until there is the certainty of something better and still effective.

INDIA AND THE UNITED STATES

July 7, 1933

Epping

[Extract] ... Upon the whole the nation stands behind the so-called National Government believing that a greater stability is imparted to its affairs by that means and no one can doubt that this Government is an enormous improvement upon the one which preceded it. That is all the more reason why we should endeavour to keep it upon the lines of policy for which it was elected. Its advantages will be offset if by going outside the conditions for which it was elected it brings a grave deterioration in the whole system of Government in our Indian Empire.

India is vital to the well-being of Britain, and I cannot help feeling very anxious when I see forces from which our population is largely supported being gradually diminished. Foreign investments are slowly shrinking and shipping is at a low ebb. If to these we add the loss of India in one form or another, then problems will arise here incomparably more grave than any we have known. You will have a surplus population here which it may be beyond the Government to provide for effectively.

We have an interest in India, and we have also a duty. I feel that if British control is seriously weakened there will be a decline in the efficiency and integrity of Indian administration bringing untold misfortunes upon millions of extremely poor people.

Mr. Baldwin the other day at Manchester spoke of the granting of self-government to Canada, South Africa, and Ireland, and he intimated that the Conservative Party had been wrong in opposing those great decisions. I cannot quarrel with him about South Africa and Ireland. In South Africa what we did has stood the test of a quarter of a century. In Ireland there has been a grievous disappointment, but still I am prepared to say that we have gained a greater advantage by separating Ireland from our Imperial affairs.

But how absurd it would be to try to apply those methods and to make a precedent of them in the case of India. If you should take steps which will darken the lives of the enormous mass of people in India you will have failed in your duty, and you will not only suffer grievously in your own interests, but in your honour and self-respect.

I have every intention of continuing my opposition to the proposals of the White Paper. I do not think that if this controversy goes on you will have cause to regret the action taken in your name. I believe the very moderate requests we have made will in the end be granted. I do not believe a Federal system will be set up in India until provincial Home Rule has been tried and found to work. I believe that before a year is out we shall have warded off the danger of a most grievous error and possibly of a fatal catastrophe.

[Editor's Note: In referring to President Roosevelt's message telling the nations of the world to balance their Budgets, Churchill said] : Such advice came oddly from the head of a State which accepted the greatest Budget deficiency in times of peace ever recorded. That being so, we should accept with some circumspection, advice reaching us from across the Atlantic where practice does not conform with the doctrines preached here for our benefit.

MONETARY POLICY

July 10, 1933

House of Commons

My right hon. Friend the Chancellor of the Exchequer [Mr. Neville Chamberlain] evidently did not feel it right to tell us anything new this afternoon, nor to admit us more closely into the grave problems which are now dominating the minds of the Members of His Majesty's Government. I do not think we could blame him for that because of the immense responsibility which attaches to the action of the representatives of Great Britain at the present time and the possibility that later on—perhaps a little later on—they would see more clearly exactly in what direction to move and would be able to make us a full, or at any rate, a much fuller statement than what we have already received. Therefore, I do not at all take occasion to complain. I merely note the fact that so far we have been told only what I may call the articulations of the conference, and no new light has been thrown upon the purposes of His Majesty's Government. [Editor's Note: Churchill was referring to the World Economic Conference held in London under the auspices of the League of Nations which had opened on June 13.] I do not think that the same conditions of silence and reticence are necessarily imposed upon private Members, and, indeed, it is a good thing, I think, that we should ventilate this subject and bring House of Commons opinion into focus upon it when the proper occasion arises, as it has this afternoon. But I speak upon it with the very greatest diffidence because, as the speech of the right hon. Gentleman the Leader of the Opposition has shown, it is a very complicated and difficult subject, and one in which one might easily lose one's way while all the time seeming to proceed along extremely promising and attractive avenues.

A year ago I ventured to suggest to His Majesty's Government that they should call an international conference on the monetary problem with a view to arresting the deflation, and I had in mind, as I said hopefully on another occasion, that the object which we should set before ourselves should be the effective revaluation of commodities up to something like the values of 1928. A year ago the world was divided between gold countries and non-gold countries and the United States led the gold countries. It seemed to me when I made this suggestion that, if the United States could be persuaded to detach herself from the gold countries and embark upon a policy of revaluation, it would become much easier and much safer for Great Britain as the leader of the sterling countries to raise wholesale commodity prices. After all, the great obstacle to price expansion a year ago was the formidable power and authority of the United States ranged behind the Gold Standard, and in that enforcing of deflation inevitably associated with the Gold Standard under the present conditions of gold hoarding. It was very difficult for us to move with any effect while the United States adhered so rigidly, so firmly and so authoritatively to that position. Very large purchases had to be made by us across the exchange every year, and the movement of our exchange in relation to the United States was one of the very serious factors we should have had to consider.

If the United States proved obdurate in her adherence to gold, it seemed a year ago that there was nothing for us but to go with what we then called the sterling convoy and steam at a pace which would encourage the largest number of countries to join the convoy and enable them to keep continuous station in it, and then the world would have ranged itself definitely into two great monetary and trading groups, as it then seemed, of almost equal power. Within each group all transactions would become increasingly easy, but between these two groups all transactions and all payments would become increasingly difficult, and we should have had—there seemed to be no alternative open—the evil of two vast rival monetary and economic worlds each of which believed that it was being ruined by the other—the gold countries believing that they were being defrauded of the debts which were due them and undercut by the depreciated exchanges of their debtors, and the sterling countries believing that the gold bloc were enforcing a policy of deflation upon the whole world with a view to enhancing the enormous masses of gold which they had hoarded in the unfortunate period preceding these world disturbances. It seemed, therefore, that there was no outcome from such a state of affairs except the wholesale repudiation of debts by sterling countries to gold countries, and the freezing up of all the exports of gold countries to non-gold countries.

That was the situation, and of the two groups I had myself no doubt, although they seemed so evenly balanced, that the sterling group would in the end prove much the stronger, even although the United States was on the other side. The sterling group, comprising as it did then almost the whole of the British Empire, and as it does now the whole of the British Empire, together with many powerful Continental countries, seemed to have the stronger position as between these two great spheres into which the world threatened to divide itself. But great friction and tension lay ahead, and a new arbitrary cleavage was opening in the world to international trade, in addition to all those other cleavages which we have known so far. I thought, therefore, that we should do our best to detach the United States from the gold bloc before we began consciously organising the sterling convoy and reconciled ourselves to the somewhat gloomy prospect I have ventured to outline.

I did not a year ago regard this as hopeless, because it was so evident to anyone who travelled about the United States, as I had recently done, that that great country was strangling itself both in respect to external and internal trade by its rigid adherence to the Gold Standard and to hoarded gold. On the other hand, when we remember how the gold obligation was soldered into the fabric of so many of the greatest American undertakings and how it was enshrined in the domestic law of the United States, with our minds dwelling upon a thousand million pounds worth of gold, including so many of our vanished British sovereigns, which had been solemnly buried in the vaults beneath the Federal Reserve Bank, when we thought of all that, it seemed that the hope that the United States would be induced to detach herself from gold and come and join the freer area outside the Gold Standard, was at any rate rather a forlorn hope. Still there was a possibility of a world conference. There was a possibility of the facts telling their own tale. In that interval there was the possibility of intimate conversations between representatives of Great Britain—which have taken place—and the United States, and one hoped that that result might be achieved.

But what has happened? The result which I had in my mind as the most hopeful that could be sought for has achieved itself. It achieved itself before the Conference ever met, freely, voluntarily, without pressure from us or bargain with us; the United States has repudiated gold. It has abandoned the leadership of the gold countries, and it is now resolutely and hopefully engaged in that very process of revaluating commodities up to the prices say, of 1926, or, it may be, 1928 or thereabouts. As far as I am concerned, while making every excuse and apology to the House for forming an opinion upon these extraordinarily complicated matters which have, nevertheless, forced themselves upon us, revaluation to the figures of 1928 was a result which I had always regarded as of paramount importance and desirability. I say "1928 or thereabouts," because, although there are many who share hopes, everone knows also the danger of the experiment upon which President Roosevelt has so courageously launched himself and his country.

If anyone had told us a year ago that the United States would join Great Britain in abandoning gold we should have thought him far too sanguine; we should have thought him a builder of air castles whose expectations were his desires and whose wishes were his beliefs. The tremendous event has happened. We get every day in the newspapers headlines of equal size, and therefore we are sometimes apt to overlook the fact that they deal now and again with matters of vast and dominating importance, and at other times with purely frivolous or trivial topics. But the great event of the United States going off gold—a greater event than our departure from that standard—has happened, and I for one frankly rejoice.

Let me submit to the Committee—and I do not intend keeping it long this afternoon—that I really would speak with great trepidation upon these matters, because, without contact with the technical experts and without the great knowledge in possession of the Government, it is very difficult to do more than express a tentative view, and that I intend to do. It seems to me that the following results have followed from the decision of the United States which are all satisfactory and beneficial to us, or may be later. First of all, there is the gold bloc. What is called the gold bloc—we are getting into a new terminology upon this matter very rightly—rests upon American support. Confronted to a certain extent with a measure of American antagonism it becomes incomparably weaker as a world force. We no longer have the two equal forces. The changed use of this enormous power has altered altogether the proportion as between the gold and the non-gold countries. The countries of the gold bloc play nothing like the part in the world's business and production as do the non-gold countries, nor do they possess their vast and varied territory and their immense reserves of raw material. We must certainly do nothing apart from what is in our own interests. We cannot deflect from our own proper policy, but apart from that we must do nothing to embarrass or hamper the countries who decide to remain upon gold and to adhere to that, but I must say that I think it is extremely doubtful, whatever we do, whether they will be able to adhere to this system now that the United States has changed sides. I do not believe that any steps which we could take—and I hope that we shall take no steps which are to our own disadvantage—would alter at all the outcome of events. Let me say parenthetically, but, I hope, in the most inoffensive terms, that these gold countries have really no grounds for reproaching either the United States or Great Britain.

I am tired of hearing these claims to superior virtue and integrity attached to the Gold Standard countries; to countries which have already like France devalued to the extent of four-fifths of their indebtedness, or countries like Germany which has destroyed its entire rentier class, relieved itself of all fixed charges and is not paying either its public or private debts. I am unfeignedly glad that there is no danger now, or very much less danger, of the creation of a crystallisation of two economic and monetary worlds. There is no danger—to borrow a word from a much more thorny controversy—of a monetary diarchy in the world as between two equally established and equally large parties. The liberation of all currencies from gold is a possibility which must certainly be taken into account for the future. That is a great event, a prodigious event, if we look back to the position where we stood last year. Hitherto, we have had to consider the case of particular countries one at a time quitting the Gold Standard, or to groups of countries departing from it, but if all the countries depart from gold for the time being—I say only for the time being—an entirely new and by no means necessarily unhopeful situation will be created. Through the period of general flux we might reach the solution, or a solution, a far better solution of this problem than anything that has been our power so far.

It is in relation to this possibility of the non-gold area being enlarged until it is almost universal that the second beneficial effect of what has taken place arises. In such circumstances it seems to me, looking at it from the British point of view, that the prestige and influence of sterling must become enormously enhanced and that consequently the position of London as the financial centre of the world will become even more secure. We in this island have shown, both before and after the abandonment of the Gold Standard, that we can manage a currency detached from gold, and manage it with sober and sedate self-control. The United States have yet to prove that, having escaped from the gold hoarder, they may not fall a victim to the paper speculator. I trust that they will succeed. Every one of us must hope and pray that this valiant experiment will succeed. They are pioneers, they are in a pioneer position, and the consequence of their failure will strike a note of despair throughout the world. I hope that they will succeed, but, succeed or fail, it seems to me very likely that once gold has been dethroned, sterling will become the world's most trustworthy measure. Already in these circumstances, for one year we have had two rival systems at work, and we have heard the expression: "It was not sterling that went off gold, but it was gold that went off sterling," and there was some considerable measure of truth behind it. How much more will the strength and solidity of sterling be apparent when gold is nowhere set up as an anchor in any part of the world. It is a great responsibility for us that this should happen, but it is also a very great opportunity, and it is an opportunity which has come to us in conditions when we have a stable Government in this country possessed of enormous powers to deal with any situation which may arise. I hope that it will not be found unequal to that opportunity should it arise.

The third result of what has happened in the United States has been to remove a barrier which has hitherto prevented us from carrying out the declared policy of the Chancellor of the Exchequer of raising the wholesale price level. I hope the removal of that barrier means an endeavour on his part to raise the prices up to at least the level of 1928. We have been told hitherto that we could not do this because other nations, especially the United States, were wedded to gold, but now that divorce has become so common, almost universal, it may be found that we in these islands have regained our freedom too. For all these reasons, I rejoice—and I do not think the right hon. Gentleman would shed many tears over it—in the action of the United States in quitting the Gold Standard. I am sorry for the World Conference because no doubt it has lost a very great part of its original purpose. The biggest thing it could do had been done before it met. But there is plenty more work, as my right hon. Friend has shown, of the utmost importance, for the World Conference to do. Anyhow, conferences exist for men and not men for conferences. I trust that the Government will keep the Conference in being. It is of the utmost importance that it should be continued in existence during the unforeseeable and not by any means unhopeful conditions which the next few months may bring about. If some nations go I hope, and I gathered so from my right hon. Friend, that His Majesty's Government will remain with others, keeping the others together. So long as the United States representatives remain in this country very few countries in the world can afford to absent themselves permanently from deliberations which at any time may assume the most decisive character.

I do not at all share, as an outsider, the naive astonishment with which some Members of the Government received the refusal of the United States to agree to a temporary price stabilisation of currency. I agree with the quotation read from President Roosevelt's speech during May, but how anyone watching the changes that had occurred in the interval could have imagined that Mr. Roosevelt, on the morrow of taking his tremendous plunge, and in the full tide of his successful experiment, having just severed his country from gold and launched himself on a revaluation of commodities, would agree to tie it all up again to gold, out of love for France, is quite beyond human comprehension. I agree with Professor Gustav Cassel, whose extraordinarily pregnant and suggestive statements have appeared from time to time during the last few years, that merely to tie up currencies even temporarily to hoarded gold—it is not gold, remember, but it is hoarded gold that you are invited to tie yourselves to at various ratios—would be no solution of the world's difficulties and certainly should not be attempted until the desired revaluation of commodities has actually been achieved.

I have indicated, I hope in language which is sufficiently vague not to fall into technical inaccuracies—we must all be particularly careful—my view, which I have sincerely held during the last 18 months while we have been compelled to address ourselves to this awful topic. Let me ask the Government what is the alternative to a real effort to revalue commodities. Now that the United States has joined the Latin countries and Germany in post-War devalorisation of their currency, we shall if we do nothing—I admit that we have done something—be the only Power which has not written off or written down past obligations at least to the level at which they were contracted, and we shall find ourselves alone in a competitive world crushed under a unique burden of debt and fixed charges, of which our rivals have freed themselves, burdens which will increase with every effort we make to reduce them and with every failure to arrest the fall in prices, while all the time our rivals will have relieved themselves in varying degrees. We shall be the only country where, above all others, the new wealth produced each year by the enterprise and toil of man is penalised to an unfair and destructive extent in comparison with the old wealth of past accumulations. We shall be the only country to assert and enforce the rights of creditors far beyond their original contractual equities, and by so doing if we go on indefinitely upon such a course with a falling price level, we may well bring about the ruin of that very rentier class who have been made usurers against their will, and without their knowledge to a very large extent, by the movement of monetary affairs, and whose lawful rights can only be guarded and guaranteed when founded upon justice, reason and public advantage.

Let the Government consider also the paralysing burden of taxation and the precarious balance of the Budget. We are incomparably the heaviest taxed people in the world. How can we expect a real revival—I rejoice in the signs of improvement which are shown, and it is no good part to minimise them—while we remain with a burden of taxation unparalleled in the past and crushing in its actual effect? While we proceed on the present lines I see absolutely no hope of any mitigation of the burdens of taxation. My right hon. Friend the Chancellor of the Exchequer has used up every conceivable resource merely to pay his way, and it is even doubtful whether he will succeed in paying his way. Very severe and much resented economies have been enforced and no others of a substantial character are now in prospect. All the yield of the tariff, the enormous yield, which has come to our aid, has been absorbed. All the savings of the skilful conversion, £20,000,000 or £30,000,000, have been absorbed. All the saving in not providing for the payment of the American Debt has been absorbed, because it was not included. All the relief of raising the entire Sinking Fund has been swallowed up, and still the balance trembles doubtfully. The explanations are only too plain. The burden of providing more than £120,000,000 a year, as we are bound to do, for 2,000,000 or 3,000,000 unemployed, has cut down the revenue at the same time that excessive taxation is drying up its sources. If a successful policy of price raising and wage raising, at the moment when the price raising had been effected, were adopted, the new wealth would be replaced in fair relation to the old.

You cannot measure by what unseen channels stimulus will come to your industries throughout the land. The burden of debt in relation to new production and to figures of revenue would also be reduced. Lighter taxation would liberate enterprise. Thousands of businesses which now make no profits at all, although they are still carrying on—a matter which was brought before me when I was Chancellor of the Exchequer—which are at present withdrawn from the tax collecting area, would come again into the revenue production area to the relief of the Chancellor of the Exchequer. You may get from lower rates of taxation, I will not say the same yield but, proportionately, a much higher yield than you get from destructive rates of taxation. Lastly, there would be a further reduction in unemployment, the most blessed economy of all, from which future Chancellors of the Exchequer alone can expect to have effective relief.

It seems to me that the course of His Majesty's Government is clear. Although they are absolutely right in not being precipitate and in watching carefully the moment at which to act, no doubt, they are justified in keeping their own counsel, as they certainly have done, I trust that this course, which is clear, is one upon which they will resolutely set forth. It seems to me that they should now proceed, or at the best moment proceed, to organise and guide a sterling convoy, in the centre of which lies the whole of the British Empire, upon a set plan of controlled revaluation; endeavour to raise prices in relation to sterling as far and as much as they can without losing touch with the Dominions and foreign countries who are keeping company with us. It is safe enough. The American navy has come over, as they did in the Great War, and although separate from us is steaming along the same course. It may be that it is steaming at undue speed considering the unchartered seas through which we are all passing, but there is no more risk of a direct monetary collision or conflict between sterling and the United States of America. We ought, I think, to follow their general movement at a prudent distance, with every possible precaution which is open to experienced navigators, and with that thought for the common interest imperative on those who move in large associations. It may well be that the whole armada will be united at no distant date, and will move forward together in one majestic array and at one uniform speed.

INDIA (ADMINISTRATIVE POLICY)

July 17, 1933

House of Commons

I am sure that, however we may differ about India, the vast majority of Members in the House, wherever they sit, will feel how frightfully out of balance has been the summing up of the hon. Member for Bridgeton (Mr. Maxton) on the British contribution to Indian progress. When I listened to those impressively uttered sentences, which did not seem to me to form at any point the remotest contact with reality or truth, delivered in that charming manner which always impresses the House, I could not help feeling how difficult must be the task which lies before any British Government who are endeavouring to convince people who hold the hon. Member's views of the merits of their administration and of the value of their mission in the East. The hon. Member spoke as if nothing but exploitation and tyranny had been the characteristics of British rule, and as if there was nothing to show for it except, as I gathered, the canals and so forth of which the Secretary of State [Sir John Simon] spoke to-day. But in 50 years 100,000,000 more people have come into being in India. It may well be, as I said to the House on another occasion, that it would have been better had fewer new people come into being, and if a greater measure of subsistence had been possible for the great mass of the people than has been, so far, within our power to achieve; but no one can possibly say that a country whose population has increased by almost two-thirds in quite a short time is a country in which there is an undue pressure by an alien Government upon the updraught of national life.

I do not rise to follow the hon. Member in his remarks, but, in the few words which I shall venture to address to the Committee, to congratulate the Secretary of State and His Majesty's Government upon the very satisfactory administrative tale which they have to tell. The right hon. Gentleman told us of progress of every kind in the last two years in India. That was most gratifying to Members of every party, and all that I can venture to say is that it seems that the progress which he has described marks, according to his statement, the arrival of a British Government in India, not by any means at its goal, but at a very satisfactory resting place at the present time. Most of all was his speech satisfactory when he spoke of the improvement in law and order.

He not only told us how there was a great diminution in the number of persons in gaol for civil disobedience, but the most satisfactory point of all was the very distinct measure of assistance given to the Government by Indians themselves in the passing of legislation to avoid the necessity for the re-enactment of the special ordinances. All that was satisfactory, and no one could deny to the right hon. Gentleman the great credit which is due to him and to Lord Willingdon for the reconstruction work in social order which they have achieved without bloodshed and without any violent commotion or tumults, but simply by firm and patient administration of the law.

But what a contrast this procedure has been to the policy of the late Government! The hon. Member behind me made a desperately far-fetched effort to make out that they were both parts of one tremendous whole. I cannot see any contrast greater than the contrast between the Gandhi-Irwin Pact and the answer which the right hon. Gentleman read out with justifiable pride which the present Viceroy has sent to Mr. Gandhi. It is impossible to place in juxtaposition that Treaty which was negotiated only two years ago and the answer which Lord Willingdon has so properly sent to Mr. Gandhi on this occasion, and of which the House, I gather, almost unanimously approves, except for the Socialist party, without seeing that, here you have a contrast as vivid and as absolute as the contrast between oil and vinegar, or black and white. There has been a great change. That is the point which I desire particularly to impress on the Committee. When more than two years ago I and others criticised very strongly the policy of the Socialist Government, it was not only upon the constitutional issue on which they had embarked that we dissented. It was as much, in some ways even more, upon the administrative weakness which was throwing India into disorder. We all remember that there were horrible events at Cawnpore, there was the occasion at Lahore when the British flag was torn down and solemnly burned by the India Congress, and there was the disobedience campaign of Mr. Gandhi. All these processes were accompanied by continued degeneration of law and order throughout India, causing the utmost anxiety, more particularly as this process of immediate administrative degeneration was accompanied by what looked like a veritable landslide in the constitutional sphere.

At any rate, in the administrative sphere the right hon. Gentleman has completely reversed the policy of the late Government. Instead of inviting Mr. Gandhi to negotiate a sort of treaty with the Government of the King Emperor, he has been refused access until he places himself within the law. That process redounds enormously to the credit of the administration. What is the use of pretending that there has not been a great change, and what would be my justification if, having seen that great change made in the direction that I urged, I should sit silent and not get up and offer my congratulations, unwelcome though I have no doubt they will be to my right hon. Friend, for having taken the advice that I offered two years ago, for having digested the reproof that I administered two years ago to his predecessor and for having accomplished this great task—this is a most important point—without any serious or horrible incidents such as may easily occur in collisions between the police or the troops and the people. Where are all those tales that we used to hear of it being impossible to re-establish order or deal with Mr. Gandhi and the Congress movement without sending out a division of troops from home—without terrible events on the spot? When we suggested to Mr. Wedgwood Benn that law and order should be maintained, that you should not make treaties with law-breakers, and so forth, when it was suggested that you would have to suppress this Congress movement of civil disobedience, the answer was that it was easy to use machine guns and artillery, but horrible massacres would be perpetrated upon the helpless civil and working-class population. There was no truth in all that. All these were defeatist tales of weakness and falsehood to lead us to take decisions which were not warranted on the merits and were not justified upon the facts. All that has been completely exploded, not by any arguments that any of us delivered but by two years of administrative achievement, the effects of which are now before us and are indisputable. It is simply straight-forward, firm administration of law and order, the avoidance of bargains struck between the Viceroy and a man in quasi revolt which have been sufficient to change the entire picture of India from the melancholy, formidable and lamentable state which it presented two and a-half years ago, to the extremely satisfactory condition—I hope not too optimistically stated—which the Secretary of State has laid before us to-day.

What of this talk about the present Central Government of India being an organism so inefficient that it had to be changed for something quite different? We have been told again and again that the present system is a very bad one, and that the Central Government is very inconvenient and must be replaced by something better. Here you had the most difficult situation you could possibly have. You had the country thrown into great disorder by the weakness of administration of Mr. Wedg-wood Benn and, I am sorry to say, the late Viceroy. You had at the same time an important constitutional change bruited about everywhere and pushed forward. You could hardly have a more difficult situation in which to restore order without bloodshed, but it has been done. This despised Central Government machine, which we are told is so bad that it must be swept away, has proved an effective engine smoothly and easily to change the whole situation and to re-establish a perfectly satisfactory condition of affairs. I am entitled to draw this moral from my right hon. Friend's speech. He has enormously improved the situation and swept away many of the evils. He has done it without any of the disasters that were foretold. He has done it with the existing machinery of Central Indian Government, and he has done it by adopting methods pressed upon his predecessor by many of those to whom in other aspects of the Indian constitutional question he finds himself opposed. [*Interruption.*] I never said so. I draw my own moral.

But I should not like the Secretary of State's speech to go out to the world as if it was a proof that the policy that the Government have been pursuing is the same policy as that of the late Socialist Government. It is the opposite policy, and it has been completely successful. [*Interruption.*] The right hon. Gentleman is premature in interrupting me. In administration it is the opposite policy. In the constitutional sphere, which we are not allowed to touch upon, it is the same. My argument will presently be having had this success in reversing the policy of the late Government in the administrative sphere, why do yourselves out of the possibility of an equal advantage if you reverse it in the constitutional sphere? I say it is an entirely different policy. It is within the rights of my right hon. Friend, and it is essential to the argumentative position of the Government, to contend that this great improvement has not been effected by the forces of repression—has not been effected by locking up 60,000 people, that these events have merely been administrative incidentals, and that the real thing that has pacified India has been the hope held out of the great constitutional changes embodied in the White Paper policy. No one can decide about that. It is a matter of assertion and counter-assertion. The right hon. Gentleman quotes some anonymous civil servant or someone, not improperly at all, in his support to show that this peaceful condition which is being re-established is due to the hopes of the Indians that their national aspirations will be realised, or words to that effect. He is entitled to say that, and to say what a great help it has been in restoring order to have this constitutional discussion going on in the meanwhile; but it is equally open to those who disagree with him to argue that his achievement is all the greater because, in spite of the extremely disturbing and subversive suggestions which have been continually made about the departure of the British Raj from India, and all the loose and vain talk that has been indulged in upon that matter, and all the hopes which have been roused, many of which are not going to be fulfilled, he has been able to restore peace and order without any serious difficulty.

There are the two views. No one can say which is proved right to-day. We shall see. But, arguing from the experience of the past, I would most solemnly urge that, just as he profited so much in the administrative sphere by taking the advice that we tendered to him and to his predecessor so, if he follows the same path in constitutional reform, he may reap another harvest. It is in my opinion a very dangerous and sinister fact that the right hon. Gentleman and the Government, and those who support the present constitutional proposals, should use the well-earned credit that they have gained by pursuing a policy of one kind in the administrative sphere in order to gain confidence for a departure of a totally different kind in the constitutional sphere. If the right hon. Gentleman had followed the policy of Mr. Wedgwood Benn, if Lord Willingdon had followed the policy of Lord Irwin, I have not the slightest doubt that this great Conservative majority in the House of Commons would have brought the policy to a standstill. But he has confronted Parliament; he has confronted the country with great administrative success, and then he misuses it by a perversion of the real facts. He has misused all the prestige he has got by this action in order to urge us on to courses which are totally different in spirit and which, if carried into effect, would rob him and rob his successor by the very means by which he has succeeded.

I have no more to say except this. The fact that order and peace have been restored in India is no ground for abandoning constitutional reform in India. On the contrary, it liberates the cause of contitutional reform from the hideous danger with which it was intermingled in the time of the late administration. Never has there been a more favourable opportunity for proposals for constitutional improvement and reforms in India since law and order have been restored by considered, sober and sedate methods. Certainly we must persevere in that course. Those who are represented as diehards and obstructives in this matter simply because they rest themselves in the main upon the reports brought to this House by the Statutory Commission, do not in any way draw from the re-establishment of peace and order in India the conclusion that nothing should be done and that no forward movement should be made. No, the conclusion which I would draw from it, with all the modesty I can, is, just as we have been right on the question of the method of dealing with disorder in India, so the wise and prudent limits which we assign to constitutional progress at the present time, will mark the best path which the right hon. Gentleman can follow in his future conduct of Indian affairs.

THE PRINCE OF WALES

July 25, 1933

British Empire Service League Conference,
London

[Extract] . . . Our memories turn back to the tremendous days when our hearts beat with a desire that those who played their part and bore the brunt of the War should not be forgotten by fellow-countrymen once the danger is past. The Prince of Wales's contributions to the nation in the years following the Great War have been enormous. (Cheers.) He upheld and emphasized the theme of unity of the British Empire, and has done his best for the Army, Navy, and Air Forces and for the Civil Service who bear so important parts in our affairs. Those are tasks to which his heart would naturally incline and to which all the circumstances of his upbringing would direct his mind. He has opened the eyes of the younger generation to a new and indispensable sphere of activity, the well-being of the working masses of the nation. His deep growing association with the welfare of the cottage home, with the life of the people, has given a definite inspiration to the younger men. (Cheers.)

It is a rough world that we live in to-day. Danger clouds are showing in more than one quarter. Many disappointments have been patiently endured in countless homes. The glories of the most complete victory ever gained under arms have not been followed even in victorious countries by any easement in the pressure of life.

Speaking at a gathering without class or party distinction I think we can feel a certain sense of satisfaction at the position we occupy to-day. We have been through the greatest convulsion the world has ever known. We have seen the greatest Empires collapsing, and almost every human institution which existed before the War has been remodelled, recast, or swept out of the way. But here we are—and I speak increasingly on behalf of the older generation—with not a bad tale to tell to the younger men who are coming on. We can say that despite all the disturbance and tumult the British Empire was steered and conducted so that not one single inch of territory was removed from our control. We preserved all that our ancestors had gained, and that inheritance we can still hand down undiminished to the younger generation.

"EUROPE'S HOUR OF DANGER"

August 12, 1933

Theydon Bois

Our country is at peace. We enjoy a greater measure of freedom and security than any other nation in the world—perhaps the greatest measure of personal freedom and security combined that has ever been achieved by any community in all history. We are suffering less than most countries from the great depression of trade. You will not expect me to tell you that all this is due to the Government headed by Mr. Ramsay MacDonald. It is due to the genius of the British people and to the vitality and strength of their institutions. It is due to the traditions which are still so widely respected in our island life. Still, we must not underrate the advantage we have of a solid, stable Government, composed of honourable and upright men, respecting the ancient Constitution of the land and obeying the laws they themselves administer.

We know we have a Government capable of maintaining law and order and of respecting and guarding our individual liberties and civic rights, which our forefathers gained for us in many a hard-fought field. We know that in all this we can rely on a House of Commons elected upon an impulse of patriotism and still only in its Parliamentary prime. When we look out upon the tragic confusion of the world and see how many countries, great and small, have fallen a prey to anarchy or tyranny or are devoured by ferocious hatreds of race, class, or faction, we should be grateful to the Providence that has thus far preserved and protected us.

I see that Mr. MacDonald told a Dutch newspaper the other day that the National Government had three more years to run and would certainly last longer. Many of us would be quite content that that should be so. There are, however, three evil and dangerous storm clouds which either overhang us or lie on the horizon.

The first is the state of Europe. Nobody can watch the events which are taking place in Germany without increasing anxiety about what their outcome will be. At present Germany is only partly armed and most of her fury is turned upon herself. But already her smaller neighbours, Austria, Switzerland, Belgium, and Denmark, feel a deep disquietude. There is grave reason to believe that Germany is arming herself, or seeking to arm herself, contrary to the solemn treaties exacted from her in her hour of defeat.

I have always opposed the rearmament of Germany and have criticized in the House of Commons all this foolish talk of placing her upon some kind of equality with France. I denounced and derided the perilous policy to which we seemed inclined to lend ourselves of putting pressure upon the French to weaken their splendid army. The same people and the same perverse school of thought in England and the United States that have already weakened the British Navy sought to weaken the French army. But the French most prudently refused to hearken to this hazardous advice, and the fact that they refused is the main foundation of the peace of Europe to-day.

I hope our National Government, and especially the Cabinet Ministers in charge of the Navy and Army and the Air Force, will realize how grave is their responsibility. They are responsible, like the Ministers before the War, for our essential safety.

I trust they will make sure that the forces of the Crown are kept in a proper state of efficiency, with the supplies and munition factories which they require, and that they will be strong enough to enable us to count for something when we work for peace, and strong enough if war should come in Europe to maintain our effective neutrality, unless we should decide of our own free will to the contrary. Always remember that Britain's hour of weakness is Europe's hour of danger. I look to the League of Nations to rally the forces which make for the peace of the civilized world and not in any way to weaken them.

The second evil cloud which overshadows us is the continuance of the enormous unemployment. We all rejoice that there has been some noticeable improvement in the summer months. But that improvement should not for a moment justify the Government in imagining that the present conditions of the industrial population—and I may add of the black-coated working men—can be tolerated with complacency.

This cancer of unemployment is eating out the heart of the people. Here in the south—the prosperous, ancient, long-settled Conservative south—we see serious unemployment. But that is nothing to what is happening in the north, or in the poorer working-class areas.

I can only say that reform of the monetary system so as to procure a steady recovery in the value of new effort compared to old debts and fixed charges is an absolutely necessary factor in revival here at home. We all should watch with sympathy and earnest attention the heroic experiment which the President of the United States is making. If he fails it will be not only an American, but a world, disaster. For myself I put far more hope in the resolute mental energy of President Roosevelt than in the venerable and chilling orthodoxy of Mr. Montague Norman.

I mention these two famous men because they represent the opposite thoughts and moods upon the economic problem. I should like to see our National Government and the Chancellor of the Exchequer, who bears so heavy a burden, find some path between the two which would bring us nearer to the realities of production, distribution, and exchange.

The third danger that menaces the Government is this absurd Round Table plan of setting up a Federal Constitution in India on the rather battered lines of Western democracy, and of handing over the control of the police and the welfare of the Indian masses to the efforts of either largely untried or provedly disloyal Indian politicians.

Now, whereas the state of Europe and the economic depression are largely beyond the control of any British Government, in their Indian policy our Government and its leading men have only themselves to thank for all their embarrassments. Why cannot they let the Indian politicians prove their capacity for giving good government to the masses and loyal duty to the Crown in the great Provinces before embarking on this Utopian dream of a United States of All India?

Surely it is fair to ask these Indian politicians to prove that they can govern the great Provinces, almost as large and as populous as France, Italy, or Spain, before handing over to them the responsible control of the stately Empire which the British have built in India instead of the endless miseries and massacres of the past. Surely we should not part with the effectual control of law and order, of peace and justice, until we have some solid facts and guarantees upon which to depend.

FINANCE AND BANKING

October 3, 1933

Lord Mayor's Dinner to the Chancellor of the Exchequer,
Directors of the Bank of England, and
Merchants Mansion House, London

I feel I speak for everyone of every party, and even for that powerful group who represent no party but an amalgam of all, when I say that we receive Mr. Chamberlain's [Chancellor of the Exchequer] encouraging reports, assurances, and declarations with the utmost gratitude and with a confidence born of the fact that the right honourable gentleman is not a man to put things better in words than they are in fact. (Cheers.) We have passed from a free country to a protectionist country, the gold standard is gone and the Sinking Fund has been very properly and wisely suspended by the Chancellor of the Exchequer. Those are great changes, but they are changes which have been forced upon us, and the general mind of the country is that we must do our best under the new conditions. Many of the old principles and ties have been wrested from their moorings. I cannot say that they are adrift—they are at sea and afloat, and under their own steam. Our experience is not alone but is an experience felt over the whole world. Enormous changes have been brought into the economic life of every nation, but we cannot say for ourselves—and the speech of the Chancellor of the Exchequer convinced us—that we are making our way through the fluidity and confusion of the world, not only as well as, but better than, any other great commercial country.

There was a time when the Governor of the Bank of England was not only one of the most mysterious but one of the most uncontroversial personages in the island. It may not be the fault of the Governor of the Bank that his functions have become matters of public controversy but we are proud of him and compliment him upon his courage and imperturbability and on the inflexible fidelity with which he discharges what he conceives to be his duty. British banks, confronted as they have been in the last four years by a phenomenon to which no parallel existed, have shown themselves capable of an adaptiveness and a resourcefulness which has been a definite contributory factor in the strength of the country.

DISARMAMENT

October 5, 1933

Conservative Annual Conference,
Town Hall, Birmingham

[Extract] ... During the last four or five years the world has grown gravely darker, and it is very timely that the resolution [on disarmament] should be passed by the Conservative Conference. We have steadily disarmed, partly with a sincere desire to give a lead to other countries and partly through the severe financial pressure of the time. But a change must now be made. We must not continue longer on a course in which we alone are growing weaker while every other nation is growing stronger.

One would expect that a Minister representing one of the Fighting Services would have come to the Conference to reassure us. They obviously share the misgivings of the Conference. (Cheers.) But the Chancellor of the Exchequer [Mr. Neville Chamberlain] is present, and nobody ought to vote for the resolution unless he is prepared to assure the Chancellor of the Exchequer that, heavy as our burdens are, we prefer the security and safety of our native land above all other benefits. (Cheers.)

THE GRENADIER GUARDS

November 4, 1933

First or Grenadier Sergeants' Club Dinner, London

[Extract] ... I remember in the Omdurman campaign coming down the Nile in a boat for three or four days with a whole company of the 1st Battalion of The Grenadier Guards on board. That is where I got my vocabulary. I never lost the firm grip I then got upon the resources of the English language. I also saw the 3rd Battalion at a small action in South Africa called Diamond Hill. I thought I saw the 2nd Battalion when they were under General Rundle, in the 8th Division, when there were very long marches and very short rations. That experience confirmed my education. So when I was for a very short time attached as officer under instruction in the late unpleasantness to the 2nd Battalion, I felt that, however much I needed instruction in that particular kind of trench warfare, at least I knew the language. (Laughter.)

My ancestor the great Duke of Marlborough received his first commission in the First Guards, and was Colonel of the regiment and commanded the British armies in which the First Guards served during the 10 campaigns of almost unbroken victories on the continent of Europe. You ought to have "Schellenberg" emblazoned on the battle honours of the regiment, for half of the officers and men engaged were either killed or wounded, and it was certainly one of the bravest and most memorable actions of its kind in Europe. Lord Beaconsfield said that we are ruled either by force or tradition. We in this country are greatly ruled by tradition. The Grenadier Guards are keeping alive those traditions which lift the ordinary man above his level and put him in touch with the great deeds of the past.

GERMANY AND THE LEAGUE

November 7, 1933

House of Commons

On October 14 Germany walked out of the Disarmament Conference; a week later she left the League of Nations. On October 26 Labour won the East Fulham by-election on a blatantly pacifist platform. It is doubtful whether this element was the dominant one in this historic election, but it made a deep impression on all politicians, and particularly on Baldwin.

Mr. Lloyd George seems to suppose that he is entitled to some special claim to interpret the Treaty of Versailles and other treaties which ended the War. It is quite true that he had a great deal to do with the making of that Treaty, but once a treaty is signed it becomes an international instrument which everyone can judge, and I personally prefer the measured opinion of the jurists upon whom the Foreign Office relies.

I believe that the Treaty has been maintained in the letter and also in the spirit. It is not true that this country or the great countries with whom we have been associated have violated the Treaty in the letter or in the spirit. So far as the letter is concerned, I rest upon the dispatch of the Government of September [18] 1932, which laid out the whole case in a masterly manner. So far as the spirit is concerned, it is well known that ever since the Treaty was signed mitigations have been constantly introduced—far more than the Treaty contemplated. The evacuations of German territory have been carried out with greater rapidity, while the whole scheme and structure of reparations has been swept away altogether, and the victors in the struggle have lent a thousand million sterling to Germany over and above anything they have been paid. It is altogether wrong, therefore, to suggest that the late Allies in the War have failed in the letter or in the spirit to carry out, broadly speaking, their Treaty obligations.

My right hon. Friend made tonight a deeply interesting speech, to which I listened, like everyone else, with admiration of the persuasive charm and skill with which he pressed his point. There is nothing that he can do so well as to draw one side of a picture in the most glowing manner and then reduce the other side to small and pitiable proportions. He gave an account of the state of Europe. He represented that Germany might have a few thousand more rifles than was allowed by the Treaty, a few more Boy Scouts, and then he pictured the enormous armies of Czechoslovakia and Poland and France, with their thousands of cannon, and so forth. If I could believe that picture I should feel much comforted, but I cannot. I find it difficult to believe it in view of the obvious fear which holds all the nations who are neighbours of Germany and the obvious lack of fear which appears in the behavior of the German Government and a large proportion of the German people. The great dominant fact is that Germany has already begun to rearm. We read of importations quite out of the ordinary of scrap iron and nickel and war metals. We read of the military spirit which is rife throughout the country; we see that the philosophy of blood lust is being inculcated into their youth in a manner unparalleled since the days of barbarism.

The Leader of the Opposition [Mr. Lansbury] said just now that he and the Socialist party would never consent to the rearming of Germany. I was very much pleased when I heard that. I agree with him. I should feel very much safer if I felt that that would not happen in my lifetime or in that of my children. But is the right hon. Gentleman quite sure that the Germans will come and ask him for his consent before they rearm? Does he not think thay they might omit that formality and go ahead without even taking a card vote of the Trades Union Congress? Then the right hon. Gentleman said, "But in order to prevent them rearming I should like to see all the other countries, their neighbours, disarm," and that has been the burden of his speech and of many other speeches. But I doubt very much whether the other Powers are going to take any notice. I do not see why they should. In the next breath the right hon. Gentleman said that if they take his advice, and if it should turn out wrong and they find themselves exposed to attacks and getting into trouble, the first thing he will do will be to call a general strike in order to prevent any aid being sent them. If he is not going to take the slightest responsibility for these people, even if they do take his advice, I am inclined to think that they will be entitled to say to him, "Mind your own business."

But it is our own position that weighs upon us most of all here in this House. I am glad that an interval has been introduced into this dangerous process of disarmament in Europe, which has played a noticeable part in raising the temperature to its present level. If we wish to keep our freedom, we should forthwith recognize that our role in Europe is more limited than it has hitherto been considered to be. Isolation is, I believe, utterly impossible, but we should nevertheless practice a certain degree of sobre detachment from the European scene. We should not try to weaken those Powers which are in danger, or feel themselves in danger, and thereby expose ourselves to a demand that we should come to their aid. I have deprecated these schemes which we have laid before the Disarmament Conference prescribing the size of all the armies and navies and air forces of Europe. I am not going to analyze the MacDonald Plan. I told the House in March that it never had the slightest chance of being accepted— never. How could you expect those countries that feel themselves in so great danger to make the very large reductions which were asked for in their armaments, their air forces and armies, while at the same time substantial increases were offered to the Germany with which we are now confronted?

I know that it is natural for Ministers, for the Prime Minister, to wish to play a great part on the European stage, to bestride Europe in the cause of peace, and to be as it were its saviours. You cannot be the saviours of Europe on a limited liability. I agree with the statement of the late Mr. Bonar Law, who said that we cannot be the policemen of the whole world. We have to discharge our obligations, but we cannot take upon ourselves undue obligations into which we shall certainly come if we are the leaders in compelling and pressing for a great diminution in the strength of France and other Powers which are neighbours of Germany. How lucky it is that the French did not take the advice that we have been tendering them in the last few years, or the advice which the United States has given them—advice tendered from a safe position 3000 miles across the ocean! If they had accepted it the war would be much nearer, and our obligation to come to their aid would be much more strictly interpreted. There should be recognition of the fact that we ought not to place ourselves continually in the most prominent position and endeavour to produce spectacular effects of disarmament in Europe, because as surely as we do a great deal of our discretionary power will be gradually whittled away.

There is a fairly general measure of agreement as to the course which we should now pursue. We should adhere to the League of Nations. I did not agree with the Member for Carnarvon when he mocked and scolded the League in a speech in the country. Nor do I agree with those poor friends of the league who say that, just because the League was incapable of dealing with the situation in the Far East, on the other side of the world, it will have no efficacy in dealing with the European situation. What could you expect of the League in far-off Asia? China and Japan—what do they care for the League of Nations? Russia and the United States—neither of them members of the League. Those four countries comprise half the population of the globe. They form another world, a world in itself, and you should not judge of the success or power of a great international institution like this by the fact that it has not been able to make its will effective at the other side of the globe. Very different is the case in Europe. In Europe you have at least erected it upon the basis of the Treaties of Peace. That is a foundation on which you can build, and not only is it erected on that foundation, but powerful nations stand fully armed to defend those Treaties and, if necessary, to make themselves the agents and authorities of the League of Nations.

I believe that we shall find our greatest safety in co-operating with the other Powers of Europe, not taking a leading part but coming in with all the neutral States and the smaller States of Europe which will gather together anxiously in the near future at Geneva. We shall make a great mistake to separate ourselves entirely from them at this juncture. Whatever way we turn there is risk. But the least risk and the greatest help will be found in re-creating the Concert of Europe through the League of Nations, not for the purpose of fiercely quarreling and haggling about the details of disarmament, but in an attempt to address Germany collectively, so that there may be some redress of the grievances of the German nation and that that may be effected before this peril of [German] rearmament reaches a point which may endanger the peace of the world.

I see in the House some of the Ministers responsible for Defence Departments. I have been in that position myself in the years of baffling uncertainty through which we passed before the Great War, and I should like to tell those Ministers my own experience. In such circumstances every kind of pressure will be put upon them to reduce what they consider and what they are advised to be the necessary provision for our security. The papers will write leading articles. The Chancellor of the Exchequer and the Treasury are bound to put their case. The economists will give their views, and in Parliament there will be pressure for cutting down this and that. But if trouble should come none of the able editors, none of the stern economists, will be at hand to defend the Ministers. When the Service Departments are found to be hopelessly lacking in the essentials of our safety it will be no use to turn round and say to a newspaper, "You wrote an article saying that there must be a great cut," or in saying to a Member of Parliament, "You voted against any increase." These people will be among the very first to say, "Oh, you took all this money, and yet you have not even provided what is necessary."

In these circumstances, proved as it is that we have disarmed to the verge of risk—nay, well into the gulf of risk—a very great responsibility rests upon the Ministers for the Defence Departments to assure us that adequate provision is made for our safety, and for having the power and the time, if necessary, to realize the whole latent strength of our country.

AVOIDING WAR

November 11, 1933

Royal Naval Division Reunion Luncheon,
London

[Extract] . . . There are few things in my life that I value as much as the respect, regard, and unfailing kindness with which I have always been greeted by the officers and men of the Royal Naval Division. When one looks back on all that has happened and thinks of all that was said about it, and of the many differences of opinion which still prevail, one might have thought that if there was one place where I would not dare to show my face—(laughter)—it would be in the midst of the survivors of the Royal Naval Division, the men who were directed, in consequence of action I took, into one of the bloodiest scenes and most formidable situations in all the Great War. But, terrible as were the scenes in which you were plunged and the crises in which you played your part, the life, vitality, and human strength of the men who made up the division, and the brave families from which they sprang, were sufficient to wear down the worst that fate could threaten. There was no place where the division served that its name was not bright with honour, and there was not one in which it did not render notable service to the general cause of the Allies.

The great effort of the Dardanelles may safely be left to history. It comes along slowly but massively like an elephant, flattening out a great deal of rubbish in its path. History will unquestionably proclaim that if the Division had been supported as it should have been—and as, God knew, I did my best to secure—the history of the world would have been much happier, the history of the War would have been much shorter, and there would have been millions of men alive to-day who now were passed untimely from the world.

What could have been written down which was more precious to the men of the Division than the words in which Lord Haig congratulated the Division on its achievement in taking more ground and more prisoners in a single day than any of the other brave units which all the Empire sent into the field? . . .

I rejoice that this country is pulling round, perhaps better than any other in the great depression. It is showing great strength and coolness and composure, and also real unity. Although we rejoice at those things, still the state of affairs on the Continent of Europe must cause us all anxiety. I can only say that I believe a wise policy will keep this country out of European wars. I hope this country will be very careful not to meddle too much with friends and former Allies when they are taking measures they think necessary for their own security in a much greater danger. I believe we can so handle our policy as not to be too closely involved. But I will also say this, that never will I tolerate the language which is used, now here, now there, to say that England can no longer do her duty: to say that people would not march, or that undergraduates would not fight, for King and country.

FOREIGN POLICY

November 13, 1933

Constituency Meeting, Chingford

[Extract] . . . The trend of the by-elections shows that under the leadership of Mr. MacDonald and Mr. Baldwin the Conservative Party will face great difficulties when the General Election comes in two years' time.

Though the Socialists led this country to the verge of bankruptcy only two years ago, and disgraced themselves a few years earlier by the general strike, and the country repudiated them at the last election, the ascendancy of Socialist ideas seems greater than ever. The debates in the House of Commons are mainly conducted by Socialists, either on one side or the other. The Prime Minister is an international Socialist and so is the Leader of the Opposition. The Lord Chancellor is a Socialist, and so is Mr. Henderson, the president of the Disarmament Conference at Geneva. With all these key positions in their hands, it is natural that the Socialists are able to propagate their views both in international affairs and about our Empire in India.

The Socialists' foreign policy, always associated with Mr. MacDonald, of interfering on the Continent and trying to weaken France and strengthen Germany and, above all, of disarming Britain, has already been carried a long way. The Socialist policy about India and the Round Table Conference and the White Paper are steadily marching forward, and Mr. Baldwin uses all the power of the Conservative Party, all its social influence and that of the Party Whips and the Central Office to crush down resistance. Well might Sir John Simon exclaim at the luncheon to the three leaders of the National Government, "We are all Socialists now."

Still I believe that there are a great many people in the country who have a different opinion and will try as well as they can, though deprived of their natural party machinery, to stand up for their opinion. That is why it is so vitally important to preserve the strength and unity in the coming confusion of as many characteristically Conservative constituencies as possible. Thus, whatever happens there will be a strong nucleus of convinced resolute Tory members to continue to fight against Socialism in all its forms both at home and abroad.

It is never the slightest use trying to conciliate Socialist opinion. The only chance is to develop a national, patriotic British policy in a confident and whole-hearted manner and then to meet the Socialists in a thoroughly aggressive spirit. Unless a new spirit comes into Tory politics in the next few years there may easily be a landslide of a most lamentable and perilous character.

It is reserved for Lord Irwin to state the foreign policy of the Government in its most bald and unwise form. We are to assure France that she can count on us in order to induce her to disarm. If the French take our advice they will be weaker and we shall be more closely bound to them. They will have the right to say: "We have weakened ourselves at your request. We are now in danger. You must come and help us."

Surely this is to have the worst of both worlds. We neither keep out of a Continental struggle, nor, if we are drawn in, have we a strong ally. We are simply condemning ourselves, in fact, to make up out of our own flesh and blood for the strength we ask France, and not only France, but the friendly Powers associated with her to give up. What conceivable British interest should lead us into such danger?

Under the Treaty of Locarno we are free to judge exactly whether we are involved in a European war or not, and no one would dare to carry this country into a war without being supported by the heart and conscience of the nation. But as surely as we meddle with the vital defences of nations who believe they are in great peril, so surely will we be deprived of our discretion and dragged in willy-nilly at their tail.

THE DISARMAMENT CONFERENCE

November 14, 1933

Devonshire

[Extract] ... The Disarmament Conference has not only turned out to be an absolute farce and fraud, but it has done very great damage to the relations of the different Powers in Europe. The nations have been nagging each other to disarm, while all the time their hatreds, jealousies, and dangers have been quite unrelieved. Of course, they will not disarm. Not one of them is thinking of doing so, except, perhaps, Great Britain. On the contrary, during the last seven or eight years those nations have increased their armaments, especially the United States, whence came the most beautiful speeches of all. Not only have those European countries increased their armaments, but other countries of pronounced neutrality, not involved in the War, like Holland, Denmark, and Switzerland, have been forced to arm, and they are making preparations to defend their frontiers. They all live around Germany, the most formidable people in the world, and now the most dangerous—a people who inculcate a form of blood-lust in their children, and lay down the doctrine that every frontier must be the starting point for invasion.

What right have we to go to the perturbed countries bordering on Germany and tell them they must disarm unless we say that, if they get into trouble through taking our advice, we will go to their aid? I do not think we should do that. Locarno served a good purpose at the time it was ratified, but why should we compromise our freedom of judgment and our right to decide whether in the event of another European war we should needlessly involve ourselves and our children? Surely it is our business, our wisdom, to detach our country as much as possible from the vehement conflicts which are gathering on the Continent of Europe. But we cannot do that if we weaken those countries and meddle in their affairs too much. Disarmament has nothing to do with peace. If disarmament becomes universal war would not be in any way prevented. I hope the Government are going to cut the loss on the Disarmament Conference. We can only reach peace by trying to settle the grievances which exist between one nation and another. Then we can have moral disarmament. I have been described as a war monger. It is a lie. I laboured for peace before the War, and if the naval holiday I advised had been accepted by Germany the course of history might have been different.

THE POLITICAL SITUATION

November 15, 1933

Chigwell

[Extract] ... I have been asked whether I really think that the anti-Socialist forces at home would be stronger without the Prime Minister, Mr. Baldwin, and Sir John Simon.

In reply I am bound to say that the leadership of Mr. MacDonald would be a very great obstacle to the success of the Conservative and anti-Socialist forces at the next election. It is quite clear that the main conflict will be between international Socialism and the patriotic British forces. Obviously the anti-Socialist forces would be hampered by having at the head of the Government an international Socialist.

One of the most effective means by which the Socialist attack can be defeated is by counter-attacking them on their own vicious and disgraceful record. I am never tired of pointing out how the Socialists reduced this powerful country to the verge of bankruptcy only two years ago and how they tried to seize political power through the agency of the general strike. That is a main and essential part of the Conservative case, but how can we urge these powerful arguments when the head of the Government which we will be trying to defend is primarily responsible for that evil behaviour?

Then we come to the question of Mr. Baldwin and Sir John Simon. Will it be better for the Conservative cause if they retire? I think the answer depends upon what they do about India. If Mr. Baldwin is going to continue to thrust the Round Table Conference policy and the White Paper about India down the throats of

Conservatives all over the country he will do so much harm to the party that a very serious political disaster will occur.

But if he shows respect for the true opinion of those to whom he owes his position, if he is as loyal to the Conservative Party as the Conservative Party has been to him, and if he separates himself from the Socialist policy on India, there is no reason why he should not be the effective captain of the coming battle. All depends upon his attitude on India.

This is even more true about Sir John Simon. He is the last man in the country who can find any excuse for going wrong about India, for every one knows perfectly well what his true opinions are. It is his duty to stand up for those opinions and not merely to try to cover and explain away the follies and weaknesses of Lord Irwin, Lord Reading, and Sir Samuel Hoare.

THE DISARMAMENT CONFERENCE
November 17, 1933

Loughton

[Extract] ... I am disturbed to see that Sir John Simon and his Under-Secretary, or Joint Secretary, Mr. [Anthony] Eden, have gone to Geneva to try to revive the Disarmament Conference and to advocate the so-called MacDonald plan.

What is so alarming is the manner in which England is being made to take the lead in pressing other countries in great danger to weaken their defences and in trying to lay down the law to the whole of Europe as to the size of their different fleets and armies and air forces. We cannot possibly do this without becoming ever more deeply involved in the fierce European situation with all its hideous dangers.

Let us drop all this mischief-making pretence of disarmament while dangers and fierce hatreds and jealousies are so rife. Let Great Britain do her part and her duty in the League of Nations and with all the other countries, small as well as great.

FOREIGN POLICY
November 21, 1933

House of Commons

After the mover and seconder of the Address have delivered their excellent speeches, after the party leaders, the leaders of great parties and the leader of a once great party, have made their contributions to our knowledge, the House will perhaps be so indulgent as to tolerate a few comments on some aspects of the situation from a back bencher and private Member. Here, let me say by way of parenthesis that it astonishes me, after having listened to the Debate on so many of these occasions, that private Members neglect the opportunities with which an occasion like this could supply them. We often have complaints from them that they have no opportunity of being called—

Mr. Tinker: They do not get a chance until the big men have had a try.

Mr. Churchill: Allow me to point out to the Hon. Member that there will be many hours to-night—the House has no need to adjourn—when a very active discussion could be maintained. With a desire to set an example in that respect, I shall offer a very few observations to the House. It is usual on these occasions for the Prime Minister to give to Parliament and the country a broad survey of public affairs both at home and abroad and to focus the main issues upon which political controversy is likely to develop in the coming Session between the different parties, but on this occasion the Prime Minister, the Leader of the House, has confined himself, except for casual mention of others, to two main topics. He dealt with Foreign Affairs and he dealt with the question of armaments manufactured by private firms. I am bound to say that I thought his argument on the latter subject was very effective and one which might have been reinforced, because I believe it is no exaggeration to say that this country, where we are so busy pillorying the armament firms is, more than any great country, devoid of the means of making weapons of defence should emergency arise. More than the industry of any country either in Europe or on the northern Continent of America this island has almost lost the capacity to make weapons of defence, if it were required to do so. It is a very odd thing that when the principle of disarmament has been carried in this island so far as that, even menacing the entire safety of the country, it should receive no recognition from the party opposite, and that those who have disarmed most in the world should still be accused of being jingoes, war-mongers, and protectors of armament firms.

But it is not with that part of the Prime Minister's speech that I wish to deal to-night. I am anxious to follow up for a very short time the discussion which has taken place upon the foreign situation. Europe to-day presents a lamentable scene. There was one phrase in the right hon. Gentleman's speech relating to Foreign Affairs—almost the only phrase in which, I am bound to say, there was any information—in which he dealt with the importance of using diplomatic machinery. He said, and I was very glad to hear him say it, that parallel and supplementary efforts would be made as a result of diplomatic machinery. That is a very desirable thing. There was a time when statesmen never left their own country and there ensued a time when they hardly ever returned. There was a time when the statesmen of different countries hardly ever met each other, but there has come a time when they must be getting frightfully bored with continual propinquity.

I was reading a book the other day by an able young writer, long versed in the affairs of the Foreign Office, Mr. Harold Nicolson, in which he referred to the evils of imprecision in Foreign Affairs. When you get two very distinguished statesmen, representing two different countries, and they meet together, naturally they wish to be extremely polite with one another and naturally they want to make the very best impression. Both desire to have something to take home to their people—this one to show what he has done for his country and what sacrifices he has made of his country's interests for the sake of peace. Each seeks to make an effect with their own particular public. It is not really a good method of conducting diplomacy. I should have thought that it was much better to use the trained diplomatists more, to use the Ambassadors more, to use the vehicle of carefully considered dispatch, in which the nice terms of meaning and the realities can be stated deftly and clearly, where the situation can be put calmly and patiently in the right way by those men who have made it their life's business to study foreign affairs, and can convey exactly the shadow of meaning which is required. Therefore, I am glad to know, because I made a suggestion on the subject to my right hon. Friend earlier in the year, that we are going to have diplomatic machinery employed again.

The position which we have now reached in Europe is a very lamentable one, and I do not think that this Debate at the opening of the Session, the greatest day in the Session, when the whole field of affairs is open, when the Gracious Speech is made on the subject of an Address from the Commons, should pass without some comment on the subject. A most unsatisfactory result has been reached in Europe, and I am going to say, as I have said before, although it will not be at all popular, that the Prime Minister's conduct of foreign affairs, whether as the head of the Socialist Government or as the head of the National, patriotic Government, has been equally attended with misfortune. I do not say for one moment that he is responsible for the tremendous turns and twists of events that have occurred in the attitude and demeanour of great countries in Europe, still I must draw the attention of Parliament and the country to the total collapse of all the main matters with which he has been personally concerned in foreign affairs.

Let us look back. There was the London Naval Conference. I do not think there is any doubt whatever to-day among those who study the position of our Navy that that has been a very great hindrance not merely to our naval strength but to our spending such little money as we can afford to spend in a manner calculated to give us the greatest measure of security. Then we come to Lausanne. I have always thought that it was a very great mistake to release our German debtors until we had some security in regard to our credit. What has been the result? We have released them and what have they done with the money that otherwise they would have had to pay across the exchange? They have been buying the nickel referred to by the Prime Minister with the money that ought to have been put across the exchange, whereas we have received no sort of effective release from our creditors elsewhere. I cannot feel that the triumph of Lausanne, the more it is examined, will bring any sense of satisfaction to those who have studied the situation.

Then there is the World Economic Conference. I have heard people say about the Prime Minister that, although he may have his faults and short comings, see how good he is at conferences; that is his speciality. Before the meeting of the World Economic Conference Parliament sent him to the United States on purpose to arrange beforehand and make sure that there were no misunderstandings. All that happened was that we allowed that conference to assemble without any effective common policy with the United States of America, with the result that the nations brought together from all ends of the globe to London were made participators in one of the most painful and melancholy fiascos of international intercourse. Future international relations have to that extent been impaired and the prospect of general co-operation impoverished.

Lastly, there is the Disarmament Conference, which is the main topic upon which I desire to speak. I have often wondered what is the secret of the Prime Minister's success. I have watched him with the greatest interest all these years and I have often been very puzzled how it is that he seems able, in the words of the poet: "to ride in the whirlwind and direct the storm." I have not the slightest doubt that it is far from his intentions, but I am bound to say that one of the qualities which have led him to the giddy pinnacle which he now holds is an extraordinary aptitude for laying the blame for failure on other people. He was for a long time, two years, the leader of the Socialist Administration, of whom I have expressed the worst possible opinion. It now appears that all the blame rests with hon. Members now sitting on the benches opposite. The right hon. Gentleman the other day spoke about the importance of having a good memory. He has the best kind of memory one can have, a memory which conveniently forgets. His anno domini, his hegira, begins with the end of the year 1931.

Now in regard to our foreign policy, the long series of breakdowns—they cannot be described as anything else—which have reduced diplomacy almost to bankruptcy in Europe, I understand that the blameworthy person is the Foreign Secretary. I have no means of information except the many channels of the public Press, but as far as I can see and from what I hear he is the guilty person. I hold no brief for my right hon. Friend the Foreign Secretary; indeed, no one has any need to hold a brief for him. He is very good at holding briefs, that is his forte. But where the Foreign Secretary makes a mistake is not in the manner in which he conducts the brief he has taken up, but in his readiness to accept any brief which is tendered to him in the proper manner and with the appropriate fee marked in the corner. He takes up anything which is presented to him, with the consequence that he finds himself, and has found himself on this occasion, placed in a very difficult position.

In regard to the Disarmament Conference, I think that the Foreign Secretary was set an impossible task. The task he was set was to persuade Europe to agree to what is called the MacDonald Plan of Disarmament. The Prime Minister placed this great plan before Europe, making enormous demands upon ourselves and prescribing to the angry and nervous Powers of Europe exactly the size of their armaments and air forces. But the Prime Minister had never worked out the figures. He presented this scheme to Europe, and, as I said at the time, France and other countries, although naturally polite, said they would read it a second time and send it to a committee. I understand that it was only read a first time and then sent up to a committee, and I gather that the Foreign Secretary was entrusted with the difficult business of handling the matter in committee. The French would never agree to let such a plan be read a first time unless they had a perfectly clear plan and method, very proper on their part considering the danger they are in to see that the plan worked no mischief. There was bound to be a breakdown when the matter came into committee.

Look at the formula put forward with so much triumph by the Foreign Secretary. He dealt with it quite tenderly, as one which would reconcile France and Germany. It was, "a system of equality within a system of general security," or was it "equality within a general system of security"? Or was it "qualitative equality within a general system of security"?

What does it all mean? What is the result of all that? When you are trying to get agreement to bridge the gap there is this absurd formula presented, which is really a contradiction in terms. You might just as well say that you are in favour of deep water bathing provided it is certain none of us get wet. Ladened with this tremendous plan, this plan which make Germany and Italy numerically stronger than France, a plan which would derange entirely existing balances of Europe, and which, I believe, if it were the rule to-day would place us in a position when we should not be far removed from war, the Foreign Secretary goes to the committee and at a certain stage, having tried to cozen the French, has to agree to something which they put in, with the result that the Germans leave the Conference. And he has to bear the blame for that. The responsibility rests on whose who, without adequate study, put forward a plan which makes us interfere in the vital life of Europe, a plan which had no chance of being accepted, and then throw the burden of carrying it through upon the right hon. Gentleman the Foreign Secretary.

The Secretary of State for Foreign Affairs (Sir John Simon): The right hon. Gentleman will allow me to correct him on one point. He will clearly understand that I am just as much responsible for the British plan as anybody else, and I do not disclaim a scrap of that responsibility.

Mr. Churchill: I am well aware of the doctrine of Ministerial responsibility and nothing that I have said contradicts it in any way. The Disarmament Conference has been a danger to the peace of Europe. It has not only made the relations of different countries much worse, but it has undoubtedly had the effect of gravely endangering the League of Nations itself. The Four-Power Pact which the right hon. Gentleman the Prime Minister has been concerned in making is undoubtedly a rival to the League of Nations; it cannot help being so. If hon. Members will watch carefully in the next few weeks the action of Italy they will see that a new centre will be set up which, if it develops, will undoubtedly lead to an immense weakening of the League of Nations as an instrument upon which we can rely. This would be a great misfortune. One of the gravest issues which arises at the present time is a weakening of the League of Nations, first by trying to do things which it cannot do, thus casting a strain on it which it cannot bear and, secondly, by the great Powers endeavouring to break away and conduct the vital matters of Europe through another agency. In my view, the prudent course for us is to associate ourselves with the League of Nations to defend safety and honour by working not with three or four nations but with 12 or 14 Powers, and doing our part, and no more, in conjunction with those Powers. I have taken the opportunity of the Debate on the Address to bring these matters once more before the House, and I thank them for their indulgence.

INDIA (CONSTITUTIONAL REFORM)

November 22, 1933

House of Commons

I do not wish to continue the Debate upon the merits of this immense topic which has been opened to us this afternoon in two such pregnant speeches as those to which we have just listened. I say "pregnant" because they contain very much matter and many statements with which all of us could agree or disagree according to our views. But I do not propose this afternoon to go into those large issues, because when we have this matter on the Floor of this House in the long stages of a Bill, we shall have lots of opportunities to thrash out every detail and every aspect.

Colonel Wedgwood *rose*—

Mr. Churchill: The right hon. and gallant Gentleman knows a great deal about India, but I have lived a long time in the House, and I certainly am of opinion that we shall have opportunities of debating this matter very fully. Therefore, I do not propose this afternoon to go at all over the ground which I, personally, endeavoured to explore and to illuminate when we last discussed this subject. Neither do I propose to object in any way to the reappointment of the Committee, and I should like to associate myself with the tribute which was paid to the Committee yesterday by the Prime Minister for its patience, courtesy and zeal in its protracted task. I think it is a great pity that the Government packed the Committee with such an overwhelming majority of their own supporters who had already made their views publicly known in favour of the White Paper. If the Secretary of State had shown a larger sense of tolerance and of fair play, and a greater detachment from his own schemes, I believe that he could have created a body whose labours would have been a real help in solving these profound Indian problems, or might, at any rate, have made some valuable contribution thereto. It was a great chance which my right hon. Friend threw away through being too greedy. But at this stage in the proceedings, after the Committee have sat for so many months, after they have examined so many witnesses, and, as I can testify myself, with inexhaustible assiduity and patience, and now that they have begun to consider that there is nothing left for them to do but to disagree upon their report, I think it would be a great pity to make any effort to change the personnel at the present time.

Therefore, I make no complaint at all of the Motion which the Under-Secretary made to us in his speech, which, unhappily, I did not hear, but which, I am told, had at any rate the merit of brevity. The point I wish to complain about this afternoon is not the appointment of this Committee nor the character of the Committee. My complaint—it is very largely a Parliamentary argument, not roaming off into the far spaces of the East, but very much directed to our own affairs at home—my complaint is directed to the fact that His Majesty's Government, while constantly assuring Parliament and the Conservative party, who, after all, are the bulk of their supporters, that we are not committed in any way beyond the Act of 1919, and while appealing to us on all occasions to wait for the Report of the Joint Committee, are, in fact, doing everything in their power to drive forward the White Paper policy, and to make it impossible for Parliament to recede from it. That is the proposition I propose to develop and examine, with the patience of the House, this afternoon.

I say that for this purpose the Government speak with two voices—one voice for home and the other for India, and very often one voice for one audience at home and another for a different audience. What is the salient face in the tactics of His Majesty's Government? It is very remarkable, when you consider how long this matter has gone on, that they have never openly sought a vote in favour of the White Paper policy. Nothing could exceed the modesty and the meekness of the Motions which the Government arrange to have proposed in their support. Every direct issue has been avoided, whether in the House of Commons or in the party conferences out of doors. The Government have never dared—I make no reproach upon their courage; it is not a question of courage, it is a question of their knowledge of the political forces at work—to ask plainly for approval of their Indian policy. They have a stock Motion which they introduce on all difficult occasions when they are brought into contact with those to whom they owe their political authority. I must read it to the House. That stock Motion is to this effect:

> Approves the caution with which the Government is proceeding in framing its proposals for a new Constitution, and believes that this country should not come to any final conclusion on the matter until the Joint Select Committee now sitting, which consists in the main of men with a wide experience of Indian administration, have finished the hearing of evidence and made their recommendations.

That seems very reasonable. Nobody could find much fault with that, but it is hardly an heroic and confident statement of the issues which the Government are putting before the country. I notice that even Ministers of the Crown have been quite ready to support a Resolution of this kind, congratulating the Government and enjoining upon the Government—that is, upon themselves—extreme caution in the development of their Indian policy. Nobody would complain of that kind of self-discipline, which may be extremely necessary.

From the beginning we have been assured that we are not committed by anything that the Round Table Conference have done to any new position in regard to India. At every stage we have been urged to wait for something that is going to happen. For a very long time we were told to wait for the White Paper. Then we were told to wait for the appointment of the Committee. Now we are told to wait for the report of the Committee. When the report of the Committee has been presented we shall be invited to wait until the Government decide upon the main headlines of their Bill, and after that we shall be told to wait until we see the actual text of the Bill. At every point we are being invited to wait, and side by side with it there goes on an insidious propaganda to this effect: "After all the expectations that have been aroused in India we cannot go back on the work of the Round Table Conference."

I am going to repeat some of the assurances that we have received. They are familiar to the House, but there is no reason why the country and the House should not be reminded of them. The earliest of them was given by the Prime Minister, in reply to a letter addressed to him during the late Parliament by my right hon. Friend the Lord President of the Council, who asked him some very pointed questions. The Prime Minister replied, on the 11th November, 1929:

> The answer to both parts of the question as to whether the Viceroy's (Lord Irwin's) Declaration implies any change in the policy hitherto declared or in the time when this status may be attained, is, "No."

Then there was the celebrated statement of Lord Hailsham, in December, 1931, in the opening Debate of this Parliament:

> You are not pledging yourself to support any Bill when it comes before this House. You are committing yourself to this, and to this only, that you endorse the action of the Government in going on with their inquiries and negotiations, in sending out their Committees, in seeing the Ruling Princes and in endeavouring to find a solution on those lines, but you reserve to yourself full liberty if, when the solution is brought before you, you think it does not meet the conditions laid down.

That was the statement made by Lord Hailsham in the House of Lords. Lastly, there is the statement of the Secretary of State for India, in the House of Commons on the 27th March of this year:

> The pledges of the past leave full opportunity to Parliament in the choice of the time and manner of constitutional advance. I accept this principle.– [Official Report, 27th March, 1933; col. 697, Vol. 276.]

Those are the assurances. Let us look on the other side. Look at the propaganda. My right hon. and gallant Friend opposite has referred to Sir John Thompson and Sir Alfred Watson, two gentlemen who have lately obtained some prominence through being particularly noticed by the "Times" newspaper. I am not aware of any other claim they have to special attention. They are the chief organisers of the Union of Britain and India, which is the propagandist society which has been set up to advocate the White Paper, and which is cherished, and I think I might almost say, though I do not say it, nourished by the Conservative Central Office. Let us see what these two gentlemen, who are conducting the propaganda of the Government and who, so to speak, are the advance guard of the Government in their Indian policy, have to say. Sir Alfred Watson wrote in the "Times" of the 10th June, 1933:

> Whatever validity attaches to the Montagu pledge, it has been rein-forced, if not superseded, by a pledge of far more significance. In December, 1931, both Houses of Parliament approved by overwhelming majorities the policy outlined in the Indian Round Table Conference, Command Paper No. 3972. That Command Paper declared for provincial

autonomy, for a Central Government with responsibility on a Federal basis, and for safeguards. The Prime Minister stated that, "In order to give this declaration the fullest authority" he was asking Parliament to approve it.

Sir John Thompson, on the 15th September, also in the "Times" newspaper, said:

> Parliament has already expressed its approval of the triple basis scheme which is now before the Joint Committee, that is, provincial autonomy, federation and partial responsibility at the centre.

What is the relation of this insidious propaganda to the perfectly definite pledge of Lord Hailsham in the House of Lords when the Resolution was being passed, and to the statement made by the right hon. Gentleman in the House so recently?

There is a much more important declaration which has been recently made, to which I must invite the attention of the House. I mean the declaration of the Viceroy upon the question of Dominion Status. The phrase "Dominion Status" was loosely used 10 or 12 years ago and all who were concerned in that, however unwittingly, are blameworthy.

Earl Winterton: Hear, hear.

Mr. Churchill: I am glad to find that my words for once have won the agreement of the Noble Lord. I am glad to find that on one point, at any rate, I am at one with him. Many things have happened in the last 10 years. The whole of this constitutional field in India has now become an area of the most closely examined and meticulously scrutinised constitutional argument, and every point, every phrase is now looked at not with the sentimental interpretation which might have been put upon it but with the exact meaning. Moreover, as the Noble Lord might remind his constituents at Horsham the next time he has the courage to face them—the Statute of Westminster has been passed in the last two years.

The House is familiar with all the details of the Statute of Westminster. The changes which that Statute made in Dominion Status are overwhelming and measureless. The changes which it made in the letter of the law of Dominion Status are overwhelming—the right to secede by mere votes of the Assemblies, the power to disallow any Imperial Acts, even the Acts which constitute the instrument setting up the Dominion, and many other points of the utmost significance which had been a dead letter between us and the self-governing Dominions but which carry great validity in regard to our relations with India. All these powers have been introduced to the Statute Book as a result of the Statute of Westminster, and I do not imagine that the Indian politicians are not fully alive to all this. We all remember Mr. Sastri's attempt to commend the White Paper to some of his friends, when he pointed out that Dominion Status included the right to secede from the British Empire, and therefore it was more acceptable than it otherwise would have been.

When this Parliament began, in its callow youth, when it first arrived here full of enthusiasm and wondering what great things were going to happen, I raised this question of the effect of the Statute of Westminster upon the proposals of the White

Paper—not the last White Paper but the first White Paper of two years ago; the Prime Minister's valedictory address to the Congress delegates. What did the Secretary of State say? He said that the Statute of Westminster had no more to do with the statement of Government policy than the man in the moon.

Sir S. Hoare: I should repeat that now.

Mr. Churchill: Very well. I am very glad to hear that. I am very glad that the right hon. Gentleman is still standing by the man in the moon. But what does he think of this statement of the Viceroy, reported in the "Times" of the 29th August of this year, in which he claimed that

> His Government's policy had been completely consistent with two main facets and the first was to push on with the reforms as hard as they could go so as to help India forward to Dominion status and absolute equality with the other Dominions.

What has the right hon. Gentleman to say to that? While he declares that what he has in mind has no more to do with the Statute of Westminster than the man in the moon, the Viceroy, with whom he is in the closest accord, speaking in India, to another audience, says that he is working up to absolute equality—note the phrase—with the other Dominions, and he uses that expression at a time when the politicians in India attach importance to the expression "Dominion Status," because they know that under the Statute of Westminster it gives them the right inter alia to secede from the British Empire. No doubt the right hon. Gentleman will explain this position when he speaks this evening, but it is very difficult to reconcile this kind of double policy, the man in the moon here, and absolute equality at Delhi with that fair dealing which we have always associated and which I hope we shall always be able to associate with those who sit on that Front Bench.

There is another aspect which illustrates the point that I am making, namely, the concealment of the issue here while all the time a march is being stolen elsewhere. That is my point. There is another aspect, and perhaps to some extent something of this might have been inevitable, but I want the House to examine it. While the country is assured that nothing is happening and that we are altogether uncommitted, step by step His Majesty's Government are advancing towards their goal. While the nation is soothed and chloroformed here, every preparation is being made to bring the policy into actual effect in India. Indeed, it is taken for granted by the Government of India in their every act that this policy is going through. A law has been passed empowering Governors to prolong the life of various local legislatures, and in view of the constitutional changes which it is assumed are going to take place governors are being appointed who are ardent supporters of the scheme. That is not unnatural, because one would hardly expect the Government to appoint opponents of their scheme.

The Civil Service have been offered the right to retire on proportionate pensions if under the new scheme they feel that they have no longer a reasonable and hopeful sphere of usefulness. This is a curious provision which does not seem to suggest any great enthusiasm on the part of the Civil Service for the new method, but it is no bar to the Government claiming that the great bulk of the Civil Service are supporters of the scheme. Contributors to the Indian military widows and orphans pension fund have been told, rather callously, that if they care to bring their funds home they can, but, naturally, their pittance will be less at home because of the lower rates of interest. We are told that it is derogatory to the Indian Government to offer any British guarantee for the payment of pensions due. The naval and military authorities have been reassured by the proposed detachment of the fortress of Aden from the control of future Indian Governments. Aden is to be saved from the wreck. It is a measure of prudence which must commend itself, but it is rather a strange mark of confidence. All this shows how constantly and by every channel the Government are proceeding as if the Report of the Committee were a foregone conclusion, as if the decision of this House and the other House were a foregone conclusion, and that the whole scheme would come into complete operation. While anxieties at home are lulled and the direct issue avoided we are every month becoming more deeply compromised by arousing Indian expectations, and at the same time His Majesty's Government, ruthlessly, behind the scenes, are making every preparation for carrying their policy into effect. They have already gone a long way.

Among all the continuous preparations which they are making and the propaganda which they are conducting behind the scenes in all the vast administrative sphere under their control, nothing is more prominent than the pressure they have put on the Princes of India. The word "pressure" is difficult to define. Pressure is difficult to prove. I am told that sometimes the Whips put pressure on hon. Members in the Lobby to vote in a particular division, but it is difficult to prove as, in the first place, some of the language used would not, I am told, be suitable for reproduction on the Floor of the House, even if it were not already safeguarded by being private conversation. Therefore I have to rely on public statements which are quotable. There are several which are quotable. I am not going to say anything about patronage. Since I referred to it in the Debate in the summer I have had a great deal of material put before me, but it is a matter which cannot be dealt with properly because it involves dealing with individual cases, and would be very painful and vexatious to the individuals concerned. Therefore, I shall not attempt to deal with this very large and obvious sphere of patronage. But let me take a statement made by Sir Akbar Hydari, the representative of the Nizam in this country. On 23rd December, 1932—he asked this question:

> Is it not the fact that the Secretary of State and His Majesty's Government have slowly but surely pressed us into the Federation? No one who has watched the Secretary of State and his colleagues ruthlessly holding us to it, can doubt that it is an All-India Federation that they want, and no lesser substitute.

Apparently this ruthless pressure had some effect on Sir Akbar Hydari, because when I was a witness before the Joint Select Committee he said this:

> May I also state that so far from there being any pressure from the Political Department of the Government of India on the different States in favour of Federation, I believe British India, at any rate, was afraid that the pressure would be exerted the other way in tearing up the Federation.

Whatever pressure has been at work on the mind of this eminent and distinguished Indian gentleman it has certainly been effective; it has produced a complete change in his statement. Then there was the exhortation, the warning, with a menace in it, given to the princes of India by the Lord Chancellor in winding up the third Round Table Conference. He said:

There was only one thing which could dim the lustre of their statesmanship, and that one thing was delay. India is thirsting . . . you have put the cup to her lips—do not delay her drinking it.

I say that it is pressure when one of the leading Members of His Majesty's Government says publicly to the princes of India that they will be responsible for denying to India the cup for which India is thirsting. There is also the incident of the Jam Sahib at Delhi, who was interrupted by the Viceroy and made to discontinue the speech he was making on the dangers of federation. It was explained to me by the Secretary of State, when I attended the sitting of the Joint Select Committee, that this was merely that the Jam Sahib was out of order, the topic was not on the Order Paper for that day, and that all the Viceroy did was to call him to order. That is not at all a complete representation of what took place. The greatest pressure put on the princes of India is the pressure of their own loyalty to the Crown, to the British Government, and to the Viceroy as the King Emperor's representative. When it is clearly shown what is the view of the Government it undoubtedly tends, through the whole of the great congregation of Native States, to make them desirous to meet the wishes of the supreme authority, of the King Emperor and his Government. One of the most pathetic features of this story is the malversation of loyalties to the British Empire, which we have by our past conduct deserved and won, and which should have been our defence and support.

I am not making any assertion but I would ask the Secretary of State to enlighten us on this matter. I have seen it stated that the residency areas, at Bangalore and Hyderabad are being handed back to the Governments of Mysore and Nizam respectively. Is that so?

Sir S. Hoare: I shall deal with these questions in my own time and in my own way.

Mr. Churchill: I am glad of that, that is perfectly right and proper. The right hon. Gentleman cannot say "no" right away, and he is entitled to make his answer in the form he likes at a later stage. There is the question of the Berars. This is an important point: I am subject to correction on this matter. The Berars are a district in the northern part of the State of Hyderabad which have been administered for a long time by the British Government. The Nizam and his advisers have been anxious to have them back under their own government, an anxiety not entirely shared by the population of the district. This is what the Secretary of State said on the 15th of December to the Hyderabad Delegation at a dinner reported in the "Times of India" on 17th December. It was not reported extensively in this country, but the text is taken from the "Times of India," on which I am entirely dependent as my authority.

If it is not correct then my argument, so far as it rests on this report, must be withdrawn. This is what the right hon. Gentleman is reported to have said:

> We have had one or two difficult questions; to take the single instance connected with the future of Berar, a territory that is part of Hyderabad but none the less administered by the British Government. Obviously, that dual arrangement might make for considerable difficulty in the way of a Federation, if there was not willingness to make an agreeable settlement on both sides. Sir Akbar—

that is the gentleman whose opinions underwent a transformation—

> and I have discussed the question at some length,, and I venture to say that the discussions all go to show that with good will on both sides—and it is quite obvious that good will exists on both sides—more detailed negotiations that are to occur in India in the next few weeks will certainly succeed. I see no reason, and I do not think that Sir Akbar sees any reason why the complicated position of Berar should in any way be an obstacle in the way of the entry of Hyderabad into the Federation.

That is an important concession made to one of the most important, perhaps the greatest, Prince of India, not, of course, as a bargain, not, of course, as a *quid pro quo*, but simultaneously with the vigorous exertion which he and his representatives are making in favour of the establishment of a federal scheme. There was the incident which fell under my own notice at the time when I visited the Joint Select Committee. There was a question from Sir Manubhai Mehta, who is the representative of Bikaner. He was examining me, and after pointing out that the Indian States had great financial grievances against the Indian Government and that they ought to have large financial concessions, he asked this question:

> 15,184. Are you aware that the Davidson Committee also reported that many States had not been fairly treated, and large financial sums were due to them and they would be paid to them only if they entered the Federation. You now stop the Federation. What becomes of their financial claims?

Whether he asked this question by accident or design I cannot tell, but I wish hon. Members had been present to see the effect it produced on the Secretary of State for India and upon the Chancellor of the Duchy. Hon. Members have no doubt seen a hen suddenly disturbed when sitting on eggs; and the Chancellor of the Duchy, the Chairman of the Committee, came clucking and cluttering up. Observe what happened. Here is a Committee presided over by the Chancellor of the Duchy, which has been dealing with the question of the sums paid by the native States to the Imperial Government in consequence of the protection they receive from British forces and for other reasons, going into the whole of this matter; and here are the States which are all complaining, as everyone does complain, that the Government ought to make large financial concessions. Here are the Government very anxious to get the States to come into the Federation, to work up to the 50 per cent. which is now all they hope for in spite of the inducements and pressure. And then comes my right hon. Friend the Chancellor of the Duchy with his report. I do not suggest for a moment that he had any intention of offering any inducement in the report, but it presents the situation that if they do come in they are going to get large financial concessions, and that if the Federation does not go through they are not, as far as we know now, going to get them, or are not going to get them in the present form at the present time.

There is an instance of pressure, of financial pressure. I am willing to accept any statement as to the good faith of the Government in the matter, though the point is not what the Government meant. The real point is what is the impression produced upon the Princes of India and the native States by the way this matter has been handled? There can be no doubt, if you read what Sir Manubhai Mehta said, what that impression was. In spite of all these inducements, it really is remarkable that the Government have had to reduce their expectations of the Princes who will come into the scheme down to as low as 50 per cent.

I have definitely limited myself to this one point, which I have tried to approach from various angles. It is not only the right but it is the duty of a Government to have a will of its own and to have a policy, and to declare that policy. I do not accuse the Government of being without a will of its own, or without a policy on India. On the contrary, I think that the Prime Minister and the Lord President of the Council have never changed their policy in any way since it was formulated around Christmas of 1930. Then the Prime Minister, head of a Socialist Government, as we know from the testimony of the hon. Member for Bassetlaw (Mr. M. MacDonald), definitely decided in favour of a federal system for India, with responsible government at the centre. Since 26th January, 1931, when my right hon. Friend the Lord President, then the Leader of the Opposition, openly declared his intention to support and implement—that was the word—the proceedings of the first Round Table Conference, these two powerful politicians, who control in one way or another an enormous part of the agencies and facilities of our public life and discussion, have steadily driven their policy forward by every means in their power, and such has been their ardour that they have subordinated almost all other considerations to their main purpose. I have no doubt—I give this as a matter of personal judgment—that their agreement upon the subject of India played a definite part in bringing about the great convulsions in our political and party life which occurred at the end of 1931.

During the whole of this long period, more than three years, they have never in my judgment changed their policy. The policy is exactly the same now as it was when the Prime Minister planned it as head of the late Government. The White Paper embodied that policy. The Joint Committee was selected to make absolutely sure that it should be supported. And every step has been taken since which forethought and calculation could suggest in order to bring it to fruition. We see infirmity of purpose, inertia and lack of energy and conviction in many directions in our affairs, but we must recognise the persistency and resolution and activity which have characterised the action of the Government in this Indian sphere. There is no complaint of that. They have as much right to press their views as some of us have to oppose them.

My complaint is not that they are pressing their views by every means open to them. My complaint is of the discrepancy between their action and the assurances which the leaders of the Conservative party are constantly giving to the public that no one is committed, that the whole matter is *sub judice*, that the Lord President is only considering the matter in all its bearings, that all is entirely open pending the report of the Joint Committee, and that all we are engaged in is inquiry and examination. That is the discrepancy to which I have directed the attention of the House this afternoon. It is a discrepancy which I think is unfair—I will not say wilfully unfair, but in fact naturally unfair to the Conservative party and the country, who have a right to be told with candour whither it is proposed to lead them, instead of being baffled and hoodwinked by endless evasions, when all the time every possible step is being taken to prejudice the decision beyond recall.

1934

"WHITHER BRITAIN?"

January 16, 1934

Broadcast, London

We had never been—certainly not for hundreds of years—so defenceless as we are now. The hideous curse of war from the air has fallen on the world. We used to say that we would have a Navy stronger than that of any two Powers. Surely the least we ought now to do is to have an air force as strong as that of the nearest Power that can get at us.

If we have that, I do not believe we shall be attacked. Or, if we are, I do not think it would last long, or do us a mortal injury. I am all for diplomacy and good intentions, but first of all we ought to make the island safe. We ought also to have a clear, honest, foreign policy which anybody can explain and everybody can understand.

I do not agree with those who say the League of Nations is no use, and can never prevent another European war. It might be the only chance of preventing one; or, if it could not prevent it, of making sure that the guilty disturber of the peace has the worst of it. If the League of Nations is not broken up by wrangles and intrigues about disarmament, it might still remain an august tribunal to which not only Great Powers but small peoples might look, if not for protection, at any rate for a declaration of where right and justice lay. We must take our place there, and bear our share in building up a confederation of nations so strong and sincere that in Europe at least no aggressor would dare to challenge them.

The cause of the world depression is not famine or scarcity. It is our very power to supply our wants more abundantly that have upset the old arrangements. Man is conquering Nature, and the problem now is to spread the plenty which science can bestow. We have got to find out the answer to that; and I believe we should find a way. If it is so easy to produce surplus food, surely it ought not to be too hard to bring it to those who need it. We do not want a revolution to arrange that. All we want is a little more common sense and a better organization.

Many powerful forces threaten our Parliamentary system. The House of Lords should be reformed and made into a strong and effective Second Chamber. It should be different in character from the House of Commons, and its task should be to keep

5319

the main structure of our national life beyond the danger of sudden and violent change.

The House of Commons should also be strengthened and brought more effectively in touch with the active life of the people. Its present state is most unhealthy. All views should be represented there, and both sides should be heard on every question. The franchise ought to be strengthened, and what is called "weighted." There is no need to take away votes from anybody. We should give extra votes to the millions of men and women, the heads of households and fathers of families, who are really bearing the burden and responsibility of our fortunes on their shoulders.

I hope that before this Parliament breaks up it will reform the House of Lords and put it in its proper place in relation to the House of Commons. I also hope that it will reform the franchise of the House of Commons itself and make it a more true and permanent expression of the real forces that are alive in the nation.

We must be a strong, successful, scientific, commercial Empire or starve. There is no half-way house for Britain between greatness and ruin. That is why I feel so anxious and so angry when I hear all these high-brow sentimentalists and chop-logic feeble minds talking in their airy philosophical detachment about letting India go, or throwing away the Colonies, or losing touch with Canada, Australia, New Zealand, or South Africa, these young nations who stretch their hands to us across the oceans. Little do these clever chatterboxes know and little do they dream of the miseries to which they would condemn the faithful patriotic wage-earners of Britain.

SIR STAFFORD CRIPPS

January 25, 1934

Conservative and Unionist Association Dinner,
North Paddington

I think English men and women have a great deal to be thankful for when they see the condition of chaos which exists throughout the world, and the tyranny under which so many nations have fallen.

We have a great country and we have a great chance. We have seen all these institutions, of which this island has been the cradle, brushed away and all sorts of ideas put forward giving great ascendancy to brutal power, but here we have preserved the liberties of the subject.

We are told that if the Socialists get into power, they will have no nonsense with the House of Commons; they will allow it to pass a resolution straight away, and then after that Sir Stafford Cripps and his friends will be telling us where we get off. But I must say I think him a poor kind of revolutionary. I am not a revolutionary. I am all for old England going on, year after year, century after century, building up each generation and losing nothing.

But if I were a revolutionary I certainly would not adopt the tactics of Sir Stafford Cripps of jumping into the middle of it and then running away, leading the excited crowd forward to overturn the British institutions and then when somebody says 'Order, order' running away like a little whipped cur.

I think that is a very poor form of revolutionary. I do not know how often you have noticed how a portion of discontented working people—and they are a very little portion—are misled by the leaders whom they hoist upon their shoulders. Some of them, as soon as they are hoisted, are delighted to mingle with the Conservative forces which preserve the greatness of our country. Others, like Sir Stafford Cripps, are off the moment they are in a hostile crowd.

DEFENCE

February 7, 1934

House of Commons

This speech was the first—and among the most dramatic—of Churchill's speeches on the perils of neglecting British air defence. The phrase "We are vulnerable as we have never been before" was not factually accurate, but this speech may be regarded as the opening barrage of a long campaign which, although initially unsuccessful, was to have momentous consequences for Britain and for Churchill.

Every one, I am sure, will share the admiration of the hon. Member for Gower (Mr. D. Grenfell) for what he called moral disarmament, and his wish that, just as duelling has passed out of our minds in this country, so the idea of war may be banished from the minds of all the civilised nations of the world. We all share those sentiments which the hon. Member expressed in his agreeable speech. But, unhappily, when we look out upon the conditions of the world we see a very different picture, and not only a different picture, but tendencies which are running in a contrary direction—the immense stimulus to nationalistic ideas which is the characteristic and the main feature of modern times, taking the form of economic self-containment and of rivalries as fierce as any. All this rise of nationalistic ideas moves directly contrary to those pleasant and bright visions of society, in which the hon. Member indulges himself and has indulged us this evening. The movement is rather the other way. What is happening now is that all those grievances and injustices, to which the hon. Gentleman who spoke from the Liberal Benches referred, between the nations of Europe and in the Far East are unsolved or unredressed, and that meanwhile all over the world countries are arming.

Thus we have an entirely different situation from that which we would all like to see. We have an entirely different situation, or a very greatly changed situation, from the one which existed only a very few years ago. I remember in the days of the late Conservative Administration, when I had the honour of serving under my right hon. Friend the Lord President of the Council, who is, I believe, going to reply on the Debate to-night, that we thought it right to take as a rule of guidance that there would be no major war within 10 years in which we should be engaged. Of course, such a rule can only be a very crude guidance to the military and naval chiefs who have to make their plans, and it had to be reconsidered prospectively at the beginning of each year. I believe that it was right in all the circumstances. With Locarno and the more mellow light which shone on the world at that time, with the hopes that were then very high, I think it was probably right to take that principle as a guide from day to day, and from year to year. No one could take that principle as a guide to-day. I am quite certain that any Cabinet, however pacific—and no one can impugn the peaceful desires of His Majesty's Government, except those who are divorced from the slightest desire for contact with truth—there is no Government, however pacific and peace-loving that could possibly arrange the basis of their naval and military organisation upon such an assumption as that. A new situation has been created, largely in the last few years, partly in the last three or four years, largely, I fear, by rubbing this sore of the Disarmament Conference until it has become a cancer, and also by the sudden uprush of Nazi-ism in Germany, with the tremendous covert armaments which are proceeding there to-day, to which the hon. Member for Broxtowe (Mr. Cocks), in a most interesting speech yesterday, drew our attention. He quoted figures, which may or may not be strictly accurate, but which now bear a very close relation to the grave underlying facts. That has changed the position very much indeed, and everyone sitting on the Government Bench knows how gravely the position has been changed. Only yesterday we defined once again our commitments to other countries. They are very serious commitments. The White Paper which we discussed yesterday contains a very grave sentence:

> They have a right to expect that, if these provisions and pledges were solemnly entered into, they would not be lightly violated, and that any violation of them would be met in the most practical and effective way by immediately assembling Governments and States in support of international peace and agreement against the disturber and the violator.

I think that those are very serious words to use in a document, and it would be most unwise for us to proceed with our diplomacy in one direction, and not make our necessary preparation in the other sphere. We had a speech yesterday from the late Foreign Secretary, my right hon. Friend the Member for West Birmingham (Sir A. Chamberlain)—one of his most lucid and powerful utterances—in which he dotted the i's and crossed the t's of this declaration, and pointed out that it was to be understood as a gentleman's agreement, as a declaration to be interpreted with a fine sense of honour; and there was no contradiction of any kind—could there have been?—from His Majesty's Government. At Birmingham this year, my right hon. Friend the Lord President went out of his way with great solemnity to issue a warning about the European situation, and he pointed out how strictly we should adhere to all the engagements into which we have entered. These are considerable facts, and we must consider our military, naval and aviation defence in relation to facts of this character.

An hon. Gentleman was asking what cause could arise for any dispute which we could have. We are engaged in demanding equality for armies, in imposing equality for armies as far as we can, upon the nations of the Continent—France, Germany, Poland and Italy. Suppose it is asked in a few years that there should be equality for navies, too? When the Government are asked about this, they say, "Oh, no, that would not apply; we should not agree to that." Suppose we are asked some time in the future to restore colonies for which we hold a mandate, the Government would say, "Certainly not; we should not open that question in any way." There are a lot of things which we will do and will not do, and this is one of the occasions when we may ask, What do we back our opinions with; what arrangements and force have we to summon behind these serious issues of opinion on which we declare our will and right? What happens, for instance, if, after we have equalised and reduced the army of France to the level of that of Germany, and got an equality for Germany, and with all the reactions which will have followed in the sentiment of Europe upon such a change, Germany then proceeds to say, "How can you keep a great nation of 65,000,000 in the position in which it is not entitled to have a navy equal to the greatest of the fleets upon the seas?" You will say "No; we do not agree. Armies—they belong to other people. Navies—that question affects Britain's interests and we are bound to say, 'No.' " But what position shall we be in to say that "No"?

Wars come very suddenly. I have lived through a period when one looked forward, as we do now, with great anxiety and great uncertainty to what would happen in the future. Suddenly something did happen—tremendous, swift, over-powering, irresistible. Let me remind the House of the sort of thing that happened in 1914. There was absolutely no quarrel between Germany and France. One July afternoon the German Ambassador drove down to the Quai d'Orsay and said to, I think, M. Viviani, the French Prime Minister: "We have been forced to mobilise against Russia, and war will be declared. What is to be the position of France?" The French Prime Minister made the answer, which his Cabinet had agreed upon, that France would act in accordance with what she considered to be her own interests. The Ambassador said, "You have an alliance with Russia, have you not?" "Quite so," said the French Prime Minister. And that was the process by which, in a few minutes, the area of the struggle, already serious in the East, was enormously widened and multiplied by the throwing in of the two great nations of the West on either side. But sometimes even a declaration of neutrality does not suffice. On this very occasion, as we now know, the German Ambassador was authorised by his Government, in case the French did not do their duty by their Russian ally, in case they showed any disposition to back out of the conflict which had been resolved on by the German nation, to demand that the fortresses of Toul and Verdun should be handed over to German troops as a guarantee that the French, having declared neutrality, would not change their mind at a subsequent moment.

That is how the great thing happened in our own lifetime, and I am bound to say that I cannot see in the present administration of Germany any assurance that they would be more nice-minded in dealing with a vital and supreme situation than was the Imperial Government of Germany, which was responsible for this procedure being adopted towards France. No, Sir, and we may, within a measurable period of time, in the lifetime of those who are here, if we are not in a proper state of security, be confronted on some occasion with a visit from an ambassador, and may have to give an answer in a very few hours; and if that answer is not satisfactory, within the next few hours the crash of bombs exploding in London and the cataracts of masonry and fire and smoke will warn us of any inadequacy which has been permitted in our aerial defences. We are vulnerable as we have never been before. I have often heard criticisms of the Liberal Government before the War. It is said that its diplomacy was not sufficiently clear and precise, that it wrapped things up in verbiage, that it ought to have said downright and plain what it would do, and there were criticisms about its lack of preparation, and so forth. All I can say is that a far graver case rests upon those who now hold power if, by any chance, against our wishes and against our hopes, trouble should come—a far graver case.

Not one of the lessons of the past has been learned, not one of them has been applied, and the situation is incomparably more dangerous. Then we had the Navy, and no air menace worth speaking of. Then the Navy was the "sure shield" of Britain. As long as it was ready in time and at its stations we could say to any foreign Government: "Well, what are you going to do about it? We will not declare ourselves. We will take our own line, we will work out our own course. We have no wish or desire to hurt anyone, but we shall not be pressed or forced into any hasty action unless we think fit or well." We cannot say that now. This cursed, hellish invention and development of war from the air has revolutionised our position. We are not the same kind of country we used to be when we were an island, only 20 years ago. That is the thing that is borne in upon me more than anything else. It is not merely a question of what we like and what we do not like, of ambitions and desires, of rights and interests, but it is a question of safety and independence. That is what is involved now as never before.

I am going to mention only this, because I am not going to stand between the House and my right hon. Friend for more than a few minutes longer, but it does seem to me that there are three definite decisions which we should now take at once, and without any delay. The first affects the Army. We ought to begin the reorganisation of our civil factories so that they can be turned over rapidly to war purposes. All over Europe that is being done, and to an extraordinary extent—to an amazing extent. They are incomparably more efficient than anything that existed in the days of Prussian Imperialism before the War. Every factory in those countries is prepared to turn over to the production of some material for the deplorable and melancholy business of slaughter. What have we done? There is not an hour to lose. Those things cannot be done in a moment. The process should be started, and the very maximum of money that can be usefully spent should be spent from to-day on—if we act with wisdom.

Then there is the question of the Navy. For the Navy, at any rate, we should regain freedom of design. We should get rid of this London Treaty which has crippled us in building the kind of ships we want, and has stopped the United States from building a great battleship which she probably needed and to which we should have not had the slightest reason to object. It has forced us to spend some of our hard-earned, poor money—the little there is for these purposes—unwisely. It has forced us to take great ships which would have been of enormous utility in convoying vessels bearing food to these islands and to sink them in the ocean, when they had 10 to 15 years of useful life in them. We must regain our freedom at the earliest possible moment, and we shall be helped in doing so by the fact that another of the parties to that Treaty is resolved to regain her freedom, too. Then there is the air. I cannot conceive how, in the present state of Europe and of our position in Europe we can delay in establishing the principle of having an Air Force at least as strong as that of any Power that can get at us. I think that is a perfectly reasonable thing to do. It would only begin to put us back to the position in which we were brought up. We have lived under the shield of the Navy. To have an Air Force as strong as the air force of France or Germany, whichever is the stronger, ought to be the decision which Parliament should take, and which the National Government should proclaim.

There is only one other point which I venture to mention— [Hon. Members: "Go on!"] —and that is the co-ordination of the three Services. A right hon. Friend of mine, the Member for South Molton (Mr. G. Lambert), yesterday asked the Prime Minister a very pertinent question as to the allocation of money between the three Fighting Services. I doubt very much whether, at this stage, there is room for economy in any of them, but at any rate it would be advantageous, in my opinion, if the problem were studied from a central point of view, because things are changing very much. The emphasis should be thrown here or there, according to the needs of modern conditions, but there should be much more effective co-ordination than now exists. I ask my right hon. Friend when he replies, after consulting with the Leader of the House, to say that sometime in this Session the Vote for the Committee of Imperial Defence should be put down—the Prime Minister's salary, or whatever is the Vote—so that we can have a discussion on the three Services combined. It would be a very valuable discussion, one such as has frequently been allowed in previous years, and was never more necessary than at the present time.

My hon. and gallant Friend the Member for Lewes (Captain Loder) has moved an Amendment to the Motion asking us to await the result of the White Paper. I see no great harm in the House placing some hopes in the White Paper, but grave harm if that is going to delay the necessary provision for security at home in the meanwhile. Who believes that the proposals of the White Paper will prove acceptable; for instance, that France, which has now between 700,000 and 800,000 men, is going to reduce her forces in Europe to the level of those of Poland, to an equality with those of Germany? Who can say that our proposals will gain any acceptance on the Continent of Europe? The Government can make their effort, if they like, they can then say they have done it, but they cannot justify delaying necessary action in the sphere of defence until they get the answers, which will be given, no doubt very politely, to the Lord Privy Seal when he embarks on his peregrinations round the capitals of Europe. We cannot delay for that. Therefore, if my hon. and gallant Friend were to go to a Division, I should vote for the Motion and against this temporising, vaporising, paralysing Amendment which my hon. and gallant Friend opposite has put down, I believe at the instigation of the Government.

I think that the responsibility of His Majesty's Government is very grave indeed, and there is this which makes it all the graver: It is a responsibility which they have no difficulty in discharging if they choose. We are told they have to wait for public opinion, that they must bring that along and must be able to assure the good people here that everything is being done with the most pacific intentions—they must make a case. But they do not need to do anything like that, and nothing like that can stand between them and their responsibility to the Crown and Parliament for the safety and security of the country. The Government command overwhelming majorities in both branches of the Legislature. Nothing will be denied to them that they ask. They have only to make their proposals, and they will be supported in them. Let them not suppose that if they make proposals, with confidence and conviction, for the safety of the country that their countrymen will not support them as they have always done at every moment. Why take so poor a view of the great patriotic support which this nation gives to those who, it feels, are doing their duty by it? I cannot feel that at the present time the Government are doing their duty in these matters of defence, and particularly in respect of the air. It seems to me that while we are becoming ever more entangled in the European situation, and while we are constantly endeavouring to weaken, relatively, our friends upon the Continent of Europe, we nevertheless are left exposed to a mortal thrust, and are deprived of that sense of security and independence upon which the civilisation of our island has been built.

DEFENCE

February 15, 1934

In Support of Sir Roger Keyes,
The Guildhall, London

[Extract] . . . These are tactics of a crowd of professional pacifists, who if you are not very careful, will land us in another horrible war, and on the losing side. These pacifists urge that we ought to disarm ourselves entirely, while all the rest of the world is arming—we ought to do it as a gesture, to set an example. The difficulty about this plan is that we have tried it and it failed. We are the only country that has disarmed. Every other country in the world has increased its armaments in the last 20 years except the defeated countries, which were not allowed to do so. And now they are all rearming as fast as they possibly can. We are the last people in the world to desire a war. Our interest, our aim, our duty is peace. With the world in its present state we ought to take reasonable precautions, so that the good cause is not overwhelmed by the bad.

The League of Nations is a great power in Europe, and we ought to stand by the League and do our duty there along with the other Powers, both great and small. This is a very much safer course than to try to disarm France and rearm Germany and bring those countries to an equality. By taking sensible precautions and by working with the League of Nations we should be able to keep clear of Continental struggles; or, if we are unhappily drawn into them, to see that we have not only the strongest forces on our side but also the public law of Europe and the public opinion of civilized mankind.

With its immense resources and almost unlimited power the present Government should be capable of acting with creative vigour and inspiration. It should maintain our rights and interests with sober but firm determination. It should make sure we are not put in jeopardy by unpreparedness. It should handle and control social and financial problems with more energy and daring. We should not be parleying away the splendid possessions which our forefathers won. We should not be content always to seek the line of least resistance or try to please everybody. We should match up against the difficulties and strive to compel events, and bear down, by the moral force and momentum of a great advance, unreasonable, unwholesome, or malicious opposition.

I see several notable Portsmouth Liberals on the platform. They are here because the greatest causes which Liberalism has fought for are challenged in the world to-day. The right of the individual against the State, the right to oppose the Government of the day, freedom of speech, freedom of the Press, freedom of public meeting, freedom often of private talk—all are denied over great areas of Europe. Some of these tendencies are alive in this country. Many of the Socialists would join in the fight against dictatorship; but there are Socialists, as Sir Stafford Cripps has reminded you, who aim at the virtual abolition of Parliament and free institutions, and would like to have the whole control of our ancient democracy in the grip of their own dirty little gang. Here in this island we have built up an order of society incomparably superior to anything that can be seen in any large country abroad. We wish to keep these advantages and improve upon them, and we do not mean them to be filched away from us by subversion at home or intrusion from overseas. It is because these causes are at stake that Liberals are supporting the National Government and Sir Roger Keyes.

"MARLBOROUGH: HIS LIFE AND TIMES"

February 21, 1934

Lecture, University College, London

Churchill's first volume of his massive biography of the first Duke of Marlborough had been published in 1933.

The age of Queen Anne was the greatest in our history. In a little more than 10 years the English race rose from being one of a dozen minor Powers to be the unquestioned leader of Europe against Louis XIV. There was military glory abroad, immense political strides at home, the union between England and Scotland, the development of the Parliamentary, constitutional, and cabinet system, advances in philosophy, architecture, literature, and painting which heralded all along the line the majestic advance of England to an age in which she showed more power, glory, wealth, and comprehension of herself than had ever been known before. It was then that the foundations were laid on which 50 years later Clive and Wolfe drove our enemies out of India and North America.

The heart and brain of all this was John Churchill, first Duke of Marlborough, who led the armies of the Grand Alliance through a succession of victories which, so far as I am concerned, were practically unbroken. For eight of these years he was the leading statesman of England, conducting foreign policy by personal negotiations with the kings and potentates of Europe. It was Marlborough who supplied whatever there was of unity of command and of cohesion and design in the war, who, from being regarded as a small country gentleman ennobled by favour of Queen Anne, dominated Europe.

[Editor's Note: Speaking of the difficulties Marlborough had to face, he said]: Marlborough was hampered by the determination of the Dutch not to take part in a decisive action, but to follow a policy of safety first—a good policy in its place but not in war. For 10 years against the best troops and their generals Marlborough never fought a battle which he did not win and never laid siege to a town which he did not take.

[Editor's Note: When describing conditions at home in those days he referred to the formation of a Tory Government with a few Whigs in the minor offices to give it a special flavour.] That is very different from anything which could occur at a time like this. (Laughter.) At the end of his life Marlborough was abused by both parties, defended by none. He wrote no memoirs, made no explanation, but that he was a true man serving a great cause became more and more apparent as the history of those times is revealed.

REPLIES TO QUESTIONS

February 23, 1934

Conservative Association Meeting,
Oxford University

Sir Oswald Mosley's New Party had vanished in 1931; Mosley subsequently formed the British Union of Fascists, which donned black shirts and uniforms on the Mussolini model. For a time the B.U.F. caused genuine concern, before the wearing of political uniforms was banned by the Public Order Act of 1936. But the British Fascist movement, despite Mosley's brilliant oratorical powers, had faded long before then. The British attitude to both Black and Red Shirts was immortalised in A. P. Herbert's phrase, "A curse on both your blouses!"

[Extract] ... I believe in the maintenance of Parliamentary democracy. To preserve it I urge the establishment of a strong second chamber by some reform of the House of Lords. The House of Commons ought also to be reformed.

If the Chancellor has the surplus of £20,000,000 or £30,000,000 which people hope he has, he should first of all take off the special cuts and surtaxes imposed by the Snowden Budget.

I admire the spirit shown by President Roosevelt and wish Mr. Elliot every success and only hope he will not spill the milk. (Laughter.)

I object to the term "hunger marchers." You may call them anger marchers, but not hunger marchers. Nevertheless, the precious liberty of allowing anyone to march to the capital to lay before Parliament a petition is worth preserving.

I am not alarmed by the spread of Fascism in this country as a threat to democracy in England. I am sure that the good sense and long-trained political freedom of the English people and our institutions will enable us to steer a course which will not make it necessary to evoke the assistance of either Black or Red Shirts.

ARMY ESTIMATES

March 6, 1934

House of Commons

I beg to move to reduce the Vote by £130,000.

I cannot feel that there is any very great validity in the complaint of the hon. and gallant Gentleman that this new charge of £1,500,000 a year is to be included on the Army Vote, and the explanation he gave of his grievance certainly made the worst possible out of it. What is the object of the hon. and gallant Gentleman? He would like to add £1,500,000 to the accounting of the Army audits, so that he and his friends can point to the terrible increase of military expenditure and to the bloated armaments which are rolling up at a time when all the world is seeking for disarmament, knowing all the time that, whatever way you look at it, it is merely a matter of bookkeeping.

Major Milner: On the contrary. I pointed out that it did not matter on which Vote this sum was put, because it would not result in an increase of armaments. I made that perfectly clear, and the right hon. Gentleman the Member for Epping (Mr. Churchill) is quite wrong in his interpretation.

Mr. Churchill: Nothing could be more misleading than to increase the nominal total of the Army Estimates by this £1,500,000 a year. The Government are justified in being candid with the public, but it is perfectly clear, as the hon. and gallant Gentleman admits, that it in no way involves an increase of armaments of any kind. I am very glad to see my right hon. Friend the Secretary of State for India in his place. I trust that he has not unduly strained the permission of his medical adviser by coming here. I very much regret if, in the course of my remarks, I should be involved in controversy with him, and he should not be in the very best of health. My right hon. Friend sometime ago accused me of hitting the Government and hitting its Members. I can assure him that that is a complete delusion, especially in his case. It is not the sinner that I hit but the sin. That rule is general in his case, on this as upon other matters.

The right hon. Gentleman had no right to try to claim me as a supporter of his policy in this matter. I notice that His Majesty's Government are inclined to claim my protection from time to time. Even the Prime Minister seemed to go out of his way to drag me in when I was sitting most inoffensively in this corner. I cannot accord to my right hon. Friend the protection that he desires in this matter. We have been associated for many years, and he must know perfectly well—though I am not entitled to make any relevation in regard to those days any more than he is to refer to my opinions of those days—that he has heard me on many occasions and in different places express consistently, over many years, the view that the balance of charge between India and the War Office was unfairly adjusted against this country. That has been the view that I have consistently held for a great many years. To suggest that the Chancellor of the Exchequer, or any Chancellor of the Exchequer in the last 25 years, would have been responsible for putting down a vote of £1,500,000 for a new grant-in-aid for India in perpetuity—and to do so in these hard times of crushing taxation and grinding economy—is altogether at variance with the known facts and with the ordinary processes of human reason. The right hon. Gentleman must stand on his own feet in this matter.

I make no complaint of the particular form of the tribunal, though I am certainly not saying that it was a wise thing to set up this tribunal. We are not concerned with the tribunal—or only very indirectly. It is not an award as the right hon. Gentleman says; it is a report. It is not an award of a judicial tribunal by which we are bound; it is a report of a body of gentlemen, a committee of very able gentlemen, to the Government, and on their report the Government have decided to take £1,500,000 per year out of the pockets of the taxpayer and to present it to the Government of India. I am certain that that would never have been allowed and would never have been agreed to by any of the Governments which have held office in the last 25 or 30 years. We had discussions following upon the Welby Commission and the Romer Commission. There were long discussions between Lord Haldane and Lord Morley, which I perfectly remember, in which the matter was threshed out in great detail by men whose Liberalism and whose desire to deal equitably with India were undoubted. They arrived at what they considered to be a fair working arrangement.

During the recent Conservative Administration the late Sir Laming Worthington Evans, who was then Secretary of State for War, felt very acutely the injustice to which the British taxpayer was subjected by the cost of maintaining the service of the Indian Army, and he pressed very strongly upon the Government of that day that there should be an inquiry into one specific point, the question of sea transport charges. That was agreed to, the matter being raised on the initiative of the War Office. That fact shows that the Government of the day felt, as I know that they did, that there was a *prima facie* case for the diminution of the burden on the British taxpayer in respect of Indian Army costs. So far from the right hon. Gentleman quoting that as a means of trying to bring me to his rescue, and to cast my aegis over his manoeuvres, if it proves anything, it proves the reverse of what he set out to show.

I want to make it clear that Parliament is free to decide in this matter. The Committee have an absolutely free hand. We are not dealing with a judicial award, but with a proposal put forward by a Minister of the Crown, on the responsibility of our own Government at home, to add to the public burden. This is a matter in which the Committee ought to take some interest. The Chancellor of the Exchequer is distributing his surplus very early this year. I hope that it is a very large and ample surplus, but it is quite remarkable when we consider the conditions under which this Government were appointed, and the tremendous insistence upon ruthless economy at the time, that there should be so much money about, and that £1,500,000 can be pulled out and brought forward on an afternoon like this, not as an amount only for the year, but as a continuing service for all time. The figure may not be quite accurate, but I think that the capital value of that sum will represent pretty nearly £40,000,000. That is what we are asked to do, and we ought certainly to look into it very carefully. I am very glad that the hon. and gallant Gentleman opposite has taken interest in it. Public money ought not to be splashed about in this manner without very grave, just and searching examination by this Committee of the House of Commons.

I have read the able report of this able committee—or tribunal if you like to call it, but it is no more a tribunal than any other committee similarly appointed to make recommendations—to the Government about this question. It seems to me that the committee were very hard put to it to find any reason for an increased contribution from Great Britain with respect to the British Army in India. On pages 8 and 9 of the report they give an account of their search for some reason, and apparently they looked at a great many promising resting places for their argument, but, upon consideration, they found that one after another would not bear the weight of any conclusion. It is not until we get to page 15 that they have at last found a foothold for this new imposition upon the British taxpayer. I hope that the Committee will look at page 15. When tribunals give decisions and do not give reasons, it is very difficult for anyone to form an opinion. But, when a tribunal or committee gives its reasons, even ordinary laymen can form their own views on them. Just let us look at the two reasons which are given on page 15. My right hon. Friend read them, but they are very important, and, if the Committee will bear with me, I will read them again. They are:

(1) That the Army in India is a force, ready in emergency to take the field at once, which does not exist elsewhere in the Empire, which is specially available for immediate use in the East, and which has on occasion been so used.

(2) That India is a training ground for active service which does not exist elsewhere in the Empire.

I do not say that there is nothing in these two statements, but there is not very much, and to a large extent they are not true. Take the first—that the Army in India is a force ready in an emergency to take the field at once, which does not exist elsewhere in the Empire. That is only true in the sense that the British troops in India are up to full war strength, whereas in this country it is necessary to call out the reserves in order to mobilise our battalions and other units. Apart from that, it is not true to say that the troops in India are more readily available or are ready in an emergency to take the field at once, because, if you consider the time it takes to prepare transport, the probably much quicker location of masses of shipping in this country, and the need for furnishing special equipment in India for the various contingencies that might arise, you would not find in many cases that they would be ready any sooner, or even, possibly, so soon. Certainly they were not ready so soon in the great instance that we had in the Great War, when our Expeditionary Force had been fighting for, I think, two months before these excellent troops from India could be brought on to the scene. This first of the two reasons, therefore, on which £1,500,000 of British money is to be expended, is really capable of considerable canvassing and modification in regard to its validity.

As regards the second reason—that India is a training ground for active service which does not exist elsewhere in the Empire—again I do not wish to underrate the manly and gallant life of our troops on these vast plains of India, but I doubt whether you can say that experience in frontier wars is any special guide in, shall I say, the great struggles of the Continent of Europe. I remember often hearing the late Sir Charles Dilke argue to the contrary, and point out how, in the war of 1870, it was considered that the French suffered by having such a large proportion of Colonial generals who had been advanced from small fightings in their Colonial possessions to high positions in the Army, instead of having men at the summit who had based their views on broad scientific study of the greatest operations of war. And the Germans, let me point out, had no India, they had none of this advantage of training their troops on a great training ground such as India. Their Army was entirely a home-trained army, trained in Europe; and I have yet to learn that they did not give a very good account of themselves in the Great War. Certainly, judged by the most awful and unanswerable test, they killed between two and three men for every one of themselves who was killed, and that without any of the advantages detailed in the second reason for which we are invited to spend £1,500,000 a year for all time.

These are fairly flimsy pretexts, found after such a very long search by this very able Committee, considering the burden which is to be placed upon us. At any rate, whatever you may think of these reasons, there is nothing new in them; there is nothing in these two proposals which has not been perfectly obvious and well known and recognised as common ground for the last 30 years in all the endless discussions between the India Office, calling itself India—"she"—and the War Office; in all those endless discussions these facts have been perfectly well known. Why should they now be given such extraordinary prominence at the present time? That is the question that we have to investigate. Before I attempt to do so, I would like to say that against these two reasons which are given on page 15 there are other considerations which might well be studied if you are going to survey the whole relationship of the British Army in India to the Exchequer and the English taxpayer. If you are going to do that, there are other considerations which far outweigh the two set forth here. I will mention two of them to the Committee now, neither of which is referred to at all in the report. I am astonished that the representatives of the War Office did not bring them to the notice of the Committee, if in fact they did not.

To begin with, the first great consideration which must be set forth is the enormous effort and sacrifice imposed upon the British nation in maintaining an army of 60,000 men permanently under the conditions of life and service in India for generation after generation. That is holding out the dumb-bell at arm's length; it is a tremendous strain. A seven years' slice is taken out of the lives of these young men. You call it short service, but by every standard in Europe it is a very long service.

Seven years are taken out of their lives, some five of which are passed under all the fierceness of the Asiatic sun, they are exposed to the trying effects of the Indian climate, and they are exposed to the temptations which naturally follow to young soldiers in that country. As we well know, the statistics of venereal disease and the general effects upon our young men sent out to serve in the Army in India are by no means negligible. I do not wish to put it too high; I make great acknowledgment of the efforts which have been made to improve the hygiene and conditions of the troops; but to suppose that you are not subjecting a body of 60,000 of your men, the flower of your youthful working-class manhood, to a long strain, and taking from them five or six years of the time during which they might be fitting themselves into the industrial field, to suppose that you are not taking from these men's lives something which is extremely important and which they may never get back again, is altogether to underrate the character of the effort which Britain makes to maintain an army in India.

It is our duty to make this effort, because, if we did not do so, if we did not maintain this Army in India, India would fall immediately into anarchy and civil war, and, after a brief period of turbulence and disorder, the probabilities are that history would see another conqueror, either from across the seas or through the mountains. [*Interruption.*] I will not pursue the topic further, except to submit to the Committee that this great strain and effort made by Great Britain for so many generations to preserve the peace, order and security of India should count at least as an equal, and I consider as an overriding, consideration to match against this second item that India is a training ground and that they get good practice at manoeuvres out there.

Let us look at the next consideration. We could, of course, have a very much cheaper military arrangement if we had only ourselves to consider. I remember often hearing Sir Charles Dilke explain the great advantages that would accrue to our military system if we divided the Army, making India pay the whole cost of a long-service Army for India, while we ourselves had a short-service Army here, with, we will say, two years with the Colours and 10 in the Reserve. Such an Army would rapidly build up a very large, flexible, homogeneous force at no greater, and probably at a less, cost than we are now put to by having to adopt the system of seven years with the Army and five with the Reserve. It is a great mistake to suppose that our Army arrangements are not gravely complicated and burdened, as anyone who has studied the matter knows them to be, by the need of rendering this great service to India; and I think that this second counter-consideration ought to have been placed against, and might well be placed against, the reason of the Committee that we have some troops there ready in an emergency. I say that there is not much validity in either of these reasons, that there is nothing new in either, and that undoubtedly far stronger points can be raised on the other side.

Then there is the reservation on the last page, by Lord Dunedin and Lord Tomlin, on the question of sea transport. I agree with the hon. Gentleman that this is a matter well worthy of our attention. Here are these two great legal authorities, dealing, not with any of those *imponderabilia* which played such a large part in every sphere in which the committee worked; they are dealing with a question on which they are absolutely competent to express an opinion, namely, whether there is a case in equity and in contract for the continuance of the £130,000 subsidy in aid of sea transport. They both come to this conclusion:

> We, therefore, though reluctantly . . . are driven to the conclusion that there is no ground for the subsidy. . . .

But that does not affect the Government at all. In this mood of generosity which has swept across them, and for which usually we search in vain, they have not hesitated to act against the opinion of these two eminent legal authorities dealing with a matter on which they are prefectly competent to pronounce. In order to bring matters to an issue, therefore, I propose, if it can be fitted in with any other Motion—I am not sure whether there is a Motion from the other side to reduce the Vote—to move to reduce the Vote by £130,000, in order to point out that the policy of the Government in this respect at any rate should be brought into line with the definite rulings of these two eminent Law Lords, who are themselves so friendly to the aspirations of India in other respects. If I get an opportunity, I shall also vote against the grant of £1,500,000 as a whole.

To return to the question that I mentioned a moment ago, why His Majesty's Government decided to convey this new grant-in-aid to India, or rather to the British Government in India, at this particular time, no doubt we shall be told that it has nothing to do with the White Paper Constitution and nothing to do with the grave financial expense and confusion in which the attempt to extend the pleasures of democractic electioneering to the Indian masses is likely to involve the Indian Government. Those who wish to deceive themselves will believe that it has nothing to do with it. I am told that the right hon. Gentleman even referred to the possibility of money from this source in one of his answers before the Committee, but I have not the reference, and, if that is not so, I will stand corrected. We shall be told it had nothing to do with it, just as we were told that the retrocession of the Bangalore Cantonment had nothing to do with the desire to make Mysore into a federal system, or that the new arrangements made about the Nizam's sovereignity over the Berars had nothing to do with any desire to include that great Indian State in Federation. It seems to me, and I believe it to be true—I regret to say it—that this extra payment of £1,500,000 which is being engineered and might slip through the House without the public attention being drawn to it is part of that elaborate crochet work which my right hon. Friend, I am sorry to say, has too often mistaken for statesmanship. Let the Committee contrast this strange liberality with the attitude of the Government and the Treasury when the question is discussed of the difference between two and three shillings in the children's allowance. Then a very different mood prevails. Then the Government are adamant. Then the Chancellor of the Exchequer is the emblem of financial austerity.

Something has happened in regard to the Indian matter which puts it in a different category, and I will tell the Committee what in my opinion has happened. When a Cabinet Minister gets into a difficulty with a policy on which the Cabinet is bent and to which it is largely committed and they do not see their way clearly through it, the money has to be found and the Chancellor of the Exchequer has to face the burden.

"Not once or twice in our rough island story" the line of least resistance has been found through the pocket of the taxpayer. Do not let the Committee delude itself with the idea that this sop—for it is no more—is or will be accepted as a settlement. India, that national entity which you are endeavouring to call into being and the nucleus of the British bureaucracy will not accept it. You have only to see the proposals which the India Office put forward. Our Secretary of State hopefully put forward five or six proposals which would have added enormously to our charges. He put them forward as matters which should be considered so that, when it came to splitting the difference, there would be a very good chance of their getting a large slice of the money of the British taxpayer. Of course, what you are doing now will be brought forward by the Indian Home Rule Government as soon as it is constituted. They will say: "You have admitted the injustice. What about the arrears of all these years?" They will press not only for the different concessions which the Secretary of State and the India Office have put before the Committee. They will take these as a starting point and will press forward much larger demands, and that will be the first phase of the new Government when it is created. This is only the first heavy drop of the thunder shower. It is only the first of the deprivations and repudiations to which we are to be subjected if the policy to which my right hon. Friend is committed is carried out. If you have so much money as all this, if you are in such a giving mood, if you are resolved to persist in the policy of giving federal home rule to India, you should have kept this £1,500,000 a year carefully as a means of guaranteeing the pensions of the British officials who have so faithfully served you and served their country and whose anxiety you might so easily thereby have allayed.

CIVIL ESTIMATES AND ESTIMATES
FOR REVENUE DEPARTMENTS

March 7, 1934

House of Commons

During the course of the Debate yesterday I ventured to hazard a suggestion that the Secretary of State for India had been influenced in fixing the scale of this grant by the need of procuring additional funds in order to carry out his policy of giving Federal Home Rule to India, and finding the money for this democratic experiment in India. I was not at that moment in possession of the quotation of his evidence before the Joint Committee which would support that assertion. I therefore did not make the case with the fullness that I should have been justified in doing. I have since looked up the quotation, with the aid of the admirable index of the evidence before the Joint Committee, and I find that the impression that I had is fully borne out. There is not

the slightest doubt that the Secretary of State had in mind the use of this contribution, this additional grant-in-aid of £1,500,000 which we are now to Vote for the
purpose of carrying forward this Federal Home Rule Scheme in India. A discussion
arose in the Joint Committee about the present financial position of India, what
money was available, and very severe and careful examination of the position was
undertaken by the hon. Gentleman who is now the Deputy-Leader of the Opposition.
Among other questions he asked this:

> Have you considered at all the possibility of any part of the burden of
> defence being taken over as an Imperial burden.

The hon. Member asked whether the right hon. Gentleman had in view any relief from
this quarter, or words to that effect. The Secretary of State said:

> It is a question, of course, that has constantly been discussed between
> India and Great Britain for many years and is one of the questions that
> will emerge out of the Capitation Tribunal decision. I would prefer, if
> Major Attlee will allow me to do so, to wait until the autumn when I
> should hope to be able to make a fuller statement of the results of the
> Capitation Tribunal than I can to-day.

Then a further question was raised as to whether other parts of the Empire paid less,
to which the Secretary of State replied:

> Major Attlee is raising a very big and a very controversial issue, upon
> which there has been a discussion for generations. What I can tell him,
> however, is that this was one of the issues referred to the Capitation
> Tribunal, composed, as he will remember, of impartial British and Indian
> judges, and I should hope to be able to make an announcement on the
> subject when we resume our discussions in the autumn.

That the right hon. Gentleman's hope was not fruitless and that he as justified in his
hope was shown by what occurred. The tribunal fixed no figure and gave no award. It
merely indicated that there should be a contribution of some kind. That was enough
for the Secretary of State. That was what he had been counting upon. He was then
able to go to the Chancellor of the Exchequer and demand from him, as colleague to
colleague and as one man in a confederation with another, the means of supplying the
finances necessary to bring his home rule scheme into operation. I expect there was a
very hard tussle between the Secretary of State and the Chancellor of the Exchequer
and that the Chancellor consoled himself by thinking that he had got out of it as
cheaply as he could when he gave £1,500,000. The award of the tribunal could
perfectly well have been satisfied by £130,000 or simply remitting the other half of
the sea transport as was done 20 years ago, but the Secretary of State required this
money as a make-weight, and as grist to his mill for bringing his home rule scheme into
operation. He demanded and procured from the Chancellor of the Exchequer this

£1,500,000, but he would have been very glad to have got more, because even that does not give him as much as he requires. That is my view and I say it is directly connected.

I see it stated in a newspaper which belongs to the Government Press—for they still have some Press left—that it was an unworthy suggestion to say that this demand for £1,500,000 had anything whatever to do with the Indian constitutional reform. I have exposed to the House to-night on the Report stage of this Resolution the direct link and the absolute proof, which no one can dispute. You may try to explain it away and wrap it up in a cloud of words, but there is not the slightest doubt that the hope of the Secretary of State was to obtain a substantial refreshment from this source for his scheme, and he has undoubtedly obtained it. I have indicated how I think the figure was fixed, by this hugger-mugger discussion between the India Office and the Treasury, with the War Office intervening.

But we had an alternative suggestion put before us last night by the Secretary of State as to how he worked out the scheme. He took all the expeditions in which India had assisted the Empire for the last 60 years. He took them all in and said there was so much due on that account. He also looked at the admirable training facilities afforded to our troops by the large expanses of the Indian plains, and said that there was so much due on that account. How much for each one he did not mention, but, adding them together—the expeditions from the sixties to the present day and these training facilities—he suddenly informed us that the answer was £1,500,000. Of course, anyone who knows anything about the working of the Governmental system knows it was nothing to do with these expeditions and training facilities, but what the Chancellor of the Exchequer thought was the least he could get off with. He did get off, in my opinion, with a very severe mauling such as no other occupant of that office would have tolerated in the last 30 years in regard to this issue. This £1,500,000 which is provided was aimed at and struggled for and fought for as part of the necessary provision for the home rule scheme of the right hon. Gentleman. He is getting it now as a burden for ever fixed upon the people of this country, and, although I do not expect for one moment that the House of Commons, which is the guardian of the public purse, is going to worry about such a bagatelle as £1,500,000 when the Government Whips are on the other side, yet I venture to say that in bringing this matter to the attention of Parliament and to the attention of the country, we have exposed one of the most disagreeable phases of the under-workings which are bringing forward this Indian policy to a conclusion which will be permanently disastrous to our interests.

THE NEED FOR AIR PARITY

March 8, 1934

House of Commons

The introduction of the term "parity" with regard to air defence caused a very considerable amount of confusion over the next two years. In reply to Churchill's speech, Baldwin assured the House of Commons that the Government would "see to it that in air strength and air power this country shall no longer be in a position inferior to any country within striking distance of our shores."

It is certain that the endeavors which have been made by the Government to procure a measure of disarmament from Europe similar to that which we have practiced ourselves as an example have failed. I have never thought that these efforts would succeed, and I have said so. Perhaps it was uncharitable to say it. I exceedingly regret that they have failed. The Government have admitted for more than a year past that in their desire to procure disarmament they have gone to the very edge of risk. Yes, Sir, and many of us think that they have gone beyond that edge. I have not been able to convince myself that the policy which the Government have pursued has been in sufficiently direct contact with the harsh realities of the European situation, but, of course, I admit most fully that they have made it clear before all the world, not only by words, which are so easy, but by actions, which are so hard, and by inaction, which is so questionable, how sincere has been, and still is, our desire to bring about a general measure of disarmament, especially in the air. That has failed, and nobody can deny it. You could not have chosen in this country anyone more qualified to bring success to his mission than the Lord Privy Seal [Mr. Eden]. It is not his fault that he has not met with success. No one could have stated our sincere case in a more agreeable manner, more simply and effectively, to the different countries which he has visited, but he has failed. In view of that failure we must now, from this moment, look to our own safety. That is the feeling which I believe is in the minds of all—that we must now betimes take measures to put ourselves in a state of reasonable security.

What are the measures that we can take? First of all, of course, there is the preservation of the peace of Europe. We should do everything that we can do to that end. I am astounded that this Government, which has laboured far beyond the bounds of practical expectation in the cause of disarmament and peace, should be abused and insulted as if it were an administration that was anxious to plunge this country into another war. But, putting the preservation of peace in the first place, what is the next great object that we must have in view? It is to secure our national freedom of choice to remain outside a European war, if one should break out. That I put as the more direct and more practical issue, subordinate to, but not less important than, the preservation of peace.

This is not the time, in this Debate, for us to argue about the duties and obligations which this country may have contracted or her interpretation of those obligations in regard to any Continental struggle that may arise. We all hope it will never take place, and I am not at all prepared, standing here, to assume that it will inevitably take place. On the contrary, I still grasp the larger hope and believe that we may wear our way through these difficulties and leave this grim period behind. But there can be no assurance upon that, and we must have the effective right and power to choose our own path, in accordance with the wishes and resolves of the nation, in any contingency or emergency which may arise upon the continent of Europe; and for this purpose we must be safe from undue foreign pressure.

We cannot afford to confide the safety of our country to the passions or to the panic of any foreign nation which may be facing some desperate crisis. We must be independent. We must be free. We must preserve our full latitude and discretion of choice. In the past we have always had this freedom and independence. I have heard reproaches about the Liberal Government before the War, that they did not make enough preparations or look far enough ahead. But we were in a position where, at any rate, we had a complete freedom of choice; much might be lost by delay, but, as far as the safety of this country was concerned, we were not in any danger. We could hold our own here and take what time we chose to make up our minds, and what time we required to raise the whole vast might of the British Empire, month after month and year after year, from a peace to a war footing.

Nothing of that sort exists today, and unless we regain that freedom of choice, this is no longer integrally or characteristically the same kind of country in which we have always dwelt, and for hundreds of years have built up our own special, insular character and culture. We have never lived at anybody's mercy. We have never lived upon the good pleasure of any Continental nation in regard to our fundamental requirements. We have never entrusted the home defense of this country to any foreign Power. We have never asked for any help from anyone. We have given help to many, but to make good the security of our own island we have asked for help from none. I recognize the strong ties of interest, of sentiment, and of modern sympathy which unite the two great still-remaining Parliamentary democracies of Western Europe. The French and British populations are profoundly bent on peace, and their Governments have nothing to gain by war, but everything to lose. There are great ties which we have in common with the French Republic, but, in spite of all that, we ought not to be dependent upon the French air force for the safety of our island home. [Editor's Note: At this time the French air force ranked first in Europe in numbers.] Although there may be no engagement, the mere fact that you cannot defend yourselves and that your friend across the Channel has additional power makes a whole series of implications which very nearly involve the condition of dependence upon overseas protection. All history has proved the peril of being dependent upon a foreign State for home defense instead of upon one's own right arm. This is not a party question, not a question between pacifists and militarists, but one of the essential independence of character of our island life and its preservation from intrusion or distortion of any kind.

Let us see what we mean by safety. It is a word easy to use, but somewhat difficult to explain. Now that the hideous air war has cast the shadow of its wings over harassed civilization, no one can pretend that by any measures which we could take it would be possible to give absolute protection against an aggressor dropping bombs in this island and killing a great many unarmed men, women and children. No Government can be asked to guarantee absolute immunity to the nation if we were attacked in this way by this new arm. It is certainly in our power, however, if we act in time, to guard ourselves, first of all, from a mortal blow which would compel us to capitulate; and, secondly, it is in our power, I firmly believe, to make it extremely unlikely that we should be attacked, or that we should be attacked by this particular method of terrorizing the civil population by the slaughter of non-combatants, which, to the shame of the twentieth century, we are now forced to discuss as a practical issue.

For this purpose we ought to use every method which is available. We cannot afford to neglect any. I am going to mention what I consider are the four simultaneous lines of defense which we should develop. The first, of course, is a peaceful foreign policy. We must continue to strive, as we are striving, by every means, by every action, by every restraint and suppression of harsh feelings and expressions, to preserve the peace and harmony of Europe. No one, unless blinded by malice or confused by ignorance, would doubt that that has been the main desire of His Majesty's present Administration, just as it was of the Administration which preceded it.

What is the second line? We ought not to neglect any security which we can derive from international conventions. We must get all we can from them. I do not agree with those who say that these international conventions are not worth the paper on which they are written. It may well be that vague, general pious affirmations like the Kellogg Pact do not carry much practical conviction to people's minds, because everyone can see that, the right of self-defense being conceded, every country which plunges into war will allege that it is fighting in self-defense, and will probably convince its own people that it is doing so. It may be an extremely good thing in itself to make this wide, general affirmation that there will be no more war, but it undoubtedly has not carried conviction, and thus it has weakened the virtue of these international instruments. A greater measure of confidence can be reposed in more definite, limited and precise arrangements. At any rate, we should be very foolish to neglect them. Whatever may happen to the discussions now going on about regulating the size of air fleets, we should strive to secure an international convention or a series of treaties confirming air warfare to military and naval objectives and to the zones of field armies.

Such schemes would have to be drawn up in full detail, but I do not believe that this would be impracticable, and I hope the House is not going to be led by very easy arguments to suppose there is no validity or virtue in such arrangements. All the experience of the world shows that they have played their parts even in the most hideous quarrels of nations, and any nation that refused to enter into discussions of a convention to regulate air warfare would consequently be left in a position of grisly isolation, proclaiming its intention deliberately to make war as a scientific and technical operation upon women and children for the terrorization of the civil population. It would be a wise thing for us to get as many nations as possible to join in a convention which would exclude, on paper at any rate, this method from the arena of recognized warfare. I deprecate anything that is said to assume that such a method is compatible at all with any form of decent civilization. His Majesty's Government have been perfectly right to make it clear that no question of the convenience of using air warfare for police purposes in savage countries and barbarous regions should stand in the way of such an agreement of convention if that police measure becomes the sole obstacle to the conclusion of an arrangement otherwise generally satisfactory. We must not balance convenience against safety. Even if we were faced with the old difficulty of expense in maintaining order in the mountain valleys of India without the facilities of an air arm, provided there was a world consensus of opinion against the use of bombing undefended areas, it would be to our advantage to make the sacrifice in order to secure a much greater gain. Even taking the lowest view of human nature, nations in war do not usually do things which give them no special advantage, and which grievously complicate their own position.

No convention of the kind of which I have been speaking would be of the slightest use between the Great Powers unless it were based on parity [*i.e.* upon our having an Air Force equal to any other country within striking distance of our shores]. That is the key to any convention which may be negotiated. If one side had an all-powerful air force and the other only a very weak defense, the temptation to use the weapons of terror upon the civil population might far outweigh any detrimental effects on neutral opinion. If, however, the two sides were in an equality and in the position to do equal and simultaneous harm to each other, then the uselessness of the crime would reinforce its guilt and horror, and the effects upon the action of neutrals. I hold that we should make conventions to limit and regulate the use of the air arm, and these conventions should be made, and can only be made, on the basis of parity. If both sides feel that they would suffer equally from a breach of an international convention and neither side can see how it can gain an advantage over the other, it seems likely that these conventions will be respected. Not only would the danger of our being attacked be greatly diminished, but the character of the attack would be confined within the limits of the convention by breaking which neither side would have anything to gain.

That is the argument for parity, and for immediate parity. I believe that conventions based on parity are the best only means of shielding the crowded populations of our great cities, and particularly of this enormous London, by making it certain that there will be no advantage to either side in departing from what has been agreed. I do not see how the most sincere lover of peace or the most inveterate hater of war in this House can dispute the good sense and reason of the argument for parity. [Editor's Note: This argument for equal air strength applies only to one particular arm, and deals only with the position of Great Britain in relation to Continental Powers. It in no way contradicts the argument in which the dangers of a general equality of armaments between victor and vanquished nations are described.]

There is, of course, one other and ultimate method of defense which we must also develop by every conceivable means. I mean the effective punishment and destruction, by an active and efficient home defense, of any invaders who may come to our shores. I do not pretend to deal with technical matters this afternoon. This is not the time for us to deal with them, nor do I think the House of Commons is the best place in which they can be ventilated, but I must express this opinion. It ought to be possible, by making good arrangements both on the ground and in the air, to secure very real advantages for the force of aeroplanes which is defending its own air and which can rise lightly laden from its own soil. I cannot believe that that advantage, properly organized, would not give an additional and important measure of protection. We should be able by these means to impose deterrents upon an invader, and even upon a potential declaration of war, and gradually to bring attacks upon us, by attrition, to smaller dimensions and finally to an end altogether. In these matters we have, of course, to trust our experts. I hope that they are busy, that they are tirelessly working out methods of defense; and we trust the Government and the Ministers concerned to guide the experts, and to make sure that the necessary funds and authority are supplied to carry out a complete scheme of home defense.

Therefore, there seem to me to be four lines of protection by which we can secure the best chance, and a good chance, of immunity for our people from the perils of air war—a peaceful foreign policy; the convention regulating air warfare; the parity in air power to invest that convention with validity; and, arising out of that parity, a sound system of home defense—in addition to all these other arrangements if they all fail. We must not despair, we must not for a moment pretend that we cannot face these things. Dangers come upon the world; other nations face them. When, in old days, the sea gave access to this island, it was a danger to this island. It made it liable to invasion at any point; but by taking proper measures our ancestors gained the command of the sea, and consequently, what had been a means of inroad upon us became our sure protection; and there is not the slightest reason why, with our ability and our resources, and our peaceful intentions, our desire only to live quietly here in our island, we should not raise up for ourselves a security in the air above us which will make us as free from serious molestation as did our control of blue water in bygone centuries.

It is not to be disputed that we are in a dangerous position today. This is a very good White Paper. The opening paragraph sets forth a most admirable declaration, but what is there behind it? £130,000. Very fine words. It must have taken the Cabinet a long time to agree to them—with the Air Minister drafting them and passing them round. They give great paper satisfaction. But what is there behind them? £130,000. It is not the slightest use concealing the facts. The Under-Secretary has given some of them. The Liberal Member who spoke from the benches opposite gave some, as I thought, most disconcerting and alarming facts about air warfare and the growth of air armaments. And we are, it is admitted, the fifth air Power only, if that. We are only half the strength of France, our nearest neighbor. Germany is arming fast, and no one is going to stop her. That seems quite clear. No one proposes a preventive war to stop Germany breaking the Treaty of Versailles. She is going to arm, she is doing it, she has been doing it. I have not any knowledge of the details, but people are well aware that those very gifted people, with their science and with their factories, with what they call their "Air Sport," are capable of developing with great rapidity a most powerful air force for all purposes, offensive and defensive, within a very short period of time.

Germany is ruled by a handful of autocrats who are the absolute masters of that gifted nation. They are men who have neither the long interests of a dynasty to consider, nor those very important restraints which a democratic Parliament and constitutional system impose upon any executive Government. Nor have they the restraint of public opinion, which public opinion, indeed, they control by every means which modern apparatus renders possible. They are men who owe their power to, and are, indeed, the expression of, the bitterness of defeat, and of the resolved and giant strength of that mighty German Empire. I am not going to speak about their personalities, because there is no one in the House who is not thoroughly aware of them and cannot form his own opinion after having read the accounts of what has been happening there, of the spirit which is alive there and of the language, methods and outlook of the leading men of that tremendous community, much the most powerful in the whole world. The German power is in their hands, and they can direct it this way or that by a stroke of the pen, by a single gesture.

I dread the day when the means of threatening the heart of the British Empire should pass into the hands of the present rulers of Germany. I think we should be in a position which would be odious to very man who values freedom of action and independence, and also in a position of the utmost peril for our crowded, peaceful population, engaged in their daily toil. I dread that day, but it is not, perhaps, far distant. It is, perhaps, only a year, or perhaps eighteen months, distant. Not come yet—at least, so I believe, or I hope and pray. But it is not far distant. There is still time for us to take the necessary measures, but it is the measures we want. Not this paragraph in this White Paper; we want the measures. It is no good writing that first paragraph and then producing £130,000. We want the measures to achieve parity. The hon. Gentleman opposite who spoke so many words of wisdom seemed to me to mar the significance and point of his argument when he interposed in it the statement that he was not committing himself to any increase.

Mr. Mander: At this stage.

Mr. Churchill: But this *is* the stage. I do not say today, but within the next week or so. The turning-point has been reached, and the new steps must be taken. There are very special dangers to be feared if any Great Power possessing Dominions and connections all over the world falls into a peculiarly vulnerable condition. How many wars have we seen break out because of the inherent weakness of some great empire, such as the Hapsburg Empire or the Turkish Empire, when they fell into decay? Then all the dangerous forces become excited. No nation playing the part we play in the world, and aspire to play, has a right to be in a position where it can be blackmailed.

I said I would not dwell on the past, but I must repudiate the unfair attacks which have been made lately upon the Secretary of State for India [Sir Samuel Hoare]. He and I have very grave differences, and I, personally, shall carry them to their conclusion, but to charge him, or to charge Lord Trenchard, to whom our small but admirable Air Force owes so much, with having failed in their public duty is monstrous. At any rate, as Chancellor of the Exchequer responsible for five Budgets before 1929 I must entirely associate myself with the Secretary of State for India, then Minister for Air. Next to the Lord President of the Council, then Prime Minister, I shared the responsibility for what was done, or not done, in those years, and I am prepared to offer a detailed and, I trust, vigorous justification—or, I hope, vindication—if it should be desired in any quarter. But the scene has changed. This terrible new fact has occurred. Germany is arming—she is rapidly arming—and no one will stop her. None of the grievances between the victors and the vanquished have been redressed. The spirit of aggressive nationalism was never more rife in Europe and in the world. Far away are the days of Locarno, when we nourished bright hopes of the reunion of the European family and the laying in the tomb of that age-long quarrel between Teuton and Gaul of which we have been the victims in our lifetime.

That hope is gone, and we must act in accordance with the new situation. Here I address myself particularly to the Lord President. I say nothing in derogation of the high responsibility of the Prime Minister, but I address myself particularly to the Lord President as he is in his place in the House. He alone has the power. He has the power not only because of the confidence which is placed by large numbers of people of the country in the sobriety of his judgment and in his peaceful intentions, but also because, as leader of the Conservative party, he possesses the control of overwhelming majorities of determined men in both Houses of the Legislature. My right hon. Friend has only to make up his mind and Parliament will vote all the supplies and all the sanctions which are necessary, if need be within forty-eight hours. There need be no talk of working up public opinion. You need not go and ask the public what they think about this. Parliament and the Cabinet have to decide, and the nation has to judge whether they have acted rightly as trustees. The Lord President has the power, and if he has the power he has also what always goes with power—he has the responsibility. Perhaps it is a more grievous and direct personal responsibility than has for many years fallen upon a single servant of the Crown. He may not have sought it, but he is tonight the captain of the gate. The nation looks to him to advise it and lead it, to guide it wisely and safely in this dangerous question, and I hope and believe that we shall not look in vain.

THE MacDONALD PLAN REJECTED

March 14, 1934

House of Commons

I was taken to task the other day for saying that the Lord Privy Seal [Mr. Eden] in his mission to the three capitals in Europe had failed. I have listened to his very agreeably delivered speech, so excellent in its phrasing and so well meant in its sentiments, and I am bound to say that the farthest I can go in altering my statement that his mission had failed is to say that up to the present at any rate it has not succeeded.

He was set an impossible task. Take one instance. He had to commend to France an elaborate scheme of disarmament which meant that the French would have to agree that their army in Europe, long the most famous in the history of the world, should be no stronger than the army of Poland, Germany or Italy. It seemed to me, even before he set out on his tour, extremely unlikely that France would agree to that at any time, least of all at a time like this. I ventured to say a year ago, when the Prime Minister's first scheme, prescribing in great detail to the countries in Europe exactly how large their armies, navies and air forces should be, was put forward, that there was no chance of it being accepted. And when this scheme had been received by the French with the greatest politeness, and with an ingenuity born of what is now a long and careful study of the Anglo-Saxon mentality and the character of public opinion in the United Kingdom and in the United States, when they accepted with great civility the scheme as a most valuable contribution to the progress of mankind and the consolidation of the peace of the human race, but mentioned that there were a few little reservations on this point and that which they might find it necessary to introduce, I predicted what the fate of the scheme would be.

The Lord Privy Seal has pointed out that the objections now are not the technical objections of experts as to the size of cannons, and so on; that is now what is holding up agreement. For a long time we were told that this was the difficulty, but as the experts have now adjusted their views we have got back to where we started. Nations are not prepared to accept a great diminution of their individual security at this juncture, and they begin to raise new and fundamental opposition to the principles of the proposals put forward. Another proposal with which the Lord Privy Seal was charged was that France should reduce her air force to 500 machines. Actually at the moment she is proposing to spend, over a certain period, £40,000,000 to £50,000,000 in order to improve the character, quality and power of her air force, which already numbers three or four times that figure. Is she likely to agree? Will the French write back to us and say that they are entirely converted from their point of view and are ready to reduce their air force to 500 machines, while contemplating an improvement in the German air force at the same time?

Is it really worth while indulging in these illusions? Can we expect the French to write back to us agreeing to the proposal? We are not going to receive from this upstanding French Government anything which will meet the first MacDonald scheme or the second MacDonald scheme. I am reminded of a famous quotation from Dr. Johnson, which might well be read and pondered over by my hon. Friend:

> Ye who listen with credulity to the whispers of fancy, and pursue with eagerness the phantoms of hope, who expect that age will perform the promises of youth, and that the deficiencies of the present day will be supplied by the morrow; attend to the history of Rasselas, Prince of Abyssinia.

I did not find much in his most attractive and engaging speech that was reassuring. On the contrary, in the most correct phraseology which could possibly fall from the lips of a Minister of the Crown he painted for us a more sombre picture of the deterioration which has been going steadily forward in Europe than any we have yet heard from that Bench. I venture to suggest to my hon. Friend, in whose career the whole House has a common interest, because we do like to see new figures emerge, to be careful not to be too obliging in his departmental duties, and not to be too ready to do what is asked of him on all occasions, because he is very valuable, and we all hope that he will be associated with real success in the domain of foreign affairs.

False ideas have been spread about the country that disarmament means peace. The Disarmament Conference has brought us steadily nearer—I will not say to war because I share the repulsion from using that word, but nearer to a pronounced state of ill-will than anything that could be imagined. First of all, you were met with a competition among the different countries to disarm the other fellow, to take away the peculiar weapons of this or that other country, while safeguarding their own special military or naval interests. Then, in the second place, at Disarmament Conferences which were persisted in again and again year after year in spite of every failure, the desire was to throw the blame of the inevitable breakdown on some one country or another. "It was not me but that other country."

So in the end what have we got? We have not got disarmament. We have the rearmament of Germany. That is the monstrous offspring of this immense labour—the rearmament of Germany. Why, it is only a little while ago that I heard Ministers say and read diplomatic documents which said that rearmament was unthinkable—"Whatever happens, we cannot have that. Rearmament is unthinkable." Now all our hope is to regulate the unthinkable. Regulated unthinkability—that is the proposal now; and very soon it will be a question of making up our minds to unregulated unthinkability.

It is always an error in diplomacy to press a matter when it is quite clear that no further progress is to be made. It is also a great error if you ever give the impression abroad that you are using language which is more concerned with your domestic politics than with the actual fortunes and merits of the various great countries upon the Continent to whom you offer advice. Even suppose that the hon. Gentleman's mission shall be judged eventually to have failed, I am not so sure that we shall be so much worse off than if he had succeeded. Suppose France had taken the advice which we have tendered during the last four or five years, and had yielded to the pressure of the two great English-speaking nations to set an example of disarmament: suppose she had taken the advice of the Liberal newspapers! Only three or four years ago we noted the derision with which they wrote about the French barrier of fortresses which had been put up. Suppose the French had followed our example. Suppose they had made this gesture which is so much talked of today and had reduced themselves to allowing their defenses to fall into the kind of disarray to which we, out of the highest motives, for which we do not always get credit abroad, have reduced ours—what would be the position today? Where should we be?

I honour the French for their resolute determination to preserve the freedom and security of their country from invasion of any kind; I earnestly hope that we, in arranging our forces, shall not fall below their example. The awful danger, nothing less, of our present foreign policy is that we go on perpetually asking the French to weaken themselves. And what do we urge as the inducement? We say, "Weaken yourselves," and we always hold out the hope that if they do it and get into trouble, we shall then in some way or other go to their aid, although we have nothing with which to go to their aid. I cannot imagine a more dangerous policy. There is something to be said for isolation; there is something to be said for alliances. But there is nothing to be said for weakening the Power on the Continent with whom you would be in alliance, and then involving yourself further in Continental tangles in order to make it up to them. In that way you have neither one thing nor the other; you have the worst of both worlds.

The Romans had a maxim, "Shorten your weapons and lengthen your frontiers." But our maxim seems to be, "Diminish your weapons and increase your obligations." Aye, and diminish the weapons of your friends. That has been the extraordinary policy of late years. Great hopes were set on the Disarmament Conference when it began, and after Locarno there were great hopes. I am not going to pretend or suggest that the nagging and harping on disarmament have been the sole cause of the degeneration of European affairs. That would be unfair. Hideous new factors have rushed up at us from the gulf. Hideous new events have taken place which no one could have foreseen. Surely now we have reached a point where we ought to make an end of this effort to force disarmament upon countries which feel themselves in danger, and to put ourselves in a reasonable position of security. That will be better for peace, and much better for our own safety if peace should fail.

We now have an urgent duty. The Lord President made an important and welcome declaration in debate last week upon air policy—that if these attempts to obtain a Disarmament Convention failed, we should then place ourselves in a position of air parity, or words to that effect. I accept a statement of that kind without any hesitation, because I am certain that with his reputation and with his responsibility my right hon. Friend would not have made such a statement merely to get round a Parliamentary corner on a particular occasion, or to stave off the fulfillment of his undertaking by dilatory processes. Therefore, I did not share the anxiety of some Members at certain passages in his speech.

But there is one point on which anxiety might have arisen. When my right hon. Friend was making his speech and saying that if all failed, *then*—we all expected him to say, "Then we shall immediately take steps to put ourselves in a satisfactory position"; but after the "then" came something different. He said that then there would be an Air Convention. That was rather an anticlimax. It would be dangerous indeed if we had to begin again in regard to the Air Convention all those elaborate discussions with all the Powers, the tremendous procedure at Geneva, to go over the whole course again for one-third of the prize, as it were, and at the same time remain ourselves in this extremely dangerous position, while all the time the situation, for all we know, might be altering from week to week by the development of the aerial armaments and facilities of Germany. Therefore, one hopes that when the Minister who is to reply speaks he will say something to reassure us that this Air Convention which is to be entered upon if the main Convention fails, will not interpose a delay of more than a few weeks in the proper review and reconsideration of our domestic defense.

I made a proposal myself that we should endeavour to have an agreement with different Powers near us to limit the use of the air weapon. That is quite a different matter. There need be no delay in consequence of that—to confine air warfare as far as you can to the zones of the armies or military objectives. There need be no delay in that, because the essence of it is that we have an equal air force. Therefore, every step we make meanwhile to secure parity would help an agreement if it could be reached on the limitations which should be imposed by either side on the use of aircraft.

There was one remark thrown out very tentatively and guardedly by the hon. Member for Caerphilly [Mr. M. Jones], a remark which seemed to me to be pregnant. He said, in effect, why, if other things fail, should not the nations who are actually in agreement about keeping the peace and so forth reach out their hands to one another? Surely that is an idea which should be pursued, but it should be pursued through the

League of Nations. It is to the League of Nations that France or Belgium or any of those countries who are alarmed by the proceedings of their powerful neighbor, Germany, should have recourse. There it is that they should make their case, and all consequential action should be taken under the authority of the League of Nations. If it be true that those countries are deeply alarmed by proceedings across their frontiers, and if no satisfaction is given to them and no explanation made of what is going on, then it seems to me that they should associate themselves one with another, under the aegis of the League of Nations. Thus you would have a large number of countries who agreed and who had powerful forces and who could stand there, armed to defend each other if necessary, but who would not be able to move in any way except by the sanction of the international body. You would thus have the strength of the individual armies plus the control and authority of a great world-wide international organization. I do not believe you will ever succeed in building up an international force in a vague and general manner, or that it can be created in cold blood. But it might well be that an international force would come into being by an alliance of national forces for a particular emergency or for particular purposes, and, once having been started, it might give the security to the world which would avert the approaching curse of war.

SUNDAY TRADING QUESTION

March 15, 1934

Hotel Victoria, London

I think the Government will all agree in principle that they did not mean to permit the English Sunday to be reduced to a Continental Sunday. They did mean it to be a day entirely different to the ordinary working day. At the present time there is great need for people to be out of doors at the week-end, because the majority of them are confined to buildings during the week. That has to be recognized, and they would have to bring legislation up to that view, while still preserving the characteristics of the normal English Sunday and preventing the burden of unnecessary labour falling upon any class of the people. They want the Home Office to have consideration for the new conditions and to recognize and preserve what is necessary and healthy in these days and to make effective laws which would not be broken or evaded. We have much to congratulate ourselves upon. When we look upon the infringements of liberty, the fierce regimentation of opinion, and the intolerance breaking out in many countries and the dethroning of Parliamentary institutions, it is a comfort to see in this country of ours that we are able to give consideration to such matters as the preservation of the dignity of our Sunday and the lightening of the hours of labour.

EX-SERVICES WELFARE SOCIAL APPEAL

March 19, 1934

Mansion House Dinner, London

[Extract] ... I want to make it clear that the society casts no reflection on the general way in which the national duty towards the sufferers of the War is being discharged. But the strictness of regulation inevitable in the administration of State funds makes it all the more necessary that that State provision should be supplemented by large voluntary subscriptions and earnest of personal effort. Rules and classifications in dealing with State funds can not be always altered to meet exceptionally hard cases, and though I am glad to say that there is increased latitude and flexibility in the methods approved by Parliament year by year, the records of the society show that there are many painful cases which do not receive the special treatment which they require. In many cases it is only now that the mental effects of the War are being shown, as is proved by the fact that, whereas there were only 2,500 cases in mental hospitals in 1919, there are now 6,000 patients, with 30,000 borderline cases. These are the people who are being helped by the slender resources of the society.

A MINISTRY OF DEFENCE

March 21, 1934

House of Commons

There is a very general agreement in the House that a Ministry of Defence should be our ultimate aim. In no other way can the best arrangements be made for economy and efficiency. There are particularisms and what the Deputy-Leader of the Opposition [Mr. Attlee] described as the vested interests—the innocent and respectable vested interests—of the various Services, and they cause much waste and confusion. Our history books are full of the dissensions between the Army and Navy which have led to the loss of such fine opportunities in the past. We are assured by the Prime Minister that everything is now brought into complete harmony from a central point of view at every moment, but when we come to look below the surface of this assurance one sees many things which do not square with this hopeful and desirable assumption.

One cannot help feeling that in the distribution of public money each Service naturally fights for its own hand. There is nothing like leather, said the cordwainer, and each Service presses its own claims. In my experience, which is, I suppose, as long as anyone's, the Minister with most information and address and backed by the Department with the largest hold upon tradition and public goodwill gets the largest share, and a larger share than would be secured if the case for the three Services were presented to the Cabinet as a whole, and in relation to what is judged to be the chief danger of the times. That seems to me to be the first argument which can be adduced for a Ministry of Defence—that it would put us in a far better position for dealing with the changed conditions of high strategy and Imperial policy.

But there is a second argument that is novel and increasing. All the three Services in modern times have a new common factor which they never had in anything like the same degree until the present century, or, indeed, until after the recent Great War. I mean science and invention. Science and invention are sweeping all before them. The same science applies to all three Services alike, and its application must play a large part in all your plans and outlook. Nothing like this was known in the nineteenth century, and in those days the segregation of the Services seemed comparatively simple. The Navy, to quote Lord Fisher, was a dismal mystery surrounded by seasickness, and had nothing in common, except good conduct, with the barrack square and the red-coated Army of those days. The Air Force did not exist.

The new science has come along permeating all these Services—a solvent which disperses their differences. Science cares nothing for the professional particularisms or the established customs or the cherished traditions of any one of the Services. In the fires of science, burning with increasing heat every year, all the most dearly loved conventions are being melted down; and this is a process which is going continually to spread. In view of the inventions and discoveries which are being made for us, one might almost say every month, a unified direction of the war efforts of the three Services would be highly beneficial. We should have a greater chance of applying the gifts of science broadly to the whole texture of our defensive arrangements if there were a reception of all these new inventions and discoveries from a common elevated point of view, removed from the prejudice of any one particular uniformed profession. That is a second argument for a Ministry of Defence.

There is a third argument, which arises out of the other two, but which also affects the very important question of public economy—the expense, the burden upon this House and the taxpayer. There are many functions which are common to all three Services, but which are now managed as separate branches. There are separate medical services to succor the three separate Services of the Army, the Air, and the Navy. There are separate Departments of chaplains to minister to the spiritual needs of the airman, the soldier, and the sailor. Research—an enormous, vital field—has not been pooled; there must, surely, be great overlapping there. Above all, Intelligence has not been pooled, and this, I may point out, was recommended to a very considerable extent by the Weir Committee. They strongly urged a movement towards the pooling of the various, almost numerous, Intelligence branches which are at work at the present time in the body of our State. But nothing has been done about it. The Committee was appointed in 1923; it reported in 1926; we are now here in 1934, and nothing has been done about it. It was a very good Committee. Their recommendations were modest. They pressed this, but nothing has been done about it in the interval.

Lastly, there is the great field of contracts, and here something has been done. I would go farther, and admit that much has been done. The Contracts Committee, which the Prime Minister mentioned, is at work, and even before that committee was set up I have never felt that it was true that the different Departments of the State have in time of peace been bidding against each other to any large extent in the common market so as to put prices up against one another. The Treasury take care of that. And our arrangements, as the Prime Minister has indicated, are often very much better in practice than they are in theory. But in the field of contracts there still is much that could be done, even in time of peace, and if ever we should be involved in a great war again it would be most important that the entire business of the purchase and manufacture of munitions and supplies of all kinds, possibly with certain highly technical exceptions, should be taken over by a central administration and unified.

When the Great War broke out, our Navy was by far the largest in the world, and its great supply departments of all kinds lay behind it in the same proportion. The Army, on the other hand, had to be multiplied twenty- or thirtyfold, but this took some time, and it was many months before the war pressure led the Navy and the Army even to impinge upon the real resources of British industry. But by the middle of 1915 we began everywhere to feel the frontiers of supplies of every kind; the bones began to appear through the skin; and thereafter, from that time onwards, there were lamentable collisions and dispute and friction between the Admiralty and the other two Services represented by the Ministry of Munitions. In the end, the Ministry of Munitions made everything for the Air Ministry and for the Army, but they had to fight with the Admiralty, who remained a separate enclave, almost a foreign Power, as it seemed, in the heart and centre of our State. I hope that arrangements will be made in the future to ensure that nothing like that occurs again, for I have no doubt, from the experience which I have had—and I had opportunities of seeing a good deal—that the public did not get the best service or the best use of the available material during the opening years of the War, owing largely to the jealous clash which took place between the Admiralty and the other two Departments.

In organizing industry, not only actually but prospectively, surely we might learn something from our German friends, who are building up an entirely new army and other fighting Services, and who have the advantage of building them up from what is called a clean-swept table—starting fair in this respect, unhampered by past conventions, by customs or prejudices of any kind. That is a great advantage indeed. I have been told that they have created what is called a "weapon office," or *Waffenamt*, which makes for all the three arms of the Service which they are so busily developing. It seems to me that this expression, "weapon office," is pregnant, and that it might well enter into and be incorporated in our thought at the present time. Not only in the current supplies of the three Services in time of peace, but still more in the organization of national industry in case war should come, it seems to me imperative that there should be one view and one control in this country.

To sum up, I urge, first of all, that the Government should affirm publicly and definitely the principle of a Ministry of Defence; secondly, that they should take forthwith every interim step towards the merging and the fusion which would render, after the passage of a number of years, such unification possible, and that this should be a steady policy pursued year after year. By doing this I believe we should increasingly fit ourselves for dealing with immediate practical problems. We should improve the value which we get for the taxpayers' money or, alternatively, we should get the same security for less money, according to whether the skies were dark or clear, and we should be moving steadily towards a sound, true organization of our resources.

INDIA (CONSERVATIVE POLICY)

March 28, 1934

Conservative Party Central Council Meeting,
London

I do not wish in any way to mar the friendliness of the meeting. Not only are we met as friends, but as friends who within two years will be engaged in a desperate struggle against all the subversive forces in this country, roused up by every form of prejudice. I agree that we should make a solid front of all the strong forces which we can get together, forces of the kind which pulled this country through the War and broke the general strike. Such forces should be led against the Socialist menace and that is our prime and foremost duty.

I deny any suggestions that the Indian problem was a "sectional job." We are bound to press our views on India. We have had a very hard night and a very long one, but we are making progress. If the present muzzling resolution had been passed a year ago we would not have had the remarkable declaration that has since been made by their leader that the National Union would be consulted. Some of us with whom the Council were angry feel that they have had to put their point of view, and we have only done our duty. We will continue to do so to the best of our ability. The National Union has played an important part in the discussion of the Indian problem. If the resolution is passed it will put a stop to the consideration for a long or a short time. I urge that the meeting should secure to the National Union its full liberty.

On previous occasions the issue has been complicated by people saying that it is a matter of confidence in the Government. Clearly in rejecting this Birmingham muzzling order there will be no such question, as it has been made plain that the resolution has no official inspiration. Some of those who have not wished to express an opinion yet on the full aspect of the Indian question, or do anything which might be considered a challenge to the Government, but who feel in their hearts that it would be a good thing to give a friendly warning gesture to the Government to go slowly could, I suggest, vote for Lord FitzAlan's amendment.

A QUESTION OF PRIVILEGE
(THE HOARE-DERBY AFFAIR)

April 16, 1934

House of Commons

I desire to ask leave to raise a question of Privilege and to ask your Ruling, Mr. Speaker, as to whether I may submit a Motion thereupon to the House. On personal grounds, I raise this question with the greatest reluctance, but I also do so with the conviction that I have no other choice. A mass of evidence has been placed at my disposal unreservedly. It is evidence of so remarkable a character that I feel bound to bring the subject before the House, and I do so in accordance with the Rules of Procedure, which prescribe that such matters shall be raised at the first Parliamentary opportunity after the facts have been ascertained by any Member of the House. I ask leave, Sir, to submit that a breach of the privileges of the House of Commons has arisen out of certain proceedings of some members of the Joint Select Committee upon Indian Constitutional Reform. I shall state the facts briefly and as far as possible without comment, because I feel that this matter in the first instance requires investigation by the Committee of Privileges.

During the month of May, 1933, last year, the India section of the Manchester Chamber of Commerce was engaged in preparing its evidence for the Joint Select Committee, which was then and is now sitting. As soon as the forecast and outline of this evidence reached the Secretary of State for India, sharp differences of opinion arose between him and the then President of the Chamber of Commerce, Mr. Richard Bond, and, as I assert, the Secretary of State from that date set himself to prevent the presentation of the Lancashire evidence in the form in which those most concerned in the welfare of the cotton industry wished to present it. A month passed, and in the middle of June, 1933, the same year, the India section of the Manchester Chamber of Commerce completed its preparation of the evidence. The evidence was printed, and 100 copies were duly forwarded to the Secretary of the Joint Select Committee, by whom they were formally received. It was then expected that the hearing of this evidence would take place on the 30th June. Actually, it did not take place until the 4th November of last year.

Early and full information of the character of the evidence, if not indeed—but I have to be very careful only to base myself on facts, which I undertake to prove—if not indeed an actual advance copy of the text, reached my right hon. Friend the Secretary of State, and thereafter, almost immediately thereafter, a dinner was held in London, on the 27th June, at Lord Derby's house, to which the principal members of the India section of the Manchester Chamber of Commerce were invited by Lord Derby. The Secretary of State and two other Ministers of the Crown were present. This was the beginning of a long series of negotiations, amounting to pressure, upon the Manchester Chamber of Commerce, and recognised as pressure by them. This body was chiefly represented, when Mr. Bond had finished his term of office, by Mr. Barlow, the new President of the Chamber, and Mr. Rodier, the Chairman of the India section.

The object of the pressure was to procure a fundamental alteration in the evidence already officially tendered to the Secretary of the Joint Select Committee and already in his possession. I stress that point. To conform with this, the hearing of the evidence was put off, as I have already mentioned. I base the statement that pressure was applied, and the use of the word "pressure," upon the terms of a conclusion reached by the India section of the Manchester Chamber of Commerce on the 28th July of last year, a month after the dinner to which I have referred. Up to this date they were still standing fast to their opinions. The members agreed unanimously that pressure might be brought upon the Chamber to revise their evidence, then agreed and tendered, and they agreed that unless a new situation arose, there should be no suggestion made of making changes in the nature of the Committee's recommendations. I mention this fact to establish the point of pressure.

Now this pressure which the India section of the Manchester Chamber of Commerce apprehended, or was already conscious of, soon came upon them, and I assert that it came primarily from my right hon. Friend the Secretary of State, through all the channels which His Majesty's Government can command, direct and indirect, and in particular that Lord Derby, a leading member of the Joint Select Committee, visited Manchester in September, interviewed members of the Chamber of Commerce, and sought to persuade them and to counsel them to alter their evidence. Eventually, the Manchester Chamber of Commerce were induced to withdraw the evidence which they had formally presented, and on a date which I cannot inform the House of as yet they procured the surrender of that evidence by the Secretary of the Joint Select Committee, to whom it had been confided and who held it on behalf of the committee as a whole. The 100 copies which ought to have reached the members in due course were thereafter recovered uncirculated.

I do not dispute—it is no part of my case to dispute—the right of witnesses to modify evidence which they have tendered in writing, or after they have tendered it orally, if their better judgment induces them to do so, but I think that when a whole document has been presented, and an entirely different document has been presented, that matter ought not to be a secret from the members of the Joint Select Committee. Anyhow, that is not the point which I have to raise in this submission which I am making. I am concerned entirely with the pressure which was brought to bear upon the members of the Manchester Chamber of Commerce to change their evidence. I am concerned with the quarters from which those pressures arose and the channels through which they were applied, and that is the only matter which is before the House at the present moment.

In the narrative which I am unfolding we have now reached the month of October. By this time there was a mission from the Manchester Chamber of Commerce, including some members of the original India section of the chamber, which was actually in India in connection with the question of Japanese competition. Attempts were made—this is another of my assertions—to persuade this mission to take the responsibility upon themselves of asking that the original evidence should be altered. The mission, however, were on the spot. They had the opportunity of being able to judge how far Lancashire interests would be injured by the publication of the original evidence. They were in a much better position to judge than the members of the Chamber of Commerce at home. There are, I believe, some members of that mission in the House, and they will be able to give their opinion upon the facts which I have stated.

This mission on the spot, who had the opportunity of seeing whether Lancashire interests were endangered and were good judges of that, refused point blank to accept any responsibility for making changes in the evidence. They urged that the evidence should be published in its original form, together with a supplementary paper, which they suggested, of a conciliatory character dwelling on the importance of good will, which we should all admit must play a large part in the solution of these matters. That was what was recommended by this mission in India on the spot, in touch with the circumstances, having an interest in getting an immediate negotiation settled satisfactorily, having a great need to keep in the good graces of the Government of India who were in touch with the Secretary of State. In spite of all that, this is what they recommended, namely, that the evidence should be published as it was originally printed and as it was originally handed in to the Secretary of the Joint Statutory Committee. They telegraphed in this sense. We are now at the 24th October, 1933. On that date, as the result of this continuous, pervasive pressure, the Indian section of the Manchester Chamber of Commerce in spite of what their mission said, took the responsibility upon themselves, under the pressures to which they were subjected, of agreeing to substantial and, indeed, fundamental alterations in the evidence. A new statement of evidence was printed. This was but a ghost of the original evidence, a poor, shrunken, emasculated thing—an acceptance of what might be thought to be an inevitable drift of events. It was but a ghost of the original evidence that Manchester wished to give and had actually deposited. This in due course was presented to the Joint Select Committee and heard by them at their session on the 4th November, the vast bulk of the members being in total ignorance of what had been going on behind the scenes before they were at last allowed to hear the opinions of the Manchester Chamber of Commerce. I must make it clear—because I have to make out the points as I go—that I am prepared to prove, although I am not going to quote any secret documents at this moment, that the differences between the original evidence and the evidence which was tendered eventually were of a decisive character and not small alterations or emendations or tonings down; they were alterations of a decisive character.

I have placed these facts before the House, and I wish now to point my claim that a breach of Privilege has been committed. The members of the Joint Select Committee sit in a judicial capacity. We have been continually assured of this, and also, of course, of their impartiality, and we have all been urged, and are repeatedly urged, in fact—it is the focus of the political situation at the present time—that we should await their decision. In fact, two members of the Joint Select Committee, to wit, the Secretary of State for India and Lord Derby, have been jointly and severally concerned in procuring a complete alteration of the evidence tendered by the Manchester Chamber of Commerce and submitted through the usual channels. Their action was no doubt well intentioned. I do not impugn their personal motives. There is no question of personal honour involved in anything I say or in the Motion I shall presently make with your permission. I do not argue on the merits of the question. Many may think that the advice tendered was wise. That is not the question which the House of Commons has to settle this afternoon. I do not argue upon the merits of the question. There is nothing to do with any views about the solution of the Indian problem in this matter. That is a question we shall have plenty of opportunities of discussing later.

But this I say, and I submit to the House and to you, Sir, as Speaker, that it is grossly irregular and highly objectionable for members or a member of the Joint Select Committee sitting in a judicial capacity to bring influence and pressure to bear upon witnesses to induce them to alter the evidence which they naturally wished to tender, to suppress the truth as they wished to tell it, and which they had officially placed in the possession of the Secretary of the Joint Select Committee. The Sessional Order relating to witnesses deals with the position in language which, though archaic, has a bearing. We pass this Order at the beginning of every Session. It says:

> That if it shall appear that any person hath been tampering with any Witness, in respect of his evidence to be given to this House, or any Committee thereof, or directly or indirectly hath endeavoured to deter or hinder any person from appearing or giving evidence, the same is declared to be a high crime or misdemeanour; and this House will proceed with the utmost severity against such offender.

Since the word "tamper" may raise a qualm in some minds, I may say that Erskine May contains precedents which show that no question of corruption is necessary for the word "tamper" or the validity of the Sessional Order. There was a case in 1809 where a gentleman was proceeded against by the House of Commons on the ground of tampering, when all he had done was to tender advice to a witness about to appear before a Committee of the House. This Sessional Order shows how serious is the view which has always been taken by Parliament of attempts to meddle with witnesses and to defeat the purposes of Parliament, namely, that their Committees should elicit the truth and arrive at right and sound conclusions, and that that purpose should not be defeated by the alteration or suppression of the evidence which witnesses of all kinds may wish to tender. Still more marked is the case when the evidence had actually been placed in the possession of the Secretary of the Joint Select Committee and was privily withdrawn and fundamentally transformed afterwards. I have mentioned incidentally that the bulk of the other members had no knowledge of this, and it is a matter which in their place and their sphere, I should think, they should raise—the acting Leader of the Opposition knows what the position was; he sat there many hours—and they ought to have been informed, and he ought to have known what was going on.

I am concerned, however, this afternoon only with the privileges of this House, and I say most of all that it is repugnant to the proprieties of public business and to the dignity of this Joint Committee, and the credentials of the Committee above all others, considering the importance of a solution of these grave matters—it is repugnant that one or more of its members should be active agent or agents in such a process of transforming the evidence to be submitted to them. Although neither malice nor corruption is imputed, the irregularity and impropriety are so gross and grave, I submit to you, Sir, as to constitute a case of breach of Privilege of the most flagrant character.

What would be said if a tribunal of judges were trying a case about which there was a keen public controversy, and on which very large issues—immeasurable issues—depended, and if one or more of the judges, hearing from the Government that inconvenient evidence was likely to be tendered by important witnesses, sought them out, got into touch with them, invited them to dinner, induced them to transform their evidence which they had already manifested their intention to submit to the court—what would have been thought of that? I have known Lord Derby since I was first a candidate for this House, more than 30 years ago, and I share the general respect and good will which are felt for him. He has great influence in Lancashire. The story of how that influence has been built up by a lifetime of services, of kindliness, and of neighbourly hospitality is one of the most honourable and agreeable features in the life of that great and sorely-stricken county. But no personal considerations either of friendship or of respect can possibly condone so monstrous a confusion of functions as arises when members of a Joint Select Committee in fact actually prevent the statement of the real evidence which an important set of witnesses are to give, and when they procure the substitution of weak, meaningless and colourless testimony which passes as representing what those witnesses wish to say.

These are not the days, alas, when Parliament can afford to be too lax and easy going in the assertion of its rights and responsibilities. Things cannot be done in such an easy, quiet, good natured manner. There must be firm assertion of principle and of decorum. Personal considerations must not affect the faithful and uncompromising discharge of public duties by Members of the House, even though the private friendships have to suffer thereby. Persons, however elevated, however virtuous, must be made to understand and to respect the proper limits of the various functions they discharge. No man can sit as a judge upon a tribunal, no man can be cited before all the country as an independent and impartial arbiter, and then, at the same time, go round and manage and whittle down the evidence which is going to be presented to his colleagues and fellow judges. The two roles are absolutely irreconcilable. I shall not, of course, attempt this afternoon to deal with the aspect which these transactions wear when contrasted with the many assurances which Ministers have given, and are always giving, to their own party and to Lancashire that everything will be laid before the Joint Select Committee and threshed out there, or when they are contrasted with their appeal that every one should await the verdict of so authoritative, so impartial and so thoroughly informed a body.

I confine myself to-day solely to the argument necessary to establish a *prima facie* case of breach of Privilege. I have made a number of statements, some of them amounting to charges, and I shall be rightly asked what evidence I have to prove what I have said. I will deal with the House with complete candour. I am in possession of documentary evidence, which cannot, I think, be challenged, to prove all the facts I have set out, and a good many more. These documents have been given to me without any conditions as to private confidence and secrecy, other than those which may be prescribed by law, but practically none of them are official documents. I have not sought this information, which has been volunteered to me, and what course have I, as a Member of Parliament, but the course which I ask the House, subject to your Ruling, Sir, to allow me to take? As soon as I saw these papers I was sure that I could not discharge my responsibility except by raising the case as a breach of Privilege—and I submit they constitute a breach of privilege—and by laying that case before the Committee of Privileges for their investigation of these matters.

I therefore ask to be allowed to substantiate before the Committee of Privileges the statements which, with great regret on personal grounds, I have thought it my duty as a Member of the House of Commons to make. I have sent notice to my right hon. Friend the Secretary of State for India, who is the officer of the House principally concerned in the matter, directly and personally concerned in the subject of my statements, in order that he might be in his place to deal with the matter should he care to do so. I now ask you, Mr. Speaker, as guardian of the rights and liberties of this House, and of the power and authority of Parliament, to rule that a *prima facie* case of breach of privilege has arisen and to allow me to move, in suitable terms which I will submit, that the whole matter be forthwith remitted to the Committee of Privileges for their consideration.

[Editor's Note: The matter was referred to the Committee on Privileges on April 18 after the Speaker had ruled that there was *prima facie* evidence to merit an inquiry. Thus the stage was set for one of Churchill's most spectacular fiascoes.]

SEA TRADE

April 20, 1934

Honourable Company of Merchant Mariners Dinner,
Mansion House, London

These are hard times for the Mercantile Marine. There is a great shrinkage in world trade. There is almost a conspiracy among the nations of the world to cut themselves off from one another. There is an improvement, which they all must welcome, and they cannot exclude the Government from consideration in contributing to the turn of the tide in their favour. (Cheers.) The greatness of England has been founded on seaborne trade and seaborne food. Seaborne trade, should a new war occur, would be attacked not only by a hideous underwater menace but from the air. No doubt they might still rely on the courage and seamanship and all those qualities which they have in their merchant seamen, but let them give the seamen that protection from the Royal Navy and from a superior Air Force which would enable them to proceed confidently to and fro on their lawful avocations.

SEASIDE CAMPS AND SETTLEMENT
ASSOCIATION APPEAL

April 24, 1934

Luncheon, Carpenters' Hall, London

[Extract] ... The work of the camp cannot be kept going without regular and generous support. What better measure can be taken to smooth off the differences between class and class, eradicate snobbery in every form, and make those who are lucky in this world understand and sympathize with the dignity of the lives of those who are perhaps born with hardly any advantages, than to bring together in a summer camp by the sea boys from the poor quarters of industrial districts and young men, their own contemporaries, from the Universities and the Public Schools? What more powerful and well conceived agency can they have to make our country one?

COMMITTEE OF PRIVILEGES' REPORT
(THE HOARE-DERBY AFFAIR)

June 13, 1934

House of Commons

The Committee of Privileges ruled that no breach of Parliamentary privilege had occurred, and unanimously exonerated Sir Samuel Hoare and Lord Derby from Churchill's allegations. Sir John Simon and Leo Amery were particularly caustic during the debate on the Committee's Report. In the end, the debate collapsed, and no division was taken. The Report was adopted. Churchill's reputation slipped even further. This was a crucial episode in the decline of his fortunes.

I think it will be convenient if I group the remarks I have to make this afternoon under three heads. First, my justification for taking the course I did; secondly, the decision of the Committee, and subsequently of His Majesty's Government, to suppress the evidence; and, thirdly, the constitutional consequences of the new interpretation, as I hold it to be, which the Committee have given to the law of Privilege. At the root of this dispute lie very grave and far-reaching issues. I am not going into the merits of the India Conference; I refer to this not for the purpose of dealing with the merits but solely for the purpose of emphasising the magnitude of the issues which lie at the root of this dispute. Manchester said in effect—I am not using their actual words—that at the moment of giving a new constitution to India, with responsibility at the centre and complete tariff autonomy leading up to full Dominion status, safeguards should be incorporated in the constitution to prevent Lancashire and other British trading interests with India being arbitrarily or capriciously ruined at the discretion of an All-India Assembly. I share that view. My friends and I hold that, while we protect India and maintain a large army for internal order, we have a right to ask for guarantees that the mutually advantageous trade which has so long flourished between Great Britain and India shall not be injured or destroyed by an unfair use of tariffs, bounties, or administrative action, and we think that the new India Constitution Bill affords an occasion when this principle must be brought into review.

The Secretary of State for India and those who think with him hold that there is no possibility of safeguards, that the so-called Fiscal Autonomy Convention must operate with added force under responsible government, and that our only hope is to trust to good will and trade negotiations. This is a grave controversy, and, of course, there are two opinions about it. I myself hold that it is a controversy which lies at the root of the whole of this discussion, all that runs through the report turns upon that issue, and, therefore, it is not a small thing, a little thing, no light matter, about which we are fighting as we are. It is a matter of such grave consequences to our country that in serving that cause one might well sacrifice personal friendships or anything else which may be necessary for the purpose. This was the issue which the Manchester Chamber of Commerce wished to raise in their evidence before the Joint Select Committee, and this was the issue which the Secretary of State for India wished to deter them from raising. Obviously, he had—not a strong personal interest, there is no such idea—a strong personal political interest in doing so, because if Lancashire had brought this claim into the full light of day before the Joint Select Committee there would undoubtedly have been considerable alignment to that opinion of all Lancashire members in opposition to the policy which the Secretary of State was conducting.

The complaint which I make and which I voice is that this claim of Lancashire has never been brought before the Joint Select Committee in the full light of day, and that they have concluded the hearing of evidence in complete ignorance of the fact that Lancashire desires to raise this question. In fact, the evidence finally and publicly tendered by the Manchester representatives to the Joint Select Committee was practically to the effect that they sought no amendment at all in the India White Paper. That is quite untrue. We are in the presence, first of all, of a substantial matter of controversy, no question of words, but a really grave fundamental variance between two parties, and, secondly, a grievance, which I conceive to exist, that that issue has not been brought to the attention of the Committee or the public.

What was the task of the Committee of Privileges? It seems to me that there were three questions which they had to decide in respect of the Secretary of State for India and Lord Derby. Did they endeavour to procure an alteration in the evidence; did they succeed; and, thirdly, in either event was this a breach of privilege? The first question is one of pure fact, the last is one of pure opinion, and the intermediate question is one in which fact and opinion both play their part. Upon the first question, I submit to the House that almost all the main facts which I submitted to them in April are accepted in the Report. The Prime Minister has said that there was no disagreement about the facts. I am glad that there is no disagreement about the facts which I put in. I am sorry that I cannot wholly reciprocate the compliment. I am glad to see that the

Commiteee put in the forefront their agreement with my declaration that nothing in these charges affects the personal honour or good intentions of the Secretary of State and Lord Derby. I said that; and they have endorsed it after a thorough examination. On the other hand, no attempt is made to dispute the charge that these two statesmen endeavoured to deter the Manchester Chamber of Commerce from tendering their evidence in its original form. I have explained, and the report shows, that the alterations for which they pressed were not small matters. They involved great principles, which I have ventured to lay before the House, which will become dominant in the near future.

In other matters I find myself in complete agreement with the Committee in regard to their confirmation of the facts I adduced in my speech. There is confirmation of the fact that the Secretary of State for India received, before the dinner on 27th June, an outline of the proposed evidence. He received it on the day of the dinner, although it is true that he had not the opportunity of reading it. So also is admitted my statement that this evidence was the subject of discussion at the dinner. There is no dispute about that. I am not going to take up the time of the House by reading out the confirmation passage in the Committee of Privileges' Report, but they say:

> This record was made at the time or shortly after the meeting, and it may be accepted as reliable.

It is quite true that they introduced this refinement:

> The impression left upon your Committee is that the main points dealt with by the evidence were, in fact, covered by the statements made at the dinner, but they were not raised or discussed as being the evidence of the Chamber.

I frankly confess that this is not a refinement which had occurred to me, and would not occur to a lay mind. I do not draw a distinction between discussing the evidence and discussing points in the evidence. I make all necessary apologies on that score. Last April I said that the Lancashire Mission to India, refused point blank to accept any responsibility for making changes in the evidence. They urged that it should be published in its original form, together with a supplementary paper of a conciliatory character. I was confirmed upon that subject by my hon. Friend the Member for Stockport (Mr. Hammersley). This is also borne out by the report of the Committee of Privileges, I think on page 16, which shows that the Mission in their telegrams of 3rd, 18th and 23rd October adhered to their view that the evidence should not be altered. Therefore, I say, and the House must forgive me for saying, that it is my duty to justify the course I have taken in invoking this grave, formidable procedure of Privilege which is the power and glory of the House of Commons and which, in this country, as in no other country in the world, enables a private Member of this House to hold the whole machinery of the State up to accountability—a procedure which has come down from our ancestors. In any other country in the world, I suppose, I should be put in a concentration camp and visited by a party of overgrown schoolboys. But here one has this right, and I would regard it as most dishonourable to have invoked this procedure unless I could offer solid reasons of duty and fact as a justification for taking this course.

I must, however, correct my original *prima facie* statement in a few particulars. First, I was not aware that after the dinner of which there has been so much talk—the so-called Derby dinner of the 27th June—Lord Derby had altered his opinion for very good reasons, because of the trade negotiations. I assumed that his opinion had been the same throughout. I did not realise that whereas before the dinner he was in agreement with the original evidence of the Manchester Chamber of Commerce, shortly after the dinner he changed his view, and, instead of being the ambassador of Lancashire to the India Office, he became very much in this respect, in the interests of Manchester, the ambassador of the India Office to Lancashire. The dinner, therefore, while quite correctly described by me in many essentials, stood in an entirely different setting from that which I had supposed. It was not an attempt—I am bound to make this admission—by the Secretary of State, through Lord Derby, to modify the Lancashire point of view. It was, in fact, an attempt by the Manchester Chamber of Commerce, through Lord Derby to modify the Secretary of State's point of view. I hope I make that quite clear.

However, the dinner has receded altogether into the background and in importance as this inquiry has developed. It has been superseded by the far more direct, tangible and incontrovertible evidence of the letters of the Secretary of State to Lord Derby, and Lord Derby's letters to the secretary of the Chamber of Commerce, Mr. Streat. Secondly, when I stated that Lord Derby sought to persuade members of the Manchester Chamber of Commerce to alter their evidence in September, I ought to have added July and August, because those months were the period of his chief activities. But these are the only modifications. I stand here with the report before the House, and I say that those are the only modifications I have to make in the *prima facie* statement, except that I ought to have been more careful every time I said "procure alteration," in following the words of the Sessional Order—"to procure or endeavour to procure" the alteration of evidence. With these exceptions, which in no way affect the validity of the change I make, I rest with confidence upon my statement to the House. I do not withdraw it or modify it in any way. I claim that the report has established that the Secretary of State and Lord Derby, jointly and severally, from the best of motives, and in a perfectly honourable manner, endeavoured to deter the Manchester witnesses from presenting the evidence they desired to present.

If the only question at issue in this matter turned upon this point of "hath endeavoured" to deter, I should rest content with the narrative contained in the report of the Committee, because about that there is really no dispute, as the Prime Minister said. But it is when we come to these issues which are raised of advice, influence and pressure that we need much fuller details and a clearer account. Where, I would ask, does advice end and pressure begin? I can conceive that one of the answers which may be made to that is that advice becomes pressure when it is offered to a witness by a member of the tribunal before whom that witness is to plead his case. At any rate, I commend that definition—certainly not exhaustive—to the considered thought of the House. It is when we enter the region of what I may call "peaceful persuasion" that we must have fuller details. You cannot judge of the quality of the influence except in relation to the particular facts of the case. It is quite impossible for the House to judge the merits from the report which is before them now. Indeed, I think it is a mystifying document. It seems to be jumbled both in topics and in chronology. References to salient points are so obscure that it fails to convey, I should think, to the ordinary reader who had to study it for the first time, any clear, and almost any intelligible, impression in many particulars. I certainly cannnot accept it as an adequate account of what took place, or as an adequate account of the evidence, and still less of the documents, to which I am coming presently.

I, therefore, protest against the decision that the evidence is to be suppressed. I quite agree that some parts of the evidence should be excluded—certainly parts which relate to the interior discussions of the Manchester Chamber of Commerce. It would not be fair or right at all that these should be made public in so far as they are likely to damage their trading affairs. But the great bulk of the evidence is quite irrelevant to the points at issue. There would be no difficulty in exercising some parts of the evidence which are said to be detrimental to the public interest, and I admit that some parts are. I was much obliged to the Prime Minister. I was going to argue the case that there was nothing to prevent certain of these documents from being published, but he has quoted an authority, the name of which I did not catch, that obviously the Committee could recommend the House to publish the whole, or part, or none of the evidence. So that there is not the slightest reason why this evidence, so far as it is material to the great constitutional issue which is raised, should not be published, and the other parts which affect Lancashire interests or wider national interests excluded. However, the Government have taken their decision on the matter and, of course, whatever they decide, they have overwhelming power; but, if the evidence is to be suppressed as a whole, it becomes all the more important that the narrative of the report should be correct, and where the documents are quoted, they should be quoted faithfully.

I was very much surprised to hear the Prime Minister claim me as being in agreement with the facts. I put in documents at the invitation of the Committee in entire disagreement with many of the facts contained in the report. Naturally, I received no answer to that. The Committee have published their report, and I have to face their final decision. I intended to raise it in Debate in the House of Commons, because it is my opportunity and my duty to raise it here, and, of course, in courtesy I sent the Prime Minister this morning the letter to which he made considerable reference in his brief speech. I pointed out that I was going to ask about certain points where, I think, the Committee have made a mistake, or commited an oversight, or not given an adequate or a true account—I do not mean in any offensive sense—of particular documents they have cited, summarised or quoted fully, and used as points in their argument. Therefore, I sent in the letter in order that he and the Attorney-General, who is by his side, might have the documents handy, so that when I asked a question about them there would not be any difficulty in finding the passages to which I should venture to refer.

I must say that this evidence divides itself into two parts. There is the evidence which I put in which was placed unreservedly in my hands, and I obtained from the Prime Minister, in writing, an assurance that the legal character of the evidence would not be in any was altered or become the property of the Government or anything like that, from the fact that I had placed it at the disposal of the Committee for the work in which they were engaged. I need scarcely say that I should never dream of publishing any part of the evidence unless I were satisfied that it would be advantageous—not merely not disadvantageous—to the Lancashire trade. The rest of the evidence has been elicited by the Committee, and it was bound to be elicited, from the body of documents which I put before them, and which afforded a continuous narrative over the whole period of these transactions when they came to be examined. The evidence put before the Committee supplements, fortifies and, in some parts, corrects the evidence which I set forward. That evidence has been shown to me and to the Secretary of State in confidence, and I shall strictly respect that confidence. But I am not prepared to submit to any mis-statement which will have the consequence of misleading the House at this time.

I shall consider myself entitled to correct points in the evidence where, by oversight or accident, there is a mistake and a wrong impression is given, and I hope, indeed, that the Prime Minister will be as anxious as I am to make sure that a true impression is given to the House, provided that in no way is there anything adduced which could have the effect of prejudicing public or Lancashire interests. I shall not embark—I can assure the House I will be as brief as I possibly can—upon any exhaustive or meticulous examination of the narrative contained in the report. I will content myself with a few major instances. The first one which I will recite is the letter from the Secreatry of State to Mr. Bond, the President of the Manchester Chamber of Commerce, which is referred to in paragraph 17 of the report. The report says:

> On 7th July Sir Samuel Hoare sent a considered reply to Mr. Bond's letter of 23rd May. He explained that he had postponed a reply in view of the dinner which the Earl of Derby had arranged, and again gave an assurance that, when the representatives of the Chamber of Commerce gave evidence, the joint Committee would examine the case of the cotton trade with every care and sympathy.

I wonder what was the point of that? Everyone would know that a Minister's reply is always a considered reply. Everyone would know that a body like the Manchester Chamber of Commerce would be listened to with reasonable care and sympathy. Why was this letter put in? There is a sentence omitted from that letter. The last sentence is omitted, I have no doubt by inadvertence or by oversight, but the last sentence is the only sentence which is the slightest degree relevant to the matter before the House— the only one which has anything whatever to do with it. It is a very important sentence and one which in no way affects the public interest. It has nothing to do with the trade between Lancashire and India; it has nothing to do with foreign relations. It is a sentence which affects only the Secretary of State but which affects him very directly and is entirely relevant to the arguments which I seek to deploy to the House.

I would ask the Prime Minister if he has any objection to me quoting that last sentence or to quoting it himself. I pause for a reply.

Hon. Members: Answer!

The Prime Minister: The whole point is this. If quotations are to be begun from one document and another, how can the House accept the report which the Commitee of Privileges has given them? This is one of the things that I should have liked very much to have had an opportunity of considering. I have not been able, since I received the letter from the right hon. Gentleman, even to see the sentence which he wishes to quote and which has been handed to me this very minute by the Attorney-General. It is not a question of whether this sentence should be quoted or not, but of whether the recommendation of the Committee of Privileges is going to be carried out.

Hon. Members: No!

Mr. Churchill: These considerations would indeed be very important if the letter had not already been quoted, but, according to all tradition and practice in the House, when a document is recognisably quoted to a considerable extent, and any party who has knowledge of that document complains that the full quotation has not been made, it is customary that that should be accorded. Of course, if the Prime Minister says that the public interest is involved in reading that sentence then I should be very much surprised but, if not, may I ask the Secretary of State for India himself. It is his letter. He is the man involved. He is very much concerned, but there is nothing dishonourable about the sentence. Is he so much concerned, after all the prominence that has been given to it, that this sentence should be concealed? I again pause for a reply.

The Secretary of State for India (Sir Samuel Hoare): I have no desire to enter into a controversy upon a point of this kind with my right hon. Friend. I am here to-day not to argue this case but to accept the report of the Committee to which he referred this question. As to whether this or that sentence would be advantageous to my point of view, or the public, that is another question.

Mr. Churchill: I am bound to say that I consider that, if this attitude is to be adopted, it constitutes a breach of confidence, and there is no breach of confidence so bad as to publish a one-sided and misleading account of a document and then to hold the other party bound in honour not to reveal it.

The Prime Minister: Well, it is very easy to start that hare, but, if the right hon. Gentleman really gets up and says that the sentence which he wishes to be quoted is a sentence which shows any desire on the part of the Committee of Privileges to suppress essential facts, than all I can say is, after perusing it now, that that really is not a true statement. There is nothing in the disclosure of this sentence which would add to the statement. [Hon. Members: "Read it out!"] It is for the House to settle the whole matter, and I do hope that the House is not going to be led away by any of these well-known debating operations. . . .

Mr. Speaker: The document to which reference has been made does not come under that Rule. This is not an official document.

Mr. Churchill: As I say, I hold that in strict equity and honourable conduct I am perfectly entitled to read that sentence, but I am not going to do so without permission because I will not let one bad act lead to another. Nothing can be more unfair than to hold one party bound, while giving an imperfect and inaccurate account of a particular document and not allowing the necessary correction to be made. I really wonder at the Government putting themselves in that position. I am not accusing them of any malevolent intention in the matter. It never occurred to me that they would not be glad that this particular sentence, if I attached importance to it, should not be read, and I may say about this sentence that it is my contention that it would have a direct bearing upon the wording of the ultimate decision of the Committee of Privileges.

The Attorney-General (Sir Thomas Inskip): This passage is not a passage which, if the House hears it, they will, I venture to think, consider as of any great importance one way or the other. . . . The House will judge for itself whether or not that is a proper course for the right hon. Gentleman to take.

Mr. Churchill: I certainly will accept that invitation, and I hope I may feel that the Secretary of State who, as I say, is not reflected on in any personal manner, associates himself with it. I should like to feel that he is with me, that it should be read. There has been such a fight about producing this sentence—it might have been produced at the first moment—that I must relieve the feelings of the House by saying that it in no way affects the personal reputation of the right hon. Gentleman. Let me tell the House that this is a very short letter. Almost the half of it is here in the report and is of no consequence in paticular, but the last sentence is this. This is what the Secretary of State wrote on 7th of July to Mr. Bond, the President of the Chamber of Commerce:

> Of course, the whole matter so far as the Constitution is concerned, is now in the hands of the Joint Select Committee and, pending their conclusions, it would not, I think, be appropriate or useful that I should go into it any further.

The Committee has been sitting for three months and that expression "not appropriate," which the Secretary of State applied to his own action, reflected on what he had done in the past and reflected more on what he was about to do in the future. I put it to the House that we are not talking about anything that is dishonourable or immoral, but we are talking about things which we allege are inappropriate, and I say that with that word figuring in the mouth of the Secretary of State himself, it is surprising that such a word found no reflection in the ultimate report of the Committee.

Sir S. Hoare: I am sorry to interrupt the right hon. Gentleman once again, but I should have thought that that was one sentence in all this correspondence with which he would have been in entire agreement.

Mr. Churchill: I was indeed and that explains my anxiety to have it brought to the light of day. Now I come to the letter of 17th July. This letter is summarised at considerable length and part of it is printed on page 5. Part of that letter shows that the Secretary of State wrote to Lord Derby seeking to enlist his help as mediator. On page 5, the Committee says the Secretary of State asked him to use his influence, or quotes him as having urged that, which is quite true. Both of these are in the same letter. Why was it appropriate, I want to know, for the Secretary of State to ask Lord

Derby, a fellow member of the Joint Select Committee, to use his great influence with the Manchester Chamber of Commerce, when at the same time he himself knew that it was inappropriate for him to do it any further? I am entitled to ask these questions. These matters do not turn, thank God, in this country upon any hideous scandals, but they do turn upon nice points of Parliamentary conduct which the House is perfectly capable of deciding. I say that this account of this letter is most unsatisfactory. Part of it is contained in one part of the document and part in another, but the letter is a most important document. The letter of the Secretary of State to Lord Derby of the 17th July has already been half, or rather quarter, published here and summarised in a manner that is colourless and bald, so that no one can see the significance of it. It was the letter in which the Secretary of State urged Lord Derby to do what he himself did not feel he ought to continue to do, and it puts, in the most categorical manner, the great alterations of principle which he wished to have induced in the Manchester evidence.

My right hon. Friend the Secretary of State—I hope he will allow me to continue to call him so—shakes his head. I am not going to ask for further quotations in this matter, but because I have opened a point on which I have been denied, I say that the Governemnt ought themselves to publish the exact requests for the alteration of the evidence on the great fundamental points which the Secretary of State made to Lord Derby and which he asked him to use his influence to procure. We ought to have that. What do we read in the very next line? What I can only call a complete misstatement.

Sir Percy Harris: Is that an attack on the Committee of Privileges?

Mr. Churchill: It is an attack on the report. Why is it brought before the House if we are not allowed to quote it? In the very next line of the quotation of this letter of the 17th is a statement about the letter which Lord Derby wrote in consequence of that letter, and this is the statement:

> As the result of this suggestion the Earl of Derby wrote to the Secretary of the Manchester Chamber of Commerce on 19th July urging re-con- sideration of the wording of certain clauses in the memorandum.

That is quite untrue. I do not mean that it is not true—he may have said it was the wording—but it is quite untrue that what he asked was re-consideration of the wording, and if the letter were published, everybody would see that that could not hold water for a moment. Great and fundamental changes were demanded by the Secretary of State. Lord Derby copied out these changes and sent them forward, line after line, with all his influence, to his friend the Secretary of the Manchester Chamber of Commerce, and yet the Committee comes before the House and writes on the face of the report the statement that this is only a matter of wording. I deny it altogether, and I say that that is a complete misrepresentation of the facts.

What is the bearing of this upon another point? Here we see the Secretary of State asking Lord Derby to press the Manchester Chamber of Commerce, through its Secretary, to make important alterations in its evidence. We are told—and the report lays great weight upon it—that they only acted when invited. There is no truth in that, in so far as this matter was concerned. There was no invitation to the Secretary of

State, or to Lord Derby at this stage, to advise them. On the contrary, the Secretary of State asked him, and when Lord Derby wrote to the Secretary of the Manchester Chamber of Commerce, what was the answer? This is all apparent in the document. It was so discouraging that, after some further interchanges, his Lordship decided that the letter should be withdrawn, so you cannot say, as the Committee attach great importance to it at one point in their recommendations, that this advice was only given when asked for. There was no invitation at all.

I put these instances forward—I could naturally multiply them—in order to show how very inconvenient it is to be working on mere summaries of the important documents on which this case turns. And let me say that the House has a great responsibility in this matter. This House is the judge of privilege. It was not to the Committee of Privileges that I appealed; I appealed to the House, and the Committee of Privileges is the instrument by which the House has investigated the matter, and the House is now asked to pronounce on these questions without seeing the documents, which, if they were published, would, I am sure, enable a true opinion to be formed upon the character of the action of which we have made complaint.

I specify the following letters which, in my opinion, ought to be published:—The Secretary of State to Mr. Bond, of the 5th May; Mr. Bond to the Secretary of State, of the 23rd May, with enclosure; the Secretary of State to Mr. Bond, of the 7th July; the Secretary of State to Lord Derby, of the 17th July; Lord Derby to Mr. Streat, of the 19th July; Lord Derby to Mr. Streat, of the 9th August, with enclosure. None of these letters in any way, if published, would have the effect of injuring Lancashire trade or really trespassing at all upon matters which could touch the public interest, but they are all essential to a fair judgment being formed of the character of the transaction which has been under review, and I say that the summaries and the account in the narrative do not put the House in a position to judge fairly what those documents convey.

I come to the last part of my remarks, namely, the technical and constitutional aspect. I submitted that the Secretary of State had infringed in general the privilege of the House of Commons, and also, in special, the wording of Sessional Order No. 1, which says, "directly or indirectly hath endeavoured to deter"—very harmless, but very searching words. I notice that the Committee refer to this as the Sessional Order of 1700. That may be true, but the wisdom of our ancestors comes down, and it is only some three or four months ago that the House renewed this Order. It is not merely archaic or obsolete procedure, but kept in full and living force from Session to Session, every year.

The Attorney-General: Does the right hon. Gentleman suggest that we described this Sessional Order as of the year 1700? When we quote the Order we expressly use the expression:

The Sessional Order first passed in the year 1700.

Mr. Churchill: I am not making a serious accusation, but these old things which were found out in the past are very well worth holding on to in these modern days. Great stress is laid upon the point by the Secretary of State that he failed in his endeavour. He admitted to the Committee that he had tried, and he admitted in the House that he had tried, through various channels, but he asserted that he had failed. Such a plea may affect the gravity of the right hon. Gentleman's action, but it does not in the slightest degree alter its character from the standpoint of privilege. The task of the Committee of Privileges was to decide whether the facts fell within the ambit of the Sessional Order, and on this they have made pronouncements of a grave and far-reaching character. If these pronouncements are endorsed by the House, as no doubt they will be, they will govern for the future the character and procedure of all Committees of the House.

The House will no doubt, on the Amendment which has been placed on the Paper by my hon. Friend the Member for East Aberdeen (Mr. Boothby) examine in more detail the effect of some of these pronouncements, which are contained principally in paragraph 21—an extraordinary paragraph to be the foundation of our Parliamentary law for the future. Any lawyer, I am told, who likes to read it will see that it is, from beginning to end, a mass of mixed thinking, bristling with *non sequiturs* and questionable points, and adorned at intervals by pious and good-natured conclusions and platitudes. Such a paragraph as this paragraph 21 cannot remain as the last word on this subject in the future in any circumstances.

Let me just mention one or two of the gems. The Sessional Order, it says, "has only a very limited application to this Committee." I confess that that surprises me very much. Then we are told that this Committee is not a judicial body, and, because it is not a judicial body, it is mainly outside the Sessional Order. If it were so obvious that the Committee was not a judicial body, and that the Sessional Order did not apply, why did you want to take two months considering this matter? It could have been settled in two days. As soon as I had finished unfolding my case, the Committee could have said to me, "Mr. Churchill, you make no charge against the honour or integrity of these gentlemen." I should have said, "No, I do not; indeed, I vouch for them." They would have said, "You do not charge bribery, malice, or corruption on any point. Let us tell you that this Joint Select Committee is not a judicial committee. Let us tell you that the ordinary rules for administering justice and ascertaining facts do not apply to it. Let us tell you that evidence given before it is not evidence in the ordinary sense of the word, that the witnesses are different from other witnesses, that the relations between the members of the Committee and the witnesses are quite different from what is the case with other committees. You have no case at all. There has been no breach of privilege, and there will be no inquiry. We wish you a very good morning."

Why did they not say that? Instead of that, we had this prolonged examination, and I do not wonder at all that they took a long time to give the ruling which they have given in this document. No doubt they realised the gravity of these new interpretations of the law and their effect upon the privileges of the House of Commons. No doubt they shrank from the contradictions which they had to introduce into the ordinary meaning of words. They saw no doubt the far-reaching effects of the discrimination between one kind of committee and another. They saw the disadvantages of narrowing the privileges of the House and the danger of opening the door to laxity of many kinds. Above all they must have shrunk from doing anything which seemed to lower the status of the Joint Select Committee by describing them as they do on pages 17 and 18:

> The Joint Committee are not in the ordinary sense a judicial body. . . . The members were chosen by Parliament in the full light of the knowledge that many of them had already formed opinions as to the proposals contained in the White Paper. . . . The ordinary rules which apply to tribunals engaged in administering justice . . . cannot be applied to the Joint Committee.

And here is a most remarkable sentence. I will read any sentence, if you tell me to. I reciprocate the courtesy with which I have been treated.

The Secretary of State for Foreign Affairs (Sir John Simon): I think the right hon. Gentleman would wish to finish the sentence he began. He unfortunately dropped it.

Mr. Churchill: Tell me.

Sir J. Simon: This is the sentence:

> The ordinary rules which apply to tribunals engaged in administering justice—

Then the right hon. Gentleman dropped it, but it goes on:

> or deciding issues of fact between contending parties cannot be applied to the Joint Committee.

Mr. Churchill: I will go on:

> It might be said that the Committee should proceed in a judicial spirit.

Surely a very audacious statement about this Committee. But then it goes on to say:

> But this could only mean that the Committee should act fairly and without suffering prejudice—

That evidently means their prejudice; I read it that way:

> to hinder the hearing—

not the weighing—

> of all sorts of opinions.

I have never been very eulogistic of the Joint Select Committee, but I do not wonder at all that the Committee of Privileges, and particularly the Lord President of the

Council, were reluctant to describe them in these extremely bleak terms; for what did my right hon. Friend the Lord President say in his speech at the Friends' House on the 29th June, 1933? He said:

> I am not going to discuss in this short space of time the merits of the White Paper. Its merits are under semi-judicial consideration to-day by the Joint Select Committee, and I leave it at that. And remember their work is of a semi-judicial nature.

I give you the "semi"; I do not wish to be at all captious about that. What a fortunate thing it is that these words are introduced:

> And remember their work is of a semi-judicial nature.

I suppose it is judicial one way and not judicial the other.

> They have been solemnly charged by Parliament to go into these matters, to examine them and examine witnesses of every point of view. They can find out who are the true witnesses and who are not.

Again and again we have been exhorted in these matters—I could multiply them with quotations—to wait while this question is *sub judice*. We have been invited time and time again to admire the restraint of the Secretary of State and other members of the Committee who are supporters of the Government in remaining silent on the public platform and not embarking in public discussions, but apparently this prohibition only extends to their public activities. There is a charter for everyone to do what he likes to carry on the good work behind the scenes so long as he marks it "Private and confidential." Nothing that is dishonourable and criminal can be done in those circumstances. These liberties are not only extended to the right hon. Gentelman in his dual capacity, which argument has not been pressed at all because he sought it himself, but are offered freely, as far as I gather, to all members of the Committee. It is open under this ruling for any member of the Joint Select Committee to do anything in his power to endeavour to deter any witness from presenting evidence as he wished to present it; to do this without informing other members of the Joint Select Committee; and to sit still while those witnesses are giving evidence contrary to what it was known was their original wish to give without informing the other members of the Committee. As I say, these rulings are authoritative. We shall have to recognise them as the conditions which will govern us and the working of our committees in future. I do not wonder that before the Committee of Privileges and the leader of the Conservative party could have brought themselves to such decisions, they thought it necessary to explore every other avenue before they broke their way out through this emergency exit.

I think, on the whole, that it may be said that this Joint Select Committee deserved a little better description than it has received, although I never expected to be here in this House to say it. It has a corporate life and responsibility. It has a corporate sense. We ourselves—those who think as I do on this topic—were offered a few seats upon the Committee for representatives of the anti-White Paper point of view. What happened? Some of those men who were put on were our keenest partisans. From the moment they became members of the Committee a gulf opened between us and them, and not one of them would have dared to break the reserve which they imposed upon themselves. With only these two exceptions the Joint Select Committee have taken their duties with very great seriousness, and it is doing less than justice to their status and character to describe them in the terms in which they are described on page 18.

Still, that is the effect of the ruling which has been given. For the first time, our committees are to be put into two classes, or I should say three—judicial, non-judicial and semi-judicial. One is governed by the Sessional Order, and the others are now, we are told, largely and mainly outside it. Not only that, but evidence receives a new classification. Evidence which is opinion can be persuaded away, or even, I gather— although it is not quite clear—over-persuaded away to any extent other than by bribery or corruption. These are very far-reaching decisions. I must admit frankly to the House that it never occurred to me for a moment that the Committee would not find a technical breach of privilege. I thought it might have been a much bolder and a more effective and satisfactory course for them. Over and over again in our history in times of emergency and difficulty Ministers of the Crown or citizens of great public responsibility have had to break the law. What has been the remedy that Parliament has adopted? They have not smirched the law. On the contrary, they have affirmed the law, but they have sought from Parliament an honourable indemnity for the Ministers concerned. That is the course I expected would have been adopted here, namely, that after a technical verdict had been given the Government would have asked, as they could have done, for every confidence to be expressed in the Ministers and for their integrity to be affirmed; and I personally would have been very glad to associate myself with them.

The Committee have chosen instead to give a new interpretation, as I hold, of the Rules of Privilege, to do violence to the plain meaning of the English language, to cast a slur upon the status of the Joint Select Committee, and to alter sensibly the procedure of Parliamentary Committees. Many here may live to regret that the custodians of the rights and privileges of the House of Commons have decided to meet a temporary difficulty by taking that course. I thank the House for the great indulgence with which they have treated me. I feel that that is due to the fact that, in a sense, I am defending my own conduct, and the House always gives a double measure of consideration to anyone placed in that position.

I have been discussing these technical matters, but far beyond the technicalities of procedure and privilege there arises an issue of blunt, stark simplicity. I present this issue, particularly to my right hon. Friend the Lord President of the Council. I have no doubt that when he spoke as he did at the Friends' House a year ago, he believed what he said, and he meant what he said; and many people have noticed that on frequent occasions the right hon. Gentleman—what is quite rare in our public life—is found to be keeping his word even in his own despite. I am sure that was what he meant when he made that speech, and I ask him whether this account set forth in this report is really the way which Parliament meant and expected this great inquiry by the Joint

Select Committee to be conducted. Is it really the way which he as leader of the Conservative party meant it to be conducted? Are these the methods, quite blameless in personal honour, these methods of management and organising, to be approved indiscriminately and even applauded? Are they to be our guide in the future? Are they to be applied in every direction? We have seen this Lancashire case to a certain extent explored, and we see all there is behind it; but let the House imagine what would happen or may have happened when such processes are applied over the whole vast field of the Indian case. Apply it to the evidence of the Rajahs and the European associations in India. Apply it to the formation and expression of opinion throughout the Civil Service. The noble Lord the right hon. Member for Oxford University (Lord H. Cecil) used a searching phrase when he spoke of witnesses being marshalled as if they were an orchestra under the baton of a conductor. In this Indian sphere, it is the rod of the ruler which would be applied. I ask the House to pause long and to think deeply before they blindly apply to the methods revealed in this report the seal of Parliamentary approbation.

INDIA (CONSTITUTIONAL REFORM)

June 16, 1934

Conservative Club, Wanstead

[Extract] ... The facts which I bring forward and which are admitted in the report, ambly justify the action I took in bringing the matter before Parliament. In order to avoid declaring that a breach of privilege had occurred, the Committee of the House has had to proclaim new readings of the law of privilege. They have a perfect right to do that as the House is the judge of its own privileges.

Apart from the technical issue of privilege arose the question of whether the action taken by Sir Samuel Hoare and Lord Derby is inappropriate, as Sir Samuel Hoare described it, and to what degree of inappropriateness it attained. This could not be judged except by the disclosure of the documents for which I have asked. As long as these are withheld no just opinion can be formed by the public of the character of the transactions of which I complain.

You will see, therefore, how right Lord Lloyd and other friends of mine are in refusing to be silenced upon the Indian question by accepting seats upon the Joint Select Committee. The Joint Select Committee is revealed in its true colours, not as a body to seek the truth without fear or favour, but as an instrument of the Government designed to gather support for the White Paper policy, and persuade every one to come along quietly towards the desired goal.

Lancashire has been persuaded to come along quietly. Efforts are being made to persuade the Princes to come along quietly. Every endeavour is used to persuade the Conservative Party and the National Union to come along quietly. But the moment is approaching when those who are pursuing these tactics with so much skill and perseverance will turn round upon them and, having said all these months, almost years, that no one is committed to anything except impartial and semi-judicial inquiry, suddenly exclaim, "Too late. You have gone too far to go back."

The fight in which I have been for four years engaged is now entering upon its sternest phase. All that has occurred has only served to make me see my duty more plainly, and not to grudge any sacrifice or relax any effort to rouse the British and Indian people to a sense of the dangers to their vital interests to which they are exposed by this policy of abdication.

We have two separate battles to fight. The first is to defeat the White Paper scheme of responsible Home Rule for all India. The second will be to reunite the strong forces of British public life which carried the country through the War and broke the general strike and to lead these forces to an aggressive attack upon the Socialist menace in the General Election of 1936.

INDIA (CONSTITUTIONAL REFORM)

June 26, 1934

Lancashire India Defence League Demonstration,
Free Trade Hall, Manchester

The House of Commons has endorsed the report of its Committee of Privileges that no breach of privilege was committed by Sir Samuel Hoare and Lord Derby when they endeavoured to deter the Manchester Chamber of Commerce from tendering to the Joint Select Committee on Indian Constitution the evidence upon which they were agreed. That decision is final and must be accepted. To sustain this decision it has also been decided that the Joint Select Committee is not a judicial, or impartial body, that its members are free to use their influence to any extent short of bribery and intimidation to persuade witnesses to give evidence different from that which they would spontaneously have given.

These rulings are of far-reaching importance. They give an entirely new interpretation to the hitherto accepted law of the High Court of Parliament, and unless that law in its new form is further defined by this or some future House of Commons they will demoralize the procedure of its Committees. These are matters of grave national interest.

[Editor's Note: After referring to the serious condition of industry in Lancashire and the need for taking action against it, he said]: At a meeting of the Joint Select Committee on India on November 3 last Lord Salisbury asked Mr. Rodier, one of the representatives of the Manchester Chamber of Commerce, if he had any proposals for an alteration in the White Paper. The answer was "No."

Now those answers, although no doubt agreed upon by the Chamber at the last moment, do not represent truly either the real views or the interests of the Manchester Chamber of Commerce, or its Indian section, or of the other bodies associated with them—the Cotton Spinners' and Manufacturers' Association and the Federation of Master Cotton Spinners' Associations. Nearly six months before, all those bodies had agreed to give evidence of a totally different character. They have printed their evidence; they have deposited it with the Joint Select Committee, and it has lain there month after month.

The evidence which the Manchester Chamber of Commerce and the other organizations desire to give is that proposals should be included in the new Indian Constitution which would have the effect of reserving power to limit the right of the Indian legislature to impose tariffs on British goods.

During the past five years Mr. MacDonald's two Governments have acquiesced in two successive increases in the Indian tariffs which have spread devastation far and wide in Lancashire. That is, no doubt, because Lancashire has never exerted herself. The Lancashire leaders of commerce have resigned themselves in a helpless manner to the drift of events. But now, when the whole face of Government in India is to be changed, and when the fiscal convention is to be superseded by a real transference of sovereignty to an Indian Assembly, with an Indian Minister of Finance responsible to that Assembly, and when full unbridled tariff autonomy is to be conferred, it seems only right, as the Manchester Chamber of Commerce feels so strongly, that there should be a new deal all round and a bargain for the future should be made.

At any rate we are all unanimous upon that. The Chamber of Commerce and all its associate bodies agree to make the demand. Lord Derby gives his full approval. That is the evidence we wish to give. That is the point we wish to raise for the judgment of the whole country, and that is the exact opposite of what when the time came we actually said.

Why is it that the chamber changed its evidence and told a different tale? It fully admitted in the Report of the Committee of Privileges that Sir Samuel Hoare asked Lord Derby to use his great influence to have the evidence altered and that Lord Derby, no doubt with a sincere desire for the welfare of Lancashire, used that great influence to the utmost extent, but Sir Samuel Hoare contends very strongly that, although he has tried his best, both directly as Secretary of State and indirectly through Lord Derby, he has failed. The chamber remains obdurate, and the Committee of Privileges has found that when they change their minds they change them of their own free will and not on account of any persuasion, over-persuasion, or pressure brought to bear upon them from either of these two gentlemen, or from the India Office, or from Whitehall, or from official circles in London.

I do not agree with that altogether. I believe that the influences exerted and the spade work done during the summer of last year has played a definite part in the final decision, but I agree with the committee that this decision would never have been reached but for the negotiations upon which the cotton mission of Sir William Clare Lees was engaged in India. The members of that mission have all strongly asserted that they never asked for the evidence to be changed. They steadfastly refuse to take so great a responsibility, but there is no doubt that the position of that mission, and the agreement it was trying to make, and eventually made, in Bombay formed an important factor in inducing the change.

You have heard of a sprat being used to catch a whale, but Lancashire has used a whale to catch a sprat. Never, I venture to say, has there been such a disproportionate transaction since Esau sold his birthright for a mess of pottage—or, as I should say, a side dish of pottage. It seems to me that the leaders of the Manchester Chamber of Commerce made a very great mistake in allowing their long and carefully considered, unitedly agreed proposals to be jettisoned for the sake of this small and fugitive advantage, if, indeed, it is an advantage at all. It is a point which should be very carefully met and considered by those who are in a position to judge, with real knowledge and with real interest, the future of the cotton trade.

If it should be found that the advantages of the Clare Lees agreement are not sufficient to safeguard Lancashire from the dangers which hang over it, and bear no proportion to the tremendous commercial and constitutional issues which are now at stake, then those leaders who took a prominent part in turning the Chamber and its associate bodies completely round in a few hours bear a very great, serious, and lasting responsibility, for which they should be required to render a strict account.

[Editor's Note: Referring to the future of India, Churchill asked] : What are the chances of good will under the new Indian Constitution? That Constitution will not bring peace to India. On the contrary it will open a fierce period of strife. There will be no good will from the Congress Party. On the one hand, there will be Indian politicians with far-reaching powers to be conferred on them. On the other hand will be the Viceroy, or Governor-General, with all the safeguards and the power of veto, and the bayonets of the British Army at his call. Each side will have enormous powers, and when they clash they will throw India into interminable tumult. In the very centre of this struggle, like a football rolls into the field, will be the trade of Lancashire.

I have come here to-night to advise you to strike while the iron is hot and to move the Chamber of Commerce to publish their true evidence, and thereafter ask the Joint Select Committee to give them a fairer hearing, so that they may hear the truth for the first time. I do not believe that this can be refused.

AIR DEFENCE

July 7, 1934

Constituency Meeting, Wanstead

[Extract] ... I want to ask where Mr. Baldwin stands. The Prime Minister has gone for a long holiday and all the power is now in the hands of Mr. Baldwin. Where the power lies there also lies the responsibility. Mr. Baldwin promised in the House of Commons last March that if the Disarmament Conference failed we should have an Air Force which would be equal to that of any other Power which could get at us. Lord Londonderry, the Air Minister, and Mr. Eden have told us in unmistakable terms that the Disarmament Conference has failed. How can it help failing when the Germans are arming night and day? Why, then, is Mr. Baldwin's promise not fulfilled?

We were told that plans were being made and that paper work was proceeding. All that ought to have been done long ago. We ought to have had a large vote of credit to double our Air Force—we ought to have it now, and a larger vote of credit as soon as possible to redouble the Air Force. We ought to concert plans for mutual protection with the French and with other peace-loving Powers which are in danger from what is happening and what might happen in Germany.

I have previously stated that minds are oppressed by the grisly events which occurred in Germany a week ago. It seems difficult to realize that a great and highly educated and scientific nation, with all its treasures of literature, learning, and music behind it, should present itself to the world in such an awful guise. We are in the presence of a tyranny maintained by Press and broadcast propaganda and the ruthless murder of political opponents. Where a band of ferocious men rise from depths to dictatorships there is no guarantee for life, or for law, or for liberty. Far greater assurances are given to society by a limited hereditary monarchy such as that under which we have the blessing to dwell.

It is likely that even more violent convulsions will occur in Germany before the German people regain coherent self-expression and make assurances of civil and religious freedom which alone make life worth living to civilized men and women. We must all hope that that day will come before Europe is dragged again into a catastrophe which might well be final for our civilization.

THE VALUE OF THE LEAGUE

July 13, 1934

House of Commons

I have never listened to a debate upon foreign affairs where there has been such a deep, wide measure of agreement upon many of the most difficult and fundamental points. There is agreement, of course, in the object. The object that we all seek is peace. We all wish to prevent war. We all wish that the horrors into which we were plunged twenty years ago may never be repeated in our time. There is always agreement on the object, but there has been today, I think, a nearer approach to agreement upon the method than anything I have seen in our recent debates.

The leader of the Opposition [Mr. Lansbury] re-stated the Labour view in regard to war and upon the present situation. His re-statement faces many of the realities and dangers in a courageous manner, and I believe that the new definition of the Labour attitude will undoubtedly be a help in preserving the peace and security of this country in the difficult times which lie ahead. Then I was very glad also to hear the tribute which Sir Herbert Samuel paid to France. He spoke of French militarism as being at an end. He spoke of the ties of sympathy and agreement which exist between us and what is now almost the only great democracy in Europe. I am not quoting him; I am carrying his thoughts forward—I trust into fields where he would not be unwilling to venture.

Those are very important declarations. When the Labour party definitely state that their abhorrence of war does not extend to passive recognition of flagrant wrongdoing, and when a member of the Liberal party, taking a very different course from that advocated some time ago by the Archbishop of York, goes out of his way to express his sympathy for France, there are the elements of a more general body of agreement than any we have seen hitherto.

I have been trying to seek out for myself what would be the best way of preventing war, and it has seemed to me that the League of Nations should be the great instrument upon which all those resolves to maintain peace should centre, and that we should all make our contribution to the League of Nations. If there be Powers alarmed at the behaviour of their neighbours, they should refer to the League, and lay their anxieties before that body. It has seemed to me perfectly legitimate that the League of Nations should encourage with the sanction of international authority the formation of regional pacts between nations who may fear danger, and who seek to join hands together for mutual security against aggression. Therefore, I had the hope that the Government would not hesitate to further such developments. I could not see how better you can prevent war than by confronting an aggressor with the prospect of such a vast concentration of force, moral and material, that even the most reckless, even the most infuriated, leader would not attempt to challenge those great forces. It seemed to me that if a number of agreements, all under the sanction and authority of the League of Nations, grew up between Powers who have anxieties, those Powers would naturally maintain forces which were adequate to enable them to discharge their duties and their obligations, and not try to weaken each other, because there is no greater danger than equal forces. If you wish to bring about war, you bring about such an equipoise that both sides think they have a chance of winning. If you want to stop war, you gather such an aggregation of force on the side of peace that the aggressor, whoever he may be, will not dare to challenge.

This process of agreements under the sanction of the League of Nations might eventually lead to a state which we should never exclude—namely, the ultimate creation of some international force, probably particularly in aviation, which would tend to place the security of nations upon a much higher foundation than it stands on at present; and it seems to me you will never get such a development by arguing on purely general grounds. If there were, over a prolonged period of time, some general cause of anxiety, which all nations, or many nations, felt, then possibly forces might come together for that purpose which, after that danger had happily been tided over, might still subsist permanently in amity. Therefore, I was very much interested to hear the lucid statement which the Foreign Secretary has made to us upon what is called the Eastern Locarno. I understood that what had been done in the east was in the same sense and spirit as that which was done in the Treaty of Locarno, and that the spirit of mutuality and reciprocity which is so important in the Locarno Treaty is, indeed, one of the principal features in this Eastern Pact for the Guarantee of Mutual Security. That brings us to a very important consideration. It involves the reassociation of Soviet Russia with the Western European system. Remember that it is an historic event. I must say that I do not see how anyone who wishes to induce Germany to come back to the League, as she has a perfect right to do at any moment, can possibly find reasons for objecting to Russia also joining that body. The statement which the Foreign Secretary has made about the welcome which would be extended to Soviet Russia in the League of Nations is one about which there will be no dispute in this country, even among those who have the greatest prejudice against the political and social philosophy and system of government which the Russian people have, I will not say chosen for themselves, but found it necessary to adopt.

I notice that for some time the speeches of M. Litvinoff have seemed to give the impression, which I believe is a true one, that Russia is most deeply desirous of maintaining peace at the present time. Certainly she has a great interest in maintaining peace. It is not enough to talk about her as "peace-loving," because every Power is peace-loving always. One wants to see what is the interest of a particular Power, and it is certainly the interest of Russia, even on grounds concerning her own internal arrangements, to preserve peace. If Russia is to become a stabilizing force in Europe and to take her part with other countries whose danger she feels herself to share, it seems to me that that would possibly have a favorable reaction upon Russian propaganda in those other countries. There certainly would be no incentive, nothing that could be reconciled with a logical process, for Russia to make the arrangements suggested in this Eastern Pact, and at the same time to seek to weaken those countries with whom she was associated. Events have their effects upon all our minds as time passes and as they present themselves to us in new forms and in different ways, and while I certainly did not expect to find myself supporting the step which has been taken, I can do so with natural feeling and without the slightest doubt that that step is in all the circumstances right and wise.

I am also very glad that the Disarmament Conference is passing out of life into history. One of the greatest mistakes that can be made is to point to the failure of the Disarmament Conference as if it were really the failure of the League of Nations, and to mix up disarmament with peace. When you have peace you will have disarmament. But there has been during these years a steady deterioration in the relations between different countries and a rapid increase in armaments that has gone on in spite of the endless flow of oratory, of well-meaning sentiments, of perorations, and of banquets. Europe will be secure when nations no longer feel themselves in danger as many of them do now. Then the pressure and the burden of armaments will fall away automatically, as they ought to have done in a long peace, and it might be quite easy to seal a movement of that character by some general agreement.

I hope, indeed, that we have now also reached the end of the period of the Government pressing France—this peaceful France with no militarism—to weaken her armed forces. I rejoice that the French have not taken the advice which has been offered to them so freely from various quarters, because I am sure that if they had done so, and if France were as weak on the land as we are weak in the air, dangers which we may now succeed in averting, dangers which we can by patience, sanity and coolness succeed in sweeping away from the lifetime of this generation, would be on top of us at the present time.

What is the dominant fact of the situation? Germany is arming. That has been the great result of the Disarmament Conference. Out of it has emerged the rearmament of Germany. Germany is arming, particularly in the air. They have already a civil aviation which is called "Air Sport" and which is, I believe, on a gigantic scale, with aerodromes, trained pilots and so forth. All they have to do is to give that vast plant a military character. It may take some time, but it will not take anything like as long as it would take us, with our very limited aviation, to develop our air armaments. I have no special knowledge of these matters, but it may well be that by this time next year German aviation will be definitely stronger than ours whatever we do. I hope that on a suitable occasion we may hear more from the Government on that point, because if that be so, it seems of the utmost importance, not only that we should lose no time in putting ourselves in an adequate position of defense, but that we should keep close relations with other Great Powers of a friendly character who have not fallen into the error which has overtaken us of late years of neglecting the essentials of our own security.

It is no use disguising the fact that there must be and there ought to be deep anxiety in this country about Germany. This is not the only Germany which we shall live to see, but we have to consider that at present two or three men, in what may well be a desperate position, have their grip on the whole of that mighty country with its wonderful scientific, intelligent, docile, valiant people of 70,000,000. We must remember that there is no Parliament where anything can be discussed, that there is no dynastic interest such as Monarchy brings as a restraint upon policy, because it looks long ahead and has much to lose, and that there is no public opinion except what is manufactured by those new and terrible engines of broadcasting and a controlled Press. We have to consider also the risks these men run, because politics in Germany are not what they are over here. There you do not leave Office to go into Opposition. You do not leave the Front Bench to sit below the Gangway. You may well leave your high office at a quarter of an hour's notice to drive to the police-station, and you may be conducted thereafter, very rapidly, to an even harder ordeal.

Men in that position might very easily be tempted to do what even a military dictatorship would not do, because a military dictatorship, with all its many faults, at any rate is one that is based on a very accurate study of the real facts; and there is more danger in this new kind of [party] dictatorship than there would be in a military dictatorship, because you have men who, to relieve themselves from the peril which confronts them at home, might easily plunge into a foreign adventure of catastrophic character to the whole world. People may say that we have no quarrel with Germany and that Germany has no quarrel with us, but do not doubt that there is very sharp resentment against England in Germany at the present time. We may find ourselves in a position in which, if offense is taken against anything we say or do in this country, we may be confronted with an ultimatum, or very grievous action even before an ultimatum is delivered. We ought not to be in a position where we are dependent upon assistance which France could give. It is our duty to place this Empire in security at the heart and center, and to rely upon our own strength; and, believe me, we should be far more likely to keep out of trouble, and to keep the world out of trouble, if we put ourselves in that position.

I do not at all understand the line which Sir Herbert Samuel took in his carefully thought-out remarks about my being a Malay run amok, which arose, possibly, from an imagination lately stimulated by contact with Oriental lands. He spoke of the pre-War Cabinet of which we were both members, and of how measures had been taken then to put our naval forces into a state of adequate preparedness, and he was proud, and rightly proud, of that. Though it was extremely obnoxious, as the Foreign Secretary [Sir John Simon] reminded us, to the members of the Government of that day, yet they did their duty, and what had to be done was done; but the situation now is in many ways more dangerous than it was then. I am not to be understood to mean that the possibilities of a gigantic war are nearer, but the actual position of Great Britain is much less satisfactory than it was this time twenty years ago, for then at least we had a supreme Fleet; nobody could get at us in this island; and we had powerful friends on the continent of Europe, who were likely to be involved in any quarrel before we were. But today, with our aviation in its present condition, we are in a far worse position. The Disarmament Conference has been carried out year after year, *ad nauseam*. It must no longer delay our taking the necessary measures ourselves.

I was also very glad to hear from His Majesty's Government that a statement is now to be made, in a few days, before Parliament rises, which will proclaim without any further delay the beginning of steps to create a powerful Air Force in this country. Never mind the details. It certainly should be an effort to double the existing Air Force, and that alone would take a long time; and it is open for us to consider the situation when we have done that. Hoping and believing that that statement will be made, and will be found satisfactory, I feel entitled to congratulate the Government on at once taking the diplomatic steps which are appropriate to collective security at the present time, and also informing us of their intention to propose the military and financial measures which are required for our own safety.

MANCHESTER CHAMBER OF COMMERCE RESOLUTION ON INDIA WHITE PAPER

July 24, 1934

London

The results of the special meeting of the Manchester Chamber of Commerce must be regarded as highly satisfactory. The resolution passed unanimously liberates the Chamber from the false and impossible position in which it has been left by the evidence publicly tendered before the Joint Select Committee on India.

Instead of Mr. Rodier's answer to Lord Salisbury's question (No. 15,356, "You have no proposal to make for an alteration in the White Paper") that the Manchester Chamber had no amendments to suggest in the White Paper, we now have a united demand for definite safeguards for the Lancashire cotton trade.

The Chamber is thus restored to a position where it can with consistency and propriety use its influence upon, and secure the insertion of, such safeguards when the Indian Constitution Bill comes before Parliament.

I am very glad that so decided an advance and recovery should have been made without reflecting censure directly upon the members of the Chamber who were concerned in putting forward the emasculated evidence.

Every one can see the difficulties in which they were placed and the pressure to which they were exposed, and it is right that every allowance should be made on these accounts.

The all-important fact is that Lancashire has been restored to the position which she occupied when the original evidence was drafted and Parliament was entitled to deal with her case on that basis.

Any trouble to which I may have been put to bring this about is well repaid by the achievement.

At the same time the utmost vigilance must be practised in order to make sure that the safeguards demanded for the Lancashire cotton trade are real and effective. It will be necessary to maintain a continuous campaign, so that the country may be made aware of the Lancashire case, and in order that the leaders of the Chamber should be constantly stimulated and kept on their guard against the wiles of Whitehall.

We are now entering upon the last year of this struggle, and its most severe phases are before us, but I have good hope that the main danger may be averted and, even at the worst, that much may be saved from the wreck.

GERMANY APPROACHING AIR PARITY WITH BRITAIN

July 30, 1934

House of Commons

This speech should be read with care. Virtually all the "facts" which it contains were inaccurate, and known to be inaccurate. But it made a considerable impression, not erased by Baldwin's unwise assurance that "parity" would be retained until the end of 1936. Baldwin's figures were also wrong.

The position which has been unfolded to us today and the state of the world leave us in no doubt that Europe is moving ever more rapidly into a tightly drawn condition. Hatreds are rampant, disorder is rife, almost all the nations are arming, and everyone feels, as the Lord President of the Council has admitted, that the danger which we dread most of all and which we seek most of all to avert is drawing nearer to us. If this be the state of Europe, what is our position in relation to Europe? We are deeply involved in Europe. We are more deeply involved, much more precisely and formally involved, in Europe than we were twenty years ago. I think that is indisputable. We have signed the Treaty of Locarno. There is no doubt that we are at the present moment under obligations in regard to acts of aggression by Germany which are far more precise than any which bound us twenty years ago.

Ministers, with the full assent of Parliament, have repeatedly affirmed the sanctity, reality and modernity of these obligations. There is the Eastern Pact, which the Houses approved so generally and warmly, which does not add to our obligations but which certainly increases the contingencies in which existing obligations might become effective. Only last week we had a declaration from the Foreign Secretary reaffirming our interest in maintaining the neutrality of Belgium, in terms even stronger than before the Great War. Then there have been declarations, made, as far as

I can gather, with the assent of Parliament, both sides as far as there are two sides, which have associated us with other great and friendly Powers in earnestly desiring to maintain the independence of Austria. We are to hear more about that tomorrow. Lord Halifax [Editor's Note: At that time President of the Board of Education.] on Saturday, in a public speech which no doubt will be studied with great care abroad, made it clear that we were not to be excluded as a factor in a possible European conflict, and, finally, the Lord President of the Council uses a phrase which I am sure by now has travelled from one end of the world to the other when he said, with his customary directness, that our frontier is the Rhine. If the Socialist Opposition had their way I gather that we should now have added the cold, unforgetting, unforgiving hostility of Japan to all these other serious preoccupations, and that the acting Leader of the Opposition would be reminding us that our frontier was the Yangtse.

What are the measures which the Government propose? We have a general scheme to spend an extra £20,000,000 in five years upon increasing our Air Force, of which we should spend £4,000,000 or £5,000,000 before the end of this Parliament. That probably means an addition to our fighting aeroplanes of perhaps fifty machines in the lifetime of the present Parliament. Instead of five hundred and fifty, which is our present home defense air strength, we shall have about six hundred by the end of the financial year 1935-6. At the present time we are the fifth or sixth air Power in all the world. [Editor's Note: It had recently become known that Soviet Russia had constructed a large air force, second only to that of France. Britain consequently declined from fifth to sixth position in the list.] But every State is rapidly expanding its air force. They are all expanding, but much more rapidly than we. It is certain, therefore, that when the Government, this National Government and this National House of Commons, go in 1936 to the country and give an account of their stewardship, we shall have fallen farther behind other countries in air defense than we are now.

If we extend our view over the five year's programme, I believe it is also true that, having regard to the increases which are being made and projected by other countries, we shall, at the end of the period, if there is continuity of policy between the two Parliaments, be worse off in 1939 relatively than we are now—and it is relativity that counts. By that time France, Soviet Russia, Japan, the United States, and Italy, if they carry out their present intentions, will be farther ahead of us than they are now. There is no dispute about this, just in the same way as there is no dispute about the gravity of the European situation or the manner in which we are involved in it. Yet even for this tiny, timid, tentative, tardy increase of the Air Force, to which the Government have at length made up their mind, they are to be censured by the whole united forces of the Socialist and Liberal parties here and throughout the country.

One would have thought that the character of His Majesty's Government and the record of its principal Ministers would have induced the Opposition to view the request for an increase in the national defense with some confidence and some consideration. I do not suppose there has ever been such a pacifist-minded Government. There is the Prime Minister who in the War proved in the most extreme manner and with very great courage his convictions and the sacrifices he would make for what he believed was the cause of pacifism. The Lord President of the Council is chiefly associated in the public mind with the repetition of the prayer, "Give peace in our time." One would have supposed that when Ministers like these come forward and say that they feel it their duty to ask for some small increase in the means they have of guaranteeing the public safety, it would weigh with the Opposition and would be considered as a proof of the reality of the danger from which they seek to protect us.

Then look at the apologies which the Government have made. No one could have put forward a proposal in such extremely inoffensive terms. Meekness has characterized every word which they have spoken since this subject was first mooted. We are assured that we can see for ourselves how small is the proposal. We are assured that it can be topped at any minute if Geneva succeeds—on which, of course, we all have expectations; I beg pardon, official expectations. We are assured of that. And we are also assured that the steps we are taking, although they may to some lower minds have associated with them some idea of national self-defense, are really only associated with the great principle of collective security.

But all these apologies and soothing procedures are most curtly repulsed by the Opposition. Their only answer to these efforts to conciliate them is a Vote of Censure, which is to be decided tonight. It seems to me that we have got very nearly to the end of the period when it is worth while endeavouring to conciliate some classes of opinion upon this subject. We are in the presence of an attempt to establish a kind of tyranny of opinion, and if its reign could be perpetuated the effect might be profoundly injurious to the stability and security of this country. We are a rich and easy prey. No country is so vulnerable and no country would better repay pillage than our own. With our enormous Metropolis here, the greatest target in the world, a kind of tremendous, fat, valuable cow tied up to attract the beast of prey, we are in a position in which we have never been before, and in which no other country in the world is at the present time.

Let us remember this: Our weakness does not only involve ourselves; our weakness involves also the stability of Europe. I was very glad to hear some admission from the Lord President of the Council of how he had found himself hampered, or his representatives had found themselves hampered at Geneva, by our weakness. If it is thought that there is nothing behind your words, when you are in fact in a position of great danger yourself, not much attention is paid to what you say; the march of events takes place regardless of it. That march has been set in motion. Who can say that we shall not ourselves be dragged into it? There is also a European duty and talk about our being good Europeans. The best way in which a British Member of Parliament or statesman can be a good European is to make sure that our country is safe and strong in the first instance. The rest may be added to you afterwards, but without that you are no kind of European. All you are is a source of embarrassment and weakness to the whole of the rest of the world.

Then we are told that this might be all right for some other time, but not now. That was dwelt on by both the Opposition speakers this afternoon. Sir Herbert Samuel begged that, at any rate, we might put these measures off for at least a few more weeks in order to see what would happen at Geneva. Eight years ago we were told that disarmament had been discussed at Geneva. For two and a half years the actual conference has been proceeding. The Leader of the Liberal Opposition has, therefore, had a good run for his experiment. His hope has been abounding. It has preserved him at every stage from seeing the facts. Now, when even those who have worked as no other Government has ever worked for disarmament, when even they say that they cannot take the responsibility of remaining in the present condition, the right hon. Gentleman gets up and asks for a few more weeks' delay.

I should have thought that the time had come when Ministers must not complicate the problems that already have to be solved by endeavouring to square the discharge of their duty with the particular formulas which have gained such popularity during the course of the Disarmament Conference. If they are only doing what is their duty they have no need to apologize to the House, and still less to the public out of doors. Of course, no one wants to spend money on armaments needlessly. But the electors of all parties in the country expect a Government to provide for the safety of the Homeland. That is what the ordinary man regards as the Government's first duty, and that is what he considers they are paid for—to make sure that the country is safe. If Ministers, especially with the record and temperaments of these, come forward and demand a certain measure of additional force and personnel, they have only to put that forward with courage and conviction to gain an enormous measure of support throughout the country.

I cannot think of anything more likely to rally their forces than that we should see the two Oppositions presenting themselves on the ground that they will not support the necessary defense of the country and that they intend to utilize all the prejudice and the cry of unpopularity which they suppose may be brought against a Government which has to propose an increase of armaments. If they do that they will only be making another of those historic miscalculations upon large issues for which they have so often been severely chastised but from which they seem incapable of learning the wisdom of silence. It is a source of wonder to me that public men who have filled high office and who aspire to fill it again should be prepared, like the leaders we see opposite, to vote for either of the Motions which are put forward from the Opposition side. Such an act is of far-reaching character. It will not affect the decisions of Parliament, but by so doing hon. Members opposite place themselves in an invidious position as to which they may be required to give an answer, in circumstances which no human being can foresee.

The need and the interest which the Government have in doing their duty turn upon whether the measures which they propose are really a contribution to our security or not. If they are not, then the Government run the risk of falling between two stools. Their duty is to provide adequate measures of defense before it is too late. Whatever they propose, they are going to be assailed by the pacifists throughout the country with all that interested and unscrupulous vituperation which we saw in the squalid election at Fulham some time ago and which finds an echo in these Votes of Censure this afternoon. Whatever the Government do, they are going to have that thrown at them, and it is vital therefore that they should so shape their course as to gather around them and behind them all the forces upon which they would naturally rely and to which they would look for support upon a question of this character. To encounter all this storm for something which is insufficient to meet the need is to have the worst of both worlds. The Government will get their abuse, but we shall not get our defense.

We must assume, of course, that Ministers have considered this aspect of the matter and that they see where their duty and their interest lie, but I must point out that there are no grounds whatever for suggesting that it is not possible to increase the Air Force more rapidly than is now proposed. I conceive that there are many ways of rapidly augmenting our Air Force which the Government have not adopted at present. The decision which they have just taken is a deliberate decision, and I confess I find it difficult to believe that it makes adequate provision against the dangers which we have to face and which are admitted.

It is no use examining national defense in the abstract and talking in vague and general terms about hypothetical dangers and combinations which cannot be expressed. Before the War the Liberal Government of those days did not hesitate to specify the quarter from which they expected danger, and they did not hesitate to specify the navy against which we were determined to maintain an ample superiority. We measured ourselves before the War publicly and precisely against Germany. We laid down a ratio of 16 to 10 against existing programs and of 2 to 1 against any additions to those programmes. Such calculations are perfectly well understood abroad. They were stated publicly, and they bred no ill-will and caused no offense. As a matter of fact, the contrary was the case, and I think I shall be borne out in that statement by those who remember what happened in those days. As the preponderance of our Navy grew stronger our relations with Germany steadily improved, and they were never better than in the last few months before the War. [*Laughter.*] It is a fact that the relations between Great Britain and Germany were never better than on the eve of the War, which arose from troubles entirely outside our relations with the German Government. The fact that our Navy was measured against the German Navy played no part in bringing about that struggle, and therefore I propose to speak quite plainly about Germany.

My question to the Government is this: What is their view about the German military air force? The Lord President used some sentences upon this point which I think were not cast by him with the intention of achieving any special degree of clarity. I understand, of course, that officially Germany has no air force at all. She is prohibited by the solemn treaties which she signed after the War from having any military aviation. But the right hon. Gentleman said that the worst crime is not to tell the truth to the public, and I think we must ask the Government to assure us that Germany has observed and is observing her treaty obligations in respect of military aviation. If so, I shall be greatly relieved, and I think the House will be greatly relieved. But if that assurance cannot be given—and, of course, it cannot be given—then I say we are bound to probe and examine what is taking place as far as we are in a position to do so. It was different when we were talking about Dreadnoughts. You could not build Dreadnoughts in boat-houses on the Elbe, and what Admiral von Tirpitz said before the War was found to be true—that nothing outside the regular program was being embarked upon. It is a different matter with regard to aeroplanes which can be so easily constructed and their component parts assembled. Military aviation shades into civil aviation by such indefinable graduations that I dare say the Government are right in not making statements which would in fact be charges and no doubt would be capable of being rebutted or denied.

I will venture, however, to assert some broad facts. I shall be delighted if the Government are able to contradict them. I first assert that Germany has already, in violation of the Treaty, created a military air force which is now nearly two-thirds as strong as our present home defense air force. That is the first statement which I put before the Government for their consideration. The second is that Germany is rapidly increasing this air force, not only by large sums of money which figure in her estimates, but also by public subscriptions—very often almost forced subscriptions—which are in progress and have been in progress for some time all over Germany. By the end of 1935 the German air force will be nearly equal in numbers and efficiency—and after all no one must underrate German efficiency, because there could be no more deadly mistake than that—it will be nearly equal, as I say, to our home defense air force at that date even if the Government's present proposals are carried out.

The third statement is that if Germany continues this expansion and if we continue to carry out our scheme, then some time in 1936 Germany will be definitely and substantially stronger in the air than Great Britain. Fourthly, and this is the point which is causing anxiety, once they have got that lead we may never be able to overtake them. If these assertions cannot be contradicted, then there is cause for the anxiety which exists in all parts of the House, not only because of the physical strength of the German air force, but I am bound to say also because of the character of the present German dictatorship. If the Government have to admit at any time in the next few years that the German air forces are stronger than our own, then they will be held, and I think rightly held, to have failed in their prime duty to the country.

I ask, therefore, for a solemn, specific assurance from the Government that at no moment for which they will have responsibility will they fail to have a substantially superior military air force at home to that which they have reason to believe has been set on foot in Germany. Can that assurance be given? Will it be given? I think it will make a great difference to the judgment which must be passed upon these proposals if the Government are in a position to say that that is their resolve.

But in this connection we must face some of the facts about German civil aviation and British civil aviation. I am assured that the German civil aviation is three of four times as large as our civil aviation, but that is only part of the story. The British civil aviation is in its character purely commercial, and the machines cannot be converted for military purposes without falling far below the standard of war machines. Our civil machines would have little war value if they were to be converted. We are the only country whose civil aviation is so completely divorced from the technical military aspects. The German machines, on the other hand, have been deliberately and scientifically planned by the Government for the express purpose of being converted into war machines. Not only have they a speed and a design suited for this purpose, going at over 200 miles an hour, but the whole scheme of conversion has been prepared and organized with minute and earnest forethought. I am perfectly ready to be corrected, and no one will be more pleased than I to hear a convincing, an overwhelming, answer on the subject, but I am informed that the bomb-racks which would be substituted for the passenger accommodation in a great number of these fast German civil machines have already been made and delivered, and it would be a matter of only a few hours to unbolt the one and fasten in the other.

The same story can be told about the pilots. Germany has a trained personnel of pilots which is many times more numerous than our own. Gliders are a wonderful means of training pilots, giving them air sense, and there are, I believe, over 500 qualified glider pilots in Germany, whereas we have only about fifty in this country. If, therefore, you have to add to the regular increase in German military aeroplanes, which we have to expect and which, I imagine, the Government are well informed about, and which alone will bring the forces almost to equality by the end of 1935—if you have to add to that an enormous and indefinite transference of pilots and machines from civil to military aviation, it would seem that there is a very obvious danger that before the end of next year we shall be definitely weaker than the German aviation. I have tried to state these facts with moderation, and, as I say, nothing would give me greater pleasure than to learn that I have discovered another mare's nest. I shall rejoice at my own discomfort if these facts are able to be overturned or superseded by other more reassuring facts. But unless these facts can be contradicted, precisely and categorically, it seems to me that our position is a very serious one, and that not only should we brush aside a Vote of Censure on this small increase, but that we should urge a much greater degree of action, both in scale and speed, upon the responsible Ministers.

Our weakness in the air has a very direct bearing on the foreign situation, and on those foreign obligations to which I ventured to refer at the beginning of my remarks. So long as our policy harmonized with that of France and that of other countries who were the allies or associates of France, the preponderance against Germany, if Germany became an aggressor, would be so large as to constitute a deterrent against any action other than action so desperate as to be almost insane. But a new series of questions arises. We must ask ourselves whether we wish to be dependent on France for our domestic safety. We must ask ourselves whether we can accept the protection of a foreign country for any long period of time without losing that freedom to place our own interpretation upon our Continental obligations which, it seems to me, is absolutely vital to the sound conduct of our affairs. We have these obligations, but we still have the right to judge according to our sense of justice and the circumstances of the time.

I should have thought that the pacifists and the isolationists would have joined with His Majesty's Government in urging that we should at least make our island independent of foreign protection for its safety. If, however, owing to the long delays to which we have agreed in the hope of arriving at some arrangement at Geneva, we have fallen behind and are not able to put ourselves in a secure position, it seems to me that we must harmonize our policy with that of France and of the other powerful countries who are associated with France. That, it seems to me, is absolutely necessary. But what is the course of those who now urge us to pass this Vote of Censure? They have been doing all they could to urge France to disarm and have pleaded for German equality of armaments.

Mr. Cocks: The Government have done that.

Mr. Churchill: The hon. Gentleman and his followers are the driving force. What I have regretted so much is the attention that has been paid to these evil counsels. The hon. Gentleman has shown more sanity than many of those among whom he sits, but undoubtedly the course which hon. Gentlemen opposite have adopted would have the effect of weakening France, and if France had disarmed and Germany rearmed I shudder to think what the state of Europe might be at this very moment. The hon. Gentlemen opposite are very free-spoken, as most of us are in this country, on the conduct of the German Nazi Government. No one has been more severe in criticism than the Labour party or that section of the Liberal party which I see opposite. And their great newspapers, now united in the common cause, have been the most forward in the severity of the strictures. But these criticisms are fiercely resented by the powerful men who have Germany in their hands. So that we are to disarm our friends, we are to have no allies, we are to affront powerful nations, and we are to neglect our own defenses entirely. That is a miserable and perilous situation. Indeed, the position to which they seek to reduce us by the course which they have pursued and by the vote which they ask us to take is one of terrible jeopardy, and in voting against them tonight we shall hope that a better path for national safety will be found than that along which they would conduct us.

AIR DEFENCE

November 1, 1934

Constituency Meeting, Woodford Bridge

There is an issue far larger than party which causes profound anxiety—namely, the state of our air defences. In spite of the plainest warnings and facts, practically nothing has been done during the whole year. Germany is arming secretly, illegally, and rapidly. A reign of terror exists in Germany in order to keep secret the feverish and terrible preparations they are making. But enough is known to make it perfectly clear that even in organized military machines alone they will overtake us before another year had passed. Besides their organized military machines, they have a gigantic civil aviation with enormous reserves of pilots and aeroplanes, many of them faster than our fastest military machines. A great number of these can be converted into bombing machines within a few days or even hours, against which we can show nothing either ready or in preparation.

When we consider the character of the present German Government, the rapidly darkening European scene, and the obligations which Ministers are repeatedly declaring we have in Europe, it is astounding that patriotic Ministers are prepared to go on month after month bearing this load of frightful responsibility, and that so many members of Parliament set their obedience to the party whips above their duty to the nation.

Mr. Baldwin has used the most formidable and far-reaching expression, astonishing and startling Europe. He has said "Our frontiers are the Rhine." Could we be sure that the men now in control of Germany would not reply to that, "Our targets are the Thames"? The Prime Minister said only last Friday that "we had let our defences down, and down, and down," in the hope of persuading foreign nations to do the same.

A national emergency is approaching which must be faced with energy and courage if a safe, coherent, and peace-keeping policy is to be found.

I appeal to all Conservatives to make strenuous endeavours to keep our party organization in the highest state of readiness and efficiency. We are within 18 months of a General Election. Perhaps the time might be even shorter. Mr. Baldwin has said that we must not go back to the party dog-fight, and from many quarters we have heard that Conservatives are to suppress their party feelings. In what fool's paradise do the holders of such opinions dwell? A party dog-fight is going on now. The whole forces of the Socialist and Liberal Parties are being ceaselessly directed against the Conservative members and candidates from one end of the island to the other. In every Conservative constituency extremely hard fights lay before the sitting members. What then is the use of saying they must not have a party dog-fight when two parties are already attacking the third?

The Conservative Party has two great battles to fight—to defeat the dangerous proposal to set up responsible Home Rule for all India and hand over the police to the Provincial Governments, and to beat the Socialists. I believe there is time to win both these battles. But it might soon be too late. If the whole of the coming year is wasted upon the India Home Rule Bill and if the Government continues to split the Conservative Party by forcing that through, it might be too late to recover before we have to face the common foe. I still hope that that will be averted, and that the party organizations will put their foot down while time remains.

INDIA (CONSTITUTIONAL REFORM)

November 1, 1934

House of Commons

No one, I think, could possibly object to the principle of the Motion which my right hon. Friend [Sir Austen Chamberlain] has just submitted to the House. We quite understand that the Joint Select Committee, after their arduous labours, are most anxious that the people of India shall learn the blessings which are to be conferred upon them at the same time as the glad tidings are imparted to both Houses of Parliament in this country. Nevertheless, although the precedent may be quite satisfactory, the extra delay, although it may be we have no means of preventing it, is serious. There have been very long delays already. I am only going to pursue my argument on this matter along the theme of time and the consequences of delay. I am not even going to dwell upon the inconveniences which undoubtedly will result if this Indian controversy in its graver aspects should be so prolonged as to tread upon the heels of a General Election. On the contrary, I shall confine myself to the immediate practical time-table which lies before us between now and Christmas.

There is to be, as I understand, publication on the 21st or 22nd; that is to be the date of the simultaneous publication. Then, before Christmas, we are to have a meeting of the Council of the National Union of Conservative Associations, in accordance with the promise which was made, and which was so scrupulously interpreted, by my right hon. Friend the Lord President of the Council. If such a meeting is to give full and careful attention to the matter, this very bulky report ought to be spread wide through the country at the earliest possible moment. There ought to be three weeks before such a meeting in order to do that, after the publication of the report, and I doubt very much whether it will be possible in the time-table to fit that in. There would certainly be a disadvantage if the study of the report is cut down to, say, only a fortnight. After the Council of the National Union of Conservative Associations has met, we are, I understand, to have a three-days' Debate in the House upon the general approval or disapproval of the report. It is quite clear, therefore, that we have no time to lose.

I think, also, that everyone would wish, and that the Government would wish, to terminate as quickly as possible this present very unsatisfactory state of affairs—this unsatisfactory phase where the Government have to go about assuring their supporters that they are committed to nothing, and all the time events are moving swiftly forward in the sense of committing them very much. Also, I think that Ministers know all about the report. It is quite obvious, from speeches delivered by the Attorney-General, that they are very well informed. I dare say my right hon. and learned Friend has been so busy defending liberty that he has not fully appreciated the natural deductions which could be drawn from his remarks, but certainly it appears that he knew what was in the report, and was strongly advising people to have great confidence in it. Anyhow, I am only using this argument—which would very quickly lead me out of order if I pursued it—on the point of time, to show how essential and important it is that the delay should be shortened to the smallest possible compass. Has it been shortened to the smallest possible compass? I am not making any assertion at all; I am simply asking for greater reassurance. My right hon. Friend suggests that everything has been done with the maximum of speed; he said than an aeroplane would be of no advantage, and so on. I am bound to say I should have thought that, if the report were signed, as it was signed, I believe, yesterday—

Sir A. Chamberlain: It was approved; it was not signed. The Report of a Select Committee of either House does not have signatures appended to it.

Mr. Churchill: Well, at any rate it was approved. If it was approved and received its final release from the Committee yesterday or to-day, it would have been possible for a duplicate attested copy to have been included in the aeroplane which leaves on Saturday, the day after to-morrow, and this would have saved at least the difference between the air and the sea journey. Then the report could have been reprinted in India in a few days—in no longer time than it takes to print it here—and could have been circulated then, saving 10 days. That might be a great convenience when we were discussing this matter, as we shall be discussing it, at the Union of Conservative Associations, and also generally for the convenience of the House and of the public.

Perhaps my right hon. Friend the Secretary of State will tell us whether it was not possible to save that time, because undoubtedly we ought to have the fullest possible opportunity of considering a matter of this kind.

There is only one other point which I venture to make in this connection, and that is as to the manner in which the report synchronises or does not synchronise with the elections which are taking place in India. I am bound to say I should have thought that a report of this character ought to have been in the possession of the Indian democracy before they gave their votes at the election which has now, I believe, already almost begun. I should have thought that it would have been entirely the wish of the Government to secure that course. My right hon. Friend will no doubt tell me that he has no power to control the working of the Joint Select Committee. I shall not argue that with him to-day, but at any rate he had perfect power, in consultation with the Viceroy, to arrange for such a minor postponement of the Indian elections that this very important document from their point of view would have been before them before the elections had begun, and when there was time for them to digest the whole matter. But, as far as I can gather, the way in which this thing is working out is that the bulk of the elections will be over before this report is made public in India. I gather that some of the most important Provinces will have voted before the report is made public. The United Provinces poll before the 20th November; the Central Provinces before the 20th November; Assam before the 14th November; the North-West Frontier Province—the key Province—before the 17th November. I should have thought that it was very inconvenient—most inconvenient—to throw this document, upon which so much interest centres, into the stormy field of Indian politics in the actual midst of the elections, and not to have arranged that at any rate all the facts were before the Indian electorate at the time when they were electing the Members for the new Legislature.

I am certainly not going to suggest that this mischance has been planned; but what would have happened if, when we were introducing the Irish Constitution, we had managed to let the actual facts of the agreement out in the middle of the election of the Dail; or, going further back, if, when we were planning the Transvaal Constitution, we had managed to bring that document out at the moment when the people of the Transvaal were already engaged in their poll. It would, I think, have been thought to be a rather unfortunate handling of the affair. I do not at all suggest that it is designed. If it were designed, it would be a bad design. But, if it has been unintentional, all I can say is that it falls very much below the standard of management in technical and tactical matters that we have been accustomed to look for in my right hon. Friend the Secretary of State for India.

BETTING AND LOTTERIES BILL

November 6, 1934

House of Commons

I intend to support my hon. Friend [Lord Apsley] in his amendment, but I should not like to do so without trespassing, though only for a few moments, on the Committee to explain the reasons which lead me to take this course. I certainly do not consider that the national finances stand in need of support from sweepstakes, lotteries or premium bonds. The national finances proceed entirely apart from the subject which we are now discussing. It is rather from the moral and ethical aspect that I think the House ought really to look at the blunt facts of the situation. I must confess I find myself completely puzzled to know what is the standard that is being set up in matters of betting and gambling. We have been discussing 20 or 30 Clauses of Part I of this Bill. I have been here a great deal, and I have given a great deal of thought to this matter. It seems to me a very extraordinary thing that the House should take it as quite a right and proper matter for them to occupy several days to deal with all the details of setting up hundreds of casinos for dog racing all over the country in which courses are to be run on 104 days in the year, and consider what proportion might be taken for the rake-off and so forth, and indulge in all these discussions blissfully unconscious of the fact that they are legislating for and establishing the evil thing of betting and that when they have finished Part I of the Bill and a proposal is put forward to have two or three large national sweepstakes on great sporting events people should say, "But that would be encouraging betting. That would be countenancing the evil idea of gaining something for nothing—unearned increment—and naturally, defenders as we are of the morals of the nation, we cannot lend ourselves to that." What nonsense! Of all the forms that gambling can take, the purchase of a 10s. ticket in a great national sweep, like those that are so unpleasantly conducted for us from a neighbouring island, that is the least injurious and the least likely to lead to a family being ruined—a workman returning home without his wages.

I entirely associate myself with the mood in which the Leader of the Opposition approached the matter. It is a dreadful thing that people should be ruined and led into crime by betting and gambling, but they are far more likely to be led into crime by going night after night to dog racing establishments than if they buy once or twice a year a 10s. ticket, or a proportion of a ticket, in a great national lottery. The very character of these competitions is such that no one can lose much money upon them. How rarely they take place! It is no good trying to buy a great number of tickets in a competition in which there are millions of chances.

What is the alternative? Do you think you are going to stop this thing? You cannot stop it. Even if you ransack the mails till you destroy the privacy of the correspondence of His Majesty's subjects you will not succeed in preventing it. You will only drive it underground. It is a very unreasonable position into which we are being led. It is a position that is accountable to no theory of logic or morality that is represented in this Bill. It may well be that the existence of three or four large national sweeps a year would diminish the amount of money hazarded on gambling. The lives of many people who are at work nowadays are very monotonous. Their toil tends to reproduce itself with exact mechanical rotation and routine. Hour after hour a particular piece of labour has to be done. In my judgment this to a certain extent would be an anodyne which would diminish the amount of gambling that would take place and not increase it. There are many admirable and useful causes to which the fruits of such a competition could be devoted.

There is one other thing I wish to say before I sit down. I understand that the Government, following their usual practice, refuse to allow a free vote of the House. I cannot understand why they refuse to do so. One of the greatest mistakes which the Government make is the taking of more upon themselves than they need in a matter affecting the interests, opinions and social habits of the people about which we are just as good judges as any Government. We are representatives of the people. We are Members with constituencies comprising 30,000 or 40,000 constituents and are re-acted upon by opinions from the constituencies. We cannot bring those opinions to any consciousness when the Government Whips are put on and Government pressure is brought to bear upon them. I cannot understand it. Where, again, is the logic of your talk? You talk about democracy and respect for the will and wishes of the people. You would not hesitate to ask the opinions of the people who are returned to Westminster whether it was the League of Nations or any other great and complicated problem. Of them you would say, "It is a matter for their good judgment." But when it comes to this question about which they are just as capable of forming an opinion, and about which they have thought a great deal, and in which scores of thousands, and millions perhaps, are deeply interested, we say, "No, we must be the angels. We must come down from on High and guide them into the true channels and proclaim for them the great modern gospel at which our Parliament has now arrived, that 'you may ruin yourself on 104 days in a year by gambling on the dog course, but if you take a 10s. ticket on a Derby sweep, then you are lost beyond redemption.' "

BETTING AND LOTTERIES BILL

November 7, 1934

House of Commons

I think the Home Secretary [Sir J. Gilmour] must carry the matter a little further, and be a little more precise. He has made a very important statement. He has said, quite plainly, that the Government did not intend to disturb those with merely a few tickets in their possession; that they were out to deal with the wholesale merchant who has large supplies, or medium supplies, of tickets in his possession. I thought that was satisfactory, but there is nothing of it in the Bill, and if the right hon. Gentleman would insert words in the Bill giving effect to his purpose it would remove the anxieties which many people feel on this point. I hope the Home Secretary is not going to suppose that just because during the passage of the Bill he makes a well-meaning and good-humoured speech pointing out that everything is easy, no difficulties will arise, and that that is a sufficient protection for His Majesty's lieges against words which are actually in the Act of Parliament. Experience shows that if there are breaches of the law they are not always treated in such a friendly, smooth, tolerant and considerate atmosphere as that which the right hon. Gentleman outlined in his statement. The right hon. Gentleman owes it to the Committee to put in words, or take from us a form of words, which will make clear the distinction between the casual possession of a few tickets and a deliberate importation of large quantities of tickets with a view of defeating the purpose of the Bill.

[Later] I should be very sorry indeed if any heat were to be imported into this discussion, and I hope that the Government will not allow their naturally mild disposition to be inflamed by the berserk fury of their Liberal allies. I only rise for the purpose of pointing out that the Home Secretary, wishing to be helpful and agreeable and to smooth the path of this business, has actually put us in a rather difficult position—and himself also. He commended this Clause to the Committee by pointing out that it was never intended to apply it to any small scale or accidental operation but only to large and wholesale—though that was not his word—undertakings. But neither he nor the learned Solicitor-General has been able to point—and they certainly would have pointed with great acumen to any such provision if they had known of it—to anything in the Bill whereby the slightest effect is given to the pious and to a certain extent genial and reassuring sentiments uttered by the Home Secretary.

I do not think that the matter ought to end there. I am sure that my right hon. Friend the Home Secretary, whose disposition has always endeared him to his fellow-Members, would not wish to gain votes for his proposal by arousing with his soothing eloquence hopes which on closer examination are found to be disappointed by the harsh, rigid, legal pedantry of this Bill. I should be sorry to have to occupy the time of the Committee with a Division, although it may be necessary to do so. I venture to make a suggestion, and, in doing so, I speak only for myself as a Member of the House attending to my duties in the House to-day, as I propose to do in the manner which seems to me fit and proper, without even asking the permission of hon. Gentlemen opposite. It seems to me that the Home Secretary might meet us on this matter, or at any rate go some way towards implementing the clear expression which he has given of his wish, if, for instance, he were willing to insert in line 32 the word "organised" so that the Clause would read:

or has in his possession for the purpose of organised sale or distribution.

That would clearly draw the line between cases of the kind which if this legislation is to be enforced should certainly be prosecuted, and the large number of petty derelictions from the strict course of civic conduct which we know occur continuously all over the country. I do not put this suggestion forward in order to embarrass my right hon. Friend in the course of business, but it seems to me that if he promised to consider such a suggestion before the Report stage, it might make it worth while for my hon. Friends not to press the matter further at this stage. I do not ask my right hon. Friend to put in such a word this afternoon. I only ask him to promise that the point will be considered before the Report stage, and if possible met. If he can do so, I think that would take some of the edge off this particular proposal.

[Later] I think we really are indebted to the right hon. Gentleman [Sir J. Gilmour] for the tone and temper in which he has dealt with this matter, and I am certain, from long experience—almost one of the longest—that the progress of Bills is often expedited by that kind of treatment on the part of a Minister. The right hon. Gentleman has not committed himself to anything definite, nor do I think it reasonable to ask the Government to commit themselves on the spur of the moment. They must naturally look over the matter and see how it affects the layout of the Bill and what consequential reactions there may be, but there is a Report stage prescribed by Parliament, and on the Report stage the right hon. Gentleman will make a further statement and will make it, as I understand, with the desire to meet the views that have been expressed, if it be possible to do so without stultifying his legislation. Such an undertaking from the right hon. Gentleman will be carried out not only in the letter but in the spirit, and in all these circumstances I must say, on this particular point, that I think we have been treated with consideration.

[Later] A very formidable proposition is contained in these paragraphs. I thoroughly agree with what has already been said very fully, that if it is the intention to attempt to prohibit by law participation in the lotteries of the Irish Free State, the main process of operation will be the prohibition of the publication of lists of winners or of advertisements in the newspapers. There I quite agree with the Home Secretary; this is the staple of his apparatus, worth all the rest of it put together, and certainly likely to be effective. Although I think that the other course would have been best, and one which would have most conduced to the public interest and been most in accordance with the public will, the House has decided that lotteries on a large scale will be illegal, and the right hon. Gentleman is fully entitled to the prohibition of the publication of lists of winners in the newspapers. There, I think, he ought to stop, and not to go further and bring in, as the hon. and learned Member for South Nottingham (Mr. Knight) has said with great experience in this matter:

> any matter descriptive of the drawing or intended drawing of the lottery.

The speech of the hon. Member for South Bradford (Mr. Holdsworth) from the Liberal benches shows what a farce it is to pretend that there is any real championship of freedom there, where it is freedom when they can do the thing they want to do. In regard to things that they do not want to do, or which they think they have an interest to prevent other people from doing, politically or otherwise, they are perfectly prepared to use all those methods of repression, restriction, legal prevention and prohibition of every kind, as we have abundantly seen, while those methods in the hands of those to whom they are opposed are always dubbed weapons of villainous tyranny.

I hope that the Government will tread the sober path in this matter. It is very hazardous to go pressing into new paths of legislation. It is entirely novel that a newspaper should be prohibited from giving an account of any event that occurs, whether in Dublin, Paris or anywhere else. The House of Commons might consent to derogate so far from the liberty of the Press which we all regard as essential as to say that lists of winners shall not be published, as in the paragraph with which we are dealing, as well as to prohibit any advertisement of what is going to take place. Those two together are quite adequate. The right hon. Gentleman shakes his head. He might quite easily sit there and overload the Statute Book with a whole lot of vicious principles which are not necessary for the faithful and adequate attainment of the object which has been consented to and prescribed by Parliament. He has an over-whelming majority; he has only to ring a bell, and his vast, blind battering ram comes into operation, but he must be moderate for that very reason, and because of that power to carry anything right or wrong irrespective of what the country thinks about it. The decision is in his hands, and that is all the more reason for him to be moderate. He has no right to overload the Statute Book with things like this, prohibiting newspapers from describing facts and to say that a fact shall be blotted out. It is the sort of thing which happens in Germany. There were horrible murders, when great numbers of people were murdered, and the authorities said: "No reference to it shall appear in any newspaper." The fact was blotted out, and most people to whom I have spoken about it have forgotten it, except the relatives.

It is not necessary for the fanatics who are pressing this matter, and who have some pull or control over the Government, some influence utterly disproportionate to their numbers, virtues, or reasoning power, to drive the Government into producing new departures in legislation which are very questionable, and are over and above what are needed to achieve the result. The Home Secretary is the guardian of public liberty; he is not merely a sort of glorified chief constable for locking people up. He ought to remember that protection of liberty is his duty, too. I sat in his place for some years, and I certainly think it is very undesirable to put one word in that you do not need. What more could you need than to prohibit advertisements and to prohibit the publication of any list of prize winners, whether a complete list or not?

Now I should like to point out that it is impossible to discuss paragraph (c, ii) without having in mind the next paragraph, which is of an even wider nature. The words in (c, iii) are protected by a special enactment in Sub-section (3) of this Clause stating that

> Proceedings . . . in respect of matter published in a newspaper shall not be instituted except by, or by the direction of, the Director of Public Prosecutions.

No such protection covers the words in (c, ii). I shall have something to say about Sub-section (3) when we reach it. I suggest that for the present, to begin with, the right hon. Gentleman might agree to leave out of (c, ii) the words as far as and including

> drawing of the lottery, or,

and confine himself to

any list (whether complete or not) of prize winners or winning tickets in
the lottery; or.

Then we can come to the discussion of (c, iii), bearing in mind that it is covered to
some extent by the fact that it is placed under the very superior discretion and
jurisdiction of the Director of Public Prosecutions. I hope that the Home Secretary
will see that he has all that he needs if he takes the last two lines of paragraph (c, ii).

[Much later] I hope and trust that the Home Secretary is going to give some
reply on this point, which really is the crux of the whole matter. It is not a small
matter. It has been debated on both sides, and we do not disagree on the major point;
we agree that the publication of lists of winners should be prohibited. But his is an
essential Clause in the Bill, and I hope we are going to hear from the right hon.
Gentleman some answer to the arguments which have been put forward—some indication either that he is considering them or has found in his mind some mental process
which enables him to reject them. I rose to ask him a specific question. Will he kindly
say why it is that the provision in Sub-section (3) that a prosecution shall not be
instituted except by the direction of the Director of Public Prosecutions in respect of
any proceeding under paragraph (c, iii) is not applicable to paragraph (c, ii), in which
general words are introduced at the beginning? If paragraph (c, ii) had nothing in it but
the precise, specific statement that a list of winners must not be published, it would
not be necessary to have these vague words:

any matter descriptive of the drawing of a lottery.

It seems to me that this, at any rate, ought to be put into operation under the
protection of Sub-section (3), for what it is worth. Can the right hon. Gentleman
assure me that that can be done? It seems to me to be the only reasonable way.

[Much later] My right hon. Friend dealt in his speech principally with the case
raised by the hon. Gentleman of the onus of proof being shifted to the person in
possession of a ticket. He promised to consult with the Law Officers to see if that
matter could be settled. I think we can certainly leave that aspect where it has now
been put, because I am quite sure he is anxious to produce the best possible form with
the desire to meet some of the objections. He has said that it is his duty to stop all
these loopholes. The air is a very wide loophole, but I should say the ether, imperceptible, tenuous, which laps the universe, is the loophole which he will have to stop.
What is the answer to that? What is the use of putting up all this tremendous apparatus
of penalties, of restrictions on newspapers, prescribing that this and that shall not be
done, no publication of winners, with all the forces of Liberalism behind it? What is
the use of obliging those gentlemen in their ardour for repression, when all the time
the great, wide world is free, and there is the fullest information coming from
broadcasting stations?

[Much later] I will not weary the Committee by prefacing my remarks but will
come directly to the point I reached in the course of my speech which was inter-

rupted, to which we must have an answer. What is the answer of the Home Secretary? How is he going to stop the loophole of perpetual broadcasts of the winners and the advertisements? Has it ever occurred to him that there was such a loophole; or has it dawned upon him now for the first time? I thought he was startled when he began to realise what he had to do in the case of newspapers coming from Ireland. Whoever is going to benefit it is certain that the Irish newspapers will benefit very largely. They will have a continuous feature in all their pages of the state of the Irish Sweep, the methods by which tickets will be drawn, all those descriptive accounts which are such a shocking offence when committed by English newspapers, and also a list of winners. These papers will come in by the thousand; their circulation, of course, will go up. People who are following this matter for their own interest will ask their news-agents to get them. Is that to be a crime; is it an offence? Are you going to make it an offence? Let us have an answer before we cast these things into the form of statute law.

Assuming that a great many people would like to have the "Irish Times" for a particular week, or for particular days, is the newsagent committing an offence if, in the ordinary course of his business, he complies with the desire of his customers and gets the necessary copies of the journal? If that be an offence, we want to know. The Home Secretary said that it is a question of those people who are trying to advertise the sweep. These people do not care anything about the sweep; they are only selling their newspapers, and they are going to do good business. That is a point which must be met. For the moment I am enlisting myself on the side of my right hon. Friend, trying to face the difficulties which will confront him, difficulties which will have to be met. I thought that he himself would have made some contribution towards a solution. If you wish to be logical and carry this thing through with the high hand, or foot, as the case may be, you will have to have a new series of provisions designed to deal with the import of foreign newspapers, or Irish Free State newspapers.

The hon. Member for Bodmin (Mr. Isaac Foot), in his desire to put down this evil at whatever cost to liberty, has tried to play upon anti-Irish prejudices; he has tried to work up our dander against the Irish Free State. He must face the consequences. If the Home Secretary is effectively to prevent the circulation of the list of winners and other advertisements of the Irish Free State Sweepstake in this country, he must take power to blot out these passages in the Irish newspapers and in foreign newspapers which contain these references, or he must seize the whole edition. There are plenty of precedents for that process. In Germany at the present time we see in our newspapers again and again that a particular edition of the "Morning Post" or the "Times" or the "Daily News" has been seized in Germany. Do you propose to do that? If you do not, you cannot handle this matter. Thousands and thousands of these newspapers may come in and the information will be given. If you are not going to take power to seize editions which have these advertisements and the results of the draw, then it is a farce to attempt to deal with this difficulty, and you are subjecting English newspapers to great injury and injustice. What are you going to do to Irish Free State newspapers? What are they going to do to you if you take power to blot out whole pages, say, of the "Irish Independent" or the "Irish Times" or to seize the whole edition? Do you think they will sit still and do nothing? They will retaliate. They might stop the "Times," a great supporter of His Majesty's Government, going into Ireland, and then what a row there would be. They might say, "Let us have a quota, let us have reciprocity"; there is no limit to the difficulties into which you might get.

The Home Secretary may be a little vexed, but we are doing him the greatest service in warning him of these difficulties. It is amazing that he has not foreseen the pitfalls which lie before him. The whole if this Clause becomes valueless unless you take power to deal with the importation of foreign newspapers and also with what has never been mentioned before until my hon. Friend mentioned it—I confess that it had not occurred to me—the fact that everything can be disseminated by the broadcast, and that with the greatest ease millions of people in this country, between five and six million people, can listen to the whole story of the Irish Sweepstake. What a zest will be added to it when it is a way of getting round a law which carries with it no sort of public sanction. Instead of listening to the Home Secretary extolling the National Government, you will find them all listening to these other broadcasts. There will be a keen hour on the air. What is the right hon. Gentleman going to do about that? Is he going to start some great station to queer the atmosphere, set up atmospherics, to strike in with a great boom? If so, he will raise further difficulties. Nothing is more dangerous than an illusory attack on liberty. Under the Liberal impulse this poor, unforeseeing Government is being drawn step by step into a series of confusions, contradictions and muddles, which will make it the laughing stock of the country.

[Much later] I think my right hon. Friend the Home Secretary should give some more effectual answer to this point than he has done. It is no use simply saying, "We did not mean to deal with it, and we are not going to deal with it, and it is not convenient, so we do not put it in, and we shall carry out our Clause, and, if you do not like it, we shall ring the bell and bring in our majority." That is not the way to deal with this matter. What is there behind it? I speak with complete ignorance of this matter. I am just an ordinary Member of the House of Commons who has never taken part in a football pool. I have at other times, I believe, been drawn into other forms of this particular vice, notably when I have been encouraged by the Noble Lady opposite to take an interest in the running of horses on the turf, but—

The Chairman: I ruled just now that we must not repeat the Debate which we have already had on this question. Therefore, although the question was pertinent up to a certain point, I do not think I can allow it to be continued.

Mr. Churchill: With very great respect, Sir Dennis, you have put the Question, "That the Clause stand part of the Bill," and the Clause contains a most important provision exempting from the scope of the Bill a particular form of gambling, which we are told is of a most vicious, injurious and detrimental character. No answer of any kind that I have heard has been given. We have to submit to that, but surely we are entitled to argue that no answer whatever has been given except that it is not convenient to deal with it. There are all sorts of suggestions that there has been some sort of deal, some sort of political pressure, that there has been voting strength behind this, that there is influence, and powerful influence, at work. Then we have to consider how that sort of talk, which I trust could all be dispersed—I hoped the Home Secretary would have dispersed it with a gesture—is all coupled up with the fine professions which the Government make, and made to us last night. We heard what a horrible thing it was for a man who had been Chancellor of the Exchequer to suggest that you might have a national sweep on the Derby. We must have some principle in this matter, and for my part one of the things which has led me to take an interest in this Measure is the smug hypocrisy which animates so many of its provisions, which on the one hand buys off people by riveting gambling in the most poisonous form on the people, and on the other hand pretends that this is an anti-gambling Bill.

[Later, on Clause 28–Penalties for offences under this Act and forfeitures] This is a serious position for the House of Commons to take up. No doubt it has bound itself to take this position by all that has gone before. We are, as we have been told throughout the day, creating new offences, making new criminals, furnishing new candidates for our penal establishments. We have passed with a gesture another Clause which must be read in connection with this one, giving the right of intrusion into the dwelling-house on a new set of pretexts. All these steps are being taken one after another; the House of Commons would not dream in its collective capacity of offering any resistance to the will of the Government. Now we have to pass Clause 28, which contains very heavy penalties. For a first offence there is a severe fine and imprisonment—the prison taint is to be inflicted for a first offence on summary conviction, and there is to be a fine not exceeding £100. In the cases of a second or any subsequent conviction the imprisonment may be for a term not exceeding three months and under Sub-section (2) the fine rises to £500 and the imprisonment goes up to one year—one year's imprisonment for those guilty people who break this law by participating in a national Derby sweepstake, who mingle with such a wicked affair.

It is quite all right in the case of football; it is quite safe in the case of the little lotteries and so forth. That is perfectly all right. There is not the slightest moral foundation for these invasions that are being made on liberty—I do not mean the liberty to gamble, but the liberty to live, to walk freely in the street, the liberty of your fellow-man. It is nothing but a deal. On these grounds I think the House ought to consider, with very much more gravity than it has, a Clause like this. One of the greatest difficulties which they have to face in the United States is the enormous volume of legislation, which is poured out like a mill by all the legislatures every year. We are getting into the same sort of mood here. The Government have only to put up a Bill, get it on to the lines of the House, turn their machinery on it, and it goes through. I believe that the penalties which are inflicted in this Clause set the stamp upon the Bill; they show the gravity, the bite that there is in it; and when we take the whole situation as presented to us to-day—the first time that this part of the Bill has really been brought under the dissection of the House of Commons—we cannot but feel that an injury is being done to our national life without the slightest warrant of moral justification.

[Later] I do not think there is very much difference between the Committee and the Home Secretary. We have had a discussion which was rather stormy at times, and there have been passages and interchanges, but it seems that towards the close we have got to a close measure of agreement on this point, and I was delighted to hear my right hon. Friend say that he shared the sentiment which had been so generally expressed in the Committee that although in the case of the promoters of illegal action there should be a financial penalty—and not only a financial penalty—sufficient to prove an effective deterrent, that nevertheless we should not bring scores of thousands of humble people, our fellow countrymen, into a position where we say to them: "Ah, you have done something which lays you open to a penalty of six months imprisonment"—or something of that sort. I thought the proposal made by my hon. Friend the Member for Barnstaple (Sir B. Peto), which was taken up so handily, if I may say so, by the hon. Member speaking from the Opposition Front Bench, and put forward in a very soothing fashion, had brought us to a point where some definite step forward might be taken. Therefore, I hope that my right hon. Friend will not shrink from the labour involved between now and the Report stage in dividing the penalties into two categories. It is not a difficult thing to do, with the staff and plant of a Government Department at his disposal, and with the aid, readily forthcoming, of the most accomplished Law Officers. There could be no difficulty in assigning the severe penalties to certain Clauses of the Bill and to have inserted elsewhere penalties for the smaller offenders. I take it from what the right hon. Gentleman has said that he is contemplating some such procedure. The Noble Lady need not look at me in that manner.

Viscountess Astor: We are all agreed. We can go home.

Mr. Churchill: The Noble Lady has all day long been engaged in pious works, and she ought not to weary in well doing.

Viscountess Astor: There is a disadvantage in being a teetotaller.

Mr. Churchill: I hope the Noble Lady is not going to delay the proceedings. It would be a great pity if, at the moment when we are in a more genial atmosphere, she should be the one to strike a jarring note. I hope the Home Secretary will seriously take into consideration the suggestion that the severe penalties should be reserved for those who commit large scale offences.

"A VERY OLD MAN"
(THE SOCIALISTS AND INDIA)

November 8, 1934

Constituency Meetings,
Harlow and Roydon

I am now a very old man. In a very few weeks I will attain my 60th birthday. Having held great offices of State for nearly a quarter of a century, I am quite indifferent as to whether I hold public office again or not. I will not think of doing so unless I am absolutely sure that I will do some good, and that it is my duty to do so. I rejoice to occupy an entirely independent position, where I am not called upon to bow the knee to anyone, and where I can give any fruits I have gathered of experience and knowledge to the service of the country.

I made my present object the defeat of the Socialist Party. They have to be beaten, or at any rate, if not beaten, they have to be held so closely that they can not do the mischief that they otherwise would do.

Mr. Baldwin said the other day that they must not go back to a party dog-fight, but the dog-fight is on now. The Socialist Party and the Liberal Party are attacking us night and day. There was a good dog-fight in the County Council and municipal elections, and at Lambeth and Swindon the other day. But what we have to consider is what is their dog going to do.

In Epping I am not going to run for protection to Mr. Ramsay MacDonald or to Sir John Simon. I think they should stand on their own Tory basis and welcome the adhesion of men and good will. The way to deal with these two dogs is to show them a little of the snarl, growl, and bite of the British bulldog.

If we are to spend the whole of 1935, the last year of this Parliament, in a desperate attempt by the Government, with the aid of Socialists and the Liberals, to carry a scheme of responsible home rule for all India, then it seems to me that, whatever may happen to that scheme, the mere process of crushing out those who will not agree to it and trying to force the Conservative Party to do the opposite to what it has been constituted to do may indeed produce the most serious injury and division.

You hear people say that we must not split the party over India. I quite agree, but that counsel should be addressed to those who brought forward the new policy introduced by the Socialists. My hope is that we shall succeed in winning the two battles we have to fight. The first is to defeat the policy of Abdication at the centre in India, and the second is to beat the Socialists. I hope we shall get rid of the first and then all join together for the second. That is what I am working for.

AIR DEFENCE

November 9, 1934

Constituency Meeting, Chingford

[Extract] ... The situation in the world to-day is far worse than before the Great War. Our greatest and most immediate danger is from the air.

[Editor's Note: Referring to the debate in the House of Commons on the activities of the armament firms he said]: The Socialists and Liberals are making a great outcry about this, and it is one of the many methods by which they hope to keep the country in its present dangerously undefended condition. The real inquiry ought to be into the alarming decline of our means of making weapons to defend us should danger come. Before the War we had enormous plants on the Clyde, on the Tyne, at Barrow, and at Coventry which undoubtedly enabled us to equip and expand our Navy and make heavy cannons at a rate which our enemies had not taken fully into account. But even so our unpreparedness to equip the millions of volunteers who beseiged the recruiting offices made an enormous prolongation of the War necessary.

Every one then alive remembers the agonies our troops went through before the Ministry of Munitions really began to function upon a great scale. Now the situation is far worse than before the Great War. We are much less prepared and have much smaller plants in being, while every other large country is prepared for emergencies upon a scale undreamed of even by the most militarist nations in 1914. Throughout Germany, France, and Italy every factory is thoroughly organized to turn over at a few hours' notice, on the mere receipt of a telegram, from peaceful manufacture to war production. Those who make sewing machines would make machine-guns. Those who make motors would make tanks. Those who make perfumes would make poison gas. Those who make chemicals would make explosives, and so on. The whole hideous process has been studied with infinite care upon the Continent.

All the knowledge and experience so dearly bought in the last War has been turned to account. In a few hours, by the pressing of a button, the whole of Germany can be turned on to one sole, single purpose—namely, the production of death-dealing machinery. Is this really the moment in our country to try to break down the few armament factories which in a wofully shrunken condition still have survived the long process of British disarmament?

As to America, although they are separated by oceans on either side of their vast self-contained country from any danger, they are building a fleet upon an unexampled scale.

Our greatest and most immediate danger is however, from the air. In spite of the plainest warnings and the most menacing facts, the whole of this year has been wasted by the Government, and next year our position would become one of marked inferiority to Germany. Now Mr. MacDonald has begun to recognize that the spectacle of a great country with vast Possessions and interests all over the world, and so weak in self-defence as to invite attack and make itself a prey and bait to hungry, ruthless rivals, is a new factor in the increasing danger and instability of Europe.

My dearest wish and main object in public life is never to see another war. But it is a melancholy fact that we are at the present time in grievous and increasing danger. With Mr. MacDonald's policy—as Socialist Prime Minister or as Nationalist Prime Minister—we have sensibly aggravated our position. In all these circumstances, I have resolved to put down an amendment to the address upon air defence which is closing in upon us.

[Editor's Note: After referring to the fact that the report of the Joint Select Committee would be made public in a few days, he said]: The most interesting and momentous point of immediate importance on India is the attitude of Mr. Baldwin. The immediate course of British politics rests with him. If he decides that he will use his control of the party machine and party funds to force the Conservative Party to become the active agents of a policy of federal home rule in India, to which their convictions and their traditions are alike profoundly opposed, he would incur the sole responsibility for the melancholy consequences which would ensue to the great organization which has followed him so faithfully and so long.

The interests of all the peoples of India, all the races and religions of a population of 350,000,000 are also at stake. The abdication of British control at the centre of Indian government, however safeguarded during what is called a period of transition, would bring upon these helpless millions miseries and confusion, before which the world would stand amazed and of which the British nation would be forever ashamed.

BETTING AND LOTTERIES BILL

November 12, 1934

House of Commons

I ask myself with some surprise whether this is really all the Government have to say in answer to the speeches we have heard from every quarter of the House in criticism of their proposals and in advocacy of this alternative. The hon. and learned Gentleman the Solicitor-General made us an agreeable speech, showing a high degree of Ministerial precocity, which I am quite sure was not at all unwelcome to the House, but he in no way attempted to face the broad, main, popular, public issue which is at stake to-day. I would first address myself to the Labour party, His Majesty's official Opposition. We have heard two voices from those benches to-day. I do not say that in reproach, but am using it to reinforce my appeal. The right hon. Gentleman the Leader of the Opposition is now in his place, and I will address my remarks very particularly to him, because I have not the slightest doubt that his authority will produce unity among those whom he leads—not perhaps on every question, but I am sure on this.

A sort of argument has been put forward that the Labour party should vote for the Government on this point of the searching of workmen's and other people's dwellings out of revenge for votes which were given by Conservatives on the Disaffection Bill. I feel sure that any man who is considering his public duty with calmness and composure will see that that argument ought not to weigh with him at all. I shall show later that there is no logic in it, but, apart from that, it is certainly not right that a representative of a working-class constituency should address himself to a topic of this kind in that spirit. We are not here to score off each other—or, rather, we may score off each other, but, ultimately, what happens here affects the lives of the people who send us here and to whom we are answerable and responsible.

There is another misconception into which an hon. Member who spoke from the second bench below the Gangway seems to have drifted. He appeared to proceed under the supposition that the doctrine that an Englishman's home is an Englishman's castle had come into existence with the present democratic constitution of this country. Far from it. It existed long before the vote had been extended even beyond the narrowest class, and is deeply ingrained in all of us. I put it to the Leader of the Opposition, who all his life has fought for liberty, that it is a melancholy fact that during the period when the Socialist forces have gained great recognition there has also been—not by their wish—a concomitant and simultaneous inroad upon the liberty of the subject which is very grievous, and they owe it to themselves and to their movement, in view of what is taking place all over the world, to be particularly careful, on all questions which arise, to preserve the liberty of the individual. Certainly they ought; and I am sure they could not allow a difference between two parties in the House upon the Disaffection Bill to bias them in giving sincere and frank consideration, and that is all I am asking, to this particular Measure.

This is class legislation of the most objectionable character. Rich people have not the slightest difficulty in gambling to their heart's content. The provisions of the Bill make it perfectly clear that the Carlton Club, and, I dare say, the National Liberal Club—although I do not often go there—will have every facility to conduct their sweeps. Everything is done to make it easy for those who are in a well-to-do position. The old Betting Acts were passed 100 years ago, and in those old days betting was an aristocratic thing and it was thought that the working classes had to be kept in good order. Their betters could do what they pleased, but it was not for the working class to have such indulgences. I am addressing myself entirely to the Opposition benches, and I suggest that they should think about all these matters before they decide to give a vote against what I may call the fair rights of the ordinary man to have his home respected.

Take the question of the domicile. We are asked to authorise a new intrusion into the domicile. It is very serious to treat that as trivial, and to say that it does not matter and that the people concerned are only poor workpeople. It does matter. I see that the Under-Secretary of State is shaking his head. He will be able to speak presently, and he had better keep that valuable organ in a state of repose. Look at this question of a constable entering a home; never mind whether he is a "common or garden" constable. That was not said in any disrespect about our admirable police force, and I am glad that the Solicitor-General realised that he could not make that quite cheap point with any effect. How would the Home Secretary [Sir John Gilmour] like to have a constable entering his home? He might be out of office in a year and a half. How would he like a constable coming to his door and someone coming up to his study and saying: "There is a policeman at the door with a search warrant. We do not know whether he is common or garden or not, but here he is with a search warrant"?

That constable might search for one thing and he might light on another thing. I am not afraid that the Home Secretary has anything more to conceal than any of us, but I put it to him that he would feel insulted. So would any of these hon. Gentlemen here. Is it not a greater injury to the ordinary working man, in his cottage standing in a long row of streets? He lives so close to his neighbours, who see everything and see everybody arrive. When the constable comes to the house, they do not know what it is about. All they know is that the police are after him. The policeman comes in and rummages his house, looking through everything that is there. It is a very serious thing. In these days, people ought not to worry too much about party feelings and that kind of thing, when it comes to firmly holding on to the good old liberties which have been build up in this island and which, thank God, we have been able, to a large extent, to preserve.

The question comes as to how you compare the procedure which is adopted in this Bill with the procedure of the Incitement to Disaffection Bill. My hon. Friend has moved that the same procedure shall be applied to this Bill as Parliament insisted upon being applied to the Disaffection Bill. There are great differences between the two. The first Bill affected very few people. Not a great number of people want to throw a seditious leaflet over the wall of a barracks. There is happily very little danger of that, but the offence is grave. It was agreed that a judge of the High Court should deal with the offence of trying to cause disaffection among the troops. But here is an offence which everybody admits is trivial, that of trafficking in lotteries or breaking the law in regard to sweepstakes—being guilty of the crime of sweepstake-mongering. This new offence upon which we are invited to turn the whole battery of British law is regarded by most people as exceedingly trivial. There is not one of us, if he searches his conscience, who will not find that there was some moment in his life when he trespassed over the strict line which divides gambling from earning.

This is a very trivial offence, and, if the Bill be passed, nobody will think any the worse of those who take part in lotteries, although the Bill will affect enormous numbers of people. That is the point. How many homes are you exposing to these inroads? Under the Disaffection Bill you could count the number in a period of five years on your fingers, but under this Bill there will be thousands, or scores of thousands of search warrants, and magistrates all over the place will be beseiged by enthusiasts—Liberal enthusiasts, who are not only found in this House but have their representatives in the constituencies—who, with all the fanaticism and energy of prohibition fanatics, will be busily trying to stop this terrible evil while a world of misery is surging around them. I daresay that magistrates will be signing thousands of these search warrants in the course of a year. If that be not so, let us take measures to make sure that it is not so. Opening all these cases where the domicile may be violated by the entry of a police officer, and where exposure and injury will be done by such an event occurring, is incomparably more injurious to our society than the successful sale of ten thousand lottery tickets. I put that to the sense of the House, for hon. Members to consider with some attention.

You have lost your sense of proportion. Because you have great power, and by ringing a bell you can bring in an enormous brigade—an army corps—you set yourselves and you say that you will appeal to the sense of the House. You will appeal to the sense of those who were not in the House. You will bring them in, and because you can do that and imagine that all power is at your disposal, you feel inclined to have your will enforced in a manner which goes beyond the spirit of the times in a matter so small. You must keep your search warrants for the safety of the State and for the detection of brutal and villainous crime. You should not extend them, as you are doing in this Bill, to matters which are considered to be petty and venial by the vast mass of your fellow countrymen. I say to hon. Gentlemen who sit on the Government benches—not because they may have been impressed by some of the advocacy which has come from the Liberal benches—that there is nothing that those gentleman would like better than to see the Conservative party put itself in the position where it is weakened by associating itself with this legislation. Having advocated it for their special anti-gambling purposes they will not hesitate to go about the country and prate liberty on the largest scale.

Mr. T. Williams: I think hon. Gentlemen should welcome the return of the Liberal Member for Epping (Mr. Churchill) who has brought back recollections of 25 years ago when he was just as irresponsible as any Member could be. He certainly ought to know all about the Liberal party's acrobatics in regard to liberty and freedom as well as their alphabet from A to Z. The right hon. Gentleman rather issues a challenge to hon. Members on these benches—

Mr. Churchill: An appeal.

[Later] I was much perplexed and even intrigued to know what was the real explanation of this football pool story. When we were discussing this matter in Committee it seemed to be wrapped in clouds of mist, and nothing was forthcoming from the Treasury Bench in any way to throw a light upon it, but now we are indebted to the Home Secretary [Sir John Gilmour] for a very frank and, if I may say so, a very naive explanation of the principles and reasons which have guided His Majesty's Government in taking the decision which they have to ignore football pools on this occasion. What is the explanation of my right hon. Friend? It is that it would have been unpopular. Here is an admission with regard to what is on the whole perhaps the worst form of gambling which is now current in the country, which is not only confined to football pools, but apparently, as the Home Secretary indicates, is shortly going to spread to racing, cricket, and other spheres. From the revelations which have been made by hon. Members, and by the hon. Gentleman opposite, undeterred apparently by the scurrilous letters that he has received—and I do not think a Member of Parliament ought to be disturbed by scurrilous letters; we should have stopped long ago if we had been disturbed by that sort of thing—the hon. Gentleman has pointed out, with very considerable knowledge of this matter, the kind of way in which the ordinary unsuspecting man in the street is fleeced, is swindled, in many cases—I do not say by any means in all cases—and how, even when he wins a prize, there is some catch in it.

I do not attempt to sit in judgment upon this particular form of gambling, but it seems to be admitted in all parts of the House—the Home Secretary drew the attention of those concerned in the Press to the fact—that this is an extremely unsatisfactory and deleterious form of gambling. Unfortunately for us, the public, but fortunately for the people engaged in this, they have already got a sufficient amount of backing and bristles for it not to be the kind of topic that the Home Secretary, acting on behalf of His Majesty's Government, cares to touch. This is a hedgehog, a porcupine, prickly, and so the right hon. Gentleman recoils. He has indeed unwittingly been drawn very near to this dangerous animal. The unsuspecting Marquess of Londonderry, in another place, had actually put out his hand to touch or even to strike the creature, but he very soon, warned by the Administration, drew it back. "No, we are reformers, we are going to deal with the evils of betting, we are not going to allow the demoralisation which follows on a Derby sweep. No, in order to stop that, we will not hesitate to enter dwellings, to black out the newspapers, to issue every kind of warrant, to enforce the most severe penalties." All that can be done, but this is another matter. "There is something in this which really would make it inadvisable to go any further. We should have to be very careful in a matter of this kind. We thought it all over very carefully, and we decided that this was an ugly customer that we did not want to tackle."

Where is your principle? Where is your policy? What right have you, when you run away like this, to come up and play the heavy father to this country and tell us what a shameful thing it is to ask that a Derby sweep should be legalised? Rather than do that, you are prepared to set up a vast gimcrack apparatus of oppression and restriction. I am amazed at the mess the Government have got into over this matter, and all their majority will not wipe this out. The people of this country are very much interested in this matter. If there were a principle in the matter, I think the Government would have some chance, but obviously there is no principle. It is simply a case of push as far as you can and as far as you dare. Where the thing can be kicked, it is kicked, but where it cannot be kicked, the Government bolt. They have bolted away from the football pool, and they imagine they can win back a reputation for consistency by enacting all kinds of severe restrictions and penalties upon a far less injurious form of a national practice which they will never be able to stop. I think it is a most lamentable matter, and I am very, very sorry for the right hon. Gentleman, whose personal character is so high and whose good nature, courage, and good will have been shown in many fields and in many ways for many years. I am very sorry for him, that he has so shortsightedly and unwittingly allowed himself to be let into a position where, neither from the point of view of popularity nor from the point of view of principle, has he a leg to stand upon.

[Later] I beg to move, "That further consideration of the Bill, as amended, be now adjourned."

I rise for the purpose of inquiring from the Government what their intentions are in regard to our further procedure to-night, and also to make them a suggestion which I trust may abridge our labours. We have now been at this Bill since Question Time, and we have not yet reached the first Clause of the Report stage of this long and complicated Measure. Any one who has been here through the hours of this Debate will know there has been nothing in the nature of obstruction. One speech after another has been informative, and I am certain that those who have been in charge of this Bill know more about its dangers and pitfalls than they did when they presented it to the House. The Amendment Paper is heavily loaded with matter which can be fertile of discussion and we have not yet begun consideration of the first Clause. I want to know from the Government how long they propose to sit. Will they really go on till 4 or 5 or 6 o'clock in the morning? Their Division Lobby will, no doubt, be sufficiently well furnished to carry their Measure through, but surely it would be better to take a more reasonable view of the position as it has developed since this Bill has been brought effectually under the scrutiny of the House of Commons, and I suggest to my right hon. Friend the Home Secretary a course which would be very much in his interests and in the interests of the Government, namely, that he should be willing to drop Part II of this Bill altogether. That is not only the opinion of the House but the opinion of the country.

There is no need to indulge in any apologetics. The right hon. Gentleman and the House are approaching the end of this Session and the beginning of what promises to be a very arduous new Session. He has dealt with an important aspect of this problem, and this other one, the question of this severe legislation against national sweepstakes, could well stand over and be treated in a private Member's Bill next year, when hon. Members would get an opportunity to look at it according to the opinion of their constituents—and the feeling of Members themselves—without its being mixed up with a Government Measure or the Government being mixed up with any of the popularity or unpopularity which may flow from it. A really sensible step, and one which I venture to suggest my right hon. Friend would be showing real statecraft to take, would be to let us have Part I, with any necessary penalty Clauses which are in

Part III, and to drop Part II, and let it be a subject of reconsideration next year in view of the opinion which has developed in Parliament and elsewhere. If he does that, I am certain the proceedings can be wound up in a very easy and convenient manner, and there will be no need for the recriminatory and comminatory summings-up which otherwise will be necessary in order to acquaint the country of the confusion which exists. Considering what admissions the right hon. Gentleman has made about football pools and so forth, he really is not in a position to come out on the high morality side. I ask the right hon. Gentleman, in considering this proposal, not to think of his pride. Pride is a very evil thing in conducting a Bill. It is far better to defer to the unerring instinct of the House of Commons, which never is wrong upon these matters, and, after all, it is the duty of the House to apprise Ministers of the position. I trust the right hon. Gentleman will consider this point, and if he agrees, I have no doubt we shall very soon end the proceedings; but, if not, I would like to know how long he proposes to keep the House sitting to-night.

[Later] My right hon. Friend will not be under any delusion on the situation in which he and his Bill now stand. He seems to think he holds some sort of whip over us. Really what he says is: "If you do not neglect your duty of discussing all the questions which arise on the Report stage, then you will not be allowed to have a proper debate on the Third Reading." But supposing that the House chooses to discuss, and thinks it is its duty to discuss, these matters all through to-morrow and to-morrow night, and right on till the next day, then the right hon. Gentleman will not be able to enforce the Third Reading debate, and all his attempts to push matters forcibly upon the House may be brought to a standstill. I think he would be well advised to allow the proceedings to be terminated now. We have only reached Clause 1 so far, and he wants to get, in the small hours of the morning, another 15 Clauses. There are a great many Amendments on the Paper besides those which he has put down, and there are many points of interest and importance which will have to be discussed; but there are other reasons, apart from keeping the House up till two or three o'clock to get a few more Clauses to-night, which I would ask my right hon. Friend to consider, and which I would ask the Government to consider. It seems to me that this is a matter where my right hon. Friend should have some consultation with the Leader of the House.

I do not know why the Leader of the House is not present. He ought to be present. I have often seen the House in great difficulties because it does not have superior guidance given it at critical junctures, the Departmental Minister unable to take his eyes off the immediate present, his *amour propre* excited and his obstinacy aroused, driving the House into a very difficult position. Those are the times when I have again and again seen the Prime Minister come in and say "You must not do this." I strongly recommend the right hon. Gentleman to press this proposition no further. If he attempts to do so, I do not think he will make progress in proportion to the labour and inconvenience that will be caused. As for to-morrow, I hope before we come to-morrow he will have had an opportunity of taking better advice.

[Later] I do not think that is at all a satisfactory explanation. I must say I was surprised that the Home Secretary should not be able to explain it and to put the House in a proper position to decide on the point. This is a question which stands in a peculiar position, because, as the hon. Member for South Croydon (Mr. H. Williams) reminded the House, it was never discussed in Committee of the whole House. That shows the slovenly manner in which this Bill has been conducted. Here is the right hon. Gentleman who during an enormous period in Committee upstairs never detected an obvious discrepancy and incongruity between the wording of Clause 1 and of Clause 20. It is astonishing that he should have overlooked a thing like that. I suppose that the right hon. Gentleman has been so busy adjusting all the little interior questions or is so buoyant with his feeling of the high morality that he has established and the blows that he has struck against gambling in this country that little matters like defining the actual year—which is of real importance in this matter—are out of his mind.

I still do not understand his preference for the word "year" instead of "calendar year." I think that "calendar year" would be much better; it is more precise. Evidently when this Bill emerged from the machine it was considered that it should be the calendar year, and I am sure that the Noble Lady the Member for the Sutton Division (Viscountess Astor) will agree with me. I do not see why this Bill should be weakened by the abolition of an expression which has a most respectable tradition attached to it. "Calendar year" is clear and plain to me. The word "year" leaves it doubtful as to whether it may not be the Income Tax or the financial year; but the calendar year is a year that corresponds most accurately to the movement of the celestial bodies and will enable us best to deal with this difficult matter. I am most anxious as the House has been discussing very seriously the question of 104 or 130 days that we should know if by substituting the word "year" for "calendar year" any complications may arise. I should like to hear the views of the hon. Member for the Scotland Division of Liverpool (Mr. Logan) on this matter. We must know the reason why the word "calendar" is to be struck out. I hope we shall not dismiss the matter in a hurry. I think we ought to stand by the word, and I shall vote in the Lobby for its retention. I feel that I should be able to make up my mind on the subject with more conviction if I had a fuller explanation of how the different interests are affected by this change. It would also be a great advantage if the Under-Secretary of State for the Home Office who has been sitting silent all the day would display those brilliant talents that have won him advancement and would give us some clear reason in support of it. After all, we have heard little from the Home Secretary, and I must say that when he chooses to speak he never attempts to bully the House. He just attempts to overlay it, bringing pressure to lay down on top of it, crushing the life out of it in the most friendly and genial manner. I can understand his desire to do right and to get rid of the word "calendar," because he wants to lighten the Bill. If he wants to get on he should lighten it still further and get rid of Part II. However, in the absence of a fuller assurance as to the effect of this Amendment I shall feel it my duty to vote against the deletion of the word "calendar."

[Later] I think it would be in the interests of progress if I again inquired at this stage, after another two hours have passed, if the Home Secretary would let us know what his ideas are as to the amount of political pressure he intends to put on the House to-night. In order not to break into the discussion which is now in progress, I would ask leave to move the adjournment of the Debate.

Mr. Speaker: I could not accept that Motion now. If the right hon. Gentleman cares to ask the Home Secretary how long he is going on, I should raise no objection.

Mr. Churchill: Of course, Mr. Speaker, I am bound by your ruling. Therefore, I will put a question to the right hon. Gentleman and ask him how long he intends to go on. Nevertheless, I would submit to you, Sir, for your ruling, that, although you may not be prepared to accept the Motion if related to some inquiry as to the intentions of the Government in respect of business, you might perhaps be prepared to accept it on the ground that it is high time that the Leader of the House was here. Are we to be left in an unprotected position, entirely at the mercy of a Departmental chief, who has not only lost his head in regard to the Measure—no, I will not say lost his head, but who has lost his sense of relationship to the House and to his fellow Members? Would you, then, Sir, accept the Motion if I put it in these terms?

Mr. Speaker: No, am afraid I could not accept it on those terms either.

Mr. Churchill: With very great respect, I was not going against your ruling in any way, but, having put my question, I was returning to the question under Debate and to the speech of the Under-Secretary. I was proceeding to point out what he has said about the complications of this provision for 104 days, and so on.

Mr. Speaker: The right hon. Gentleman misunderstood me. If he is making a speech, it must be founded on something. I could not allow him to move the adjournment, and I said he must confine himself to merely asking the question.

Mr. Churchill: May I ask for your ruling, Sir. If I confine myself to merely asking how far the Minister is going, shall I exhaust my right to speak on the Amendment?

Mr. Speaker: No, the right hon. Gentleman will not have exhausted his speech on the Amdenment now before the House.

Mr. Churchill: Then I will confine myself strictly to asking the Home Secretary how far he intends to go.

Sir W. Davison: On a point of Order. You, Sir, have said that it is customary for the Leader of the Opposition to raise this point. Are you aware that the Socialist Opposition have on this matter become the supporters of the Government and that it is the people on this side of the House who wish to make the inquiry? The Lord President of the Council or the Prime Minister said, when I asked him, that he was aware that the Eleven o'Clock Rule had been suspended every night since the House resumed, and I asked him whether he intended to force things through.

Mr. Speaker: That has nothing to do with the Question before the House.

Sir J. Gilmour: We are discussing this group of Amendments. We have now had a considerable discussion upon them, and I should hope than an early decision will be reached. One is a drafting Amendment of mine, and on Clause 7 there is another drafting Amendment. Then there is an Amendment which I understand an hon. Member wishes to move, and a further drafting Amendment follows on Clause 16. I shall be quite satisfied if we reach Clause 16. The Amendments in my name are really drafting Amendments.

Sir W. Davison: Why not leave them until to-morrow?

Mr. Churchill: I expected that answer, and I propose now to deal with the subject before the House. We understand from the right hon. Gentleman that we are to go on. I wish to deal with the speech delivered by the Under-Secretary in which he described the discussion of the issues before us—104 days, eight hours each day, and what he prefers to call—using a very vulgar and common expression borrowed, apparently, from the gambling dens of Chicago—the rake-off of 6 per cent. He explained that if any one part of this meticulously studied and most beautifully balanced system were deranged or disturbed, everything else would have to be disturbed. For instance, if the 104 days had been 130, then I suppose the races that take place would have had to be reduced or increased and that would have had its effect on the rake-off. I think it is very demoralising to see the way in which His Majesty's Government have gone into the gambling system.

The discussion on this subject really raises the issue how far we are to consider it our duty to favour the development of dog racing in this country. I do not agree with my hon. Friend opposite, for I look with a tolerant eye on the establishment of this system. As a matter of fact, this is a frightfully important Clause for it is the motive power of the Bill. It is this charter to the dogs which is giving the right hon. Gentleman a great measure of support in carrying forward his proposals. It is a very unsatisfactory state of affairs. I cannot complain at all. The Under-Secretary has given us a very full explanation—the kind of explanation to which the Chief Whip takes exception because of its length. At any rate, it was very clear; in fact, so clear that I turned to the hon. Member beside me, and said: "I believe that he has been put up to kill his own Bill, but that cannot be true." I hope it may be possible for us to have a gleam of light on our discussions before the sun enters the Chamber for it would be very refreshing. If you go across the Channel, you will see that dogs are used to draw carts; but, although it has always been considered an unusual method of using dogs in this country, that is the principle on which this Bill is based.

[Later] However this matter may be viewed—and I think the explanation of the Home Secretary was very exiguous and lacking in clarity—it is perfectly clear that the point raised is due to carelessness in the preparation of the Bill. Why have we had to wait for these drafting Amendments to be introduced? We have been all through the Committee stage, and why was it not put right before, seeing that it was an original error in the Bill? Here these words "adjoining district" which the House was invited to carry in the Committee stage are now found quite unsuitable. The right hon. Gentleman has explained that they might be thought to relate to a racing track, whereas they relate to municipal or other political boundaries drawn between different districts. How is it that this has previously escaped the attention of the Home Secretary? Does he not go through the Clauses with his draftsmen in the morning? It is an extraordinary thing that this sort of drafting Amendment should be introduced at the last minute? If the House had not examined the matter very carefully, I doubt if such Amendments would have ever been put in. When I looked at this matter in the first place before hearing the statement of the Home Secretary, I said that this was mere pedantry, and I asked myself: "Why is the House being kept up at this hour on such a nicety of language and what is the refinement of meaning to discriminate the one proposal from the other."

Now that we have heard the explanation, it seems to me much more than a drafting Amendment. It is an Amendment of substance which would never have been discovered but for the careful attention which the House has given to the matter. The omission seems to indicate a lower standard in the preparation of details than is customary. I fear the present generation of Ministers falls far short of former days. I remember being brought up in Opposition under the guidance of the late Lord Balfour and seeing how that great man prepared Bills, and the hours he used to spend with his draftsmen going through them systematically and cross-examining the draftsmen on every doubtful point so that when the Bill came before the House he was complete master of it. Here we have the right hon. Gentleman treating us rather harshly, and yet he says that these are mere drafting words. Every footprint he has left behind him to-night is a sign of inadequate attention to the task for which he has assumed the responsibility of guiding this House.

[Later] Before the right hon. Gentleman [Sir John Gilmour] rises I beg to move, "That further Consideration of the Bill, as amended, be now adjourned."

I venture now at three o'clock, when more than three hours have passed since the matter was put to you, Mr. Speaker, to submit again a Motion for adjournment. I venture, very respectfully, to suggest to you that if the Government would make some suggestion as to how they wish to proceed we might make progress. The Home Secretary told us that all he was thinking about were mere drafting Amendments. There is one on the Order Paper, but there are two other heavy Amendments in the name of the hon. Member for the Scotland Division of Liverpool (Mr. Logan). It is quite true that the Amendment which we are now about to consider [Clause 7—Discretion of licensing authority as to grant of licenses] may not take very long, but the other two are heavy Amendments, and I do suggest to the Home Secretary that we shall certainly have to go on all through to-morrow night. That is inevitable. Then we shall have the Third Reading coming on in the early morning hours of Wednesday. If the Home Secretary really is going to try to get these Amendments to-night, it will keep us here until morning, for we have some heavy work in front of us.

Would it not be possible to take now the Amendment which the Home Secretary says is purely drafting, and, having disposed of that, come back to-morrow, for many opinions have to be reconsidered and our energies re-created. The right hon. Gentleman would then have been able to discuss these matters with the Prime Minister—if he is available—or with the Lord President of the Council.

I do not put it to the Government that they are not going to get anything out of this by taking these Amendments at about six o'clock in the morning. On the other hand, I have not the slightest doubt that if the right hon. Gentleman said he would stop at the end of Clause 7 the House would endeavour to facilitate him in winding-up his business as quickly as possible. We are certainly not resisting all these points out of any feeling of faction at all. We are really trying to show the Government that they are getting in very great embarrassment in the country. That is why we are looking at all these points with such meticulous care. I hope the right hon. Gentleman will meet us.

Mr. Isaac Foot: In view of the nature of the Debate we have had on such trifling matters as the calendar year and the rest, when obviously time was taken, not upon the substance of Amendments, but in order to delay the proceedings—

Mr. Churchill: On a point of Order. The hon. Gentleman has no right to say that. I submit it has frequently been ruled unparliamentary to suggest that action has been taken to delay the proceedings. The hon. Member has no right whatever to say it and it is really intolerable at this late hour of the night.

Mr. Speaker: Was the right hon. Gentleman appealing to me?

Mr. Churchill: Yes. I am complaining of the charge of deliberate dilatory conduct.

Mr. Speaker: I have heard these charges often made before.

[Later] Captain Crookshank: I beg to move, in page 7, line 25, after "Act," to insert: "or under the First Schedule to this Act."

My right hon. Friend said just now that these were largely drafting Amendments. The right hon. Member for Epping (Mr. Churchill) has said that he and I must share the blame, because this is consequential on Clause 6, which went through in the Committee stage. It was partly my fault not to have seen that it was inserted there. The right hon. Gentleman was not present when we discussed it, so he may share the blame too. In Clause 7 we are dealing with cases in which licences are refused and where an applicant has been convicted of any of the offences under the Act or with falsifying or other dishonesty. By error we omitted the offences under Schedule 1, such as refusal to give full information regarding the working of the totalisators. I am sure the right hon. Gentleman would agree that a person who has done these things is not suitable to be given a licence to carry on either dog racing or a totalisator. It is only a drafting Amendment, but I may tell the House that the next Amendment in my right hon. Friend's name uses the same words for the same reason in the Clause dealing with the revocation of licences.

Mr. Churchill: I must admit that I stand rebuked by my hon. and gallant Friend. I think the remarks he has made about the slurring over of this point in the Committee stage—and he has frankly taken his share of the blame—are fully justified in so far as they cast some aspersion on me. I was not in my place in the Committee stage. Indeed, I must confess that at that time I was not at all informed about the enormities which this Bill contains; otherwise I should have been in my place. The hon. and gallant Gentleman has referred to my absence, and I can only express to the House in terms of unaffected sincerity my extreme regret. In the meantime, the hon. and gallant Gentleman has made this reproach on the private Member, and when it has been done in such a way as not to be offensive at all and when the Minister associates himself with the offence and in no way casts an invidious comparison as to the relative apportionment of the blame to be borne between us, I can assure him that, while I accept his reproof, I bear no malice and feel but little sting. What a lesson this should be to us all. Indeed, I am grateful to him. The hour is late, and at this time of the morning the human body flags and we are overcome by the strain and stress of the day, but it is at this very moment that a stern reminder of our duty is called for. Though the flesh may be weak, a double effort of the spirit may enable us to discharge the tasks which we have to perform.

This I say by way of preliminary to addressing myself, under the exhortations of my hon. and gallant Friend, to the very serious and complicated proposals which he makes in this Amendment. He proposes in this Amendment to make a penalty applicable not only to offences under the Clause, but to offences under the First Schedule, and to throw, therefore, incontinently into the area of discussion a whole series of minor delinquencies, all of which may be made the motive power and the fulcrum upon which the decision as to licences will turn. That is not a small matter. We have been talking of these great dog race tracks and how the Government are going to make a memorial by giving a Magna Charta to the totes. Some of them have cost an enormous sum of money to erect. The shareholders' money is invested in them, and not only the money of the proprietors and the general public is affected. The employes of these tracks are very numerous. We have been told that there are 30,000 employes in the dog racing industry. Yet the refusal of a licence would automatically injure or ruin the whole of these powerful interests—capital and labour alike. Such a thing as the refusal of a licence when it comes up for periodical renewal would have the effect possibly of destroying the finances of a powerful company, it might be not only for a period of years, but they might never open again. Then the whole of the employes, who perhaps had moved into the district and had bought a house and sent their children to school in the area, would have all their educational and cultural careers interrupted suddenly and violently.

Let us see what are the kinds of offences which are concerned in this Amendment. It is all very well to say that these are only drafting Amendments and to try to get us to believe that it is not a serious matter. It is all very well of the right hon. Gentleman to show us by his silence that he is an honest man, for all the members of the Government excel in honesty, but a more candid course would be to make sure that we are not left to trip over and avoid dealing properly with points of this kind. Let me indicate some of the kinds of thing which this First Schedule deals with, and which might conceivably lead to conviction for an offence. If a man has been convicted under the First Schedule, then his licence may be revoked, and that enterprise, with all the consequential reactions which I have ventured to indicate, may be swept at a stroke from life into history. May I just ask my hon. and gallant Friend to look at the Schedule, the First Schedule, the provisions regulating the establishment of totalisators on race courses? Take paragraph 3, line 15. It reads as follows:

> The operator shall before receiving any bets in connection with any race, post in a conspicuous position on the track a notice showing the minimum stake (hereinafter referred to as the "betting unit") which will be accepted at the totalisator from persons betting on that race, and shall distribute or cause to be distributed the whole of the moneys staked on any race or races by means of the totalisator among the persons winning bets made by means of the totalisator on that race or those races, after deducting or causing to be deducted such percentage, not exceeding six per cent., as he may have specified in the said notice.

That is a very complicated procedure that this man has to carry out. He has to place the notice in a conspicuous place. Suppose he places it in a place which is not deemed to be conspicuous, and a court may decide that it was not conspicuous—and even justice may err. It is a thorough justification for a magistrate bringing down ruin, bankruptcy, squalor, and poverty on a man for an error. I read out what he had to do and how careful he had to be, and here is a point. Observe the next words in Clause 7, Sub-section (1, b):

Convicted of any offence under this Part of this Act or of any offence involving fraud or dishonesty.

These may just be ordinary, simple cases of negligence under which a conviction is obtained under this Bill.

Captain Crookshank: The right hon. Gentleman is dealing with the regulations of this Bill in the Schedule; but it has nothing to do with the Amendment. The only offences covered by the Amendment are those under Section 7.

Mr. Churchill: I am much obliged to my hon. and gallant Friend for that information, which I observed he obtained from under the Gallery [*Interruption*]. Surely we are not going to be so delicate of pussyfooted as all that. I am glad he has got the information, but I am sorry he did not have it before. Now that we know where we are, let me address myself to Section 7 of the Schedule. It says:

The accountant and his technical adviser and their respective servants authorised in that behalf in writing may, at all reasonable times, enter the premises in which the totalisator is set up, and examine any part of the mechanism and test and watch the working thereof.

Now may I ask, in regard to this important passage, what is the offence that is being aimed at? As far as I can make out, this Section is merely permissive. Is the offence which you have in view the fact that they did not exercise their option to ask for information or, if they did ask for it, that obstruction was put in their way? Now I will turn to the next point. The Under-Secretary of State, when he is asked if it refers to the persons who fail to exercise their option or to persons who refuse to facilitate him in his duty, he gives no answer at all. It is not as if he is a Minister who is not glad to give information. When he has it, he is glad to give information. [*Interruption.*] . . .

Captain Crookshank: The right hon. Gentleman has been reading from the middle of the Section. If he had read the whole of it before he started his speech, he would have had the answer.

Mr. Churchill: I do not want to mislead the House by making an imperfect quotation and I will certainly read it all:

Every person who—(*a*) obstructs the accountant or his technical adviser or any duly authorised servant of either of them in the exercise of any of the powers conferred upon him by his paragraph.

As I see it, that is an important extension of the penal Clauses and hon. Members have found it out only during the rigour of debate. Here it reads that if a person "obstructs the accountant or his technical adviser." If that is so plain, why did not the hon. and gallant Gentleman state it? I suppose he has not read it, or has forgotten it altogether. Paragraph (*b*) reads:

neglects or refuses to give to any such person as aforesaid any such information, or to produce to him any such document, as may have been called for by him in pursuance of this paragraph; or

And paragraph (*c*) reads:

> knowingly gives to any such person as aforesaid any information which is
> false or misleading.

If a man knowingly gives information which is false and misleading, he partakes of that general fraud or dishonesty. I hope I am not wearying the House.

Viscountess Astor: We are spellbound.

Mr. Churchill: I am glad to know that the noble lady has returned rested and refreshed. I shall not attempt to dilate upon paragraph (*c*), because it is quite clear that that is covered by the terms of the paragraph which refers to offences involving fraud or dishonesty. It seems to me that the first two paragraphs, (*a*) and (*b*), only amplify what is brought out in the paragraph I have just read. He gets them both ways. They are beset with difficulties and legal pitfalls. Should these persons fall into error in the discharge of their complicated duties, the error will be held to be an offence, even although it does not involve any moral turpitude, even although they leave the court with no stain upon their characters, no effect on their position in the world, on their social relations, or in their homes. All that is provided for by the words about fraud and dishonesty. Yet the fault, which is admitted to be one of error, to be one arising from the inevitable and in some way irremovable frailties and shortcomings of human nature, may be letting down these men's employers and their hapless fellow workers—indeed, ruin will be at once sudden and final.

[Later] The Parliamentary Secretary to the Treasury (Captain Margesson): I beg to move, "That further Consideration of the Bill, as amended, be now adjourned."

Mr. Churchill: On that Question, it may be convenient that we should hear from the Government a little more of the intentions they have for the conduct of this Measure. A great many people will have to make their arrangements, if they can. It will be for the public convenience that a statement should be made as to whether the Government intend in the sitting to-morrow to take, not only the Report stage, but the whole of Part II and Part III, which are also full of controversial points. Do they then intend to take the Third Reading? They cannot blame us for the Third Reading being put off to a very inconvenient time. We have got, with much toil and pain, to the point prescribed. The Home Secretary has got his Clause 16, and I hope he enjoys it. If the remaining stages of this Bill, and the Third Reading, cannot be taken at a reasonable time(I hope the right hon. Gentleman will think the matter over before we meet again. Either he should drop Part II of the Bill, or he should let the Third Reading be taken on Thursday, on the day following the discussion on the depressed areas. I understand that it would not be possible to closure the Debate on the Third Reading if we came to it after 11 o'clock. At that time the Debate is entitled to run. I think that this House will debate the Bill at great length on the Third Reading, if it is taken in the early hours. It would be important to the country that a large part of the discussion should take place during the hours of daylight when the public was here.

The right hon. Gentleman the Home Secretary has had a marvellous success—I hardly remember a more signal success—through the tact, adroitness, and grasp of his speeches. He has had the aid of the patronage Secretary. Having been victorious and trampled on his enemies, he may be more yielding. He may be content with the remaining part of the Report stage without Part II, or, if he insists on going through with the whole Bill, he may give part of Thursday to that. If he would give us three or four hours on Thursday, I have no doubt we should arrange to finish at a reasonable hour to-morrow night. If not, we shall simply have to go on fighting as well as we possibly can in order to prove to the country the injury which is being done.

BETTING AND LOTTERIES BILL

November 13, 1934

House of Commons

I venture to adumbrate, for I can do no more, to the House a suggestion which may be for the convenience of the House and the efficiency of our Debates and which I dare say would not be unacceptable to Members who took part in the long discussion of last night. In order to do so, I venture, purely, for technical reasons and to put myself in order, to move "That the Debate be now adjourned." I wish first to say that although we sat very late last night it was a very good-tempered discussion.

Hon. Members: No!

Mr. Speaker: The right hon. Gentleman cannot move that Motion, because there was no Debate in progress when he rose to speak.

Mr. Churchill: I presume, then, that this must be treated as a party conversation. I was saying that the Debate of last night although protracted was good-tempered, and for my part I certainly acknowledge the good temper which was preserved by the great majority of Members. The position which we have now reached is that we may consume the whole of to-day's sitting in the discussion of Amendments and only reach the Third Reading of the Bill in the late hours of to-night or the small hours of to-morrow morning. Thus there would not be a proper opportunity for any general discussion at all. Is there no means by which we could have a general discussion or a discussion as general as possible on Part II of the Bill? We have now reached Clause 21, the Clause which you, Sir, were about to call upon, and if it were agreeable to this House I suggest that we might have on Clause 21 a discussion covering the whole question of Part II of the Bill. That would enable a discussion on wide lines to take place, and I imagine it would greatly lighten the proceedings on the Third Reading of the Bill, although the two discussions would not be strictly analogous and would not cover exactly the same ground. Yet there would be an opportunity during the afternoon to cover the main issues raised in Part II and that should certainly abridge the discussion upon the Third Reading. I only throw that out as a suggestion which would be of advantage to the House.

Mr. Speaker: I am not sure whether the right hon. Gentleman is addressing his suggestion to me or to the Government.

Mr. Churchill: I was hopeful that I might first see that such a course would be agreeable to them, provided that you, Sir, saw fit to associate the House with it.

[Later] We are fortunate that through the flexible procedure of the House of Commons and through the interpretation which you, Sir, and the House have given to our Rules, it has been found possible upon this occasion to secure a Debate upon the issues raised in a vital portion of this Bill, and to secure that Debate during the afternoon, when it can be followed by the country. That, I think, is very satisfactory. We shall, I trust, have as long as possible, up to the time when we hope to be able to dispose of the remaining Amendments before we devote ourselves to the renewal of general discussion upon the Third Reading. In the course of this Debate not the least interesting feature has been the chastened attitude of the hon. Member for Bodmin (Mr. Isaac Foot). Only a few days ago he was here as a tyrant. Now he is apologising, I will not say for his existence, but for his general attitude, and is most anxious to persuade us that really he is no kill-joy or spoil-sport.

It very often happens that a man who, in his public life, adopts the most sour and stern and drab principles and colours, at home or in private circles is an unfailing fountain of gaiety and good fellowship, and that I have no doubt is the case with the hon. Gentleman, once he feels that he has discharged his public duty of making himself as disagreeable to his fellow mortals as he possibly can. I think I noticed that some of the criticisms which have been levelled at him from this side had made an impression upon the hon. Gentleman's inner consciousness, and I do not think that he will ever again feel entitled to speak with the same freedom and confidence in the cause of liberty after the impression which undoubtedly has been established of the truth of his position, namely, that he is in favour of everyone having the opportunity to do anything of which he does not disapprove.

The Home Secretary [Sir John Gilmour] had also emerged from this controversy with a mingled record. Certainly, I cannot retract any of the criticisms which I have made about the manner in which he has used the force of his majority and the exigencies of time to drive this Measure through the House. Also I must say that there is so much trick work in the articulation of this Bill that it is difficult to reconcile it with the candid open character of the right hon. Gentleman. The way in which one part of the Bill has been dealt with by a different procedure from other parts, the way in which the time factor has been made to work to procure decisions before they have been given that discussion which the House would like to give them, and the way in which this suggestion, the very reasonable suggestion, of an anti-Irish problem has been made to serve the cause of anti-gambling—all this argues an amount of finesse and calculation which one hoped were foreign to the character of a Minister whose simplicity and uprightness have always endeared him to the House, and especially to those who know him best. But I will say that the good temper shown by the Government and their supporters in these long Debates has been quite exceptional in my experience of the House on these occasions. I trust that it will continue as long as we have to enter into clashes upon these proposals.

Let us see what is the main criticism that can be levelled at Clause 21 and Part II of the Bill? It seems to me that the Government had two courses open to them. One was to introduce a regular anti-gambling Bill and courageously to face the unpopularity which would attach to it, to attack as boldly as they possibly could—we know that there are lengths to which one could not go—all the evils of gambling and particularly the worst and most injurious forms which gambling takes. If they had done that, they would have established a moral case to come forward and say, "We must carry out Part II otherwise we should stultify the dignity, the consistency, the integrity of the work we have already done." They would have been able to say "It is true that we are going to make new crimes, to put men in prison, to inflict heavy fines, and to impose many restrictions to liberty, but we are doing so from motives of high conscientious conviction. Our loathing and detestation of the crime and the vice of gambling, our deep realisation of the miseries and ruin which it causes in so many homes have hardened our hearts, and just as we are feeling these strong, poignant emotions ourselves, so we are entitled to lay the lash upon the shoulders of the delinquents who fail to conform to our standards." But nothing of that kind is open to my right hon. Friend to-night.

He had that course and he had another course which was, frankly, to recognise that there are many features of gambling and betting which have grown up in the life of the nation and which no Government and no series of Governments will be able to eradicate. These have taken new forms and have acquired vested interests and voting strength, and they cannot be dealt with, and nobody wishes them to be dealt with, in a rough and ruthless manner. But if the Home Secretary accepts that view as the view which animated him in Part I, then certainly he has no right to come forward and to take this highly austere and would-be imposing attitude of superiority, of moral rectitude or correctitude, and to say that anyone who ever held responsible office in this country could associate himself with the idea of a public lottery being allowed in this land, passed his comprehension. Any crimes which can be laid to my charge in that matter are the most innocent peccadilloes compared with the mass of shocking faults and abuses of which the right hon. Gentleman has made himself the perpetrator.

This Bill consists, in the first place, of what I shall call "the charter of the dog totes and the football pools"; the second part is the high morality recovery of banning anything in the nature of a large sweepstake while providing conveniently for the small ones; and the third part is the pains and penalties and restrictions on liberty indispensable to Part II. Of these three, the first, I say frankly, is rather disreputable, the second is evidently hypocritical, and the third, I believe, will be largely futile. It seems to me that it would not have been at all a bad plan for us to have set up three or four large British national sweepstakes in this country each year, under some body like the stewards of the Jockey Club, independent and regulated, which would in a moment have blotted out all foreign competition in this matter and solved all the problems of people sending money out of the country, and which would, I believe, have met the wishes of the great majority of the people of this country and would, I further believe, have done them no harm. I agree with what the hon. Member for West Willesden (Mrs. Tate) said, that the fact that a man has a lottery ticket or a share in a lottery ticket cannot do him very much harm. It only happens a few times a year, and it enables his mind, in the toil and monotony of life, to rest occasionally in the mere contemplation and the excitement and pleasure of the hope of a fortune coming to him. At any rate, it is not comparable in its evils to the evils which we are definitely sheltering and legislating for and establishing on a new modern legislative basis in Part I of this Bill.

It seems to me also that the true opinion of the House was probably expressed very fairly, very frankly, when my hon. Friend two years ago obtained leave, under the Ten Minutes Rule, to introduce a Bill setting up national lotteries in England. He tells me—I have not verified the figures myself—that 176 Members voted for it and only, I think about 120 against, so that it was a fairly full House, fuller, at any rate, than we have had in many of these discussions. That, you see, was the true and honest opinion of the House. I agree that you may say that a First Reading Division usually comes to nothing, but, if there was this moral stigma, if it was so horrible, the unclean thing, with the sort of sense of evil surrounding it from which the hon. Member has always made it his first duty in life to flee, if it really was instinct with this vice, how was it that so many hon. Members were prepared to entertain the discussion and voted on a Division for the introduction of such a Bill?

Here I come to the case of my right hon. and gallant Friend the Patronage Secretary. Here is where he comes on the boards. I remember quite well that occasion. I think we walked through the Lobby together, almost arm in arm. Well, my right hon. and gallant Friend has been converted. He has seen the light in time. He is, as it were, a brand snatched from the burning, and as was said of the illustrious trimmer, the great Lord Halifax, by Dryden:

> "Nor changed alone, but turned the balance too,
> So much the wit of one brave man can do."

I must say that I believe that Part II of this Measure will be found very largely unenforceable, and it will certainly breed a great deal of resentment. People have written to me to say that they have never taken a ticket in a lottery and that they will not endeavour to do so. A new kind of warfare, an artificial, unnecessary warfare, will be set on foot in the bosom of our anxious and harried land between the persons who wish to assert what they think are their rights to take part in a sweepstake, even though it be a large one, instead of confining themselves to the small ones of which the Home Secretary approves, and the agents of the Home Secretary, working through the law and under the Attorney-General and Solicitor-General. That war is going to take the form of an immense amount of evasion and subterfuge, of a great many regrettable practices on the one hand, and on the other the right hon. Gentleman advances in all the panoply and with all the batteries of the law upon these evildoers of a minor kind.

These unfortunate delinquents will be pursued by every means. First of all, we are to rummage the mails. There must be almost continuous rummaging of His Majesty's mails, and this is a very serious thing. There are certain reasons of State and reasons connected with the administration of criminal justice which may occasionally authorise a Minister to take advantage of the fact that when letters are in the Post Office they are His Majesty's property for the time being, but with that principle used on a large scale, in scores of thousands of cases, to tamper with the privacy of the correspondence of people in this country, many letters being opened without the need—for to catch one, you must open many—is a very great abuse. At the present time, when we have a good constitutional system in this country, when, whether the party opposite is in power or this party is in power, no one feels that the sort of things are going to be done in this country that are habitually done all over the world to the citizens of many other countries, namely, every form of espionage and intrigue, I assert that it is the most serious disadvantage inherent in Part II of this Bill that there should be this rummaging of the mails and tampering with private correspondence for what I consider, and what nine men out of 10 in this House and this country consider, a very trivial matter.

The right hon. Gentleman is to search the homes. He has the right to enter the homes on a new pretext. It is this Part II that makes it necessary particularly, or certainly as much as Part I, and we discussed yesterday how great an evil and injury that was. I am delighted that the opinion has been so strongly expressed on this side that one of our great duties is to limit the intrusions upon the home and very strictly to guard the ordinary, plain people of this country from anything like contact with police officers. The right hon. Gentleman said that he would not mind if a warrant to search his house were issued. I do not believe it. He does not mind a friendly constable coming to his door to make sure that he has renewed his game licence or with any other inquiry connected with his motor car or something like that—a perfectly friendly transaction—but suppose he was out of the Government and was even in great hostility to the Government, and found that he was no longer respected as he is in the great position which he holds, but that a warrant had been issued to search his house, and he had to submit to the searching of all his boxes and every cabinet and cupboard in the whole place, and explain to a constable, on the warrant merely of a magistrate, because, forsooth, it was alleged—and it might only be alleged; it might be a mere pretext under a bad administration—that he, falling away from the high principles with which we are familiar in these Debates, had taken part in selling a few tickets in a sweepstake, I think he would be very much annoyed indeed.

Lastly, there is the question of the censorship of the Press. To the rummaging of the mails, to the intrusions in the home, is added the censorship of the Press. Obviously that is a big step, and if you are going to try to deal with this problem, I feel that the publication of the lists of winners and so forth is necessary. There is an Amendment on the Paper, which we shall reach presently, which seeks to provide for the Irish papers and papers printed on the Continent, but it certainly in no way stops the loophole to which I drew attention. These papers have great circulations. They undoubtedly can and will be brought in and will gain over the English Press, their English rivals, by the fact that they will contain this news. Then there is the question of the broadcast referred to by my hon. Friend, about which no answer has been given. A gentleman, a correspondent, has written to me, since these Debates began, showing me a scheme by which I can well imagine, without the slightest breach of the law under this Act, it would be possible to frustrate to a very large extent the purpose of the Home Secretary, but I am not going to reveal it. I am going so far to act with him and to leave such matters to work themselves out. But, believe me, all over the place thousands of cunning brains will set to work to see how they can steer their way through this legislation, and as long as you have not got the conscience of the people on your side, you will find, in these venial matters, that it is very difficult to enforce strict obedience.

Then an hon. Friend of mine not now in his place, the hon. and learned Member for Central Nottingham (Mr. O'Connor), suggested to the Government that a much better way would be to say that you would take all the winnings by law, a 100 per cent. tax on the winnings of anybody who entered a sweep. As far as I can make out, that would only make sure that all the money went out of the country, because a man who won, with a 10s. ticket, £10,000 or £20,000 would probably just go abroad to spend it until the hue and cry had died down. Therefore, I cannot see that from any point of view the right hon. Gentleman is in a position to enforce this legislation. In spite of endless friction an enormous amount of breaches of the law would occur, not only to the detriment of this Bill, but to the detriment of the general respect for law and obedience to law which have been the characteristic of the English people, in such marked contradiction to the state of things which has occurred in some transatlantic countries with which the Noble Lady opposite is so well acquainted. I must, however, say this, because we have to face a serious issue, that I hope that the resentment which this Bill will create will not induce people to endeavour to frustrate the intentions of Parliament, because undoubtedly it is an evil that money should be sent to the Dublin sweepstake and out of the country in large quantities.

Why are we put in that dilemma? How much better it would have been to handle Part II on lines of principle in accordance with Part I. How much better it would have been to provide a lightning conductor of a few sweepstakes, which would have relieved you from the whole of your troubles. Even now why not drop Part II? When we cannot compel you by any resistance in the House, believe me it is enormously to the interest of the Government that they should do that. If Part II were dropped, a Bill could be introduced, preferably by a private Member, which with the assistance of the Government would place this matter in a situation in which it would meet the wishes and desires of the country. In the case of the old parable of the sun and the north wind, when the north wind blew the young man pulled his coat more tightly about him, but when the genial sun came out he cast it from him; when the genial sun of commonsense comes out the cloak of subterfuge can be cast away. The Government would achieve a real diminution of gambling if they adopted that course. When we ask the Home Secretary to do this, he replies that they have made up their minds to do this because they are going to do it. Might we not learn some of the springs of thought that have led to this process, which have led to the thought—"This is our view, and we are going to stick to it." If you look at this Bill, the kind of gambling that is allowed is decided on the caprice of the Home Secretary, not on commonsense. They say, "We will allow this and not allow that. This is a shocking crime and from this—which is the same thing—we will take a rake-off and also have a profit from Income Tax." There is no principle in this, no reason given. The Home Secretary has decided on an act of power—not reason. The German Emperor at the Royal Proclamation at Munich said: "Hoc volo, sic jubeo; sit pro ratione voluntas" which, for the benefit of the Treasury Bench I will translate, having, for greater security, brushed up my knowledge on the subject, "So I will, so I order; let my will stand for a reason."

It is not quite the way the House likes to be treated, and because of that some of the friction that has been expressed in a courteous manner has arisen. When I come to look at this Bill I must say it conforms to no principle either of policy or of morals. The morals of Part I are entirely different from those of Part II, and the policy of the Bill as a whole is most detrimental. As to the row of able men on that bench who are never tired of telling us how vital they are to the country, that they should continue to guard and guide our course, nothing could be more unfortunate for the National Government than that two Bills should occupy us all this time, on one of which we are going to vote to-night. One Bill will dismiss thousands of Liberals to their old allegiance. Undoubtedly this one will cause widespread discontent, certainly resentment and scorn among the working-class supporters of the Conservative party.

We are now going to divide upon Clause 21. Many of us are going to vote against it. Nobody must vote against Clause 21 under any illusion of what that vote means. It is no use concealing the fact that if defeated it will destroy Part II of the Bill. A vote against Clause 21 is equivalent to the omission of Part II of the Bill, although technically expressed in a different form. I shall give my vote for the Amendment for that very reason, in the hope that in the near future there will be national sweepstakes under proper safeguards, and that they will be authorised by Parliament, and that all this detestable apparatus of restriction and penalties for new and minor offences will pass away from us like the fogs that sometimes afflict us in November.

REFORM OF PARLIAMENTARY PROCEDURES

November 15, 1934

House of Commons

I am not entirely in agreement with all that has been said in the speech to which we have just listened, but I am sure that the House will agree that it was a far more valuable contribution, a critical and constructive contribution, to our discussion, than the usual echoing applause with which the Socialist party so frequently greet the proposals of the National Government. To this particular set of proposals their attitude has naturally been, if I may say so without disrespect, that of hungry cats purring at the prospect of a brimful dish of cream, about to be handed to them, they hope, at no great distance of time. We are indebted to the Lord President of the Council [Mr. Stanley Baldwin] for his succinct—as he called it, and quite rightly—lucid and uncoloured account of what is now proposed. I must say in passing that it would have been more in accordance with precedent if a statement of this kind as to the conduct of Debate and upon the procedure of the House had been made by the Leader of the House of Commons, but we have to recognise that in the right hon. Gentleman we have one who has previously held those great offices with distinction. The right hon. Gentleman mentioned in the first place the proposal that the Reports of the Select Committee on Estimates and of the Public Accounts Committee could be placed more conveniently before us on a Supply Day. I think we shall not make any objection to that. It seems a very valuable and desirable reform.

Upon the question of the selecting of the Chairmen of Committees by you, Mr. Speaker, instead of their being selected by the Committee of Selection as has been the long traditional custom, there is, I think, some matter for debate, as the speech to which we have just listened from the Liberal benches has shown. It is a change which the House may decide to make—indeed, I cannot doubt that the House would make any change it was asked at the present time by the Government, supported as they are by the Opposition—and it would be a pity if hon. Members made that change without realising the setting in which these circumstances lie. I was not aware, in the first place, that the old system had broken down. I had thought that the Committee of Selection and the Chairman of the Committee of Selection had exercised their function in a manner which in no way called for stringent reform, or for the removal from them of the discretion and authority which they had hitherto exerted.

I understand from the Lord President of the Council that you, Sir, have expressed willingness to accept any additional function in this respect that the House may desire to cast upon you, but I must say that this proposal to remove decisions of this kind from the purview of a Parliamentary Committee to the authority of Mr. Speaker—to whom I refer, I need scarcely say, with the most profound respect—is contrary to the general drift of Conservative opinion in other matters connected with Parliamentary affairs. For instance, one of the most important issues with regard to the Parliament Act, the certifying of money Bills, was that this matter must be removed from the *ipse dixit* of Mr. Speaker and placed upon a joint Committee of Privileges conferring between the two Houses. This is a proposal which runs counter to what may be considered in much larger matters to be the main stream of Conservative opinion.

There is another aspect of this matter. The old view, the traditional view, has been that the Members of the House of Commons, the ordinary Members—I think we had the expression the other day, "the common or garden" Members of the House—

Mr. MacQuisten: Led up the garden.

Mr. Churchill:—were capable of conducting the business of the House to a very large extent without undue interference by the Executive. Ordinary Members were chosen by the Committee of Selection from other ordinary Members, because of qualities which had become known in the ordinary course of Parliamentary business, to discharge the function of a Chairman of Committee. That was the idea. The whole procedure was in the hands of the House as a whole, and was left there unmanaged either by the executive government or by the august authority of the Chairman of Committees, which have been limited to the major and main aspects of our Parliamentary life. This proposal seems to have the elements of creating a peculiar class of Members who specialise in selecting Amendments and other matters of Parliamentary procedure, and who would be, as it were, removed by an invisible but no less perceptible barrier from the ordinary run of the Members of the House of Commons. Whether that is a good thing or not every Member must judge for himself, and I am not at all seeking to pronounce in any decided manner upon it.

It is a new feature altogether that there should be in the House 10 Members associated with the Chairman of Committees and with the Deputy-Chairman, all under the nomination of Mr. Speaker, and who would, as it were, specialise in this class of work, and that those responsibilities will be transferred to this special class from the general body of Members of the House of Commons. It must be well worthy of consideration by the House whether any slight gain in efficiency—I fully admit that there is some—is not more than offset by the change in Parliamentary custom and tradition. On this, let me point out that while everyone has the greatest confidence in your decisions, impartiality and great knowledge of the aptitudes of Members of all parties, we cannot legislate upon the basis that you will always be the occupant of the Chair.

We have to think also of the future in dealing with the Procedure of the House of Commons. Parliaments come and go, and there have been many precedents in our history for the election of partisan Speakers. Indeed, the greatest strife and struggle, when a new Parliament began its labours, used to be that which occurred in choosing a Speaker who would be the effective agent of one party or another. Suppose that a period should come of violent political strife, a period of revolutionary change, when there would be a whole mass of enormous Bills to be passed through, with all the Committees working at once, as well as the House, with the greatest activity; and suppose that a Speaker were appointed by the dominant and triumphant party, and the whole of the 10 Chairmen of Committees were equally so appointed. The conditions would be wholly different from any that we live in at the present time, and it seems to me that in these hypothetical but possible conditions you might easily get a sort of uniformity throughout the whole of the chairmanships of these Committees which would be very detrimental to the fair play which is the right of minorities, and might conceivably be even more detrimental to the prosperity and well-being of the State. I think, Mr. Speaker, that on the question of the creation of a special *corps d'elite* of chairmen under your eye or the eye of your successors, as against the practice of letting it, as it were, well up from the good sense and good feeling of the ordinary Members of the House of Commons, the House should balance the two alternatives in their minds before they give their decision.

I come now to what is to my mind the much more important question of the powers which are to be given to this new class of Chairmen of Committees. The hon. Gentleman who represented the Liberal party made, in his interesting speech, no concealment of the fact that this is a very important change, and not the sort of change that ought to slip through without anybody in the House even taking the trouble to mark it. Although we may see our liberties and rights fading away, or falling away, step by step, and although we may have no power to resist the will of the administration in collusion—or rather, I will not say in collusion, but in association— with the will of their political opponents, nevertheless it is only right that the steps on this downward path should be registered and marked, and that Parliament and the public should be well aware of what they are doing.

This kind of proposal, if my right hon. Friend will allow me to say so, arises from what I think is a wrong view of the major functions of Parliament. Parliament is not a mere apparatus for passing Bills. A not less important function is preventing bad Bills from passing. Parliament has many functions apart from its legislative function, and it seems to me to be absolutely essential that people should not try to shape our procedure as if perfection would be attained when legislation was most easy. Most Bills, I believe, cost money, lose votes, create officials, and worry the public, and certainly Parliament has to stand between the great mass of the public and the strong pressure of organised sectional interests, or organised party interests, which from time to time endeavour to imprint their special wishes, or convictions, or fads, upon our Statute Book.

The practice of Parliament must be judged, not by quantity, but by quality. You cannot judge the passing of Bills by Parliament as you would judge the output of an efficient Chicago bacon factory. Out of doors this ignorant idea is much cherished, and you frequently hear people say: "Why don't they sit all the year round, and pass all the Bills they are asked to pass?" But the country would be thrown into great confusion if there were not corrective counter-checks, and if there were not Conservative elements in the country which are not anxious to see continuous rapid change, and all our affairs thrown into a state of flux. It is important, in a well-governed country like this, where so much has been achieved in the past, that a certain amount of time should be given for people to accommodate themselves to circumstances, and for troubles and difficulties to pass away, rather than that they should always be dealt with by petulant and impatient legislation.

In the last 25 years out of the 34 that I have been in the House—indeed, almost since I was first elected, but in the last 25 years particularly—possibly I have conducted through this House more legislation, social and other, than anyone except perhaps the right hon. Gentleman the Member for Carnarvon Boroughs (Mr. Lloyd George), and possibly my right hon. Friend the Member for West Birmingham (Sir A. Chamberlain). I have done it in all sorts of conditions, sometimes when there were the most tremendous controversial issues at stake, and when the two great parties, with only a majority of 100 between them, were ranged upon these benches fighting every inch—every Clause, every Sub-section, every word, every syllable, almost every comma; and I was never aware that it was not possible for the Government of the day, with patience and with a reasonable use of their Parliamentary powers, to get their legislation through. What has happened all of a sudden to this Government that it is not able to get its legislation through? I should have thought that the Government had no difficulty about getting their legislation through—that their only difficulty was to think of good legislation to bring before us. What is the trouble? When the Government have this overwhelming power, this colossal majority, this perfervid affection and agreement by the Opposition, what is the need for coming forward at this juncture and making new prunings from the limited shrub of the rights of private Members and of Parliamentary liberty? I have heard nothing from my right hon. Friend which shows us where we are. It looks to me as though we were called together for a month to deal with matters which I imagine would far better have been left undealt with, and, there being a little spare time, this additional improvement in the powers of the Executive and of the Government, in conjunction with the Opposition, over the House of Commons, has been thought to be a very good topic to introduce on one of the closing afternoons of our Session.

I have never argued, and never will argue in this House that a minority should have the power of resisting the settled will of Parliament by dilatory processes, but that has never been the case. They ought not to have that power, they have never had it, and they have not got it now. Surely, the Government have quite enough power at the present time, without seeking to add to that great mass of authority which in many respects they seem unable to use. This proposal that the House should make a further surrender of its powers and rights to the Executive—for that is what it comes to—must also be judged in connection with the decision which the Government enforced upon the House, or extracted from the House, about moving Bills from the consideration of a Committee upstairs down to the Floor of the House, or, as one may imagine *per contra*, from the Floor of the House to a Committee upstairs. That is a principle which has now been established by the House. It seems to me that a very unsatisfactory situation will arise if, when great Measures are going through the House, parts of them are shifted upstairs, and then parts of them are brought down here—a new Parliamentary process which I venture to define, even before it is put into practice, as shuttlecocking—moving Measures from a Committee to the House and back again, so that neither the Committee nor the House will give full, comprehensive study and debate to the Measure in its integrity, but only to a clipped and shorn series of proposals, some dealt with upstairs and some dealt with here. Proposals of this kind, used by an unscrupulous Government, or a Government which desired to carry through really revolutionary legislation, might perhaps at no great distance of time be found to be of immense consequence to all of us who sit here.

It seems to me that the proposal to extend the power of selecting Amendments to the Chairman of Committees upstairs ought to be very carefully watched by the House. I must say that I myself prefer the Kangaroo Closure. I believe that the Kangaroo Closure is a perfectly effective agent for the passing of Bills, and greatly preferable to the power of selecting Amendments. I remember that we used it a great deal in the struggles before the War, and, although it often excited anger, it is not the same kind of thing as the arbitrary power of selecting Amendments. [Hon. Members: "The Guillotine."] I am not talking about the Guillotine at all; I am talking about the Kangaroo Closure. Let us be clear about the terminology. By the Kangaroo Closure I mean the power of the Minister to move, with the assent of the Chair, that a Clause, or even two Clauses, shall stand part down to a certain line or word. The Kangaroo Closure moves on along the face of the Clauses, and it is a very great power. It cuts out all the Amendments relating to the parts which have been dealt with up to that point.

But I would put it to the House and to my right hon. Friend that, with all its severity, the Kangaroo Closure rests in the hands of the House, because the House has immediately to pronounce upon it. A vote is put to the House, and it is the act of the House; and, if a lot of Amendments are cut out, they are cut out by the House. If after the Closure has been carried and a second Division has been taken, there is great feeling in the House—and I have often seen it on these occasions—it is open to those who are opposing the Bill to obtain the assent of the Chair to a Motion to report Progress or to adjourn the Debate. It is then possible to consider the matter, and very often some easier arrangement is made, and some reparation afforded on the Report stage to those who have been prevented from discussing important Amendments.

I consider that the Kangaroo Closure, severe as it may be, and perfectly capable, as it is, of carrying the largest legislation—we carried the Home Rule Bill and the Parliament Act under it—is entirely adequate, and is preferable to what occurs now, which, although I need scarcely say it, is perfectly agreeable to everyone because of the great fairness and discretion and scruple with which it is administered, is inherently an arbitrary procedure. Any number of Amendments may be simply ignored without any reason being given, or any power or right on the part of any Member to ask for reasons or make a protest. To extend that power to these ten Chairmen upstairs, who are to be controlled by the Chairman of Committees and the Deputy-Chairman, is, I think, unduly and needlessly to curtail the rights of the House. It is, of course, quite easy to understand why hon. Gentlemen opposite support all this. They look forward eagerly to the assumption of power; they have a firm belief that they will be able by passing Bills to make everything much better for everyone in this country—

Mr. Rhys Davies: Will the right hon. Gentleman allow me—

Mr. Churchill: I do not want to give way. I do not want to delay the House unduly, because I am sure we all want to get on with the Debate on the distressed areas. If the hon. Gentleman will allow me to say so, it seems to me to be very natural that the Socialist party should wish to have this.

Mr. Davies: The right hon. Gentleman seems to be critical of the power of Mr. Speaker to select Amendments on the Floor of the House. Was he not a member of the Government that gave him that power?

Mr. Churchill: I fully accept what has been decided, that there was given to Mr. Speaker and the Chairman and the Deputy-Chairman this power to select Amendments, but I consider that procedure a more arbitrary one than what is called the Kangaroo Closure—giving the Closure on a considerable number of lines on the face of the Clauses of a Bill. Power to use the Kangaroo Closure already belongs to Committees upstairs provided the House assents in any particular case. Then why, if this very effective and powerful Kangaroo Closure be already in their power, is it necessary to substitute this power to select Amendments?

I hope the House will consider that there are two sides to this question, and I hope it will not be supposed, because the Government and the Opposition are in agreement, that no one need worry or be anxious about it. I have put these few remarks before the House in order that they may be considered during the course of the Debate. I address myself particularly to the Lord President of the Council when I say that the vitality and life of the House of Commons is one of the real interests of those who wish to see constitutional government maintained. To crush out the liberty of the House of Commons and make it an organised voting machine will detract from its influence in the country. I am shocked that, when a whole afternoon is available for discussing these reforms in Parliamentary procedure, no more constructive plans have been put forward. I saw a report of a Conservative Committee which had most admirable plans for improving the Procedure of the House, for enabling us to have Debates with short speeches and so forth. I am sorry that when my right hon. Friend has come to put these Measures forward, he has not found it possible to adorn them with constructive measures which would have the effect of adding to the dignity of the House, but has only found it possible to make proposals for larger encroachments upon our old liberties.

My right hon. Friend [Stanley Baldwin, Lord President of the Council] in spite of his most agreeable and genial speech, has not responded adequately to the requests made to him from the Liberal benches. He has hardly made an adequate return to the hon. Gentlemen on those benches for the vigour of their support on this occasion. In view of the rhetorical exertions made by the right hon. Gentleman the Member for Caithness (Sir A. Sinclair) on behalf of the Government the Lord President of the Council might have paid a little more attention to the humble and not wholly unreasonable request of his followers. The right hon. Gentleman opposite is carrying this Debate into an atmosphere which it had not otherwise entered. For him to describe these few gentlemen who feel it their duty to make some observations about the curtailment of the rights of private Members as a motley gang of conspirators against the National Government is rather extreme. I really wonder whether the Government ought not to make some special act of concession on account of the Billingsgate that the right hon. Gentleman has been slinging. Considering that he is himself the leader of a party much smaller than those who represent what I may call the traditional Conservative view on this question and considering that he is the leader of a handful of Members nearly all of whom can vote on this question with great impartiality because they are not likely to be troubled with the consequences of it in another Parliament, I think he might have kept within reasonable bounds in this Debate, especially as most of us said nothing provocative and most of us listened with great pleasure to the eloquent speech and watched with enthusiasm the expansive gestures with which his harangue was adorned. But I am not going to return evil for evil. My right hon. Friend has not repaid good with good, but I will not repay evil with evil.

I am bound to say I think there is something to be said for the proposal that has come from the hon. Gentleman who proposed this Amendment. I was astonished to see that this matter, which undoubtedly will give more latitude to the House to discuss subjects in which it is interested, should actually have received a measure of lukewarm support from the official Opposition. It is most refreshing to see any steps on their part towards discharging the customary functions of an Opposition, and insisting on reasonable opportunities for the raising of topics in Debate. We must remember that the old practice of the House in relation to a Motion for the Adjournment of the House on a matter of urgent public importance was that the Motion should come on directly at a quarter to four. When I first entered the House that was the invariable rule, and many a great debate have I heard spring up in a flash. [An Hon. Member: "Surely not!"] Oh, yes, I am speaking of times long before my hon. Friend was even born. Straight away I have heard the late Mr. John Morley and others raise a point and a debate spring up. There often resulted a dramatic debate in which the whole country was interested, because the things that the House was discussing were the things that the country was thinking about at the moment.

Then it was thought by the Conservative Government of 1900, of which I was not a member, that it was a little hard on Ministers to have to face some of these large and important issues of public policy, connected with the South African War or foreign affairs and so forth, on the spur of the moment across the Floor of the House. Therefore, the system was introduced of holding over the debate until after the dinner hour, until 7:30. That, of course, took all the spring and snap out of these Parliamentary occasions, and that was one of the many steps taken in my lifetime which have tended to make the Debates of the House less and less a mirror of the thought of the country, and of less and less interest to the public at large. That change which has been enforced prevents these matters being raised and surely a little more latitude might be given, as the hon. Gentleman suggests, at the other end of the day.

There are all sorts of questions which ought to be raised. There is no absolute obligation for Ministers to attend, but there are questions which ought to be raised, and which Members and their constituents wish to raise here at the very first opportunity. As I understand it, all that the hon. Gentleman says is that there shall be always half-an-hour after eleven o'clock and that if there is a Division, or possibly two Divisions, the half-hour shall begin when the Divisions are over. I am glad to have got it right, because I was not sure that I saw quite what the hon. Gentleman wanted. I do not think that this is a very unreasonable request. I think that the Lord President ought to consider it, particularly a request coming like that from a small and ardent band of his supporters who do not often make any requests but who generally do all they can to play the game of the National Government—though they were unhappily sundered from the Government on one particular issue. A misunderstanding arose. It would have been more generous on the part of my right hon. Friend had he been able to meet the hon. Gentleman. We have heard rumours, and I believe it has also been stated in the newspapers, that in the next Session the time of private Members is to be taken by the Government. If that is to be the case much more then it is necessary that this safety valve should be kept open, and that there should be some time or other in the course of the 24 hours when urgent matters affecting a group of Members or a part of the country can be brought forward.

Would it not be possible for the Government to agree to the Amendment providing that it was understood that this was only applicable in any Session when the private time of private Members was taken by the Government? I suggest that as a compromise, because I am most anxious that the unity between the Liberal party and my right hon. Friend here should be restored. I should have thought that a compromise of that kind was thoroughly in accord with the English spirit, which my right hon. Friend always extols and often exemplifies. If that could be done, I am quite sure it would enable this Debate to terminate in a far more satisfactory temper than that unfortunate lapse from good taste, good manners and good feeling which we have witnessed in the right hon. Gentleman opposite.

[Later] May I ask the right hon. Gentleman [Mr. Baldwin] in connection with the statement which he has made, in view of the fact that this important proposal requires further consideration on the part of the Government and that he is willing to give it further consideration, whether it would not be better, considering the length of time that we have already spent upon this matter and the work which we have already to do, that further consideration of this subject should be postponed. That would give an opportunity to the Government in the new Session to present in entirety their schemes for the reform of Procedure, including some of the proposals put forward by the Noble Lord. I take advantage of the right hon. Gentleman having admitted very candidly and very fairly that this is an open matter which requires further consideration, cannot be dealt with piecemeal and cannot be settled at the present time to ask whether he cannot allow the Debate to be adjourned so that we may get on to the far more grievous issue of the distressed areas, in regard to which so many Members have been waiting for a long time in the House to enter upon Debate?

"THE CAUSES OF WAR"

November 16, 1934

Broadcast, London

As we go to and fro in this peaceful country, with its decent orderly people going about their business under free institutions, and with so much tolerance and fair play in their laws and customs, it is startling and fearful to realise that we are no longer safe in our island home. For nearly a thousand years England has never seen the camp fires of an invader. The stormy seas and our Royal Navy have been our sure defence. Not only have we preserved our life and freedom through the centuries, but gradually we have come to be the heart and centre of an Empire which surrounds the globe. It is indeed with a pang of stabbing pain that we see all this in mortal danger.

> A thousand years scarce serve to form a State,
> An hour may lay it in the dust.

What shall we do?

Many people think that the best way to escape war is to dwell upon its horrors, and to imprint them vividly upon the minds of the younger generation. They flaunt the grisly photographs before their eyes. They fill their ears with tales of carnage. They dilate upon the ineptitude of generals and admirals. They denounce the crime and insensate folly of human strife.

All this teaching ought to be very useful in preventing us from attacking or invading any other country, if anyone outside a madhouse wished to do so. But how would it help us if we were attacked or invaded ourselves? That is the question we have to ask. Would the invaders consent to visit Lord Beaverbrook's exhibition, or listen to the impassioned appeals of Mr. Lloyd George? Would they agree to meet that famous South African, General Smuts, and have their inferiority complex removed in friendly reasonable debate? I doubt it. I gravely doubt it.

But even if they did, I am not sure we should convince them, and persuade them to go back quietly home. They might say 'You are rich, we are poor. You seem well fed, we are hungry. You have been victorious, we have been defeated. You have valuable colonies, we have none. You have your Navy, where is ours? You have had the past, let us have the future.' Above all, I fear, they would say 'You are weak and we are strong.'

After all, only a few hours away by air there dwells a nation of nearly seventy millions of the most educated, industrious, scientific, disciplined people in the world, who are being taught from childhood to think of war and conquest as a glorious exercise, and death in battle as the noblest fate for man. There is a nation which has abandoned all its liberties in order to augment its collective might. There is a nation which with all its strength and virtues is in the grip of a group of ruthless men preaching a gospel of intolerance and racial pride, unrestrained by law, by Parliament or by public opinion. In that country all pacifist speeches, all morbid war books, are forbidden or suppressed and their authors rigorously imprisoned. From their new table of commandments they have omitted 'Thou shalt not kill.' It is but twenty years since these neighbours of ours fought almost the whole world, and almost defeated them. Now they are rearming with the utmost speed, and ready to their hands is this new lamentable weapon of the air, against which our Navy is no defence, before which women and children, the weak and frail, the pacifist and the jingo, the warrior and the civilian, the front line trenches and the cottage home, lie in equal and impartial peril.

Nay worse still, for with the new weapon has come a new method, or rather has come back the most brutish methods of ancient barbarism, namely the possibility of compelling the submission of races by terrorising and torturing their civil population. And worst of all—the more civilised a country is, the larger and more splendid its cities, the more intricate the structure of its social and economic life; the more is it vulnerable, the more it is at the mercy of those who may make it their prey.

Now these are facts—hard, grim indisputable facts—and in face of these facts I ask again, what are we to do?

There are those who say 'Let us ignore the continent of Europe. Let us leave it with its hatreds and its armaments to stew in its own juice, to fight out its own quarrels, and cause its own doom. Let us turn our backs upon this melancholy and alarming scene. Let us fix our gaze across the oceans and lead our own life in the midst of our peace-loving dominions and Empire.'

Now there would be much to be said for this plan, if only we could unfasten the British islands from their rock foundations and could tow them three thousand miles across the Atlantic Ocean, and anchor them safely upon the smiling coasts of Canada. I have not yet heard of any way in which this could be done. No engineer has come forward with any scheme. Even our best scientists are dumb. It would certainly take a long time. Have we got a long time? At present we lie within a few minutes' striking distance of the French, Dutch, and Belgian coasts, and within a few hours of the great aerodromes of Central Europe. We are even within cannon-shot of the Continent. So close as that! Is it prudent, is it possible, however we might desire it, to turn our backs upon Europe and ignore whatever may happen there? Everyone can judge this question for himself, and everyone ought to make up his mind about it without delay. It lies at the heart of our problem. For my part I have come to the conclusion—reluctantly I admit—that we cannot get away. Here we are and we must make the best of it. But do not underrate the risks—the grievous risks—we have to run.

I hope, I pray, and on the whole, grasping the larger hope, I believe, that no war will fall upon us. But if in the near future the Great War of 1914 is resumed again in Europe after the Armistice—for that is what it may come to—under different conditions no doubt—no one can tell where and how it would end, or whether sooner or later we should not be dragged into it, as the United States were dragged in against their will in 1917. Whatever happened and whatever we did, it would be a time of frightful danger for us. And when the war was over, or perhaps while it still raged, we should be left face to face with the victors whoever they might be. Indeed, we should, with our wealth and vast possessions, be the only prize sufficient to reward their exertions and compensate them for their losses. Then certainly those who had tried to forget Europe would have to turn round very quickly indeed. And then it would be too late. Therefore it seems to me that we cannot detach ourselves from Europe, and that for our own safety and self-preservation we are bound to make exertions and run risks for the sake of keeping peace.

There are some who say—indeed it has been the shrill cry of the hour—that we should run the risk of disarming ourselves in order to set an example to others. We have done that already for the last five years; but our example has not been followed. On the contrary, it has produced the opposite result. All the other countries have armed only the more heavily; and the quarrels and intrigues about disarmament have only bred more ill-will between the nations.

Everyone would be glad to see the burden of armaments reduced in every country. But history shows on many a page that armaments are not necessarily a cause of war and that the want of them is no guarantee of peace. If, for instance, all the explosives all over the globe could by the wave of a magic wand be robbed of their power and made harmless, so that not a cannon or a rifle could fire, and not a shell or a bomb detonate, that would be a measure of world disarmament far beyond the brightest dreams of Geneva. But would it ensure peace? On the contrary, war would begin almost the next day when enormous masses of fierce men, armed with picks and spades or soon with clubs and spears, would pour over the frontiers into the lands they covet, and would be furiously resisted by the local populations and those who went to their aid. This truth may be unfashionable, unpalatable, unpopular. But it is the truth. The story of mankind shows that war was universal and unceasing for millions of years before armaments were invented or armies organised. Indeed the lucid intervals of peace and order only occur in human history after armaments in the hands of strong governments have come into being. And civilisation has been nursed only in cradles guarded by superior weapons and discipline. To remove the causes of war we must go deeper than armaments, we must remove grievances and injustice, we must raise human thought to a higher plane and give a new inspiration to the world. Let moral disarmament come and physical disarmament will soon follow. But what sign of this is there now?

When we look out upon the state of Europe and of the world and of the position of our own country, as they are now, it seems to me that the next year or the next two years will be a fateful turning point in our history. I am afraid that if you look intently at what is moving towards Great Britain, you will see that the only choice open is the old grim choice our forbears had to face, namely, whether we shall submit to the will of a stronger nation or whether we shall prepare to defend our rights, our liberties and indeed our lives. If we submit, our submission should be timely. If we prepare, our preparation should not be too late. Submission will entail at the very least the passing and distribution of the British Empire and the acceptance by our people of whatever future may be in store for small countries like Norway, Sweden, Denmark, Holland, Belgium and Switzerland, within and under a Teutonic domination of Europe.

The difficulty about submission—I state it calmly—is that we have already in this island the population of a first-class Power. And on our new scale of life as a smaller state we could not feed more than perhaps half those who now live here. Great stresses will arise in deciding which half should survive. You have perhaps read the story of

'The Raft of the *Medusa*.' I will not dwell on that repulsive scene. These are the disadvantages of submission and of Britain definitely relinquishing her great situation in the world.

Preparation on the other hand involves statesmanship, expense and exertion, and neither submission nor preparation are free from suffering and danger.

I should not speak in this way if I were not prepared to declare to you some of the measures of preparation by which I believe another great war may be averted, and our destruction, should war come, be prevented. First we must without another day's delay begin to make ourselves at least the strongest air Power in the European world. By this means we shall recover to a very large extent the safety which we formerly enjoyed through our Navy and India. They are doing so because absolutely in the forefront of their programme is the rejection of the so-called 'Communal Award,' that is, the proposed allotment of seats between Hindus and Muslims in the provincial legislative councils under the forthcoming Constitution. It is said that this allotment is unduly favourable to Muslims, particularly in the two important provinces of Bengal and the Punjab.

Against these two parties is the Muslim Conference Party. Its candidates, all over India, stand for the Communal Award, the whole Award, and nothing but the Award. There is also a Muslim Independent Party—a little more to the left in general politics than the Muslim conference, but on the whole determined to uphold the Communal Award.

Away in the south of India, confined to the Presidencies of Madras and Bombay and the Central Provinces, is the Justice Party. This is a Centre Party, prepared to embrace all castes and communities. The Justice Party's main strength is in the Madras Presidency, where it has for years been predominant.

So the general composition of the new legislative Assembly may be expected to be: On the left, the Congress, and allied groups and parties normally opposing the Government of India in everything. Opposed to them will be the Government bloc and nominated members usually assisted by the elected British members, and, very often, by the majority of Muslims. There are always some members who belong to no party, of whom it can never be safely predicted on which side they will vote.

The Congress and their allies may be expected to have about 50 members, which is roughly equal to the Government bloc, the nominated non-official members, and the elected Europeans put together. The key position of the Muslims and the non-party members is obvious.

PARLIAMENTARY DEBATE

November 21, 1934

House of Commons

This is a very drastic and unusual proposal. The Government are making a demand which I have not often heard made in all the time that I have been here. Not since 1921 or 1922 has such a demand been made. This Parliament has not hitherto shown itself careful of the rights of private Members, and it is a remarkable fact that that should be so, in view of the high hopes that were entertained by the new Members who came into the House. One might have hoped that they would have developed a very strong and vigorous sense of its position. Considering that party politics are practically extinct, because of the overwhelming majority of the Government, one hoped that those Members would have been most zealous to preserve the opportunities for freedom open to private Members in the limited time allotted to them. We are always hearing that private Members are not showing that fertility, ability and originality which are necessary to keep alive our Parliamentary institutions, and yet here are the Government taking away those opportunities of legislating and of ventilating large general issues which have always given, to private Members and to young Members in many cases, an opportunity of establishing themselves as Parliamentary figures who would, in time, replace those who sit upon the Front Bench. Why is it necessary for the Government to do this? They have an enormous majority, far larger than they require. But, quite apart from that, on the particular Bill which is to be the main topic in the new Session, the India Bill, they have the promised support of the Socialist Opposition—[Hon. Members: "No!"] The right hon. Gentleman was very careful to say that he was anxious to go as far as possible and to get the Bill if he could not get anything better. That is what I understood him to say yesterday; I do not wish to misquote him.

Mr. Lansbury: I wish to be quite clear on this matter. I said that we should put before the House our views as to what the Bill should be, and we should move what Amendments we thought necessary, but we should do nothing to obstruct the passage of the Bill—that we should act as I think an Opposition ought to act in dealing with a Measure of that kind.

Mr. Churchill: I do not think that that was quite what was conveyed to my mind. The idea conveyed to my mind was that the right hon. Gentleman indicated that, although the Bill did not go as far as he and his friends might wish, at any rate they were supporters of getting the Bill through if they could not get anything better—or, as we should say, worse. I think that that is the position. Certainly it is very remarkable how often the Government are supported by their Socialist and Liberal opponents. That ought to make it quite easy for them to get their legislation through. When I came back to the House after the Election of 1931, I was most desirous of voting against the Socialist party, and I do so whenever I get an opportunity, but I always find that the National Government is in the Lobby with them; it is very difficult to separate them. And yet, with this enormous majority, with an absolute docile House of Commons—the most docile that I have ever seen—and with the great measure of support which comes from the Labour benches, and on many occasions from the Liberal benches, the Government have to ask us to make this very great mutilation, in fact complete elimination, of the liberties of private Members.

I must point out that no answer has yet been given by the Government to the very reasonable suggestion which was made by the Leader of the Opposition—on this occasion, as an exception, functioning in his normal constitutional capacity—that, if the India Bill takes longer than is expected, it should be carried over to the Autumn

Session, and Parliament should come together at such earlier date as may be necessary to secure a fair and full discussion of so momentous a Measure. No answer has been made to that suggestion. The Prime Minister's argument is quite watertight and holds together as long as you assume that at the end of July Parliamentary activities must necessarily come to an end, and the Session must be brought to a close before the House adjourns. But nothing of the sort is the case. We can go for a short recess to the country, and then come back to resume our labours. We ought not to scamp our duties on a matter which may effect, perhaps permanently, the whole fortunes of this people and the great Empire in India.

Let me point out that, if we are in this difficulty, the fault is entirely that of the Government. We have been called back for the last month to waste our time upon two Bills, the Betting and Lotteries Bill and the Disaffection Bill—two Measures singularly ill-conceived and of very questionable utility. We have been wasting a whole month, taking the glamour off the beginning of a new Session, wearying the House with late sittings almost every night. If those days since we were recalled here at the end of October had been saved, and the Session begun then, there would not be the slightest need to take these 21 days from the private Members. It is sheer mishandling on the part of the Government that has got us into this position. Having blundered on, plodded on, forced their way ahead with this resistless, dumb, blind force which they have at their disposal, having thrust their way on in spite of every warning, they have now got into a difficulty, and who is to pay the price? They are breaking their way out through the procedure and privileges of the House of Commons, and the private Members are to be the losers. That is where we stand to-day. Do not let it be said for a moment that the reason why the private Members have to give up their time is that, besides the usual time for the India Bill there is to be a great programme of social reform. The reason is that the Government are reluctant to call the House together in the early Autumn, and they have got into such a mess with their Betting and Lotteries Bill and their Disaffection Bill that they have taken the whole bloom off the new Session of Parliament.

There is another way in which I imagine the right hon. Gentleman might endeavour to facilitate the progress of our business, and that is if he would develop the practice, which he has observed to-day, of coming down himself and leading the House. Really, the right hon. Gentleman need not look so impatient. I have seen greater men than he occupying his position, who have valued, quite as highly as the position of Prime Minister, the honour of leading the House of Commons; and a great deal of facility is given to business by the personal touch and personal contact and relationship established between the Prime Minister and the House when he acts as Leader of the House in Parliament. I remember the late Lord Balfour, who was always most assiduous in his attention to his duties in the House. It is really no use the right hon. Gentleman keeping aloof from his fellow Members—standing off like an absentee landlord giving orders to evict, collect rents, and so forth, and having the estate managed for him. I am sure that, if he were able to come down and watch the proceedings for himself, he would not be called upon to adopt the drastic and roughshod measures which he has found it necessary to propose to us to-day.

I am not sure that I should have risen to take part in this discussion at all but for the remarks which the Prime Minister made yesterday about the India Bill. He seems to have adopted a tone of menace with regard to that Bill. He would give what he thought fair time, but no licence. But since when have Members of Parliament had to get a licence? We have our rights, and you, Mr. Speaker, are the judge of our exercise of those rights. It is certainly not for the effective Government to be the sole interpreter of what is reasonable in discussion and what is stepping beyond those bounds which they think convenient to their conduct of public business. It seems to me to be a most unusual, and, in fact, I think unprecedented, thing to suggest, as the right hon. Gentleman has suggested quite plainly, the adoption of a Guillotine procedure before a Bill has even been presented to the House. It is customary, as indeed, the Leader of the Opposition has indicated, to allow a Bill to run a certain distance, and then, if it is seen that discussion is being pushed beyond what is due and normal, the feeling of the House supports the Government in asking for a special time-table for their Bill.

At the moment nobody has seen the Bill. Theoretically it does not exist. We were told that the Government could not make up their minds about it until certain conferences had been held, and so forth. The report has only come into our hands this afternoon. But the Prime Minister knows that the Bill contains 300 Clauses. What grounds are there for assuming that the tactics by which it will be resisted will be dilatory tactics? As I said the other day, I do not consider that it is justifiable, or ought to be possible, for a minority to resist the settled will of Parliament by means of purely dilatory tactics, but there must be upon a great Measure of this kind party and controversial discussions and occasions when there are sharp differences, which perhaps afterwards are composed and a more smooth passage assured for the Measure.

It is a great pity to destroy the whole freedom and life of Parliamentary discussion by making the House Debate within the Guillotine. I certainly think it most unusual and most undesirable, and a bad precedent, that the Prime Minister, months before the Bill is introduced, should already be threatening private Members with the application of these drastic proceedings. Moreover, it is not only unusual. It is a very unwise thing from his point of view to let the country know, when many important discussions have to take place in the country, that the Government are perfectly resolved, if they can have the power and if authority is given to the Leader of the Conservative party as well as to the Prime Minister, with the aid and support of the Opposition and in association with them, to ram this Bill through Parliament by the most drastic measures. I hope that will be widely known throughout the country and borne in mind by all persons who are taking an interest in this controversy.

It is quite true that with the power at the disposal of the Government they certainly will be able to steam roller and plough down the opposition. That is why people in the country who have an opportunity of considering these matters should walk very warily, because of the greatness of the responsibilities which are thrust upon them in a matter of this kind. It seems to me that we have before us a sombre, a melancholy and an ill-starred Session. What is going to happen may give great satisfaction to hon. and right hon. Gentlemen opposite. We are going to witness, first of all the deprivation of all the rights of private Members, secondly, the application of the Guillotine Closure with great severity to enormous constitutional measures of historic importance, and, thirdly, the process of the Conservative leaders trampling down and dragooning their followers amid the cheers and war whoops of both the opposition parties which are constantly and busily engaged in attacking the Conservative party in the constituencies.

THE GERMAN AIR MENACE

November 28, 1934

House of Commons

I beg to move, at the end of the Question, to add the words:

> But humbly represent to Your Majesty that, in the present circumstances of the world, the strength of our national defences, and especially of our air defences, is no longer adequate to secure the peace, safety, and freedom of Your Majesty's faithful subjects.

To urge the preparation of defence is not to assert the imminence of war. On the contrary, if war were imminent preparations for defence would be too late. I do not believe that war is imminent or that war is inevitable, but it seems very difficult to resist the conclusion that, if we do not begin forthwith to put ourselves in a position of security, it will soon be beyond our power to do so. What is the great new fact which has broken in upon us during the last 18 months? Germany is rearming. That is the great new fact which rivets the attention of every country in Europe, indeed in all the world, and which throws almost all other issues into the background. Germany is rearming, that mighty Power which only a few years ago, within our own experience, fought almost the whole world, and almost conquered. That mighty Power is now equipping itself once again, 70,000,000 of people, with the technical apparatus of modern war, and at the same time is instilling into the hearts of its youth and manhood the most extreme patriotic nationalist and militarist conceptions. According to what we hear, according to what we are told and what comes in from every quarter, though little is said about it in public, Germany has already a powerful well-equipped army, with an excellent artillery, and an immense reserve of armed trained men. The German munition factories are working practically under war conditions, and war material is flowing out from them, and has been for the last 12 months certainly, in an ever broadening flow. Much of this is undoubtedly in violation of the treaties which were signed. Germany is rearming on land; she is rearming also to some extent at sea; but what concerns us most of all is the rearmament of Germany in the air.

In my Amendment other aspects of defence besides the air are comprised, but I shall confine myself absolutely to the danger from the air. I shall be specially careful not to exaggerate. Indeed, I hope that every statement that I make will be admitted to be an understatement. I shall try my utmost to keep within the limits of what is really known and proved. Let us, first of all, look at the dimensions of the danger as it affects this country at the present time. However calmly surveyed, the danger of an attack from the air must appear most formidable. I do not accept the sweeping claim of the extreme votaries of the air. I think that a great many statements which are made are calculated to frustrate the purpose of reasonable precautions by presenting the problem as if it were one which was insoluble. But without accepting these claims no one can doubt that a week or 10 days' intensive bombing attack upon London would be a very serious matter indeed. One could hardly expect that less than 30,000 or 40,000 people would be killed or maimed. I see that General Seely, now known as Lord Mottistone, in the other House made some calculations on this subject. They were said to be of a reassuring character. But even those reassuring figures and calculations, I think, at least justify the statement I have just made, that a week or 10 days of this kind of intensive attack would result in 30,000 or 40,000 being killed or maimed.

The most dangerous form of air attack is the attack by incendiary bombs. Such an attack was planned by the Germans for the summer of 1918, I think for the time of the harvest moon. The argument in favour of such an attack was that if in any great city there are, we will say, 50 fire brigades, and you start simultaneously 100 fires or 80 fires and the wind is high, an almost incalculable conflagration may result. The reason why the Germans did not carry out that attack in 1918 must be stated. It was not at all, as Lord Mottistone suggested in another place, that our air defence had become so excellent that we were protected against it. It was because the advance of the Allied Armies, with the British Army in the van, already confronted the heads of the German State, the Imperial Government of Germany, with the prospect of impending defeat, and they did not wish to incur the fury of retribution which would follow from such a dreadful act of power and terror as that which would have been involved in such a raid. Since those days the incendiary thermite bomb has become far more powerful than any that was used in the late War. It will in fact, I am assured by persons who are acquainted with the science, go through a series of floors in any building, igniting each one simultaneously.

Not less formidable than these material effects are the reactions which will be produced upon the mind of the civil population. We must expect that under the pressure of continuous air attack upon London at least 3,000,000 or 4,000,000 people would be driven out into the open country around the Metropolis. This vast mass of human beings, numerically far larger than any armies which have been fed and moved in war, without shelter and without food, without sanitation and without special provision for the maintenance of order, would confront the Government of the day with an administrative problem of the first magnitude, and would certainly absorb the energies of our small Army and of our Territorial Force. Problems of this kind have never been faced before, and although there is no need to exaggerate them, neither on the other hand is there any need to shrink from facing the immense, unprecedented difficulties which they involve.

Then there are the questions of the docks of London and the estuary of the Thames. Everyone knows the dependence of this immense community, the most prosperous in the whole world, upon the Eastern approaches by water. I need say no more about that. We studied it very carefully in the War, and I have not the slightest doubt that it has weighed very much on the minds of His Majesty's Government. It ought not to be supposed that the danger of an air attack, assuming that such a thing occurred—I am only making an assumption and not by any means saying it will come to pass—would necessarily be confined to London or the area around it. Birmingham and Sheffield and the great manufacturing towns might all be made the subject of special study, and every part of the country is equally interested in whatever measures of security can be taken to provide against such a peril. Not less dangerous than the attack upon the cities and the great working-class areas and upon the manufacturing centres, would be that directed upon the dockyards and the oil fuel storage which, unless proper precautions are taken, as I trust they have been or are being taken, might actually paralyse the Fleet, with consequences which no one can fail to perceive.

Therefore, I suggest to the House in this first part of the argument, that the danger which might confront us, however moderately put, would expose us not only to hideous suffering, but even to mortal peril, by which I mean peril of actual conquest and subjugation. It is just as well to confront those facts while time remains to take proper measures to cope with them. I may say that all these possibilities are perfectly well known abroad, and no doubt every one of them has been made the subject of technical study. I, therefore, have stated to the House as briefly as possible—and I trust I have not overstated the case—the kind of danger which reasonably ought to be taken into consideration should, unhappily, a breakdown in European peace occur.

I come to the second part of my remarks which deals with the much more difficult and much more debatable question of what remedy can be applied. What measures can we take to provide against these very great perils, or at any rate mitigate and minimise their effects? I do not think, to give a personal opinion, that it is much use planning to move our arsenals and factories over to the west side of the island. When one considers the enormous range of foreign aeroplanes and the speeds at which they travel—200, 230 and 240 miles an hour— it is evident that every part of this small island is, I will not say equally, but almost equally, within range of attack. If enormous sums of money were spent in displacing our arsenals from their present position, it might well be found that before this cumbrous process was completed, improvements in aeroplanes would have more than discounted any advantage which might have been gained. The flying peril is not a peril from which one can fly. It is necessary to face it where we stand. We cannot possibly retreat. We cannot move London. We cannot move the vast population which is dependent on the estuary of the Thames. We cannot move the naval bases which are established along our southern coasts with the great hereditary naval populations living around them. No doubt, where new factories were being created the factor of distance would be an important consideration, but in the main I am afraid we shall have to face this peril, whatever it may be, where we stand.

I think it would be a great mistake to neglect the scientific side of defence against aircraft attack—or purely defensive action against aircraft attack. Certainly nothing is more necessary, not only to this country but to all peace-loving and peace-interested Powers in the world and to world civilisation than that the good old earth should acquire some means or methods of destroying sky marauders. It is a matter which is of interest to us all that we should be able to meet this present menace which no generation before our own has faced, which shakes the very fabric and structure of all our civilised arrangements, and, by spreading fear and danger far and wide, makes it more and more difficult to preserve security and tranquillity in the minds of the different great States. If anything can be discovered that will put the earth on better terms against this novel form of attack, this lamentable and hateful form of attack—attack by spreading terror throughout civil populations—anything that can give us relief or aid in this matter will be a blessing to all.

I hope that the Government will not neglect that aspect of the question. There is a committee, I have no doubt, studying it. It ought to be the strongest committee possible, it ought to have the greatest latitude possible, and it ought to be fed with the necessary supplies to enable experiments of all kinds to be made against this danger. I have heard many suggestions with which I would not venture to trouble the House now, but they ought to be explored and explored thoroughly and with all the force of the Government behind the examination. It ought to be not merely a question of officers of a department doing their best, but of the force of the Government, and I do hope that my right hon. Friend when he replies will tell us that steps of this kind will be taken; that there will be no danger of service routine or prejudice or anything like that preventing new ideas from being studied, and that they will not be hampered and subjected to so many long delays as were suffered in the case of the tanks and other new ideas during the Great War.

The fact remains that when all is said and done as regards defensive methods—and all that you can say now has been said already—pending some new discovery, the only direct measure of defence upon a great scale is the certainty of being able to inflict simultaneously upon the enemy as great damage as he can inflict upon ourselves. Do not let us under-value the efficacy of this procedure. It may well prove in practice—I admit you cannot prove it in theory—capable of giving complete immunity. If two Powers show themselves equally capable of inflicting damage upon each other by some particular process of war, so that neither gains an advantage from its adoption and both suffer the most hideous reciprocal injuries, it is not only possible but it seems to be probable that neither will employ that means. What would they gain by it? Certainly a Continental country like the one of which I have been speaking, with large foreign armies on its frontiers, would be most unwise to run the risk of exposing itself to intensive bombing attacks from this island upon its military centres, its munition establishments and its lines of communication at a time when it was engaged or liable to be engaged by the armies of another first-class Power.

We all speak under the uncertainty of the future which has so often baffled human foresight, but I believe that if we maintain at all times in the future an air power sufficient to enable us to inflict as much damage upon the most probable assailant, upon the most likely potential aggressor, as he can inflict upon us, we may shield our people effectually in our own time from all those horrors which I have ventured to describe. If that be so, what are £50,000,000 or a £100,000,000 raised by tax or by loan compared with an immunity like that? Never has so fertile and so blessed an insurance been procurable so cheaply.

Observe the reverse of the picture. Assume that one country has a powerful air force and that the other has none, or that the other country has been so decisively beaten in the air that it has hardly any air force left. Then not only war machines but almost any flying machine that can be fitted to carry bombs will be employed to go over and to torture every part of the State and the community in that other country until it surrenders all that is asked from it. Absolute subjugation could in the end be enforced by such air attack, once a country had lost all power to fight in the air. Once complete ascendancy in the air had been secured, the victor Power might almost at leisure pick out any aircraft factory and make a special study of it, an intensive attack upon it, and thus there could be no recovery. It is almost the only form of war that we have seen in the world in which complete predominance gives no opportunity of recovery. That is the odious new factor which has been forced upon our life in this twentieth century of Christian civilisation.

For all these reasons, it seems to me, and I submit to the House, that we ought to decide now to maintain, at all costs, in the next 10 years an Air Force substantially stronger than that of Germany, and that it should be considered a high crime against the State, whatever Government is in power, if that force is allowed to fall substantially below, even for a month, the potential force which may be possessed by that country abroad. That is the object with which I have put this Amendment on the Paper. I am not going into other questions than those with which I am specially concerned to-day, but I must just mention that if, to this provision which I have suggested, you add those measures towards collective security by what I would call placing special constables upon the dangerous beasts in Europe and perhaps later on elsewhere, under the aegis and authority of the League of Nations, I firmly believe that we may have it in our power to avert from this generation the supreme catastrophe of another war. The idea that we can intervene usefully in sustaining the peace of Europe while we ourselves are the most vulnerable of all, are the beggars in fact, is one which cannot be held firmly by any man who looks at this in the faithful discharge of his duty.

I have now spoken of the danger, and I have indicated, as far as I can see, what is the only remedy or mitigation which is in our power, and I have suggested that it is a good and effective mitigation and a very reasonable security. I now come to compare the actual strengths, present and prospective, of Great Britain and Germany, as far as I have been able to form an opinion about them. Here again there is no reason to assume that Germany will attack. In fact, the German people have very friendly feelings in many ways towards us, and there is no reason at all why we should expect that they would attack us; but it is not pleasant for us—I will put it to the right hon. Gentleman the Leader of the Opposition—to feel that it may soon be in the power of the German Government to do so unless we act.

I will not dwell this afternoon on the character of the present German Government, because the House knows it all, and there is no need to repeat all that. I will content myself by saying that the decision of a handful of men, men of the 30th June, is all that is required to launch an attack upon us, if such an attack were possible, and that only the shortest notice or no notice at all could be counted upon. Never in our history have we been in a position where we could be liable to be blackmailed, or forced to surrender our possessions, or take some action which the wisdom of the country or its conscience would not allow it to do. Never have we been in a position where we could be subjected to that or, alternatively, have to face the horrible ordeal I have tried, very briefly, to place before the House. It is a danger to all Europe that we should be in that position, and I do not think His Majesty's Government ought to put us or leave us in such a plight, where we, with our wealth and Empire, exist on the good behaviour and good faith, which may not be lacking, but which may not be present, of the present rulers of Germany. I am sure our people are not willing to run such risks, and yet, as I am going to show, I think indisputably, this is the kind of danger which is coming upon us in a very short time unless we act upon a great scale and act immediately.

According to the Treaty of Versailles, the German Government are not allowed to build any military aircraft or to organise any military air force. Now this stipulation was intended to be a protection to the other countries and for their greater security and assurance, but it has in fact become an additional danger. What was meant for a safeguard for the Allies has in fact become only a cloak or a mask for a potential aggressor. With any other country, the facts about its air development would have been stated quite promptly. We could have put an unstarred question on the Paper as to the strength of the air force of France, or the United States, or any other country. In fact, the League of Nations collects these figures. It is part of the process of waging war against war that there shall be full disclosure, that people shall know where they stand, at any rate, if you cannot remove fear, that at least you can remove suspicion. With any other country this would make no difficulty, but it is just because Germany is under this special disability. I understand how it has arisen. It has not been considered etiquette, or at any rate the Government have shrunk hitherto from stating the facts which they know well—I am sure they know—about the German rearmament, and very naturally, because, if the Foreign Secretary had said there was this or that that they were doing contrary to the Treaty, he would immediately have had to make good his statement, or perhaps stand by his statement, that he was charging a great Power with a breach of the Treaty, and I can understand that until certain disclosures which have been made on the Continent had been made, it was necessary for the Government to proceed with great caution in this respect.

But the time has come when what was meant to be a protection for others must no longer be a cloak or a mask for Germany. The time has come when the mystery surrounding the German rearmament must be cleared up. We must know where we are. The House naturally in these matters leaves the main responsibility to the Executive, and that is quite right, but at the same time it cannot divest itself of responsibility for the safety of the country, and it must satisfy itself that proper measures are being taken. I will therefore this afternoon assume the duty of stating what, to the best of my belief, are the strengths and programmes of the German military air force which is being built up in contravention of the Treaty, and I invite my right hon. Friend the Lord President to confirm, correct, or contradict me when he speaks, as I believe he is going to do immediately after I sit down. If he does not contradict me or correct me, the House should assume that the statements which I make are true or at any rate that they are understatements; that is to say, I have not revealed the real state of things. In order that my right hon. Friend might be able to deal effectively with these issues and might not be confronted with them abruptly in the House, I sent him in the last week a précis of the exact points which I propose to put to him, and I understand that he has had an opportunity of consulting with the high expert authorities upon this matter.

I therefore assert, first, that Germany already, at this moment, has a military air force that is to say, military squadrons, with the necessary ground services, with the necessary reserves of trained personnel, and material—which only await an order to assemble in full open combination—and that this illegal air force is rapidly approaching equality with our own. That is my first submission to the Government and to the House. Secondly, by this time next year, if Germany executes her existing programme without acceleration, and if we execute our existing programme on the basis which now lies before us without slowing down, and carry out the increases announced to Parliament in August last, the German military air force will this time next year be in fact at least as strong as our own, and it may be even stronger. Thirdly, on the same basis, that is to say, both sides continuing with their existing programme as at present arranged, by the end of 1936—that is, one year further on, and two years from now—the German military air force will be nearly 50 per cent. stronger, and in 1937 nearly double. All this is on the assumption, as I say, that there is no acceleration on the part of Germany, and no slowing down on our part. So much for the comparison of what may be called the first line air forces of the two countries.

I come to the second line—civil aircraft which are capable of being used for military operations, the dual purpose machines, as they are called in Germany. Here the story is very much worse for us. Germany has already between 200 and 300 machines of long range with great speed, 220 to 230 miles an hour, which are now ostensibly employed, or actually employed, many of them, in carrying mail bags and to some extent in carrying passengers, which machines can be converted into long-distance bombers of the highest efficiency in a few hours. All that is necessary is to remove some parts of the passenger accommodation and fit bomb racks in their place. Those bomb racks, I told the House five months ago, are already made and kept in close proximity to the machines. That is the position at the present time. Germany has already between 200 and 300 of these machines. This time next year the number will have risen at least to 400 of these machines, which in the case of war will be a direct addition to the German military air force.

Against that we, as I understand, can set nothing that is in the slightest degree comparable for military purposes. Our civil aviation is valueless for war purposes. Indeed, it has been the custom of Ministers and others to boast of this fact as proof of our pacific intentions, if, indeed, proof were needed. Everyone knows that we have built for comfort and for safety, and without the slightest contemplation of convertibility. Therefore, I assert, and I invite the Government to contradict the statement if they can, that by this time next year, taking both the military and the convertible civil aircraft into consideration, Germany will have a substantially stronger Air Force than we. Frankly, I do not think that the country has prepared itself to realise this fact. The conditions in 1936 and 1937 if the German convertible machines are added to the military machines, will be that the German Air Force will, of course, be far more adverse to this country than the purely military figures, which are bad enough, that I gave a few moments ago.

I come to what I may call the third line—the ordinary civil aviation. It is difficult to compute the value of this for war, but it represents reserve pilots, mechanics, landing grounds, factories, aerodromes and a general familiarity with the flying art, which is, indirectly, of great importance. I think you may say that civil aviation bears the same relation to the fighting force as the mercantile marine has for so many generations borne to the Royal Navy. It is quite certain that the German pool of civil aviation, from which a military air force can be expanded and developed, is already far larger and far more closely related to military purposes than ours. The principle underlying German civil aviation, and all the regulations and subventions, point to their being made efficient for rapid transformation into military machines, or, as far as possible, into training machines.

Nor is Germany neglecting defensive preparations. Air alarm arrangements, gas drill and so forth are taking place all over Germany as well as in many other parts of the Continent of Europe. The House must not miss the bearing of this upon retaliation, upon the protection one can get from the power of retaliation, because if of two populations, both exposed to attacks of this kind—which God forbid—one has all kinds of protection which enable it to avoid the loss of life, it is perfectly obvious how great will be the injury to the one unprepared. I know that the Government have been considering this matter, and I understand the reason why nothing has been done is the fear of frightening the population. I say that it is much better to be frightened now than to be killed hereafter. It is much better to be frightened before it happens than when the danger actually comes to pass.

There is another point which, I notice, was referred to in a Question and Answer in the House to-day. I am assured that many of the German aerodromes are proof against air attack. They build earth concrete embankments round the shelters where the aeroplanes are stored, so that the place is quite safe; whereas you have only to look at our aerodromes for our Air Force to see that they are vulnerable to any attack of that kind, and might be put out of action altogether. Anyone, however pacific he may be, must admit surely that there is no proper protection of our aerodromes. I think that this is a primary and an urgent duty of the Government. I heard the Debate the other day upon the devastated areas of our country. Many suggestions were made for remedying the situation. Suppose there is a great deal of work to do in earthing up these aerodromes which will have to be constructed, why not give it to those unemployed people? Recruit 20,000 or 30,000 men from those areas on good wages, and let them go about the country and do this necessary work, instead of being employed on relief work and so forth. Let them act, not as unemployed, but as a labour reserve, and let them go forward and revivify their own homes by sending back the wages which they earn by doing the most necessary and urgent of public tasks. I throw that out by the way.

I have now completed my review of the two countries and I invite my right hon. Friend the Lord President to state, if I am wrong, where I am wrong, and to what extent I am wrong. But I cannot leave this subject without also referring to another cause of anxiety. So far, I have dealt with what, I believe, is the known, but beyond the known there is also the unknown. We hear from all sides of an air development in

Germany far in excess of anything which I have stated to-day. As to that, all I would say is: Beware. Germany is a country fertile in military surprises. The great Napoleon, in the years after Jena, was completely taken by surprise by the strength of the German army which fought the war of liberation. Although he had officers all over Germany the strength of the army which fought him in the Leipzig campaign was three or four times as strong as he expected. Similarly, when the Great War broke out, the French general staff had no idea of the reserve divisions which would be brought against them. They expected to be confronted by 25 army corps; actually more than 40 came against them.

It is never worth while to underrate the military qualities of this most remarkable and gifted people, nor to underrate the dangers that may be brought against us. I only say it does not follow that, in stating the figures I have to-day, I am not erring grievously on the side of under-statement. It sounds absurd to talk about 10,000 aeroplanes, and so on, but, after all, the resources of mass production are very great, and I remember when the War came to an end the organisation over which I presided at the Ministry of Munitions was actually making aeroplanes at the rate of 24,000 a year, and planning a very much larger programme for 1919. Of course, such numbers of aeroplanes could never be placed in the air at any one moment, nor a tenth of them, but the figures give one an idea of the scale to which manufacture might easily assume if long preparations have been made beforehand, and a great programme of production is launched.

The danger I have dealt with. I have mentioned the remedy so far as it can be described, and I have compared the two air forces. But what have we done in the last year? This is the last aspect with which I wish to deal. We had a Debate last March, and there was a good deal of anxiety expressed. My right hon. Friend the Lord President made a very weighty declaration, and he broke the back of the Debate. But in the evening the Debate revived, and a great deal of anxiety was expressed for a more explicit statement, and my right hon. Friend showed a little less than his usual imperturbable urbanity and patience, and said, "If you are not satisfied, you can go to a Division." What was the use of going to a Division? You might walk a majority round and round the Lobbies for a year, and not alter the facts by which we are confronted. What happened after the March Debate? Very little—so far as I can see, nothing happened for five months. Then we came to July. In July, the right hon. Gentleman came down to the House with the full authority of the Government and announced the programme of the 42 new squadrons to be added to the Air Force in five years. I pointed out there and then that this scheme did not propose to strengthen the Air Force even by one additional squadron before 31st March next, and only by 50 machines—that is to say, 50 machines in their proper squadrons with all their reserves, and so on—by 31st March, 1936. Another five months have passed, and we now know that nothing has been done, and that nothing will be done before 31st March which will involve a Supplementary Estimate. I am well aware of all that has been rightly said of the complication of this service and the necessity of preliminary preparation, and so forth. I will deal with that not now, but when an opportunity occurs upon the Air Estimates. I submit to the House that to continue this dilatory process in the present situation, even for a few more months, and certainly for another year, will deprive us of the power ever to overtake the German air effort. I therefore invite His Majesty's Government to tell us, firstly, what are the facts; and, secondly, if the facts are admitted, what will be their action?

I have only one more thing to say, and I address myself to the Liberal and Labour Oppositions. We read almost every day—certainly every week—in their great popular newspapers the most searching and severe criticism of the existing German regime. Nowhere is that criticism put with greater force and ability and from no quarter is it, I believe, more resented by the present rulers in Germany because it is in the main true. Things are said which are capable of raising the deepest antagonism, not in the breasts of the German people, because they have nothing to say as to their own destiny, but in the breasts of those powerful men who control the people. How can hon. Members opposite reconcile that criticism with the other parts of their policy, which is to cover with contumely and mockery and odium every attempt to secure a modest and reasonable defence to maintain the safety of the country? I have not always found myself in full agreement with this House of Commons, but I have never lost all hope that it will prove itself to be what its creators hoped for it, a great House of Commons in the history of the country. The election which brought this House into power was one in which the greatest number of voters ever called upon to record the franchise in this country voted, above all things, for the maintenance of the strength and the security of their native land. That was the emotion which brought us into power, and I would venture to say: Do not, whatever be the torrent of abuse which may obstruct the necessary action, think too poorly of the greatness of our fellow countrymen. Let the House do its duty. Let the Government give the lead, and the nation will not fail in the hour of need.

INDIA (CONSERVATIVE POLICY)

December 5, 1934

Conservative Party Central Council Meeting,
Queen's Hall, London

If as a result of what we do today we find India in a few years' time reduced to the anarchy and misery of China, the word "irrevocable" is one which will haunt us all their lives. Nothing in the Report of the Joint Committee altered the main principles of the White Paper, which in turn emerged substantially unchanged in character from the Round Table Conference held by the Socialist Government in 1930. We are to force democratic Parliamentary institutions upon India when democratic and Parliamentary institutions are in so many great countries failing even to give the elementary guarantees of justice and freedom. We are to make far-reaching transferences of power—abdication, we should call it—to the Indian democracy at a time when all over the world we see other countries reaching out and hurriedly arming in order to acquire oversea possessions and markets and empires. Let us look round the world! Outside these islands are forces of Imperialism and Nationalism such as the modern world has never seen before. At home we have defeatism, of which every one complains, and indifference which seems almost to chloroform us.

I think Mr. Baldwin was absolutely right when he reminded us that what we have in common and what we have to unite against is the Socialist menace. I wish that by agreeing to the prudent proposals of Lord Salisbury we could be brought into line together. I do not under-rate that menace. There are Socialists everywhere—both at the head of the Government and at the head of the Opposition; they have captured the control of London, and, according to Mr. Amery, they might expect a victory at the polls. Wherever we look we find that the Socialists are preaching doctrines, sapping the foundations of every structure which our forefathers have raised. Ought there not to be some force or party in the State which will stand vigorously to arrest this process of degeneration and decay? Ought not the Conservative Party to be that force? Ought it not to be the rock in this uncertain situation, or is the Conservative Party to sit gaping while the foundations of the Empire are being frittered away?—not sitting still, but becoming the active agents to overpower those who are trying to save what they can from this Indian wreck.

I ask whether this plan will work, whether it will last. Will it give a better Government to the Indian people? (Shouts of "Yes" and "No" and some cheers.) Will it give Indians more food? Will they have less taxes to pay? Will there be peace in their streets, greater justice in the courts, and higher security against the oppression of class and race? Will it give what the Indian politicians themselves asked for? Is there any finality in it; any hope of tranquillity even for a breathing space to follow on the passage of this constitutional scheme? India is to be subjected to a double simul-taneous convulsion.

Whom does this White Paper Home Rule satisfy? The Socialist Party takes it only as a step for a further advance. The Congress Party would use it as a valuable lever to carry out their purpose. The Conservative Party—ah, if they could only say what is in their hearts! Will any other country behave about the interests of great oversea possessions as this country does?

INDIA (CONSTITUTIONAL REFORM)

December 12, 1934

House of Commons

Everyone will agree with the Foreign Secretary [Sir John Simon] when he speaks of the importance of this Debate, dealing, as I think he said, with a subject as momentous as any upon which the House has had to come to a decision in the last hundred years. Who touches India touches history, and when, as the hon. Gentleman the Member for Orkney and Shetland (Sir R. Hamilton) reminded us, we are dealing with the lives and fortunes of one-fifth of the globe or one-sixth of the human race, we touch not only history but world history. I feel that it will be the endeavour of all who take part in these Debates to try their best to raise them as far as possible to a level worthy of the subject and worthy also of the tradition of this House, which in former generations has lavished time and thought upon the study and discussion of the affairs of India. Those of us who are in a minority here will certainly exert ourselves in that way.

I may say that, speaking for this minority, we claim in this matter belligerent rights. We are concerned in defending a cause and putting a case whose dignity and magnitude are such that we are entitled to those rights, but we realise that it is quite impossible—it would, indeed, be intolerable—that the settled will of the House of Commons should be arrested by merely dilatory procedure. Let the Government give a fair opportunity for discussing this great controversy. Let us discuss it in such a way that the 20 or 30 items of principle and cardinal points of method can be debated fully, and I am sure that the Government will find that those who differ the most strongly from them will be the first to render them aid in achieving the execution of their plans within a reasonable and orderly period of time. I hope, indeed, that it may be possible to come through the whole of these Debates on the India Bill which, when we consider the procedure in the other House as well as the procedure here, may well take us into the latter part of next year without the application of those processes of Guillotine and Closure which were introduced in the latter part of the nineteenth century and are an excrescence on the traditional Procedure of the House of Commons.

I know that there is a mood in some quarters to ride rough-shod over the minority, and I am very glad to find that it has received no encouragement from the Prime Minister and from the Government. I have also heard it said that modern democracy takes no great interest in India—it is too remote, too vague, too complicated—and will resent the occupation of our time upon the Indian problem. I hope that that is not true. If it were true, we should have ceased to be an Imperial people and shown ourselves unfitted to continue to fill that considerable place in the world to which the exertions of previous generations have raised us. I was so much encouraged by the fine Parliamentary action of the Prime Minister in regard to a suggestion which was made to send the Bill to a Standing Committee, that I will persevere on this favourable wind, and I am emboldened by the speech of the Attorney-General a few days ago in the country in which he talked about the splitting of the Conservative party from end to end. The Attorney-General—who is a great authority on these matters, though not so great an authority as the Lord Chancellor, who keeps the King's conscience, but still always ready to advise on matters of correctitude as well as law—the Attorney-General laid down the principle that it was unworthy for anyone in dealing with this India question to consider such an issue as the unity of a party. Unworthy! I think that is a very heroic doctrine and a very heroic mood, and I hope that we shall rise to it. As far as we are concerned, I may assure the Government that there is nothing that we should like better than that this issue should be decided on its merits according to what Members really think about it, and without any introduction of adventitious or extraneous influences or suggestions from anywhere. I hope that the Government, following the high line which the Attorney-General sought to take, will ask my right hon. Friend the Patronage Secretary, who is very busy these days, to desist from his systematic and official "unworthiness" and allow us all to have a free and open vote this evening when the Division is called.

I listened, as did all the House, with deep attention to the speech of the Foreign Secretary. I listened to his lucid, luminous explanation of such points as he considered it was necessary to draw our attention to on this occasion, but when he had finished I am bound to say that there came across my mind this feeling: Here is the greatest event for 100 years. Is this all that you have to say to induce Parliament to take the step which it is now being asked to take? Is this all the reason which you are prepared to give us before we embark upon this, as you admit yourselves, hazardous voyage? As I listened to his speech I had the feeling that the right hon. Gentleman with his sweet reasonableness was reducing this matter to petty proportions, to the mere matter of a few provisions here and there, putting the Liberal soul at rest on the troubles of indirect election; and that these were insufficient arguments to induce the House to launch this country into something which may well turn the whole history of the State. The feeling came across my mind that I was on a ship which was going down in a calm sea, and that some very reassuring observations were being addressed to the passengers, because there were no boats, I will not say by the captain but, at any rate, by the chief steward.

Let me say, first of all, that I do not think the Socialist Opposition have treated the Government very generously or even very fairly. Whatever advance has been made at any time to meet them, and immense advances have been made, they have accepted it only as a starting point for a new departure. Take the Statutory Commission. Representatives of all parties were on the Statutory Commission. They reached a unanimous conclusion. Many of us did not like the report of the Statutory Commission. Many of us thought that it might have been well said that the use made of the Montagu-Chelmsford reforms did not warrant at this stage a further advance. Still, when a commission of that quality goes to India, travels all around, comes back and makes its report, people try to submit, even if they cannot have their own point of view given effect to. I suppose the Conservatives on the commission made derogations from their view. Certainly members like the late Vernon Hartshorn did. To his memory a very worthy tribute has been paid by the Foreign Secretary. He was a charming, gifted and patriotic man. Members from all sides came back and endeavoured to produce, and did produce, a unanimous report. That was a very considerable fact, and it marked a great advance on the part of those who are doubtful whether further advances should be made.

What happened to that report? The Foreign Secretary reminded us that it had never been debated by Parliament. No sooner had the report been presented—the ink was hardly dry upon it—when the Prime Minister pitched it into the wastepaper basket and called together a Round Table Conference, which reopened the whole topic from the beginning; true, in the light of the information collected by the report, but, still, a complete reopening of the whole subject. Out of this Round Table Conference came the point that really divides us to-day and really has caused the trouble and the whole division which is growing in the country. The cause has been the additional surge forward, the lurch downwards I should describe it, at the first Round Table Conference from the basis which had been reached by the Simon Report. Again, I must point out that it was the Socialist party who had their way. It was their plan. It was their plan which was accepted. It was their plan which was recommended by the first Round Table Conference. It was their plan which was embodied substantially in the White Paper, and it is their plan which emerges, with certain additions and improvements, from the report of the Joint Select Committee. Does anybody dispute that it is the Socialist plan, the plan of the Socialist Government?

Sir S. Hoare: Yes, I do.

Mr. Churchill: I am glad to hear that remark, because there is a certain amount of controversy as to the parentage of the interesting progeny before us. The hon. Member for Bodmin (Mr. Isaac Foot) laid claim to it for Lord Reading, and he was rather controverted from the Socialist benches. Now there is another competitor for this dubious honour. As there is some difference on the subject, I will read the perfectly plain statement which was made by the hon. Member for Bassetlaw (Mr. M. Macdonald), whom we know as the most popular, agreeable, and competent Under-Secretary of State for Dominion Affairs. This is what he wrote in a newspaper in his constituency. It is very important that we should know these facts, because there is a dispute. This is what he wrote three years ago:

> How accurate was the Government's calculation of what would be the ultimate conclusions of the Conference, and of what policy it would finally be able to announce with the approval of all delegations, is illustrated by an interesting fact. The drafting of the Prime Minister's concluding statement of the Government's policy, actually delivered on the 19th January—

that is, January, 1931—

> was already in hand before Christmas. The text of the statement was completed during two all-day conferences between the Prime Minister and his principal Government advisers, which I attended at Chequers on 27th and 28th December. This was several days before the Conference itself began to consider the all-important question of Indian responsibility in the Central Government. It was before the Indians themselves had stated their ideas in detail.

Here I must disappoint the hon. Member for Bodmin—

> before Lord Reading had made his famous speech announcing the Liberal party's support of the Indian claims, and before the Conservatives' definition of their policy. Yet only minor alterations had to be made in the Government's statement as a result of these events following its original drafting. So much for the tactics of the Government.

So much for the statement of the hon. Member for Bassetlaw. There can be no dispute about the origin and the genesis of this scheme which we have before us, on the part of anyone who will consider that frank and open avowal. It may be asked: Why bring this up? I bring it up because it is challenged in some quarters. I also bring it up to show hon. Members opposite what obligations they have towards this scheme. Their paternity is proved without any doubt, and they are not going to escape the consequences by merely abusing the wretched brat which has been foisted on the guileless Conservatives. What did we then see? No sooner had the compliance of the Conservatives been achieved, no sooner had they agreed—no doubt they agreed of their own free will, and no doubt they agreed with the scheme on its merits; I do not argue that it was done under any duress—but no sooner had the matter been pushed forward to this stage than hon. Members opposite started moving on another downward march along the slope.

I must really warn His Majesty's Government that they will never be able to reach an agreement with the Socialist Opposition. The more they go forward the more they will be led on. Even now, if they were to meet all the suggested amendments which were made by the hon. Member for Limehouse (Mr. Attlee) in the Joint Select Committee, it would only be the starting point for a new departure. The Socialists are ready for that. The right hon. Gentleman who leads the Opposition is much ahead of the hon. Member for Limehouse, and is careering along the path towards the abyss, with a policy all of his own. I am told that the highest caste in India boasts of the distinction of being twice born. The party opposite—if they will allow me to say so in no offensive way—have been twice brought in regard to this matter. What is the result? The result is the formal opposition of the whole of the Socialist party and extreme denunciation by that party of the whole of this scheme, after the Government have done so much to meet them, and which they have carried on so far at such great risk. That is a very formidable fact.

We hear a lot about national unity and the importance of acting as a nation and not as parties in this matter. Where is the national unity if a party which represents a very large proportion of the country and is advancing confidently, as it believes—there may be more to be said about that before they reach that point—to power, definitely dissociates itself from such a scheme, and denounces it and opposes it formally in the House of Commons? My hon. Friend the Financial Secretary to the Treasury made a very thoughtful speech the other day. He does sometimes make very thoughtful speeches. He referred to the Irish parable. Let me say, as I am going to quote his words, that I do not intend to shirk my responsibility for any concern in that. The hon. Member, with great force and great cogency, said:

> We allowed the Irish question to become a party question, and from that moment we were lost. Once the Irish realised that they had two opposing parties to contend with their success was assured, for they could, and did, play one party off against the other until Great Britain was reduced to the most shameful surrender in her history. The Indians are not less astute than the Irish. They are more numerous and more powerful. Once allow them to believe that they can get more from one party than from another and there will be no end until we retreat from India with the same ignominy that attended our retreat from Ireland.

There you have the analogy. Here you have the alternative party, the only party which can replace this Government, and it has definitely come forward in direct opposition to and denunciation of your policy. The Government are entitled to review the situation in the light of the fact that what they have to offer now to the Indian people is not any more the gift of the nation. It cannot be pretended to be so. It is only the gift of a number of gentlemen who at the present time are able to marshal a Parliamentary majority in the House of Commons.

Many false analogies are drawn from past events, and we have had in these Debates continuous references to Ireland and South Africa. Of course, we all try to learn lessons from the past, but in extracting those lessons we naturally draw and extract the ones which are the most agreeable to our mood at the moment. I had something to do with most of those decisions. It fell to my lot to carry the South Africa Constitution Act and the Irish Free State Act through this House. I will tell hon. Members the particular lessons which have remained in my mind from them. First as to the South Africa Constitution Act. The lesson there was that it is not enough to be right and well meaning, but that you must find big men with whom you can make a bargain which will be faithfully observed. In General Botha and General Smuts we found two great men, two great warriors, and fathers of their country, who, for a quarter of a century, have used their extraordinary gifts in order to preserve the solemn compact which was signed between the two belligerents in the Treaty of Vereeniging, and subsequently in the South Africa Constitution Act. It is no use comparing the South Africa Constitution with what we are now asked to do for India. It is only to darken counsel to bring that in. I am sorry that General Smuts, for whom I have such admiration and a long friendship, seemed to make some comparison the other day. I wonder what the distinguished General would say if a proposal was put forward to give seats in the Union Legislature to Indian immigrants to South Africa, or to the native inhabitants of South Africa? I think the fine and expansive phrases of his Liberalism would shrink to a very much more narrow and effective practical demonstration of his will.

In Ireland also, I shared in that sombre decision, and I am not going to attempt to elaborate it to the House now except to say that there, again, we tried to make a bargain with the men who really controlled the opposite forces, and, if that has failed, it is largely because those men, Michael Collins, Kevin O'Higgins and Arthur Griffiths, gave their lives quite soon in an effort to maintain the honour, as I believe it to be, of the Irish people in the faithful execution of Treaties entered into with good faith on both sides. We have had great disappointment and disillusion in Ireland. I wonder whether the then leader of the Conservative party, the right hon. Member for West Birmingham (Sir. A. Chamberlain), feels that disappointment. I certainly do, poignantly, and every reproach which naturally attaches to it; to the prophecies which were made, the hopes which were aroused, but which the passage of time and the march of events have falsified. I feel it very much indeed. Although one must act according to the circumstances of the moment, and grave indeed were the circumstances of that moment, I cannot feel that one ought not to accept to some extent the hard teachings of experience.

But how much worse lies the Indian situation? There you have no one to deal with, nobody that can execute their side of the contract or agreement. There you have no one who can answer you; you have only vague noises coming back to us across the ocean, incoherent noises, as the result of all we say and do. The House must ask itself:

How shall we stand on this Indian matter, not in a year or two, but 10 years hence? After all, the lesson that you may learn from Ireland is that at the beginning things may go fairly well, that the first lot of men you deal with will keep their word. There are in India men trained under your system, their minds habituated to a certain course. But the second lot of men, who come along and get into office by attacking the first lot, care nothing for the contracts which have been entered into or the agreements which have been made; they brush them all aside; they are nothing to them. And thus we have been insulted, derided, defrauded and mocked in our Irish policy.

Where shall we be 10 years hence in our Indian policy? Ten years is a very short time. I have been twice engaged in big matters in my experience as a Minister in which 10 years was the limit when they were to be reconsidered—the Washington Treaty and the Montagu-Chelmsford Reforms. It seemed to be all right and that we need not worry about them any more. They are both here. Where shall we be 10 years hence in this Indian matter? That is the question we must ask before the House votes to-night. In 10 years time the foundations and pivots of British authority will have simultaneously weakened in every part of India. You will have shifted the axis of India. You will have altered the focus of Indian loyalty. Everywhere the waves of so-called popular government and democratic movements will be lapping against the foundations of your institutions and pressing upon the structure of your power. Where will hon. Members in this House find themselves in 10 years time? If you resolve to proceed upon this path, to take this step now, it will be absolutely no use afterwards complaining of the consequences. We were criticised, the Lord President of the Council, the right hon. Member for West Birmingham, and I, for what we did in regard to Ireland, sometimes very harshly. Believe me, what you are going to do now is far more risky and ten times as large and lasting.

But we are told by the Secretary of State for India that the case of India is different, that we are keeping an Army in India and kept none in Ireland. I do not believe that that really affects the issue. At this stage of the difficulties in front of us it is not a question of the Army. If it comes to that the British Army is not so far away from Ireland. If the Irish trouble could have been settled by the use of military forces, we should not have put up with the treatment which we have received. No one dreams of using military forces against Ireland, great and grievous as are our complaints against the Irish Free State; nor would anyone. Once you engage yourself in this constitutional process and deliberately hand over power, set up a responsible Government with Ministers and Cabinets, who may present to the Governor-General their minutes according to the Constitution, you are upon a path where you may suffer mortal injury before any situation arose, and without any situation arising where military power had to be employed.

One other lesson I learned from the Irish Treaty proceedings, and I am sure that the Lord President of the Council learned it too, and a great deal better than I did. It was this. On a great Imperial issue the votes which are given by Conservative Members in the Lobby or at the National Union of Conservative Associations are no true measure of the feelings of the party on the subject at stake. They are naturally influenced by their trusted and honoured leader. I well remember when we were both engaged in the Irish matter that everything seemed to be going very well—I think there were only 30 or 40 who voted against us in the Lobby on the decisive Division—we had the great advantage of Lord Derby's assistance in bringing Lancashire along quietly and in turning the opinion of the National Union, and at the Liverpool conference only 70 delegates voted against the Irish decision out of 1,800 delegates. The "Times" newspaper recorded this with lively satisfaction. But the right hon. Gentleman knows perfectly well that underneath the surface passions and feelings were boiling and that deep injury was done to the structure of unity and harmony within the party. So well did he judge this that within less than a year he went off to the Carlton Club and blew the Government sky high.

I venture to draw a lesson also from the Montagu-Chelmsford Commission, and it is this. It is not the slightest use the House of Commons depending on a Joint Select Committee to give them good advice about India. We had a very fine Joint Select Committee, not quite so loaded, arranged and marshalled as the one over which the Secretary of State for India has reigned, but it was a very authoritive Committee and contained many men of intelligence, experience and authority. We took its advice. Many people think the advice given by that Committee has been the seed of the difficulties and evils we are suffering from to-day. For a long time I felt some reproach when hon. Members came along and said: "Mr. Churchill, it is all very well your coming forward now, but what were you doing when the Montagu-Chelmsford reforms were passed?" There, we took the advice of a Joint Select Committee, and the lesson I draw is that the House of Commons should not allow itself to be too easily gulled by an array of complacent notabilities and dignatories, but should address itself with earnestness to the topics which come before it and form an opinion of its own. That is what we shall endeavour to do in the months before us.

I will not linger longer upon the past, although I have, I hope, extracted some gleams of guidance from it. The past is over, the long process of examination has come to an end, and with it many hot controversies which were associated with it. When the House has approved of the report of the Committee, which no doubt it soon will do, the Constitution Bill will be brought before us, and then we shall have to take a new view of that piece of work as a whole. We shall have to try it, as I ventured to say out of doors the other day, by the test of a few simple questions. Will it work? Will it last? Will it satisfy the people for whom it is designed? Will it make a better government in India and a more assured and permanent connection between India and the Crown? These are the questions we shall have to determine next year, and we must go into them fully in the time allowed, which is enough to make it possible for us to do so. It is by the results of its work that the House will be judged. It is no good saying that we were at it for seven years, that we had a Joint Select Committee, and that we took enormous pains, the test by which our work will be judged will be: Is it good? Is it vital?

The great Napoleon said that a Constitution should be short and obscure. Although we have not yet seen the text of the Bill, we know enough about it to know that this particular Constitution will never fulfil one of these desiderata. But you may ask of any Constitution two questions: First, will it make a better Government; and, secondly, will it be acceptable to those for whom it is intended? Justification is, I think, possible on either of those counts. You may say that it will be unpopular in the country, that they will not like it, but that it will be a much better Government for the great mass of the people; or you may say that the people will have to put up with a lower level of administration, that the conditions will not be so good, but that it will gratify their ideals and that that is what they really want. Either of those defences can be made. But can His Majesty's Government make either of them upon this proposal? I believe it is possible to demonstrate that your policy fulfils neither of those conditions in any way. I know what we are going to hear. We are going to be told: "Here are the extremists of the Labour party; here are the Die-hards; and in the middle this great central phalanx of the sober-minded, steady, prudent, patriotic, matter-of-fact, common-sense, British Members of Parliament moving forward along the middle way." But it does not always follow that the middle way is the best way, as the man found who fell between two stools.

That is the difficulty of the Government. However large may be the number of people with them, they are still confronted with that difficulty. I do not agree with the party opposite; I disagree violently with the proposal they put forward. But at any rate they have a theme. Their theme is to do what the Indians wish. We also have a theme; it is to discharge the mission of Britain in the East. But what is your theme? That is what we want to find out in the months that lie before us. This scheme offers neither efficiency nor consent. We are launched upon a project which political India rejects. We parade it as grand and magnanimous; they reject it as a hollow sham. We consider that it is an immense relinquishment on our part of vital control; they accept it, if they accept it at all, only as the means of wresting further controls from us. We have deserted our duty to the Indian masses. Well I know that. But we have not gained the consent or gratitude of the Indian intelligentsia. We have wrested, wrenched, plucked the roof-beam from our house in the hope of building a bridge across a gulf, and when we have torn it down we have found that the beam is much too short. That is the answer which I give to those who say: "Go along in the middle with the moderate people." It is not the least use doing so unless they have a policy which somewhere or other achieves a definite purpose.

I was very glad to see that the report of the Joint Select Committee does not in any way under-rate the importance of provincial government. It speaks of it as a fundamental departure from the present system, and indeed Indian Ministers who have had so little experience can really not consider themselves slighted when they are asked to take over the government of countries as great as France or Germany, or Spain, or Italy, and when they have the whole of these vast populations and their affairs submitted to them. No one can complain at all that these tasks are unworthy. On the contrary, they constitute, I believe—provincial Governments alone, whether the police is fully transferred or not—a rulership as great and as august as is being exercised by any body of men in the world.

But there is this objection to the provincial scheme. I should have acquiesced in it and supported it and submitted to it, although from many points of view I do not like it, but there is this objection to it: Absolutely no provision is made for ensuring that we discharge our responsibility to the mass of the Indian people—none whatever. It is quite callous and disgusting the way in which the whole of their services are transferred without any desire to follow up and see what happens and to make sure that efficiency is maintained. I ventured to submit to the Joint Select Committee a proposal to have a system of grants-in-aid similar to those which we have in this country, which ensure the efficiency of our education system, and inspectors from the centre who would get in touch and make the conditions of the people between one province and another attain a certain standard. This could be done without the slightest derogation from the dignity of those whom it affected. There is not the slightest derogation. It is only what the Chancellor of the Exchequer and other Ministers here, who are giving money to local bodies, are continually doing.

There is no reason why something should not have been done. But the right hon. Gentleman yesterday boasted in a very pointed way that there would be no question of grants-in-aid or inspectors following up or anything of that kind. He can do that, and no doubt his Indian friends, as he rightly called them, will be pleased. Of course they will be pleased. But where does he stand himself? He stands himself in the position of one who has announced that the British Government completely disinterests itself in the welfare of this great mass, handing them over without caring even to inquire whether or not their hospitals, their schools, and all their different social services undergo a great deterioration. I call that a lamentable thing.

Sir S. Hoare: They are transferred now.

Mr. Churchill: Yes, but there are many other things that are going to be transferred. At any rate, the right hon. Gentleman in rejecting the suggestion I made at the time made it clear that he did not interest himself at all in any way in what happens there. I noticed that the hon. Member for Limehouse made a very far-reaching and rasping statement upon this subject. He said: "Let us suppose that we have this Constitution"—he was speaking generally of the Constitution—

> what will be the position of the masses under it? Self-government is only a means to an end. We do not want to hand over the workers and peasants of India to the Princes, the landlords, the moneylenders, the industrialists and the lawyers. I fear that that is what we are doing.

It is a very serious matter for the Government that that should be said by the official speaker of the Socialist party, because it is going to be repeated on hundreds of platforms throughout the country, and I believe it will find an echo in many Conservative hearts when it is known, especially among those who have great personal experience of India, that a lot of this talk about liberty for India only means liberty for one set of Indians to exploit another.

But the crux of the dispute between us is the question whether you should limit yourself to the provincial scheme or whether you must go forward and have federal autonomy. My Noble Friend yesterday put that very fairly. He said: "That is the great issue between us." It is true that without that undoubtedly the Bill would have an easy passage, even among those who very much dislike many features of it. But the Government are very conscious of this weakness, and an elaborate argument is being fabricated to prove that you cannot have provincial autonomy without central autonomy, that provincial autonomy without central autonomy would be rejected by the Indian people, and even that it is impossible—some go as far as that—not only is it pernicious but physically impossible to have the one without the other.

Evidently this is the sensitive spot. Anyone who has listened to the Debates will see that this is the point upon which the advocates of this policy feel most uncomfortable. They have to prove that the one form of autonomy is inseparable from the other, and it is this link between the two that causes them the greatest anxiety. Consequently there is a regular chorus of protestations whenever it is approached. I have heard the Secretary of State here, the Chancellor of the Duchy at Manchester, and the First Commissioner of Works here last night, and my Noble Friend, and no doubt we shall presently have my right hon. Friend the Member for West Birmingham, all engaged in proving that you must have the central if you are to have the provincial, and if they cannot have the central some of them even go so far as to say that they would rather have nothing at all and drop it all. It is rather rash to put the case so high.

After all, the Statutory Commission made a plan which presumably was a watertight plan, which envisaged provincial government only. They might have liked to have had something more, but they never said provincial autonomy alone was impossible, and Lord Irwin's Government in India, writing an elaborate critique upon that plan, went even further and treated federation as even more remote than the Simon Commission did. They contemplated a workable scheme without it being necessary to introduce this federal scheme. How can you pretend that it is unworkable when these bodies definitely made their plans upon that basis, and put them before us at such great length and with so much force? Besides, supposing in the course of our Debates we are able to prove, as we may well be able to do, that the federal structure and apparatus will not work, will not stand and will break down because of the many anomalies and contradictions and unsolved difficulties; or supposing that the Princes do not come in. What happens then? The Secretary of State for Foreign Affairs placed that in the very forefront of his argument and held it up as the most notable fact.

I am not now going into the question of the Princes' action, because we shall see in due course, before the Second Reading of the Bill; but if we are able to show that the scheme is unworkable, if we riddle it and hold it up to the censure of Parliament as bad workmanship, or if the Princes do not come in even in the reduced number that you want to come in, where will you be after you have been persuading your followers that the provincial scheme is impossible without the central, and in a few months' time you have to come to this House and say what a splendid thing the provincial scheme alone is all by itself?

I must address myself to this weak point—the junction between the two schemes; because that is the point on which all our batteries will be firing in the months ahead. Talk of the unity of India! We hear a great deal about it and of the danger of centrifugal forces from the Chancellor of the Duchy. He is very much against them. But my right hon. Friend must remember that, after all, it is the centrifugal force which now keeps the earth, including the Duchy of Lancaster, from falling into the sun, when our destruction would be total and immediate. But we are told that the unity of India must be the goal. The unity of India is not an end in itself. I think there is danger in assuming that it is axiomatic in our arguments that we should work for the unity of India as the end. Unity is not the end in itself. The welfare of India is the end, and the unity may or may not be the means of attaining that end, according to circumstances. However, let those who seek the unity of India listen to these words of John Stuart Mill. I knew that my hon. Friend the Member for Bodmin would like to hear them, so when I came across them I thought I would save them for him. They are taken from the volume on Representative Government already quoted by the Foreign Secretary:

> When nations thus divided are under despotic Government which is stranger to all of them, which ... chooses its instruments indifferently from all, in the course of a few generations, the identity of situation often produces harmony of feeling and the different races come to feel towards each other as fellow-countrymen ... but if the era of aspiration to free government arises before this fusion has been effected the opportunity has gone by for effecting it.

These are remarkable words from a remarkable man, whom Lord Morley said he approached as a calm lamp of benignant wisdom at which he was glad to kindle his rushlight. These are remarkable words. Are we to hand over the unity of India which is simply the result of British rule? There is no real, practical unity in India apart from British rule. Endeavour as you may to diminish British control and influence and Indianise the services of Government, to that very extent, step by step, you will see the unity of India decline. The only unity left when your rule has sunk will be a unity of hatred of all foreigners, particularly the foreigners with whom they have been brought into close contract. Then we used to be told that if provincial autonomy were offered without central autonomy, it would be rejected. As they are rejecting every-thing offered, obviously that argument has lost some of its force. If provincial autonomy is set up without central autonomy we are told that provincial governments, instead of concerning themselves with the great responsibilities entrusted to them, will be occupied in trying to obtain control of the central administration, and that they will exhaust themselves in that. I think that that is a very far-fetched and unconvincing argument. If Indian political classes who control provincial legislatures are not satis-fied, if the Congress party, who are the same party throughout the country, are not satisfied, obviously they will endeavour to press for changes in the central legislature. Will they not be able to use more power if, in the central legislature, they have already got an advance guard, a dyarchy established, and have got their foot in the door, not only in the central legislature but in the Cabinet? You will not escape this agitation; you will only arm it. On the contrary, if you are to look at this question of the interests of the Provinces as compared with the dual system of the Provinces and the Centre, I have heard great authorities on India say what a pity it would be if in the provincial legislatures the best men were drawn away from their work and forced to engage in the sterile constitutional struggles which, on the passage of this Bill, will begin at the Centre of India.

But then we are told—"Alas, the central government is so weak. The poor, weak central government cannot continue like it is; we want a stronger government." What do you mean by a stronger government? The Secretary of State must declare whether he seeks an act of liberation or to have a stronger government. Never was there a government so strong in relation to its subjects as the existing Government of India. It is quite true that it does not use its strength, that it defers more than is desirable to the opinions of the unsatisfactory representative legislative assembly which has been gathered together at Delhi. But the inherent, latent power of the Government is indisputable. We have seen that power exercised, and skilfully exercised. Why, the whole of the formidable movement of civil disobedience led by Mr. Gandhi, was completely defeated without the use of a single British battalion, and with hardly any loss of life. Such a demonstration of power, of strength of the central government has never been surpassed. Of course we are told that reforms are needed, that members of the legislature ought to become members of the executive council and so forth, but to pretend that the condition of the central legislature is so weak that you cannot allow it to continue, that you must strengthen it by setting up a dyarchy, a parliament of 600 men with, as the hon. Member for Limehouse told us, "Very little to do or few subjects to deal with," is an argument which ruptures the bounds of reasonable thought.

Lastly, we are told that the Princes have offered to come into the Federation, and that the opportunity may never return. Why will the opportunity never return? Do you anticipate failure in the Provinces? If you go on with them alone, will failure be so marked that once the Princes see it they will not consider the possibility of re-entry? For only if you anticipate failure must you expect they will not return. If provincial governments are a success, there is a far greater inducement for them to associate themselves with it. When the units are found to be of real purpose, the Princes will surely wish to join in the central system. However, we are told that when the Princes made their offer to come in they stipulated that in return there must be responsible government at the Centre. I thought it was a very odd thing that these autocratic Princes with lineages that go back for hundreds of years insisted that the central government must be responsible. I share the objection of my Noble Friend to the word "irresponsible." I note the curious terminology which describes as "responsible" the antics of the parliament of Ceylon, while the Select Committee dubs on page after page as "irresponsible" the majestic policy which has raised India from the misery and anarchy of former centuries. How anyone can abuse the English language, the English achievements in that way, passes my wit. What they meant was "non-responsible." Consultation of a dictionary would have relieved them from that error.

How was it that the Princes made their offer? In the dark and dismal days of the Irwin-Benn regime in India, a feeling, quite unwarranted, that the English really meant to hand over their responsibilities in India resulted in a tremor passing through the country. Every toiler who could spare a moment stopped to find out what was happening. Everywhere people were thrown into confusion. You saw one manifestation in the second horror of Cawnpore. You saw another manifestation when between some Princes and the Congress party there was an agreement reached, that if the Princes asked for responsible government the Congress party would guarantee them their hereditary despotic power in their own States. The idea that the Princes were enthusiastic about the proposal is arrant nonsense and humbug. It could never have been put across if there had been a Conservative party in this country doing its duty. But when "The Times," the "Daily Herald," the "News-Chronicle" and the "Manchester Guardian" all sing the same tune in cacophonous chorus a great imposture can be maintained against the public for a considerable period of time. I could go further into this matter, but I will not, for I do not wish to trespass on the time of the House. But I have tried to put some arguments forward which, in my opinion, show that no case has been made out that Federal and Provincial Governments are inseparable, and that the desperate efforts made to bridge the gulf between them have not succeeded.

I hope that the right hon. Member for West Birmingham will, perhaps, be able to address himself to that. One other favour I would venture to ask him is that I do hope he will tell the House the charming story of his conversion. I have heard it myself before, but I would enjoy it very much again. There are some in this House who have never had the opportunity of hearing it at all. I ask the right hon. Gentleman to tell us what sturdy feelings of independence led him to undertake the task of joining the Select Committee, with what grave misgivings he viewed the kind of policies and proposals upon which he might have to pronounce, by what infinite soul-stresses, he was forced inch by inch by the logic of inexorable fact to come to the conclusion that he must vote in the Government Lobby on this subject as he had always done on previous occasions.

The Lord President told us that unless we accepted this scheme we should lose India in two generations. That is a long way to look ahead. I do not know what is the exact measurement of a generation; it has never been computed. It seems to me that a remark of his old friend the late Mr. Bonar Law would be applicable—That you cannot argue with a prophet; you can only disbelieve him. As a matter of fact, looking even a few years ahead, it is a great mistake to assume that the future is a mere continuation and extension of the present and the past. The most unexpected turns back are taken by mankind in their journey. The trees do not grow up to the sky. Very often we see the sharpest zig-zags here and there, saving nations and saving great areas of the world from disaster at the last moment by sudden revulsions. You cannot look as far ahead as that but you ought to look ahead as far as you can, and ask yourself where you will be in 10 years time? This particular scheme which no one believes in really, not even the most enthusiastic Samuelite Liberal, is by no means the only way in which we can maintain our connection and our honourable contact with India.

I should like to point out to the House that we are now asked to adopt this scheme of Federal Home Rule at the Centre, and that not one of the conditions, which were envisaged at the time when it was first discussed, has been made good. There is no acceptance of it by the Indian political classes. There is no agreement between Mohammedans and Hindus upon the communal issue. The communal award made in default of their agreement has not been accepted by them. The anomalies of in-and-out voting in the Federal Assembly have not been solved. The franchise is wholly unsatisfactory. I daresay I prefer the one which you have now adopted but consider what it is. You are adopting a franchise which the Secretary of State and the whole India Department and the Commission which you sent to India considered was not the right franchise. He tosses to and fro on his feverish bed, now to one side and now to the other, finding nowhere in which to rest. All that is unsolved and unsettled. The financial stringency is unrelieved—though we have not heard much of it in these Debates—and there is not the wherewithal even to start the Provinces off with certainty still less the Federal conditions.

Nevertheless, in spite of all that the House of Commons is now asked to sign, as my Noble Friend the Member for Aldershot (Viscount Wolmer) has said, what amounts to a post-dated cheque, to be presented three or four or five years hence, by unknown hands, in circumstances which no man can foretell. That is what we are asked to do. Of course, the Government will win. We do not doubt that. But when they have won, when their vast majority has shuffled through a hundred lobbies, what will they have gained? They will have gained the right to impose upon India a system wholly unsuited to the welfare of its people and abhorrent to all who speak in their name. They will have plunged vast regions into prolonged political agitation and disputation which will proceed, not only in every Province, but also at the centre and summit of the Government of India. Meanwhile, every political agitator in India will look forward to the arrival in power here of a Socialist Government which has announced beforehand that it is prepared to out-bid your proposals at every point. Meanwhile, you will have injured, baffled, discouraged and divided the great political force and party which, in a world of gathering fears, must remain one of the chief instruments of British strength, and, more important than any question of party, you will have depressed the vital heartbeat of Britain all over the globe.

1935

GOVERNMENT OF INDIA

January 25, 1935

India Defence League Meeting, Bristol

Ten days before the end of a by-election in Wavertree, Liverpool, Mr. Randolph Churchill presented himself as an Independent Conservative candidate. This was seen as an action deliberately inspired by the elder Churchill, but in fact he had had no prior knowledge of his son's venture. But he supported him, and the rage of the official Conservatives was great.

In the event, Randolph Churchill polled more than 10,000 votes, but Labour won the seat. The Conservatives' estimation of the Churchills plummeted to new depths.

Sir Samuel Hoare spoke the other day as if the fight against his India policy were over. He was wrong. The real fight has only now begun.

We are told that the Government Whips can command an overwhelming majority for any proposals that the Government might choose to make during the remaining months of this moribund Parliament. Even if that were true we will not be daunted. This great issue will not be settled by mere numbers. It will be settled by argument, by will-power, and by the general political situation.

Whether we are few or many, we are enough to carry on this great debate, and we will not falter or shrink in courage, in effort, or in sacrifice in resisting to the utmost limit of human power, under the Constitution of what is still a free country, what we believe to be ruinous to the fame and splendour of the British Empire. We will carry on our struggle in both Houses of Parliament, and in all the organizations of the Conservative Party as opportunity might serve, and, above all, at this stage we will carry it forward in the country. We will not be deterred by abuse; still less will we be deterred by threats.

[Editor's Note: Referring to his son's campaign in the Wavertree Division of Liverpool, Mr. Churchill said]: I do not need to speak to you about him. You have already found that he can speak for himself. But what a spectacle you presented to the nation of the Conservative party machine working frantically night and day, its wealth, its wire-pulling, Ministers of the Crown in shoals, agents by the dozen, all employed to prevent a young man of 23 making his way as a Conservative into Parliament where for so many generations his forebears had borne their part. It is a pitiful spectacle, humiliating to the present leaders of the National Government.

If the ideas and causes for which Mr. Randolph Churchill is fighting at Liverpool are to have no part in the composition of the Conservative Party, if the only object of our party managers is to get rich, tame, futile men into Parliament, how will we ever be able to retain our hold upon the new generation, which is already here knocking at the door to claim its rights and to accept its responsibilities?

If the patriotic youth of Britain finds that their path is everywhere barred by the older generation—indeed, I will say by a worn-out generation—I fear that the great party which Mr. Disraeli inspired will cut itself off from the harvest of the future.

To such a pitch have the nerves of this Government, with its 400 majority, been shaken by this by-election that we are actually told in our inspired Press that members of Parliament who go to speak on Mr. Randolph Churchill's behalf, and for the cause of which he at this moment has the honour to be a representative, will be subjected to what is called "disciplinary action" by the party machine. I do Mr. Baldwin the justice of saying that there is no reason to suppose that any such intolerant folly entered his mind. If it were so, then indeed dark days would lie ahead for the Conservative Party and for its present leader.

What does this threat amount to? The only measure at the disposal of the party managers is to withdraw the Whip, which informs Conservative members of the course of Parliamentary business and asks them to help the Government to deal with it. The withdrawal of the party Whip from any member is only effective if his constituency turns against him and calls on him to resign his seat. But if the constituencies reply, as they most certainly will reply, by passing votes of confidence in the excommunicated members, the only result will be a rebuke to the Government from a number of the strongest and safest Conservative seats throughout the country.

No one except the most abject of mortals would be deterred by such processes from doing what he thought right. I think I speak for all my friends in the India Defence League if I say that we have not embarked on this controversy lightly or inadvisedly, and that we will, if necessary, be prepared to face final exclusion from public life rather than fail in what we conceive to be their trust.

I make no claim on your account or my own to be a hero in this matter; for there is hardly a Conservative member throughout the country who will not—once he has taken the plunge—find himself in a stronger position in the forthcoming Election if he is relieved from all connexion with the India policy of the Government, and, I must add, from all connexion with the present Prime Minister, Mr. MacDonald.

My hope is that we will so handle this India Home Rule Bill in the House of Commons as to prevent an irrevocable abdication of British sovereignty over India, and that thereafter there will still be time to close the ranks and to unite against the common enemy all those strong forces which carried our country through the Great War, which broke the general strike, and which, acting altogether, can still command the destiny of Britain. I may of course be disappointed in that, but that is the end to which I and my friends are marching and in which we will persevere.

INDIA—THE BETRAYAL

January 30, 1935

Broadcast, London

[Extract] Sir Samuel Hoare boasted in his broadcast of all the ex-Viceroys, all the ex-Governors, and other important magnates whom he has roped in on the side of Indian Home Rule. He says he has all the authorities behind him. But what nonsense this is! These great personages who have sailed over the surface of Indian affairs, these political dreamers and schemers who love to air their theories, these exalted officials bound by their duty to the Government of the day, are not the only people who know about India. There are several hundred thousand practical people in this country who have lived or served in India. If you took a ballot on this India Home Rule Bill among the British electors who have lived in India and gave them each one vote for every year they have lived there, the verdict would be 20, 30, 40 to one against the policy which we are now told commands a preponderance of expert Anglo-Indian opinion.

We are told that the working classes or black-coated working men take no interest in India? India has quite a lot to do with the wage-earners of Britain. The Lancashire cotton operatives have found that out all right. A hundred thousand of them are on the dole already; and if we lose India, if we have the same treatment from a Home Rule India as we have had (to our sorrow) from a Home Rule Ireland, it will not be 100,000, it will be more like 2,000,000 bread-winners in this country who will be tramping the streets and queueing up at the Labour Exchanges. . . .

Why should the leaders of the Conservative Party present themselves as the apologists of our rule in India. Future ages, will regard it as incomprehensible that a handful of men, less than half-a-dozen, but with their hands upon the party machine, could have twisted the whole mentality of the Conservative Party into its present abject mood. By giving them one sharp dig in the ribs you can recall the Conservative Party to its traditional duty. Why don't you do it? You'd be all the better for it, and so would they.

Sir Samuel Hoare has thrust upon Parliament the most bulky Bill ever known. If it was as luminous as it is voluminous, it would indeed command respect. But what is this India Home Rule Bill? It is a gigantic quilt of jumbled crochet work. There is no theme; there is no conviction; there is no simplicity; there is no courage. It is a monstrous monument of shame built by the pygmies.

India is to be subjected to a double simultaneous convulsion in the Provinces and at the Centre by a crazy attempt to create a Federal system before the units which compose it have even been formed. The wall before the bricks are made; the faggot before the stakes are cut! The faithful, trustworthy Indian police, the mainstay of peace and order, are to be disturbed and harassed by divided allegiances arising from unsure, irrational compromise. The supreme government of India is to be racked by Dyarchy—rival authorities clutching at the levers of power. In a period of severe economic and financial stress India is to be launched upon another 10 years of furious, costly, sterile political struggles fought out in the heart and brain of the Central Government, as well as in those of the Provincial Administration. There are to be 11 Governors, armed with dictatorial powers if they dare to use them—that is to say, 11 potential kinds of the seventeenth-century type. There are to be 11 actual Parliaments on the twentieth-century model. And these two opposite forces are to begin a wearing struggle with one another which will plunge India into deepening confusion and will impose upon these helpless millions, and hundreds of millions, living as they do already on the very margin of existence, a cruel new burden of taxation and mis-government.

Even the authors of this policy show by a multitude of shifts and safeguards that they have little confidence in what they do. They give and they take back, and then half give again. They concede a principle, they deny it in performance. They refuse, and then they furnish the weapons by which that refusal can be upset. They tempt and they disappoint. They speak with double voices: one to the House of Commons, the other to the Indian politicians. They will be disbelieved by both. They deserve to be disbelieved by both.

I do not take so poor a view of our moral rights in India as is fashionable nowadays. We are no alien Power in India. We are the latest of many conquerors, and we are the only conquerors who have ever made the well-being of the Indian masses their supreme satisfaction. What is the chief shame of this Indian Home Rule Bill? It is that we finally withdraw our guardianship from this teeming myriad population of Indian toilers. We withdraw our protection from their daily lives. We withdraw it, not merely as an experiment which can be brought to an end at any moment; but as a solemn abdication and repudiation of duty. We are henceforward to shrug our shoulders about their education and their hospitals, the canals which water their fields, the Courts of Justice upon which they rely, and we cut them from the House of Commons which has so long been their shield.

Mr. Attlee, the official spokesman of the Socialist Party, said:—"We do not want to hand over the workers and peasants of India to the Princes, landlords, money-lenders, industrialists, and lawyers. I fear that that is what we are doing." Those are terrible words, and I, as a Conservative opposed to his party on so many points, tell you that they are true. There is no exaggeration in them. They are the brutal truth. By this deed we abandon our mission in the East, the faithful discharge of which has been our greatest glory. By it we blacken the face of Britain with an indelible stain and rend the life of India with an incurable wound.

"TAME AND DUMB" CONSERVATIVES

February 5, 1935

*Address in Support of Randolph Churchill,
Liverpool*

There are times when I wonder whether our British greatness has not passed and whether the future holds anything for us other than a great decline. In view of such a situation personal and party questions, bandied about by political organizations, take their own proper small place. How anyone can put loyalty to a party, or to a local organization, or to a government, or to a leader like Mr. Baldwin or Mr. MacDonald, in the balance against a vital and overdue long-needed reassertion of our will and resolve to remain a great power in this competitive world passes my comprehension.

We are told by Mr. Baldwin that these are not the days to go back to party dog fights. In what fool's paradise does he live if he believes that a party dog fight is not going on all over the country at the present time? What are the Socialists and the Liberals doing all over the country? Taking all they can from the Government. The only difference is that whereas two dogs are biting us, our own dog is not fighting back; he has got a Socialist muzzle on him. The great Conservative Party to which the country would have so gladly given their confidence in 1931 is paralysed.

Never has a party of men been driven from power with so much contumely as the Labour minority Government. Yet, on the morrow of this unparalleled punishment and humiliation, they are everywhere in the key positions throughout the land. There is a Socialist at the head of the Government, a Socialist at the head of his Majesty's official Opposition; and a Socialist representing Great Britain—one of the same old gang—(laughter and cheers)—at the Disarmament Conference at Geneva; and a lot of good we have got out of that so far.

There is a Socialist Lord Chancellor; the Socialists have captured the government of London, the enormous London County Council for the first time is in their hands, and they have got their grip on many municipalities throughout the country. They have affected the universities and turned the heads of a lot of silly, callow youths who have not examined the great problems which confront us.

It is the Socialists who have foisted this Indian Federal policy on the Conservative Party. It is entirely their own plan. It was the foundation of their policy which they made out before the Liberals or Conservatives were even consulted, and they are now trying to make the great Conservative Party use its strength to force the measure through Parliament.

Meanwhile the Conservative Party, which is the bulwark upon which we have to rely, lies tame and dumb while its leaders and party managers mouth slogans and incantations which have no relation to the realities of the time or the immediate approaching problems of the future.

[Editor's Note: Mr. Churchill taunted Mr. Platt with having forgotten to put the word "Conservative" on his election literature.] Great parties have disappeared because public opinion has been unfavourable to them. But never has there been a party which, while it had five-sixths of the Legislature in its control and a great majority in the other branch of the Legislature, has faded and passed out of existence through a clerical error. (Laughter and cheers.) In my view the time has now come for the Conservative Party to assert its strength and proclaim its principles. We should take no narrow or ungenerous view. We should welcome the assistance of able and patriotic men of any party who will come and help in the work of national salvation. But is the famous Liverpool Working Men's Association to try to send a candidate to Parliament who, but for Randolph, would never have put the word "Conservative" upon his bill? That, I think, would be a mockery for all time.

INDIA (CONSERVATIVE POLICY)

February 8, 1935

Reply to Constituents, London

Churchill was responding to the resolution "That the Nazeing branch of the West Essex Conservative and Unionist Association, in annual meeting assembled, deplores Mr. Churchill's consistent opposition to the National Government in the House of Commons, and further desires to point out to Mr. Churchill that the position of the India Defence League in connexion with the Wavertree election creates a highly dangerous precedent for the adoption of an Independent Conservative candidate in the Epping Division, who would undoubtedly now be welcomed by many loyal supporters of Mr. Baldwin and the present Government."

I make no complaint of this expression of your opinion. I claim and practise a wide measure of independent judgment upon public questions, and I do not resent equal freedom among friends and supporters. Indeed, I believe that it will be far better for the Conservative Party, and for the country and Empire of which it is the bulwark, if the honest differences arising from the painful plight into which we have been led should be fearlessly brought to the fresh air instead of ranking underground. Even serious open differences between friends are better at the present difficult juncture than that sullen apathy and dumb discouragement which would be fatal to our chances at the General Election.

For the last four years I have been repeatedly authorized by the West Essex Central Association, in formal resolutions, to oppose the Indian policy of the late Socialist Government, which has now become the policy of the present National Government. I hold that the issues now at stake in India transcend all party and personal considerations. Hard fighting in a high cause means the readiness not only to inflict but to suffer severe blows, and every one must march where his sense of duty leads him.

You are wrong, however, in supposing that I am "a consistent opponent" of the present Government, still less that I am opposed to the principle of an Administration broader than the Conservative Party. On the contrary, I hope to stand at the next election, as I did at the last, as a Conservative and National candidate, and I trust that by that time there may be a sincere and effectual reunion of all those forces which carried us through the Great War and broke the General Strike, and whose strength is still predominant in the British democracy.

I feel, however, that the present National Government, which is opposed by two out of the three great parties in the State, which is headed by an international Socialist (still proclaiming himself a Socialist), and whose principal measure now being driven through Parliament will, as I believe, wreck and ruin our Indian Empire, is not a Government which can inspire or represent the national spirit of Britain.

The Conservative Party before the next appeal is made to the electorate must recover its pre-eminence and cohesion. This it can do only upon a commanding theme. That theme can only be the maintenance of the strength and integrity of the British Empire and the protection of the wage-earners whose livelihood depends upon the endurance of the Empire. For such a truly national and imperial policy we should welcome the aid of able and patriotic men, whatever their party labels may have been. But we should not injure the cause or derogate from the theme to gain weak and encumbering allies, nor must the Conservative Party be made the agent of policies against which its traditions protest and its instincts revolt.

You have asked that your resolution shall be brought before the West Essex Central Association, and I am in thorough accord with that. I shall welcome the opportunity of laying before them once again a full statement of my views in plain and unmistakable terms, and I shall ask for a direct vote of confidence.

GOVERNMENT OF INDIA BILL

February 11, 1935

House of Commons

I am very glad to feel, from what I have heard, that our differences on this Bill, which are serious, are not likely to be aggravated by any differences about the time to be alloted to its discussion. I understand that my right hon. Friend the Lord President of the Council will possibly give us some information upon this matter when he speaks to-night. I can assure him that those of us who are the Conservative opponents of this Measure do not wish to resist it by dilatory methods. We rest our hopes upon argument and upon reason. Personally, I have always felt that every Government, any Government, has a right to pass the main and major Bill of the Session in that Session, and if a fair, reasonable time is allotted for this Bill, which is one of great length, and in which many points of view are involved, I say on behalf of all my friends, that we will co-operate with the Government and with the other parties in order that the different stages of the Bill may be properly and adequately discussed over the whole area of the Bill, and that the Debates may be brought to a conclusion at a convenient point. We will do our very best to help and assist the Government in every way.

Surely it would be a very great credit to the House and to the Government, and especially to my right hon. Gentleman the Patronage Secretary, if a Bill of this extraordinary size and intricacy were to pass through Parliament, when feelings run so high about it, without there being the necessity of any formal Guillotine Resolution or without the necessity even of applying the Closure at any point. That, I believe, is not beyond our power to achieve, and if so, it will greatly enhance the procedure of this House and get us back to the period before our procedure was mutilated during the latter part of the nineteenth century. There is one advantage which will come from this to which I may, perhaps, refer. We are now at the beginning of these long debates on India. How shall we come out? How shall those of us, on this side of the House at any rate, who are political friends and in many cases personal friends, emerge from this long, rigorous controversy? No one can tell. This I will say, that if the minority can feel that the issue has been fairly tried, that they have had every opportunity which reason can afford for stating their case and for putting the really searching and questionable points in the case to debate; if they feel that they have done their best, then at any rate, they can feel that they are guiltless of any evil consequences that may result, and if anything could remove a lasting bitterness it would be that this matter has been thrashed out thoroughly in the House of Commons.

Of course, the grave new fact which is now before us is the declaration of the Secretary of State the other day reaffirming Lord Irwin's statement of October, 1929, about Dominion Status. My right hon. and learned Friend the Attorney-General said in the course of his speech that the Viceroy had the express authority of the Government of that day behind him in 1929; there is much more in it than that. Our memories are very short, and I must ask a few minutes' attention from the House to remind hon. Members of what really happened in 1929. The Statutory Commission were completing their report, and everyone was waiting with the very greatest respect and expectancy. Suddenly, Lord Irwin, as he then was, made this declaration. This phrase "Dominion Status" had been very loosely and unwisely used—by me, among others, certainly—in the years immediately after the War, that is, about 15 years ago, but time had passed by 1929, and in the interval it was felt among people in many quarters, and in Parliament, that so vague and indefinite a phrase ought not to play a part in the revision of the Indian Constitution. It was thought then especially wrong that such a phrase should be revived in the most solemn manner by the Viceroy, and on the eve when Parliament was expecting the report of its Statutory Commission.

We were told on Friday by the hon. Member for Broxstowe (Mr. Cocks), and I have no doubt that it is a perfectly valid explanation, that Lord Irwin's object was to create a favourable atmosphere for the publication of the report; but what this statement did was to overbid and to destroy the report of the Statutory Commission. It cut the ground from under their feet. The report was superseded before it was presented, and never since has it been thought worth while to bring this immense, invaluable and incomparable document to the formal consideration of the House of Commons. There was an immediate general protest at this statement. The indignation was intensified when it was found that the Statutory Commission—I hardly dare call it the Simon Commission any more—had themselves disapproved of this most improper departure.

Let me recall to the House the names of those who disapproved: Lord Reading, my right hon Friend the Member for Carnarvon Boroughs (Mr. Lloyd George), my right hon. Friend the Member for West Birmingham (Sir A. Chamberlain), and, of course, Lord Birkenhead. All these authorities upon the subject, leading men, disapproved in the strongest terms. My right hon. Friend the Lord President of the Council stood in a somewhat different position. He had been overtaken while on his holiday at Bourges by an emissary of the then Prime Minister—the present Prime Minister—and, in the belief that the Simon Commission—the Statutory Commission—favoured this declaration, he gave a conditional assent to it. The other day I saw in a newspaper: "Trial of the Tory rebels." What happened on this occasion was something very like the trial of the Tory commander-in-chief. I was not a member of the court. I was returning on the high seas, and when I arrived I acted, if I acted as anything, in the capacity of prisoner's friend. I hope my right hon. Friend will bear that in mind should the occasion arise. The right hon. Gentleman found it necessary to make a personal explanation to the House about it in which he said, about this declaration which the Attorney-General wishes us to suppose was almost taken for granted, and which had the full authority of the day, and so on:

> I pledged myself alone, and that only conditionally upon the assent to the proposed publication being obtained from the Simon Commission. In this matter my colleagues and I acted in full agreement.— [Official Report, 7th November, 1929; col. 1305, Vol. 231.]

This account is given by the then Secretary of State, Mr. Wedgwood Benn, speaking in this House on 7th November, 1929:

> Lord Reading made it perfectly plain from the beginning that he objected to this declaration. . . . In the second place, we learned that the Statutory Commission did not wish to be associated with the issue of any declaration, and, finally, the right hon. Gentleman, the Leader of the Opposition, and his colleagues, ex-Secretaries of State for India and others, dissented most strongly from the course which the Government proposed to take. Therefore, we had first, Lord Reading from September onwards objecting; then the commission not wishing to join in, and then the right hon. Gentleman opposite, on behalf of the Opposition—

that is, my right hon. Friend the Lord President of the Council—

> making the most strenuous objection. That was the situation which faced the [Socialist] Government in October. They wished to do this thing and they were faced with this powerful opposition. . . . The Liberals were against it, the Conservatives were against it, and the commission were

unwilling to participate. What did the Government do? They governed.—
[Official Report, 7th November, 1929; cols. 1325-6, Vol. 231.]

How we laughed; but he laughs best who laughs last. Confronted as we are with the
situation in which we now stand, I will say that the then Secretary of State has made
good his boast. The strange occult influences of Socialists, wherever they may sit, the
power of those ideas to which no resistance is made, have compelled us—have induced,
permeated and pervaded this Parliament, with its gigantic Conservative majority—to do
what in those days was scouted by everyone except those in the minority Government
of the Socialist party. I agree that the great opposition has disappeared. I do not see
my right hon. Friend the Member for Carnarvon Boroughs; he seems to have lost
interest in this all-important manner, in which he has played so great a part. Lord
Reading—
        Hon. Members: Where is the Prime Minister?
        Mr. Churchill: The Prime Minister has carried his point, certainly. He is the only
one who has. Lord Reading, released from the guidance of Carnarvon, rapidly slid over
to the opposite pole and developed his own point of view. My right hon. Friend the
Member for West Birmingham was, as he says, converted; the Foreign Secretary, of
course, then quivering with indignation, has been what has been called, in American
parlance, taken care of. So we find that this Declaration which was condemned then
by the leading authorities, is now exhumed, resuscitated, and foisted upon the House
of Commons, and that the House of Commons is expected to swallow it without
further question.
        What I ask, and what I think we should consider is, what has happened since
1929 to induce this change of view? The first thing that happened is this: The
Statutory Commission have published their report and it was found that they unanimously concurred in omitting any mention of Dominion status from their report. I
think that was a rebuke, in a way, to the persons who, like myself, in the atmosphere
after the War, when these matters had not become closely debated and hammered out
as counters of discussion, used such language. I accept the rebuke. I think it is right
that people should be reproached for language that they have used 10 or 15 years ago
in different circumstances if that should be found subsequently not to conduce to the
interests of the country. What is the second fact? The Joint Select Committee, the
body in which we are told such immense authority resides—the Government seem to
ride through all difficulties on the back of the Joint Select Committee—deliberately
omitted mention of Dominion status. Deliberately; it was not accidental. I cannot
believe that it was accidental. They are no longer in existence; I wonder what that
committee would have said if by a vote they had been asked to express their approval
of the insertion of that statement in the speech of the Secretary of State last week.
That the omission was not accidental cannot be disputed.
        I was reading in the public print a few days ago a speech by the Archbishop of
Canterbury in which he said:

        I think it is time that we got rid of such a misleading phrase as
    "Dominion status." It has proved capable of infinite misunderstanding

both in this country and in India. No one knows whether it means constitution or position. If it is to mean constitution, is it conceivable, considering the circumstances of India, and the necessary relations with the Imperial Parliament which these circumstances involve, that in any time which any of us can contemplate, India should have a constitution identical with those which have been achieved in countries so entirely differenct as South Africa, Australia, or Canada? Therefore, it is no use thinking that there can ever be a constitution in India identical with the Constitutions of those Dominions.

I was delighted to read those sagacious words of the Archbishop of Canterbury, because they are, as the hon. Member for Caerphilly will probably recollect, almost an exact replica of the explanation which I myself gave in this House, 3-1/2 years ago, of my own previous unfortunate utterances on the subject. We have, therefore, the Statutory Commission deliberately abstaining; we have the Joint Select Committee, four years afterwards, deliberately abstaining; and yet now the Government ask us to re-incorporate with the utmost formality this deliberately avoided phrase in the policy for which we are asked to vote to-night.

There is a third event which has occurred since 1929, since the Irwin Declaration. It is the Statute of Westminster. Whatever reprehension may have been attached to the use of such a loose phrase as "Dominion status" before the Statute of Westminster, surely that is slight compared with the censure which should fall upon those who use it now that we have seen the Act of Westminster in all its repellent legalism. Before the Statute of Westminster, the relations of the various Dominions to one another and to the Mother Country were largely undefined; but now we have a written Constitution, or what is very largely a written Constitution.

My hon. Friend the Member for Springburn (Mr. Emmott) asked the Attorney-General a number of pointed questions at the beginning of our Debate this afternoon. The Attorney-General bore them with a stolid face and with his usual composure. But when he came to approach the point in his speech where he should give some answer to them, I thought his discomfiture and agitation and obscurity were painful to witness. My right hon. and learned Friend, who, of all men, can make things clear, was found to be also the man above all others who could enwrap and envelop them in the thickest of fogs. I think we must try to get a little clarification of the position from the right hon. Gentleman. There was one thing that he said in response to an interruption of mine. He said, as I gathered, that it was no use asking what were the differences between Dominion status in 1917 and in 1935, or something to that effect. I said, "Which is it that you are doing now? What is the meaning of your solemn promise? You have made a solemn promise; you tell us how solemn it is; you are forcing us to endorse it. Will you tell us whether it means that the Statute of Westminster applies to Dominion status when it is mentioned by the Secretary of State, or whether it does not?" That is a fair question, and it ought to be possible to give an answer to it.

My right hon. and learned Friend did give an answer—a very characteristic answer. I will not say it was characteristic of him; that would be discourteous; but it was characteristic of the method which is now in vogue in this matter. When I asked him, "Which is it—pre-Statute of Westminster or post-Statute of Westminster, 1917 or 1935?" he said, "Both before and after." That is very good. For his faithful followers it is all right, it is before the Statute of Westminster; for Indian consumption it is after the Statute of Westminster. That is a very dangerous method to apply, and one which, as I shall show, is frequently being resorted to, in the course of the Debates on this Indian matter, by His Majesty's Ministers. But there is no doubt whatever as to what the answer means. The Statute of Westminster does apply and does govern this Declaration, and is meant to govern it. It may be that the right of secession is not implicit in the Statute of Westminster; that is another matter; but the promise made was intended and meant to carry the force of the Statute of Westminster. The ultimate Dominion status which India is to achieve will be Dominion status as defined by the Statute of Westminster. You say it is not defined—I beg pardon—as expressed, as exemplified, as embodied in the Statue of Westminster. That is what it means. This shows the way in which we are treated. Three-and-a-half years ago, when I raised this matter first and when we had the first White Paper, with the Prime Minister's valedictory address to the delegates of the Round Table Conference—when that was before us, and the Government demanded approval for the White Paper, which was the forerunner of the policy which is now being carried out, I put it to my right hon. Friend the Secretary of State, did it or did it not carry with it the implication of the Statute of Westminster which we had just passed? He said:

> The Statute of Westminster has no more to do with the statement of Government policy than the man in the moon.

Let the House consider, and let the country consider—because they are going to take an interest in this matter—how we are being edged, and shoved, and wheedled, and drawn ever nearer and nearer to a position to which, if it had been frankly, boldly and fairly placed before the Conservative party, they at least would never have committed themselves.

No wonder, with this guilty record, they did not dare to put in in the Bill. There, again, is another instance of this equivocation which, I am sure, is the worst way of dealing with India. It is not in the Bill, so that it can be said, "Well, it has no statutory effect." That is a re-assurance to the followers of the right hon. Gentleman. On the other hand, the language used by the Attorney-General, the language used by himself, this solemn Declaration, this deliberate, considered statement on behalf of the Government and so forth, is meant to have its advantage over their in India. Nothing can be worse than this. Let your yea be yea and your nay be nay in dealing with Asia and with the Indians. They may dislike what you say, but they will respect it. But the kind of very nice balancings and dodgings which I see too often in this matter are calculated, not merely to win their dislike, but to excite their contempt.

It is, I think, most important in these Debates that we should try as far as possible to answer each other's arguments. I used a lot of arguments when we last discussed this subject, but no attempt, as far as I can see, has ever been made by the Government to answer any of them. They make their own speeches from their own point of view. We shall never get to grips with this matter unless we really try to face up to the awkward points and posers which are put to us from the other side of the argument. I will try to deal with a few. The first important point to deal with is one which has been put by the Secretary of State, and implied in his answer to an interruption of mine about our complaint of the omission of any care for the welfare of the masses of India in all this great Bill and in all these reports and commissions. If I rightly interpret my right hon. Friend—and I am trying to do so—this was the position: We complained that the welfare of the Indian masses is virtually ignored in all these reports—their agriculture, their education, their hospitals, their water, their forests, their labour standards, their social services. The Imperial Power divests itself of interest and control over all these matters, grasps solely what is essential to its own self-interest, and, with a shrug of its shoulders, leaves this enormous peasant proletariat to take their chance in the inexperienced hands of whatever may be the dominant party in the different Provinces or in the Central Legislature.

That is our complaint. What is the answer of my right hon. Friend? If I may give what I conceive to be his answer—he will correct me if I am mis-stating it, but I am really his advocate for these few moments—he says: "The Act of 1919 transferred the bulk of the services; as for the rest, you and your friends are willing to support Provincial Autonomy, which covers the rest and governs the future. What right, then," he says, "have you to accuse us of being indifferent to the welfare of these masses, when you are equally committed to leaving them to shift for themselves?" I do not know whether that does justice to his point of view, but I certainly felt that it was an argument which we had to meet. What is our answer? We have an answer; it is this: The first 10 years of the Montagu-Chelmsford reforms showed a marked deterioration in the transferred social services—such a marked deterioration that we cannot allow this process to continue unchecked. Now that we are extending a far fuller measure of House Rule to the Provinces, we must make a new provision to secure reasonable and decent efficiency. We are handing over services of immense consequence, for instance, irrigation and the forests—irrigation, that highly artificial system upon which a quarter of the food of India depends; and the forests, the cutting down of which would affect the humidity, and also the springs and the whole drainage and canal system on which great Provinces and communities exist in what would otherwise be blistering desert. These are handed over, in contradiction, I gather, of the whole advice of the Simon Commission—I have their report here. I cannot find an absolute positive veto, but the whole page which I have here deprecates this course in the strongest manner.

It seems to me that there is only one way for us to preserve this control, and that is by the system which was mocked at by the hon. Member for Caerphilly in a personal sense, but not in a Parliamentary sense. It can only be done by a portion of the money available for the Provincial Governments being meted out to them from the Central Government under some system and with an inspectorate similar to that to which we are accustomed here in regard to education and other matters, which will ensure that there is not a grave administrative breakdown or a serious decline in the Provinces. That is our answer, and it is the only safeguard against progressive deterioration. Moreover, it is the Government's only defence against the charge that they have abrogated their present responsibilities to the people of India, and that they are not caring any more what happens to these poor people. We shall place upon the Paper a series of Amendments to give effect to this method and system, which, I firmly believe, we are bound in duty to do if we are to proceed even with the Provincial sections of this Bill.

The hon. Member for North Bristol (Mr. Bernays) put a series of questions to us on Friday, one of which was: "Do you or do you not believe in democracy?" That is a fairly large question. We all remember the gentleman who, on being shown an elephant for the first time, said he did not believe it; and there was the lady who wrote a metaphysical treatise, whose name, unfortunately, escapes me. Perhaps my right hon. Friend the Lord President, whose various and numerous excursions into literature adorn the culture of our political life, will be able to supply the missing name. This lady began her treatise with the words: "I accept the Universe." And, as we all know, Mr. Carlyle made the celebrated comment: "Gad, she'd better." That is rather like my feeling about democracy. I accept it. But I am a good deal more doubtful whether democracy believes in Parliamentary institutions. There was a very fine article, which greatly impressed me, written by the hon. and gallant Gentleman the Member for Hitchin (Sir A. Wilson) reminding us of the utter failure of all the Parliaments that have ever been set up in the East. We have only to look across the Channel in Europe to see how democracy tends in its present manifestation to be injurious to the Parliamentary system and to the personal liberties which are dear to the Liberal heart. I should like to ask the hon. Member, does he call this Bill democracy? Is the communal franchise democracy? Is caste reconcilable with democracy? Is the idea of 60,000,000 untouchables reconcilable with any sort of democratic system? The foundation of the democratic idea is that one man is as good as another, or better. Are the second chambers in this Bill democracy? Is it democracy to have indirect election—four or five men in a room, we were told, choosing the delegates of a great Province? The hon. Member takes us to task as to whether we believe in it. I ask him the kind of democracy he is voting for. Is it democracy to spatchcock into the midst of your central elected chamber one-third of the representation of the stewards and bailiffs of the hereditary Princes, who are autocrats? The hon. Member had really better go to the Liberal Summer School without delay and brush up his fundamentals, or else he will run a very grave risk of forfeiting his deposit.

It is fashionable, wherever the influence of the Government extends, for prominent Conservatives and high officials to take a needlessly poor view of our rights and our position in India. I was sorry to read of a high military officer in India speaking of us as aliens. The Joint Select Committee repeatedly stigmatised our rule in India as irresponsible. The Lord President made a reference to the Indians having an increasing preference for putting their confidence in men of their own race and language. To-day the high water mark is reached by the Attorney-General, who, on being challenged by me, exulted that the influence of the British district officer was now no longer so paramount as it used to be. I am very sorry to hear of this downcry of our national credit. None of it is true. All of it is utterly untrue. We are no more aliens in India than the Mohammedans or the Hindus themselves. We have as good a right to be in India as anyone there except, perhaps, the Depressed Classes, who are the original stock. Our Government is not an irresponsible Government. It is a Government responsible to the

Crown and to Parliament. It is incomparably the best Government that India has ever seen or ever will see. It is not true to say that the Indians, whatever their creed, would not rather have their affairs dealt with in many cases by British courts and British officers than by their own people, especially their own people of the opposite religion. Any Hindu would prefer to have his case dealt with by a British officer than by a Mohammedan, and vice versa. I have been told that there are frequent instances, and modern instances, of peasants who have a quarrel in a village and both parties walking 40, 50 or 60 miles to find a British district officer who can adjust the trouble between them. Talking about going to people of your own race and language and so forth, when Mr. Gandhi had his appendix removed he was very careful to insist upon a British surgeon. Instances like this could be multiplied indefinitely and it is wrong, indeed it is heartbreaking to find the great name of Britain in India so wantonly and improvidently depreciated by the very functionaries whose prime duty it should be to defend them.

A similar mood of disparagement affects the defence of our commercial rights with India. I always pay great attention to what my Noble Friend the Member for Horsham (Earl Winterton) says of India. The line that he has taken upon it is remarkable. As the old song says, his propensities are all the other way. He asked me whether we who constitute the Conservative Opposition adhere to the so-called Fiscal Convention of 1919. I do. But I place a very different interpretation on it from that of the Government spokesmen. The Fiscal Convention of 1919 is not a convention in the sense of being a policy. It does not confer fiscal autonomy upon India or upon the Government of India. It does not transfer British sovereignty to an independent external body. The Government of India is not an independent body. It is a projection, to a very large extent, of the Government of Great Britain. It is open to the Secretary of State to address and, if necessary, to instruct the Viceroy, and through him the Government of India. The closest consultation in practice—the weekly letter—prevails, or ought to prevail. Many representations in my own recollection have been made by Secretaries of State to Viceroys in regard to tariffs affecting different branches of British trade. The Crown appoints the Viceroy, the Crown appoints the Finance Member of the Viceroy's Council, the Crown appoints the important functionaries who compose the Government of India, and in the ultimate issue these functionaries can be recalled by the authority of the Crown and others appointed in their stead whose views are in harmony with those of Parliament. Of course, it might not be right or expedient to do that. That would entirely depend on the circumstances of the case and the time, but to say that we have transferred fiscal sovereignty, that India has complete fiscal autonomy, is not warranted either by the letter or by the spirit of the so-called Fiscal Convention. It has always been understood, until the last five disastrous years of these relations, that both the Viceroy and the Secretary of State owe a duty to both countries in the maintenance of healthy, fruitful, fair trading conditions. While we maintain an Army in India at a great burden of expense to this country, while we give the protection of our fleet, while we give the fruitful advantage of our trade, we are entitled on the highest grounds of justice, as well as empowered by hitherto unimpaired sovereignty, to proper and special consideration in regard to our trade.

Sir S. Hoare: Is my right hon. Friend in favour of continuing the system under which we do not interfere when the Viceroy and the Legislature agree on tariff questions, that is to say, would he impose a tariff upon India if India were unwilling to have it?

Mr. Churchill: If my right hon. Friend had followed my argument he would see that it entirely covers the point. I have pointed out that, if the Viceroy and the Assembly are in accord, the Secretary of State does not interfere, but, as the Secretary of State is in special relation to the Viceroy, it is not an agreement of two external independent bodies. Do you think you could let a point like that slip when the livelihood of millions in this country might depend on the interpretation of our rights? It may be well and wise to give way and to interpret your rights with prudence and discretion, but that our own Minister, the representative that we have in this House, should take such a very low and poor view of the valid rights and authority that we possess in this House is indeed much to be regretted. [*Interruption.*] During the last five years certainly it seems to me that duties have been raised out of all relation either to the trade between the two countries or even to the interests of the Indian revenue. The hon. Member for Caerphilly and the hon. Member for North Bristol speak of this matter as if in trade matters what becomes an advantage to one country can only be obtained to the detriment of another. That is an absolute contradiction of all Free Trade principles. One of the first maxims that I honoured, and still honour, in the Free Trade armoury is that all legitimate interests are in harmony, and that the good of one country may well be the good of another, whether within or without the Empire, and all the more stimulating and all the more beneficial if within the Empire. It is not a question of one country exploiting another, but of both deriving reciprocal benefits through the interchange of goods and services upon the largest possible scale.

Of course, we are confronted with the old choice of self-government versus good government. We are invited to believe that the worst self-government is better than the best good government. That is going too far, but I think no one would look at it in that way. It is a matter of degree. It is a matter that can only be judged in relation to the actual circumstances and conditions. Everyone is, in fact, approaching it on those lines. The modern view is not concentrated entirely on the sovereign virtues of self-government. On the contrary, there is the idea of the external aid to be given by one nation to another. How happy we should be if the United States were willing to place her fleets and armies at the disposal of the League of Nations to protect countries in Europe against an aggressor. How we should rejoice. Yet it is those very functions which we have discharged and are discharging in India that have given India its immunity from the perils, the anxieties, the disorders and the burdens which oppress the strongest and most civilised nations in Europe. That is not the principle of self-government. It is the principle of beneficial aid from an external source for a virtuous object.

This protection and security cannot be removed from India. They have grown with our growth and strengthened with our strength. They will diminish with our diminution and decay with our decay, if I may paraphrase a famous sentence. In so far as they are withdrawn and this external aid withheld, India will descend, not quite into the perils of Europe but into the squalor and anarchy of India in the sixteenth and seventeenth centuries. It seems to me that the present infatuation of the Liberal mind, and I must say of the more intellectual part of the Socialist mind, is at this moment very serious. Their error is an undue exaltation of the principle of self-government. They set this principle above all other principles; they press it to the destruction of all other principles. Let satisfaction be given to the idea of self-government and in the end, they assure us, all will come right, and the consequences, however evil, will fade into the background. Let there be self-government and all will be well. But see the absurdity of this in application. Let me take an instance. The Bombay and Ahmedabad mill-owning millionaires, we will say, obtain a corrupt influence over the Congress Party and so exercise a dominating influence in the new Legislature; and the Legislature, under their influence, sets up a prohibitive tariff which causes widespread distress in Lancashire, which affects the Indian revenue and which horribly denies and stints the vast agricultural population of India in its legitimate needs.

In the result enormous profits are reaped by this handful of exploiters. And then what does my right hon. Friend say? That he must regard that with sombre acquiescence as an example of the less successful working of his system of self-government: But if, on the other hand, the Viceroy and the Secretary of State in close association influence the Government of India to limit the tariff to *bona fide* revenue purposes and to the degree within which the interests of the Indian consumer are adequately considered and protected from monopoly, then that wise and prudent and righteous measure would be condemned as the shameful exploitation of one country by another. No other country in the world would consider such an argument for a moment. No other country in the world having Asiatic possessions would for a moment look at such arguments—and other countries are as intelligent in their own spheres as we are.

The French, I believe, export 50 per cent. of their whole exports to their own Colonies; and the Dutch also. None of these countries would submit to this extreme interpretation of a theoretical doctrine, pushed beyond all bounds of common sense and beyond all bounds of common humanity, either to the people of India or to the people of this country. I accept the so-called fiscal Convention with the interpretation which I put upon it. I have been at the centre of affairs for a very long time, and I know the interpretation that has been put on it for many years by people just as competent as many of those who now direct our affairs.

Mr. Hammersley *rose*—

Mr. Churchill: I am afraid that I cannot give way. The hon. Member as a Lancashire Member ought to be helping. The moment you set up responsible Government at the Centre, you begin to make effective the transfer of sovereignty. Then you make the great change, and that is the moment at which, we hold, as a condition of making this transference you should obtain sure and lasting guarantees for mutually advantageous trade between the two countries. If the Federal Clauses of this Bill are persisted in by His Majesty's Government, we shall certainly endeavour to introduce such provisions into this Bill and to take the opinion of the Committee upon them. My Noble Friend the Member for Horsham set out to convict us of inconsistency and want of logic in our position. He said, if I rightly interpret him, that we did not really believe in the spread of Western democratic methods in India and yet we were willing to agree to a far-reaching scheme of Provincial Home Rule, imputing to us want of logic in that. Any concession made to the opinion of others may be turned against us in that way. But that is not a very hopeful way of approaching these long Debates, when obviously there must be a good deal of give and take on both sides. I answer that, not by logic, but by an appeal to history in this controversy.

I have always felt bound to a very large extent and in principle by the great compromise and settlement between representatives of all British parties embodied in the report of the Statutory Commission. I do not agree with it in every detail, but in the main I have felt greatly under the impression of its authority. I should have been glad if the commission had reported, in view of the lack of co-operation by Congress and other elements and in view of the deterioration of the transferred Services, that no further advance was justified at the present time. I have not the slightest doubt that that would have been the best and most sensible decision to be reached, and I have no doubt that many people in their heart of hearts, not only here but in India, would take that view. But we bowed, as often we have to bow to a practical working proposal. People ought not to underrate the work of the Statutory Commission. They condemn dyarchy in all its forms and sought to eradicate it from Indian polity. What they gave they gave fully; what they withheld they withheld firmly. They gave full Autonomy to the Provinces but maintained integral cohesion at the Centre. If the experiment in the Provinces came to grief, then it could be stopped and the powers resumed. Meanwhile, none of the grave complications attendant upon All-India Federation would have been raised. I still think that after all these five years of discussions and inquiry no advance or improvement of any sort has been made upon the report of the Statutory Commission. There has been no advance towards efficiency, no advance towards finality, and, above all, no advance towards agreement. All these protracted, tumultous confabulations which followed Lord Irwin's unfortunate Declaration in 1929—all this labyrinth through which we have been led has brought us nothing that has been good for this country or India.

We have gone further, and we have fared worse. We have gone into infinite worries, bitter quarrellings, toils unending, and ever-deepening confusion, with sharper disagreements between friends at home and with fellow subjects in India. There has been no foothold for us to stand upon. The hon. Gentleman who spoke last argued that no one should pay attention to the opinions of anyone holding our views. It seems to me that their opinions should not be overlooked entirely. Then comes this extraordinary point. The present position of the Indian Legislature, judged by this Resolution which they carry by so large a majority of elected members, is almost identical with the recommendation of the Statutory Commission set up by us some five years ago. It is extraordinary that they recommend that Provincial Government should be proceeded with, although they do not like it in its present form, and that the Federal system should be dropped. They say:

> With respect to the scheme for central government called All-India Federation this House is clearly of opinion that it is fundamentally bad and totally unacceptable to the people of British India, and therefore recommends the Government of India to advise His Majesty's Government not to proceed with any legislation based on that scheme.

That is identical with the position disclosed in this magnificent and monumental Report of our own Statutory Commission which was prepared with so much pains and trouble by the Commission as a result of their journeys through the East. Therefore, it seems to me that if we are illogical in this matter we have good justification in the fact that the Statutory Commission and the Indian Legislature seem to be of the same opinion. Let me retort upon my Noble Friend that if we are inconsistent in going as far as the Statutory Commission, although farther than we wished to go, where is his consistency and where is the consistency of the Government of which he is the champion? They use fine language about meeting Indian aspirations, but they do not meet them. They speak all the time as if they had agreement with Indian political forces and reproach us for marring the harmony when there is the most violent disagreement.

The Government proclaim their trust in the Indian political classes—but they show their distrust by the multitude of Safeguards they have introduced. Take the question of the provisions with regard to the handing over of the police. We hear all this talk about the educative value of responsibility, and it is beautifully expressed, but what is the responsibility that will really be given to the Indian Minister of a Province in regard to this? It seems to me that it is very seriously inroaded upon. He must not interfere with the internal government of the police; he cannot appoint or dismiss the chief of the police; and he is not to know the information on which the police act, although he will have to bear the responsibility of action which may involve blood-shed. It is no good saying that one should not tell them these things for they must be well known to Indian lawyers and others who have studied the matter. Here, again, you have made the great mistake of using all kinds of language not fully justified by the act and facts for which you are responsible. The Government are floundering in the old bog of government by consent with consent not forthcoming.

But there is one matter upon which the Indian Legislature will have great power and great temptation to use its power, and that is in the matter of trade relations between the two countries. When this Trade Pact, this poor meagre Pact for the sake of which the Manchester Chamber of Commerce sacrificed its opportunity of stating its whole case before the Joint Select Committee—when this Pact was rejected the other day, some of our friends who support the Government Bill met us with a superior, but at the same time rather sickly smile and said: "This means nothing; they are not responsible; they have not yet got the healing, educative, steadying, stabilising force of responsibility operating upon them; when they have that it will be all very different." I do not know about that. If there is a man who wishes to kick you but has not the power, are you to say: "Give him the power and you may be sure you will be quite safe"? It may be true. No one can say that it is not conceivable, but it is not at all a convincing or alluring argument.

Here our Irish experiences ought to be relevant. It ought to be relevant upon this question of the healing, educative virtues of responsibility. We gave them full re-sponsibility and everything necessary to full autonomy. We had a solemn treaty and there you had able and resolute men who had pledged their faith to that treaty. But what happened? It was this. Both the Government in Ireland and the Opposition were forced to vie with one another in showing who could be the most disagreeable to

England. The Government would have liked, as I know, to show us friendly feeling, but they did not dare for Opposition Members gained popularity throughout the country by showing how they could beat the Government hollow at the game of twisting the lion's tail. Because the Government were not so good at kicking England as they were the Opposition finally installed themselves in their places, broke the treaty and ruined the country. That is what happened in Ireland. Of this healing virtue of responsibility this certainly is not an encouraging example. It is not at all proof that the medicine in which you have such unbounded faith will in all cases produce immediate recovery.

You have not got, as you have in Ireland, a practical and complete autonomy. This new Parliament will be obstructive at every point. The Opposition said the other day that they would have very little to do. They could criticise the administration and attack the safeguards, and you have furnished them with a means to attack the safeguards. What is the means by which they can attack the safeguards? It is by maltreating the trade. They will have Lancashire as a hostage, they will be able to torture Lancashire, and they will be able to extract from the Government and extort from the Viceroy diminution of the safeguards. They will have that in addition to all the other mighty persuasive powers of Parliamentary procedure.

I have watched this story from its very unfolding, and what has struck me more than anything else about it has been the amazingly small number of people who have managed to carry matters to their present lamentable pitch. You could almost count them on the fingers of one hand. I have also been struck by the prodigious power which this group of individuals have been able to exert and relay, to use a mechanical term, through the vast machinery of party, of Parliament and of patronage both here and in the East. It is tragical that they should have been able to mislead the loyalties and use the assets of the Empire to its own undoing. I compliment them on their skill, and I compliment them also on their disciples. Their chorus is exceedingly well drilled. We listen to their parrot cries—"We have set our hands to the plough; we must plough the furrow to the end, even if the course is folly, and even if the end is disastrous."

We are told that something must be done. My father Lord Randolph Churchill was often credited with saying that when he heard people going about saying that something must be done, he had noticed that something very foolish was done. We are told that you cannot put the clock back. What nonsense. We put the clock back every year with highly beneficial results. Why do we put it back? That is what I want the House to notice. We put it back to place ourselves in more harmonious relation with the great facts of nature. We do not try with our little clocks and watches to run counter to nature. That would bring us into confusion or be entirely ineffectual. The error of the Government is that they are trying to put the clock forward without regard to the true march of solar events. They are trying to put it forward in the hope that the sun will alter its process because of their little dodges. So much for the argument that you cannot put back the clock.

There is one final argument that remains. I will endeavour to compress and put it as shortly as possible, but it is one that must be met. We are told that by opposing the India Bill and India policy here and in the country we are running the risk of putting the Socialist Opposition into power, and that they will pass a much worse Bill. If that doctrine is to be accepted, it means that right hon. Gentlemen opposite, whether in office or in Opposition, are always in power. It really destroys the Conservative and Liberal parties. But in actual practice the passage of this Bill as it stands will make very easy the path of a Socialist Government in carrying a solution of the India problem which not one of those who are going to vote on the Government side to-night would for a moment contemplate or tolerate. One Parliament cannot bind another, but there are certain practical securities. The first is well organised parties expressing their national and traditional view, balancing each other and reacting upon a healthy public opinion in the country—that is the great security against foolish or dangerous legislation.

But there is another, and it resides in the Procedure of the House of Commons, which I am glad to know the Government themselves are respecting in this case. This Bill is a gigantic barrier against hasty or imprudent legislation. Imagine the party opposite installed on these benches having to pass through Parliament a Bill with hundreds of Clauses during their first or second Session. They would never be allowed by their followers. They would say: "Get on making the new order of society; get on with your cure for unemployment; get on with your nationalisation of the banks, and so forth; do not spend all your time on these intricate matters." A Bill of this kind is an immense deterrent with all its complications, but you are doing all this work and you are sweeping all this barrier out of the way. When this Bill is passed it will be quite an easy matter to amend it. There will not be the slightest difficulty. A dozen or 15 Clauses in a little, light paper Bill would be quite sufficient to tear away all these safeguards which are comforting so many hon. Gentlemen to-night, and which they are laying to their hearts as the grounds to justify them in what they are doing and to quiet their misgivings—the natural pricks and stings of conscience by which they are undoubtedly afflicted. Take the question of the Federal Clauses of the Bill. I have not been able to estimate how many there are. Perhaps the Secretary of State will tell us some other time. At any rate, there are hundreds of them.

Sir S. Hoare: Certainly not hundreds.

Mr. Churchill: Let us say a large proportion. We will ascertain the figure later. As we stand at present, if this Bill is passed as it is, the Federal system can be brought into operation in three, four or five years, when the circumstances may be wholly different from what they are now and when, in our opinion, it would be most unwise and unnecessary to bring them into operation. But they can be brought into operation by a single vote; an Address in both Houses of Parliament. Can you expect the House of Lords, which the Lord President has so persistently refused to reform or strengthen, to stand up in these circumstances against a Measure, the principle of which has been conceded, and against a Socialist Administration in power, on a matter which would be said to be vehemently demanded in all parts of India? No, the security against bringing into operation the Federal system at an unsatisfactory time is that the Federal system should stand over from this Parliament and be left to be brought in when the circumstances are apt and ripe for it.

I will make an appeal to the right hon. Gentleman, if he will allow me to do so, an appeal which is earnest and governed by sincere respect. Will he not consider the division of this Bill into two parts and the omission of the Federal Clauses? That will enormously relieve the whole position and follow on the advice and wishes expressed by the Indian people through the only channels and organs which are open to them. Moreover, it does not in any way prevent the Government exposing their whole design. They have already exposed it in this Bill, which has passed the First Reading, and which is going to pass through Second Reading. You have unfolded your great plan of Indian Parliaments of the future, and you can put it up in the tea room for everyone to see. There is only one block which you can build now and for a good many years to come, for which you have the funds and for which you have the agreement, or measure of agreement. Put that up, and when, later on, the time comes, it will be possible to relate the other parts of the building to what has already been erected.

The Vote we are going to give to-night will be a vote against the Second Reading of this Bill. As it is put from the Chair it gives a perfectly clean, clear, simple vote against the Second Reading on the Question of whether the word "Now" and other words stand part. That Vote in no way involves the terms of the Amendment placed on the Paper by the Opposition. If we were successful in our vote against the Second Reading of this Bill, another Question would have to be put from the Chair, that their words be there inserted. There could be no question of their coming before the House if we were successful in the first Division. We should vote against the words of the Socialist Amendment in the second Division and, I trust, that we shall be assisted by any debris of His Majesty's Government who may still find it necessary to take an interest in public affairs.

This is the first time that this extended and elaborate Bill has been brought out into the open and exposed to the criticism of the House of Commons. I believe that it will be possible to convince the House and the country that the Federal proposals are untimely and unworkable. I believe that they could be riddled in fair and free Debate, and that if the scheme which is now being pressed forward—the whole of it, not only the Federal, but also the Provincial—were dropped by the Government it would be the cause of great relief not only throughout this country, but from one end of India to the other. We shall endeavour to conduct our opposition as far as in us lies to show the fatal faults and defects of this Bill. But we shall aim at doing more. We shall try to instil into the minds of the peoples of Britain and of India a different and a new conception of the relations between the two countries. We hope once and for all to kill the idea that the British in India are aliens moving, with many apologies, out of the country as soon as they have been able to set up any kind of governing organism to take their place. We shall try to inculcate this idea, coming now to be mentioned more and more in many quarters of the House, that we are there for ever as honoured partners with our Indian fellow subjects whom we invite in all faithfulness to join with us in the highest functions of government for their lasting benefit and for our own.

GOVERNMENT OF INDIA BILL
(CLAUSES 1, 4, 5, 6)
February 19, 1935
House of Commons

On a point of Order. I would wish to make it quite clear that I consider myself, personally, strictly bound to assist the Government in getting this Bill through in the 30 days of the Committee stage, but I do not at all want to be bound beyond that, and I think it would be a pity if it went forth that Members were engaged beyond that general acceptance of the total time. For instance, I hoped that perhaps I might draw from you some statement in public that the particular allocation of the stages now put down for this Bill is intended to be elastic and provisional and can be modified at the convenience of the House, the sole obligation which we have entered into with the Government being to abandon opposition to the Committee stage within the 30 days, if the Government majority hold together. I should like to have it on record that these provisional allocations are of an elastic character. It would seem, looking at this time-table, that probably more time will be required on the early stages of this Bill. They are fertile in large points of principle—the first 60 Clauses of it are peculiarly fertile in large points of principle—and it would seem that the 30 days would give an opportunity for a very full and free Debate upon the main selected points which the Committee would wish to discuss. I should deprecate our starting upon this discussion with any feeling that we have from the beginning to hustle through our task, to hurry on our task, and that everything has to be got through with the very greatest despatch. The Committee, I trust, will be permitted to work its way into the Bill in the ordinary manner, the agreement and understanding that we finish within 30 days being, of course, paramount. I put these observations forward in order that none of us may be held bound by detailed interpretations proceeding far beyond the subject matter of the main agreement.

[Much later] I do not care to give a vote for this Amendment [Clause 1—on the short title] without offering in a few sentences my explanation to the Committee. I admit, quite frankly, that there are disadvantages in this proposal, as there were disadvantages in the previous proposal we discussed this afternoon. Anyone can see how we trespass, or seem to trespass, upon the plenary responsibilities of the Government of the day, and to some extent on the liberty of discussion in this House. But the defects are but the shadow of the far greater defects inherent in the structure of the Bill. I agree that these kinds of remedies would not be proposed were the disease which we are resisting and endeavouring to check as far as we can, not so grave and desperate. A public functionary is being created under the Bill unique in character. Nothing like it has ever been conceived, or ever will be conceived after an experience which future years will no doubt bring. This is not the time to enlarge upon the functions of the Viceroy, but to suggest that they will not be functions exciting the fiercest controversy and almost continuous friction is to miss the whole point.

Hon. Members opposite seem to suppose that now that responsible self-government is being given to India, the Viceroy will have nothing to do. It is not merely the vast range of subjects with which he will have to deal, but also their highly controversial nature. At any moment he may be called upon to resume autocratic government of a Province, to sweep away a Constitution. At any moment he may be called upon to dismiss Ministers, to dissolve Parliaments and veto legislation. Now that the Government by their Measure have dragged India into party politics, and have raised issues which will not slumber during a whole generation, the position and actions of the Viceroy will be the subject of continuous criticism in this House, whichever party occupies the seat of power or opposition. There will be criticism. The Viceroy will be expected to act in regard to the reserved powers to maintain security of defence, and great anxiety will be caused as to whether he is, in fact, discharging that duty. You may see that movement from this side of the House. On the other hand, in India you may have great resentment of his exercise of safeguards, and pressure being put upon him by his Ministers, complaints of the autocratic temper of the Viceroy, Ministers in conflict with them. Is it to be wondered at that in these circumstances, when you have this official lifted up so entirely out of the common run of all political devices and arrangements, around whom these storms are going to beat—is it strange that we should in the best way we can, and by the best amendments we can propose, seek, in the first place, to free his appointment as much as possible from partisanship, to ensure continuity in the appointment of any such functionary and to secure him a certain reasonable stability once he has undertaken these duties?

Those are the objects of the Amendment. It may be that the actual wording of the proposal shows defects—many of us can see them—but, nevertheless, the object is of the most serious character. The speeches which have been made from the Government Bench, and the speech of the Noble Lord the Member for Hastings (Lord E. Percy), have indicated the serious character of the difficulties we are endeavouring to meet. The Government have brushed them away and leave the Viceroy, confronted not merely with the difficulties I have mentioned, but with crises of a most extraordinary character, to be dismissed from his office in the ordinary manner as if he were no more than a simple official placed in this extraordinary position. It seems to many of us that his dismissal ought to be affected in the broad, open light of day, and by the full act of Parliament. It should not be a matter which should rest exclusively with the executive. It is true that the executive, if it wished to dismiss the Viceroy, would presumably command a majority of the House, and I cannot myself conceive that in these matters the present House of Lords would use its veto on Indian questions, which I observe are not subject to the Parliament Act.

It seems to me that when you are placing the Viceroy in this position, charged with these peculiar functions, he is going to be the storm centre for many years, and the least you can do is to fortify his position in some way, not relieve him from the criticism of Parliament, but make sure that his dismissal, if it is decided upon, shall operate only through the most formal, ceremonious and grave methods in which such an act can take place. It is too much to expect that the Government will accept the

Amendment in its present form any more than they did the pertinent Amendment by which the right hon. Member for Hillhead (Sir R. Horne) sought to mitigate the defects of the Bill; but while pointing the moral of the danger in which we stand we may still express a hope, a faint hope, and, therefore, a hope which requires to be cherished all the more, that as our discussions continue the Government will take steps to reassure the sincere and urgent fears which are held not only in this House, but with increasing force throughout large parts of the country.

[Later] I should like to move, "That the consideration of Clause 5 [Proclamation of Federation of India] be postponed." If that be assented to, I shall also move, "That the consideration of Clause 6 [Accession of Indian States] be postponed."

The Deputy-Chairman: Perhaps it would be for the convenience of the Committee if the right hon. Gentleman moved that both Clauses be postponed.

Mr. Churchill: I beg to move, "That the consideration of Clauses 5 and 6 be postponed."

I am very much obliged to you Sir, for bringing to my knowledge the fact that it is in order for me to do so.

I ask the Secretary of State if he will agree to their postponement, because it would be a very right and proper thing to do, and it would not in any way delay our proceedings. Part II is one of the most important features of the Bill, because it raises the great issue of the Federal System and the conditions under which the States will accede to it. I always understood that this matter would not be raised this week. There are a great many reasons why it should not be raised. To begin with the text of the Bill has only just gone out to India—about a fortnight ago—and the Princes and others will be studying it in detail. They will have very little time in which to take decisions which are so important and to decide what Amendments, if any, are required. I understand that the view of the India Office is that any Amendments of that kind can be inserted on the Report stage, but the consideration of this matter on Report will be very much abbreviated, and there will be very little time to do anything. It seems most undesirable that we should have to decide Clauses 5 and 6 before the discussions which are taking place among the Princes in India have reached a conclusion. I understand that a meeting is to be held on the 27th, and, if this Bill had taken the course which I was led to expect, namely, that it would not be brought on until next week, we should not have to debate these very important Clauses without knowing what the main view of the Princes in India was going to be.

If the Princes decide not to come in at this stage, it will not be necessary to move various Amendments to a Clause to which I will presently refer. If, on the other hand, they are coming in, and we are faced with the question of the institution of the federal system, it is absolutely necessary that Amendments should be moved to make that system a reality; for instance, the question of the anomalies of Princes voting in and out on Income Tax, and so forth, must be settled, as must the various questions, which one would not wish to press until they are necessary, as to their becoming naturalised British subjects if they accede to the Federation. All sorts of questions arise as to what kind of Instrument of Accession and terms of accession the Crown will accept. Suppose that a Prince accedes with such limitations as to make him a partner and a participator in the Assembly and yet, at the same time, withhold any very large derogation from his own internal powers. Those matters will all have to be looked into and studied, and will have to be the subject of Debate and Amendment in this House, and the House will decide upon them as it sees fit.

It is, in my opinion, very improper to bring on the Committee stage of the Bill so close to the Second Reading, to hustle the House and other people who are concerned, and to force them to the gravest decisions and discussion of the gravest matters in the Bill within such a very short time of the Second Reading being disposed of. The Bill, which is of enormous complexity, has been printed under a month, and the task of putting down Amendments and relating one set of Amendments to another is one of very great difficulty to a person not possessing the organisation of the great Departments of State. These two Clauses would far better be discussed at a later stage when we shall know much more of the position in India, and when still more mature consideration can be given to the various aspects of the Bill, and to the Amendments which are appropriate to it. I hope that the Secretary of State will agree to this postponement.

Mr. Morgan Jones: No, he will not.

Mr. Churchill: Ah, I suppose you have arranged it. There is too much of that. That is one of the things which have been commented on outdoors, the way in which the Socialists on the Front Opposition Bench and the Socialists on the Government Bench are doing their deals behind the backs of the Conservative party. I did not expect to hear this subterranean process so nakedly exposed by the hon. Gentleman, who already knows beforehand exactly what the Secretary of State will do. I expect it is all pretty well laid out and drawn up from start to finish. I dare say the hon. and learned Member for East Bristol (Sir S. Cripps), who has re-entered, is to be put up to make one of those firework speeches to give a sort of sham opposition to the Bill to cover his eager scuttling into the Government Lobby.

I regret very much that this interruption from the Front Opposition Bench led me from the more calm and temperate manner in which I had hoped to couch my appeal. I hope that the right hon. Gentleman will consent to these Clauses being postponed. He will, by so doing, enable a better discussion to take place, and will not be taking an unfair advantage of the House, and he will clear himself altogether of any desire to force a decision from the House on these Clauses before the Princes' decision in regard to their coming in or not has taken place. I will not say any more at the moment because, as we are in Committee, I can easily return to the topic. I will merely content myself by asking the right hon. Gentleman whether he will agree to the Motion I make.

Sir S. Hoare: Let me first call attention to the curious way in which the right hon. Gentleman makes an appeal of this nature. He indirectly accuses me of wishing to take an unfair advantage of the House, and of conspiracy with hon. Gentlemen opposite. There is no reason for postponing these Clauses, first of all because everybody has been in possession of the substance of them ever since the Joint Select Committee reported. The two Clauses follow almost exactly the Recommendations of the Joint Select Committee, and they do not come as new proposals to the House about which hon. Members have only heard in the last few weeks. Every hon. Member who has followed the details of the discussion has known all about them since last

November; so also has everybody in India. The Clauses follow the Recommendations of the Joint Select Committee's Report, which has been in the possession of everybody, here and in India, who is interested in the question, since last November.

Mr. Churchill: Is it not a fact that the most important part of the discussion now taking place among the Princes in India is upon the differences which exist in the text of the Bill from what is to be found either in the White Paper or in the report of the Joint Select Committee, and that upon those differences important decisions turn? How can it be said that all those matters have been known all that time? It is those very differences which will determine the Princes' decision.

[Later] As I have been subjected to severe criticism from the Front Opposition Bench, I think it right to point out to the Committee how very reasonable is the proposal which I am making. If normal constitutional practice and the reasonable orderly custom of Parliament had been followed, and at least a fortnight had been allowed to intervene between the Second Reading and the Committee stage of a Bill of this magnitude, the difficulty would not have arisen. That is the course which I understood was to have been taken. Then the Government decided to bring the matter forward a week earlier, and get these two very decisive Clauses dealt with at this stage, which happens to be before the discussions which are proceeding in India will mature. That is a limitation of proper and regular constitutional procedure and custom, and, in addition, it is an alteration of the original course which we were led to believe would be taken. I make no charge of any kind against the Government in this matter. I have been assured that the ante-dating of the Committee stage to this week had no ulterior motive, and I accept that assurance completely, but nevertheless the inconvenience remains, even if the purpose does not exist, and, if the proper normal course had been taken, that inconvenience would not have existed at all. The inconvenience is patent to every one. Hon. Gentlemen opposite would like, naturally, as it were, to force the Princes' hand by getting a decision in this House beforehand, but I think it is a very great pity that the Princes cannot be allowed to decide this matter before we have been subjected to the necessity of taking our decision. I certainly shall press my Motion to a Division.

GOVERNMENT OF INDIA BILL
(CLAUSE 5—PROCLAMATION OF
FEDERATION OF INDIA)

February 20, 1935

House of Commons

I do not rise for the purpose of continuing the Debate so much as to ask when we are to have some reply from the Government to the prolonged discussion that has taken place. Since dinner time last night debate has been in progress upon an Amendment of consequence, and so far we have had no information from the

Government whether they will accept it or not. We have had no attempt to meet any of the arguments that have been employed in favour of the Amendment and against the policy of the Government. This is a very far-reaching and weighty Amendment and you, Sir, following the convention that is ruling us, that our arrangements give more and not less liberty to the House of Commons of discussion, have allowed us a full discussion of this super-imposition of the federal Constitution upon the broad foundation of the Statutory Commission's Report. That really is the issue. It is not the only time the issue will be raised. It comes up on a great many Amendments. There are a score of Amendments any one of which, if carried, would be fatal to the federal scheme, but this is the first major time at which the matter comes before us. There has been this Debate and there have been all these arguments. We have had no answer whatever from the Government. I suppose the Secretary of State is going to make sure that he has the last word in the Debate.

The Secretary of State for India (Sir Samuel Hoare) *indicated dissent*.

Mr. Churchill: Then, may I suggest that really on this occasion he might run a little risk and give some guidance as to what his purposes are? For my part, I am prepared to discuss the matter and support the Amendment, and show, as far as I can, the many vicious Clauses which render the Government policy of Federation at the centre injudicious and most pregnant with evil consequences. We have had already two long Debates in which this topic has been greatly raised, and many arguments have been used against the policy of Federation at the centre and no Minister has given any answer of any sort or kind to any of those arguments. Statements have been made in previous Debates on this matter by the Lord President of the Council which have not dealt at all with the arguments used in the Debate, not in the least. They have dealt with questions in connection with groupings of party votes and so forth. No attempt has been made to answer all these arguments. I really consider there is a great volume of argument against the introduction of this federal scheme to which my right hon. Friend might find it worth while to address himself. I am sure that, if he did so, he would strengthen the volume and current of the Debate in the Committee and put us in a position to know the mind of the Government. So far many arguments have been used against Federation, and all that has happened is that Ministers and supporters of the Government who have spoken have confined themselves to saying, "You must have Federation because the princes made an offer and said that their offer only held if there was responsible government. Consequently, there is nothing for it but to put the Bill through." We ought to have something better than that, and I ask my right hon. Friend: Will he reply now to the Debate?

[Much later] The Committee will feel indebted to the Secretary of State for the clear and full exposition he has given of the views and position of His Majesty's Government on this serious issue. If I found it necessary to apply a blister in order to procure from the right hon. Gentleman this highly agreeable exertion, I can only feel that it has been attended with success, and, if he is satisfied with his efforts, we are entirely grateful to have received from the Government some guidance as to their views on this subject. The Secretary of State has reaffirmed the Government's case without attempting in any way—naturally he could hardly do so in so short a time—to deal with the arguments which have been advanced. He has restated the Government's main position. The Princes made their offer to come into a federal system; the Princes said that if they came into a federal system they must be responsible and, therefore, it is necessary for the Government to set up this federal system now. That, in short, is the main position of the Government. The right hon. Gentleman also said that if we were to proceed only with provincial home rule, a centrifugal tendency would be developed in the provinces, and the united focus and harmonious action of India would be destroyed. That is a clear statement of the position taken up by the Government, and also by the Joint Select Committee.

When it is given out, as it has been to-night, with an air of expert authority which the Government quite rightly are entitled to assume, one is entitled to be allowed to point to the fact that other expert bodies, who have given great consideration to this matter, have taken an entirely different view of the philosophical and fundamental basis on which this issue turns. My hon. and gallant Friend, in asking his question was really leading up to a quotation I am about to make from the report of the Statutory Commission. [*Interruption.*] I do not know why hon. Members opposite should laugh; I am surprised at such irreverence. This was a body which contained eminent Liberals, the most pre-eminent Liberal was at its head, and hon. Members laugh because I venture to quote him. I have always noticed that the hon. Member for Bodmin (Mr. Isaac Foot) mocks at every authority which does not suit his argument at the moment, but I will admit that he is not the only man in the House who does that. This is what the Statutory Commission said:

> Even if we were to ignore the Indian States and were to rest content with the provinces as at present constituted, the necessary conditions for bringing a full federal constitution into being are not yet present. The provinces must first become political entities.

I should have thought there was some importance in that. Before we can become political entities, before we can join ourselves together in political parties, we must first be born into this world of sin and woe. The commission go on:

> Even when our proposals for the constitution of the Governors provinces have been embodied in a Statute, the process is not completed. The provincial constitution only begins to exist as a living thing when the forces which operate it are at work and provincial opinion gives it inspiration and direction. Every federal union means the coming together of constituent elements which, while preserving their identities, look to the Centre to deal with matters common to all. Thus the nature of the constituents themselves has a great influence on the form which the federation takes. It is a difficult task.

These are not my words; they are not the words of Tory diehards. This is the Statutory Commission, with the Foreign Secretary at its head, surrounded by Liberals and Labour representatives.

It is a difficult task to combine the process of devolution with that of integration on a new basis.

These are solid propositions and arguments provided for us in the House of Commons and Lords by our own Statutory Commission, which was sent out and worked in India for two years. They gave us these solid bases of argument and, therefore, I am not so hopelessly divested of authority when I am confronted with the statements of the Secretary of State, which are absolutely contradictory to these main basic propositions. It is by no means the only time that we shall raise this federal issue in its different aspects, but it is the prime occasion. Having listened to many able speeches made by the supporters of the Government from time to time—there are some of them, certainly, who are very able in their statement of their views—I must say that I remain bewildered as to the initial motive power and impulse which lead the Government to insist on bringing a federal system into operation now, and forces us to take this position on the Bill. I have searched to find some adequate and satisfactory reason for it. Nobody wants it in India. With great difficulty the Princes are being brought up to scratch or not, as the case may be. We do not know. The Government have a great advantage over us in this respect, because the Debate is taking place without our knowing the decision of the Princes. With the greatest difficulty the Secretary of State set himself out to have three-quarters of the Princes as the test, but very quickly he had to write it down to one-half—

Sir S. Hoare *indicated dissent.*

Mr. Churchill: A larger number than the present number was originally put forward by the Secretary of State.

Sir S. Hoare: I do not think so.

Mr. Churchill: It is not a question of thinking, it is a question of fact.

Sir S. Hoare: If the right hon. Gentleman doubts my word, I will say "No."

Mr. Churchill: I do not doubt my right hon. Friend's honesty and good faith in the matter, and I hope that such things are not going to be suggested. In this controversy many things have happened during the last four years and I certainly was under the impression, just as honestly or almost as honestly as the right hon. Gentleman, that a higher number of Princes was chosen in the first instance, and, in fact when we put down our Amendment about the three-quarters we understood that we were basing ourselves on the original view. However, the Princes are to be represented, they made this offer and demanded responsible government at the Centre. It reminds me of a saying of the Duke of Wellington to a man who accosted him with, "I believe you are Mr. Smith?" The Duke said, "If you believe that you will believe anything." Why these autocratic Princes should demand responsible government at the Centre I cannot conceive. What happened, as far as we have heard—names have been mentioned, but I will not repeat them—was that some of the Princes, believing that under the Secretary of Stateship of Mr. Wedgwood Benn England was really determined to move out, lock, stock and barrel, met representatives of Congress and did what in ordinary English language is called a deal. The Princes were to be left to run their territories as despotic and hereditary rulers and to help Congress to get responsible government at the Centre. That was the situation which preceded the so-called offer of the Princes, and that is the explanation, and the only explanation, of their enthusiasm for responsible government.

What will be the plight of the Princes in this new Assembly? Anything more lamentable can hardly be conceived. They will be expected to uphold stability, the Conservative point of view, to sustain the Imperial authority, and be as it were behind the Viceroy. The Chancellor of the Duchy made a most interesting and revealing speech a few days ago, in which he spoke of the advantages of having the Princes in. He made a confession of faith on the matter, very characteristic, very natural and very sincere, in one who has been a party manager. He said: "Here is this large block of votes, one-third of the Assembly, they will put things straight and counteract the evil of democratic and revolutionary tendencies which are manifested in the Congress of India." That is the position. The Secretary of State has shown how much hope he is putting upon this. What is to be the position of the Princes under this ordeal? Congress are not going to be idle in the new Assembly, and any Prince who makes himself prominent in defending Imperial interests and in acting in accordance with his sentiments of loyal allegiance, will be a marked man. He will be the subject of a double attack. Agitation will be raised in his dominions behind him, disorders will occur, comments and criticisms will be made, and there will be pressure at the centre, to show how he is a reactionary, is neglecting his State and how much happier they are in the States of those Princes who have conformed to the views of Congress. I say they will be in a dreadful position. If you imagine that they are going to be an element of stability, I believe that you make a profound mistake. There will be no element of stability there. Once the British power has definitely disinterested itself in this aspect of our affairs in India the Princes of India have no choice whatever but to throw in their lot with their own fellow-countrymen, and that is what they will do under the remorseless pressure of political events.

Mr. MacQuisten: Safety first.

Mr. Churchill: As my hon. and learned Friends says, "Safety first" will not necessarily be a motto confined to the Treasury Bench. In regard to this new register, by going forward in this matter and enforcing a federal system on top of this very large measure of provincial home rule you create, and set Parliament to authorise, a structure of constitutional polity, a legislative assembly more curiously constituted, more illogically framed and based than any which has ever been seen in the whole history of constitution-mongering. Here is this body, and you say that it is responsible. I thought that the demand of the Princes for responsible government at the centre was a sham. But the response is also a sham. This is not responsibility at the centre; it is a pretence of responsibility. Almost every conceivable function in which responsible government resides, has been reserved. The protection of minorities, defence, the foreign situation; finance, except 20 per cent. of it—the whole basis is reserved.

What you are giving at the centre is not responsibility. What you are giving is the power to extort responsibility. What you are giving is, by Parliamentary method and by Parliamentary arguments, you having conceded all the argumentative positions, the power to extort inch by inch, and month by month, the full responsibility. But you are not giving it now. In the meantime a constitution is being created, infinitely laborious, infinitely complicated, people voting in and out according to instructions, people voting as representatives of the ancient monarchies, and as newly-elected representatives in the new Assembly, an Assembly which cannot be rectified by any dissolution, just the Princes, representatives and others elected by indirect election— [Hon. Members: "No!"] Yes, it is so! It is an extraordinary situation, a piece of work most laborious but most lamentable when completed. The industry and labour and good will put into it do not remove the fact that the result is wholly undesirable and one which is resented and disliked and repudiated everywhere. You cannot get the Princes, or you will very doubtfully get the Princes, to come forward.

I am not going at this moment into all the methods that have been used. I may have something to say about them later on. But as for the Indian Assembly, as hon. Lady who spoke last night—an independent Member, an independent lady Member— made it quite clear that the dominating opinion in India now is that, rather than have this Bill, they would have the matter reconsidered from the beginning. And that would be a very good thing. You would get a better result, because after all the fighting and nagging and general badgering that have been going on we are getting to a fairly proper comprehension of the situation.

Would it not be wise of the Government, therefore, not to drive the scheme through this Parliament just because they have a very large number of gentlemen here who are ready during the closing months of this Parliament, to walk through the lobbies behind them? The scheme cannot come into operation for four or five years. Why not look a little further ahead? I know the lust of power, the sense of having such a very large majority in both branches of the Legislature, so that what you put on paper with your initial is settled. It is very affecting to the mind. I am bound to say that when I continue my search for any reason which the Government could possibly have had for assenting to the federal system at such great cost to themselves, at such great cost to their party, at such great cost to the people of India, and forcing the system through, I find that a handful of individuals of reputation and strong conviction were engaged at the beginning of this matter, and that these men have had their hands on the lever of power and can pull the great machine of party and Government. I find that to be the principal explanation of the situation in which we find ourselves to-day. It would be perfectly simple for the Government to proceed with the provincial, and to say that the federal system would come into being if the provincial aspect is found satisfactory, if it has made good in the provinces; and that the Government of that day in another Parliament—not this Parliament, but another Parliament—must face the responsibility and the burden of passing the detailed Clauses, instead of bringing the scheme into operation by an Address to the Crown from both Houses, and ramming it through after a single Division.

It is a very grievous thing. I do hope that we are not going to drag the House of Lords into this fight. We are told to attach great importance to an Address from both Houses. As far as I have been able to inform myself, the passing of an Address is not a matter governed by the Parliament Act. So that here you have not the dilatory veto of the House of Lords as affirmed by the Parliament Act. Here you have the absolute veto of the House of Lords, without any reference to the Parliament Act. But this is a very serious thing. If you suppose that the House of Lords is going to be put into the position of standing against the House of Commons on a matter of this kind, when no doubt there will be a situation of great excitement in India at the same time, I think you are resting absolutely upon an unsure and insecure foundation.

We consider that the plan which is put forward in this Amendment, which may be called the Salisbury Plan—it is not a bad name, for, after all, Lord Salisbury took a great deal of trouble in studying the matter—is really what the Statutory Commission advised, with certain modifications. In principle it is what the Statutory Commission advised: that there should be provincial government, provincial home rule, that integral control should be maintained at the centre and that a consultative body should be provided. That is, in substance, the Salisbury Plan. That is the issue. Imagine what would happen if we heard next week that the Princes were not coming in. There would be a sigh of relief from all over India. But that would be nothing like the sigh of relief which would go up all over the Tory party, and indeed far outside the bounds of party—a feeling of great relief that this wedge which is being driven in to split a great political organisation had ceased to operate and that there would be unity. Not only would there be relief in India, but a greater measure of unity at home, and we should have freed ourselves, we should have prevented the writing of one of the most melancholy, one of the most perverse, one of the most unnecessary chapters in the whole history of the British people.

[Much later] The essence of the Government's scheme has been based upon the offer of the Princes. That was the statement made by the Lord President of the Council—whom I do not see in his place to-night—at the critical meeting of his own party. We were told the Princes had come forward with their offer and the suggestion was made "How can you reject these good gifts which are so freely proffered to your hand?" Now we are right down to the bones of the offer. There was the speech of the Secretary of State in which he said that the Indian States would come in. By a misprint in the Official Report, such as often occurs to us, he was reported to have said that "all" the Indian States would come in. My right hon. Friend the Secretary of State says he did not say "all" and, whether he said it or not that he did not mean to say it, which is quite the same thing. No one is going to hold a Minister in high office and in a great critical position, responsible for the exact terms of the phrases which fall from his lips, but at any rate it was said that the Indian States would come in.

That is a very important point. The whole essence of the matter as presented to us was, "They want to come in." We were told that they had come forward with their offer and that all they said was, "Do let us be responsible. Do let us have democracy. Do let us have the will of the people prevailing." But they were to come in. Here was this great offer, enabling us to build up this vast megalomaniac palace of Indian Federation. This thing was presented to us because of the Indian States. All was put upon their offer. Now we are told it is only to be half. I am not going to argue with my right hon. Friend. He says he did not say "all" or did not mean to say "all" and that is the end of it. But between "all" and 50 per cent. there is a pretty wide margin. He brushed that aside, but the Government are basing their case on the offer of the States. We are told that we ought to give up our views because of this great ugly rush of the Princes of India to get into the Federation—on a purely democratic basis, of course. That is understood all the time. But between "all" and 50 per cent. cannot we come to an agreement with the right hon. Gentleman? Cannot we split the difference and accept this Amendment of 75 per cent.—three-quarters instead of half?

What is all this talk about the blackmail which is to be exerted by the outstanding of a few States or whatever it may be—that if you ask too many to come in the last lot might make conditions, and that you have to ask a very few to come in so that you can square that lot—and you have got them very well sized up I must say? Add up the big States of India and see the ones that have been dealt with—Travancore, and Bangalore, and so forth. But when you come to the focus of this matter you find that this point diminishes under the criticism of the Committee. Personally I think this is the weakest point in the Government's case. I think they make a great mistake to force it so much. If the great mass of the Indian States were really so sincere in their desire to participate in the newly created Federation of All-India, with responsible government, with the full surge of democratic processes operative at the centre, you would not have had this awful comedown to 50 per cent. and that 50 per cent. just about what can be managed and manipulated.

The right hon. Gentleman will tell me, no doubt, that the Joint Select Committee have considered all this, and settled it all, and examined it all so nicely. My right hon. Friend made a great mistake in not having a better committee of inquiry, people who would really make a searching examination of these problems. [An Hon. Member: "What did not you join it?"] Because the composition of it was so unfair—about four to one, between three and four to one. Let us be quite frank about it. An hon. Member looks at me in a questioning manner. We are fighting this policy, fighting this Bill, and we have to judge whether we shall fight it, on the committee or outside the committee, entirely from the point of view of whether we can make a better fight; but if the committee had been a fair one, if it had been one which gave a fair representation—and we are not fighting it with such ill-effects as you suppose or as your majorities in this House may lead you to imagine—if the committee had been a fair one, it would have been quite possible to go on it. The right hon. Gentleman, however, so managed this committee that, instead of being a committee to inquire into these matters, it was a sort of recruiting agency for supporters of the Bill. But I am not going to discuss the committee. On the contrary, all I say is that if this matter had been properly thrashed out in the committee, the right hon. Gentleman would not be in the position in which he finds himself at the present moment.

Mr. Amery: Why did not you thrash it out then?

Mr. Churchill: If I am to take up the point which has been flung at me by the right hon. Member for Sparkbrook (Mr. Amery), I may have to put some strain upon your indulgence in presiding, Mr. Chairman, but I will leave it entirely with this observation, that it was not a committee of inquiry; it was a mutual admiration society, with a few increasingly embarrassed spectators. I come back to the point that, in default of fair and searching criticism, this is the first criticism which has come upon these plans. This is the first time they are dragged to the light, I will not say of day, but to the broad light of Parliamentary discussion, and here we have—

Sir S. Hoare: This percentage has been in the White Paper, all through the Indian discussion, and the Round Table Conference, and the Indian Princes themselves have agreed to it throughout.

Duchess of Atholl: May I ask the right hon. Gentleman if I was not right in saying that he first publicly mentioned this percentage at the end of the last Round Table Conference?

Sir S. Hoare: I do not know whether that is so or not, but even so, that was how many years ago? [An Hon. Member: "Two years."] I should have said much longer.

Mr. Churchill: We know that India is progressing at an enormous rate. We are told that it is progressing at such a rate that any man who came home before the Secretary of State took office has no opinion about it worth considering, so no doubt his own views will change from time to time. But let me put before the Committee the brutal fact that whereas the sort of general idea was that it was to be the offer of the Indian States, that they all wanted to come forward, now it has been cut down to 50 per cent., and those 50 per cent. can be pretty well made up out of the States which we allege, and will increasingly assert and endeavour to prove, have been in one way or another got at, approached, developed, by the right hon. Gentleman through all the sources that are open to him. What is the use of telling me that there is this talk about pressure and bribery? Let us withdraw all invidious expressions. The facts are quite good enough. Here are these territories which are to be retroceded. Here are these tributes which are to be forgiven. Here are these alterations in the financial arrangements with the Government of India. We heard representatives of the Princes appealing that these concessions should be made to them, and they were only to be made if there were Federation. All this only operates on the basis of 50 per cent.

One could have understood if, with all these adventitious aids, the right hon. Gentleman had worked it up to 75 per cent., but 50 per cent. is all he is able to get. With all the pressure of the Government and all the power and might, majesty and dominion at the disposal of a National Government in the full plentitude of power, they can get only 50 per cent. This is the crux of the whole matter. Here is the basis on which the Conservative party were induced to consent to this measure; they were told that here was this offer of the Princes. I must say we thought it was a stream, but it is a pump, and the pump only works to the extent of 50 per cent. The right hon. Gentleman would be well advised to accept the Amendment; there is no reason why he should not. Why should he not accept three-quarters? He says that the odd balance of States would blackmail him. On the 50 per cent. he thinks he has got them pretty well fixed up now. The Committee can judge between those two propositions. If the Government are going to give a foundation to your Indian policy, if the great States of India are to come into a federal system, and if they desire to come in so long as it is democratic, have not the Government the courage to put their convictions to the test of 75 per cent.?

The right hon. Gentleman is here on the weakest point of his case. I should say the weakest point of his case up to the present time. I can only speak as a political friend of the right hon. Gentleman, and even that would be subject to some discount, but if he would accept the Amendment, on which we intend to divide, and take three-quarters as a broad test of the willingness of the States to come in and as a broad guarantee and vindication of the statement of the Lord President of the Council as to the offer being the thing that moved him—this offer which is petering out and shrinking down, and all the available pressure only working it up to 50 per cent.—if he would take this on the basis of three-quarters, even if they do not all come in, even if the decision were adverse to it, would he be so much the worse off? Would the Government be so much the worse off? Would India be so much the worse off? Who would be the sufferers by it? The right hon. Gentleman would be well advised to accept this further definition. If he has faith in his policy, cannot he trust it beyond an even-money chance?

CONSERVATIVE LEADERSHIP AND AIR DEFENCE

February 22, 1935

Loughton

The real cause of the unemployment "muddle" and of many other failures in the Government is the fact that there is no Prime Minister, in the sense of a commanding mind ranging comprehensively over the whole field of public action. [Editor's Note: Churchill was referring to a recent speech by Mr. Baldwin in which he said: "I do not believe our party alone could win a clear majority in the United Kingdom today with the amount of split votes there would be between itself."]

Now if this means anything, it means that the leader of the Conservative Party pursues a policy which at the General Election will produce a large amount of split votes among Conservatives, and that therefore, in order to carry his policy, he must go in search of Socialist and Liberal votes to make up the losses he is suffering in Conservative votes.

I had hoped that at the General Election there would be no split votes among Conservatives, and that our leaders would give us a policy upon which the whole strength of the Conservative Party could unite. But if Mr. Baldwin is going to pursue a Socialist and Liberal policy which the Conservative Party cannot unitedly support, and is then going to seek the votes of Socialists and Liberals, instead of Conservatives, then the question arises whether as a party leader he is entitled to take such a course.

The duty of the party leader who owes everything to the support which his party is giving him is to keep that party together, to pursue policies on which it can act unitedly, and not to split up a large portion of his own party in the hope of making converts and allies of the Socialists and Liberals. I hope we shall have some reassuring explanation of this menacing statement by the leader of our party.

There has been a very unfortunate breakdown in the Government's unemployment policy. As usual, the Conservative Party get the worst of both worlds. The Conservative Chancellor of the Exchequer has to find a very large sum out of the profits of the income-tax payers. This money is given to the unemployed, and the Socialists will claim all the credit of having extracted it from the Government.

The economics of the Means Test have been largely dissipated: still, on the other hand, all the unpopularity of enforcing this test is still going against the Conservative

Party in the constituencies. I do not think it is at all fair to throw the blame of this disaster upon the new Minister of Labour. If the qualities of industry and sympathy were among those required in a Minister of Labour, Mr. Oliver Stanley possesses them in a high degree. The fault is not his. The real cause of the muddle and of many other failures in the present Government is the fact that there is no Prime Minister in the sense of a commanding mind ranging comprehensively over the whole field of public action.

In Mr. Ramsay MacDonald the country, the Government, and, above all, the Conservative Party are carrying a burden of the most grievous kind. If Mr. Baldwin decides that we should go to the General Election under such leadership, I shall certainly not be able to agree to that course.

The interests of the country must come before a personal consideration. The nation requires confidence and vigorous leadership as well as a man at the head of affairs who commands the respect of patriotic men and women of every class.

The great fact is that Germany is arming and to a large extent has already armed. I fear Germany. I fear greatly for the peace of the world when I see her gathering in strength and putting on that terrible panoply she wore in 1914. Even at the height of war we had never allowed ourselves to be dominated by such a passion of national exclusiveness as was exhibited by Germany to-day. When I saw what happened on June 30 and the hideous medieval spectacle a few days ago of the decapitation of two women, I felt very uncomfortable.

I see that terrible power which fought the whole world—and nearly beat the whole world—laying its hands on all the new tackle of war, and particularly the air.

Before 1914 this country was safe in her island home. I do not think the government has made adequate provision for our air defence. We have been promised an air force at least as strong as Germany's, but I believe before the year is out that the German air force will be substantially stronger than our own.

An air force cannot protect one population from another, but the fact that we had one as strong as another country would deter them. I hope there is still time to take the necessary measures. Whether the assurances of the Government will be carried out has yet to be shown.

We are making an air pact with France. I am in favour of that so far as it goes. But if you get a foreign country to protect you, you only get that on the promise to protect that country, and you may be drawn into all manner of quarrels that seem very remote from us in England.

The only safe line is to be strong and independent. Have a strong defence, and then be animated by a sincere love of peace. In that way you may escape the perils that still loom upon us in the future.

GOVERNMENT OF INDIA BILL
(CLAUSES 5, 6)
February 26, 1935
House of Commons

I beg to move, "That the Chairman do report Progress, and ask leave to sit again."

The Committee will not, I am sure, be surprised at my venturing to submit this Motion. I do so because of the momentous news which has been received from India, and which we learn from every side in the public Press. I do so for the purpose of commenting upon that news and pointing out the position in which we stand with regard to the Clauses which have now become the immediate subject of debate; and also for the purpose of giving the Secretary of State the opportunity, which no doubt he will desire, of making a statement on the subject. According to the reports which have appeared, and which I do not understand to be in any way challenged as official reports, the Princes of India, at their meeting in Bombay yesterday, passed a resolution which no doubt is present to the minds of hon. Members of this Committee, and the closing paragraphs of which indicate very definite rejection of the Government's scheme for the Federation of India. What strikes me about this resolution, the summarised reports, and the telegrams which, it is said, the Princes have addressed to the Secretary of State, is the variety, the gravity, and the substance of the differences which exist. These are not differences which can be described in any way as matters of drafting, as small points which can be adjusted, minor matters which make for some misunderstanding which can easily be cleared up later on on Report. It is said that these differences touch the following matters:

The form and mode of accession to the Federation.

The provisions for the preservation of treaties and agreements concluded with the States.

The special responsibilities of the Governor-General in respect of the States.

Then there is a most important point, touching the efficacy of the safeguards in the event of grave public disorder supervening in India and its being necessary to suspend the Constitution.

Measures to be taken in the event of its being necessary to suspend the Constitution.

The treatment of privileges and immunities.

Enforcement of the Federal laws and the powers vested in the Governor-General to give directions to the rulers of States.

The extent of the executive authority of the Federation in regard to the States.

There are further differences which have arisen on finance, and also upon what I should have thought was a very essential matter to federation, namely, the working of the statutory railway board in relation to the competition between State railways in the possession of native States and State railways in the possession of the Government of India. I venture to submit that this resolution constitutes a new political situation so far as the future of this Bill is concerned. Certainly I cannot conceive how, in the face of all these Amendments and alterations which are put forward by a body whose concurrence is indispensable to the entire process of the Bill, we can be asked to discuss the remaining general question of Clause 5 [Proclamation of Federation of India], and still less Clause 6 [Accession of Indian States], which deals with this very topic of accession.

I have pointed out already the inconvenience to which the Committee would be put in embarking upon these discussions before we knew what the Princes' decision was, and, indeed, it seemed quite likely that we should have already disposed of Clause 6 by this time. Happily, it is still in the possession of the Committee, but how is it competent for us to discuss it? Here are Amendments which affect the whole basis, and we do not know what the Amendments are, nor, I suppose, is the right hon. Gentleman in a position to tell us exactly what the Amendments are or to place them on the Paper. If we were able to put them on the Paper in two or three days, we could easily postpone the Clauses until the Amendments were there, but to discuss the Clauses without knowing what are all the alterations in the structure of the Bill, to discuss the whole question of federation in all the Clauses in the Bill without knowing whether in fact the indispensable condition, namely, the accession of the Princes is going to be achieved, is purely to confront the House with the prospect of discussing a hypothetical matter with the prospect of embarking on a great waste of time, thus condemning us in all probability to a prolonged and dreary farce. This question of the accession of the Princes is, as everyone recognises on both sides, the Government and the Opposition, and those of us who dissent from the proposal of the Government, the foundation of the whole policy. I am not going to burden the House with any more quotations than one which is necessary to establish the case. The Secretary of State in his broadcast speech on 1st January said:

> There cannot be provincial autonomy without federation, and federation must be all-India federation embracing the States and British India. If there is to be federation, there must be responsibility in the central Government if only to satisfy the requirements of the Princes, who will not enter a federation controlled by Whitehall.

There is the foundation, and it has been the whole story that the Government have told from the beginning of the discussion. It was for this that they made their departure from the more or less solid ground of the Statutory Commission. It was at this point that the landslide at the first Round Table Conference occurred. This was the point where they threw the train of coaches off the line with the disaster that we have suffered from ever since. I could give a dozen instances of the Secretary of State's insistence on this point. On this everything stands. This is the rigmarole that he taught all his followers to proclaim with so much insistence.

I see the Lord President in his place and I am bound to address myself to him amicably but pointedly. The Lord President met his party at Queen's Hall at a meeting to which great importance was attached and around which a great deal of interest

hung. What was the crux of his appeal? It was that you must not reject this offer of
the Princes. My right hon. Friend would not have thrown all that weight on to that
topic at this moment if he had not honestly believed that there was a prospect of a
great new situation, and to seize that prospect, to enjoy that opportunity, was what he
urged them to do. He quoted first of all the Foreign Secretary's recantation of the
Simon Report. He quoted the Foreign Secretary as saying:

> But since we reported there has been a new fact.

There has been another new fact.

> We were commissioners, but we were not prophets, and it was not until
> after we had reported that the new fact emerged.

He went on to describe the action of some of the Indian Princes which led to the
changes in the Government policy in 1931. The Lord President said to his followers—I
can see them visibly wilt under the impact of the appeal—

> It would, indeed, be a great responsibility to reject the prospect of a
> closer union between the Indian Princes and their great territories on the
> one hand, and the British India, for which we have a special responsibility,
> on the other.

This is the linch pin of the whole story, and the linch pin has been pulled out. I
contend and submit substantially that that is the fact.

I must revert for a moment to the resolution of the Princes. It is not only what
they say; it is the tone in which they say it that the House should note. If these were
minor difficulties to which a happy outcome was expected, you would not expect a
manifesto of this kind containing some very serious things considering the body from
which they emanate, considering the relations of those Princes to the Viceroy and to
His Majesty's Government.

> This meeting desires to emphasise that in many respects the Bill and the
> instrument of accession depart from the agreement arrived at during the
> meetings of the representatives of the States with Members of His
> Majesty's Government.

Only the other day Lord Halifax was saying:

> My right hon. Friend the Secretary of State is confident that the report
> of the Committee does, in fact, substantially meet the reasonable appre-
> hensions of the Princes as they were explained to the Joint Select Com-
> mittee.

Here the Princes have declared that in many respects these proposals depart from the
agreement arrived at. There is a direct conflict of testimony between the two parties.

It is always very serious when people who are supposed to be in the closest relations say that there is a breach of an agreement arrived at. You may be sure that there is a great deal of feeling behind the differences. The resolution continues:

> And regrets to note that the Bill and the instrument of accession do not secure those vital interests and fundamental requisites of the States on which they have throughout laid great emphasis.

Surely this matter cannot be dismissed as a mere question of drafting. It is without a knowledge of the Amendments that will be required to meet these vital interests and fundamental requisites that the Committee is going to be urged to proceed with the discussion of Clause 6 and the other federal Clauses. It went on to say:

> This meeting is of the definite opinion that in their present form, and without statutory modification of and alteration to the fundamental points, the Bill and the instrument of accession cannot be regarded as acceptable to the Indian States.

Who are these Princes who made this proposal and committed themselves to this very far-reaching and weighty pronouncement? They were unanimous in the first instance and they are representative of the Princes of India in an overwhelming degree. The little States were there as well as the great, though not by any means all the little States. The States to whom the greatest inducements have been offered to join the Federation, Mysore, Hyderabad and Travencore—all these States concurred in this resolution, and they are the greatest States in India. They are meant to be the main part of the 50 per cent.—the old guard—upon which the right hon. Gentleman is hoping to rely to carry his proposals. He cut it down to 50 per cent., and here are those great States which were an essential part of the 50 per cent. In addition to that, it is not only the Princes who were lukewarm, who had secret misgivings, who have been talking pretty freely of their misgivings and fears about the Bill and some of them declaring their definite hostility, who are represented in this resolution, but the Princes who were most in favour of this policy, the very Princes who made the original offer, the unauthorised offer as we contend and as many of the other Princes have contended, the very Princes who came forward and have always been paraded as the special champions of this policy and deflected the course of events at the Round Table Conference—these are the Princes who are associated with others in this resolution they have presented to us in this form.

The Committee, I think, will see the difficult position in which it is this afternoon in embarking upon the discussion. I must confess that I am not at all surprised at this change of opinion of the active minority of the Princes on whom the Government have hitherto rested as the champions of the Government policy. In fact, I think that this change in their opinion—a very decisive change it is—bears out what some of us have ventured to submit to the House and to the Committee. These were the Princes, these were the minority, who were led to make the so-called offer in 1931 as the result of a bargain with some of the representatives of the Congress, and some of the advanced parties in India. The terms of this bargain—an unholy bargain—were that if the Princes demanded responsible government at the Centre, then the Congress party would leave them to govern their estates as they liked. That was the outline of it.

I want the Committee to see exactly how this matter has worked. These were the Princes most susceptible to the influence of the Indian political classes in British India, and in those days the opinion of those political classes was in favour of a federal system, with responsible government at the Centre. But now that the whole matter has been examined and discussed, those very political classes are in full retreat and in recoil from the proposal. They have carried a resolution against it by an overwhelming majority in the Indian Assembly, and they are undoubtedly bringing their influence to bear upon the Princes with whom they were originally in touch in exactly the contrary sense of four years ago, with the result that those Princes, who are working more or less in close association with those political elements, are moving in the opposite direction just as strongly as they moved in the direction of the Government in 1931.

That is the explanation, and one can see it working. Thus those Princes who were most amenable beforehand to the Government project, are now falling back into the main line of all the rest of the Princes who never liked it, and were only embarrassed by the many influences brought to bear upon them to draw them into the main body. Hence the unanimity of all these Princes. The names of the States have only to be read out to dispose of any argument that they are not the dominating force with the Indian Princes, and that is the reason of the unanimity among them. There is another thing not less remarkable which should not be overlooked, and that is that the Ministers are in agreement with the Princes. The Ministers of the States are represented as being in agreement with the Princes. That is very remarkable, because one always can see that the Ministers had everything to gain with regard to their personal position, because once they became the nominees of those States in the Federal Assembly their position would be vastly different, their status would be vastly raised and they would no longer hold their position purely at the pleasure of the Princes they served. The idea that when some great Minister of State was playing a great part in the Federal Assembly he could be recalled owing to the fact that the Sovereign under whom he was serving wished to have another nominee, even if it were entertained would be very difficult to carry out in practice. Any assembly worthy of its salt would rally to such a man who was suddenly recalled by an outside power. The Ministers who were to gain this great accretion to their strength have associated themselves with the Princes in these far-reaching declarations.

Thus all the articulate elements in Indian political life from Congress up to the Princes are arrayed against this Bill, and the reason why I move to report Progress is in order to ascertain what course His Majesty's Government wish to pursue. No doubt the Secretary of State will try to minimise the difficulties. He will promise vaguely further important concessions, while at the same time hurrying on these vital Clauses, getting them through the Committee stage without disclosing the details of the concessions at all to the House or the Princes. If the Committee lends itself to his imposture, and if the Government, by using their enormous majority, enforce it upon the House, all I say is that they will only put off and only aggravate the inevitable day of reckoning. It is quite certain that the attitude of the Princes is now definitely against this kind of federation at this particular time. The safeguards may be whittled down. You may relax some of the precautions in the veto of the Viceroy which you believe indispensable to the discharge of the responsibilities of this House. The power of the Viceroy to deal with an emergency may be crippled by the concessions which you will propose. The coherence of federal India may be impaired by further awkward concessions in regard to railways and finance, and the small benefits which were offered to us as a result of this enormous change in the structural organisation of the Indian polity will be lost.

Although this may be the method which the right hon. Gentleman is about to adopt, and which has been enforced upon the House, and may condemn us to discussion utterly meaningless, which is an affront to Parliament, yet we predict with confidence that nothing will change now the resolve of the Indian Princes to disengage themselves from what they have realised is a dangerous project, and, while so many things are in flux, nothing will lead them, and nothing should lead them, to quit the solid rock of their treaties with the King Emperor. Now that we have reached this point, we see the improvidence and the short-sightedness of the kind of arguments used by the Secretary of State, and by my right hon. Friend the Member for West Birmingham (Sir A. Chamberlain), my right hon. Friend the Member for Sparkbrook (Mr. Amery) and by the Noble Lord the Member for Hastings (Lord E. Percy). These are the arguments of which I warned them when I addressed the House before. [*Interruption.*] I am in the recollection of the House, that they were very short-sighted in declaring that nothing in this Bill is worth anything without the federal Clauses, and unless the Princes come in, and that without federation they would rather not go on with it, and that we had better drop it altogether rather than proceed with this provincial home rule, without this super-home rule at the summit. That seemed to me to be a most improvident argument at the time when it was uncertain whether the Princes would come in or not. The right hon. Gentleman kept on assuring us that it would be all right. Of course they would come in. Of course there would be minor difficulties, and so on. So have all the Government spokesmen said everywhere, but our opinion has, I think, proved more accurate upon this matter—more accurate, at any rate, than any opinion the right hon. Gentleman has yet given to the House or the Committee.

As I say, it seems to me that my right hon. Friends have placed themselves in a position of great difficulty, and so has the Secretary of State, because now, if the Princes do not come in, they have used arguments which will be used against them, or might be used against them, to vitiate even that provincial extension of home rule which was proposed to us by the solemn, carefully worked-out report of our Statutory Commission four years ago. However, we shall leave the Government and its Ministerial supporters to disentangle themselves from these foolish and unforeseeing arguments which were so freely used thus to get round the momentary corner of a Debate. It is clear that the federal scheme is dead. Every day its decomposition will be more evident, and, as the summer advances, more offensive. But even now His Majesty's Government have a chance—perhaps the most blessed and fortunate chance—to get back to the broad proposals of that Statutory Commission to which nothing useful has been added in the last four years. Although we consider, as I have often said, and I am bound to repeat now, that these proposals are a most hazardous experiment, they do not contain the mortal perils of this federal plan. Let the Government discard the federal plan. Let the right hon. Gentleman put aside pride and obstinacy. Let him imitate the prudence and the wisdom of Sir Robert Walpole on the great Excise Bill when, having seen what the situation was, he told his followers and supporters with the greatest conviction, "This dance can no further go."

[Much later] We are all indebted to the learned Solicitor-General for the cogency and the compression of his statement on this series of Amendments (Clause 6—Accession of Indian States), which play an important part in the Government's alterations to the Bill. I feel, after what my hon. and learned Friend has said, that the Committee is now in full possession of all the points at issue. As we are anxious to get on as rapidly as possible, I shall not find it necessary to delay the Committee by exploring this matter further, but there are one or two questions I wanted to ask. As far as I am able to throw myself into the full stream of the right hon. and learned Gentleman's discourse, I gather that this series of Amendments is designed to placate the Princes, a very legitimate and a very necessary task, designed to placate them upon the varying and complicated type of their Instruments of Accession. The rather vulgar commonplace word "declaration" has been put into a suitable background, and the expression "Instrument of Accession" is given due prominence. That is the specific Amendment, and it inaugurates a series of Amendments all designed, as I take it, to enable the Secretary of State to go round to these Princes one by one. Perhaps the right hon. Gentleman will give me his attention. Perhaps he was telling the learned Solicitor-General of something which the latter had forgotten to say. They are all designed to enable my right hon. Friend to go round to these Princes one by one—not having them in a great bunch of 100, as we saw the other day in Bombay—but one by one and take from each according to what he can give—from each according to his power, to each according to his need. It will be a case of an indefinite succession of individual dealings. After all, some will contribute a good deal to the Federation, others may only be able to give very little, but he needs them all, and this Amendment gives him the power to arrange anything that he likes with any Prince in order to gather his force together.

I take it that is the object of the extremely powerful technical exposition from the Solicitor-General. We can quite understand the purpose; although some of us, not having a legal training, may not be able to follow every one of those refinements, yet, nevertheless, the purpose is nakedly clear. It is to enable the right hon. Gentleman to gather his party together among the Princes. But there are one or two questions I must really ask. There must be some limit, some minimum test, before he can say he has got a Prince. Of course, the larger the party the more generous are the conditions of association, but this is rather a small party, on the narrow verge between the 50 per cent. who we thought were associated with the whole party and the 75 per cent. where a lot of vulgar blackmailing considerations might intrude upon the course of the Imperial Government. Therefore, the right hon. Gentleman must have a more or less precise test. I hope he will tell us what is the least concession of individual State rights which he will accept as suitable for the Crown to concur with. I gather we shall have all kinds of Instruments of Accession. Some will come in for a lot, and some for less, and some for hardly anything—some will hardly pay the green fees. At any rate, however they are in there must be some test, and I hope the Secretary of State will tell us quite shortly what it is. I would not wish him to go over all the legal points again. We have got them. Quite shortly, what exactly is the least that will qualify a Prince to be told, on the authority of the Crown, that he has executed an acceptable Instrument of Accession—I think I have got that right?

Another question which arises is a little more complex, but I think I can put it without any legal complication. All these Instruments of Accession will be of varying types and varying values. Some will be whole-timers, some half-timers, others will only just chip in for a bit and go away again. All these Instruments of Accession are of varying values. There may be four, five or six different types, or many more. How do those varying values affect the principle of 50 per cent. of the Princes coming in in order to constitute the basis of the federal system? It is obvious that these react upon one another. You cannot count the half-timers as whole-timers. For the purpose of 50 per cent. you cannot count a man who only comes in for one thing or another, and who says, "I come into Federation on this limited liability principle; I quite agree with it as far as that is concerned." You cannot count him as a 100 per cent. factor of the 50 per cent. necessary quota.

These react upon each other, and we are getting into an extremely complicated notation in this matter. I hope the right hon. Gentleman will tell us quite plainly whether, when he says there must be a 50 per cent. minimum of the Princes by population and territory, as set out in the Bill, he means 50 per cent. *bona fide* Instruments of Accession and not merely a number of Princes who may have paid a certain lip-service to the principle, although they may have a certain population and territory. Are these obligations to be reciprocal? Is everyone—including those who come in for a very little—also to be excluded from voting in the Debates of the Federal Assembly in respect of matters which they have not, as it were, put into the pool? If you are to carry out this immensely complicated scheme, the like of which was never seen on earth, in Heaven or in the waters under the earth, and will never be seen again after we have finished with it, at least you should lay down the broad principle that no one shall take out of the federal pool more than he puts in, and that no Prince shall take out of the federal pool more than he puts in. I hope I shall be able to have an assurance that that is definitely embodied in the law.

I am sure my right hon. Friend will clear up these points of difficulty which remain over; he really owes it to us to do so. He said earlier in the day that the House had instructed him to produce this Bill, but I think responsibility does not rest entirely upon the House. He forgot to mention that before the House instructed the Government to produce this Bill, the Government instructed the Whips to instruct the House to instruct him to produce exactly the Bill that he requires.

GOVERNMENT OF INDIA BILL
(CLAUSES 6, 8)

February 27, 1935

House of Commons

I wish to thank the Secretary of State for the illumination which he has thrown upon a complicated aspect of the Bill and on his Amendments. I couched my remarks in an interrogatory form. I was not drawing a picture, but I was asking a certain number of questions in order to obtain reassurance that the picture when drawn by the Secretary of State would be free from some of the blemishes which might appear in some versions. I think the Secretary of State has made it very plain that the accession of the Princes must be great and substantial accessions. If they come in they are to come in for substantially the whole body of the subjects up to 45. There is no question of their being allowed only to take up two or three, or half-a-dozen, or fifteen. They must come in substantially for the whole of these 45 important elements in the Federal Constitution. That, I think, is very satisfactory. I agree that in a sub-Continent as vast as India certain differences here and there might allow of some mitigation in respect of a particular State, but I gather that that is only to be for a very small proportion of the 45 subjects and is not likely to occur except in a few of the States. That being so, I think that undoubtedly the core of the Federation will be sustained by the Princes who subscribe to this particular list.

I gather that it is optional in regard to the other list to come in with or without reservation. It appears to me, if I understand rightly, that in regard to the first list of 45 subjects—I notice that it stops short of State lotteries, in which my hon. Friend the Member for South Kensington (Sir. W. Davison) is interested—some of the services may be handed back, as it were, to the Princes for administration in their own territories, instead of being administered by the Federal Government, if that is found to be satisfactory. That is so, is it not?

Sir S. Hoare: Yes.

Mr. Churchill: But, of course, the discussion of the affairs of those States in the Federal Legislature will range equally over any branches that have been reassigned to the States and to those which are being administered by the Federal Legislature and which the Princes have surrendered to the Federal Legislature. That is very important, and I am very glad that we are going to see exactly what the consequences of the situation will be. There will be this enormous block of subjects, 45 subjects, which touch the States at so many points, and the whole of them can be made the subject of debate at any time in the Federal Assembly. That is certainly right, because obviously if the services have been surrendered they are amenable to discussion, and if once surrendered and then handed back *a fortiori* the supervision must be maintained. The internal affairs of the States which join the Federation will be continually open to debate and discussion in the Federal Assembly. That is most important to establish, and I am very glad that the Secretary of State did not find himself in agreement with the hon. and learned Member for East Bristol (Sir S. Cripps) who seemed to think that it would be, as it were, outside the purview of the scope of the Federal Legislature to discuss and to have debates on the internal affairs of the different States. It now appears that they will be brought fully and fairly on to the floor of the Federal Assembly. Having regard to the fact that the list is a substantial list and that those States that accede to the Federation will be subject to having the whole of these matters constantly discussed in the Assembly it seems to me that no one can deny the reality and the gravity of the act which each one of the Princes will take when he subscribes irrevocably to the Instrument of Accession.

[Much later] The Secretary of State talks about coercing the Princes. There is no question of anyone being coerced. If they wish to come into federation, as we are told they have offered to do, it will be a voluntary act. My right hon. Friend has repeatedly assured us that in no circumstances is pressure to be put upon them to take this step. But, if they take the step, surely we are entitled to press upon them the importance of this class of subject being included in those to which they subscribe. Surely we are entitled to do that. The Imperial power does interest itself in the fortunes of the masses of India and in their well-being, and now Parliament is asked to leave this on one side. The object is to get federation. Surely if we are going to have federation, if this great design is to be carried to completeness, it should be a federation which has as one of its central points a desire to raise and to unify labour conditions throughout India. In the present circumstances the very greatest difficulties will arise. One very revealing remark fell from my right hon. Friend when he said he thought the Federal Assembly would not be so favourable to progressive social legislation as would be the federal units. Here is a clear admission that he is trying to set up what is thought to be a reactionary—

The Deputy-Chairman: I do not think we can discuss federation again on this Amendment.

Mr. Churchill: I was merely replying to the statement of the Secretary of State. He said that the body at the centre would be less likely to concern itself with the well-being of the masses, with factory legislation and so forth, than the federal units, even than some of these despotically governed Indian States. It is a terrific statement.

Sir S. Hoare: My right hon. Friend is unintentionally misrepresenting what I attempted to say. It is obvious, if he looks at the list, that the subjects concerned with the daily life of the people are provincial subjects, and always have been. That being so, it must be the Provinces which will be most closely connected with questions of social reform, and the movements for social reform are much more likely to come from the Provinces.

Mr. Churchill: The proposal that is put forward is that an effort should be made to clothe the centre also with these functions, and that the Princes who accede to the Central Legislature should place themselves in a great area in which there will be an endeavour to establish uniform labour conditions as far as possible, and it is obvious that if there is not that attempt, all progress is arrested. Here is an opportunity for Parliament to strike this note in favour of not neglecting our duties to the great proletariat of India, and of placing before the Princes the fact that, now that they are coming into this system of federalism, which the Government assure us and them will be so greatly to their advantage, the least the Government can do is to endeavour to negotiate with them and ask them whether they cannot be induced to take on this burden. The most effective way of influencing the Government in that respect is for us to support our opinions by our votes. In all these matters Great Britain is making enormous sacrifices, and if the Princes wish to have this federal system they should, in my opinion, share in those sacrifices too.

[Much later] We have now reached the conclusion of this Debate on the Question, "That Clause 6 [Accession of Indian States] stand part," and I venture to think that there is hardly any other question more momentous than the one with which we have to deal now. Here is the crux of the Debate. We have considered many Amendments, and we have now reached the point where the main issues are clearly before the Committee, and we are entitled to review them, seeing that the Committee have to take a decision of such consequence. This Clause deals with, as the Chairman has pointed out on several occasions, the accession of the Princes. Without the accession of the Princes there can be no All-India Federation, and without an All-India Federation we are assured, though I do not myself adopt that view, that there can be no hope for the present Government of India Bill. Therefore we are absolutely at the cardinal point of our discussion. The Government attitude throughout has been that it would be of the very greatest advantage to the Princes if they accede to the Federation.

The right hon. Member for West Birmingham (Sir A. Chamberlain), and others who have been enlisted in the Government scheme of very effective orators, through their association with the Joint Select Committee, has expressed on his high authority the view that it would be greatly to the advantage of the Princes if they were to sign the Instrument of Accession. That is the position of the Government. The Princes are, by association with an All-India Federation, to gain great facilities and great improvements in their customs arrangements and so forth, and in joining in general matters of interest for the great sub-Continent of India. That is the position of the Government, their official and public position, but when one has a Debate such as we have had to-day one sees how very thin and threadbare that kind of argument is, what a bold bluff it is, what a sinking there is, what a hollow feeling there is behind all the confident asseverations of the advantage to the Princes, the great demand of the Princes, the surging of these princely figures towards the portals of All-India Federation.

In spite of this tremendous tendency to federation, this irresistible demand for federation, on the part of the Princes, the Secretary of State, with his liberal and humanitarian sentiments, has not dared to speak a word for the poor millions of India; he has not dared to say one word on their behalf. So near, so narrow, is the margin that he has not dared to say to any of these Princes, not even to the most enlightened of them whose labour conditions are better than those which prevail in British India, "Surely, in your Instrument of Accession you will agree to uniform laws for labour and social and health conditions." He would not dare to do it. The sense of advantages which the Princes have is not strong enough to bear the weight of that demand, and the Secretary of State, intent upon the political aspects of the great design which he has carried so far and fought for so valiantly and boldly, which he has lost himself in, absorbed himself in, has brushed aside all considerations affecting the well-being of the masses of India, who are regarded as pawns in this great game of empire unbuilding. His Majesty's Government do not dare to ask that any steps shall be taken in the Federation to secure decent conditions for the masses of the Indian people. That is an important point. One of the lines of the attack we make on this Bill, not only now but which we shall make as long as it is in any way presented as an issue in our public life, is that the interests of the masses of the people of India have been totally ignored.

The hon. Member for Bodmin (Mr. Isaac Foot) made a speech which I am bound to say did more credit to his fidelity to the engagements and associations into which he has entered than to the interests of working democracy. It was the sort of speech of a very old Liberal school. As long as they could preach liberty they cared little what were the conditions of the poorer people. But I must not allow myself to be drawn outside the scope of the discussion, and I think I rather caught your eye, Mr. Chairman, as though you were, shall I say, on the pounce. Therefore, I will not press my advantage against the hon. Member for Bodmin any further at the moment. I say clearly that the Government do not believe that this will be to the advantage of the Princes, or that the Princes have that idea, because they dare not ask us to insert the provisions. Indeed, the position of the Princes will be most poignant. I said so in the Debate on the Second Reading, and to-day we have had full confirmation of the fact. I did not know at the time of the Second Reading Debate that the Instrument of Accession would be interpreted to cover the very wide series of subjects, 45 topics, of which the great majority are obligatory. Then there is the expectancy that the voluntary list shall also be acceded to by the Princes.

I did not know, I was surprised like the hon. and learned Member for East Bristol (Sir S. Cripps), that all matters of the internal government of the States would be debatable on every occasion, on almost every pretext upon which you can hang a Parliamentary Debate. As hon. Members know a discussion may be raised on one point and at almost any distance from that point; but little did I realise that this would be possible by direct debate. I thought that by a side wind they would be able to call the Princes over the coals in regard to questions about internal administration, but only by a side wind. To-day the Secretary of State, speaking with great clearness, explained that in all matters of labour legislation and so on the Ministers will be advising the Viceroy and the Assembly will be influencing Ministers, although there is no direct surrender on the part of the States. It is clear that the whole of the affairs of these independent States will be debatable from day to day on the floor of the Indian Assembly. If we tried to debate the affairs of the Irish Free State in this House, I think we should be pulled up. I thought it would be only a limited debate which would prevail in the Federal Legislature as against the States. Not at all. It is clear that all these matters can be debated. It illustrates the poignant position, the terrible position, of the Indian Princes.

What are they expected to do when they sign the Act of Accession? That is the core of our discussion. They are expected to be the stabilising influence in the Assembly. They are expected to be the conservative and loyal influence. If they move in that direction, and in so far as they do move, they will excite the animosity of those who hate our rule and who hate law and order in every form. They will be attacked first of all in their States, where disorders will be raised by agitators. They will be attacked in the Central Assembly, where the Secretary of State assures us there will be limitless opportunities for calling in question and debating every one of their actions. In the third place, these matters undoubtedly will have their repercussions over here. When a Prince has stood out for the Imperial connection and gained unpopularity in India, has been attacked in his own State where agitation has been fomented against him, he may easily find people who will criticise him again over here. A horrible position for the Princes to be placed in. Is it to their advantage? I do not wonder that the Government dare not put another straw on the camel's back and ask them to agree to decent conditions for the labouring people. The ice is far too thin for that.

But what is their actual view? What has astonished me more than anything else in the course of these discussions, through which we shall arrive at a true conviction of the issues in this enormous Bill, is that the Secretary of State, whose ability is so obvious, whose industry is so praiseworthy, who is so saturated with his subject and whose courage and qualities as administrator and parliamentarian are nowhere more readily admitted than by those who are fighting him in this matter, has not been able, as well as many of those who are acting with him, to understand the simple dynamics of the Indian situation. Why is it that the Princes are now boggling at the Act of Accession? Why are they now rising in such hostility and wrath against it, when you thought you had them all so tame and friendly? Why is it? The right hon. Gentleman said he was surprised. I am not surprised at all, and my friends are not surprised, not because of special information which reached us, but because it is quite clear to anyone who has followed this thing what are the dynamics and the articulations of the Indian situation.

You have a different situation from that of 1930. You are four years removed from then; this is 1935. In 1930 the Indian Princes had an invitation from the advanced political forces of British India to join them in a Federation, which it was believed, in the bad days of the Irwin-Benn regime of 1930, would have speedily led on to their practically taking over the goodwill of the whole business of British Government in India, lock, stock and barrel. But things have changed since then. They have changed from another cause. They have changed because of the right hon. Gentleman's firm administration and the much improved administration of Lord Willingdon compared with the previous regime, and also because some other people have put up a fight all the time to keep a strong resisting force operative; and now the Princes are not so willing to adopt this Instrument of Accession. Why? Whereas they were invited by the political forces in British India in 1930 and 1931, there is no invitation to-day. The invitation is withdrawn; the political forces are not saying to the Princes, "Come on and share this Government of Federal India." They say, "No. Stand out of this. Do not you associate yourselves with this scheme, which we have repudiated. If you do, it will not be comradeship we shall give you. On the contrary we shall pay you out by all the means which this Bill will give us the power to pay you."

That is the explanation of the Princes' change. What is the good of pretending to be surprised at it? It is the working of remorseless laws, and I am astounded that the

Government have not seen that that would be the reaction which would occur as a result of these four years, and of the continued process of change which has governed their own course during that time. What is the present view of the Princes? My right hon. Friend the Secretary of State read this afternoon a telegram which he had received from Reuter's Agency in Bombay. I must say that if it had been an official telegram I should have given it equal credence—yes, equal credence. But we have now in our possession statements made by the leading personages upon this very question of Clause 6 and the act of accession. What is so remarkable is that it is the very men on whom the right hon. Gentleman has been relying who are now most vehement against the Bill—the Maharaja of Bhopal, the Maharaja of Bikaner, Sir Akbar Hydari and Sir C. P. Ramaswami Ayyar. These are the Ministers and Princes who are most concerned in this matter, who are most in touch with the intelligentsia in British India, the Indian intelligentsia. They are the very ones who have most denounced this Measure. That is a great fact. You may vote them down; you may vote us down; you may call your 200 gentlemen from the Lobbies and the smoking-rooms and Library and vote us down, good and plenty. Yes, that is what happens. You may do that, but nothing can alter the facts or the march of events. There is the point. The Maharaja of Bhopal said:

> The present scheme as put forward before us in the shape of the Government of India Bill and the draft Instrument of Accession, falls far short of many of our vital demands, and in regard to certain matters ignores agreements reached with His Majesty's Government in London.

And then Sir Akbar Hydari, the able Minister, said two days ago:
Hon. Members: It has all been published.
Mr. Churchill: Yes, but there is no reason why the House of Commons should not hear the facts. He said:

> These are matters to which we attach vital importance, and I really, for one, cannot understand why Section 6 (1, *a*) has been allowed to be provided in all its brutal absoluteness.

I do not say whether that is right or wrong. I am not associating myself with the statement. But this is not our man. He is the Government's own man, and he is surprised that the Government have inserted Clause 6 in the Bill "in all its brutal absoluteness." It does not sound very much like mere trouble about drafting Amendments, a little difference here or there or some small matter of adjustment. It is most extraordinary. The quotation goes on:

> We cannot accept the entire Act as it has been enacted by Parliament. We have always protested against any acceptance of that kind. We have always held that we will be parties to a federation with regard to specific things and specific provisions. Here we are first asked to accept the entire Act, and then we are allowed to make reservations, not with regard to sections of it, but with regard to one particular Schedule of it, and in regard to all other matters we are asked to accept the Act. I think we have

all unanimously agreed that this is a position which under no circumstances whatever we shall be prepared to accept.

Then Sir C. P Ramaswami Ayyar said:

> I appeal with all the force at my command that this Clause 6 is a dangerous innovation—

What a comment on the brutal ease of a majority to violate the decent sequence of Parliamentary procedure when here at this moment you are going to vote on this Clause and carry it, no doubt with the usual 200 gentlemen. I hope they will long be. Here you are, and at this moment you do not know what are the opinions of the people on whose agreement you depend for the existence of your Bill. The right hon. Member for West Birmingham took a very strong line the other day and said: "We will take our path as the British Parliament and not pay any attention to these opinions." What nonsense, when you have said that the accession of the Princes is vital to your scheme. How can you stride off and say that you care nothing for all this? But if you are doing your duty and they do not agree, the result is that all that is done will be ploughing the sands, a wasting of the time of Parliament. Sir P. Ramaswami Ayyar said:

> I appeal with all the force at my command that Clause 6 is a dangerous innovation. It marks the culmination of a process which began in 1930. From then down to 1934 it has been a progressive inclined plane and we are now at the bottom of the plane. This Clause is full of dangers, and I ask Your Highnesses with all the force at my command not only to disclaim Clause 6, but the spirit underlying this Clause.

Ought we not to know that before we vote upon the Clause? Are we not right to tell this to the House? Is it not relevant to the Debate and to the decision that we have to take? The quotation continues:

> It is fraught with the utmost mischief. I am deliberately and firmly of the opinion that those features to which the Committee of Ministers has drawn attention are fundamental and vital, and unless there is a change in the spirit with which the Act is going to be dealt with hereafter, it would be a thousand pities if your Highnesses should join in a compact of which you know not the end.

There are many more opinions of that kind. We are a small minority here, even though, on questions affecting the well-being of the masses of the Indian people, we have associates to whom in other matters we are bitterly opposed. But we are a small minority. You can mock at us because in the Division Lobby we can only produce 50 or 60 Members against hundreds brought up by the Whip and waiting to fall in when the moment comes. We know that. But this is not going to be fought out by numbers.

From the very beginning I have been sure that it is not going to be fought out by numbers. It is going to be fought out by the force of events, and by the decisions which are taken in the minds of men outside this House and by the effect which is produced upon the spirit and determination of the Conservative party. There is what we rely upon in our resistance, and never did I feel more hopeful than I do to-night.

The Attorney-General mocked me—mocked us—the other day. He said: "We see your game." Our game! I suppose for Members of Parliament to devote years of time to this subject and to sacrifice many friendships and, in the case of some of the younger men, their political careers, in order to fight for this issue—that we are told is a game. But for the Attorney-General to take any brief which is offered to him—that is professional business. We have done the best in our power, and it seems to me that we are entitled to-night to ask the Committee not to pass this Clause in view of the vital decisions which depend upon it, and in view of the fact that we do not know any of the essential points upon which our decision ought to rest. The right hon. Gentleman has conducted his case so far with the very greatest skill and the very greatest courage. I am bound to say that I admire his performance in everything except its direction—its objective. But I think he would add greatly to his reputation if he said that in view of the facts placed before him now he did not think that it would be fair to ask the Committee to-night to come to the decision of placing this Clause among the approved Clauses of the Bill.

[Later] This is a very serious Clause [Number 8—Extent of Executive Authority], and the explanation given, and, indeed, the text in the Bill, are typical of the extraordinary contortionary methods now considered the best way of dealing with the innumerable peoples of the East. In the first place, the King Emperor devolves his authority on the Federal Executive, and that authority is devolved in Clause 8 in regard to the most vital matters which can possibly be concerned. The Federal Executive is given power to raise in British India naval, military and air forces, and the government of all these powers is freely conceded in order to give a feeling of real responsible government. Then, by a later Clause, the whole of this is taken back. First it is given, then taken back. It is perfectly true, and it is no good contradicting it. Here is power given to the Federal Executive to do all this and at the same time it does not mean that the Indian people or Ministers have any power, the whole thing being withdrawn and reserved under the purview of the Viceroy himself by a later provision not in the Bill but in a statement made to cover the Bill.

When Dominion status is given, the whole of these powers are to go to the Federal Legislature, and there will be nothing to prevent them from taking over the whole of these powers under the Statute of Westminster. First they are given, then temporarily withdrawn, but only for a transitional period, for in the ultimate stage they are to be handed over under Dominion status and the Federal Executive is then to have power. This temporary arrangement is, to be quite frank, the best way, in the opinion of the Government. They are to raise and command forces in India, including any forces of British extraction, which may be so unfortunate as to be left in that country at that time. What is the value of paragraph (c) in Clause 8 about the enlistment of foreigners? Once the Statute of Westminster is operating in India it will be perfectly possible to tear up the whole of this instrument, to enlist foreign officers, to organise the Indian army, with not one word of security. In view of the expectations held out, I would ask the Committee to consider not only the consequences—we are not in a position to resist this Clause—but to see the frightful elaboration of the process considered necessary to appeal to the Oriental mind. First, they say, "We will give you everything." Then it is taken back, and then—"Ah, but never mind, in the distant future, perhaps not so distant, for the coming of which we will not specify any date—we might say 150 years, you may call it five years or when the next Government comes in—you are to have complete Dominion status, and then you will be able to tear this up and possibly engage Swedes, or Germans, or Japanese to officer your Army if you want to." All this farce is gone through in the hope of pleasing the sentimental feelings of Indians. No, Sir, they are much too clever: one of the reasons why you have lost contact is that you have never been able to deal with them on a dead level.

GOVERNMENT OF INDIA BILL
(CLAUSE 9–COUNCIL OF MINISTERS)
February 28, 1935

House of Commons

It is, of course, a very convenient distinction between the two functions, and, if my memory serves me right, it is fully explained in the report of the Joint Select Committee. Undoubtedly there is great difficulty in describing this action and the rights of a Governor-General under the two specific and separate methods. I am bound to say that I agree with the Solicitor-General that if there is a difference between the Governor-General and his Ministers and he exercises his individual judgment because previous consultation with them has broken down, he will not be under the need of consulting them any more. All parleys having come to an end he will take the matter into his own hands and act freely. I gather that that is so?

The Solicitor-General: Yes. Of course he can, if he thinks proper and if all friendly relations have broken down, proceed to act on his own responsibility. I do not mean to imply that in those circumstances he is precluded from consulting his Ministers. At any point he may think it right to consult them.

Mr. Churchill: Even when they differ? I may be in error, but I have not seen any definition of these two convenient terms in the Bill. I do not think that there is any definition. This Amendment is an attempt to give a definition to these two new terms of art which are being introduced into our legal terminology. Are the Government sure that there is no need for definition? In what way will this definition be conveyed after the Report of the Joint Select Committee has been relegated to the Library and this Bill constitutes the only current vehicle for the transaction of business? It may be that there is no need for this definition?

The Solicitor-General: My right hon. Friend will appreciate that I did not deal with that point because the Mover of the Amendment did not do so. I quite appreciate the point. As my right hon. Friend will see, this matter will not be a matter in the ordinary sense of going to the courts. That was dealt with in Sub-section (4). These definitions are not definitions in the ordinary sense of the word. My right hon. Friend asked what would be the position when the report of the Joint Select Committee has faded from our minds. The method of application and explanation of these words will occur in the Instrument of Instructions. In our view that is the right place for them.

Mr. Churchill: I am much obliged for that explanation.

[Later] But is it not an occasion when it is open to discuss whether this definition of these two new terms of art, if any definition is to be given, should figure on the face on any Instrument of Instruction?

The Chairman: That may be, but even then it is a very narrow one.

Duchess of Atholl: That is the point that I wish to make, the necessity for having those powers put beyond a shadow of doubt in the Act of Parliament. When these powers were reserved under the 1919 Act, I do not believe there were Indians who then objected to them, but the Indian delegates to the Joint Select Committee made clear—

The Chairman: The Noble Lady must not discuss the powers but only the definition.

Duchess of Atholl: I do not wish to discuss the powers, but it seems necessary to put them in the Act of Parliament. As a matter of fact, a very strong opinion came from Europeans in India as to the importance of showing that these powers were intended to be used if necessary, and were not merely illusory powers.

Mr. Churchill: I hope the Secretary of State will say a word on this. I have an open mind, but I should like to hear what there is to be said. I thought from what the Solicitor-General said that the Instrument of Instruction was satisfactory, but it would be better if the Secretary of State made it clear that the strength of these two new terms of art will not in any way be detracted from if they are not put on the face of the Statute. At first sight it appears that they would seem to be detracted from, because the Instrument of Instruction can be varied by an Address to the Crown by both Houses, whereas the Statute requires an amending Bill. Therefore, there is a change. We should be much obliged if the right hon. Gentleman would give us guidance on the point.

[Later, after remarks by Sir S. Hoare] *Prima facie* it would seem to be the opposite. The mysteries of the law are profound, but, *prima facie*, if a man is required to do a thing it is more limited than if he is not debarred from doing it. But I think we must rest content with the undertaking that the Secretary of State has given that, if there be any substantial point in the matter, we may refer to it at a later stage.

[Much later] My Noble Friend the Member for Horsham (Earl Winterton) has introduced a temporary breeze into the debate this afternoon, which I certainly think does not tend to accelerate our procedure.

Earl Winterton: It was good-humoured.

Mr. Churchill: I am not so sure that it was good-humoured. The Noble Lord had no right to prescribe to my hon. Friend that he ought to state both sides of the case. I do not know how we shall ever get to the end of this Bill if it is to be an obligation of fairness and honour on each one of us to state not only our point of view but the point of view of the other side. I cannot imagine anything more likely to embarrass our proceedings. And then, of course, if we begin to state the point of view of the other side the further question will arise whether we are doing justice to that point of view. I think the debates would be endless if we were to embark on that course. The Noble Lord is a very keen supporter of this Measure, one of its principal promoters, one who has had the honour of sitting on the Joint Select Committee, and he has always, naturally, nursed a proper pride in his own handiwork. I must say that when he suggested to my hon. Friend the Member for Springburn (Mr. Emmott) that he had not read this report, he did him a very severe injustice. I took the liberty of borrowing—I had almost said of purloining—his actual copy in order to refresh my own memory, and I have my hon. Friend's copy in my hand, underlined and underscored at every point, showing a most careful and meticulous study of it.

Earl Winterton: Is that why my right hon. Friend was good enough to ask me privately if I could show him the place?

Mr. Churchill: The Noble Lord—I am in the recollection of the Committee—referred particularly to paragraphs 32 and 33, and I was not quite sure whether I heard him aright. He then said, "Read down to paragraph so-and-so," and I was not quite clear as to what he had said. But I was quite able to find the place, because it was handed to me. I took the book from my hon. Friend when he had it open. But what is all the point of this interruption by the Noble Lord? Does he mean that I have not read the report? Is that what he is trying to suggest? I think it is rather unmannerly to criticise in this House the way in which Members give their time to the discharge of their duties. I am not aware that the record of the Noble Lord entitles him to any special distinction for perspicuity in the discharge of his public duties. If he has a claim to any special distinction in that respect, it has passed singularly unrewarded in his long career.

Mr. Molson: May I ask the right hon. Gentleman whether the carefully annotated copy of the hon. Member for Springburn (Mr. Emmott) is his own copy or is the copy of the Noble Lady the Member for West Perth (Duchess of Atholl)?

Mr. Emmott: I think it is my own copy which the Noble Lady at some time or another has borrowed from me.

Mr. Churchill: It is quite clear, Sir Dennis, that an apology is due from the hon. Member for Doncaster (Mr. Molson) to my hon. Friend the Member for Springburn (Mr. Emmott). The hon. Member for Doncaster asked me to give way in order that he might make an intervention, and now he is proved conclusively wrong on a matter of fact. No doubt the hon. Gentleman will get up and say that he was wrong.

Mr. Molson: I asked a question, and if the Noble Lady the Member for West Perth will say that property in the book vests in the hon. Member for Springburn, I will certainly apologise.

Mr. Churchill: It is usual when an hon. Member makes a statement in this House, as did the hon. Member for Springburn, for other hon. Members to accept his bona fides, especially in a matter of a personal character of that kind. Now that the Noble Lord the Member for Horsham has forced into the centre of our discussion this general question of dyarchy, I am bound to address myself to it. I do not agree that this is the only point where the question can be discussed; the vice of dyarchy runs throughout this Bill. That is the hideous blemish. That is the cause of the evils which we see and apprehend. Again and again I have heard dyarchy condemned. I have heard supporters of the Bill like Lord Lytton, with great experience, condemn it in unmeasured terms. There are the words of the Statutory Commission's Report, words of the greatest weight, declaring that this very thing that you are now doing at the centre is inadmissible, and giving weighty reasons why it is impracticable and full of vice. You are departing from the Report of the Statutory Commission and you have cast that upon one side, although it was agreed to by all parties. You have left that safe, sure ground and you have embarked upon the very precarious and unstable footing of the Round Table Conferences, the White Paper and the Joint Select Committee.

Compare the Report of the Statutory Commission and the way it deals with dyarchy with the jejune apologetics of the Joint Select Committee; look and see how the Statutory Commission approached this subject with a view to ascertaining the truth, while the Joint Select Committee approached it with a view to carrying out the policy which was put to them by the White Paper. They were, as has been properly stated, a body to find reasons for supporting preconceived conclusions. When you compare and read those passages, I wonder that the Noble Lord had the face to get up and draw any conclusions. He mentioned paragraph 32 of the Report of the Joint Select Committee. Here is the explanation of why the solid arguments of the Statutory Commission have been thrown over by the Joint Select Committee. Paragraph 32, which the Noble Lord mentioned, furnishes the reason. Here is the reason for the tergiversations of the hon. Member for Finchley (Mr. Cadogan) and of his catherine-wheel contortion on that subject. He was once associated with the weighty words of the Statutory Commission. As soon as he got into the Joint Select Committee he fell under the evil, ministerial influences with which that body was packed—hopelessly packed—and, of course, lacking the moral strength to stand against the tide and the prevailing currents of opinion—[Hon. Members: "Oh!"] Perhaps I ought not to put it in that way. Shall I say, allowing himself to succumb too easily to the seduction of drifting with the sea and floating with the tide, if my hon. Friend will allow me to substitute those words for the others which I inadvertently used? What is the reason given for the desertion of the opinions of the Statutory Commission on the subject of dyarchy and the substitution of the opinions of the Joint Select Committee? It is this—and I am going to read only a sentence:

The Princes have ... stated ... that they are willing now to enter an
All-India Federation—

and they insisted on responsibility. I wonder indeed that the Noble Lord should raise that point to-day, because he is like a man standing upon the trapdoor of a scaffold, leaning forward to draw the bolt and to precipitate himself, in hopeless logical and argumentative confusion, into the pit. The Noble Lord has certainly not helped the case of the Government by the intervention, which, however ardently intended, has not been a fortunate one.

We take the strongest exception to this Clause, although, until we were provoked by the Noble Lord, the discussion had been conducted in a very quiet and good-tempered spirit. Yet it would be a mistake to suppose that the greatest objection cannot be taken to this Clause, and we are bound to vote against it. We are bound to testify against it, as it embodies the principle of dyarchy. The position of the Viceroy we begin to see in detail in this Clause, how he is to combine his strong executive function with the delicate handling of Ministers. We see the different points of view brought to a collision in the very central organism of the Government, and we see this central organism racked and strained in this way and in that by all those innumerable stresses at the very moment that, over the whole expanse of India, 11 provincial governments are being brought into existence. We are forced to express our repugnance and our destestation of this Clause at this time; it is certainly our duty to do so.

I do not intend to repeat upon this question arguments which I have used on Second Reading and at other times, but let the Committee realise quite clearly what they are going to do when they vote that this Clause stand part. They are introducing dyarchy into the centre of India on the sole pretext that the Princes wish to come in, which is not true, and that they have demanded responsibility. For that hon. Members are voting—for a basis which is going to be shorn from under their feet; for the establishment of a system so vicious that it has been condemned by every authority which has dealt with it, and by the highest authority which could be accepted in this House, namely, by our own Statutory Commission.

[Much later] Before I address myself to this proposition [concerning Clause 12: Special responsibilities of Governor-General] may I appeal to the Secretary of State to give us the view of the Government? I do not think the debate could proceed satisfactorily without our knowing the reaction of the Government to the proposal [to provide that the Governor-General shall have special responsibilities for prevention not only of any grave menace to the peace or tranquility of India, but also of any grave menace to health] submitted by the hon. Member for St. Albans (Sir F. Fremantle). The question far transcends the ordinary questions of party politics or non-party politics, or even national affairs: it is concerned with the great warfare of mankind against disease. Here we make a common front against the common foe. I should think that, on the whole, the Government would be very much disposed to include "disease" in the ambit of the Governor-General's powers; but it may be there are objections to it. It may conflict on some of the political theories which underlie the Measure. Our discussion would, I think, be abridged if we proceeded with a knowledge of what is in the mind of the Secretary of State, and with a clear comprehension of what are the purposes of the Government.

[Later] I must say that I think the extremely well-expressed and competent speech of the Under-Secretary was not at all adequate to the issue before the Committee. He gave a very clear account of the elaborate provisions of the Bill and threaded his way through that labyrinth with every proof of the assiduity and thoroughness with which he has studied its details. But, after all, let us get back to the central fact. We are not now pressing to set up machinery at all; all we are pressing to assert is a principle and a duty. Let me read the words of the Sub-section as it is proposed that it should be amended:

The prevention of any grave menace to the peace, health or tranquillity of India.

Health is probably going to extract a far graver toll of slaughter, casualties of a blind impotent approach, than anything that will happen in the communal riots which will follow the passing of this Bill, and to the peace of India that is a matter formidable in its character. Surely, the Government ought to assert, and allow the House of Commons in this clause to assert, that fact among the supreme reserved responsibilities of the Governor, so as to shield India from any grave menace to its health. It is not very much to ask that it should be put in here, and in this form. You may say, that all this sort of arrangement with local and Provincial Governments of this and other lands will not work. Everyone knows that when we are dealing with pestilence you want supreme direction. That is what you require. I remember, many years ago, living in an Indian city during a hot summer when 40,000 people died of bubonic plague, and the resistance of the population to the necessary measures of the Government was quite marked. It even reached the ears of the European community, the trouble there was in enforcing the necessary provision of feeling under their armpits to see if the tumour had begun to swell and so forth; and in these examinations the greatest trouble was shown. All this rests in the highest mission which the British have in India.

It may be that you will ask how it should be expressed in later Clauses. Certainly we are not saying that the Governor-General is to interfere in every matter affecting the health of the community. He has all the local bodies and other splendid institutions which are dealing with it, and why, you might say, interfere on every occasion?—Certainly not, but this is a supreme ultimate responsibility, just as vital as the defence of India and the maintenance of tranquillity in India, in order to shield enormous masses of the human race from the ravages of pestilence, and from pestilence which may sweep like the black death through the land. And to say that the Governor-General has not that responsibility is, surely, a menace and a grisly hiatus in the scheme which you are putting up for the future government of India. I do not think that it is at all satisfactory. The Secretary of State refuses to deal with the matter. He will not allow it. There is a special adjuration in the Clause as to the matters in which the Governor-General is to interest himself. In 99 cases out of a hundred it would not constitute "a grave menace," but even when there is a grave menace to the teeming population crowded together in circumstances which seem incredible to western experience, you will not arm him with or summon him to the discharge of that duty. You leave it out of the Bill. My Noble Friend has just said that he has the power to-day, but you take it away from him by the Bill, which you call a reform. You take away from him the right, the power to lift the shield of Britain against sweeping pestilences which may devastate India. You will not even give him the invocation to do the duty, and you call it a constitutional reform Bill.

GOVERNMENT OF INDIA BILL
(CLAUSES 12, 13)

March 5, 1935

House of Commons

I beg to move, "That the Chairman do report progress, and ask leave to sit again."

I desire to put a question to the Secretary of State and to offer him an opportunity of giving some information to the Committee. I quoted the other night some extracts from speeches alleged to have been made in the Assembly of the Princes at Bombay, which seemed to show how wide, various, vital and fundamental were the Amendments which they would require in the Government of India Bill. The Secretary of State had then no knowledge of what had occurred, but I wish to know whether, in what is practically a week since then, he has been able to obtain and is able to give us further information about the discussion which took place, whether those extracts were accurate, and whether he can tell us anything about the consequential effects which they will necessarily have on the Bill.

I see in the "Morning Post" to-day verbatim reports of speeches by Sir Akbar Hydari and Sir Ramaswami Aiyar which certainly disclose differences with the Government which, if they are to be met, will entail a complete remodelling of the Bill. They already affect Clauses 2, 6 and 8, and we have dealt with them. Unless entirely new information is forthcoming, a case is disclosed for a motion to recommit the Bill in respect of these Clauses, because it is perfectly clear that, if they stand in the form in which they have been passed by the Committee, the Princes will not accept the Bill. Then, according to the arguments of the Government, it is impossible that their scheme can go forward; that is the Government's case. I do not know how many Members have read the report which appears in the "Morning Post" to-day. It seems to me that there ought to be an official report in matters of this kind which become public in this country. Whether they should become public is another matter, but they have become public, and we are bound to judge the facts as they are presented to us. Anyone who has not read these two columns in the "Morning Post" should really do so without the slightest delay, because it is essential to an appreciation of all the matters which are under discussion. Anyone who has read them will see what a serious position we are in. Take the Clause we are now discussing, Clause 12 [Special Responsibilities of Governor-General]. Sir Akbar Hydari says:

> Then there are Clauses 12 and 127, by virtue of which the Governor-
> General can at any time really interfere in the internal administration of
> your State on the ground that you are not doing your federal duties.

That is what he is reported to have said. Did he say that? Is this an authentic speech, or is it invented from beginning to end? If it be true, then this is a most grave and serious matter. Perhaps the Government are not ready to answer to-day, but they should fix a day in the near future when they will be able to tell us what are the differences between then and the Princes on this Bill, what are the Amendments for which the Princes are asking, and whether, and if so to what extent, they are able to meet those differences. Otherwise, are we not simply wasting our time? Are we not debating the whole Measure upon a false footing? I am advised that the Princes require vital and specific amendments to Clauses 2, 6 and 8, Clause 12—that is the Clause before us this afternoon—paragraphs (*a*) and (*g*), Clauses 45, 99, 127, 145, 147 and 156.

Where do we stand? Where do the Government stand? I have no doubt that we can arrive at a perfectly amicable arrangement, because anyone can see the difficulty in which the Government have been placed. To use the words of the "Statesman," that friendly newspaper that always supported them, they have been "duped and misled." Those are the words of the "Statesman." But that may not be the fault of the Government. It is certainly their misfortune, and we have to be careful that it does not become our misfortune. It seems to me that a new situation has arisen, and that the Government should make a comprehensive statement. If these facts are true, they should tell us how they propose to deal with the situation; and if they are not true they should relieve the anxiety of their followers upon the matter at the earliest moment. I am sure it will be much more simple to deal with this Bill when we know where we are. The Secretary of State said that it was desirable that we should know where we are at the earliest moment. When we know exactly what it is that the Bill is going to be we shall be able to give our attention to it. Meanwhile, I await with the customary respect, and even unusual interest, the answer which I invite from my right hon. Friend.

[Later] Will the right hon. Gentleman answer the question as to whether at this meeting of the Princes in Bombay the Speeches were taken down in shorthand or not? There appears to be a direct conflict of testimony. The two Ministers he has quoted say that their speeches were not taken down. Some explanation is usually forthcoming in a case of discrepancy of that kind. Will the right hon. Gentleman also say whether these transcripts have been forwarded to the Viceroy? Surely he can inquire of the Viceroy whether it is true that he has received a report of what happened; and, if so, surely he can lay it before the House later on?

[Later] If I had misled the Committee, wittingly or unwittingly, I should certainly make my disclaimer and apologise, but I have done nothing of the sort. I quoted certain extracts which were placed in my hands. [Hon. Members: "No."] They were given to me by the "Morning Post," and were to appear in the paper next morning. They appeared to be authentic and to be highly relevant to the particular Clause, and I thought at the time that I was not only justified in bringing them to the attention of the Committee, but was bound to do so. I do say, and, in fact, after a week has passed, it is found that these extracts are accurate and authentic. [Hon. Members: "No."] If the hon. Gentleman would read the reported—the alleged— speeches, he would see that they bear the mark of genuineness and authenticity in every line. All that I have to ask is that the Government should say whether these speeches are authentic or not. The hon. Gentleman argued just now as though he did not care what was the truth. [Hon. Members: "Oh."] Well, he argued as though he did not wish this point pressed as to whether these grave matters have in fact been said by the important Indian ministers to whom I have referred. We ought to know the truth. What are we debating here for, unless to find out the truth and to place our debates on a fair and reasonable basis?

I am far from having reached the end of this matter, and I hope and trust that when the report is in due course received by the Viceroy, to whom I am informed it has been sent, the right hon. Gentleman will endeavor to lay the facts before the Committee in a White Paper. Until he does, or until he contradicts this matter in the same definite manner in which the speeches are repudiated and we know exactly in what terms they are repudiated and what lines and what paragraphs are inaccurate, I shall accept them as accurate and true and shall argue upon that basis. I hope and trust that the right hon. Gentleman will endeavour to place the Committee at an early date upon that reasonable basis.

The hon. Member for Limehouse (Mr. Attlee) has been indisposed for the last 10 days. I am sorry if one of the symptoms of what we now see is a happy convalescence should be bad temper. If the hon. Gentleman had been fortunate enough to enjoy his usual health and to be present at the Debates he would have seen how admirably they had been conducted, how sensible has been the feeling on every side that there was no obstruction, and also how admirably his colleagues have filled his place in his absence. He would then not have gone out of his way, on no information, and not having been in touch with the Committee and its work, to deliver such a very striking and dictatorial lecture to me. How much time has been taken up? Half-an-hour has been occupied in raising these extremely important matters, which he will find will be examined and reported in all parts of the country, and very much more than some of the orations with which the hon. Gentleman will presently favour us.

[Later] I am going to ask leave to withdraw my Motion. I think this discussion has shown the usefulness of this procedure in bringing important matters into Parliamentary discussion. May I in doing so suggest to the Secretary of State a perfectly simple course that he can take. I suggest that he shoud take this good advice; when the English newspapers, or some of them, contain long reports purporting to be verbatim accounts of speeches delivered at this confidential meeting, those reports, if they are not true, should be contradicted, and if they are true he should decide whether it is not desirable that the whole of the proceedings should be published, or at any rate that an official report of the proceedings should be made and communicated to the Viceroy. The Secretary of State is in touch with the Princes; he should put this to them and point out that some of their confidential matters had been disclosed apparently and that it is desirable that we should have fuller information on the matter for Parliament.

Sir S. Hoare: I am not prepared, so long as I am in this office, to have my telegrams to the Viceroy drafted for me by the right hon. Gentleman the Member for Epping (Mr. Churchill). I have placed this matter frankly before the Committee, and I have nothing to add to what I said.

Mr. Churchill: In spite of the refusal of the right hon. Gentleman to clear this matter up in any way, or to elicit more information which might be unwelcome to him, I beg to ask leave to withdraw the Motion.

[Much later] I think my right hon. and gallant Friend the Member for Newcastle-under-Lyme (Colonel Wedgwood) was well advised to raise this question. I am bound to say that when I read the Clause [Number 12—Special Responsibilities of Governor-General] it did not occur to me that there was all this significance to be attached to the word "legitimate." Obviously, and on the face of it, we would not expect the Viceroy to protect the illegitimate interests of minorities, but after the explanation of my right hon. Friend the Secretary of State, it is clear that a definite and important significance is attached to the introduction of this word "legitimate." In the ordinary course, this sentence would have read simply "safeguarding the interests, etc." One would have thought that the Viceroy, on whom we are showering all these various functions, to whom we are entrusting this immense process of discrimination in all these matters and the power of deciding when to intervene, on whom we are imposing these many extraordinarily subtle and complex tasks—one would have thought that this high functionary, this gifted being, would be able to distinguish between interests which were legitimate and those which were not legitimate, without the necessity of stating it in the terms of the Statute.

It seems to me that we are here in the presence of some understanding which has been reached with certain classes in India—and for what? My hon. and gallant Friend the Member for North Islington (Colonel Goodman) raised the question of the untouchables. What does the Secretary of State regard as the legitimate interests of the untouchables? We know what their interests in the ordinary sense are. Their chief interest is to be treated as human beings. But what are their legitimate interests? How much are their interests narrowed down by this word "legitimate"? I should have thought, now that British protection was going to be withdrawn from the minorities, in the first instance, that the Government would have been most anxious to confer upon the Viceroy the widest and most unfettered discretion in dealing with the minorities and giving them protection.

We have not heard from the Attorney-General or the Solicitor-General anything upon the legal aspect of this question but obviously, if ever such matters could be brought to examination in a court, the court would put a construction upon these words. I know that the acts of the Viceroy are not subject to examination by a court, but in so far as these words can be constructed by a court, it is perfectly clear that a very definite construction will be put upon the word "legitimate." I say that this word has been put in to safeguard and to shelter abuses and oppressions which have lasted so long and are so deeply rooted and so widely spread that it is not found convenient to attack them. I should have thought that the Government, in making this charter for India, would have considered it worth while to write boldly and simply that the Viceroy was to be responsible for protecting the interests of minorities. The right hon. Gentleman the Secretary of State has, for purposes which have certainly not been made clear to this Committee, introduced this limiting word, and I trust that we shall hear from someone on the Front Bench a fuller explanation. We have been told to look into the Instruments of Instructions. It may be legitimate—I beg the Committee's pardon, I should say reasonable—to go to the Instruments of Instructions for guidance upon the point, but why is it necessary to write this word "legitimate" upon the face of the statute? I cannot understand it. There is evidently something obscure behind it and, in my view, the Government ought to offer the Committee a further explanation.

[Later] If that be the case, if the word "legitimate" is not needed, why is it in the Bill? The right hon. Gentleman has stultified his other speech as far as I can understand and contradicted himself. Having consulted his legal advisers, he now says there is no virtue in the word. I never thought there was. It is one of those expressions which, apparently, have a soothing effect on certain people, but does not alter the character and meaning of the statute at all. Why do you want to put it in? The Bill is surely long enough without seeking to find excuses for interpolating superflous adjectives. There is no point in it at all. The right hon. Gentleman ought to accept the Amendment if it makes no difference and if he wishes to give some guidance to the Governor-General to say that, in protecting interests, it does not mean that he is to make himself the champion solely of those interests without regard to any other considerations. I hesitate to make any suggestion of a drafting character lest my right hon. Friend should retort on me with pontifical severity, but I would ask him, if this Amendment makes no difference, to accept it and leave out the word "legitimate."

[Much later] Surely the speech of the Secretary of State is at once revealing and disquieting. It was quite clear why the words "United Kingdom," are to be retained and the words "British Empire" are not included. It is because the Secretary of State desires to give to the new Indian Assembly the power of striking at Canada and Australia through the medium of trade, if they are not satisfied with the treatment of Indians who have emigrated to those Dominions. The Secretary of State seemed even to relish the prospect that in the near future India would have an opportunity of dealing with those delinquent Dominions. That is a serious thing, and it is an extremely dangerous thing that that should be said. This is, in fact, a Bill to give to the Indians the power, among other things, of imposing discriminative and penal trade restrictions against Canada, South Africa and Australia. It is hardly possible to have anything more uncomfortable than that. I agree with my hon. Friend who asked whether the high commissioners have been consulted in this matter. The Secretary of State did not answer that question.

There is a certain weight in the argument that negotiations, commercial treaties and so forth should be conducted between the Government of India and the individual Dominions; also the question of immigration and so forth can be a matter of discussion and of reciprocity to some extent between them, and the Government in many matters are well advised to stand out, but here you have an Empire Government placing a new power in the hands of a new assembly, a power which they have not exercised up to the present, and that power is capable of being used—as it is intended to be used—to enable each of those Dominions to be proceeded against by India. What will happen when this process begins, and when the new Indian Assembly, if it ever comes into being under this Bill, starts out to punish South Africa for their treatment of Indians in Natal? I imagine that South Africa will feel that we have brought this new evil upon them, and that they will be very much inclined to find fault with the Imperial Government, and possibly will themselves retaliate against our trade.

I feel that this Amendment is very well based. I am astounded at the naked candour with which the Secretary of State for India has practically avowed, not merely with sombre acquiescence but with an actual appetite, that the new Indian Government can make use of the new powers to spread ill-feeling and trade restrictions throughout the British Empire.

[Much later] Could the right hon. Gentleman [Sir S. Hoare] enlighten us a little further on this aspect [of Clause 13—Provisions as to Instruments of Instruction]? I understand that the Instrument of Instructions can only be varied by an Address from both Houses—that there would have to be a majority in a single division in each of the two Houses of Parliament to justify any alteration, or any serious alteration, because I presume that the entire Instrument could be redrafted and altered in 50 different ways, and a single division in each House of Parliament would carry this out. It is not a question of every Amendment having to be passed through, as in the case of a Bill. The right hon. Gentleman seems a little to associate these two processes, but nothing could be more different than the process we are now going through, of passing a Bill through Parliament, and a mere vote by a temporary majority in the House of Commons. They are two entirely different things. The right hon. Gentleman talks about an amending Act—if there were large alterations in the Instrument, there would be an amending Act. But there is no means of enforcing that on the Government of the day in possession of a temporary majority. They can redraft the Instrument of Instructions in such a way as completely to transform the emphasis and character of the Bill, and a single division, a majority of 20 or 10, will be enough in this House. What happens in the House of Lords? This is a very important point, and raises very far-reaching constitutional issues. I wonder how it strikes the Lord President of the Council, who, I see, is in his place. Both Houses of Parliament have to concur in the alteration; you have to have a majority in the House of Lords. The right hon. Gentleman is very proud of his majority in the House of Lords at the present time.

Mr. Isaac Foot: You were hoping for it.

Mr. Churchill: I am always hoping for the support of the respectable elements in our community in defence of the main assets and glories of the British Empire. Sometimes those hopes are not fully borne out by events, and the hon. Gentleman has the pleasure of exulting on those occasions. The point that I want to put to the Government, the Secretary of State, and the Lord President, turns on this veto of the House of Lords. As far as I make out, the passing of an Address by the House of Lords is not a matter covered by the Parliament Act—I mean that it is not a matter amenable to the procedure of passing the Address through the House of Commons in three successive Sessions in the space of not less than two years. It is not a question of a mere time veto; it is an absolute veto that is being provided in this respect in the House of Lords. The absolute veto of the House of Lords is being revived in this matter. I see that a great constitutional revolutionary wishes, with legal authority, to instruct us, and I gladly give way.

Sir S. Cripps: The right hon. Gentleman will agree that you can pass a Bill to abolish the House of Lords.

Mr. Churchill: That has nothing to do with the fact, because we have not passed that Bill yet.

Sir S. Cripps: Under the Parliament Act you can. If they refuse in a matter of this sort, you can abolish them, and then they could refuse no longer.

Mr. Churchill: The hon. and learned Gentleman talks about abolishing the House of Lords, but it is very much easier said than done. The House of Lords are like a great many things that he wishes to abolish; they have a vitality and power of resistance that has never yet dawned upon our budding Socialist lawyer. The point that I put to His Majesty's Government is this: At the present time we are entrusting a first-rate function, one of the most responsible decisions, to the House of Lords without even the Parliamentary time limitation which was enforced by the Parliament Act, thus reverting to the pre-Parliament Act situation. That is what is called strong meat. It seems to be a formidable assertion for the Government to make, and particularly for the Lord President, who has so long refused to do anything to reform the Second Chamber in accordance with the Schedule to the Parliament Act. An unreformed Chamber, vulnerable as it has been found to be in the past, happens to be working with you at the present time in your policy. This body is to be put into the forefront of politics and, if in 15 months time a Socialist Government is in power, it proposes to remodel the Instrument of Instruction and to do various other things under the Bill which are to be done by a simple Address to the Crown.

I suppose the Conservative party are invited to lay comfort to their souls by the fact that they can rely upon a veto—none of your whittled down Parliament Act vetoes. This is a good pukka veto. Are not the Government deluding their followers? Are not they inviting them to take their stand upon a most precarious and most insecure platform? Is it not clear that it would be most unfair to ask the House of Lords to take the responsibility of standing up against a widespread Indian demand supported by a majority in the House of Commons? In that case, where is security at all? Whichever way you look at it, whether you take the point of view of reverting to the earlier form of veto which was abolished 20 years ago—[An Hon. Member: "By you."] Certainly, and no Measure that I have supported do I feel has better stood the test of time than the Parliament Act. It is true, as the hon. and learned Gentleman said, that it is open to the Socialist party, if they obtain a majority, immediately to introduce an amending Bill cutting out the whole of these safeguards or any other provisions in the Measure that they do not like, and run it under the Parliament Act for three Sessions in two years and it becomes law automatically. At the same time they can carry a Bill abolishing the House of Lords altogether, but still two and a half years is a certain security. The point that I invite the Government to pronounce upon is the old unlimited veto of the House of Lords, and I hope we shall have an authoritative answer from either the Lord President or the Secretary of State before we go much further in the Debate.

GOVERNMENT OF INDIA BILL
(CLAUSE 16–ADVOCATE GENERAL)

March 6, 1935

House of Commons

I feel bound to support this Amendment, because it seems to maintain as far as possible the *status quo* at the centre. I expect that the federal part of this Bill will fail and that the centre will continue for the time being, probably for a good many years, in its present condition, which is not satisfactory, though we might go further and fare a great deal worse. I therefore vote for the Amendment to preserve the nominated element at the centre, just as I voted to preserve to the Indian electors their direct election to the centre, of which they have been deprived by this Bill. We are in fact depriving the electors on the one hand of the method of direct election, to which they have become used and which they value, and at the same time we are depriving the Governor-General of the forces of stability represented by the nominated element.

In every way you are making the Central Assembly much poorer. It is a Central Assembly which will be based not upon election by the people but upon indirect election by the Provincial legislatures. All the more necessary is it that there should be nominated element which will redress the balance and provide what is left out by these close corporations. I feel that we ought to press this question without any hesitation at all because undoubtedly it will serve to emphasise the importance of maintaining successfully the experiment which has hitherto been made—so far as it has gone—in India of a body at the centre which, although it is full of faults and shortcomings has nevertheless maintained a certain existence and identity for a period of time. If we are to strip it on the one hand of its popular pretensions and on the other hand of its nominated element we are creating a condition of affairs far more unsatisfactory than anything of which we have had experience up to the present.

GOVERNMENT OF INDIA BILL
(CLAUSES 18, 26, 33, 38)

March 12, 1935

House of Commons

In respect of the guidance you have been good enough to give us, might I venture, first of all, to say that I think it is over-sanguine to expect that we should conclude Clause 45 this evening? There are several Clauses of considerable importance and many of great interest, and I should have thought that to-morrow we should be certain to be clear of this most important Chapter of the federal part of the Bill; but, naturally, we must do the best we can in view of what you have said. I had been thinking that it would be necessary for us to-day to ask for a more general statement from the Government as to our position on this Bill, either on a Motion to report Progress or on a Motion to recommit the Bill in consequence of the very great uncertainty which exists as to the permanency of all the work we are now doing, but I feel that in view of this friendly arrangement which we all wish to see a success, and a precedent for future House of Commons procedure, it would be better to accomplish Clause 45 and finish this part.

I gather from an answer which my right hon. Friend the Secretary of State for India gave, or which was given on his behalf, that he will to-morrow be in a position to make some statement as to laying Papers before the House in regard to the later developments of the negotiations with the Indian Princes. If that were so, and we could accomplish Clause 45 satisfactorily this week, and perhaps get some little way beyond it, it would appear most desirable that we should have a general review of the position on the first day this Bill is taken next week, because otherwise we are discussing the Bill upon a basis which seems to be very ill-related to realities. May I add how glad we are to see the Secretary of State back and recovered in his health? I earnestly hope that if we are to sit up till 12 o'clock to-night, he will not feel that his presence is necessary. I am sure that we shall not make less progress if he finds it necessary to withdraw.

[Later] I find myself in general agreement with the condemnatory epitome of this Clause [Number 18–Constitution of the Legislature] which has fallen from the lips of the hon. Member for Broxtowe (Mr. Cocks). It is one of the most important Clauses in the Bill, because it presents to us the structure of the new Assembly which is to exercise responsible government over all India. I have asked myself whether, upon the whole, the scheme of this Clause, set where it is in the general articulation of the Bill is not the worst legislature that ever was planned. Perhaps I ought to abate a little the rigour of my assertion, because no one can have an exhaustive knowledge of all the legislatures that ever have been planned, but certainly this is the worst that I have ever seen brought before this House and the one least likely to give contentment or proper government to the persons for whom it is designed. What the hon. Member for Broxtowe has said seems to be true. The Government have taken away from the people of India, from the electors, 1,500,000 of them, direct election to the existing Assembly, and in place of that they have substituted indirect election, which the Secretary of State opposed, which the Government of India opposed, which the Government of India opposed, which the White Paper opposed and which was introduced into the Joint Select Committee as the result of all kinds of negotiations, over which the veil of hitherto unviolated secrecy had been thrown.

I certainly was told that one of the reasons which weighed with the Commissioners who went out there in advocating direct election was the danger of a caucus, the danger of corrupt influences being brought to bear on the comparatively small number of people who now will choose. That danger resumes itself in all its force, and at the same time the salutary relief of a dissolution is practically robbed of its efficacy. The same answer will to a large extent be returned even if the Assembly is sent about its business. One of the greatest safeguards of parliamentary institutions is the power of dissolution, the certainty, that assemblies can be scattered to the winds, and there is what is called a new deal operating in parliamentary and political affairs. But for that destruction would overtake all legislative assemblies. They would become odious to those in whose name they presume to act. In this system you will have an assembly increasingly hide-bound and stable. You will take away altogether from your Indian polity that indispensable device—namely, a dissolution, and a new set of men, which has everywhere been found necessary for parliamentary procedure.

As for the second Chamber, I suppose it will be about the richest body in the world, man for man. It will certainly be a chamber which will be well able to protect the rights of property, I do not mean the rights of British property, but Indian property. They may not take a very high view about the interests of British merchants and manufacturers, or of the Lancashire traders, but I think it will be very strong in interpreting the rights of property when it is a question of the interests of the Ahmenabad or Bombay mill-owners, who are large subscribers to the funds of the dominant party in India. It will be strong in enforcing the sanctity of contracts and the interests of the money-lending classes, and will no doubt take a robust view of the interests of landed proprietors. In religious matters it is highly probable that their bias will be strongly conservative. As for the general questions of social legislation and so forth, it is unlikely that any strong initiative will come from this body. And remember that this institution which you are now imposing on India, which you are now ramming down the throats of Indians, whether they like it or not, will be largely unalterable. There they will be, and there they will remain. You are riveting the shackles of the worst aspects of capitalism without its progressive reforms, and without its continued elections and refreshed assemblies. And you are riveting these shackles upon the people of India for an indefinite period.

Compared with the present Assembly this new federal structure is at a serious disadvantage. We are told how much stronger it is to be, and how we are escaping from the defects of the present weak Assembly. It has not worked so ill. The people have got used to it, they have voted for it, and have associations with it. It is true that the Government defer too much to it, although not perhaps too much, having regard to the tolerant working of British rule in India. In its place you are substituting this new body in Clause 18, this new organism, with what are called responsible powers. I think that the Government have throughout proceeded upon a wrong assumption in regard to the part which will be played in the Chamber by the Princes. All through our Debates we have heard the suggestion that you can safely dispense with the official bloc; that you can safely entrust what is called responsible government to the new Assembly because of the representatives of the Princes of India who will be there, who are expected to sustain British interests and give stability and responsibility to the structure. We are asking the Princes to become as it were the champions of British action in the Assembly and the defenders of the prerogatives of the Governor-General and the safeguards. That is a strain to which it is very unfair to expose them in the eyes of their fellow countrymen.

I believe also that you are putting a burden on the Princes which they will not accept, even if they come in. Nothing is more remarkable than the quickness with which solidarity has been established between the Princes and political forces in India. The Secretary of State and the Conservative party who are going forward on this issue, suppose that they are going to have a bulwark and security in the Princes which will counteract the subversive and violent forces which exist in India. I think they will find that they are on very insecure foundation. You are asking more than you ought of the Princes in asking them to undertake such responsibilities. In principle this abstraction, which you are clothing with reality and which you call the Indian nation, will act together in all matters or in almost all matters on which the cleavage is between Indian national aspirations and the safeguards retained by the British executive.

I have not had time to count the numbers accurately, but I think there are some 600 gentlemen, or 615, who will be gathered at Delhi. I agree with the hon. Member for Limehouse (Mr. Attlee) that they will have very little to do. What are they to do? You have only to read Clause 12 [Special Responsibilities of the Governor-General] and see what they may not do to realise that it utterly destroys the reality of responsible government. No one can read that Clause and the Clauses which immediately follow, which enable the Governor-General himself to legislate by ordinance or by proclamation, or to take over at any time the entire Constitution, in conjunction with Clause 18, and imagine that what is being given to this new body, to these institutions, is responsible government or anything like it. It is a farce and a mockery on the name of responsible government. When we are told that the Princes insisted on responsible government and now say that they will not come in, they have a right to say that the condition of responsible government has not been made good.

You are not giving them responsible government. What are you giving them? You are giving them something which is more dangerous than responsible government; you are giving them the power to extort responsible government by all the weapons of Parliamentary procedure. They will have very little to do except to find fault, to press for the abolition of the safeguards. They will have very little to do except to carry out those tariff wars against South Africa and Australia, to which the Secretary of State referred the other day in terms from which a suspicion of gusto was not wholly excluded. They will be able to deal with tariffs—they are under their control—so long as they do not discriminate against British trade; and by raising their tariffs they will be able to bring endless pressure to bear on the Governor-General by maltreating Lancashire trade and British trade until he accepts their point of view or the Government dispenses with these indispensable safeguards. And you are inducing the Conservative party to become the draught animals to drag this Bill through. It is not responsible government.

The Clause sets up an arena of strife, in which will be fought a controversy not novel in the world, a struggle which we went through in the 16th and 17th centuries, between representative institutions, which had one set of ideas, and the prerogative of an almost potentially absolute monarch on the other. The friction will be endless. This will be an assembly given over to politics. It will occupy its time with politics. It will seek to gain for itself those attributes of that responsibility which you have pretended to confer upon it, and in that process you are inaugurating a decade of friction, tumult, disturbance, disorder, irritation and anger in India, at a time when the healing processes of constructive economy and of industry should repair the depression through which the country is passing and make some definite inroad upon the awful poverty in which the great masses of the Indian people are plunged.

We see in this Clause a bad piece of work. Happily I do not think that it will come to fruition. I do not think that it will ever emerge from the paper form in which it has darkened the pages of this bulky Bill into actual operation. I predict that that will not be so. The Princes will not come in, and, if they do not, then obviously the whole of the structure is meaningless and invalid. The Lord Chancellor said some time ago that the Princes would not dash the cup from the parched lips of India. They have dashed the cup from the parched lips of India, from one end of the country to the other, and drawn forth a chorus of jubilation hailing them as deliverers. The policy of the Government, the aim and the ideal they set before themselves, is a united India. We may congratulate them. They have united India from one end to the other, from Karachi to Rangoon, from the Khyber Pass to Tuticorin, from rajah to ryot, from untouchable committee to mahasabha. All, without exception, have joined together, united, speaking with one voice and one heart, and repudiating this scheme of which Clause 18 is one of the central and perhaps the most peccant parts.

[Later] I wish to take the Committee to witness and also the larger public out of doors, that although for over two hours arguments have been used against this Clause [Number 18] from every quarter and every section of the Committee not the slightest attempt to answer any of those arguments has been made. The Secretary of State contented himself with the imputation of motives and with vague generalities. In no way did he attempt to meet the serious case, as I submit it will be found, which I unfolded upon this subject and which has been reinforced from almost every part of the Committee. Of course, when you have a majority of 200 gentlemen waiting in the Library and Smoking Rooms whom you can summon, you do not need, I suppose, to go into arguments and to deal with serious contentions when they are advanced. You merely call for your legions and invite them to perform what the Lord President of the Council once extolled as footwork—and so you move forward. At each stage of this weary process we shall endeavour to point out to the country at large that the ordinary processes of reason have ceased to operate on the side of those who are driving forward this policy and are simply relying on the remaining momentum and force of what I expect will be found to be a moribund majority.

I see that my right hon. Friend the Member for Sparkbrook (Mr. Amery) has returned, and I must refer to one note which he struck to which I must take exception. It was when he appeared to voice the opinion of a great many Members that I should not address the Committee so often or at such length. Let me say that any intolerance of that kind on his part would not at all facilitate the speed with which this Bill is being carried through. We had great hopes of making considerable advance to-day and to-morrow, and I should very much deprecate this perfervid supporter of the Government introducing an element of warmth and even of acrimony which has so far found only a feeble echo in the speeches of the Ministers themselves. There is one thing which my right hon. Friend said for which I am very grateful to him. He referred to the length of my speech, which was only a quarter of an hour, and he warned me on that point. I can assure him that on any question where I might be in danger of boring the Committee I will gladly refer to him for his advice and assistance, for I cannot feel that one can possibly have a greater expert authority on such a subject.

[Much later] I think it has been a very good thing that we have explored this question. I raised my aspect of the matter for the purpose of eliciting from the Government a statement on the situation, but I little expected that the consequence of that would be the very grave offer and admission to which the Secretary of State has just given expression. When I spoke in perhaps a jocular manner of persons returning from the Andaman Islands to the Indian Parliament, I little thought that my right hon. Friend, in terms of the gravity of which the Committee must have felt immediately conscious, would have told us that there is real danger of dangerous terrorists, persons engaged in the gravest forms of terrorism, standing for the Legislature of Bengal in particular and being elected for the Bengal Assembly, unless this bar is put in their path. Be it observed that it is indirect election that we are talking about. Therefore, it is not a question of—I think the right hon. Gentleman said—mass emotion sweeping a constituency and influencing poor and more or less ignorant electors. These dangerous terrorists—the importance of the admission must not be lost sight of in the country— guilty of the worst of crimes, will be likely to be elected in Bengal by the Provincial Legislature of Bengal and sent to the Federal Assembly from that Legislature. That is the admission that has now been put before us. [Hon. Members: "He did not say that!"] If I am wrong I shall be delighted to be corrected.

Sir S. Hoare: I was arguing the question on general lines. This Clause trenches on the provincial chapter as well as the federal chapter. In my argument I may have been arguing the provincial case more than the federal case and I should certainly say that it is to me almost inconceivable that a terrorist could be returned by indirect election in any Province. But I equally say that if the disqualification remains in the federal part of the Bill it is difficult to remove it from the provincial part.

Mr. Churchill: The right hon Gentleman wants to have it both ways. But the fact remains that he was dealing with the federal part, and the federal part is the only one which it is in order to discuss or this Clause. We all heard what he said clear and plain, that but for this bar dangerous terrorists would be chosen for the Federal Legislature by the Provincial Legislature of Bengal. That is a most grave and serious admission, and after such a statement I cannot support the Clause. If it is a fact that under this constitution the Provincial Legislature of Bengal may select dangerous terrorists and send them to the Federal Legislature then all I can say is that I hope this will be noticed by people outside these doors.

We ought not to let this matter pass with such very vague general explanations as that. [Editor's Note: Churchill is referring here to paragraph (f) of Clause 33—sums to finance the Governor-General when he is acting as the representative of the Crown.] This paragraph provides for the payment to His Majesty of any sum that may be required for the Viceroy to deal with the Indian States, and the Under-Secretary has represented it as if it had nothing more in its purpose than the financing of the Indian political department.

Mr. Butler: I said that we must read the actual document before us. If the right hon. Gentleman will refer to it he will see reference to expenses incurred in discharging the functions of the Crown in its relation to the Indian States. They would be covered by this paragraph.

Mr. Churchill: That is the point, but when my hon. Friend made his speech what he dwelt on was keeping the political department going, and what he kept in the background was the discharge of the functions of the Crown in relation to the Indian States. That is the point on which I think the searchlight should be turned. I suppose that if an Indian State is ill-governed and the Rajah misbehaves himself in any way, and coercion has to be applied to him, that is the paragraph from which the fund will be supplied. Is not that so?

Mr. Butler *indicated assent*.

Mr. Churchill: That is so; exactly. If any question of paramountcy arises, this is the paragraph which covers it. Let us have our law right on the subject.

The Solicitor-General: My right hon. Friend is stating in quite general form that if expenditure was incurred as a result of misgovernment in a State the expenditure necessary would fall on federal revenue. But there might be a levy on the State concerned. We should reimburse the federal revenue out of the State.

Mr. Churchill: My hon. and learned Friend has helped greatly in the discussion. This is a very important Clause for the Indian Princes, because this paragraph provides the fund from which the means of disciplining them and keeping them in good order in the federal system is to be provided. Suppose that one of the States misbehaves, or the Congress representatives in the Federal Assembly put pressure on the Viceroy, the political department would be put into motion and the pressure would be applied, and the funds for the pressure would come out of this paragraph (f). That is so. I am not saying that it is not desirable. It may be very necessary indeed. But when passing so many clauses with great rapidity we ought to notice all the important points with which we are dealing. The question of paramountcy falls under this sub-section. Questions arising out of paramountcy will be sustained by the funds under this paragraph. Has the Secretary of State seen the declaration of the Maharaja of Bhopal? [Hon. Members: "The Nawab!"] I am not so conversant with these Indian titles as some hon. Members. We are always told that we should never quote French in this House with a French accent. I do not pretend to be versed, like the Private Secretary to the Under-Secretary, in all these details. Has the Under-Secretary read the declaration of the Nawab of Bhopal, in which he says that it is vital and fundamental to his agreement with the Bill that as regards paramountcy there should be an independent tribunal between the paramount Power and the Princes' States?

The Chairman: I think that is hardly relevant to this discussion.

Mr. Churchill: With great respect I am not using it as a text but only as an incidental illustration and I pass from it rapidly to say that, should a case like this arise, a dispute about paramountcy, it is upon that topic that the fund provided by this subsection would be used. In a dispute on paramountcy involving the use of coercion the funds would come from this Subsection. Is not that the case?

Mr. Butler: I think I have on several occasions told the right hon. Gentleman that all the moneys necessary to the Governor-General for the exercise of his functions as Representative of the Crown will be found under this Subsection.

Mr. Churchill: That is a very nice way of answering my question in the affirmative. I am not objecting. Undoubtedly if the Princes come into the Federation they will have to be subject to severe disciplinary control, and the moneys will have to be found, from federal revenues in the first instance. I agree with the Under-Secretary that later on the expense may be transferred from the federal revenue, and recovered from the delinquent State. There is no reason why that should not happen if such a lamentable situation as has been suggested should arise. I think it well however that we should note these facts. These Clauses and sub-sections slip through very fast, and people sometimes do not realise what is in them and wake up afterwards with great surprise to find what they have done. Here we have the armoury, the arsenal, in which the means of coercing States and disciplining them are to be found. This is the authority for placing on the federal revenue the means of reducing States to a proper subjection to the federal scheme.

Mr. Amery: Is not the actual purpose of the Sub-section simply to preserve the position of the Viceroy *vis-a-vis* the Princes as it is at present, in that sphere of paramountcy which lies entirely outside the Federal Constitution. What then, is the object of trying to make the flesh of the Princes creep with the idea of the new terrors to which they are to be subject if they should come into the Federation? It seems to me that that is one of the interventions in our debates which have nothing to do with the merits of the Bill but are intended to frighten the Princes.

Mr. Churchill: I object altogether to the suggestion of my right hon. Friend. He is always imputing motives. It is a thing which can be done from time to time with delicacy, with courtesy and with moderation, but when it becomes the staple of a right hon. Gentleman's speeches in debate, it occupies a position rather below the general level over which the attention of this Committee should range. This is about the third time to-day that the right hon. Gentleman has dealt with arguments advanced by me by simply saying "Oh, you want to frighten the Princes." I certainly admit, indeed I avow, and glory in the fact, that I should like to give my words of warning and counsel to the Princes to keep clear of this misshapen scheme. I am not afraid of that, and I should be ready to take on my own shoulders the responsibility of persuading them to stand out of it. But to say that because I avow that perfectly legitimate and proper Parliamentary position, the right hon. Gentleman should therefore feel himself absolved from using his fine intellect to provide any arguments at all in regard to the matters under discussion in the Committee, is not a deduction that can be drawn. I wish my right hon. Friend would try to address himself to the arguments instead of simply contenting himself with raising the crudest points of prejudice.

Mr. Amery: If I did impute any motives, my right hon. Friend glories in the fact. What I was addressing myself to was the fact that the argument he advanced was entirely irrelevant to this Sub-section.

Sir John Wardlaw-Milne: I do not impute any motives to my right hon. Friend, but I would ask him what bearing his illustration has on this paragraph? He gave us an illustration and then dealt with some position that might arise if some far-fetched proposal, about which nobody has heard, was accepted by some future Government of India. As far as I can see, that cannot be an illustration of this paragraph at all. It deals entirely with the position which at present exists between the Crown and the States, and surely it is no illustration of the working of this paragraph to deal with some hypothetical case which might arise if some proposal, which a great many members know nothing about, is at some future time accepted by some future Government of India.

Mr. Churchill: It is not true to say that this deals with only the present position. It deals with the position which will be created when the Federal Government is brought into existence. There is no such Government in existence now, so that it does not deal with the present but the future position, which is the position we are being asked to create.

Sir J. Wardlaw-Milne: That position as between the Viceroy and the States is exactly the present position, that is to say, the powers of the Viceroy in connection with the States continue after federation as they exist now.

Mr. Churchill: No, because new obligations are to be undertaken by those who sign the Instrument of Accession and the enforcement of the whole of the complicated process of new obligations will be met under paragraph (f) of this Clause. I agree that funds must be provided, but very large funds will probably be necessary owing to the extensive disagreements which will occur. All I am saying is that as we pass along through the long corridors of this Bill we ought to mark at each stage the significant passages, and this is one of the most significant.

[Later] The Government are to be congratulated on the exuberant character of the support they have received on this Amendment [to Clause 38—Rules of Procedure] from the hon. Member for Bodmin (Mr. Isaac Foot). So far as I could follow his argument, he said that what was proposed was very bad, but any other alternative would be even worse. "This is full of anomalies, but anything else would have been fuller still." Then why do it? Here is a system obviously illogical, irrational, awkward, inconvenient, cumbrous, failing at every point to give satisfaction to those for whom it is designed, and causing innumerable points of friction in its day to day work. Why go on with it? Why break your necks over this federal system?

Mr. Isaac Foot: Why not smash the whole Bill?

Mr. Churchill: That is not what I say. That is the anarchistic method of the hon. Member. "Ah," he says to us, "why do you attempt to discuss these great matters? We have considered them on the Committee." He has settled it all for us. But, you know, we are still the House of Commons. We are much more important than the Joint Select Committee. We are superior to them. We put them in their proper place. We review their work. We descry the many defects in their labours. We point out the inconsistencies and the absurdities of the project with which they have finally confronted us. It is no use the hon. Member coming here and saying, "Ought you to presume to interfere? You can put your trust in the Joint Select Committee." This is the old dilemma which faced Mr. Gladstone. I am sure the hon. Member will like a reference to Mr. Gladstone. He is familiar with his career and knows perfectly well that this is the old dilemma that faced him on the Irish question of Members with seats in Parliament on the basis of in and out voting. Are they to vote on all topics or are they to vote on some? That is the real issue. Because it is an old dilemma it does not follow that it has ever been satisfactorily solved. There are many riddles of the world which have never been satisfactorily solved. If they were, I suppose the world would come to an end. When one is solved, another presents itself.

In this case, all the dilemmas and anomalies are brought before us in the most acute form. Here you have the Princes coming in on a variety of Instruments of Accession, some on a limited liability principle, some going the whole hog, and all taking the same out of the federal pot. It is abhorrent and repulsive to the human mind, it grates on the core of reason; no one can bear a thing like that. One of the most profound ideas of life is that you can take no more out of it than you put into it. Here are these Princes, who are to come in with every kind of reservation for themselves, and at the same time are to sprawl broadly over the entire politics of British India.

Miss Rathbone: Hear, hear!

Mr. Churchill: I am very glad to have the hon. Lady's agreement in that progressive sentiment. I ask the Government the question which I asked at the beginning. Is it worth while going on with this when it is such a very bad thing, when the confusion and the worry are so great, and when everybody is asking you not to do so, everybody in India and everybody at home? I am afraid that the hon. Member for Bodmin (Mr. Isaac Foot) is almost the sole supporter of the Bill. When we come to look upon the support for the Clause and the federal system which hangs upon it, it is the Liberals, represented by the hon. Member for Bodmin, who show the only enthusiasm. There are two or three unfortunate Ministers who have burnt their fingers in this business and do not know how to get the sting out of them. It is a most dismal affair, and, if the Government had the sense and the manhood to cut themselves adrift from it, they would stand erect, freed from the cruel and crushing burden, relieved from an infection which, if they do not take the most stringent methods of isolation and inoculation, will prove fatal to their life.

GOVERNMENT OF INDIA BILL
March 13, 1935
House of Commons

This Clause only deserves momentary notice, because it is the Clause which prescribes the use of the English language in the Federal Assembly. Indeed, it is not necessary to prescribe it, because it is the only language in which the many different races of India can transact common business, and I think that it is worth public notice that this vehicle of the English language and everything else that is being done through the influence and authority of the British Raj has promoted and built up such unity of India as exists. When we hear the talk which goes on about all India a nation, and India is represented as an identity, it is worth while realising how very superficial, artificial, and recent is this veneer of British civilisation and organisation which has been spread over this vast and heterogeneous area. Certainly it would be a pity for us to pass this

Clause, with which I am entirely in accord, without noticing the fact that when even the most hostile conspiracies are levelled against this country by different Indian races, the preparations for them have to be conducted in the English language, and surely as our influence and authority diminish, so surely will the hope of any form of Indian unity die.

[Later] I am sorry the Under-Secretary of State [Mr. R. A. Butler] went out of his way to criticise my Noble Friend the Member for Perth (Lord Scone). As a matter of fact, there is a great deal to be said for querying the proviso, because the proviso seems to a very large extent to take away the sense of the Clause, and, if worked in a certain manner, it would destroy the sense of the Clause; but it is sufficient, as the question is raised, to state that the matter has worked well on this basis. But why, when my Noble Friend did not move his Amendment in order to expedite business, the Under-Secretary of State should go out of his way, in the hope of making a score at his expense, to occupy several minutes of our time, I am unable to say.

[Much later] I must say I think there is a great deal of force in the point made by the hon. Gentleman who moved the Amendment. I hope the right hon. Gentleman the Secretary of State will be able to meet it in some way or other. It is certainly not at all objectionable to those who think with my hon. Friends that the conduct and control of Parliament should be lively and continuous. The object of this proposal is to provide, as it were, for a refresher of the authority given by Parliament in an emergency measure. It is not desirable that measures brought in as emergent should gradually become permanent. Parliament should keep permanent supervision. I hope the Secretary of State will find it possible in some way or other to meet this point.

[Later] One would wish that the Government, which, in the first instance, regularises this exceptional legislation would assume the burden itself of bringing before Parliament after six months a further debate. It is quite different when a private Member is told he can move an Amendment to confine its operation to six months. In order to keep this exceptional procedure in being, Parliament ought to have to make a new and spontaneous effort every six months.

[Later] It seems to me that the right hon. Gentleman [Sir S. Hoare] has thrown out a much larger proposition than that which we were discussing, one to which I do not hold him to be committed. Obviously, it is reasonable that fresh legislation would be required if the entire Act should lapse after a certain period of years. This is a much larger question, one which my right hon. Friend should not be led into without examining all the consequences that would follow. Suppose in these circumstances the existing Constitution is demolished. Hardly a vestige will remain when the new one is suddenly pulled away, because it is necessary to supersede it by emergency measures. It seems quite evident that what you would require is not a provision in this Statute but new legislation by Parliament. Therefore, while assenting to the proposal to give some further safeguards against emergency measures becoming permanent through lapse of time, we would not like to be committed to such larger measures contemplated by him.

[Later] The Conservative party have been cajoled into making enormous surrenders of the control of Parliament over India on the basis that all this power is to be placed potentially and under reserve in the hands of the Viceroy, so that if a serious situation arises he can, as it were, resume the power indirectly which Parliament now exercises. This proposal seeks to reduce the Viceroy, into whose hands these great powers have been placed. It is going beyond what is desirable.

The Chairman: May I remind the right hon. Gentleman that this is not a question of the Viceroy? We have got on to the Provinces.

Mr. Churchill: But the principle is exactly the same. Having entrusted the whole of these powers to the Governors of the Provinces, you are now to reduce the Governor to the position of a constitutional sovereign who only acts on the receipt of minutes from his Ministers and remains isolated and remote until some very rare constitutional crisis arises. That is a position which is even more destructive of any attempt to give guidance to the Indian Provinces than any thing we have heard of in this Bill.

The Chairman: I am afraid that I cannot allow the right hon. Gentleman to develop that. This Clause is an exact repetition of the one regarding the Federal Legislature, and I was only moved to select this one particular Amendment at the special request of the Members of the Opposition who explained to me the particular reason for which they wanted to move it. But nothing connected with this Amendment has any effect on what is provided by the rest of the Clause, which has already been decided. It is merely a question, as I see it, whether one of these ministers shall be described as prime minister or not, which is a very narrow point.

Mr. Churchill: With very great respect, Sir, the formal appointment of a provincial prime minister is really not a technical point, and the avowed intention of those who moved this Amendment—and I suppose I am in order in discussing the Amendment—was to create a prime minister and to push the Governor out of the discussions of the Provincial Cabinet, a very grave proposal. It is the kind of proposal which shows how we shall develop in this matter. No doubt the same process will be applied at the centre.

The Chairman: I am afraid that if that is the meaning of the Amendment I must rule it definitely out of order.

Mr. Attlee: On a point of Order. I hope that you will take the meaning of the Amendment from its Movers and not from the right hon. Gentleman.

The Chairman: I am afraid I must ask the rest of the Committee to discuss it as it was interpreted by the Mover. It was accepted by the Chair on that basis.

Mr. Churchill: I am a little puzzled how you can discuss the question of the appointment of a prime minister without in any way trespassing on the significance of such an event. It seems to me that we are invited to discuss this question *in vacuo*. What is the point of calling him prime minister if it is not to convey any constitutional change? Hon. Gentlemen, terrorised by your mild authority, for fear their Amendment should be declared out of order, now profess that all that they mean is to call some particular member by the title of "prime minister," but that it is not going to make the slightest difference. Are we going to take up our limited time in Committee in endeavouring to bestow mere honorific titles. If it be merely a question of calling some minister "prime minister" and it is clearly understood that it will have no effect on the body, I agree that we need not waste our time in speaking to the Amendment. But if there be any question of embarking upon the idea that there is to be erected from these ministers a personage, a potentate who will replace the Governor in council then obviously that is a point upon which we must take a Division.

SUNDAY TRADING QUESTION

March 14, 1935

Presidential Address, Early Closing Association Annual Meeting, Hotel Metropole, Westminster

[Extract] ... The movement has reached a stage when there should be no slackening of effort in the campaign to maintain and to improve the lot of the retail trader and his employees.

[Editor's Note: Referring to the question of Sunday trading by Jewish retailers, Mr. Churchill said]: That difficulty raises the question of some Jewish traders who claim, with a very considerable measure of reason, that if their religious beliefs oblige them to close their shops on Saturday, they should have some latitude given to them on Sunday. Then, against that, there should also be set the argument that the hours to be opened on Sundays, when the Christian shops would be closed, would be far more valuable than on Saturday, when competition was general. That is a difficulty both sides should face in an earnest desire to arrive at a decision with a minimum of hardship to the individual. I am glad to hear that the policy of the association is to allow certain compensatory concessions in respect to Sunday trading to Jewish traders who strictly observe their own religious observance on Saturday. At one time that view was not shared as it is to-day.

AIR ESTIMATES

March 19, 1935

House of Commons

In response to this formidable speech, the Government gave assurances that Britain had not lost her air superiority. As we now know, this was correct, but on March 25 Hitler announced German "parity" in air power. For the first time, Conservative uneasiness was apparent.

In the comparisons of air strength we suffer very much because there is no accurate knowledge and definite terminology by which it can be compared. Happily this difficult matter is not complicated by any differences about the standard towards which we should work. The Lord President of the Council [Mr. Stanley Baldwin] in March 1934 laid down, in the most plain and solemn manner, his view of what our air-power standard should be. I must read what he said from the Official Report:

... Any Government of this country—a National Government more than any, and this Government—will see to it that in air strength and air power this country shall no longer be in a position inferior to any country within striking distance of our shores.

Therefore, those of us who accept that statement have no need to go into questions of alliances, or difficult aspects of foreign policy, or questions of international morality and pacifism which have played, and ought to play, a part in these various debates. We have a perfectly definite objective proclaimed in March last by the highest authority on a most serious occasion, and I take that as the starting-point of the argument that I wish to put before the House. In November of last year, supported by some friends of mine, I moved an Amendment to the Address representing that

> In the present circumstances of the world the strength of our national defenses, and especially of our air defenses, is no longer adequate to secure the peace, safety and freedom of your Majesty's faithful subjects.

I do not think that the course of events has in any way stultified those who put down that Amendment. I must apologize for quoting what I said in that Debate, but it is necessary to my argument today. I said:

> I therefore assert, first, that Germany already, at this moment, has a military air force—that is to say, military squadrons, with the necessary ground services, with the necessary reserves of trained personnel and material—which only await an order to assemble in full open combination—and that this illegal air force is rapidly approaching equality with our own.

In reply to that statement the Lord President made a momentous announcement, and confirmed the fact that Germany was forming, or had formed, a military air force. Hitherto the official view had been that Germany was observing the Treaty which precluded her from having a military air force. But, as a result of that Debate in November, the statement of the Lord President to which I have referred was made. Subsequent events have shown how true it was. In reply to the further statements which I made my right hon. Friend uttered very definite contradiction, and it is with those contradictions that I wish to deal. He said:

> It is not the case that Germany is rapidly approaching equality with us. ... Her real strength is not 50 per cent. of our strength in Europe today.

That is to say, half our strength in Europe. That directly contradicted the assertion which I had made. My right hon. Friend further proceeded to say, "As for the position this time next year" (that would be November 1935), so far from the German military air force being at least as strong as, and probably stronger than, our own, we estimate that we shall still have in Europe alone a margin of nearly 50 per cent. I cannot look farther forward than the next two years.

Does my right hon. Friend adhere to that statement today? I wonder whether he will tell us when he speaks whether further information has led him to modify those very striking statements. Certainly, if they are true they are enormously reassuring. If, by any chance, my right hon. Friend has been misled into making an understatement or an erroneous statement I am sure that he would wish to correct it at the first opportunity. At any rate, I propose to examine and analyze those two statements. But before I do so I must say a word on the question of terminology. The Lord President warned us on that same 28th of November of the danger of making false comparisons. He said:

> The total number of service aircraft which any country possesses is an entirely different thing from the total number of aircraft of first-line strength. The total number, of course, includes the first-line strength and all the reserve machines used in practice and many things of that kind. I would like the House to remember that one may get a wholly erroneous picture in making comparisons, just to mention the aircraft of our own country, when perhaps the figures that have been mentioned are but the figures of first-line strength.

That is perfectly true, and we are indebted to my right hon. Friend for establishing these definite categories, so that we can carry on something like intelligent discussion upon air matters. Military aircraft and first-line strength are two different categories. I wish, therefore, this afternoon to examine the air power of Great Britain and Germany in both categories—that of military aircraft and that of first-line strength. I will deal with the position last November, when, dealing with the German position, the Lord President said:

> The figures we have range from a figure, given on excellent authority, of 600 aircraft—600 military aircraft altogether—to the highest figure that we have been given, also from good sources, of something not over 1000. The probability is that the actual figure ranges between those two, near which limit I cannot say; but it is interesting to note that in the French Chamber the French Government—and I do not think their tendency would be to minimize figures—gave the figure of the military aircraft at 1100.

I believe it will be found that my right hon. Friend, or those who advised him, mixed up the two classes that we were asked to keep separate in our minds. Instead of saying that Germany had 600 military aircraft, he should have said that Germany had 600 first-line air strength. However, taking the basis of those figures for comparison, let us see what are the comparable figures given by my right hon. Friend for Great Britain. The Lord President said:

> The first-line strength of the regular units of the Royal Air Force today, at home and overseas, is 880 aircraft. Of these, including those of the Fleet Air Arm, 560 are at present stationed in the United Kingdom. There are also at home the Auxiliary Air Force and the Special Reserve squadrons, with an establishment of 127 aircraft, making a total of just under 690 aircraft available today in the United Kingdom that could be put into the first line. But the House must realize that behind our regular first-line strength of 880 aircraft—

my right hon. Friend seems to have used the total figure for the British Empire in dealing with home defense—

> there is a far larger number either held in reserve to replace the normal peace-time wastage or in current use in training and experimental work.

I must draw the attention of the House to certain defects in that statement. My right hon. Friend says that 560 first-line air strength aircraft were available for the defense of the United Kingdom, and in order to make those figures look larger 127 auxiliary aircraft were added to produce a total of 687. Those auxiliary aircraft are not fairly comparable to the whole-time regular units of the Royal Air Force. There is the same kind of gap between them and the Royal Air Force as there is between the Territorial Army and the whole-time professional Army.

The actual facts are perfectly well known abroad. If those 127 auxiliary aircraft are to be added to the British first-line strength, then at least 300 fast commercial dual-purpose bombing machines which exist in Germany, ready and available for immediate conversion, will have to be added on the other side, which would alter the count even more to our disadvantage. Therefore, from a study of all that has been said it is apparent that in November on a comparable basis the German first-line air strength was 600 and the British home defense, including the Naval Air Arm, was 560.

Now I come to military aircraft. The 1000, or 1100, military aircraft then possessed by Germany no doubt include 300 fast dual-purpose bombing machines. What is the comparable British figure? The Lord President did not mention it in November; he left it veiled. But the Under-Secretary has told the House this afternoon that the military machines at the present time consist of 890, plus 130 of the auxiliary force, which makes exactly 1020. On this basis the British and German air forces at the end of November would appear to have been as follows: first-line strength, Great Britain 560, Germany 600; military aircraft, Great Britain 1020, without training machines, and Germany 1100. Beyond all question these are much the most favorable figures from our point of view which could possibly be cited. But even taking them as they are, they altogether disprove the first assertion of the Lord President of the

Council on the 28th of November, because they show the two countries virtually on an equality, neck and neck, whereas the Lord President said:

> It is not the case that Germany is rapidly approaching equality with us. . . . Her real strength is not 50 per cent. of our strength in Europe today.

I come to the second and more disquieting stage of my argument. Since our Debate in November four months have passed, and during that period our position has sensibly changed for the worse. The German Government have announced, formally and publicly, that on the 1st of April—that is, in thirteen days' time—it is their intention to constitute a military air force. They are going to assemble all those elements which have hitherto been altogether unofficial in strong units of the German regular air force. It involves no great change. It only means officers putting on their badges of rank which have hitherto been tacitly understood. We do not know what proportion of the vast pool of their military, commercial and sporting aviation Germany will declare as their first-line air strength, but I have no doubt that they will declare the lowest figure—that is, 600 first-line air strength—and it may easily be doubled, and more than doubled. I must point out that I have been using only the minimum figures, but although they are minimum figures, they are amply sufficient to prove the case. I do not wish to use alarmist figures unless they are forced upon me by the fact that one cannot close one's eyes to them. But I take no responsibility—and I wish to make this clear in case there is any inquest afterwards into all these statements. I must not be understood to be giving even as a private Member any assurance that the actual truth may not be much worse than the figures I have cited.

Last November in the same Debate the Lord President of the Council gave the figures of the German army which has been formed contrary to the Treaty as 300,000 men in 21 divisions. Only four months after, Germany declared on Saturday last, what we knew that there are 500,000 men in barracks, for compulsory universal service to sustain 36 divisions. The 21 has grown to 36. It may be—indeed, it is—only natural to assume that the expansion of the German air force will bear the same proportion of the new German army as the air forces of other conscript countries bear to the armies of those countries; it will undergo the same expansion; and it may be that an even more unpleasant surprise awaits His Majesty's Government on the 1st of April than occurred when the Germany army scheme was declared on Saturday last.

But what will be the relative position a year from now—that is, at the end of the next financial year? We are to add during the year 11 squadrons of nine machines each—let us say 100 machines to our first-line air strength. Eleven new squadrons will come into being with all their appurtenances and reserves. The Under-Secretary said, evidently with great pleasure, that the Air Ministry were ordering over 1000 new machines. We want to know how many new machines are being delivered. The machines may be ordered so late in the year as not really to be anything but paper decisions; and we must deal with realities in this matter. When I looked at Vote 3 I found that only £1,000,000 more was being taken for this part of the construction vote—that is, £6,800,000 instead of £5,800,000—and I do not see how the addition of £1,000,000 can possibly make such a very large addition to our Air Force. Nor does it in fact, because the Under-Secretary, with complete candor, has shown exactly the amount of the advance in British military aircraft during the year, and has told us that we now possess 1020, and that at the end of the year we shall have 1170—that is, an increase of 150 machines.

We know that the financial provisions only permit of an addition of 150 machines of this type and the addition of 11 squadrons, which will raise our first-line air strength for home defense to 659 and our military aircraft to 1170, exclusive of training machines. What, then, will be the German first-line air strength at the end of this year? We cannot tell. We shall learn officially on the 1st of April, and it is no use speculating on what they will declare as their first-line air strength. I must confine myself to the other factor, German military aircraft.

Here, again, mystery shrouds all German preparations. At various points facts emerge which enable a general view to be taken. Enormous sums of money are being spent on German aviation and upon other armaments. I wish we could get at the figures which are being spent upon armaments. I believe that they would stagger us with the terrible tale they would tell of the immense panoply which that nation of nearly 70,000,000 of people is assuming, or has already assumed. But there are certain things which strike one. For instance, the population of Dessau increased during last year by 13,000. Dessau is a center of the great Junkers aeroplane works, but it is only one of four or five main factories of Germany. There are at least twenty others of a secondary but important character; and 13,000 people are known to have entered the town of Dessau—I do not say that they are all workers—in the course of last year. One can see what the scale of production must be. Further, owing to the fact that the Germans had to prepare their air force in secret and unofficially, there has grown up a somewhat different method of producing aircraft from that which obtains in this country and in France. Much smaller elements are actually made outside the main factories than over here. Nuts and bolts and small parts are spread over an enormous producing area of small firms, and then they flow into the great central factories. The work which is done there consists in a rapid assembly, like a jig-saw puzzle or Meccano game, with the result that aeroplanes are turned out with a speed incomparably greater than in our factories, where a great deal of the earlier stages of the work is done on the spot.

I must set forth these facts because they are very important. According to yesterday's *Daily Telegraph*, between 250 and 300 military aircraft have been added to Germany's total since November. I fear it will be found that the German factories are working up from their present rate of output of more than 100 a month to some unknown monthly increase. It may be 100, 120 or 140 a month; I do not pretend to be able to say. Nothing I have gathered from the newspapers enables me to judge what the ultimate result will be, but it seems to me that if you take the next twelve months at an average output of 125 machines a month—I am sure there are a great many people who will scoff at such a low figure, and I may be only making myself ridiculous by using it and may afterwards be mocked at for doing so—even if you take that moderate figure of 125, it will mean an addition to Germany's military aircraft in the financial year 1935-36 of 1500, of which a portion will go to replace wastage, and the rest will be a net addition to their total military aircraft strength. That is many times larger than any program of deliveries provided in this Estimate, which we see is concerned with an increase of 150, plus the natural wear and tear and wastage. Therefore, I am unable to accept the second statement of my right hon. Friend the Lord President in November last, which I have read to the House and will read again:

> As for the position this time next year ... so far from the German military air force being almost as strong as, and probably stronger than our own, I estimate that we shall have in Europe alone a margin of nearly 50 per cent.

On the contrary, I must submit to the House that the Lord President was misled in the figures which he gave last November, quite unwittingly no doubt, because of the great difficulty of the subject. At any rate, the true position at the end of this year will be almost the reverse of that which he stated to Parliament. We must remember also that Germany's scale of reserves, judging by the lectures which are being delivered at different times by those who have been presiding over German aviation development, is 200 per cent. The reason is this: it will take them three months to get their peace-time industry working at full blast on a war-time basis, and they calculate on a loss of 100 per cent. of aeroplanes per month in time of war. They hope to transfer the whole of the civilian industry to maintain their air force on a wastage of 100 per cent. a month. They have, of course, made preparations for converting the entire industry of Germany to war purposes by a single order of a detail and refinement which is almost inconceivable. I am certain that Germany's preparations are infinitely more far-reaching than our own. So that you have not only equality at the moment, but the greater output which I have described, and you have behind that this enormous power to turn over, on the out-break of war, the whole force of German industry.

It is admitted at the present time that the only effective means of defense against air attack is retaliation and counter-attack, and, from the point of view of counter-attack, the Germans seem to have a great advantage over us. Although they declare that their force is purely defensive, it has a much larger percentage of long-distance bombing machines than any other force—far larger than we have ourselves.

The next point is a matter of geography. The frontiers of Germany are very much nearer to London than the sea-coasts of this island are to Berlin, and whereas practically the whole of the German bombing air force can reach London with an effective load, very few, if any, of our aeroplanes can reach Berlin with any appreciable load of bombs. That must be considered as one of the factors in judging between the two countries. We only wish to live quietly and to be left alone. If it is thought that the power to retaliate is a deterrent—I believe it is—to an outrageous attack, then it seems that we are at a disadvantage in that respect, quite apart from any numerical disadvantage. I was very glad indeed that the Prime Minister today, in answer to Sir Austen Chamberlain, spoke about the committee which is to examine defensive measures against aeroplane attacks. That is a matter in which all countries, in my opinion, have a similar interest—all peaceful countries. It is a question not of one country against another, but of the ground against the air, and unless the dwellers upon earth can manage to secure the air above their heads it is almost impossible to forecast the misfortunes and fears which this invention, of which the world has proved itself so utterly unworthy, may bring upon them.

One of the factors to be remembered is the preparation made by the civilian population on either side to guard themselves against an air raid. Obviously if one side has made good preparations the loss inflicted upon it will be very much less than that inflicted on the side which has made no preparation at all. Great panics may arise if this is not foreseen. Up to the present what has been done on the Continent is incomparably ahead of anything that has been even presented on paper publicly here. It takes a frightfully long time to get anything done in this country. We move like a slow-motion picture in all these matters.

I do not think my right hon. Friend's solemn pledge, that we are not inferior to any country within striking distance, is being kept, or that it will be kept, because the efforts which are being made will not be made by this country alone. The great advance of German aviation is only now beginning to assume its full force. The program which was announced in this country in August last was hopelessly inadequate. Its leisurely, stinted execution has so far made no appreciable addition to our strength. The provision for this year is hopelessly inadequate. We are told that we are expanding as fast as we can, but that the preparations have to be made, that aerodromes have to be bought, the training schools enlarged, and that all this takes time. There are many arguments which the Government can use to show how slow and difficult the work is. I do not accept those arguments at their face value.

I am sure that if the vigorous measures that the situation requires were adopted to put ourselves in a position of defensive security, very much more rapid progress could be made in every branch. But even if the argument were true and there is to be this great delay, if we can only proceed by such very gradual stages, then I say that the responsibility of the Government and of the Air Ministry will be all the greater. If the necessary preparations had been made two years ago when the danger was clear and apparent, the last year would have seen a substantial advance, and this year would have seen a very great advance. Even at this time last year, if a resolve had been taken, as I urged, to double and redouble the British Air Force as soon as possible—Sir Herbert Samuel described me as a Malay run amok because I made such a suggestion—very much better results would have been yielded in 1935, and we should not find ourselves in our present extremely dangerous position.

Everyone sees now that we have entered a period of peril. We are faced, not with the prospect of a new war, but with something very like the possibility of a resumption of the War which ended in November, 1918. I still hope, and I believe—the alternative would be despair—that it may be averted. But the position is far worse than it was in 1914, and it may well be found to be uncontrollable. We are no longer safe behind the shield of our Navy. We have fallen behind in the vital air defense of this island. We are not only far more deeply and explicitly involved in Continental affairs than we were in 1914, but owing to the neglect of our own defenses we have become dependent upon other countries for our essential security.

From being the least vulnerable of all nations we have, through developments in the air, become the most vulnerable, and yet, even now, we are not taking the measures which would be in true proportion to our needs. The Government have proposed these increases. They must face the storm. They will have to encounter every form of unfair attack. Their motives will be misrepresented. They will be calumniated and called war-mongers. Every kind of attack will be made upon them by many powerful, numerous and extremely vocal forces in this country. They are going to get it anyway. Why, then, not fight for something that will give us safety? Why, then, not insist that the provision for the Air Force should be adequate, and then, however severe may be the censure and however strident the abuse which they have to face, at any rate there will be this satisfactory result—that His Majesty's Government will be able to feel that in this, of all matters the prime responsibility of a Government, they have done their duty.

INDIA (DISTURBANCES AT KARACHI)

March 20, 1935

House of Commons

The Secretary of State for India (Sir Samuel Hoare): I regret to state that trouble arose yesterday morning at Karachi after the execution of Abdul Qaiyum, who was sentenced to death for the murder of a Hindu in the Judicial Commissioner's Court last September. The burial of the body in a selected graveyard some distance from the city was interrupted by a crowd of Mahommedans who swelled to 20,000 or more. Half the crowd attempted to rush the body by surprise into the city and overpowered the police. In these circumstances, and in view of the certainty of a grave communal disturbance if steps were not taken to disperse the crowd, British troops were brought up and ordered to fire as a last resource. A detachment of 25 men fired nearly two rounds each, causing casualties at present reported to be 29 deaths and 87 injured. The firing was strictly controlled, but, owing to the density of the crowd and the shortness of the range, casualties were high. As the result of the firing the crowd retreated and buried the body of Abdul Qaiyum outside the city. According to the latest report in my possession, the situation yesterday evening was quiet but was being carefully watched.

Mr. Churchill: Would my right hon. Friend say why it is that the Government of India, in dispersing these crowds of excited people, do not use lachrymatory gas capsules, such as used in America, instead of firing bullets, which pierce three or four bodies at the same time, and why humanity and commom sense cannot lead to reform in the matter of dealing with crowds of this character?

Sir S. Hoare: The Government of India have already considered that possibility. So far as I remember, lachrymatory gas has been used in the Punjab. I will look again into the suggestion, but I will say nothing that would lead the House to suppose that I have not full confidence in the troops in dealing with the situation in the best possible manner.

Mr. Churchill: Will my right hon. Friend most carefully discriminate between any suggestion that there is lack of confidence in the troops or in the judgment of the people on the spot, and a decision on a matter of high policy which is required from the Imperial Government?

Sir S. Hoare: Certainly.

GOVERNMENT OF INDIA BILL
March 20, 1935
House of Commons

This Debate has been remarkable for the unanimity of the criticism and condemnation which have been directed at this stage upon this government of India Bill as it now presents itself to us. The speeches from every quarter of the Committee have converged and concentrated their fire upon the position now occupied by my right hon. Friend the Secretary of State and those who have been associated with him in the long task of promoting this Bill. We have had a notable speech from the Noble Lord the Member for Oxford University (Lord H. Cecil)—a very rare pleasure to us in this House. He brings to us the fruits of profound reflection and of absolute disinterested sincerity. Then we have had the speech delivered by the hon. Member for Caerphilly (Mr. M. Jones) representing His Majesty's Opposition, who has given proofs of his sincerity and is known to be a very strong supporter of what is called advance in India. That speech certainly requires an answer from the Treasury Bench. Certain facts which he adduced and which have been brought forward from every quarter ought to be answered if we are to continue to be a reasonable and reasoning debating assembly.

Sometimes one wonders what is to happen if British Members of Parliament lose all contact with each other by means of reasonable processes. It is very difficult to know how we should get on in such a case, and we are in great danger of it. The Government persist in their policy. The right hon. Gentleman recites at intervals the formulae at which he has arrived. He publishes his despatches and memoranda in a highly specialised and technical jargon which only occasionally forms contact with the English language. For the rest, matters are left to the Patronage Secretary and to a large number of gentlemen who, if they were only giving to this problem the attention which they gave to it a year ago or two years ago, when they began to make up their minds, would rush this Bill out of the House. Unhappily, they have taken their decision. They are not with us here, but they will be in the Division Lobby. So the machine goes on. That you can roll the Bill forward I do not deny. We cannot doubt that you have the power, during the continued lifetime of this Parliament, to roll this Bill through, in defiance of every fact and every appeal, but the consequences will not be dispersed so easily.

My Noble Friend has moved to report Progress this afternoon because of this White Paper with its unofficial companion the verbatim report of the Princes' speeches—its handmaiden and concomitant. The White Paper undoubtedly presents us, officially, formally and directly with a new situation. No one can deny that it is a new situation. I do not believe that even the hon. Member for Bodmin (Mr. Isaac Foot), who has suffered in political controversy from being at bottom a fair-minded man, would deny that he feels himself in the presence of new facts in the situation produced by this White Paper and the speeches of the Princes. Whether we have a National Government or not is arguable, but evidently there is a National Opposition in the sense of all parties reaching a certain general basis of agreement on the fact that there is a new situation.

This White Paper and its companion represent—what? They represent the Princes' offer. I had not meant to be controversial, but it seems almost a joke. This White Paper is the Princes' offer on which the Government have gone into action for the last four years. This is the Princes' offer which induced the Foreign Secretary to abandon all the conclusions which he and his commission had reached as a result of their study. This is the Princes' offer which my right hon. Friend the Lord President of the Council dwelt on as the ground on which he solemnly advised his party to adopt this policy. I read in the "News-Chronicle," the organ of the Liberal party—I beg pardon, I am not so sure about that, but an organ at any rate of the Liberal and Labour parties—[Hon. Members: "No!"] Do not repudiate any support. You may need it all. I read that paper's epitome of this situation—their headline—and what was it?

The Princes reaffirm their faith in Federation.

Can any reasonable person who has read the White Paper and also read the actual text of the Princes' speeches imagine that we are going to make progress in our affairs by taking such nonsensical views as that? What is the moral of this White Paper? It is the final refusal of the Princes to have anything to do with this Federation scheme. [Hon. Members: "No!"] I believe we are going to have a reply from the Attorney-General. I am sure that if he were consulted in a legal capacity and if he saw this document, especially if he saw the report of the speeches, he would say that on the correspondence there was a complete breakdown. On the correspondence there appears a total and utter breach. Mind you, it is not only a question of a breach such as might arise between a willing buyer and a willing seller who were still haggling about how the thing should go and who was to get some advantage here or there. Not at all. This is a deliberate decision on the part of the Princes of India to break from this scheme of Federation. Do not delude yourselves. There is no compromise, no alternative possible.

Let me point out that it is a question of paramountcy. Paramountcy, the Secretary of State says, is not in the Bill. "I rejoice," he says, "that our differences are narrowed by the fact that I need not discuss paramountcy." But why do the Princes raise this question of paramountcy? I must say it astonishes me that my right hon. Friend, with all his ability, does not seem to be in touch with the actual way in which the forces in India are working. Why do you suppose the Princes have raised this question of paramountcy and dragged it in by the heels? Not because they expect the Government to grant their wishes, but because they wish to put up a barrier against being involved in this scheme of Federation. It may be said that there are 30 points of difference, and the lawyers may discuss them and write them out in great detail and make proposals for compromise, for arrangements and for accommodations. But the Princes were not going to trust only to that. No, they raise the question of paramountcy, and they now say "Before we come into this Federation you have to define paramountcy and deal with us on that subject." They twice use the expression that this is a "condition precedent" to their joining the Federation.

What does the right hon. Gentleman say? He says what any Secretary of State would say, the only thing which any Secretary of State could say. "I am not prepared to entertain a discussion at this time with the Princes of India upon their relations with the King Emperor." Could you possibly have a more complete and absolute breach than is disclosed by that position? On the one hand, the Princes say, "We will not enter the Federation until, as a condition precedent, our wishes about paramountcy are met." On the other hand, you have the right hon. Gentleman saying, as it was his duty to say, "We are not prepared to discuss the high relationship of these princely States with the sovereign Power." There is a complete breach. I do not think there can be any doubt about it. You may work for several months, you may spend a lot of time, trouble and money with the lawyers in trying to work out a compromise but this means that the Princes have definitely decided not to come into this Bill.

Why they have so decided it would take a long time to tell, but there is one reason that the right hon. Gentleman ought to appreciate because I think it is the dominant, the actuating reason, the motor muscle of their position. It is because their compatriots in the political classes of India have told them not to come in. It is because from all over India they have received appeals, protests, even threats, all with the object of inducing them to stop out. It is because they are making common cause with the rest of Indian educated intelligentsia and public opinion against this Measure, and therefore the Princes have withdrawn from it. There may be many other reasons, such as their position and their sovereign rights, and many of them have never liked the idea of Federation; but the decisive fact undoubtedly is that the Princes have refused to come into Federation because those forces in British India which asked them five years ago to come in have now in the most explicit and earnest manner begged them, urged them, exhorted them to stay out. Therefore, they have erected this insuperable obstacle of paramountcy.

That is the position. It is a very serious position. I really must ask my right hon. Friend the Lord President of the Council—I am always having to ask him questions—to think over very carefully what he said to the National Union of Conservative Associations. I am absolutely sure that the last thing in the world my right hon. Friend would do is to obtain support, to get round a difficult corner by anything in the nature of false pretences. I am sure that when he sees that the facts on which he presented his case to the Conservative associations are not borne out and have actually fallen from beneath his feet, he will take the earliest effective opportunity of either detaching himself from the policy or of explaining that new circumstances have arisen which induce him to base his advocacy of the Measure on different grounds from those he then put forward.

I am glad to see the Prime Minister back. It gives me great satisfaction, and I hope he will not mind my pointing out to him how different the situation is now from what it was in 1931. In those days he had the offer of the Princes; there was an offer then. In those days he had the assent and agreement of British Indian politicians. In those days he had a large amount of support among Indian Liberals—active support from that great body of central opinion of which we have heard. In those days also he had hopes of obtaining the Congress party and Mr. Gandhi—"My Dear Mahatma" we had then. In those days he had the official support of the Conservative party and Liberal support, and he was himself the head of a Socialist Government. In those days four or five years ago he had every expectation, as it seemed at the moment—although I did not share it—of being able to make a great settlement for India with an equally broad basis of public assent here. Every one of those factors has been swept away; not one vestige of that structure remains. You may say that you will continue with the Bill, but every man who has studied the matter knows that the situation has no resemblance in any way to what occurred at that time.

What do the Government say should happen now? They say, "It is quite all right, it makes no difference." The Indian Liberals will not have it. Congress will not have it, the Princes will not have it, and the Labour party will not have it. It is not an agreed Measure here, it is not a Measure which can be said to be, as it were, high and dry above the ebb and flow of party conflict. All that has vanished. Still, the Government say, "It is all right, wait until the Division bell rings, and we will get them through the Lobbies, and it will be all right." Their newspapers—they still have some in their support—their devoted newspapers will read to-morrow. "The House of Commons decided by an overwhelming majority that there was no substance whatever in those ridiculous and obstructive tactics put forward against the Bill." All this, and a reference to the fine speech of the Secretary of State, in which he depicted himself in action on behalf of a cause which has got into a somewhat ramshackle condition, will be, no doubt, admirably portrayed.

But what is the Government's policy? It is to place this Bill on the Statute Book, no matter what happens and whether they have agreement of all parties or not. They wish to place the Bill upon the Statute Book. What will happen then? I see that Lord Lothian made a speech the other day. He is a very important person and has a great influence in our relations with Germany and in our relations with India. I quote from the report of his speech in the "Times" of the 8th March:

> Lord Lothian, discussing the Indian Bill, said they had nothing to do to-day but to put the Bill on to the Statute Book and make a fresh start from that position.

I ask the Conservative party, I ask the Government and their faithful supporters, if that is the position they take up? I ask particularly my Noble Friend the Member for Horsham (Earl Winterton). If faith holds between man and man, we are entitled to know where we stand in a matter of this kind. This Bill has been represented as the most that we can give and the furthest we can go. All its safeguards have been drawn carefully in order to salve the consciences of members of the Conservative party and to make it easy for the great mass of that party to do what without their support would never have been done in this country. Now, when it is to be put on the Statute Book, what is it to be? A settlement? No, it is to be the point from which a fresh start is to be made. The Attorney-General is a Conservative. He is a sincere patriot. Has he any bottom to his convictions in this matter? Is there any point where we shall reach finality? He is going to force the Bill through, but is he prepared to take it as a starting point for some great new lurch, some downward slurge? We ought to know. Of course, you can vote us down, but if there is no sort of attempt to meet propositions of this kind, you cannot blame us if we try to fight not only in this House, but elsewhere, by every method open to us, because, once all contact is lost on a basis of reason and argument, then the only thing people can do is to organise and to endeavour to express their opinions as effectively as they can. I hope that we shall have some answer upon that point—how far do you mean to go?

This Bill is now to be placed on the sideboard like a ham from which anyone can come and cut a slice if they feel inclined before it gets mouldy and rotten. There is your Bill, there is your settlement of India, and of course it will be the starting point for any further legislation if it is passed. Every concession you have made, the most extreme point which you have reached, will be the starting point for new legislation. The Attorney-General made a speech in the country the other day. He usually indulges himself at week-ends in the country by giving us orations which are most interesting and nearly always afford food for controversial comment. He made a speech in which he said that it ought to be five or ten years before the policy of this Bill could be carried out. In five or ten years there will be a change of Government in this country. However sanguine may be the hopes that are entertained, one cannot imagine that in such a period there will not be a change. But when you have passed this Bill of 400 or 500 Clauses and put it on the Statute Book, it will not be difficult to pass a Bill of 20 Clauses. It will be quite a manageable matter. It will slip through this structure and completely transform it; it will completely prune out, excise, eliminate and excavate every one of the particular points upon which the Conservative party have been induced to carry this policy so far.

Why press this matter further? It is not any longer a great measure of Indian constitutional reform. The right hon. Gentleman has no doubt to introduce a great many Amendments to meet the objections of the Princes. I suggest that at the same time he should change the title of the Bill. He should no longer call it the Government of India Bill, but the Chelsea Hospital (No. 2) Relief Bill. He should call it by the name which far more accurately delineates its purpose, namely, to enable a number of officials and powerful people to escape from a difficult situation without undue loss and countenance and face. This Bill has nothing whatever to do with India. India will have nothing whatever to do with the Bill. The whole position has now become one of will power, of clash of opinions and wills here at the centre. Why can we not relax this position? The right hon. Gentleman spoke of the temptation of abandoning this Bill in the face of the universal opposition which it has excited among those for whom it was designed. Why can he not yield to that temptation? Temptation which is a natural instinct is not necessarily wrong. You beg the question when you say that all that reason and all that convenience and all that public interest urge is temptation. You ought to yield to these things, and this is the time to yield. This is the time when the

Government ought to lay aside every impediment. There is great need of simplifying our policy here and abroad. There is great need of uniting forces which are harmoniously blended and must act together. Surely this is the time to take a reasonable step.

It is little that we ask, and how very little it is now that we have reached the point when, as far as arguments and facts are concerned, it is admitted by all parties in the House that the case has been made out. Surely it is not much to ask that the Federal Clauses should be dropped, that they should not be placed on the Statute Book until or unless the Princes have concurred in them, that they should, as my Noble Friend has suggested, be brought to the Third Reading and then be left out with any other ancillary parts as may be required. Then we could go forward. If that were done, very useful legislation would still rest in the hands of the Government, but, if they persist in the course which they have adopted, if they simply go forward using the dull brute force that they can demand. [Hon. Members: "Hear, hear.] The right hon. Gentleman the Member for West Birmingham (Sir A. Chamberlain) has taken very great responsibility in this matter, and I hope he will not be left high and dry when the subject is concluded. If the Government go forward, using their force, they must not suppose the trouble will end with the passage of the Bill. That is not possible. While this Bill remains on the Statute Book it claims from all those who disapprove of such policies and principles a consistent and persistent effort to establish forces, continuing and organised forces, which will resist the repetition of such Measures in the future, and will endeavour, as far as possible, to repair the mischances of the past.

"AS DEAD AS MUTTON"
(GOVERNMENT OF INDIA BILL)

March 21, 1935

India Defence League Demonstration,
Albert Hall, London

[Extract] ... We are fighting against hard and heavy odds. We are fighting against our friends who have misunderstood their duty, and against leaders who have misused their authority.

The Joint Select Committee is packed, the delegates from India were picked. (Laughter.) The Lancashire evidence was cooked. The National Union of Conservative Associations was for a long time muzzled and its final assent was only procured on a basis now proved to be false. Who wants the Bill? In India, Indian political classes of every kind have repudiated its proposals. The Government preaches the doctrine of a united Empire. The only India they have united is an India united against their proposals. At home the Conservative Party loathes the Bill. It has been rammed down their throats.

The Bill is dead. It is as dead as mutton. But nevertheless the Government assures us it must be placed on the Statute Book. The corpse must be carried forward as a trophy. A docile majority who have closed their minds to reason and facts pay no attention to the change in or the collapse of the Government case. If they think they are marching with the *cortège* of the India Bill they may find they are attending their own funeral as well.

We have months of fighting yet before us and after that there will be a fight in the House of Lords led by Lord Salisbury. (Cheers.) I trust the Bill will come back to the House of Commons with a goodly stock of amendments. Much may happen in these critical months. Do not lose heart. Now is the time we are going to reap the result of our long uphill fight. Many things may happen in the central organization of the Government in the next four or five months. We may have a new Prime Minister. (Cheers.) If we do, then will be the moment when we shall ask that Conservative opinion shall be considered as a whole.

The storm-clouds are gathering over Europe. Our defences have been shamefully neglected. So cowed are our leaders that they actually boast that they have neglected defences in the hope of placating the clatter of the Socialist Opposition. There is danger gathering. Others are waiting to to fill our place in the world. Is this a time to plunge our vast Oriental dependency into the melting-pot and to divide and dishearten all those forces on which the strength and destiny of Britain depends? (Cheers.)

GOVERNMENT OF INDIA BILL
March 28, 1935
House of Commons

Subject to your observations to the Committee, surely it is asking too much of the Committee to go so far as the end of Part VII to-night. That would take us up to Clause 174. It means an enormous hurrying through the necessary business, and in view of the way in which the Government are forcing this matter from day to day and departing from the spirit and principle on which this matter should have been conducted—[Hon. Members: "No!"]—I say yes; I do not think you will really be well advised in counting on our making that amount of progress to-night, although we shall no doubt try our best to do so. The attempt to carry Clauses in great batches, in long hops, when ten to fifteen Clauses are taken or may be taken in a single bound, presupposes that ample opportunity will be given to those Members who are participating in this arrangement to consider the effect of skipping so many Clauses. When a number of Clauses are passed by a single Motion from the Chair, by general consent, those hon. Members who are responsible for seeing that the Bill is adequately discussed must have an opportunity of considering not only what is discussed but, still more, what is withheld from discussion. Otherwise we may find some very serious hiatus arising in the procedure on the Bill. Therefore, I do not think that we can reach anything like the end of Part VII to-night. It may be that our business may lag if we are supposed to watch with special care what we are doing on account of the way in which the matter has been forced upon us.

The Secretary of State for India (Sir Samuel Hoare): I am sorry that my right hon. Friend has made the suggestion that we have been guilty of a breach of faith. I can assure him that there is no breach of faith.

Mr. Churchill: I never said anything about a breach of faith. The right hon. Gentleman is always using this sort of method. You make a modest criticism, and up he gets and says: "You accuse us of a breach of faith." I said that what was being done was not in harmony with the spirit of the arrangement.

[Later] Far be it from me not to pay every tribute to the manner in which you have facilitated the working of this difficult and very important arrangement, but the fact that on a large block of Clauses there are no Amendments—an Amendment could be put down in a few minutes—is a proof of the desire of hon. Members, after careful consideration, to facilitate the procedure on the Bill as much as possible. The mere fact that no Amendment has appeared to any of these Clauses which are put in a group in no way means that there has not been heart-searching about it. It means that with a view to trying to make a success of the arrangement for getting the Bill through hon. Members have been willing not to press Amendments. If, however, we are to go through the process of endeavouring to help forward the actual progress of a Bill which we consider so disastrous to the country, we must do it within limits, and it is all the more necessary that we should not be hustled by sitting *de die in diem*. It is not possible in those circumstances to exercise a proper study of the Bill both from the point of view of what must be raised, and from the point of view of what may be done and what may be dismissed without debate. I venture very respectfully to make these observations in consequence of the statement which you have made with a view to helping the Committee.

GOVERNMENT OF INDIA BILL
(CLAUSES 177, 196)

April 1, 1935

House of Commons

I shall not, I trust, endeavour to retrace at all the arguments which others have used, but I must address myself for a few moments to the basic foundation of the argument of the Secretary of State [on Clause 177—Directions and Principles to be observed by Railroad Authority]. His reasoning, his advice, is that we must trust entirely to good will in this matter, that good will will bring us a richer harvest than anything that could be obtained by any mandatory injunction in a measure; and I need not say how he was warmly supported in that contention by the hon. Member for Bodmin (Mr. Isaac Foot). Indeed, it is remarkable how the Secretary of State and the hon. Member for Bodmin think alike. It is a case of two hearts that beat as one. They might have collaborated for a lifetime in the same Government, so harmonious and sympathetic are their views.

But let us look at this question of good will on which everything is to depend. Where is your good will? We are told to look at the past, and that in the past, since the

Montagu-Chelmsford reforms, 75 per cent. of the orders have been placed in the British Empire and only 25 per cent. elsewhere. But, as my hon. Friend the Member for Barnstaple (Sir B. Peto) pointed out, this is entirely a new situation. This is a new deal. Here we are to have an entirely fresh Constitution, involving a transfer of sovereignty such as did not exist before. Very often, after the sun has gone down, there is a glow in the sky, but even in that case 25 per cent. of the orders went elsewhere, even in those periods, when we are told that we have had good will, 25 per cent. went elsewhere, to our very great disadvantage. But now you are not going to have good will. This Bill is regarded as an affront by every section of Indian opinion, and I must point out that it is these orders which will be used as counters of warfare, not necessarily for trading purposes or on economic grounds, but for counters of political warfare.

Of course they will be used. The tariff is one of the great levers by which the Indian Assemblies will set to work to extort diminutions of the safeguards and to wrest away from the Government those powers that are withheld from them. The right hon. Member for Sparkbrook (Mr. Amery) told us how terribly effective the tariff could be, how by a stroke of the pen, with no discrimination, they could shut out the entire produce of this country and confine purchases entirely to India.

The Deputy-Chairman: The right hon. Gentleman is again going, like other hon. Members, far beyond the scope of the Amendment.

Mr. Churchill: With very great respect, may I, on the point of Order, submit that I was directly addressing myself to the arguments of the right hon. Member for Sparkbrook? I certainly had no intention, I can assure you, of going any further upon my own initiative into that field. I only thought I might venture as far as you had permitted him to go, because his statement was so very present in my mind, and no doubt in the mind of the Committee. His statement that it would be possible to confine Indian railway purchases to India alone by merely raising the tariff struck me as so very sinister and disquieting that I thought I might certainly emphasise it.

The Deputy-Chairman: So long as the right hon. Gentleman confined himself to the statement of the right hon. Member for Sparkbrook (Mr. Amery), that by the use of tariffs on railway material this Amendment could be rendered nugatory, he would be in order, but it seemed to me that he was going far beyond that to the general question of the use of tariffs by the Indian Government.

Mr. Churchill: I have finished entirely with this point, because it does not arise upon this question except in so far as it was brought in by the right hon. Member for Sparkbrook, and that only as an illustration. The point that I want to make, however, with your permission, is the question of the first set of leverages to procure political advantages, by means of the tariffs, and the second set of leverages by the placing of orders. What will you have when this Bill is in operation? We have been told that it will bring the greatest resentment among all classes in India, and you will have a great political struggle continuing year after year. The Viceroy will be forced to use his powers, and that use of his powers will be resented. What is the remedy? The remedy is to place a large order, unreasonably, irrationally, in a foreign country, and to pick out the foreign country, no doubt, with which it would be most offensive to the people of Great Britain to see this large order placed. I remember very well, when the

Irish Free State were given their plenary powers, when there was supposed to be a settlement between us, that the first thing they did when they came to build their great electric plant was to place the order in Germany. Where did they go to buy coal? They went to Poland, to anywhere but Great Britain. That was not because of economic considerations or of any commercial balancing of pros and cons, or profit and loss, but because of political malice. Here also you will have political malice, and the way in which the British Government in India, the Secretary of State, and, under him, the Viceroy will be subjected to pressure will be by the invidious, unreasonable, and hostile placing of orders—orders which could quite well come here, which possibly ought to come here, on economic grounds—abroad. I think that shows how very serious this situation is.

The right hon. Gentleman assumes himself to possess the good will of India. On the contrary, these are the actual counters of political warfare, and I think we must consider it from a new point of view. You cannot predicate good will. You have no right to predicate good will. You dare not even attempt to obtain the assent of any section of Indian opinion for your Measure. You are forcing this upon them, and, of course, they will resent it. Here in their hands is an indefinite series of means of irritation, of means of retaliation and pin pricks, which can be exercised at the expense of British trade and to the annoyance of the British people. Then, no doubt, we shall hear the hon. Member for Bodmin coming forward and saying, "Ah, well, it is true there is not that good will for which we had hoped; now you must remove those political checks which you have hitherto introduced, and then the full flow of sweetness and sympathy will once again be passing between India and Great Britain." I can hear the speech which the hon. Member would make about that. It seems to me that when we are transferring sovereignty, as we are doing, and when we are confronting ourselves with a decade of strife, tumult and irritation such as India has never seen for several generations, we are entitled to take a new view and to make reasonable provision in accordance with modern opinion.

As has been said, no other country in the world would even debate such a matter; it would be taken as a matter of course that an effort should be made to give a distinct bias in favour of and a preference to inter-Imperial goods or goods produced in Great Britain. All the more is that right when the power which claims that consideration is the protecting power by land and sea, and, in addition, is the source from which the credit originates. It is not an unreasonable proposal which has been put forward by my hon. Friend. I am very glad to see the hon. Member for Moseley (Mr. Hannon), because we have not really had in this matter the support for which we had hoped from that great city in the centre of England from whence he comes. On the contrary the hon. Gentleman's case up to now has been a case of what might be said: "So shines a good deed in a naughty world." There is another text which occurs to me which says that there is more joy over one sinner that repents than over all the rest of the body that has hitherto continued to march steadfastly forward together. I would urge my hon. Friend to press his Amendment to a division. I shall certainly support him if he does so. It seems that on this occasion we are proposing the special precautions which are appropriate to the situation which is to be created by this Bill, and I trust that in any further discussions we shall not hear from the Secretary of State any more of this fallacious and misleading talk about good will. He says that we must not put anything in about trade because it would upset the Indian four-sevenths of the railway authority; it would upset them terribly and confront their ideas of autonomy and sovereignty and so forth. When, however, you stick in safeguards of every kind which they repudiate and against which they are going to war, that, of course, is not to be considered in any way.

This is only one of many points at which the evils and absurdities of this Bill can be plainly viewed by the British public. There are many such, and as we move along through this long labyrinth of clauses and arguments, we reach a point from which we can turn round and survey the scene. Here is one such point from which you can see that you are creating a political system, a consequence of which will be that the irritation in India will be worked off in striking at British trade by the placing of orders in foreign countries. That is the course upon which the Secretary of State has launched himself and it will have an undoubted result, at the end of all his labours, which will be to our extreme misfortune and suffering.

[Much later] We ought to dwell on this point [Clause 196—Power of Federal Legislature to enlarge appellate jurisdiction] a moment. I should really have thought that it was a matter that appealed enormously to the Opposition, for obviously, in this Clause we are laying down in the most naked and blatant terms that there is one law for the rich and another law for the poor. It does not at all follow that cases over 50,000 rupees are more important than cases under 50,000 rupees. It was a maxim in Roman times, and the great Augustus is stated to have said, that magistrates should always make a point of attending to the small cases, because the small cases revealed the life of the people who bore upon their shoulders the pressing weight, the necessarily inevitable pressing weight, of an elaborate social organisation. Why should the Committee be ready to pass in a casual manner a Clause such as this? Why are the representatives of Labour, the broad proletarian masses, dumb when these things come up? They seem to say, "It is a matter involving 50,000 rupees; what do we care for that?" It may be that a poor widow is asserting her right to live—rather difficult, I believe, in some cases in India. There may be a case of a humble agricultural labourer who has been paid a wage which does not give him even the daily subsistence which is necessary to support body and soul. "Oh, well," they say, "this is nothing." It may be some small tenant farmer, oppressed by some rich landlord, who has rack-rented him and ill treated him very much, taking perhaps the whole value of his poor holding, with all the improvements which he has put into it. That is not a matter of 10,000 rupees, let alone 50,000 rupees.

I am not saying that some arrangement of this kind may not be necessary. There is a maxim, *De minimis non curat lex*, but I have never known that *de minimis* was regarded as having a pecuniary standard, or that there was any idea that wealth and wealth alone is to be the test by which the course of justice is to be regulated. I know that this may easily strike a rather unexpected and perhaps uncomfortable chord in the breast of the right hon. and learned Gentleman. Among the hierarchy of the law there are wealthy and famous and skilful advocates, and a litigant does get very well attended to when such a one puts his case. There are a lot of people who might manage to put a case effectively, and it would go through in the ordinary way, but with nothing like the careful and considerate attention to detail with which it is handled when eminent K.Cs. appear on one side or the other. That may be one of the practices which grow up irresistibly in the ordinary workings of a complicated civilisation, but there is all the difference between that and putting principles into the cold lead of an Act of Parliament. I am bound to say that I think this is a little characteristic—though I am sorry to have to say so—of the kind of outlook and view, and temper and touch and mood in which this Bill has been shaped and framed by His Majesty's Government. There is nothing like a careful procedure reserved for the appeals, the cries for justice, which arise from people whose case does not involve 50,000 rupees, none of the elaborate precautions which are available in cases above that mystic figure.

How does the right hon. and learned Gentleman arrive at his figure of 50,000 rupees; The Attorney-General, in an audible aside which I think we may fairly say has become the common property of the Committee, mentioned that the present figure was 10,000 rupees. Now it has to be 50,000 rupees before a man can get the full and careful consideration of the courts. That is very typical of the Bill; it is the exact measure of the Bill. In the future it is to be five times as difficult for poor people to get their affairs attended to in India as it was before this Bill was passed. I wish I had a legal training which would enable me to do justice to these matters, but, lacking that, I must study the text of the Bill as best I can in bringing these points forward. It is a bad thing for a great Empire when it definitely draws the line in this cold, cynical and brutal manner between the rich and the poor, especially in a population which, as my hon. Friend has reminded us, is miserably poor, brushing aside the poor and selecting only the affairs of the wealthy, of the Ahmedabad millowners, the wealthy corporations of Bombay, the enormous landowners and others. I think something should be done to make it clear that money is not to be the test. I am delighted to hear my right hon. and gallant Friend laughing, because, generally speaking, he seems to be oppressed by a melancholy disposition.

Major Hills: Surely I am allowed to laugh if I am amused.

Mr. Churchill: And surely I am allowed to derive a momentary and transient personal satisfaction at having lifted the clouds of depression from my right hon. and gallant Friend. But I will return to the topic before us. I press the point no further except to proclaim the moral, which is very clear and rather ugly. But I should like the learned Solicitor-General, or the Attorney-General if he is disposed to do so—because there is nothing like going to Number 1 in these matters—when he is replying and freeing our minds from the anxiety we have that a sordid discrimination is being established on the face of our Statute Book, to deal with Sub-section (2). As far as I can make out, though here I must plead my lay disqualification, this Sub-section enables the Federal Legislature, by passing some law, to withhold appeal to His Majesty in Council in an enormous class of civil cases in India. If I am wrong I should like to be corrected, but it seems to me that that can be the only purpose of that Sub-section. Of course, one does not want to have the Privy Council here oppressed by an immense volume of litigation coming across the Indian Ocean and, after a long process both of time and space, arriving to be decided here; but I happen to know that the right of appeal to the Privy Council is deeply valued by our Indian fellow subjects. Till they have been taught worse manners by their new masters they will, no doubt, greatly value the power of appealing to what is the most august Court that has ever been in existence in modern times so far as justice between man and man is concerned.

I remember the late Lord Haldane, who was a colleague of the Leader of the Opposition, and one who was always treated with great respect, telling the story of how men were found at sacrifice in a remote village of India. It was not a human sacrifice; they were sacrificing the ordinary domestic animals, which were valuable to them; but they were sacrificing them to the god called Privy Council, which had reached out an arm across the ocean and had given back to the humble dwellers of the village land which had been wrongfully taken from them. I am alarmed by both Sub-sections (1) and (2) of this Clause. The first appears, as far as I can see, though I await an explanation, to draw this property qualification in a manner more crude and more barefaced than I have ever known before, and the second seems to authorise and even to encourage the Federal Legislature to bar whole classes of appeals to the Privy Council in certain circumstances. I shall be glad to have these doubts removed by the legal exposition of the Attorney-General or the Solicitor-General, but what will not be removed by their exposition, however admirable it may be, is that sense which I have, and which I think the Committee has already derived, that the language of this Statute is contrary to the entire principles upon which British civilisation has been built up, and, still more, British administration of Eastern lands has been built up, and that as it stands it is a blot and a defacement upon the statute law of Great Britain.

[Later] As there seems to be an agreement on the part of the highest legal authorities in the land on both sides of the Committee, irrespective of party divisions, I feel some temerity in asking a further question. May I put this case? Suppose there is a case being tried in the Federal Court and that one of the Rajahs, a very small Rajah, in a very remote State, makes a comment upon the case which constitutes by all the principles of jurisprudence contempt of court, there is no redress at all against the Ruler? That, I understand, is the ruling. Although these Princes are to put themselves under this Federal Court which we are to set up above themselves, yet they, after they have done this act, after they have conceded a part of their sovereign rights, those sovereign rights are to remain intact and they are completely above the law, as much above the law as a sovereign in a constitutional country. All you can do is to proceed against the Home Secretary or the Vizier or whoever is the Prime Minister of the State. Is that the position? They are inviolable in all circumstances, whether before the English or before the Federal Court in India. If that is so I should like to have it in terms which are quite unmistakable, and I reserve my right to make my comments on the reply I receive.

[Later] It is evident that the Government are in a muddle about this matter. From what has already emerged during our conversations this evening that is perfectly clear. They are torn between the fear of offending the Princes on the one hand, and on the other hand their own words written in this Bill. They are putting an interpretation on this Clause, which according to the plainest meaning of the English language, it does not bear. They have to declare that a ruler is not a person—

Sir W. Davison: Or an authority.

Mr. Churchill: Or an authority, civil or judicial. At any rate I do not think we ought to take up any more time upon it. [Hon. Members: "Hear, hear."] I am glad I have carried the Committee with me on that point. With a view to bringing the discussion to a conclusion I ask the Attorney-General a question which he cannot say is vague or general because it is on the contrary a concrete and rigidly defined proposition, namely whether he will accept an Amendment to Sub-section (2) in line 22 to insert after the words "any person" the words "not being a ruler of a native State or a Federated State."

Lord E. Percy: Or the Governor of a British Province?

Mr. Churchill: I must appeal to the Noble Lord not to bring in new topics and start new hares at this late hour. He has long been one of the Government's most assiduous supporters, and I am sure they will not thank him for raising these other questions at this stage, just as I am endeavouring to make a definite proposal to the Government, putting a fine direct point upon this matter, which would bring it to an end. Will the Attorney-General accept words to the effect I have suggested?

The Attorney-General: I should have thought the answer would be "No," since we are already on the Question, "That the Clause stand part of the Bill." If my right hon. Friend put down an Amendment on the Report stage to that effect, the answer to it would be that the words are not necessary. If he reads the Clause further, he will see that this Court is to have power to make the orders which any High Court in British India would have power to make in regard to the territory over which it has jurisdiction.

Mr. Churchill: If the Attorney-General assures us that the meaning of the Clause would not be made more clear or precise by the addition which I have suggested and that its meaning is that no ruler can be summoned, then I accept that assurance. After a great deal of difficulty which might easily have been avoided the Attorney-General has at last afforded us a full comprehension of the purpose of the Government in this Clause. I thank him for that, but he could have said straight away without any of these hesitations and consultations, these to-ings and fro-ings, that this Clause had no effect upon the princely status of the Rulers, every one of whom will be in a position, though they have subscribed to the Federation, to defy the law and flout the Federal court.

GOVERNMENT OF INDIA BILL
(CLAUSES 202, 204)

April 2, 1935

House of Commons

I ventured to put a point of Order to you last night, Mr. Chairman, but you thought it might be more properly dealt with on the question being proposed "That the Clause [Number 202—Law Declared by Federal Court and Privy Council To Be

Binding on All Courts] stand part of the Bill." May I ask you to give your Ruling upon this point, which has arisen out of the arrangements which have been made for the discussion of the Bill? It has been agreed that a number of clauses may be put *en bloc* if there is no amendment to any clause; but last night there arose a case where six clauses were to be put, and there was an Amendment to the third of those Clauses. It was an Amendment which you did not select, but it was not an Amendment out of order. If it had been out of order it might be argued that it did not exist at all, but as it was an Amendment that you did not select it came into that category which I think you described as coming within the more questionable area of the selective power of the Chair in respect of amendments. We have always understood that that selective power related to making sure that the particular topic for discussion was taken at the best point which was on the Paper, and by no means related to the shortening of discussion and the excluding of any topics from discussion.

That being so, it would appear that an Amendment which was on the Paper and which you did not choose to select would nevertheless be an Amendment for the purpose of barring the putting of a series of clauses *en bloc*. I should very much like to know how you have decided upon that matter, and I must of course say that if you have decided that an Amendment may be put on the Paper and you may not select it and that then a whole block of clauses may be put, obviously it would be necessary for those who are watching over the careful and thorough discussion of this important Measure to safeguard themselves from anything going with a run, by putting on the Paper an Amendment to omit every Clause in succession from the beginning to the end. I hope that I may receive some Ruling from you on the point.

The Chairman: I think it is necessary, in the interests of the Chair and of the Committee, to say that I cannot accept what the right hon. Gentleman has stated as to the Chairman's power of selection of Amendments. That, as the right hon. Gentleman knows, is a discretion the exercise of which is a great responsibility, and the purpose of it has not been hedged with any rules or acknowledged usages. The right hon. Gentleman's first point of Order is to some extent mixed up with a second one. At any rate, it deals broadly with the question of taking a number of Clauses *en bloc*. . . .

Mr. Churchill: I need not say with how much good will and gratitude the minority in this Committee will receive the statement which you have made and which ought to be satisfactory to all.

The Chairman: The question is "That Clause 202 stand part of the Bill."

Mr. Churchill: If I may say so, Sir, you were rather "on the pounce" in rising to put that question. There are very important issues to be raised on this Clause. The Clause involves a point which we raised last night, namely, the question of the amenability of the Princes. It also touches the question of appeals to the Privy Council. These four Clauses numbered 200 to 203 inclusive combine to give us a picture, as it were, of the relations between the Federal and the State Legislatures. On these Clauses we have raised certain definite issues with the Attorney-General and the Solicitor-General which have not yet been very clearly or fully determined. This Clause 202 relates to the procedure between the Federal Courts and the Privy Council. It is of considerable consequence, and I think we might have from the Government some explanation of its exact purpose, having regard to the discussion which took place late last night. Perhaps in the light of that discussion the Government could now make a statement which would relieve some of the doubts and anxieties prevailing in certain quarters in the Committee at present.

[Later] I am most grateful to my hon. and learned Friend [Sir Donald Somervell] for his explanation. Of course, the pith and point of this matter is the extent of the intrusion upon the sovereignty of the Federated States which is involved. It now appears, and it would normally appear, that the Federal Court dominates the States which are parties to the union. There is nothing wrong about that so long as it is recognised and properly understood. But, of course, one must note in passing the very serious abrogation of sovereignty involved, and what is required from the federating units for the sake of federal union. Here we come to the important question of judge-made or court-made law, and that process by which there is built up on a substructure of statute law, a whole new superstructure. Here I think the right hon. Gentleman the Leader of the Opposition will be with me. He, I am sure, remembers the Taff Vale case, and the cases of Quinn against Leathen and Lyons against Wilkins, and all those successive judgments by which the statute law—so it was contended by the Socialists and Radicals of those days—had been changed, and the real purpose of Parliament had been gradually subverted, and diverted from the direction in which it was launched by the Conservative legislation of Disraeli's Government of 1876, into an entirely different course, very much more favourable to the employers and property owners. I am sure the Leader of the Opposition has those matters in his mind.

Mr Lansbury: The right hon. Gentleman wants to give me a headache.

Mr. Churchill: Not at all. On the contrary, I only want to rouse the right hon. Gentleman to greater activity in the discharge of his constitutional duties.

The Chairman: I hope, however, that the right hon. Gentleman the Member for Epping (Mr. Churchill) will not seek to lead the right hon. Gentleman the Member for Bow and Bromley (Mr. Lansbury) into wrong paths of irrelevancy.

Mr. Churchill: I am sure, Sir, you would not seriously think that I should attempt to induce the right hon. Gentleman into any wrong course or into referring to the Taff Vale decision or these other decisions otherwise than as illustrations to emphasise the actual argument now under discussion. The point is this. It ought to be marked that the Federal Court will move forward on its path making interpretations of the law in advance of the legislation—that is to say its interpretations will, until new statutes are passed, govern the actual practice. It is only from time to time that Parliament can pass Acts, but the courts are functioning continuously, and like the coral insects, they build up layer after layer until after a certain point has been reached you observe a new situation. At that point the legislature sometimes intervenes.

The question which we have now in view is what is the position of the Indian States in the Federation in this respect. It is clear that they are amenable to the Federal Court. They are not amenable only to the statute law which is now going through. They are not amenable only to the India Constitutional Bill, or Act as it may some day become—which God forfend. Not at all. They are amenable to the continuous law making propositions and decisions which arise from the working of the Federal Court. Of course, we cannot resist this proposition. The Government must bear the consequences, but I think it necessary that the Princes of India and the Prime

Ministers of these Federal States should realise that what they are subscribing to—if they should subscribe to it—is not a mere agreement to come into the Federal Constitution embodied in the Statute. There will be a ceaseless, perennial process of judge-made and court-made decisions in the far flung meshes of which they will certainly be enwebbed.

The Secretary of State for India (Sir Samuel Hoare): My right hon. Friend is needlessly anxious and seems to think that he has made a great discovery that the sovereignty of the Princes and the Indian States may everywhere be undermined. Let me assure my right hon. Friend that he has made no discovery at all. This Clause has always been accepted by the Indian Princes.

Mr. Churchill: No; surely in the speeches which were made at the Bombay conference, Clause 202 was specifically mentioned as one that would require amendment.

[Much later] My hon. and learned Friend has made a very fertile contribution to our discussion, but as he reached the closing period of his remarks I found that he was arriving at a different conclusion from my own. I am in favour of "champertous" being inserted in the Bill. The decision before the Committee [Clause 204—Rules of Court, etc.] is whether they will inflict upon India the Scottish or the English conception of the law in this particular. I must proclaim myself a partisan of the English conception. Champertous actions are banned with the idea of preventing litigation being fomented—although it may sometimes help some small person—by interested parties who are to be paid their fees out of the proceeds of the judgment if it should go in their favour. English opinion has always been opposed to champerty and, after all, England does still exist, although its nationality is submerged. For many generations that has been one of the essential propositions of our jurisprudence.

Why should we not extend this benefit to India? Why whould we not give them the whole of our message? "Champertous" is certainly part of the British message. Why should it not be included in this India Bill? Is there any portion of the earth in which it is more necessary that a prohibition against champertous transactions should exist than in India? China is a vast Asiatic country, but in China there is anarchy. Russia also is Asiatic; and there may be other parts of Asia which are under various forms of tyranny. But in India we have at present peace and order and legality, and we have this vice of Asiatic races, which the English themselves, inventing this word "champertous," have discovered is a matter to be corrected, and therefore why should we not confer this prohibition against champerty upon India together with all the other benefits which the hon. Member for Bodmin (Mr Isaac Fot) wishes to bestow.

Mr. Isaac Foot: The right hon. Gentleman has just said that in India there is a condition of law and order. They have no prohibition of champerty at present, and why should he desire to change the position?

Mr. Churchill: There is a condition of law and order because the judiciary of that country is influenced and dominated at the present time by English traditions, and inherent among those English traditions is this hatred of champerty; but now we are reaching to a new regime, another dispensation. Gradually English control of the judiciary will fade, and in consequence it is all the more necessary to bequeath to them our full inheritance while we are about it. I should have thought the hon. Member for Bodmin would have been the very first to have supported this proposal. He is surely not going to confer upon India all the blessings of modern democracy and deny them this English provision against champerty. Let them have the whole dose. It is a terribly dangerous thing to give a very strong and severe medicine to a whole nation and yet to leave out some essential element in the prescription I appeal to the Government to prohibit champerty in India just as they have put down dacoity, suttee and other vicious practices.

Why should the Government not accept this Amendment? What harm does it do? It is sound of itself. It will be beneficial to India. It would make no difference to the Bill, only the Government have got into such a habit of refusing everything and of thinking that all they have to do is to ring the bell and bring in the crowd that they will not even address themselves to a proposition seriously put forward upon careful and reflecting legal authority? Why cannot the Government accept this Amendment? I do not suppose they will, having said they would it would have been in the Bill. Now that they are cutting the painter, now that India is drifting apart, surely they might leave India with this principle of the law. I think I see the Attorney-General is moved. He and his learned brother are consulting together. May I hope that some consideration will be given to this point? If not, I really think the House has a right to feel ill-used, not because the Government are not courteous and polite, but because they pay no attention whatever to anything that is said. No reason whatever has been given to us. What is this statement that the language is not the same? If they put the word "champerty" into Tamil or Hindustani or any other dialect the people would not understand it, it is said. What nonsense! They will gulp down the word "champerty." If the Government imagine they will not understand what "champerty" means they are under a delusion. It is a real link of Empire between ourselves and them. If the Government insert the word "champerty" they will not need to translate it. They have only to tell the Indian people what it means in simple terms, and the Indian people will see the immense significance of it, and all over that vast sub-Continent there will be appreciative thanks.

[Later] No, Sir, [the Chairman], but might we hear from the Government some reasons why, in this matter of making rules, together with the words "frivolous or vexatious" we should not also insert the word "champertous." The only reason we have heard from the Government is that the word "champerty" is not familiar in India, but the practice is all too familiar there, and, if we are conferring upon India our British system of democratic government, we ought not to deny them this extremely valuable element in our system. We have had no answer from the Government, and the Debate has been prolonged because the answer given by the Solicitor-General was so utterly inadequate. He merely said that there was not a native word for "champerty," or something like that. It is because they have not given us any reason for not adopting these words or have not accepted the Amendment which would have been a reasonable course which almost any other Government wishing to associate the House of Commons with their legislation would have adopted, that this discussion has been, perhaps, protracted beyond the particular point. The responsibility rests with the Government. Let the Solicitor-General give some reason other than the difficulty of translating the word "champerty" into the Indian language, or let the Government accept the Amendment. We can then immediately proceed to the next Clause upon which further important points arise.

[Much later] May I venture to ask whether my Noble Friend the Member for Hastings (Lord E. Percy) is satisfied with the answer he has received? After all, my Noble Friend sat on the Joint Select Committee, whose report on this subject, I gather, differs from the action of the Government. [An Hon. Member: "No!"] He said so, at any rate, but you must fight that out among yourselves. We are not usually associated with the Noble Lord, who is a most vehement supporter of the Government in these matters, but now he differs from the Government.

> "There is a length to which, I trow,
> Colonial bishops cannot go."

I did not mean to refer to his pontifical qualities; but the Noble Lord has now pulled up. He has gone thus far with the Government, but he has now entered a serious *caveat*. I could not gather whether his objections were to the Amendment or to the whole Clause. I rather think he objected to both. He asked the Government to withdraw its Clause or to remodel it, and the point he raised was one of substance. He pointed out what confusion worse confounded would have resulted in the United States if there had been two Supreme Courts which might have given divergent rulings on, for instance, the gold dollar question. This is part of the amazing policy that you are constructing for India. There are to be two supreme courts, or the supreme court is to divide itself into two tribunals, which may give opposite opinions, but all is to be entrusted to the good sense of the chief justice, who will naturally divide the business as he may choose.

I must say that my part in this matter will be determined by the Noble Lord. He has raised the issue; he has opposed the Government and taken the responsibility—I admit he has the Joint Select Committee at his back—of confronting the National Government with a very definite point of divergence. He has been given an answer which, as anyone who has listened to it will agree, is no answer at all. He has been fobbed off with this vague and airy assurance, which I must say the learned Solicitor-General does in a most skilful manner, that "perhaps at some future time, before the Report stage, we will bear the matter in mind and see if some words cannot be inserted which will perhaps go a little nearer to meeting the point of view advanced by my Noble Friend," etcetera, and so on. Is he satisfied with that? Will he accept the rebuff which he has received? I think it is a rebuff. The mocking cheers of my right hon. Friend the Member for West Birmingham (Sir A. Chamberlain) do not at all alter my view that it is a rebuff. When a Member who has followed all the process of the Government for two or three years with the faithfulness of a hound for his master, and who suddenly asks for a bone, has something flung to him, however small—and he has a legitimate and substantial point—and is told by the learned Solicitor-General to go off and eat his own tail, I must say that I think that constitutes all the elements of a parliamentary rebuff. At any rate, I shall hold my judgment in suspense as to what I do on this Amendment until I have heard further from my Noble Friend.

[Later] Sir S. Hoare: We were under the impression that the Amendment was making more clear the intention of the Joint Select Committee. That intention undoubtedly was that there should be a division between constitutional and appellate cases, and it was to make that clear that we proposed this Amendment. My noble Friend is not satisfied with the wording of the Amendment, and I suggest that probably it will be most convenient if we pass the Amendment now, and I give him an undertaking that we will look into the question further, keeping in mind the fact that he and I are agreed that the division should be between constitutional and appellate cases.

Mr. Churchill: I do not think this matter ought to be settled in this fashion. Here is the Secretary of State doing a private deal with the Noble Lord, keeping in mind, as he said, the fact that they were agreed. After all, we are dealing with the Committee of the House of Commons, and I do not think that these transactions should be of such an extremely selective character as all that. I quite understand that a Member who presses a point with a great deal of knowledge, as the Noble Lord did, has the right to an answer specially by the Secretary of State. But I should have thought that when the Secretary of State intervened at the end of the discussion on this particular point he would have given his pledge to the Committee rather than make it one of these many compliments which he extends to those who have supported his fortunes so long.

Major Hills: Would not the real solution be to make all constitutional appeals go as a matter of course to the full Federal Court of six judges? These will be the most important appeals. There will not be many of them, and it is quite reasonable that the full court should share these decisions. For the ordinary appellate jurisdiction of the court, split up your court into two or even three divisions if you like. Those appeals will be by far the most numerous and they could be very well taken by a smaller court than the full court. If you split the court up into two divisions and apportion one to the constitutional appeals, I think you lose something in a smaller court. The Supreme Court of America is certainly much larger than three judges. I think you may have a difference of personnel which would affect a smaller body more than it would affect a bigger body. For those reasons, I hope the right hon. Gentleman will consider whether he could not in the amended Clause consent to constitutional appeals going to the full court of six judges, making two divisions for the purpose of dealing with the ordinary appellate jurisdiction of the Federal Court.

Mr. Churchill: Is not that possible? Here is a practical suggestion. I am most anxious to preserve the accord for the time being between representatives of the Joint Select Committee and the Secretary of State, and here it seems to me that my right and gallant Friend has come forward with a perfectly practicable—and as it seems to me *prima facie*; I do not commit myself—a thoroughly reasonable and sensible proposal. What is the answer to that? After all, the Government may be prepared to deal with those who oppose the Bill with all the roughness and rigour of Parliamentary power, but here are their faithful supporters! Here are men with deep anxieties, though with them in the general purpose of handing over the sovereignty of India. Surely the Government will answer their own supporters. What is the answer to what they have said? Here are three Privy Councillors who have spoken against the Government case. They are three supporters of the Government who are all members of the Privy Council—and senior members, long established. Two out of the three have sat all through the discussions of the Joint Select Committee. They have put their proposal. What is the answer of the Government? Will they accept the proposal made by the right hon. and gallant Gentleman who has just spoken, or will they give a specific assurance that on the Report stage a definite statement will be made on this point with a view to trying to give satisfaction? After all you are giving away our Indian Empire, and you may as well be agreed one with another about the proposals. At least be solid. Do not be breaking up at this stage; otherwise, one cannot tell how far the rot will spread. What is the answer to my right hon. and gallant Friend, who seems to have contributed a point of substance and one helpful to the House? It is a point on which the Government might at any rate tell us whether this would be the kind of thing they would be likely to favour and embody in the Bill when we get to the Report stage.

REARMAMENT QUESTION

April 3, 1935

House of Commons

Further on the question of business, might I ask the Prime Minister—and I apologise to him for not having been able to give him longer, or fuller, or more definite notice—whether, in view of the answer given by the Foreign Secretary to Question No. 5 this day about the relative strengths of the British and German Air Forces, he will reconsider the answer which he gave to my Noble Friend the right hon. Member for Horsham (Earl Winterton) yesterday in respect of providing some occasion to debate these urgent and serious matters?

The Prime Minister: I am sorry I have had no notice of this question, but, if I had, I am afraid I could only give the answer that I will give now, that the State of public business is so pressing that we cannot, at any rate for the moment, set aside any special day for a discussion on this subject. There will be opportunities, like the adjournment, for raising the question, and the other adjournments that are available. I am sorry, but if I asked the right hon. Gentleman to give me notice, I am afraid I should be compelled, in view of the state of public business, to give him the same answer.

Mr. Churchill: But will not the right hon. Gentleman, attaching all the weight which he no doubt should to the state of public business, also take into consideration the fact that the answer given by the Secretary of State for Foreign Affairs to-day is in direct contradiction, in respect of the relative strengths of the Air Forces of the two countries, to the solemn, deliberate, and reiterated Ministerial statements which have been made on behalf of His Majesty's Government, and that it is a matter of such grave importance that some special arrangements should be made to enable the House of Commons, which shares with the Government responsibility for the safety of the country, to participate and to take stock of the existing situation?